T0199299

COMPUTER, INTELLIGENT COMPUTING AND EDUCATION TECHNOLOGY

SELECTED PEER REVIEWED PAPERS FROM 2014 INTERNATIONAL CONFERENCE ON COMPUTER, INTELLIGENT COMPUTING AND EDUCATION TECHNOLOGY, CICET 2014, HONGKONG, 27–28 MARCH 2014

Computer, Intelligent Computing and Education Technology

Editors

Hsiang-Chuan Liu
Asia University, Taiwan

Wen-Pei Sung
National Chin-Yi University of Technology, Taiwan

Wenli-Yao
Control Engineering and Information Science Research, Hong Kong

VOLUME 1

CRC Press
Taylor & Francis Group
Boca Raton London New York Leiden

CRC Press is an imprint of the
Taylor & Francis Group, an **informa** business

A BALKEMA BOOK

CRC Press/Balkema is an imprint of the Taylor & Francis Group, an informa business

© 2014 Taylor & Francis Group, London, UK

Typeset by V Publishing Solutions Pvt Ltd., Chennai, India
Printed and bound in Great Britain by CPI Group (UK) Ltd, Croydon, CR0 4YY

Published by: CRC Press/Balkema
 P.O. Box 11320, 2301 EH Leiden, The Netherlands
 e-mail: Pub.NL@taylorandfrancis.com
 www.crcpress.com – www.taylorandfrancis.com

ISBN: 978-1-138-02469-4 (set of 2 volumes)
ISBN: 978-1-138-02639-1 (Vol 1)
ISBN: 978-1-138-02640-7 (Vol 2)
ISBN: 978-1-315-77556-2 (eBook PDF)

Table of contents

VOLUME 2

Information science and education technology

Computer, Intelligent Computing and Education Technology – Liu, Sung & Yao (Eds)
© 2014 Taylor & Francis Group, London, ISBN 978-1-138-02469-4

Preface

In the past twenty years, Computer Science and Information Technology have become involved in many varied applications throughout the world, with multiple products and rapid market services. They have not only provided industries with new methods, new tools and new products from design, material processing to operation and management process, but are also changing the manners, thinking styles and working environments of people in all fields.

This book contains selected Computer, Information and Education Technology related papers from the 2014 International Conference on Computer, Intelligent Computing and Education Technology (CICET 2014) held in Hong Kong, March 27–28, 2014. The aim is to provide a platform for researchers, engineers, and academics as well as industrial professionals from all over the world to present their research results and development activities in Computer Science, Information Technology and Education Technology.

This conference will promote the development of Computer Science, Information Technology and Education Technology, strengthening international academic cooperation and communications, and the exchange of research ideas.

I am very grateful to the conference chairs, organization staff, the authors and the members of the International Technological Committees for their hard work. We hope that CICET 2014 will be successful and enjoyable for all participants.

January, 2014
Wen-Pei Sung
National Chin-Yi University of Technology

CICET 2014 Committee

CONFERENCE CHAIRMAN

Prof. Hsiang-Chuan Liu, *Asia University, Taiwan*
Prof. Wen-Pei Sung, *National Chin-Yi University of Technology, Taiwan*

PROGRAM COMMITTEE

Xue Chaogai, *Zhengzhou University, China*
Viranjay M. Srivastava, *Jaypee University of Information Technology, Solan, H.P., India*
Zhao Weiguo, *Hebei University of Engineering, China*
He Qing, *North China Electric Power University, China*
Mir Mahdi Zalloi, *National Iranian Gas Company (NIGC), Iran*
Zhou Liang, *Donghua University, China*
Liu Yunan, *University of Michigan, USA*
Wang Liying, *Institute of Water Conservancy and Hydroelectric Power, China*
Chenggui Zhao, *Yunnan University of Finance and Economics, China*
Hsiang-Chuan Liu, *Asia University, Taiwan*
Gang Shi, *Inha University, South Korea*
Bhagavathi Tarigoppula, *Bradley University, USA*
Tjamme Wiegers, *Delft University of Technology, The Netherlands*
Anita Kovač Kralj, *University of Maribor, Slovenia*
Wei Fu, *Chongqing University, China*
Ramezan ali Mahdavinejad, *University of Tehran, Iran*
Chen Chi-Hua, *National Chiao Tung University, Taiwan*
Mostafa Shokshok, *National University of Malaysia, Malaysia*
Hong Sheng, *Beijing University of Aeronautics and Astronautics, China*
Yang Yan, *Guangxi University for Nationalities, China*
Xu Chungeng, *Nanjing University of Science and Technology, China*
Liu Zheng, *Shangdong Economic University, China*
Wen-Sheng Ou, *National Chin-Yi University of Technology, Taiwan*
Hao-En Chueh, *Yuanpei University, Taiwan*
Li Zhong, *North China Electric Power University, China*
Lixin Guo, *Northeastern University, China*

CO-SPONSOR

International Frontiers of Science and Technology Research Association
Control Engineering and Information Science Research Association

Computer science and intelligent computing

Computer, Intelligent Computing and Education Technology – Liu, Sung & Yao (Eds)
© 2014 Taylor & Francis Group, London, ISBN 978-1-138-02469-4

The study of Tibetan text clustering based on hybrid parallel genetic algorithm

Yu-Gang Dai, Pei Li, Tao Jiang & Tao Xu

Key Laboratory of China's National Linguistic Information Technology, Northwest University for Nationalities, Lanzhou, China

ABSTRACT: The domestic and foreign research on text clustering be too numerous to enumerate, related technology is becoming mature. Clustering algorithm is the key technology of text clustering; the choice of algorithm will also affect the final clustering results. At present, the domestic and foreign experts are working on improving algorithm and clustering algorithm integrated application research. However, the research on minority language's text clustering is relatively less, especially the research results about the Tibetan text clustering is very little. In this paper, the Tibetan text clustering of genetic algorithm and K-means algorithm will be research. So as to realize Tibetan text clustering based on hybrid parallel genetic algorithm, and has achieved good clustering results.

Keywords: clustering; Tibetan text; k-means algorithm; genetic algorithm

1 INTRODUCTION

The concept of genetic algorithm is proposed by Bagley J. D in 1967; and the theory of genetic algorithm and method of systematic studied in 1975. This groundbreaking work is initiated by the professor J.H. Holland who works at the University of Michigan.[1] At that time, its main purpose is to illustrate the adaptive process of natural and artificial systems.[2] Genetic algorithm as an efficient parallel global optimization search tools has already accepted by many fields, the application of it in the aspect of data mining is a great value, is an important research topic in the field of data mining.[3,9] Using genetic algorithm to solve the problem with chaos, random and nonlinear for typical characteristics, for the complex problem which other science and technology cannot solve or is difficult to solve provides a new calculation model.[4] For noisy chaotic characteristics of large amounts of data, the genetic algorithm effectively solves the problems.[5]

Genetic algorithm is a global search algorithm, it randomly generated a population, and then simulates the natural evolution towards better evolution, and the individual can be evaluated by the size of the fitness.[6] Genetic algorithm has the self-organizing, adaptive and self-learning characteristics, and evolution of natural selection and make the calculation simple genetic operators are not affected by its search space restrictive conditions (such as continuous and differentiable, unimodal) constraints, and do not need other auxiliary

information (e.g., adjustable guide), so the genetic algorithm can obtain higher efficiency, and has the characteristics of simple, easy to operate and general.[7]

Text clustering is a fully automatic processing of text set grouping process; machine learning is a kind of typical guidance process. Text clustering goal is to find such a collection of classes, the degree of similarity between classes as least as possible, and the maximum similarity within the class. As a kind of unsupervised machine learning method, clustering doesn't need training process, also does not need to manual annotation category document in advance, so the clustering technology is very flexible and has higher ability of automated processing, now has become the effective organization, the text information and an important means of navigation, more and more researchers are paying attention on it.

As information processing technology, especially the automatic word segmentation technology and the development of the semantic similarity measurement technology, based on the study of the Chinese text clustering technology got rapid development. However, the research on minority language's text clustering is relatively few. Especially Tibetan information in the direction of research is extremely scarce; just rely on some domestic colleges and universities and scientific research institutes and research department of the Tibetan local related research is not enough. Therefore, through the existing Chinese text clustering technology is applied to the Tibetan text clustering will research on Tibetan text clustering produces extremely profound significance, to promote the development of Tibetan information processing technology also is significant. This paper mainly studies how Chinese biotechnology based on genetic algorithm is transplanted into Tibetan text clustering, clustering of Tibetan text quickly and accurately.

2 THE KEY TECHNOLOGY OF TIBETAN TEXT CLUSTERING

2.1 *Tibetan text representation*

First met in automatic text clustering is the basic problem of how to make the form of text representation into a computer can understand. Text representation model is the key part of the text clustering, because it directly determines the next parts by use of methods, and finally the accuracy of clustering results. Text representation can be divided into the following four models: Concept Model and Probabilistic Mode, Set Model and Algebraic Model.

1. Concept Model, the Model for the center with concepts rather than with the word or phrase, is a kind of brand-new retrieval Model, with mesh or tree structure to classification and organization, using the distance between concepts of document similarity calculation.
2. Probabilistic Mode, this Model is based on the statistical probability to describe information samples. Probability model by considering entry documents between the statistical probability, than the Boolean model and vector model had greatly improved. Its advantage is the ability to sort information according to the related the descending order of probability sample. The disadvantage is that the probability model does not consider index entries in the information in the sample frequency. And it still assumes that the index entries are independent of each other; In addition, the probability model need to guess initial sample information, and is divided into relevant and irrelevant two collections.
3. Set Model, this Model will be a document representation as only 0 and 1 binary keywords Set forms, it is a Boolean Model. It is a typical representative. The advantage of the collection model is easy to realize. Weakness: the Boolean expression of exact match can lead to retrieve data redundancy or too little, its precise semantics is difficult to transform the general information needs into a Boolean expression, and it is the base of twelve value standard, does not take into account the approximate concept. As a result, the collection model is considered to be the weakest classic methods.
4. Algebraic Model, according to the Algebraic Model, documents consist of a set of n independent eigenvector, and each feature is endowed with a weight. Vector Space Model is a typical representative of the Model, in addition, there are representative of the neural network Model, the latent semantic indexing Model. Similar to the concept of the model is described by characteristics of weight, so can accurately measure the similarity between the documents and improve the efficiency of information processing, in addition, the part of the model matching strategy applicable to extract more similar samples.

This article uses the Vector Space Model, Vector Space Model is to use the mathematical Model of Space Vector to represent text information, and one of the most famous of the retrieval system of this Model is the smart system. In vector space model, each dimension represents a keyword, when a keyword in the text, it corresponds to a weight of non-zero value. When to feature selection in text, do not need to consider a lot of syntax and grammar information, also do not need to semantic processing documents. Vector space model of the specific said is as follows:

Given a document $D = \vec{D}$ ($Term_1$, W_1; $Term_2$, W_2;...; $Term_n$, W_n), if $Term_k$ in the text can be repeated and there should be a sequence, the relationship between analysis still has the certain difficulty. In order to simplify the analysis, can temporarily don't consider $Term_k$ order and require different $Term_k$ in the document, it can be consider $Term_1$, $Term_2$, ..., $Term_n$ as an n-dimensional coordinate system, and W_1, W_2, ..., W_n for the corresponding coordinates, thus $D(W_1, W_2, ..., W_n)$ is as a vector of n-dimensional space, called $D(W_1, W_2, ..., W_n$ text D vector said. Among them, the $Term_i (i = 1, 2, ..., n)$ of the vocabulary of the text, $W_i (i = 1, 2, ..., n)$ said its corresponding weights.

VSM's main advantage is that it simplifies the representation of a natural language, converts the complex language simple algebra content, and can be applied in mathematics calculation method for processing text; greatly reduce the complexity of the problem, at the same time to ensure the time complexity requirements of many applications. At the same time, VSM does not depend on a particular field; the spatial similarity can be utilized to approximate the semantic similarity.

2.2 *Tibetan text clustering*

Clustering is the process of a data set is divided into several groups or classes, and the data objects within the same group have high similarity, and the data objects in the different groups are significantly different. Similarity is calculated according to the description object attribute values. Clustering and classification of the difference is that the latter learning obtain classification of prediction model used by the data is known (class-labeled, belongs to supervised learning method, clustering analysis and the data analysis and processing are no pre-determined category of belonging, the class mark in clustering analysis of the data set is not exist, belongs to unsupervised learning, in many cases has stronger practicability.

2.2.1 Formal description of the text clustering

Text clustering formalized definition as:

$$D = \bigcup_{i=1}^{N} d_i$$

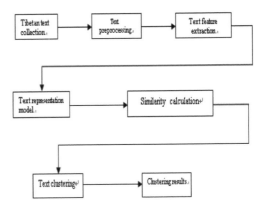

Figure 1. Tibetan text clustering process model.

on behalf of a text data set. C_j is a subset of D, then the task of text clustering is divided D into k subsets, satisfy its:

$$D = \bigcup_{j=1}^{k} C_j, \; C_{j1} \cap C_{j2} = \varnothing$$

Above as the basic conditions, only the text clustering is more important which is to make a bunch of the text on the semantic similarity and as far as possible and text as far apart or different from other clusters, namely:

$$max\left(sim(d_i, C_j) \right), \; d_i \in C_j 1$$

$$min\left(sim(d_i, C_j) \right), \; d_i \notin C_j$$

2.2.2 Tibetan text clustering process

Tibetan text clustering is a complex data process-ing; it has essentially different with other cluster-ing methods. Research clearly Tibetan process and contents of the text clustering is very important. In this paper, the model of Tibetan text clustering process is shown in Figure 1.

Text clustering to the pretreatment of the docu-ment in the first place, then the text said the final clustering. Text preprocessing approach usually cut including word processing; remove the stop, filtering web symbols, etc., as a result, the docu-ment processing into space vector or keywords list. The Chinese document representation is divided into feature extraction and feature reconstruction step or two. First by feature extraction algorithm according to the characteristics of the evaluation function and the setting threshold, from all the characteristics of the concentrated extract an opti-mal feature subset; Again after feature extraction of the optimal feature subset request according to

the clustering method, weight adjustments, high-light the important word clustering and build text representation model; According to the definition of Chinese text strings' similarity, judge the dis-tance between the text; After the use of text clus-tering algorithms, clustering results are obtained and displayed.

3 HYBRID PARALLEL GENETIC ALGORITHMS

Text and indenting Genetic Algorithm is a kind of very effective global optimization Algorithm, is proposed by Holland in the United States in the 1960s, is mimic natural biological evolution mech-anism of random search Algorithm, and used in processing of traditional search method is difficult to solve complex optimization problems. With the acceleration development of the follow-up related research work, the content of the genetic algorithm has been further supplement and improvement of basic formed a set of complete theoretical system. Therefore, the study of the genetic algorithm will gradually turn to the improvement of genetic algorithm, (such as adaptive genetic algorithm, hierarchical genetic algorithm and parallel genetic algorithm, genetic algorithm based on niche tech-nology, etc.) and based on the genetic algorithm be combined with other hybrid intelligent opti-mization algorithm (such as quantum genetic algorithm, genetic algorithm and immune genetic algorithm together, etc.).[8]

Among them, the parallel genetic algorithm is an effective genetic algorithm for solving the prob-lem of premature convergence, it take full advan-tage of the parallelism of genetic algorithm, the efficiency has been greatly improved, guarantee the accuracy of the algorithm are also obtained. But the efficiency is only through the parallelism

5

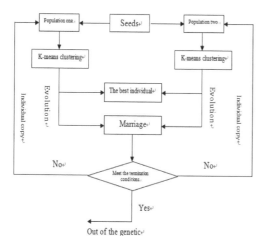

Figure 2. Hybrid parallel genetic algorithm model.

of the algorithm to obtain, has not been given in the process of calculation using heuristic approach to local optimization.

K-Means algorithm, however, is a kind of strong local search ability of clustering algorithm, it fully considered in the process of operation using heuristic method for clustering center of the excavation, so the algorithm efficiency is very high. However, K-Means algorithm is global search ability is bad, for the selection of the initial clustering center is relatively sensitive, so the algorithm precision is not guaranteed.

Therefore, this article on the choice of clustering algorithm priority hybrid parallel genetic algorithm, the hybrid parallel genetic algorithm can give full play to the efficiency of the K-Means algorithm and local search ability, and parallel the parallelism and global optimization ability of genetic algorithm, so as to rapidly and accurately find the initial clustering center. The model is shown in Figure 2.

4 FEATURE SELECTION BASED ON HYBRID PARALLEL GENETIC ALGORITHM

The main purpose of the feature selection is to reduce the dimension of feature vector and don't change feature vector representation. Feature vector selection also produces a feature vector; the result of the characteristics is one of the items in the original feature vector subset. Feature selection based on hybrid parallel genetic algorithm includes: chromosome coding and the initial population establishment, set of fitness function, genetic operator design (including selection operator,

crossover operator and mutation operator), the setting of the termination conditions.[10]

4.1 Chromosome coding and the establishment of the initial population

Chromosome coding with binary coding, coding method is as follows: for an individual (chromosome) S, and the original eigenvector v, if v is an n-dimensional vector, then the Si is encoded into a bit binary number, everyone in Si is equal to a gene of the chromosomes. If the value of first x in Si is1, meant V in the x dimension feature is selected; if the value is 0, meant y dimensions of V on the characteristics of the item is not selected. Obviously, the characteristics of any kind of combination, there is only one string with the matching.

The selection of initial population with random method, using random function to produce N chromosome form the initial group.

4.2 Fitness function

Natural selection, survival of the fittest" is the center of the genetic thinking, how to determine the individual fitness problems is the key to evaluate the individual effect. This article uses the average similarity to represent the fitness of the individual. Text is represented as feature vector, the whole text collections as a vector space, this text vector space can be calculated the average similarity between the feature vectors. If a word has a good degree of differentiation, as it has joined, the average similarity becomes smaller; On the other hand, if a degree of differentiation of words is poor, so the average similarity. Feature selection task is to select the degree of differentiation of good words, namely small characteristic collection of the average similarity, such as genetic algorithm with the average similarity of individual fitness is appropriate.

For an individual S_i, its average similarity function computation formula is as follows:

$$C(i) = \frac{1}{N} \sum_{j=1}^{N} D(S_i, S_j)$$

Among them, $D(X, Y) = (\Sigma(X_i - Y_j)^2)^{1/2}$ can be used to calculate the Euclidean distance of individual X and Y, and $X_i = W_i * b_i$. W_i is the original feature vector of the ith feature weights, bi is the ith binary values of individual X. $D(X, Y)$ value, the greater the degree of similarity between X and Y is smaller.

Therefore, the fitness function is:

$$F_i = \frac{1}{C(i)}$$

6

The greater the value of F_i is, the higher the fitness of the individual will be.

4.3 Select operator

The selection operator is the process of choosing the relative good individual adaptive value from the current group to generate the mating pool. At present, there is mainly the choice of fitness proportion, the Boltzmann selection and sorting, etc. In this paper, I will use the Boltzmann selection. Different stages in the process of population evolution require different selection pressures. Early stage selection pressure is small, because I want to poorer individuals to have certain opportunities, to make groups maintain higher diversity; Later stage selection pressure is bigger, we hope that the genetic algorithm to reduce the search neighborhood, to speed up the current optimal solution to improve. In order to evolutionary selection pressure in the process of dynamic adjustment group, Goldberg Boltzmann selection method is designed. Individual selection probability is:

$$P_s\left(a_j\right) = \frac{e^{f(a_j)/T}}{\sum_{i=1}^{n} e^{f(a_i)/T}}$$

Among them, $T > 0$ is annealing temperature. T as the iteration to gradually reduce, selection pressure will rise accordingly.

4.4 Crossover operator

Crossover operator in the genetic algorithm is an evolutionary algorithm with the primitiveness of unique characteristics. Crossover operator is to imitate the genetic recombination process of sexual reproduction nature, which plays a role in passing on to the original good genes to the next generation of individuals, and generating a new individual which contains more complex genetic structure. Crossover operator is usually a single point crossover and multipoint crossover and uniform crossover, etc.

This article will adopt the method of single point crossover, randomly setting an intersection in the string of individual coding. According to the set of the crossover probability of Pc, at this point will have an exchange of two matching individual part of the chromosome, and it will produce two new individuals.

Single point make righteous operation schematic is shown below:

Before cross is as follows:
X: 1010 0110 | 00
Y: 0011 1101 | 11

After cross is as follows:
X: 1010 0110 | 11
Y: 0011 1101 | 00

4.5 Mutation operator

Mutation on chromosome mimic natural biological evolution a genetic mutations occur, thus changing the structure of the chromosome and physical properties. In genetic algorithm, we can through the mutation probability Pm stochastic inversion of one allele of a binary character values to realize the mutation operator. Mutation is determined by the mutation probability, mutation probability though only affect the local search ability of the algorithm. However, if the mutation probability is too low, some useful genes will not be able to enter the choice; if the mutation rate is too high, future generations may lose from the parent generation inherit good features; In general the value of the mutation probability Pm is between 0.001 and 0.10.

4.6 Termination conditions

When the fitness of the best individual to a given threshold, or the fitness of the best individual and group fitness rise no more, or the number of iterations reaches algebra, termination algorithm. Default algebraic average generation is set to 100–500.

5 RESULTS AND CONCLUSION

Experiment is an effective way to judge the algorithm is good or bad, because the new method in the aspect of theory has not been proved strictly, so it is hard to avoid errors, we should carry on the objective evaluation, and try our best to improve in the later research.

5.1 Experimental data

Experimental data of this article is obtained from major Tibetan sites, involving politics, economy, culture and education, information technology, religion, ecological environment, health care, and there are 600 Tibetan texts. As shown in Table 1.

5.2 Experimental steps

The steps of Text clustering as follows:

1. Text segmentation for the test data;
2. The text is represented by vector space model;
3. Decreasing dimensions;
4. Using genetic algorithm to optimize the data which has been decreased the dimensions;

Table 1. Experimental data.

Subject category	Politics	Economy	Culture and education	Information technology	Religion	Ecological environment	Health care
The number of text	100	50	100	50	50	100	150

Table 2. Experimental results.

Algorithm	K-means	GA	HPGA
The average accuracy	60%	63%	67%
F_1	0.65	0.71	0.76

5. Using the K-means algorithm to cluster analysis for optimized data;
6. Calculating the value of F_1 and analyzing.

5.3 *The evaluation method of clustering results*

Estimating the evaluation of clustering results is good or bad basically has the following several indicators: Precision, Recall and F_1. P_r is used to show the correctness of the clustering, and R_e is used to characterize the integrity of the clustering. P_r and R_e must be considered at same time, so we introduce a new evaluation index F_1. As shown in the following formula:

$$F_1 = \frac{P_r \times R_e \times 2}{P_r + R_e}$$

The greater the value of F_1 is, the effect of clustering will be better.

5.4 *Experiment results analysis*

The experimental results are shown in Table 2.

From the experimental results, we can learn that the k-means algorithm clustering accuracy is lower. Comparing to the k-means algorithm, GA algorithm improved. Tibetan text clustering based on hybrid parallel genetic algorithm works best. Errors mainly concentrated in Tibetan word segmentation, feature selection and calculation of similarity between texts, these will be our next work.

ACKNOWLEDGMENT

This work is supported by Science and technology major special project in Gansu province (1203FKDA033), The central college funds under Grant (NO. ycx13014).

REFERENCES

[1] J.H. Holland. Adaptation in Natural and Artificial Systems[M], Ann Arbor: Univ. of Michigan Press, 1975.
[2] He Ling, Wu Linda, Cai Yichao. Clustering algorithm in data mining[J]. Computer Application Research, 2007, 1:10–13.
[3] H. Spath. ClusterDissection and Analysis: Theory, Fortran program examples[M], Ellis Horwood Ltd, 1985.
[4] Shi Jianqiang, Liu Xiaoping. The study of the data mining technology based on genetic algorithm[J]. Computer and Information Techonlogy, 2003, 1:9–14.
[5] Zhou Ming, Sun Shudong. The principle and application of genetic algorithm[M]. Beijing: National Defense Science and Technology Press, 1999.
[6] Xuan Guangnan, Chen Runwei. Genetic algorithm and engineering design[M], translated by Dingwei Wang. Beijing: Science Press, 2000.
[7] Dai Xiaohui, Li Minqiang, Kou Jisong. Dynamic clustering method based on genetic algorithm[J]. System Engineering Theory and Practice, 1999, 19(10):108–116.
[8] Zhang Liping, Chai Yueting. The present situation and development direction of the genetic algorithm[J]. Information and Control, 2001, 30(6):531–536.
[9] Zhang Tian. A New Data Clustering Algorithm and its Applications[J]. Data Mining and Knowledge Discovery, 1, 141–182 (1997).
[10] Zhang Yong. Research of Text Clustering Based on Genetic Algorithm[J]. Nanjing University of Aeronautics and Astronautics.

Computer, Intelligent Computing and Education Technology – Liu, Sung & Yao (Eds)
© 2014 Taylor & Francis Group, London, ISBN 978-1-138-02469-4

The PVDF-based method for wind turbine blades structural health monitoring

Yi-Yang Li, Zhou Wan, Zhuen Chen, Hao-Hua Liu & Xi-Cun You
Faculty of Information Engineering and Automation, Kunming University of Science and Technology, Kunming, P.R. China

ABSTRACT: Wind energy is paid more and more attention by the countries all over the world. With the rapid development of wind power, the accidents of wind turbine damage is also increasing year by year, especially the accidents caused by the blade breakage are the most common. Monitoring the structural health of wind turbine blades is a problem that urgently needs to be addressed. However, the domestic researches of wind turbine blade are mainly concentrated in manufacture and design. As a result, a method for monitoring the blades' structural health has been put forward and the PVDF monitoring sensor has been designed and produced. The sensor can measure the blade's resonance parameters at the frequency of 6~2000 Hz. Further, collecting these parameters will support qualitative analysis to judge whether the blade is cracked.

Keywords: wind turbine blade; PVDF; structural health monitoring; resonance displacement; frequency response curve

1 INTRODUCTION

With the advent of 1970s world energy crisis, wind power has been paid more and more attention by the countries all over the world, and the main use of wind energy is wind power generation. With the rapid development of wind power, the accidents of wind turbine damage are also increasing year by year. Any position of wind turbine is likely to damage, such as generator, gearbox, blade and so on. The damage caused by the blade breakage is the most frequent in statistics and also causes the greatest loss. What's worse: this kind of damage is often accompanied by serious secondary disasters (destroy of the building nearby, vehicle damage, casualties, etc.). The blade is the first step to switch wind energy into electricity. The blade damage will directly lead to the paralysis of the wind turbine. In order to reduce the risk of loss during the operation of a wind turbine, and reduce the maintenance cost for wind turbine blades, the health of the blades must be paid high attention, and the study on blades damage identification must be strengthened.

Wind turbine blades structural health monitoring is a problem which urgently needs to be addressed, but the domestic researches on wind turbine blades are mainly concentrated in design and manufacture. This paper presents a method for monitoring the blades' structure health. By utilizing PVDF film which has the advantages of fast response, high sensitivity, and good mechanical properties and

so on, the monitoring sensor has been designed and produced. The sensor can measure the resonance displacement of a blade at the frequency of 6~2000 Hz. After acquiring the inherent frequencies of a blade when it is in healthy state and when it is in cracked state, the frequency response displacement curves can be recorded. By comparing the two different frequency response displacement curves, it is intuitional to judge whether the blade is cracked.

The remainder of this paper is organized as follows. In Section 2, we introduce the chemical constitution and advantages of PVDF film at first. Then we describe the design and producing of the PVDF monitoring sensor. At last, we test the sensor and obtain the performance indicators of the sensor. After analyzing the wind turbine blade health monitoring experiments' consequences, Section 3 expounds the principle of the monitoring method and the procedure of using it in an actual monitoring. We end our paper with a summary in Section 4.

2 THE PVDF MONITORING SENSOR

2.1 *PVDF film*

PVDF (Polyvinylidene fluoride) is a high molecular polymer type of new sensing material, and its molecular formula is:

$$-\left(CH_2 = CF_2 \right)_n - \tag{1}$$

It is constituted by two fluorine atoms which substitutes ethylene molecules in the two hydrogen atoms. PVDF film has the advantages of fast response, wide frequency response, linearity, good reproducibility, wide dynamic range, easy to match the acoustic impedance, high sensitivity force electrical conversion, high strength mechanical properties. Besides, PVDF film is light, flexible, extremely thin, impact-resistant, invulnerable to the pollution of water and chemicals, and easy to make into any shape ranging from tablets or tube. Polarized the PVDF film, the film will have a piezoelectric characteristic. Further explanation is that when withstands the pressure of a certain direction, PVDF film will generate a charge which is equal in magnitude and opposite in direction in the upper and lower plane of polarization. Piezoelectric effect reflects the interplay between electrical and mechanical quantities. PVDF film is used as vibrating sensor, which the influence on system vibration is little. So the PVDF sensors have been widely used in vibration measurement and monitoring structural mode of beam.

2.2 Sensor design

After consulting literature and doing experiment repeatedly, we selected a sine curve boundary as the shape of the PVDF monitoring sensor, as shown in Figure 1. Thus the sensor will obtain the best frequency response performance, and minimize the influence on the wind turbine operation.

In the case of one dimension, the sensor attached to the surface of the object will not affect the dynamic balance and fluid characteristics of the object. The relationship between vibration response and output charge of the PVDF monitoring sensor is:

$$q = -Ze \int_0^l \sin\left(\frac{\pi y}{l}\right) \frac{d^2 w(y)}{dy^2} dy \quad (2)$$

In the formula, e is piezoelectric stress constant, $\sin(\pi y/l)$ is boundary shape function, l is length of sensor, $w(y)$ is the displacement function and Z is thickness parameter. The sensor can acquire the resonance parameters of the wind turbine blade, such as resonance displacement, etc.

The conductive silicon rubber is used as the base substrate of the sensor. After cutting the PVDF films and conductive silicon rubber into the shape we designed, bond them together with conductive silver paste. The structure of the PVDF film which is domestic produced is composed of three layers, as shown in Figure 2.

2.3 The sensor's performance indicators

Using function signal generator, power amplifier, vibration exciter and digital oscilloscope, apply sinusoidal excitation signals on the sensor for testing. Change the amplitude and frequency of the excitation signal continuously, the response of the sensor is changing accordingly, and the response waveforms coincide with the excitation waveforms. Change the given frequency excitation signal and repeat the test. The record of the frequency responses from the tests is drawn in Figure 3. The deviations of the frequency responses are calculated respectively, as shown in Figure 4.

The figures show that the response frequency deviation is the minimum when the excitation frequency is 750 Hz, and the response frequency deviation will reach or even exceed 5% when the excitation frequency is below 6 Hz or above 2000 Hz. Hereby, the wind turbine blades health

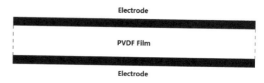

Figure 2. The three-tier structure of the PVDF film.

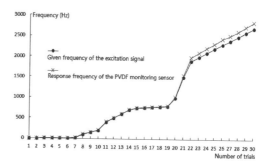

Figure 3. The test of the PVDF monitoring sensor.

Figure 1. The shape design of the PVDF monitoring sensor.

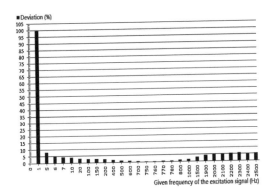

Figure 4. The deviation of the response frequency.

monitoring experiment is implemented at the frequency of 6~2000 Hz.

3 WIND TURBINE BLADE HEALTH MONITORING EXPERIMENTS

In the process of the wind turbine operating, the amount of data collected is very large, so the multi-function data acquisition card is used for the signal real-time processing, which is able to cut a certain scientific research cost meanwhile. The PVDF monitoring sensor has high internal impedance, so the signal must pass through the signal conditioner for impedance matching, signal amplification and filtering processing before entering the multifunction data acquisition card. The multi-function data acquisition card and the host PC communicate by USB2.0. In addition, the experimental instrument also need white noise signal generator, power amplifier, oscillator, wind turbine blade model (the experiment dedicated) and so on.

The PVDF monitoring sensor is attached to the wind turbine blades by silver conductive adhesive. The white noise signal generator generates a white noise signal which drives the oscillator after being amplified by the power amplifier. The oscillator applies a vibration force on one end of the wind turbine blade, and the blade starts to vibrate. The sensor feels vibration and generates electric charge. After the processing through the signal conditioner and the multi-function data acquisition card, the signals enter the host PC to store.

In the experiment, set 6~2000 Hz as the output range of the white noise signal generator. There are two pieces of wind turbine blade model which are processed by the 8th beam tablets (length 80 mm, width 20 mm and thickness 5 mm). One wind turbine blade model is cracked in varying degrees artificially, and the other one

is keep intact. Conduct the experiment four times with different blades and identity the differences between the healthy blade and the slight, moderate and serious cracked blade, as shown in Figures 5–7. From the figures, we can obtain the following conclusions:

1. The maximum amplitude of the frequency response displacement curve is about 1050 Hz if the blade is healthy. At this frequency, the resonance displacement of the blade is the max. The blade's inherent frequency is $f_0 = 1050$ Hz.

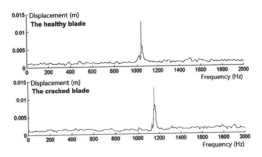

Figure 5. Contrast of the healthy blade and the slight cracked blade.

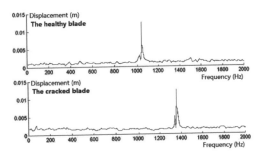

Figure 6. Contrast of the healthy blade and the moderate cracked blade.

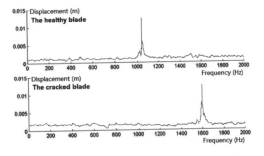

Figure 7. Contrast of the healthy blade and the serious cracked blade.

2. When the blade is cracked slightly, the maximum amplitude is about 1150 Hz, and the blade's inherent frequency is $f_1 = 1150$ Hz.
3. When the blade is cracked moderately, the maximum amplitude is about 1350 Hz, and the blade's inherent frequency is $f_2 = 1350$ Hz.
4. When the blade is cracked seriously, the maximum amplitude is about 1600 Hz, and the blade's inherent frequency is $f_3 = 1600$ Hz.
5. It is apparent that $f_0 \neq f_n (n = 1, 2, 3)$.

By comparison, the response displacement curve of the cracked blade has changed obviously. The changes of the blade's inherent frequency concomitantly lead to the three different frequency response displacement curves. In other words, the changing of the blade's inherent frequency means that the blade is getting to crack.

In an actual monitoring, we firstly measure a new quality wind turbine blade under a white noise signal excitation and record the frequency response displacement curve, get down f_0 as the healthy standard. After the turbine operating, measure the blade under the same white noise signal excitation at set intervals, record the frequency response displacement curve and $f_n (n \in N^+)$. Comparing f_0 and f_n is able to judge whether the blade is cracked intuitionally.

4 CONCLUSION

This paper puts forward a method to monitor the blades' structural health. By utilizing PVDF film which has the advantages of fast response, high sensitivity, and good mechanical properties and so on, the PVDF monitoring sensor has been designed and produced. The sensor can measure the resonance displacement of a blade at the frequency of 6~2000 Hz. After acquiring the inherent frequencies of a blade when it is in healthy state and when it is in cracked state, the frequency response displacement curves can be recorded. By comparing the two different frequency response displacement curves, it is intuitional to judge whether the blade is cracked. This method is of effectivity, utility, simple operation, intuitive judgment, and momentous engineering value. Based on this method, there is a broad application space in the research field of wind turbine blades damage identification and flexible rigid (windmill blades, turbine blades, helicopter blades, etc.) structural health monitoring.

REFERENCES

Daihua Wang and Shanglian Huang. 1999. Theoretical and Experimental Research on PVDF Sensors for Monitoring Vibrations' Parameters. Chinese Journal of Sensors and Actuators 4:250–255.
GB/T 25383-2010. 2011. Wind turbine generator-Rotor blades: China Zhijian Publishing House, Beijing.
Haiyun Zhao. 2000. The performance and applications of the PVDF piezoelectric-film. Technology and Application Publications 28(6):24–26.
Jinhai Zhu. Preparation and performance study of pvdf piezoelectric film and sensor 2011 (Master thesis): Harbin Institute of Technology, Harbin, Heilongjiang.
Peiwen Liu and Kaijian Huang. 2012. Wind turbine blade damage analysis and repair recommendations. East China Science & Technology 11:326 Zeqiang Long. 2001. Wind Power-Green Energy for the 21st Century. World Sci-tech R&D 23(04):32–34.
Shuxin Wang and Yizhe Li. 2004. The Design of PVDF Sensors and its Application to Measurement of Vibration Parameters. Piezoelectrics & Acoustooptics 25(5):374–376.
(UAE) S.M. Muyeen 2013. Wind Energy Conversion System-Technology and Trends: China Machine Press, Beijing.
Xiangui He, Xia Lu, Yuejin Yang and Wankun Liu. 2009. Wind turbine design, manufacturing and operation: Chemical Industry Press, Beijing.
Yang Zhou, Jianguo Wan and Baoqi Tao. 1996. Structure, Mechanism and Applcations of PVDF Piezoelectric Film. Materials Review 5:43–47.
Yongkai Zhu, Renqian Pan, Shengpiao Chen and Guiyun Tian. 2010. Structural Health Monitoring of Wind Turbine Blade Based on Sensor Array and Acoustic Emission. Nondestructive Testing 32(10):753–756.
Zhou Wan and Tao Ji. 2009. The PVDF-based metal structural damage crack detection. The China Intelligent Automation Conference Proceedings: 988–992.

Computer, Intelligent Computing and Education Technology – Liu, Sung & Yao (Eds)
© 2014 Taylor & Francis Group, London, ISBN 978-1-138-02469-4

Research on universal data push mechanism based on XMPP protocol and IAIDL for smart home

Y. Wang, D.L. Shi & Z.Q. Wei
Ocean University of China, Qingdao, Shandong, China

X. Wang
Haier Group, Qingdao, Shandong, China

ABSTRACT: The universal data push mechanism is considered for smart home to implement data push service between terminals with different systems. With the development of smart home and mobile devices, demand for integration between smart home terminals and mobile devices was growing rapidly. In order to solve the incompatibility between smart home terminals and mobile devices, a universal data push mechanism based on XMPP protocol and IAIDL was considered to integrate different terminals in smart home and process internal and external data push services simultaneously. So connections inside and outside of smart home can be better implemented, and expansibility, efficiency and user experience of smart home can also be improved.

Keywords: smart home; data push; XMPP protocol; IAIDL

1 INTRODUCTION

Smart home is the main direction of the study of household electrical appliances. It is the combination of communication technology, computer technology and consumer electronics technology, and this combination enable traditional home appliance to implement digitalization, intellectualization and networking.[1]

With the development of smart home and mobile device, demand for integration between smart home terminals and mobile devices was growing rapidly. In this paper, based on the existing research results, the main contribution is to combine the XMPP protocol push mechanism and IAIDL language, and put forward a universal data push mechanism suitable for smart home. This mechanism can integrate different terminals in smart home and process internal and external data push services simultaneously. So connections inside and outside of smart home can be better implemented, and expansibility, efficiency and user experience of smart home can also be improved.

2 RELATED WORK

In the implementation of data push for smart home, XMPP protocol communication and connections between mobile devices and home appliance equipment are two important research aspects.

XMPP protocol uses client–server system architecture. Data transmission between terminals should all go through XMPP server. XMPP introduces the TLS in server communication mechanism for data encryption to ensure the data security in the process of transmission, and uses SASL protocol on XML stream authentication.[4]

As is shown in Figure 1, XMPP protocol contains three types of entities, which are XMPP client,

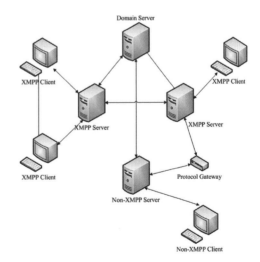

Figure 1. XMPP framework.

XMPP server and protocol gateway respectively. Among them, the protocol gateway is responsible to interconnect XMPP system with the non-XMPP system, meanwhile the XMPP server can also communicate with each other, which forms the distributed network composed of XMPP server.[5] The terminals connected to XMPP network can not only communicate with the terminals connected to the same server, but also communicate with the server on the Internet.[6]

Current mainstream systems for smart terminals such as Android and iOS have already had comparatively mature push mechanism based on XMPP protocol. For instance, XMPP protocol can be applied on the iOS platform to build Instant Messaging system, and real-time data push in the system can be implemented by adopting the technology of real-time compression of XML data in wireless network.[6] XMPP protocol can also be applied on the Android platform to build push platform by using the Node—XMPP libraries and ASMACK repositories.[7]

IAIDL specification language was originally put forward for the study of universal remote control in smart home system. The state of each terminal can be described by IAIDL specification language, and this information enables terminals to interact with universal remote by smart gateway which is running IAIDL interpreter and embedded database applications in order to implement universal control's manipulation to the entire smart home system.[1] A method has already been proposed to express IAIDL specification in the XML document.[3]

3 SYSTEM ARCHITECTURE

Studies above have shown that to implement data push in smart home, the combination of XMPP protocol and IAIDL specifications written in XML is more feasible.

The universal data push mechanism designed in this paper is shown in Figure 2. Each terminal is connected with management through smart home gateway, and the management server is the core of the mechanism, which applies XMPP protocol to handle internal and external data push services simultaneously. Push server also applies XMPP protocol, and it is responsible to send a variety of data to the management server from the cloud push server, and send status information and subscription request to the cloud push server from the management server. The cloud push services include real-time weather push, subscription push and program recommendation, etc. which can be customized according to the current status of smart home and user's subscription request.

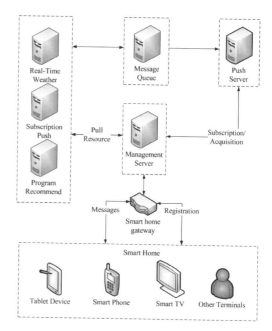

Figure 2. Universal data push mechanism for smart home.

When interacting with home appliances terminals, firstly we will define function interfaces of smart home appliances according to IAIDL specification and their function, and create interface definition text.[4] Then, interface registered senior text and interface invocating framework senior text will be created by IDL compiler, and compiled into an executable program with XML protocol high-level language text by high-level language compiler. Once the smart home appliance terminal is to be registered in smart home gateway, equipment registration packet created according to XML protocol will be sent to the gateway, and complete the registration of equipment interface service. Once push request is received, the corresponding interface will be invoked by interface adapter, and the equipment API will be invoked by execute interface program. Finally driver will drive hardware interface to complete the operation requested.[4]

4 PUSH MECHANISM

4.1 Communication module

The main function of XMPP communication module in the smart home terminal is to communicate with the management server, and to implement the push operation between the management server and terminals. XMPP communication module is mainly to implement the following functions:

1. Registration: registration is needed when new equipment is deployed. Terminal accounts should have been registered in advance before the system is deployed.
2. Login: terminals will automatically login to the XMPP server after starting up, and do some message communication after login.
3. Subscription: predefined alerts between terminals and servers will be implemented by using subscription mechanism.
4. Send messages: communication module will receive messages from control module, transform them into XMPP message encapsulation format, and send them to the XMPP server.
5. Receive messages: communication module will transform command messages received from management server into local message format, and transmit them to the control module.
6. File transfer: communication module will implement file transfer between smart home terminals and management server.

4.2 XML stream format

In push mechanism for smart home, XML node and XML stream is the carrier of messages transferred between different entities. XML stream contains XML elements transferred between two entities, and each XML node represents its own information, which implements different functions.[7] XMPP protocol defines three top XML nodes: <presence>, <message> and <iq>. Among them, <presence> node represents the subscription state of the corresponding entity, with which each terminal can release their online status, and can also query the online status of its subscribed entities; <message> node represents messages pushed from one entity to another, and it describes contents such as source node and destination node of the message, form and content of the message, etc.; <iq> node manages the conversion between two entities in XMPP server, and supports the query and response of the XML format between entities.[5]

In the internal data push, the state information and operation information of electrical appliances terminal can be represented by XML nodes written in IAIDL specifications, and these messages can be included in <message> node while transmitting. XML written in IAIDL specifications includes nine kinds of XML nodes. Among them, there are four kinds of nodes describing attributes of the home appliance: <id> represents the unique identification of the type of home appliance, <name> represents the English name of the equipment, <manufacture> represents the name of the manufacturer, <model> represents

the unique identification of each home appliance. Besides, there are five kinds of nodes describing operation information: <operationname> represents the name of operation, <operationtype> represents the type of operation displayed on the interface, <operationcurrent> represents the current state of the home appliance, <operationvalue> represents the new status value user want to change into, <operationdefault> represents the default value of the operation when the requested operation fails.

4.3 Internal data push flow

Internal data push for smart home includes the push operation of real-time state information and operation request between terminals and management server. Figure 3 depicts the data push flow between terminals through the management server. Specific communication flow is:

Step 1, XMPP module of the pusher terminal will establish a TCP connection with XMPP server.

Step 2, XMPP module of the terminal will send an XML initialization stream to the XMPP server in order to get the server's response, so as to determine whether the server is available. An XML response stream will be sent back to the terminal if the server is available.

Step 3, the management server will attempt to shake hands using established TCP connection. If it fails, XMPP server will disconnect the TCP connection. If it is succeed, XMPP module of the terminal will send a new XML stream to the XMPP server, and the server will reply a certified stream. If the client authentication is succeeded, the terminal will request to establish a conversation. If the stream the server returns contains resource binding characteristics, XMPP module of the terminal will bind a specific resource to the stream by IQ node.

Step 4, after the conversation is successfully established, the pusher terminal will encapsulate its

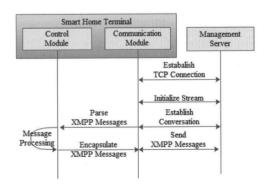

Figure 3. Internal data push flow for smart home.

status information or operation request into XML stream, and send them to the management server.

Step 5, the management server will classify information pushed from the terminal, and if the information needs to push to another smart terminal, then the server will connect to the corresponding terminal according to steps 1 to 3.

Step 6, after receiving the pushed information, the receiver terminal will parse it from XML to the local information, and then execute the corresponding operation. After the operation is completed, the terminal will encapsulate the response information into XML, and send it back to the management server.

4.4 External data push flow

External data push for smart home includes the push operation of customized information from the cloud to smart terminals and the push operation of real-time state information and operation request from terminals to the cloud. Figure 4 depicts the data push flow from the cloud to a specific terminal through the push server and the management server. Specific communication flow is:

Step 1, the cloud will send push request to the push server, and establish conversation with the management server through the push server. The process is similar to steps 1–3 in 4.3.

Step 2, the push server will establish connection with the corresponding target terminal, and send messages to the communication module of the terminal after conversation is established.

Step 3, after receiving push information, the smart terminal will parse the XML stream into local information, and display it to the user. The push flow of alert information ends here. If the user needs to request the corresponding resources

from the cloud after selecting the particular information, then the flow continues.

Step 4, the communication module of the smart terminal will encapsulate the user's requests into XML stream, and send them to the cloud through the push server. After parsing, the cloud will send the corresponding resources to the management server. Then the management server will send an XML stream to the smart terminal to complete the resource-binding operation, and then send the corresponding resource to the smart terminal. After parsing the resource into local resource, smart terminal will display it to the user.

5 CONCLUSIONS

This paper put forward a universal data push mechanism suitable for smart home, put forward the concept of external and internal data push, and by adopting the XMPP protocol architecture, enabled terminals with different system to access to smart home using unified communication protocol. In the mechanism proposed in this paper, the management server based on XMPP protocol could handle external and internal data push simultaneously, which laid the foundation for the push data's intelligent unified handling. Current mainstream mobile operating systems have already had comparatively mature XMPP protocol communication mechanism, therefore at present most of the mobile terminals can better access to smart home applied with the push mechanism proposed in this paper.

ACKNOWLEDGEMENT

This work is supported by National 973 Plan (2012CB724104) and Professor Zhiqiang Wei as the corresponding author.

REFERENCES

[1] Peng H. & Tang Z.Y., Liu H. 2008. The research of Push-Pull Technology based on Information Appliance. Microcomputer Information, 13:53–55.
[2] Milojicic D.S. & Kalogeraki V., Lukose R., et al. 2002. Peer-to-peer computing. Palo Alto: Hp Laboraries.
[3] Huang M. & Xia L. 2001. Research and design of universal remote control for information household appliances based on IAIDL, Network Security Technology and Application,12:51–53.
[4] Sun R.P. & Jia Z.P., Wu S.P. 2006. Design of Distributed Monitoring and Control System Based on OPC XML-DA. Computer Engineering, 32(14):274–276.
[5] RFC6121. 2004. Extensible messaging and presence protocol (XMPP): instant messaging and presence.

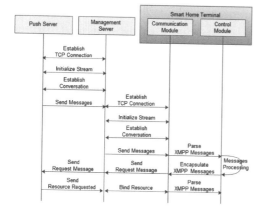

Figure 4. External data push flow for smart home.

[6] Saint-Andre P., ed. 2004. Mapping the Extensible Messaging and Presence Protocol (XMPP) to Common Presence and Instant Messaging (CPIM), IETF proposed standard, RFC 3922.

[7] Liu Z.F., 2012. Research and Implementation Of IM Client On IOS Based on XMPP Protocol. South China University of Technology.

[8] Wang Y.F. 2011. Realization of Push Mechanism in Android Platform. Computer Programming Skills and Maintenance, 22:29–31.

[9] Shieh W.G. & Wang J.M., Wen B.H., 2008. Secure remote control model for information appliances, Intelligence and Security Informatics, IEEE International Conference.

Computer, Intelligent Computing and Education Technology – Liu, Sung & Yao (Eds)
© *2014 Taylor & Francis Group, London, ISBN 978-1-138-02469-4*

Stereo vision calibration based on Elman neural network

Bing-Wen Chen

28th Research Institute of China Electronics Technology Group Corporation, Nanjing, China

ABSTRACT: In order to improve the accuracy and stability of stereo vision calibration, a novel stereo vision calibration approach based on Elman neural network is presented. The Elman neural network is utilized to build spatial mapping relationship. In the process of modeling, the Levenberg-Marquardt optimization algorithm is introduced as a criterion to train the neural network. Experiments demonstrate that the proposed approach is capable of calibrating 3D location more accurately. It is a convenient way to calibrate the stereo vision without specialized knowledge of stereo vision.

Keywords: stereo vision calibration; Elman neural network; Levenberg-Marquardt optimization algorithm

1 INTRODUCTION

Stereo vision calibration is an important issue in computer vision (Wang 2010, Zeng 2010). Accurate calibration is especially crucial for stereo vision application, such as depth measurement, three dimensional reconstruction, robotic location and object tracking.

The objective of stereo vision calibration is to learn the mapping from 2D image plane to 3D world. Several stereo vision calibration approaches have been proposed, while some camera models have also been presented to model the imaging procedure. A comprehensive status of stereo vision calibration is given in Weng's review (Weng 1991). Gonzalez also evaluates some famous calibration approaches in respect of stability and accuracy (Gonzalez 2005).

In recent years, more and more calibration approaches based on neural network (Xing 2007, Ge 2008, Wen 1991, Chen 2012) are proposed. In contrast with traditional calibration approaches, this kind of approach is capable of calibrating stereo vision without some special explicit distortion models. Some approaches learn the spatial mapping relationship based on Back Propagation neural network (BP) (Xing 2007, Wen 1991), while some researchers base their methods on Radial Basis Function neural network (RBF) (Ge 2008) or GMDH neural network (Chen 2012).

In this paper, we present a comparison between some calibration approaches based on neural network, and propose a novel stereo vision calibration approach based on Elman neural network. The remainder of this paper is described as follows: Sec. 2 introduces the Elman neural network.

In Sec. 3, we describe the proposed stereo vision calibration approach based on Elman neural network. Then the experimental evaluation of the proposed approach is described in Sec. 4. Finally, Sec. 5 includes some conclusions and further research directions.

2 ELMAN NEURAL NETWORK

Elman neural network is a partial recurrent network model first proposed by Elman (Elman 1990). It is a special kind of feed-forward neural network, which has extra local memory neurons and feedback loop. The Elman neural network is capable of approximating a nonlinear system without an explicit physical model.

An Elman neural network has four kinds of layers (Fig. 1): input layer, hidden layer, context layer and output layer (Chen 2008). The context layer is utilized to constitute the back-forward loop, from which the hidden layer selects input. In comparison with other forms of feed forward neural network, the Elman neural network is sensitive to history of input data by this mechanism.

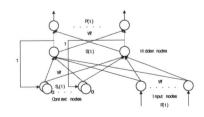

Figure 1. Structure of the Elman neural network.

3 STEREO VISION CALIBRATION USING ELMAN NEURAL NETWORK

Stereo vision calibration is actually to build the mapping model between 2D image plane and 3D world. However, this model exhibits a serious nonlinear phenomenon owing to all kinds of distortion, such as radial distortion and decentering distortion (Weng 1991), and all current imaging models cannot fix it well.

In this paper, a novel stereo vision calibration approach based on Elman neural network is proposed to approximate this complex model, and learn its nonlinear spatial mapping relationship implicitly. Moreover, in the process of modeling, the Levenberg-Marquardt (LM) algorithm (Martin 1994) is utilized to overcome some drawbacks of Elman neural network, such as: stucking in local shallow minima, and help the model slide through local minima and converge faster.

The proposed calibration approach works as follows:

1. According to the collected left and right images, the image coordinates of feature points in left and right images are extracted as input features of the Elman neural network, and then the LM algorithm is applied to train it with the training samples.
2. For the mathematical model of the Elman neural network, obtain the predictive value $\hat{p}$.
3. According to the LM algorithm, we define a performance index E (Equation 1), and adjust the weights until it reaches the minima or satisfies performance index (Equation 4, Equation 5), where the parameter μ is multiplied by some factor (β) when the performance index E increase, and μ is divided by β when the performance index E decrease.
4. Finally, for each point of targets, according to its image coordinates in left and right images, its corresponding 3D world coordinates are given by the trained Elman neural network.

$$E = \frac{1}{2}\sum_{q=1}^{Q}(\hat{p}_q - p_q)^2 = \frac{1}{2}\sum_{q=1}^{Q}e_q^2 \tag{1}$$

$$e_q = \hat{p}_q - p_q \tag{2}$$

$$\mathbf{e}(\mathbf{w}) = \left[e_1, e_2, ..., e_Q\right] \tag{3}$$

$$\mathbf{w}(t+1) = \mathbf{w}(t) + \Delta\mathbf{w}(t) \tag{4}$$

$$\Delta\mathbf{w}(t) = \left[\mathbf{J}^T(\mathbf{w})\mathbf{J}(\mathbf{w}) + \mu\mathbf{I}\right]^{-1}\mathbf{J}^T(\mathbf{w})\mathbf{e}(\mathbf{w}) \tag{5}$$

$$\mathbf{J}(w) = \begin{bmatrix} \dfrac{\partial e_1(\mathbf{w})}{w_1} & \cdots & \dfrac{\partial e_1(\mathbf{w})}{w_N} \\ \vdots & \vdots & \vdots \\ \dfrac{\partial e_Q(\mathbf{w})}{w_1} & \cdots & \dfrac{\partial e_Q(\mathbf{w})}{w_N} \end{bmatrix} \tag{6}$$

Here, $\hat{p}_q$ denotes the output value of neural network for the qth sample; p_q denotes the true value for the qth sample; e_q denotes the error of the qth sample; Q denotes the total number of training samples; w denotes the weights; N denotes the length of w; $\mathbf{J}(w)$ denotes the jacobian matrix.

4 EXPERIMENTAL RESULTS

To evaluate the performance of the proposed approach, we test the approach with some real collected datasets and compare with other approaches.

Experimental installment and dataset extraction: In the experiments, two TaiDian L300 A cameras are used to capture images whose resolution is 640 * 480. A planar checkerboard with 7 * 9 grids (the size of each grid is 28 mm * 28 mm) (Fig. 2) is used to gather the calibration point samples. The distance between two cameras and the base line (z axis, z = 0) sets as 740 mm; the distance between two cameras sets as 455 mm; the angle between two cameras sets as about 45°. The planar checkerboard moves to 310 mm, 150 mm, 0 mm, −310 mm and −465 mm five locations along the z axis of a know reference frame to generate five images for each camera respectively. The upper left corner point is supposed as the origin of world coordinates, and the calibration points are gathered by calculating the grid corresponding coordinates in the images. Only 48 corner points in central part of each image are applied to calibrate stereo vision. Three datasets of 310 mm, 0 mm and −465 mm locations which consist of 144 pairs of points are utilized to train each neural network, while two

Figure 2. The planar checkerboard.

datasets of 150 mm and −310 mm locations which include 96 pairs of points are applied to test these neural networks.

The proposed approach is compared with other three approaches: BP neural network approach (Xing 2007), RBF neural network approach (Ge 2008) and GMDH neural network (Chen 2012). For parameter setting, RBF neural network approach adopts $4 \times 8 \times 3$ network structure, gauss kernel basic function and gradient descent learning rule; BP neural network approach adopts $4 \times 5 \times 5 \times 3$ network structure, LM learning rule and sigmoid basic function for hidden layer and linear basic function for output layer; GMDH neural network approach adopts second-order for basic polynomial function; the proposed approach adopts: $4 \times 4 \times 3 \times 3$ structure, LM learning rule and sigmoid basic function for hidden layer and linear basic function for output layer.

In order to evaluate the stereo vision calibration results objectively and quantitatively, the Root Mean Square Error (RMSE) (Ahmed 1999) and the Relative Root Mean Square Error (RRMSE) (Jekabsons 2010) are adopted to evaluate each approach. While the RMSE indicator assesses the global accuracy and stability, the RRMSE indicator assesses the accuracy and stability in individual dimension. Both lower values of RMSE and RRMSE indicators indicate a better calibration performance.

$$\text{RMSE} = \sqrt{\frac{\sum_{i=1}^{n}\left[(x_i - \hat{x}_i)^2 + (y_i - \hat{y}_i)^2 + (z_i - \hat{z}_i)^2\right]}{n}}$$

(7)

$$\text{RRMSE}(c) = \frac{RMSE(c)}{\text{var}(c)}, c = x \text{ or } y \text{ or } z$$

(8)

Here, $(\hat{x}_i, \hat{y}_i, \hat{z}_i)$ denotes the estimated world coordinates which is calculated by calibration approach; (x_i, y_i, z_i) denotes the true world coordinates; $\text{RMSE}(c)$ denotes the individual RMSE indicator in dimension c; $\text{var}(c)$ denotes the variance in individual dimension c which indicates the complexity of datasets.

The quantitative calibration results of four approaches across train and test datasets are shown in Tables 1 and 2 respectively. From these tables, we can see that: the BP and GMDH approaches perform well for train dataset, but relatively poor for test dataset; RBF approach performs relatively poor in both global and individual dimensions for train and test datasets; In contrast, the proposed approach has both lower RMSE and RRMSE indicators, and is very stable.

Table 1. The comparison of calibration results between four approaches for train data.

Calibration approach	RMSE	RRMSE (X)	RRMSE (Y)	RRMSE (Z)
BP	0.9806	0.0036	0.0042	0.0029
RBF	35.8273	0.1319	0.1034	0.1082
GMDH	1.0090	0.0072	0.0055	0.0027
Elman	0.9434	0.0047	0.0046	0.0027

Table 2. The comparison of calibration results between four approaches for test data.

Calibration approach	RMSE	RRMSE (X)	RRMSE (Y)	RRMSE (Z)
BP	19.122	0.0081	0.0238	0.0616
RBF	33.4	0.1061	0.0917	0.1045
GMDH	2.9158	0.0119	0.0359	0.0072
Elman	2.2235	0.0176	0.0332	0.0035

To sum up, some quantitative experimental comparisons are presented, and the results demonstrate that the proposed approach has both lower RMSE and RRMSE indicators, and performs very stable. It is capable of calibrating stereo vision effectively.

5 CONCLUSIONS AND DISCUSSION

We present a novel stereo vision calibration approach based on Elman neural network. The proposed approach introduces Levenberg-Marquardt algorithm to build spatial mapping relationship adaptively. It does not rely on any prior knowledge. The quantitative experimental comparisons demonstrate that the proposed approach is capable of calibrating stereo vision more accurately and is stable.

In the implementation of the proposed approach, we do not take account of the processing speed. To further improve calibration performance, we are going to study how to speed the model up in the future.

REFERENCES

Ahmed, T., Elsayed, E. & Farag, A. 1999. Neurocalibration: a neural network that can tell camera calibration parameters, *Proceedings of IEEE conference on computer vision*, 463–468.

Chen, B.W., Wang, W.W. & Qin, Q.Q. 2012. Stereo vision calibration based on GMDH neural network, *Applied Optics*, 51(5): 841–845.

Chen,Y., Qi, W. & Zhao, J. 2008. A new Elman neural network and its dynamic properties, *Proceedings of International conference on cybernetics and intelligent systems*, 971–975.

Elman, J. 1990. Finding structure in time, *Cognitive Science,* 14(3): 179–211.

Ge, D., Yao, X. & Chen, W. 2008. Research of machine vision system based on RBF neural network. *Proceedings of International conference on computer science and information technology*, 218–222.

Gonzalez, J., Gamez, J. & Artal, C. 2005. Stability study of camera calibration methods. *Proceedings of IEEE Workshop en Agentes Fisicos*, 271–350.

Jekabsons, G. 2010. Adaptive basis function construction: an approach for adaptive building of sparse polynomial regression models. *Machine Learning,* 1(10): 127–155.

Martin, H. & Mohammad, B. 1994. Training feed forward networks with the marquardt algorithm, *IEEE Trans. On Neural Networks,* 5(6): 989–993.

Wang, X.J. 2010. Investigation into the keystone correction of the perspective projection of 3D scene, *Command Information System & Technology,* 1(6): 70–74.

Weng, J., Paul, C. & Herniou, M. 1992. Camera calibration with distortion models and accuracy evaluation. *IEEE Trans. on pattern analysis and machine intelligence,* 14(10): 965–980.

Wen J. & Schweitzer, G. 1991. Hybrid calibration of CCD cameras using artificial neural nets. *Proceedings of International joint conference on neural networks,* 337–342.

Xing, Y., Sun, J. & Chen, Z. 2007. Analyzing and improving of neural networks used in stereo calibration. *Proceedings of 3rd international conference on natural computation,* 745–749.

Zeng, A.L., Zhang, J.K., & Wang G.H. 2010. Research of the VVP-3D military visual simulation engine, *Command Information System & Technology,* 1(5): 17–23.

Computer, Intelligent Computing and Education Technology – Liu, Sung & Yao (Eds)
© 2014 Taylor & Francis Group, London, ISBN 978-1-138-02469-4

Compressed sensing algorithms for direction-of-arrival estimation with nonuniform linear arrays

W. Zhu & S. Shu
School of Mathematics and Computational Science, Xiangtan University, Xiangtan, Hunan, China

L.Z. Cheng
College of Science, National University of Defense Technology, Changsha, Hunan, China

ABSTRACT: The paper addresses the problem of Direction-of-Arrival (DOA) estimation with Nonuniform Linear Arrays (NLA), and proposes several Compressed Sensing (CS) algorithms to solve the problem. These algorithms are proposed based on CS method and the traditional DOA estimation algorithms. In the proposed algorithms, the CS method is used to recover the data of a Virtual Uniform Linear Array (VULA) from the data of a NLA, and the traditional DOA estimation algorithms are applied on the recovery data to estimate DOA. The experiments show the good efficiency of the proposed algorithms, especially of the CS-MUSIC and CS-RMUSIC algorithms.

Keywords: direction of arrival; compressed sensing; nonuniform linear array; orthogonal matching pursuit

1 INTRODUCTION

In the array signal processing, Uniform Linear Array (ULA) is very important and has extensive applications. However, in practice, some sensors of ULA may stop working, or the sensors cannot be uniformly spaced due to the complex acquisition conditions. Moreover, people often want to get good results with low cost. These cases yield the design of Nonuniform Linear Arrays (NLA) and algorithms for DOA estimation with NLA. For all designs of NLA, the Minimum Redundancy (MR) arrays and the Nonredundant (NR) arrays are well known (Moffet 1968, Vertatschitsch & Haykin 1986). Except the MUSIC and RMUSIC (root-MUSIC) algorithms, the traditional algorithms for DOA estimation are almost based on the ULA. Many algorithms, such as BF and ESPRIT, cannot be directly applied into the data of NLA (El Kassis et al. 2010). So many works have been done to obtain the data of a Virtual Uniform Linear Array (VULA) from the data of a NLA, such as (El Kassis et al. 2007).

A developing theory called Compressed Sensing (CS) can recover the sparse signal from incomplete and inaccurate measurements (Candes et al. 2006). The CS theory has been applied into DOA estimation with ULA (Gurbuz et al. 2012). Compared with the data of the corresponding VULA, the data of a NLA is incomplete and inaccurate. Therefore, we can apply the CS method into estimating DOA with NLA. In this paper, we use the CS method to recover the data of VULA from the data of NLA, and then apply several traditional DOA estimation algorithms on the recovery data to estimate the true DOA. We call these proposed algorithms the CS algorithms, including CS-BF, CS-MUSIC, CS-RMUSIC, CS-ESPRIT algorithms, and so on. The experiments show that the proposed algorithms are efficient, especially the CS-MUSIC and CS-RMUSIC algorithms.

The remainder of this paper is organized as follows. The preliminary knowledge is introduced in Section 2, the CS algorithms for DOA estimation with NLA is proposed in Section 3, the experiment results are reported in Section 4, and finally the conclusion is given in Section 5.

2 PRELIMINARY KNOWLEDGE

2.1 *Signal model with NLA*

Throughout the paper, we consider a NLA [$d_1 = 1$, $d_2, ..., d_M$] $\lambda/2$ ($M < d_M$) and L far-field incoherent narrowband sources impinging on the NLA come from distinct directions $\theta = (\theta_1, \theta_2, ..., \theta_L)^T$. where λ denotes the wavelength of the source signal and the superscript T represents the transpose. Then the received signal at time t of the NLA takes the form

$$x(t) = A(\theta)s(t) + n(t), \qquad (1)$$

where the $M \times 1$ vector $x(t)$ represents the received signal, the $M \times L$ matrix $A(\theta) = [a(\theta_1), a(\theta_2), ..., a(\theta_L)]$ is the array manifold matrix, the $M \times 1$ vectors $a(\theta_i) = [1, e^{-j\pi(d2-1)\sin\theta i}, ..., e^{-j\pi(dM-1)\sin\theta i}]^T$ $(1 \le i \le L)$ are the steering vectors, the $L \times 1$ vector $s(t) = [s_1(t), s_2(t), ..., s_L(t)]^T$ is the source vector, and $n(t)$ denotes a complex additive white Gaussian noise vector.

A VULA corresponding to the NLA is an ULA of d_M sensors, and the received signal at time t of the VULA can be expressed as

$$x_v(t) = A_v(\theta)s(t) + n_v(t), \qquad (2)$$

where the $d_M \times 1$ vector $x_v(t)$ represents the signals of VULA, the $d_M \times L$ matrix $A_v(\theta) = [a_v(\theta_1), a_v(\theta_2), ..., a_v(\theta_L)]$ is the array manifold matrix, the $d_M \times 1$ vectors $a_v(\theta_i) = [1, e^{-j\pi\sin\theta i}, ..., e^{-j\pi(dM-1)\sin\theta i}]^T$ $(1 \le i \le L)$ are the steering vectors, and $n_v(t)$ also denotes a complex additive white Gaussian noise vector.

Suppose a $M \times d_M$ matrix G, whose entries are zeros and ones, satisfy

$$A(\theta) = GA_v(\theta). \qquad (3)$$

Similar to the array interpolation technique (Weiss & Garish 1991), which aims to estimate the data of VULA from a NLA, the matrix G can be obtained by using

$$G = A(\theta)A_v(\theta)^H \left(A_v(\theta)A_v(\theta)^H\right)^{-1}, \qquad (4)$$

where the superscript H denotes conjugate transpose.

Inserting (3) into (1), we have

$$x(t) = GA_v(\theta)s(t) + n(t). \qquad (5)$$

2.2 Compressed sensing

A vector is called sparse if the number of its nonzero entries is much less than its length. Furthermore, a vector with length N is called k-sparse ($k << N$) if the number of its nonzero entries is not larger than k. CS theory is introduced to recover the sparse signal from compressed measurements which can result in significant reduction in the sampling (much less than Nyquist-sampling rate) and computational cost (Candes et al. 2006, Donoho 2006).

Suppose the vector signal $y = (y_1, y_2, ..., y_N)^T$ is sparse in the $\Psi \in C^{N \times N}$ domain, the representation is $y = \Psi Y$, and the vector Y is k-sparse. Suppose

the signal y is measured by a $P \times N$ ($P << N$) matrix Φ, and the measurement signal is denoted by $y_m = \Phi y = \Phi \Psi Y$. The sensing matrix is defined by $A = \Phi \Psi$, so $y_m = AY$. The sparse noisy signal recovery problem can be formulated as

$$\min_{Y \in \mathbb{C}^N} \| Y \|_0 \ s.t. \| y_m - AY \| \le \varepsilon, \qquad (6)$$

where $\varepsilon > 0$ is a bound on the magnitude of the error.

The above optimization problem can be solved with OMP algorithm (Tropp & Gilbert 2007) and other sparse recovery algorithms (Tropp & Wright 2010).

Furthermore, the sparse noisy signal recovery problem can also be formulated as the following convex optimization problem

$$\min_{Y \in \mathbb{C}^N} \| Y \|_1 \ s.t. \| y_m - AY \| \le \varepsilon, \qquad (7)$$

which can be solved by the basic pursuit (BP) algorithms (Donoho & Tsaig 2006).

In order to recover the signal with high probability, it requires that the sensing matrix A obeys Restricted Isometry Property (RIP) (Candes & Wakin 2008). That is, for all k-sparse signal x and some constant $\delta_k \in (0, 1)$, the matrix A satisfy the following inequations

$$(1 - \delta_k) \| x \|_2^2 \le \| Ax \|_2^2 \le (1 + \delta_k) \| x \|_2^2 . \qquad (8)$$

The RIP of the matrix $A = \Phi \Psi$ is related to the coherence of (Φ, Ψ), which is defined by

$$\mu(\Phi, \Psi) = \sqrt{N} * \max_{1 \le k < j \le N} |\langle \varphi_k, \psi_j \rangle|, \qquad (9)$$

where ϕ_k is the normal k-th row of Φ, and ψ_j is the normal j-th column of Ψ. Observe that $\mu(\Phi, \Psi) \in [1, \sqrt{N}]$ (Candes & Wakin 2008). Reference (Baraniuk 2007) pointed out that both the RIP of A and incoherence of (Φ, Ψ) can be achieved with high probability simply by selecting measurement matrix as a random matrix. Therefore, we can illustrate the RIP of A by illustrating the incoherence of (Φ, Ψ).

2.3 The traditional algorithms for DOA estimation

There are many algorithms for DOA estimation, such as BF, MUSIC, RMUSIC, ESPRIT, and so on. References (Krim & Viberg 1996, Van Veen & Buckley 1988) have given a good summary for these algorithms, and the reader is referred to them for more details.

3 CS ALGORITHMS FOR DOA ESTIMATION WITH NLA

As mentioned in subsection 2.2, we know that two processes, representing and measuring, corresponding to the representation matrix Ψ and measurement matrix Φ respectively, are very important in the CS method. Then in order to apply the CS method into DOA estimation with NLA, we should design Ψ and Φ firstly. For DOA estimation, the received signal is sparse in angular domain (Malioutov et al. 2005). A natural idea for designing Ψ is to expand the manifold matrix $A_v(\theta)$ on an angular grid formed by uniformly sampling $2N$ points in the angular interval $(-\pi/2, \pi/2]$ and define Ψ as

$$\Psi = \frac{1}{\sqrt{d_M}}[a(\varphi_1), a(\varphi_2), ..., a(\varphi_{2N})], \qquad (10)$$

where the steering vectors $a(\varphi_i) = [1, e^{-j\pi\sin\varphi_i}, ..., e^{-j\pi(dM-1)\sin\varphi_i}]^T$ $(1 \leq i \leq 2N)$ and the coefficient $1/\sqrt{d_M}$ is used for normalizing the columns $a(\varphi_i)$, where $\varphi_i = (i - N)\pi/2N$. If the grid is fine enough to include the true DOAs, the steering matrix $A_v(\theta)$ can be represented by

$$A_v(\theta) = \Psi X, \qquad (11)$$

Where X is a $2N \times L$ matrix, which is L-jointly sparse. Specifically, only the rows corresponding to the true DOAs are nonzeroes, and the other rows are zeroes. Combining (2), (5) and (11), we have

$$x_v(t) = \Psi X s(t) + n_v(t). \qquad (12)$$

Obviously Xs is L-sparse, and hence the signal x_v is L-sparse in the Ψ domain.

In the CS theory, it is better that the representation matrix has the orthonormal or approximate orthonormal property. The following proposition illustrates that the matrix Ψ has the approximate orthonormal property.

Proposition 1. The representation matrix Ψ like (10) has the approximate orthonormal property.

Proof. We prove the approximate orthonormal property of Ψ like (10) by proving that the matrix $|\Psi^H\Psi|$ approximates the identical matrix. We consider the entries $|\Psi^H\Psi|_{n,l}$ $(1 \leq n, l \leq 2N)$ of the matrix $\Psi^H\Psi$

$$|\Psi^H\Psi|_{n,l} = \frac{1}{M}\left| 1 + e^{i\pi\left[\cos\left(\frac{n\pi}{2N}\right)-\cos\left(\frac{l\pi}{2N}\right)\right]} \right.$$
$$\left. + \cdots + e^{i\pi(M-1)\left[\cos\left(\frac{n\pi}{2N}\right)-\cos\left(\frac{l\pi}{2N}\right)\right]} \right|. \qquad (13)$$

Observe that for any real number x and y, $e^{i\pi x} = \cos(x) + i\sin(x)$ and $\cos(x) - \cos(y) = -2\sin[(x+y)/2]$

$\sin[(x - y)/2]$ both hold. We define the matrix Γ whose entries $\Gamma_{n,l} = \cos(n\pi/2N) - \cos(l\pi/2N)$. Then (13) can be simplified as

$$|\Psi^H\Psi|_{n,l} = \frac{|1 - e^{i\pi M\Gamma_{n,l}}|}{M|1 - e^{i\pi\Gamma_{n,l}}|} = \frac{1}{M}\left| \frac{\sin\left(\pi M\frac{\Gamma_{n,l}}{2}\right)}{\sin\left(\pi\frac{\Gamma_{n,l}}{2}\right)} \right|. \qquad (14)$$

Because $|\Gamma_{n,l}| < 2$, only when $\Gamma_{n,l} = 0$ (i.e. $n = l$), we have $|\Psi^H\Psi|_{n,l} = 1$. When $0 < |\Gamma_{n,l}| < 2$ $(n \neq l)$, we have $\lim_{M\to\infty}|\Psi^H\Psi|_{n,l} = 0$. However, M is always finite in practice, and then when $\Gamma_{n,l} \approx 0$ or $\Gamma_{n,l} \approx 2$, $|\Psi^H\Psi|_{n,l} \approx 1$ holds. Consequently, the approximate orthonormal property of Ψ holds.

Therefore, the representation matrix Ψ not only ensures the sparsity of the received signals but also has approximate orthonormal property, i.e. the representation matrix Ψ is well designed.

In the following, we will design the measurement matrix Φ. Firstly, we introduce the random sub-sampling matrix $\bar{\Phi}_{m\times M}$ $(m < M)$, which randomly selects m rows out of a matrix with M rows. Define $\Phi = \bar{\Phi} G$, and it is easy to know that Φ is also a random sub-sampling matrix, which is used to select m sensors from the NLA.

In this paper, we will design the random sub-sampling matrix like $\Phi = \bar{\Phi} G$ as the measurement matrix. As mentioned in subsection 2.2, we would better design Φ which is incoherent with Ψ, and proposition 2 will prove it in the following.

Proposition 2. Suppose the matrix Φ is any random sub-sampling matrix, and Ψ is the representation matrix like (10), the coherence of (Φ, Ψ) is 1.

Proof. Suppose φ_k is the k-th normalized row of Φ, the entries of vector φ_k $(1 \leq k \leq m)$ including $M - 1$ zeroes and a single one, and ψ_j is the j-th column of Ψ. From (9), the coherence of (Φ, Ψ) is

$$\mu(\Phi, \Psi) = \sqrt{M} \max_{1 \leq k \leq M, 1 \leq j \leq 2N} |\langle \varphi_k, \psi_j \rangle|$$
$$= \sqrt{M} \max_{1 \leq l \leq M, 1 \leq j \leq 2N} \left| \frac{1}{\sqrt{M}} e^{j\pi(l-1)\sin\varphi_j} \right|$$
$$= 1. \qquad (15)$$

Therefore the proposition 2 holds.

From proposition 2, we know that the random sub-sampling matrix $\Phi = \bar{\Phi} G$ and a representation matrix Ψ like (10) have the maximum incoherence. Then the matrices $\Phi = \bar{\Phi} G$ are well designed as the measurement matrices. Reference (Candes & Wakin 2008) pointed out that when the coherence is 1, we do not need more than $L\log d_M$ samples, but we cannot do with fewer either.

In summary, the CS model for recovering the signal $x_v(t)$ from the measurement vector

$$x_m(t) = \Phi x(t) = \bar{\Phi} G \Psi X s(t) + \bar{\Phi} n(t)$$
$$\triangleq Ay(t) + N(t), \tag{16}$$

can be established as the following optimization problem

$$\min \|y\|_0 \quad s.t. \ \|x_m - Ay\| \le \varepsilon, \tag{17}$$

where $y = Xs$, $A = \Phi\Psi$ and $N = \bar{\Phi} n$.

We can obtain the recovery signal $\bar{X}_v = \Psi y$ by solving the problem (17) with the OMP algorithm or other sparse recovery algorithms, and then apply any traditional DOA estimation algorithm on the recovery data $\bar{X}_v$ to estimate DOA. Specifically, applying RMUSIC algorithm to $\bar{X}_v$ yields CS-RMUSIC algorithm, applying ESPRIT algorithm to $\bar{X}_v$ yields CS-ESPRIT algorithm. Similarly, we can obtain other CS algorithms for DOA estimation, such as CS-BF and CS-MUSIC, and so on.

The procedure of the proposed CS algorithms for DOA estimation with NLA can be summarized as follows:

Step 1. According to the configuration of the NLA, form a matrix G using (4);

Step 2. Construct a representation matrix Ψ like (10) and a measurement matrix Φ of the CS model;

Step 3. Recover the data of the VULA at time t by solving the problem (17) with some sparse recovery algorithms (such as OMP algorithm).

Step 4. Apply any traditional DOA algorithm on the recovery data to estimate DOA.

4 EXPERIMENT RESULTS

In this section, we give three experiments for DOA estimation with NLA using the proposed CS algorithms. We consider L incoherent narrowband farfield sources imping on a NLA of M sensors. The angular space $(-\pi/2, \pi/2)$ is divided into $2N = 180$ possible angles equally. Because the coherence

between any random sub-sampling matrix and the represent matrix Ψ is 1 from proposition 2, the measurement number in each CS algorithm takes about $L \log d_M$. We sample 500 points in the temporal domain, and the results are averaged over 100 Monte-Carlo runs for each CS algorithm. OMP is used to solve problem (17) in the experiments. In the proposed CS algorithms, CS-BF and CS-MUSIC are spectral searching algorithms, and their results are illustrated in the figures; whereas other proposed CS algorithms are search-free algorithms, and their results are illustrated in the tables. The results are compared with EM-ESPRIT (El Kassis et al. 2007) and "BF with VULA", where "BF with VULA" means applying the BF algorithm to the ideal noiseless signals of VULA. The results for EM-ESPRIT algorithm are based on 500 trials in each case, and the maximum number of iterations in EM-ESPRIT algorithm is 30 (El Kassis et al. 2007). The ESPRIT algorithm used in the experiments is the least square ESPRIT (LS-ESPRIT) algorithm.

Example 1. Suppose a NLA $d = [1, 3, 6]$ $\lambda/2$ of $M = 3$ sensors, a single signal comes from the direction of 10°. In this example, we consider four cases of the signal received by NLA: noiseless, SNR = 20 db, SNR = 10 db and SNR = 0 db. In this example, the measurement number $m = 2 \approx \log 6$ in each CS algorithm. The results of EM-ESPRIT, CS-ESPRIT and CS-RMUSIC algorithms are listed in Table 1, and the results of CS-BF and CS-MUSIC algorithms in the case of SNR = 10 db are shown in Figure 1.

From Table 1, we find that the EM-ESPRIT algorithm is efficient, but the error is large even though SNR is high. For the same recovery data from the data of NLA, the CS-ESPRIT algorithm cannot well estimate DOA when SNR is low, whereas the CS-RMUSIC algorithm always performs very well. From Figure 1, CS-BF and CS-MUSIC algorithms both perform well when SNR = 10db.

From the results of Example 1, we find that EM-ESPRIT and CS-ESPRIT algorithms perform poor when SNR is low; the reason is that LS-ESPRIT is biased when the data are noisy (El Kassis et al. 2007). Then we will not consider EM-ESPRIT and CS-ESPRIT more in the following two examples.

Table 1. Results of CS-RMUSIC algorithm for example 1.

Angle/deg.	Noiseless	SNR = 20 db	SNR = 10 db	SNR = 0 db
EM-ESPRIT	10.2828	10.2668	10.1334	8.7928
CS-ESPRIT	10.0000	9.9866	9.9686	2.0227
CS-RMUSIC	10.0000	9.9955	10.0274	9.5720

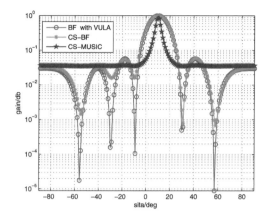

Figure 1. The spatial spectrum of the CS-BF and CS-MUSIC algorithms when SNR = 10 db for example 1.

Table 2. Results of CS-RMUSIC algorithm for example 2.

Angle/deg.	SNR = 20 db	SNR = 10 db	SNR = 0 db
CS-RMUSIC	−14.9862	−14.9403	−14.7684
CS-RMUSIC	10.0184	10.0374	9.6645

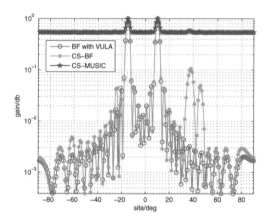

Figure 2. The spatial spectrum of the CS-BF and CS-MUSIC algorithms when SNR = 10db for Example 2.

Example 2. Suppose the NLA is a MR array of 9 sensors, that is, the NLA is $d = [1, 2, 3, 15, 19, 22, 25, 28, 30] \lambda/2$. Two signals come from the directions of (−15°, 10°). In this example, we consider three cases of the received signal by NLA: SNR = 20 db, SNR = 10 db and SNR = 0 db, and takes the measurement number $m = 7 \approx 2\log30$ in each CS algorithm. The results of the CS-RMUSIC algorithm are listed in Table 2, and the results of CS-BF and

Table 3. Results of CS-RMUSIC algorithm for example 3.

Angle/deg.	SNR = 20 db	SNR = 10 db	SNR = 0 db
CS-RMUSIC	−14.9996	−14.9403	−15.4048
CS-RMUSIC	9.9808	10.0210	10.3140

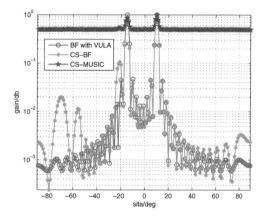

Figure 3. The spatial spectrum of the CS-BF and CS-MUSIC algorithms when SNR = 10db for Example 3.

CS-MUSIC algorithms in the case of SNR = 10db are shown in Figure 2.

Example 3. Suppose the NLA is a NR array of 8 sensors, that is, the NLA is $d = [1, 2, 5, 10, 16, 23, 33, 35] \lambda/2$. Two signals come from the directions of (−15°, 10°). In this example, we also consider three cases of the received signal by NLA: SNR = 20 db, SNR = 10 db and SNR = 0 db, and takes the measurement number $m = 7 \approx 2\log35$ in each CS algorithm. The results of the CS-RMUSIC algorithm are listed in Table 3, and the results of CS-BF and CS-MUSIC algorithms in the case of SNR = 10 db are shown in Figure 3.

From the results of examples 2 and 3, we find that CS-BF, CS-MUSIC and CS-RMUSIC algorithms perform well for estimating DOA with NLA, especially the CS-MUSIC and CS-RMUSIC algorithms.

5 CONCLUSION

With the developing CS method, we have proposed a novel model and several CS algorithms for DOA estimation with NLA. These algorithms firstly recover the data of corresponding VULA from the received data of NLA, and then apply any traditional DOA estimation algorithm on the recovery data to estimate DOA. The example results show that the proposed CS algorithms are efficient, especially the CS-RMUSIC and CS-MUSIC algorithms.

ACKNOWLEDGMENT

The corresponding author of this paper is Li-zhi Cheng. This work was supported by the National Science Foundation of China under grants (No.61271014 & No. 51371156), Specialized Research Fund for the Doctoral Program of Higher Education (20124301110003) and the Graduated Students Innovation Fund of Hunan Province (CX2012B238).

REFERENCES

Baraniuk, R.G. 2007. Compressive sensing [lecture notes]. *IEEE Signal Processing Magazine* 24(4): 118–121.

Candes, E.J. et al. 2006. Robust uncertainty principles: Exact signal reconstruction from highly incomplete frequency information. *IEEE Transactions on Information Theory* 52(2): 489–509.

Candes, E.J. & Wakin, M.B. 2008. An introduction to compressive sampling. *IEEE Signal Processing Magazine* 25(2): 21–30.

Donoho, D.L. 2006. Compressed sensing. *IEEE Transactions on Information Theory* 52(4): 1289–1306.

Donoho, D.L. & Tsaig, Y. 2006. Extensions of compressed sensing. *Signal processin* 86(3): 549–571.

El Kassis, C. et al. 2007. EM-ESPRIT algorithm for direction finding with nonuniform arrays. *Proceedings of the 14th Workshop on Statistical Signal Processing.* IEEE. pp. 453–457.

El Kassis, C. et al. 2010. Advantages of nonuniform arrays using root-MUSIC. *Signal Processing* 90(2): 689–695.

Fang, H. & Yang, H. 2012. A new compressed sensing-based matching pursuit algorithm for image reconstruction. *2012 5th International Congress on Image and Signal Processing (CISP).* IEEE. pp. 338–342.

Gurbuz, A.C. et al. 2012. Bearing Estimation via Spatial Sparsity using Compressive Sensing. *IEEE Transactions on Aerospace and Electronic Systems* 48(2): 1358–1369.

Krim, H. & Viberg, M. 1996. Two decades of array signal processing research: the parametric approach. *IEEE Signal Processing Magazine* 13(4): 67–94.

Malioutov, D. et al. 2005. A sparse signal reconstruction perspective for source localization with sensor arrays. *IEEE Transactions on Signal Processing* 53(8): 3010–3022.

Moffet, A. 1968. Minimum-redundancy linear arrays. *IEEE Transactions on Antennas and Propagation* 16(2): 172–175.

Tropp, J.A. & Gilbert, A.C. 2007. Signal recovery from random measurements via orthogonal matching pursuit. *IEEE Transactions on Information Theory* 53(12): 4655–4666.

Tropp, J.A. & Wright, S.J. 2010. Computational methods for sparse solution of linear inverse problems. *Proceedings of the IEEE* 98(6): 948–958.

Vertatschitsch, E. & Haykin, S. 1986. Nonredundant arrays. *Proceedings of the IEEE* 74(1): 217–217.

Van Veen, B.D. & Buckley, K.M. 1988. Beamforming: A versatile approach to spatial filtering. *IEEE ASSP Magazine* 5(2): 4–24.

Weiss, A.J. & Garish, M. 1991. Direction finding using ESPRIT with interpolated arrays. *IEEE Transactions on Signal Processing* 39(6): 1473–1478.

Computer, Intelligent Computing and Education Technology – Liu, Sung & Yao (Eds)
© 2014 Taylor & Francis Group, London, ISBN 978-1-138-02469-4

An improved particle swarm algorithm for distribution network reconfiguration

Fu-Chao Liu, Gang Zhang & Zheng-Yuan Li
Gansu Electric Power Research Institute, Lanzhou, China

Wei Xu
Zhengzhou Da Fang Software Company, Zhengzhou, China

Hao Liu
Henan Electric Power Research Institute, Zhengzhou, China

ABSTRACT: PSO algorithm is one a kind. But PSO is easy to be prematurity and fall into local optimization. So this paper provides an particle swarm optimization algorithm based on the organizational evolutionary (OEPSO). The evolutional operations are acted on organizations directly in the algorithm, and gained the global convergence ends through competition and cooperation, and overcome the shortcomings of the traditional PSO. Based on analysis of the distribution network reconfiguration model and the traits of OEPSO, the mathematical model and the procedures for solving the optimized distribution network optimization by using OEPSO were proposed in detail. A case study about American PG&E network system indicates that OEPSO has better convergence speed and computational accuracy, whereby providing a novel effective method or way for the settlement of the problem of distribution network reconfiguration.

Keywords: particle swarm optimization; organization; evolutionary computation; unconstrained optimization; distribution network reconfiguration

1 INTRODUCTION

Particle Swarm Optimization (J. Kennedy et al., 1995) was come up with Kennedy and Eberhartin 1995. The main method to resolve this problem is to gain the size of particle swarm, which there is some change in calculated performance, but there is also some lack: first, this method can not overcome the problem of premature convergence radically; second, this method will gain the calculated amount of algorithm. In case to this lack, many improved PSO algorithm is come out, for example Shi Yuhui and Eberhart (Shi Y et al., 2001) proposed a faintness PSO; according to the circumgyration stretch method combined with PSO algorithm change the form of the objective function, a global optimization algorithm was proposed by Konstantions Parsopolos, A et al.,); Ratnaweera (Ratnaweera, A et al.,) introduced time-varying acceleration constant and put forward variant time-varying particle swarm algorithm, self-organization hierarchical time-varying particle swarm algorithm and so on.

From the perspective of organization, this article composite different tissues by the individual form, makes full use of inter-organization individual collaboration characteristic and self-study characteristics, puts forward organizational evolutionary particle swarm algorithm. The algorithm thinks about the general particle memory characteristics, self-organizational of competition and mutual cooperation, so the particles can better adapt to the environment, guide the particle swarm evolution and achieve the goal of global optimization ultimately. In order to make full research the algorithm property, the algorithm is tested by twelve unconstrained standard of tested function, compared with three kinds of particle swarm algorithm and fast evolutionary programming algorithm (Yao X et al.,) and the algorithm used in the parameters to the algorithm performance is analyzed. The results show that the algorithm for function optimization is effective.

2 EASE OF USE PARTICLE SWARM ALGORITHM BASED ON ORGANIZATIONAL EVOLUTIONARY

2.1 Particle swarm algorithm

Considering the global optimization problem

$$\min\left\{f(x): x \in \Omega \subset R^n\right\}, f, \Omega \subset R^n \tag{1}$$

The potential answer of optimization problem is regarded as a particle in the search space without mass and volume. It has certain flight speed and position, represented in ordered three-dimensional (x^i, v^i, h). Among them, $x^i(t) = (x_1^i, x_2^i, ..., x_n^i)^T$ is the ith current location of particle, $v^i(t) = (v_1^i, v_2^i, ..., v_n^i)^T$ is the ith current speed of particle, $h^i(t) = (h_1^i, h_2^i, ..., h_n^i)^T$ is the ith best location of particle by self-experience, n is the search space dimension. Make all the particles which experienced the global best position is $h^g(t) = (h_1^g, h_2^g, ..., h_n^g)^T$, t is evolutionary iterative algebra, so the speed and position updating formula of the particle in $t+1$ generation is:

$$\begin{cases} v_j^i(t+1) = v_j^i(t) + c_1 r_1(h_j^i(t) - x_j^i(t)) + c_2 r_2(h_j^g(t) - x_j^i(t)) \\ x_j^i(t+1) = x_j^i(t) + v_j^i(t+1) \end{cases} \quad (2)$$

where c_1 and c_2 are acceleration constants, r_1 and r_2 are obey uniform distribution of random variables in [0, 1] range. From the velocity update can be seen, the constant c1 particle was adjusted to itself through the optimal position of flight of the maximum amplitude, constant c2 particle was adjusted to the global best particle maximum range flight. In addition, for preventing the particles go out of the search space, its speed VI is often limited by a maximum speed V_{max}. The first part of speed update formula express particle previous speed in type (2); the second part is "cognition", which express thinking of particles themselves; the third part is "social", which express the information sharing and cooperation between particles (Van den Bergh, F).

2.2 Particle swarm algorithm based on organizational evolutionary

In this paper, the individual uses real vector representation, we only consider the minimization problem, so the individual fitness is defined as: organization is some collection of individual, these individual are known as the member of organization, the best fitness of member is organization leader. If an organization has multiple members with the same optimal value and randomly selected one as a leader. The fitness of leader is the fitness of organization, the intersection of different organization is empty. Here are four applied to the particle swarm algorithm for organizational evolutionary operator.

2.2.1 Design of particle swarm algorithm for organizational evolution

1. Splitting operator
   In this operator, the condition to split organization org is:

$$|org| > Max \quad (3)$$

where $|org|$ express the number of org member, $Max_{os}(< N_0)$ express allowed the max number of members, N_0 is the number of all the organization members in initialized. Max_{os} and N_0 both are preset parameter. If a father organization org satisfy (3), it will be divided into two sub organization, org_{c1} and org_{c2}: in org_i we randomly select $|org_i|/3 : 2|org_i|/3$ member to compose the sub organization org_{c1}, the other members compose the sub organization org_{c2}. Then form the current population to delete organization org_i, and the organization of org_{c1} and org_{c2} joined to the next generation of evolutionary population.

2. Annexation operator
Two father organization are $org_{i1} = \{x^1, x^2, ..., x^{m_1}\}$ and $org_{i2} = \{y^1, y^2, ..., y^{m_2}\}$, m_1 is the number of organization org_{i1} member, m_2 is the number of organization org_{i2} member, and $F(org_{i1}) \geq F(org_{i2})$, so use org_{i1} to annex org_{i2} to produce a new sub organization $org_c = \{z^1, z^2, ..., z^{m_1+m_2}\}$, where $z^i = x^i, i = 1, 2, ..., m_1$. If $U_{j+m_1}(0,1) < AS, j = 1, 2, ..., m_2, z^{j+m_1}$ will be produced by annexation strategy 1, otherwise it will be produced by annexation strategy 2. Here the subscript representation of $U_{j+m_1}(0,1)$ expresses to produce a random number for each $j + m_1$, $AS \in (0,1)$ is preset parameter. The two annexation strategy is respectively given by (4) and (5).

To set the leader of org_{i1} is $(a_1, a_2, ..., a_n)$, the new one is $r_j = (r_{j,1}, r_{j,2}, ..., r_{j,n})$, $j = 1, 2, ..., m_2$. So in the annexation strategy 1, r_j is produced by (4):

$$r_{j,k} = \begin{cases} \underline{x}_k & d_{j,k} < \underline{x}_k \\ \overline{x}_k & d_{j,k} > \overline{x}_k \\ d_{j,k} & otherwize \end{cases} \quad k = 1, 2, ..., n \quad (4)$$

where, $d_{j,k} = a_k + U_k(0,1) \times (a_k - y_k^j)$.
In annexation strategy 2, r_j is produced by (5):

$$r_{j,k} = \begin{cases} \underline{x}_k + \beta_k \times (\overline{x}_k - \underline{x}_k) & U_k(0,1) < 1/n \\ a_k & otherwize \end{cases}$$
$$k = 1, 2, ..., n \quad (5)$$

where $\beta_k = U(0,1)$ and it is different to each x^k.
After r_j is calculated, z^{j+m_1} is determined by (6):

$$z^{j+m1} = \begin{cases} r_j & F(r_j) \geq F(y^j) \\ r_j & F(r_j) < F(y^j) \text{ and} \\ & \{U_j(0,1) < exp(F(r_j) - F(y^j))\} \\ y^j & otherwize \end{cases} \quad (6)$$

In fact, annexation strategy 1 is a kind of heuristic crossover operator; annexation strategy 2 is a kind of mutation operator. From the type (6) we can see when the fitness of r_j is better than y^j, r_j will progress the fitness of organization by entering org_c. When the fitness of r_j is worse than y^j, r_j will enter org_c probability, namely the fitness of r_j is more close to y^j, the more greater, this helps to keep the population diversity. Finally, from the current population we delete org_{i1} and org_{i2}, and let org_c join to the next population.

3. Cooperation operator

Let two father generation organization as $org_{i1} = \{x^1, x^2, ..., x^{m_1}\}$ and $org_{i2} = \{y^1, y^2, ..., y^{m_2}\}$. If $U(0,1) < CS$, two offspring organization org_{c1} and org_{c2} are produced by cooperation strategy 1, otherwise produced by cooperation strategy 2, here $CS \in (0,1)$ is preset parameter, two cooperation strategy are given by type (12) and (13).

Let the leader of org_{i1} as $(a_1, a_2, ..., a_n)$, the leader of org_{i2} as $(b_1, b_2, ..., b_n)$, two new individuals which are produce by cooperation are $u = (u_1, u_2, ..., u_n)$ and $l = (l_1, l_2, ..., l_n)$, so in the cooperation strategy 2, u and l are produced by (7).

$$\begin{cases} u_k = \beta_k \times a_k + (1-\beta_k) \times b_k \\ l_k = (1-\beta_k) \times a_k + \beta_k \times b_k \end{cases} k = 1, 2, ..., n \quad (7)$$

where, $\beta_k = U(0,1)$.

In cooperation strategy 2, u and l are produced by (8), where $1 < i_1 < n, 1 < i_2 < n$, and $i_1 < i_2$.

$$\begin{cases} u = (a_1, a_2, ..., a_{i_1-1}, b_{i_1}, b_{i_1+1}, ..., b_{i_2}, a_{i_2+1}, a_{i_2+2}, ..., a_n) \\ l = (b_1, b_2, ..., b_{i_1-1}, a_{i_1}, a_{i_1+1}, ..., a_{i_2}, b_{i_2+1}, b_{i_2+2}, ..., b_n) \end{cases}$$
$$(8)$$

After u and l produce, org_{c1} and org_{c2} are respectively determined by type (9) and (10):

$$org_{c1} = \begin{cases} \{x^1, x^2, ..., x^{i-1}, u, x^{i+1}, ..., x^{m1}\} \\ \quad \exists x_i \in org_{i1}, \quad F(x^i) < F(u) \quad (9) \\ org_{i1} \quad otherwize \end{cases}$$

$$org_{c2} = \begin{cases} \{y^1, y^2, ..., y^{j-1}, l, y^{j+1}, ..., y^{m2}\} \\ \quad \exists y_j \in org_{i2}, \quad F(y^j) < F(l) \quad (10) \\ org_{i2} \quad otherwize \end{cases}$$

Finally from the current population delete org_{i1} and org_{i2}, and let org_{c1} and org_{c2} join to the next population. In fact, cooperation strategy is arithmetic crossover, cooperation strategy 2 is a kind of discrete crossover operator.

4. Speed renewal operator

Let be $h^g(t) = (h_1^g, h_2^g, \cdots, h_n^g)^T$ expresses the best leader experience over its location in all organization, $h^i(t) = (h_1^i, h_2^i, \cdots, h_n^i)^T$ expresses the

ith organization for experience its best location, so the ith tissues of particle are updated in the 2th of speed and location as follows:

$$\begin{cases} v_j^i(t+1) = w(t)v_j^i(t) + c_1 r_1(h_j^i(t) - x_j^i(t)) + c_2 r_2(h_j^g(t) - x_j^i(t)) \\ x_j^i(t+1) = x_j^i(t) + v_j^i(t+1) \end{cases}$$
$$(11)$$

Speed and location vector are updated by using inertia weight method.

2.2.2 *Particle swarm algorithm for organizational evolutionary description*

Algorithm 2: particle swarm algorithm for organizational evolutionary

Step 1: Initialize population Q_t with N_0 organization and every organization only have one particle, set $t \leftarrow 0$;

Step 2: If the condition is satisfied, then output the result and stop the operation; otherwise, return Step 3;

Step 3: Each organization in Q_t, if splitting condition is satisfied, then executive splitting operator;

Step 4: If the number of organization in Q_t is larger than 1, then return Step 5, otherwise return Step 6;

Step 5: From Q_t randomly to select two father generation organization orgi1 and orgi2, then randomly select annexation operator or cooperation operator to function in those two father generation organization, return Step 4;

Step 6: Surplus organization in Q_t join in $Q_t + 1$;

Step 7: update the speed and location of particle, set $t \leftarrow t+1$, return Step 2.

3 DISTRIBUTION NETWORK RECONFIGURATION PROBLEM

According to the operating conditions, distribution network are reconfigured for three purposes: (1) reconfiguration for loss minimization, (2) reconfiguration for load balancing, and (3) reconfiguration for service restoration. In this sense, the efficient operation of distribution network can be achieved by modifying the open/closed status of the different switches in order to transfer load from heavily loaded feeders and substation transformers to relatively less heavily loaded feeders and transformers. By reducing the level of loads on feeders and substation transformers the power losses are reduced and the voltage profile along the feeders is improved. Therefore, the Distribution Network Reconfiguration (DNR) problem can be conceptualized like the task of identify a new configuration with minimal power losses, while all the system constraints are satisfied.

This is a combinatorial optimization problem where the aim is to determine the open/closed status of all switches in order to obtain an optimum configuration in a large scale distribution system.

In this paper, loss minimization is considered as the objective. The DNR problem is described as below:

3.1 Objective function

In this paper the objective function for the DNR is to minimize the power losses, which can be calculated as follows:

$$\min f_{ploss} = \sum_{i=1}^{L_1} k_i r_i \frac{P_i^2 + Q_i^2}{V_i^2} \qquad (12)$$

where L_1 is the number of the branches. k_i is the state of ith tie switch (0 = open, 1 = close). r_i is the resistance of line section i. P_i and Q_i are the net injected active and reactive powers at the ith bus. V_i is the voltage magnitude of bus i.

3.2 Main restriction conditions

1. Power flow restriction

$$\sum_{k=1}^{n} Sub_k = \sum_{j=1}^{m} Load_j + \sum_{i=1}^{L} Loss_i \qquad (13)$$

where Sub_k is the complex power of substation k. $Load_j$ is the load of node j. $Loss_i$ is the power loss of bus i. n is the number of substation. m is the number of node.

2. Capacity restriction

$$I_l \leq I_{max,l} \qquad l = 1, 2, ..., L_2 \qquad (14)$$

where I_l is the current of element l. $I_{max,l}$ is the maximum current of the lth element. L_2 is the number of element.

3. Voltage restriction

$$V_{max,j} \leq V_j \leq V_{min,j} \qquad j = 1, 2, ..., m \qquad (15)$$

where V_j is the voltage of node j, $V_{max,j}$ and $V_{min,j}$ are the maximum voltage and minimum voltage of node j, respectively.

4. Radical distribution network restriction

$$g \in G \qquad (16)$$

where g is the present distribution network. G is the admissible radial network configuration of all.

4 APPLICATION OF OEPSO TO DISTRIBUTION NETWORK RECONFIGURATION

In order to validate the possibility and reliability of the OEPSO algorithm, OEPSO was used to solve the American PG&E distribution network reconfiguration problem. Figure 1 shows the American PG&E distribution system.

American PG&E distribution network have 69 nodes, 73 branches and 5 tie switches: nodes (11&66), (13&20), (15&69), (27&54), (39&48). The rated voltage is 12.66 KV, the total load is 3802.19+j2694.6 KVA.

With Pentium IV 2.0CPU and 512M memory hardware and Delphi6 + MS SQL Server software circumstance, PSO algorithm and OEPSO algorithm are used to solve the DNR problem with American PG&E distribution system. The distribution results by PSO and OEPSO algorithms are show in Table 1.

It is seen that before reconfiguration, the initial losses and minimum voltage in per unit are 225.712 and 0.9052 KW, respectively. After reconfiguration, 6 tie switches has changed and the OEPSO

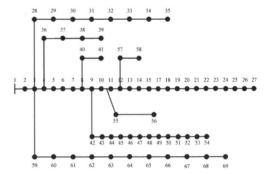

Figure 1. American PG&E distribution system.

Table 1. Result before and after reconfiguration of 69-node.

Comparative index	Base system	PSO	OEPSO
Open line sections	11–66	11–66	11–66
	13–20	13–20	13–20
	15–69	14–15	14–15
	27–54	44–45	47–48
	39–48	50–51	25–26
Power losses (KW)	225.712	100.810	100.696
Minimum voltage (pu)	0.897	0.933	0.933
Generations		300	28
CPU time (s)		57.3	1.42

algorithm give the global optimum configuration. The comparison results between the PSO and OEPSO show that the power loss of the OEPSO is a little less than PSO, but the generations and executions time of OEPSO are significantly short in respect with PSO and provides a general idea. In other words, OEPSO reaches a better optimal solution compared with PSO. All of the comparative index prove that the OEPSO is an better algorithm than PSO, which has stability of global optimization and a higher speed of calculation.

5 CONCLUSIONS

Combining the fast optimization function of PSO algorithm and the global optimization function of SA algorithm, OEPSO algorithm is presented and introduced into distribution network reconfiguration problem. The solution of distribution network reconfiguration problem based on it is put forward too. It is testified by theory and practice that the algorithm can escape from partial optimal problem PSO faced, then the reliability of global optimization is greatly promoted, which offers a new way to solve the distribution network reconfiguration optimal problem.

ACKNOWLEDGMENT

This work is supported by the Science and technology project of the China State Grid Corp (No. 5227221303A0; 5227221302A2).

REFERENCES

Kennedy J., Eberhart R.C. Particle swarm optimization. In Proceedings of IEEE International Conference on Neural Networks, Piscataway, NJ: IEEE Service Center. 1995: 1942–1948.

Parsopoulos, K.E. Vrahatis, M.N. On the computation of all global minimizes through particle swarm optimization. IEEE Transactions on Evolutionary Computation 8(6): 211–224.

Ratnaweera, A. Halgamuge, S.K. Watson, H.C. Self-organizing hierarchical particle swarm optimizer with time-varying acceleration. IEEE Transactions on Evolutionary Computation, IEEE, 8(3): 240–255.

Shi Y. and Eberhart R.C. Fuzzy adaptive particle swarm optimization. In Proceedings of the Congress on Evolutionary Computation, Seoul, Korea, IEEE, 2001: 79–85.

Van den Bergh, F. Engelbrecht, A.P. A cooperative approach to particle swarm optimization, IEEE Transactions on Evolutionary Computation 8(3): 225–239.

Yao X, Liu Y, Lin GM. Evolutionary programming made faster. IEEE Transactions on Evolutionary Computation 3(2): 82–102.

The legal risk rating for food enterprise based on artificial neural networks

M.X. Cai
College of Science, Central South University of Forestry and Technology, Changsha, Hunan, China

Y.G. Jiang
Department of Law and Administration, Changsha University, Changsha, Hunan, China

ABSTRACT: Strengthening legal risk management by rating the legal risk for food enterprise, will play a great role in food enterprises' internal self-discipline and avoid the occurrence of food safety crisis. BP artificial neural network has self-adaptive function of fault tolerance and error correction, which can make identification and rectification to the chaos of food enterprise legal risk under high uncertainly environment and evaluate the legal risk for food enterprise precisely. This paper chooses 20 food enterprises in Changsha City as sample, and establish artificial neural network rating model for food enterprise legal risk.

Keywords: food enterprise; artificial neural network; legal risk

1 INTRODUCTION

The earliest study about risk and its management is in BC. Today, risk and its management theories are more and more mature. But the studies about legal risk and its management research started at the beginning of this century, which is still a hot research up to now. Crouhy (2005) attributed the legal risk together with market risk, credit risk and liquidity risk into the bank risk to manage. Xiang & Chen (2006) carried preliminary discussion on the enterprise legal risk assessment, introduced risk value method and risk income method into legal risk rating, and proposed the risk of default method.

Artificial neural network research began in the 1940s. In 1943, The Psychologists McCulloch & the mathematicians Pitts (1943) first proposed MP model. Hebb (1949) put forward the Hebb learning role after summarizing the research achievements of conditioned reflex in 1944. After more than ten years, Rosenblatt (1986) presented the theory of perceptron and put the artificial neural network research to a climax. Hopfield (1982) gave the stability criterion using HNN mode, and explored new ways for associative memory and optimization calculation in the 1980s. Hinton and Sejnowski (1986) presented Boltzman model, which using the learning method of multi-layer network to ensure that the system as a whole tend to be the globally stable point. Rumelhart & Hinton (1986) proposed the PDP theory, which developed the multilayer network of BP algorithm and became the most common network up to now. Kosko (1986) presented bidirectional associative memory network for learning. HechtNielsen (1989) introduced back propagation network model which can be used for image compression and statistical analysis. Chua (1990) proposed cellular neural networks model, which as a large-scale nonlinear analog system and make the artificial neural network research on a new step. Some domestic scholars applied artificial neural network to the credit risk assessment, but there has no literature for applying them to enterprise legal risk assessment.

Once the food safety events occurrences, for the consumers, will harm their healthy and influence their physical quality, for the food enterprises, will make them face to the legal risk loss. Therefore, strengthening the legal risk management will play an important role in food enterprises' internal self-discipline and avoid the occurrence of food safety crisis. The legal risk rating is the key for legal risk management of food enterprises.

2 ESTABLISH THE LEGAL RISK EVALUATING INDEX SYSTEM FOR FOOD ENTERPRISE

Lay In the current research literature for company legal risk management, the legal risk evaluating index system for companies has not been put forward, but the factors which will make the companies exist general (overall) legal risk has been studied preliminarily. Lovells international law firm issued the report of legal risk for China top 100 companies in 2005, said that they make industries, organization form, the place which companies set up, intellectual property, procurement and sale behaviors (foreign) as the risk factors for risk assessment. The legal risk evaluating factors which have listed by Xiang-fei and Chen-youchun are similar to the Lovells', including the Legal environment factors, the jurisdiction area, the organization form of legal entity, business model, industry factor, the intellectual property rights, and the place of management behavior, etc.

However, the general (overall) legal risk factors of companies are mainly two types, which are the external environmental factors and internal law behavior factors. The external environmental factors mainly include legislative environment, judicial environment and law enforcement environment. The internal law behavior factors are mainly include enterprise organization form, scope of business and the legal risk management mechanism. The classification framework is in Figure 1 as follows.

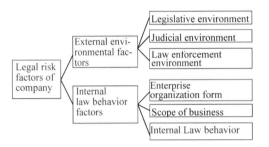

Figure 1. The tree diagram of legal risk factors of companies.

3 DETERMINE AND STANDARDIZE THE SAMPLE FACTOR VALUES FOR FOOD ENTERPRISE LEGAL RISK RATING

The samples of this study are from Changsha city (including six areas and three counties), which have 20 food enterprises, including 6 primary food production companies of agriculture, forestry, animal husbandry, sideline occupations and fishery, and 7 high processed food enterprises, 3 catering companies, and 4 rough machining food enterprises.

Due to the company legal risk index is difficult to be expressed directly in quantitative, we take the expert scoring method to quantize. The first step is dividing the grading standard of all input factors as follows.

Enterprise organization form = (Senior, Medium, Simple) = (5,3,1),

Scope of business = (Complex, Medium, Simple) = (5,3,1),

Table 1. The factor values of legal risk for the 20 food enterprises.

Company number	Enterprise organization form	Scope of business	Internal law behavior	Legislative environment	Judicial environment	Law enforcement environment
1	4.1	4.5	2.8	4.3	3.2	4.8
2	4.5	2.8	2.5	2.8	4.1	4.2
3	4.0	4.8	4.6	3.5	4.2	3.6
4	5.0	2.9	3.2	2.6	2.7	4.1
5	2.2	3.7	1.8	2.9	3.9	3.9
6	5.0	4.0	4.1	4.8	4.7	2.7
7	5.0	5.0	3.8	3.9	4.3	4.5
8	4.2	4.8	3.7	4.7	4.0	4.2
9	4.3	2.5	4.5	3.1	4.7	1.8
10	4.1	1.7	4.6	2.7	3.9	2.7
11	3.5	3.9	4.0	1.7	2.4	4.6
12	2.2	4.5	3.5	5.0	4.5	3.1
13	1.8	1.4	3.0	2.6	3.6	2.7
14	4.8	4.2	4.7	4.6	3.8	4.9
15	2.5	3.2	2.6	4.2	3.4	3.0
16	3.8	3.5	4.1	4.1	1.6	5.0
17	4.6	2.9	4.3	4.0	4.7	4.7
18	3.8	4.5	3.8	4.8	4.1	2.8
19	1.8	4.0	4.3	4.7	4.3	3.4
20	2.9	3.8	3.9	3.3	3.6	2.6

Table 2. The standard factor values of legal risk for 20 companies.

Company number	Enterprise organization form	Scope of business	Internal law behavior	Legislative environment	Judicial environment	Law enforcement environment
1	0.82	0.90	0.56	0.86	0.64	0.96
2	0.90	0.56	0.50	0.56	0.82	0.84
3	0.80	0.96	0.92	0.70	0.84	0.72
4	1.00	0.58	0.64	0.52	0.54	0.82
5	0.44	0.74	0.36	0.58	0.78	0.78
6	1.00	0.80	0.82	0.96	0.94	0.54
7	1.00	1.00	0.76	0.78	0.86	0.90
8	0.84	0.96	0.74	0.94	0.80	0.84
9	0.86	0.50	0.90	0.62	0.94	0.36
10	0.82	0.34	0.92	0.54	0.78	0.54
11	0.70	0.78	0.80	0.34	0.48	0.92
12	0.44	0.90	0.70	1.00	0.90	0.62
13	0.36	0.28	0.60	0.52	0.72	0.54
14	0.96	0.84	0.94	0.92	0.76	0.98
15	0.50	0.64	0.52	0.84	0.68	0.60
16	0.76	0.70	0.82	0.82	0.32	1.00
17	0.92	0.58	0.86	0.80	0.94	0.94
18	0.76	0.90	0.76	0.96	0.82	0.56
19	0.36	0.80	0.86	0.94	0.86	0.68
20	0.58	0.76	0.78	0.66	0.72	0.52

Internal Law behavior = (Not perfect, Medium, Perfect) = (5,3,1),

Legislative environment = (Unstable, Medium, Stable) = (5,3,1),

Judicial environment = (Strict, Medium, Loose) = (5,3,1),

Law enforcement environment = (Bad, Medium, Well) = (5,3,1)

The second step is determining the factor values according to the mean value of all experts, the legal risk factor values of the 20 companies are shown in Table 1.

We use linear scaling transformation method to standardize the factor values of company legal risk rating. Divide each value by the highest score of 5, and standardize the rating matrix, we have the data as Table 2.

4 CONSTRUCT ARTIFICIAL NEURAL NETWORK MODEL FOR THE LEGAL RISK EVALUATING OF FOOD ENTERPRISES

Because the food enterprise legal risk rating indexes have 6 items, we set the BP neural network inputs unit number as 6, i.e. the 6 standard data are the unit number for input layers, which are shown in Table 2. The unit number for output is 1 item, i.e. the values of company legal risk rating. For the hidden layer, the more, the more complex for the process of error backward propagation, and the training time will greatly increase. Moreover, while the hidden layer increasing, the local minimum error will increase. In addition, how to select the unit number for hidden layer is also a technical question. Selecting too more, will increase the training time and make the network handle too much messages, including some meaningless message. Selecting too less, will reduce the tolerance of the network and can't get ideal result for some complex problems. We set the unit number of hidden layer is 5 for rating the company legal risk. Finally, the selection of initial values for learning convergence effect is significant, which require each neuron status value near to 0 when add up the initial weights, where the right is a random value between [−1, 1], generally. We select the learning factor is a = 0.1. So, we construct the BP artificial neural network for the food enterprise legal risk rating as Figure 2.

In the BP artificial neural network model, each neural layer satisfying the following conditions:

$$Z_j = f\left(\sum_{i=1}^{6} W_{ij}X_i - \theta_j\right), Y_t = f\left(\sum_{j=1}^{5} V_{jt}Z_j - \gamma_t\right) \quad (1)$$

where $f(u) = 1/(1+e^{-u})$, which function graph is shown in Figure 3.

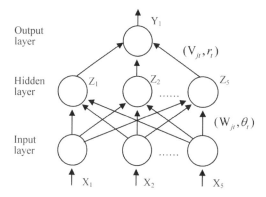

Output layer

Hidden layer

Input layer

(V_{jt}, r_t)

Z_1 Z_2 Z_5

(W_{jt}, θ_t)

X_1 X_2 X_5

Y_1

Figure 2. The BP artificial neural network for the food enterprises legal risk.

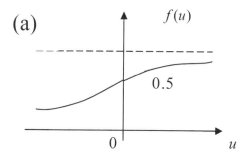

(a)

$f(u)$

0.5

0

u

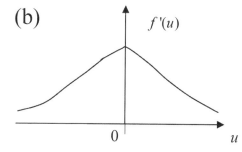

(b)

$f'(u)$

0

u

Figure 3. (a) Sigmoid impact function, (b) The derivative curve of (a).

5 THE TRAINING FOR NEURAL NETWORK MODEL AND THE RATING OF THE FOOD ENTERPRISE LEGAL RISK

By the computer simulations, training the number 1–10 company legal risk rating, we get the evaluating results as Table 3.

According to the data in Table 3, the neural network training values are near to the expected values of experts, and the training can be finished.

Table 3. The training results of the neural network for food enterprise legal risk rating.

	Training results of the neural network			The expected values of experts	
No.	Training result	Grade	No.	Training result	Grade
1	0.7825	3	1	0.73	5
2	0.7159	7	2	0.69	7
3	0.8920	1	3	0.81	1
4	0.7342	6	4	0.67	8
5	0.7016	8	5	0.62	10
6	0.7722	4	6	0.75	4
7	0.7653	5	7	0.79	2
8	0.8010	2	8	0.77	3
9	0.6583	10	9	0.70	6
10	0.6800	9	10	0.65	9

Table 4. The rating results of the company legal risk.

No.	Rating result	Grade	No.	Rating result	Grade
11	0.7258	7	16	0.8342	4
12	0.8134	5	17	0.8520	3
13	0.4720	10	18	0.8723	1
14	0.8656	2	19	0.7452	6
15	0.7005	9	20	0.7254	8

Using the neural network training values, we make the rating for the number 11–20 companies by the BP artificial neural network model and get the results as Table 4.

Rating the company legal risk by BP artificial neural network model not only provides the premise for the company legal risk managers to avoid, accept or select decisions, but also provides strong basis for the company legal risk managers to establish legal risk prevention and control mechanism.

6 CONCLUSIONS

In the case that the other evaluation methods are difficult to be applied in company legal risk rating, artificial neural network method plays more and more important role in the process of company legal risk rating.

Firstly, the factors of company legal risk are difficult to be expressed by using accurate data, which only can be given some general score by the expert scoring method with strongly subjectivity. While the method of BP artificial neural network make learning and training by using the estimated values which are given by experts, and weaken subjective factors of data by the adaptive function in training process. So, we can get the optimal solution of the problem.

Secondly, company legal risk general is nonlinear, which is difficult to make decision by linear method. The method of BP artificial neural network provides effective means and ways to solve this nonlinear problem.

Thirdly, BP artificial neural network has self-adaptive function of fault tolerance and error correction, which can make identification and rectification to the chaos of food enterprise legal risk under high uncertainly environment and find out the developing role of company legal risk and provide right decisions for company risk managers.

Finally, BP artificial neural network as a kind of multi-objective legal risk decision-making method, not only can be used to rate the multiple food enterprise legal risk, but also can be used to select legal action plans of the multiple food enterprise, and can be used to analyze and study the legal risk factors of multiple food enterprise, which precisely meet the needs of the diversity and complexity of the company legal risk decisions.

ACKNOWLEDGEMENTS

The research work was supported by Hunan Soft Science Foundation of Hunan under Grant No. 2011zk2004, and Science and technology plan project of Changsha under Grant No. K1205056-11, and Hunan Provincial Natural Science Foundation of China No. 13 JJ4088, and National Nature Science Foundation of China No. 11361067, 11301551. The corresponding author of this paper is Yungui Jiang.

REFERENCES

Chua, L.O. & Yang. L. 1990. *Celluler neural networks: theory and applications.* IEEE Trans. CAS, 35(10): 1257–1290.

Crouhy, M. & Mark, R. 2005. (Translated by Zeng, G. & Luo, X.J. & Lu, S.). *Risk Management.* Beijing: China financial economic publishing house.

Hebb, D. 1949. *The organization of behavior.* NY: John wiley & Sons.

Hecht-Nielsen, R. 1989. *Theory of the backprogation neural networks.* NY: IEEE Press.

Hinton, G. & Sejnowski, T. 1986. Learning and relearning in boltzmannmachines. *Parallel distributed processing: Explorations in the microstructure of cognition,* 1: 282–317.

Hopfield, J. 1982. Neural networks and physical system with emergent collective computational abilities. *Proceedings of the national academy of science USA,* 79: 2554–2558.

Kosko, B. 1986. *Fuzzy entropy and conditioning. Information science.*

McCulloch, W.S. & Pitts, W. 1943. A Logical Calculus of the Ideas Immanent in Nervous Activity. *Bulletin of Mathematical Biophysics,* 5:15–33.

Rumelhart, D. & Hinton, G. & McClelland, J. 1986. A general framework for parallel distributed processing. *Parallel Distributed Processing: Explorations in the microstructure of cognition,* 1: 45–76.

Rumelhart, D. & Zipser, D. 1986. Feature discovery by competitive learning. *Parallel Distributed Processing: Explorations in the microstructure of cognition,* Volume One: Foundations Cambridge, MA: MIT Press, 151–193.

Xiang, F. & Chen, Y.C. 2006. *Assessment of Enterprise Legal Risk.* Beijing: Law publishing house.

Computer, Intelligent Computing and Education Technology – Liu, Sung & Yao (Eds)
© 2014 Taylor & Francis Group, London, ISBN 978-1-138-02469-4

Adolescent attachment and the mobile phone addiction: Mediating effects of social support

X.H. Ge
Shandong Transport Vocational College, Weifang, China

ABSTRACT: Objective: To examine social support as mediators of the relationship between adolescent attachment and mobile phone addiction tendency. Methods: Totally 891 adolescent students selected with cluster sampling were interviewed using Experiences in Close Relationships Inventory (ECR), the Mobile Phone Addiction Tendency Questionnaire (MPATS) and the Social Support Rating Scale (SSRS). Result: The testing of mediating effects showed that adolescent attachment had both direct and indirect effects on the mobile phone addiction tendency, with the direct effect as the main effect. Conclusion: Adolescent attachment has direct effects on individuals' mobile phone addiction, but also has indirect impacts through social support.

Keywords: adolescent attachment; mobile phone addiction; social support; mediating effects

1 GENERAL INTRODUCTION

There are more and more so-called "mobile phone families", "mobile phone parties", "mobile phone persons", "bow clans"and "electronic servants" among adolescent students, who are keen to read e-books, update twitters, chat by micro messages, play electronic games, do shopping, and so on. Recently, it was reported that mobile phone addiction perhaps has become a new trend of the internet addiction among adolescents.[1] Mobile phone addiction is a new phenomenon of human behavior after the internet addiction, and it is an obsessed state which is obviously damaged psychologically and physiologically by overusing mobile phones due to some kind of motivation.[2]

Mobile phone addiction has taken many negative influences to adolescent students, such as inducing physiological diseases, influencing their rest, sleep, relationships and learning efficiency at classroom, increasing economy burden, reducing comprehension and leading to some personality disorders.[3][4]

Attachment refers to a special emotional relationship in which people are close and attached to each other. Social support is a kind of behavior and information of carefulness and confidence which is collected by an individual from his or her social members, which directly reflects the extent and quality of an individual with his or her social relationships.[5] Attachment may have important regulation functions to shape, maintain, and use[6] Psychoanalytic theories suggests that addictive behavior is a manifestation of attachment disorders.[7] A research showed that the scarce of social supports might be one of the main reasons of behavior addictions among adolescent students.[8]

Mobile phone addiction has taken many scholars' and experts' concerns. At present, there are few studies on the relationship among the mobile phone addiction, attachment and social support. This study mainly discussed the relationship between the mobile phone addition and attachment, and whether social support is a mediator of the relationship between attachment and mobile phone addiction.

2 METHOD

2.1 Participants

Nine hundred students from two vocational colleges in Shandong province were recruited by stratified sampling. 900 questionnaires in total were circulated, of which 881 were returned (a response rate was 97.9%). Of the questionnaires returned 4 were blank and 877 were completed for adequate use in the study, hence resulting in 877 participants in this study (287 females, 590 males). Age ranged from 14 to 19 years with an average of 18.1 (SD = 1.6).

2.2 Materials

This study utilised the Experiences in Close Relationships Inventory (ECR), the Mobile Phone

Addiction Tendency Questionnaire (MPATS) and the Social Support Rating Scale (SSRS).

The Mobile Phone Addiction Tendency Scale (MPATS). The Mobile Phone Addiction Tendency Scale is a 16-item questionnaire, which was devised and validated as a reliable self-report by Xiong Jie, Zhou Zongkui, et al,[9] developed to measure the mobile phone addiction, including four factors: withdrawal symptoms, salience, social comfort and mood changes. Items are related on a 5- point scale. Higher scores indicate heavier mobile phone addiction. The cronbach's alpha of each item in the test ranged from 0.689 to 0.856, and the cronbach's alpha of the whole scale was 0.919, showing the high level of internal consistency and suggesting that items are homogenous.

The Experiences in Close Relationships Inventory (ECR).[10] The Experiences in Close Relationships Inventory is a 36-item questionnaire, which was designed to assess the attachment conditions of adolescent students, including attachment anxiety and attachment avoidance two factors. Items are related on a 7-point scale. Higher scores indicate higher anxiety of avoidance degree. The cronbach's alphas of the two factors were 0.727 and 0.886, and the cronbach's alpha of the whole scale was 0.794.

Social Support Rating Scale (SSRS).[11] The Social Support Rating Scale was designed to assess an individual's social supports from others, including four factors: the objective support of society, subjunctive support of society and the utilization extent of social support, with 10 items. The total score of the scale is the norm of social supports, higher score indicates more individual's social supports. The cronbach's alpha of the whole scale was 0.92, and the consistence of each item was from 0.89 to 0.94.

2.3 Data analysis

The total score for each questionnaire or scale was calculated by summing the scores of each item per participant. The statistical procedures used were the correlation analysis and the testing of mediating effects. The data were analyzed using SPSS (version 17.0). The levels of significance were 1% and 5%, respectively.

3 RESULTS

The correlation analysis about mobile phone addiction, social support and The relationships among the attachment, social support and mobile phone addiction were showed in Table 1.

As shown in Table 1, there was a significant negative correlation between the mobile phone addiction and social support. And there was a significant positive correlation between the attachment anxiety and mobile phone addiction. The attachment avoidance was significantly negatively correlated with social support. The attachment anxiety was significantly negatively correlated with social support and attachment avoidance. But there was no significant correlation between the mobile phone addiction and attachment avoidance ($P > 0.05$).

3.1 The testing on the mediating effects of the social support between the attachment and mobile phone addiction

In order to further examine the relationship mechanism between the attachment, social support and mobile phone addiction, we had a mediating effects test, taking attachment anxiety as independent variable (X), mobile phone addiction as the dependent variable (B), and the total score of the social support as the intermediate variable, according to the correlation results above and in accordance with the mediating effects test procedures proposed by Wen Zhonglin, Zhang Lei, et al[12] (Table 2). For the correlation between the attachment and attachment avoidance was not significant, we didn't consider the mediating effects test of the social support between the attachment and mobile phone addiction.

As shown in Table 2, the regression coefficient (mobile phone addiction tendency as dependent variable, and attachment anxiety as independent variable) was 0.469. But when the variable of social support was added into the regression, the

Table 1. Correlation of mobile phone addiction social support and attachment.

Item	Mobile phone addiction	Social support	Attachment avoidance	Attachment anxiety
Mobile phone addiction	1			
Social support	−0.149**	1		
Attachment avoidance	−0.010	−0.207**	1	
Attachment anxiety	0.469**	−0.139**	−0.075**	1

**Level of significance 0.01(two-tailed).

Table 2. Mediating effects of social support between attachment and mobile phone addiction.

Steps	Standardized regression equation	Test of regression coefficient
1	$Y = 0.469\ X$	SE = 0.022 t = 15.69**
2	$M = -0.139\ X$	SE = 0.063 t = −4.163**
3	$Y = -0.085\ M$	SE = 0.012 t = −2.842**
	$0.457\ X$	SE = 0.022 t = 15.205**

**Level of significance 0.01(two-tailed).

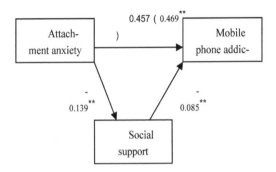

Figure 1. Path of the mediating effect model of social support.

regression coefficient reduced to 0.457, showing the social support has mediating effects between the attachment and mobile phone addiction. Attachment anxiety had direct influence on the mobile phone addiction, at the same time, had indirect influence on mobile phone addiction. The mediating effect took up 0.025 of the total effect.

The mediating effect model of the social support between attachment and mobile phone addiction is described in Figure 1.

4 DISCUSSION

The result showed that there was a significant positive correlation between the mobile phone and attachment anxiety factor. Fuendeling found that the individual with attachment anxiety is prone to notice and express their nerviness and emotion, through a lot of practical researches about attachment and emotion adjustment.[13] In order to loosen the nervous emotion, their notice would naturally turn to the use of mobile phone, so which will increase the mobile phone addiction tendency. Some studies showed there were close relationship between the mobile phone addiction and anxiety.[14]

The study found that the higher the social support score from others is, the lower the mobile

phone addiction tendency among adolescent students. This is accordance with the former studies about the relationship between social support and behavior addictions. Wei Yaoyang pointed out in his study social support negatively correlated with mobile phone addiction,[15] but the correlation between the social support and mobile phone addiction is no significance ($r = -0.08$, $P > 0.05$). Because the studies about relationship between the mobile phone and social support are not so much, we then analyzed some studies about the relationship between the internet addiction and social support, found that there was significant negative correlation between them. Mobile phone addiction and internet addiction belong to the behavior addiction naturally, so this study also proved the scarce of social support is an important factor leading to behavior addictions.

The result of the mediating effect test showed social support played some mediating effect partly between the attachment and mobile phone addiction. That is to say, the attachment conditions not only influenced mobile phone directly, but also indirectly influenced the mobile phone addiction by social support. Social support as the evaluation or cognition about an individual's own social resources available is based on the relation conditions with the people around.[16] While the individual characteristic of the individual with attachment anxiety is afraid of being rejected or abandoned, the mobile phone with powerful functions and convenience provides a good platform for them. However, it is apt to cause mobile phone addiction if of a mobile phone is excessively abused, which will take many serious negative influences on their health, learning and life.[17] This study also proved that social support as a favorable protection factor, could help adolescent students ease their attachment anxiety; reduce the mobile phone addiction tendency directly and indirectly.

REFERENCES

[1] Y. Yang & Y.X. Huang, "Cutting off the network timely to avoid children's Internet addiction by mobile phone", Chongqing Economic Times, 1–31(A04), 2013.
[2] J.G. Shi, "Mobile dependence syndrome", Journal of Clinical Psychiatry, NO. 19(2): 138–139, 2009.
[3] S.Q. Zhou, "The effects and countermeasures about mobile internet addiction on college students ", Education and Vocation, NO. 2: 58–59, 2013.
[4] S.M. Tao, J.L. Fu, H. Wang, et al, "Development of Self-rating Questionnaire for Adolescent Problematic Mobile Phone Use and the psychometric evaluation undergraduates", Chinese Journal of School Health, No. 3(1): 26–29, 2013.

[5] T.G. Li, "Some Hot Topics in Attachment Theory—Comment on Hu & Meng", Acta Scientiarum Naturalium Universitatis Pekinensis, NO. 42(2):18–25, 2006.

[6] J.B. Fu, "Relationships between Undergraduates' Internet Addiction Tendency, Self-Efficacy and Social Support" Huazhong Normal University Journal of Postgraduates, NO. 16(1): 124–127, 2009.

[7] J. Xie, P. Fang, H.C. Zhang, et al, "Internet Addiction Behavior and Adult Attachment among College Students", Chinese Mental Health Journal, NO. 25(7):454–456, 2011.

[8] L.J. Ruan, L. Zhang and W.T. Li, "Mediating Effect of Self-consistency and Congruence Between Social Support and Tendency of Internet Addiction", China Journal of Health Psychology, NO. 19(8):992–994, 2011.

[9] J. Xiong, Z.K. Zhou, W. Chen, et al, "Development of the Mobile Phone Addiction Tendency Scale for College Students", Chinese Mental Health Journal, NO. 26(3):222–225, 2012.

[10] T.G. Li, K. Kato, "Measuring Adult Attachment: Chinese Adaptation of the ECR Scale", Acta Psychologica Sinica, NO. 38(3):399–406, 2006.

[11] S.Y. Xiao, D.S. Yang, "The Influence of Social Support on Mental and Physical Health", Chinese Mental Health Journal, NO. 1(4):183–186, 1987.

[12] Z.L. Wen, L. Zhang, J.T. Hou, et al, "Testing and Application of Mediating Effects", Acta Psychologica Sinica, NO. 36(5):613–620, 2004.

[13] Fuendeling, JM. Affect regulation as a stylistic process within adult attachment [J]. Journal of Social and Personal Relationship,1988,15: 291–322.

[14] Y.F. Zou, Y.Q. Zou, Y.S. Yao, "A Crosse-sectional Study on Mobile Phone Users and Mobile Phone Dependence in Cllege", Acta Academiae Medicinae Wannan, NO. 30 (1):77–80, 2011.

[15] Y.Y. Wei, "Research on the relationship between social support and mobile phone dependence among college students", Journal of Jilin College of Finance and Taxation, NO. 28 (4):91–93, 2012.

[16] Y. Wu, Y.L. Deng, C. Pan, "Childhood Psychological Abuse and Emotional and Behavioral Problems: Mediating Effects of Social Support", Chinese Journal of Clinical Psychology, NO. 19 (4):494–495, 2011.

[17] Kenichi ISHII. Mediating Effects of Social Support Mediating Effects of Social Support [J]. Keio Communication Review, 2011, 33:69–83.

Computer, Intelligent Computing and Education Technology – Liu, Sung & Yao (Eds)
© 2014 Taylor & Francis Group, London, ISBN 978-1-138-02469-4

Study on training approach for microsystem design and fabrication

P.Y. Zhang & Y. Li
School of Physics and Electronics, Henan University, China

ABSTRACT: Microsystem technologies, which is the fundamental field that students should know, is a cutting-edge interdisciplinary leading humanity into the microcosm. Based on analysis on the course of Microsystem Design and Process, the course content, training approach, experimental methods are discussed. The tactics include appropriate choice of course contents, establishing of diversified teaching methods, strengthening of practice part. At the same time, communication platform for both teacher and student are set up to make full use of modern multimedia and Internet platforms and the diversity of assessment system is employed. The requirements on teachers are provided. The cultivation of students' innovative ability is discussed.

Keywords: reform in education; training approach; microsystem technology; MEMS

1 INTRODUCTION

Microsystem technology is an advanced interdisciplinary emerging, developed in recent twenty years [1]. It covers almost all fields of natural science and engineering technology, Including electronics, mechanical, materials, manufacturing, information and automatic control, physics, chemistry, biology and other disciplines, and associated with many sophisticated and intensive achievements of modern science and technology. It has extensive applications in information, communication, aviation, aerospace, automotive, medical, biological, environmental protection, industrial control and other areas [2,3]. Microsystem technologies will be one of the most influential high-tech in twenty-first century, and a new growth point of high-tech industry. It is considered a new industrial revolution in twenty-first century. The research in this field is developing rapidly during to enormous human and material resources in the main countries of the world. Investment of this field also increases in China, and many famous domestic universities also set up this course.

As an advanced emerging discipline, it is still in the initial stage of exploration from the aspects of course content, teaching methods, experimental practice. This paper attempts to explore from aspects above, so that the students can have a comprehensive understanding of the latest research achievements in the course characteristics as soon as possible, broadening the students' knowledge, mastering the basic theory of the field, which is to build good foundation in scientific research or engineering application. And the cultivation of students' innovation ability is also discussed.

2 CHARACTERISTICS OF THE COURSE

The early development of microsystem technologies, the meaning and technical characteristics of this area have various understandings for different people. The world's main countries in the world have their own naming according to their own development histories of the field. It is called Micromachine in Japan since their development thought is from large machining to small machinery, and to micro machine [4]. It is named Microelectromechanical System (MEMS) during to its development based on microelectronic fabrication technology in North America [5]. And it is called Microsystem Technologies for it is considered as system in Europe. What the name is not unified shows that the development of this field is still at an early stage of development. Despite the different names, but the contents are in convergence. It the early stages, named Micromachine is proper slightly due to from large machining to small machinery, and to micro machine; With nearly twenty years of development in this field, especially the mainstream processing is based on the microelectronics technology the, Moreover, its products are from a single separation part to the small system, some even a system of micro electro mechanical system, called micro machinery is inarticulate. Obviously, MEMS is worthy of the name; With the further research in this field, its product even is a complex system. It also comprises a light, sound and other parts beside machine, electric parts. Called microsystem seems more appropriate, deserved.

3 DISCUSSION AND ANALYSIS OF THE CURRICULUM CONSTRUCTION

The construction of education and teaching in Colleges and universities is to implement the construction of three level discipline construction, specialty construction and curriculum construction. Among them, the curriculum construction is the foundation, the concrete implementation of discipline and specialty construction, the decisive factor to ensure the quality of teaching. The curriculum construction is an important part of the basic construction of school teaching. Strengthening the curriculum construction is the effective implementation of teaching plan, an important guarantee for improving the teaching level and the talent training quality. realization of students innovation ability and knowledge innovation system are based on the curriculum construction [6].

3.1 *Reasonable arrangements of the course content*

The course content is very complicated owing to characteristics of its interdisciplinary, and students involve multiple disciplines students in this course, but lesson hours are limited. Therefore, for the arrangement of teaching content, it is necessary to consider the multi disciplines. The main technologies in the field are Including microsystem design, micromachining technology, MEMS devices, microsystem integration and package. Among them, the microsystem design is the base of the subject. Micromachining technology is the key of the subject, and microsystem is available only to employing the micromachining technology. So, the two parts need to emphasize on. MEMS devices are mainly focus on the technical status of the field as well as the latest developments.

3.2 *Enriching the diversification of teaching method*

The rapid development of microsystem technologies in recent years, traditional teaching methods have been difficult to meet the needs of course teaching. It is important to establish a wide range of diversified teaching methods. Multimedia technology has enriched the course teaching, and the introduction of multimedia courseware and electronic teaching plan have brought great vitality to the teaching.

Moreover, the prospects about the latest microsystem technologies, the advanced technology application and development are through employing teaching animation and video to provide sound, images, graphics and other information. So that students will have intuitive understanding of perceptual on abstract and boring knowledge on principle and design, which greatly improve the students' participation desire and interest in learning.

In addition, because of time constraints, the contents that are not taught or explained in class can be discussed via the Internet web sites and/or discussion groups. The students who have a will to further understand and study may have way to extend their own knowledge via to set up communication channels and platforms.

3.3 *Strengthening the practice part*

The course of Microsystem Technologies is the one which has high requirement for practice and hands-on abilities. The practice teaching is an important means to cultivate students' innovation ability. This course is based on the existing conditions, and reasonably arranges for experimental teaching. The experiments are including photolithography, CVD, etching and other basic micromachining process. Students are arranged in group due to less equipment. Up to date, the students participate in discussing the overall scheme of experiment, and after the discussion and analysis on experimental plans, the students can deepen the understanding of the micromachining technologies.

3.4 *Listing and numberin implementing diversity assessment methods*

The curriculum performance evaluation system is the means and the guarantee to assess grasping the knowledge and ability evaluation of students. Reasonable evaluation system can make students free from examination oriented education mode and meet requirement to strengthen comprehensive ability of students. It is beneficial to the cultivation of innovative talents. Diversification of assessment means can in lead guides beneficial to cultivation for students' abilities in scientific logical thinking and problem solving. So that students may pay more attention to the cultivation of practical ability. Assessment system is including the assessment in class, homework, experiment and practice. For instance, Through writing a small paper in group, the comprehensive practical ability and the spirit of team work are trained. The score of the course is divided into the one of homework, small paper, experiment (practice) and test.

3.5 *Requirements on the quality of teachers*

Teachers are the implementers of curriculum construction and teaching reform. Since the field is still at primary stage of development and an interdisciplinary subject, these make the theory system of the curriculum is not yet perfect and there is no mature theory system. Because of reasons above, the teachers' quality is put forward higher requirements. To properly complete the teaching task, the teacher should not only have good teaching ability and solid professional knowledge, but experience of scientific research on MEMS. Having sufficient knowing of the main content, the teachers have a clear understanding of the key technology of this field and have the ability to grasp the global field. So the teachers can make many ways appropriate choice of teaching content, and can do a good job with skill and ease in the teaching process.

4 CULTIVATION OF STUDENTS' INNOVATION ABILITY AND FORMATION OF INNOVATION KNOWLEDGE SYSTEM

Because we built the microsystem technologies lab which is an open lab, it has modeling, design and comprehensive experiments. students can enter the laboratory to participate in scientific research in their spare time, or take the class knowledge into practice.

Interested students can also expand their own ideas for college students' scientific and technological competition through the open laboratory. Those means can play an important role in cultivating students' innovation ability and can effectively promote the gradual formation of students' innovation system.

The practice means above can make students master the basic knowledge of course, and train students' independent thinking and self-learning ability. At the same time, teachers can know the learning effects, so that the ones can timely adjust course contents and teaching plan, and make the teaching more targeted.

In the specific implementation, we adopt a real case combined with my research experience, for example, modeling and micromachining process of microneedle array, the problems how the model is built and process arrange reasonably should be paid attention to. So the students can know of the real research work, understand cultivation for innovative ability and innovative thinking, enables the student to have the feeling of be personally on the scene.

5 CONCLUSION

As a new subject, it is very necessary for research on curriculum construction and practice of teaching method. This paper discusses on curriculum construction of the microsystem technologies and proposes some suggestions in course contents, teaching methods and experiment teaching. The cultivation of innovative talents is also discussed. In the implementation of teaching, the learning enthusiasm of the students is increased, and the teaching effect is improved obviously.

REFERENCES

[1] P. Rai-choudhury (2000), MEMS and MOEMS Technology and applications, SPIE Press, 2000.
[2] M. Bourne (2007), A Consumer's Guide to MEMS & Nanotechnology, Scottdsdale-based Bourne Research LLC, 2007.
[3] N.T. Flynn, Y. Li & etc. (2004), A BioMEMS Review: MEMS Technology for Physiologically Integrated Devices, Proceeding of the IEEE, 92(1): 6–21, 2004.
[4] T. Hirano (1995), Japanese Activities in Micromachining. MST News, 14: 14–17, 1995.
[5] J. Fluitman (1996), Microsystem Technology: Objectives. Sensors and Actuators, A56: 151–166, 1996.
[6] B. Huang & G. Xiang (2007), Analysis and discussion on curriculum construction of national course, China higher education research, 9, 2007.

Computer, Intelligent Computing and Education Technology – Liu, Sung & Yao (Eds)
© 2014 Taylor & Francis Group, London, ISBN 978-1-138-02469-4

Development of three-phase smart meter based on dual ATmega128L and its applications in power quality

L.F. Cheng & T. Yu

Electric Power College, South China University of Technology, Guangzhou, China

ABSTRACT: In order to solve the problems of distribution management and power quality improvement of large electricity users, a new design of three-phase smart meter based on dual high speed ATmega128L and Zigbee is proposed in this paper, and introduces its hardware interface circuit design and its applications in improving power quality, and its feasibility is verified by field test. High precision MAX125 and ATmega128L are used for data synchronous acquisition, calculation, analysis, display, SD card storage and results record, moreover, Zigbee is used for uploading data which are used for the upper system software to make power quality analysis, thus can strengthen electricity management of users, improve power quality and save energy. The instrument has advantages of easy portability, low cost, high precision, strong anti-interference ability and easy to promote, thus can effectively meet the needs of dedicated large users' power quality managements.

Keywords: power quality; comprehensive control; smart meter; dual ATmega128L; wireless communication technology of Zigbee; MAX125; Matlab

1 INTRODUCTION

China has implemented large-scale transformation and construction to the grid in recent years, thus cause a large number of dedicated users increase continuously, and strengthen the management of electricity enterprises.[1–6] The concepts of improving power quality and realizing the energy saving and consumption reducing is paid more and more attention, as a result, the multifunctional intelligent electric meters have been widespread attention and application.[7–13]

So, a portable three-phase smart electric meter based on dual AVR and ATmega128L is presented in this paper. The meter utilizes two ATmega128L MCUs as its control core and makes full use of their rich on-chip resources and peripheral equipment, thus can real-time monitor, record, display and large store big users' three phase voltage, current, active power, reactive power, apparent power, power factor and other electrical parameters which exist in low voltage side of users' distribution system, meanwhile, the use of Zigbee wireless communication mode[14] realizes that the measurement data are uploaded on time to the upper software and which makes real-time comprehensive power quality treatment analysis. The software is designed based on Matlab and according to China's power quality standards; it makes corresponding analysis with the data transmitted through Zigbee, and puts forward the improvement scheme, which can effec-tively improve the power quality of users. Through the laboratory environment test and field test of enterprise internal distribution system, the smart meter runs normally and its feasibility is verified. It proves that the smart meter conforms to the design requirements of current smart meter market, thus can effectively improve the efficiency and ability of distribution network power quality managements in enterprises. What's more, the three-phase multifunctional smart meter designed in this paper has advantages of low cost, strong intelligence, high measuring precision and easy to be popularized.

2 HARDWARE DESIGN

2.1 Working principle of the system

The working principle of the system is schemati-cally shown in Figure 1.

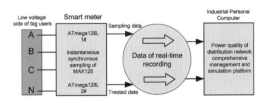

Figure 1. System principle and structure block diagram.

Smart meters put forward in this paper are connected to low voltage side of large users, three-phase voltage and current signal and zero phase voltage and current signal from big users' measuring lines are sampled in the way of instantaneous synchronous by the chip MAX125, and this data sampling process is controlled by 1# ATmega128L, such as real-time tracking frequency signal, synchronous A/D conversion control, voltage and current channel magnification control, and so on. 2# ATmega128L receives sampling data from 1# ATmega128L through SPI synchronous serial communication interface, then implements a series of calculations on these data. On one hand, these data are displayed by LCD module and stored by SD card; on the other hand, the Zigbee Control Module in the Zigbee wireless communication unit is controlled by 1# ATmega128L to receive and send data to the power quality comprehensive management and real-time simulation platform based on Matlab, and this platform utilizes the powerful data analysis functions of Matlab to implement effective distribution management and power quality improvement analysis on the big electricity dedicated users.

2.2 Hardware structure desgin

The structure of system is shown in Figure 2, the hardware system is mainly composed of frequency measurement signal conditioning circuit, voltage channel signal conditioning circuit, current channel signal conditioning circuit, high precision instantaneous A/D sampling circuit, dual AVR MCU signal processor, SPI bus, function display and handle unit (keys, real-time clock, temperature sensor, LCD display), oscillation circuit, SD control module, SD card, Zigbee control module, industrial personal computer and so on. Among which, the computer is arranged on the software of power quality comprehensive management and simulation platform, which is the core power quality analysis software of dual ATmega128L smart meter.

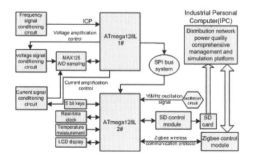

Figure 2.   Structure of hardware system.

The voltage and current channel signal conditioning circuit are respectively composed of PT, CT, and programmable amplifying circuit, among them, PT uses voltage output type voltage converter TR1102-1C, CT uses voltage output type current converter TR1102-2C, two kinds of converters are connected to the voltage follower, which realizes impedance matching.

A/D sampling circuit utilizes high precision and fast AD sampling chip MAX125, this chip is 14 bits synchronous converter with 8 channels, and it has 8 Sample/Hold (S/H) circuits, which collect 8 channel analog signals each time, and under the S/H circuit, realizing ADC conversion, and the switching time of 8 channels is 3.7 s. The output of MAX125 is 14 bits digital signal DB0-DB13 which is transmitted to 1# AVR for further processing.

1# and 2# AVR are both use ATmega128L, this type MCU is as the core digital processor of smart meter designed in this paper has the following characteristics: low power consumption and high speed 8 bit MCU, 128 KB FLASH program memory, 4 KB RAM and 4 KB E²PROM are integrated, and the E²PROM is very suitable for parameter setting, and it doesn't lose data under power off. In addition, this chip also integrates with JTAG interface which is used for online simulation debugging and program download, thus is very convenient for program modification and upgrading online.

The functions of 1# and 2# are different, 1# AVR is mainly responsible for the four roads voltage and current signal amplification control, frequency tracking and synchronous AD conversion control, and in addition, it transmits the digital signal real-time to the 2# AVR through SPI bus. The SPI bus system is a synchronous serial peripheral interface, it can make the MCU and various peripheral devices communicate to exchange information in a serial manner, and it has a total of 3 registers: controlling register SPCR, status register SPSR and data register SPDR.

The 2# AVR utilizes its rich on-chip resources and peripheral instruments, can real-time monitor, record, display, communicate and large capacity store basic distribution network electrical parameters such as three-phase voltage, current, active power, reactive power, apparent power and power factor. Furthermore, it can calculate and obtain the maximum, minimum, and average value of these basic electrical parameters in a set time. The operation process of the smart meter is shown in Figure 3.

2.3 Design of dual ATmega128L inner main program and sampling program

The program of lower-computer is written in C language, and is finally written into the ATmega128L

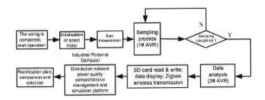

Figure 3. Smart meter application flow chart.

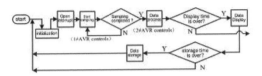

Figure 4. Main program flow chart.

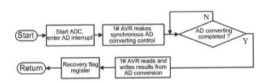

Figure 5. Sampling program flow chart.

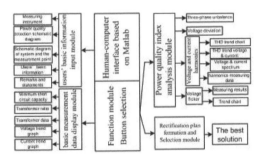

Figure 6. Structure of main computer software.

Flash. The main program and sampling program flowchart of smart meter is respectively shown in Figure 4 and Figure 5.

2.4 Design of distribution network power quality comprehensive management and simulation platform based on Matlab/Simulink

The distribution network power quality comprehensive management and simulation software is based on Matlab/Simulink and written in C language. This simulation platform constitutes the upper computer system software, and is composed of 4 parts, such as users' basic information input module, basic measurement data display module, power quality index analysis module, rectification plan formation and selection module. A comprehensive analysis of the upper computer system software outputs the final power quality rectification report of users. Its structure is shown in Figure 6.

3 EFFECT OF APPLICATION IN PRACTICAL ENGINEERING

3.1 Measuring results

Field measurements were conducted in a cement production enterprise in Shaoguan city of China, the basic situation of the factory is: two 35 kV lines, of which the voltage is stepped down 6 kV through 2 sets of S7-8000/35 main transformers; another 6 kV branch transports to the mine substation. I segment and II segment 6 kV lines are stepped down 380/220 V through two level variation, and used for low voltage equipment. The system and measurement points are shown in Figure 7 and Table 1.

Due to space limitations, only make a detailed analysis on measurement point 1 (3#3). Basic load situation is shown in Table 2, and based on which, the software of power quality analysis obtains the statistical graphs of users' power quality index, including the voltage deviation detection results (shown in Table 3), the A phase voltage and current total harmonic distortion and harmonic spectrum (including the maximum, minimum, average, 95% probability spectrum) (respectively shown in Figures 8 and 9), the voltage unbalance detection results (shown in Table 4), the voltage fluctuation detection results (shown in Table 5), and the voltage flicker detection results (shown in Table 6).

3.2 Rectification solutions

Aim at the power quality problems shown from the testing results above, three solutions are presented as following.

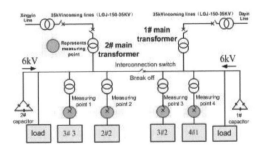

Figure 7. Schematic diagram of scale measurement points.

51

Table 1. Transformer data of the measuring point.

Transformer number	Capacity (kVA)	Type	Impedance (%)	Connection group
3#3	1250	S7-1250/6	4.5	Y,yn0
3#2	630	S7-630/6	4.5	Y,yn0
4#1	1250	S7-1250/6	4.5	Y,yn0
2#2	1600	S9-M-1600/6	4.65	D,yn11

Table 2. Basic load situation of measuring point no. 1.

Power relevance	Maximum value	Minimum value	Average value	95% value
Voltage (V)				
Phase A	235.710	208.000	226.897	232.520
Phase B	236.890	210.410	229.135	234.160
Phase C	239.430	212.430	229.977	234.820
Current (A)				
Phase A	12.000	3.000	4.570	6.000
Phase B	2623.000	627.000	1100.939	1400.000
Phase C	2454.000	556.000	999.731	1275.000
Apparent power (kVA)				
Phase A	538.350	137.500	292.567	397.750
Phase B	553.800	145.700	305.191	413.500
Phase C	522.900	129.300	279.942	382.000
Active power (kW)				
Phase A	407.000	94.000	244.863	329.000
Phase B	429.100	102.000	258.944	347.300
Phase C	384.900	85.800	230.782	310.700
Power factor				
Phase A	0.99	0.97	0.98	–
Phase B	0.99	0.97	0.99	–
Phase C	0.99	0.97	0.99	–

Table 3. Voltage deviation of measuring point no. 1.

Voltage deviation (%)	Maximum (%)	Minimum (%)	Average (%)	International value (%)	Qualified rate (%)	Qualified
Phase A	*7.270*	*−2.324*	*3.417*	*(−10, +7)*	99.618	*FLASE*
Phase B	*7.767*	*−1.080*	*4.437*	*(−10, +7)*	98.438	*FLASE*
Phase C	*8.396*	*−0.396*	*4.821*	*(−10, +7)*	93.993	*FLASE*

*Note: bold italics indicate that the type of data does not meet Chinese Industrial Standards (CIS).

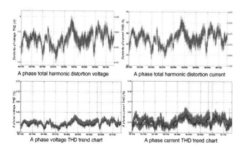

Figure 8. Voltage and current harmonic THD of A phase.

Solution 1: install capacitors and passive filter.

In order to filter harmonic currents, multiple groups of passive filter can be installed. Aim at higher harmonic content in load current, and the main characteristics of harmonic current are generated as 3, 5, 7, 11, 13 times, thus can install 3, 5, 7, 11, 13 times single tuned filter. In order to filter high times harmonic, a group of high pass filter can be installed, and the cutoff frequency selected as 15 times.

Solution 2: install STATCOM and hybrid active power filter.

Install a STATCOM device can effectively improve the voltage flicker and voltage deviation

52

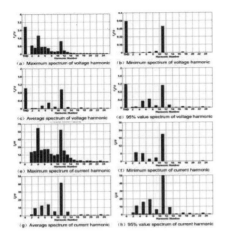

(a) Maximum spectrum of voltage harmonic (b) Minimum spectrum of voltage harmonic
(c) Average spectrum of voltage harmonic (d) 95% value spectrum of voltage harmonic
(e) Maximum spectrum of current harmonic (f) Minimum spectrum of current harmonic
(g) Average spectrum of current harmonic (h) 95% value spectrum of current harmonic

Figure 9. A phase harmonic voltage and current maximum, minimum, average, probability value frequency spectrogram.

etc. When refers to STATCOM configuration, a double winding transformer should be equipped as connection transformer, STATCOM is connected to the low voltage side of transformer, the output channel of STATCOM is connected in parallel with the 10 kV or 6 kV bus through the transformer.

Solution 2 is shown in Table 7.

Solution 3: install hybrid APF and capacitor banks.

According to load operation, packet switching capacitor banks, supplying respective phase compensation for load, thus can effectively improve the voltage flicker and other problems. In the 10 kV or 6 kV bus of factory, install a double winding transformer.

In the low voltage side of the transformer, a set of hybrid APF can be installed, thus can effectively filter load harmonic current, when necessary, the load reactive power can also be compensated. Solution 3 is shown in Table 8.

Table 4. Voltage unbalance of measuring point no. 1.

Maximum	Minimum	Average	95% value	International allowable value (95%)	International allowable value (maximum %)	Qualified
0.210	0.013	0.065	0.130	2	4	TRUE

Table 5. Voltage fluctuation of measuring point no. 1.

Voltage fluctuation frequency (/h)	Phase A	Phase B	Phase C	International value	Qualified
$r <= 1$	2.367	2.041	2.209	4	TRUE
$1 < r <= 10$	0.596	0.546	0.511	3	TRUE
$10 < r <= 100$	0.085	0.086	0.084	2	TRUE
$100 < r <= 1000$	*4.088*	*3.619*	*3.369*	*1.25*	*FALSE*

*Note: bold italics indicate that the type of data does not meet Chinese Industrial Standards (CIS).

Table 6. Voltage flicker of measuring point no. 1.

Long time flicker (2 h)	Maximum	Minimum	Average	International value	Qualified rate (%)	Qualified
Phase A	*1.305*	*0.449*	*0.972*	*1*	*58.125*	*FALSE*
Phase B	*1.645*	*0.443*	*0.881*	*1*	*88.264*	*FALSE*
Phase C	*1.863*	*0.431*	*0.866*	*1*	*91.076*	*FALSE*

*Note: bold italics indicate that the type of data does not meet Chinese Industrial Standards (CIS).

Table 7. Control measures of scheme two.

Device	Capacity	Inlet point	Note	Cost (ten thousand RMB)
STATCOM	5 Mvar	Connected to low voltage side of transformer		20
Hybrid APF	5 MVA	Connected to low voltage side of transformer		20
Connection transformer	10 MVA	10 kV or 6 kV bus of factory	Transformation ratio: 380/11000 or 380/6600	10

Table 8. Control measures of scheme three.

Device	Capacity	Inlet point	Note	Cost (ten thousand RMB)
Hybrid APF	5MVA	Connected to low voltage side of transformer	–	20
Capacitor banks	1200 kvar each phase	35 kV inlet line of load	Compensate each phase	4
Connection transformer	6 MVA	10 kV or 6kV bus of factory	Transformation ratio: 380/11000 or 380/6600	10

4 CONCLUSIONS

A three-phase smart meter based on dual ATmega128L and Zigbee wireless communication protocol was designed and presented in this paper, and its practical engineering application in power quality analysis of industry was described in detail.

1. This smart meter is in coordination with the software which is based on Matlab/Simulink platform, on basis of accurate, rapid detection and analysis of power quality, this system including smart meter and software can put forward reasonable improvements for big dedicated electricity users, and then make compares with these schemes.
2. Testing data of this system is real-time, meanwhile this smart meter utilized MAX125 to ensure the high sampling precision. The analysis function is comprehensive and the simulation ability is strong, thus can laid a good foundation for the scientific management of users' distribution network and make effective and rapid power quality analysis and supply optimized rectification measure for the big dedicated electricity users.
3. Aim at voltage deviation, voltage fluctuation, voltage flicker, harmonic and three-phase unbalance, implement comprehensive managements, not only can reduce the loss of power equipment, but also optimize operating environment, prolong the service life of equipment, and reduce pollution of power grid.
4. Comprehensive treatments and simulation results of power quality problems in certain large manufacturing enterprise of Shaoguan city show progressiveness and high effectiveness of this system.

REFERENCES

[1] R. Sanhueza, H. Rudnick and H. Lagunas, 2004. *DEA Efficiency for the Determination of the Electric Power Distribution Added Value*, IEEE Trans. Power Syst., vol. 19, no. 2.

[2] Marc A. Rosen 2007. Improving the Efficiency of Electrical Systems via Exergy Methods [J]. *2007 IEEE Canada Electrical Power Conference*, 467–472.
[3] Presuhn R. RFC3418 Management Information Base (MIB) for the Simple Network Management Protocol (SNMP)IS. 2002–12.
[4] M. Ali Azadeh, Sara Sohrabkhani 2006. Annual Electricity Consumption Forecasting with Neural Network in High Energy Consuming Industrial Sectors of Iran [J]. *Industrial Technology*, Page(S):2166–2171.
[5] Ananthan, R., Ameer, Sadam, Shiyamini, R. 2006. Comparative Study of energy Assessment from Apparel Industries. Industrial and Information Systems. *First International Conference*, Aug. 8–11. Page(S): 217–220.
[6] Lee W., Kim T. 2007. Control of the thyristor-controlled reactor for reactive power compensation and load balancing [C]. *2007 Second IEEE Conference on Industrial Electronics and Applications*.
[7] X.F. Ma, W.B. Lu, H. Wang etc, 2002. Research on automatic IC power meter reading scheme based on LV power line carrier communication [J]. *Electric Power Automation Equipment (in Chinese)*, 22(7): 53–55.
[8] J. Wu, M.C. Zhu 2004. Electric carrier meter and carrier communication [J]. *Electric Power Automation Equipment (in Chinese)*, 2004, 24(6):78–80.
[9] M.J. Wang 2009. Development and Application of Electricity Consumer Information System [J]. *Power System Technology (in Chinese)*, 2009(16):9–13.
[10] J.D. He, Z.S. Teng, H. Wen 2009. Design of single-phase multi-function energy meter [J]. *Journal of Electronic Measurement and Instrument (in Chinese)*, 25(1):89–95.
[11] S.B. Shu, J.R. Luo, Q.Y. Wang, etc 2010. Design and implementation of a portable power quality monitoring device based on DSP and ARM [J]. *Power System Protection and Control (in Chinese)*, 2010, 38 (24):185–189.
[12] X.Y. Luo, K.Peng, Y.Q. Tang 2007. New multiple-user meter design based on DSP technology [J]. *Converter Technology & Electric Traction (in Chinese)*, 2007 (2):44–47.
[13] W. Liu, F. Yang, Y.C. Fan 2007. Design of 0.2 grade multi-rate watt-hour meter based on DSP [J]. *Journal of Northeast Agricultural University (in Chinese)*, 38(6): 829–831.
[14] J.Zhou, X.C. Shi, C. Xu 2010. A Design of Multi-user Smart Meter Based on ZigBee [J]. *Electrical Measurement & Instrumentation (in Chinese)*, 47(1): 57–61.

Computer, Intelligent Computing and Education Technology – Liu, Sung & Yao (Eds)
© 2014 Taylor & Francis Group, London, ISBN 978-1-138-02469-4

Precision measurement of the spatiotemporal evolutions of a long laser pulse during nonlinear propagation

S.G. Deng, Y.B. Deng, C.X. Xiong, G.F. Zhang & Y. Tian
College of Communication and Electronic Engineering, Hunan City University, Yiyang, P.R. China

ABSTRACT: A method for measuring the spatiotemporal evolutions of the long laser pulse during nonlinear propagation is proposed, which not only has advantages of operation simple, convenience and high resolution, but also can measure the fine structure of the long pulse in time domain. The spatiotemporal evolutions of a picosecond laser pulse propagating in different lengths of CS_2 medium are measured by this method. It is found that the pulse width has a trend of slight narrow because the picosecond laser generates slight self-focusing effect in space with increment of the length of CS_2 medium.

Keywords: spatiotemporal evolution; synchronized ultrashort pulse; precision measurement; nonlinear propagation

1 INTRODUCTION

With the rapid development of ultrafast laser technology, the pulse width is from a femtosecond level into an attosecond, for example, 10 as ultrashort pulses have been generated in the ultraviolet and X-wave band. Ultrashort pulse laser technology has a broad application prospects in many fields, such as optical communication, laser-plasma interaction, laser-atom or laser-molecule interaction, and pump-probe spectroscopy[1–7]. The ultrashort pulse is used as a very short time probe, which provides an important tool for investigation of ultrafast chemical reaction in the microscopic world. For an instance, ultrashort pulse is used to detect the ultrafast chemical reaction of atoms-molecules and measure the fine structure of a long pulse in time domain. We know whether the long pulse generates modulation phenomena in time domain by measuring the fine structure of this long pulse. When the long pulse with an initial modulation propagates and amplifies in the large-scale Nd: glass laser system, the modulation will be accumulated and enhanced, which leads the output laser pulse has serious distortion in time domain. So a corresponding measurement method to characterize the fine structure is necessary.

There are two types of methods for measuring the temporal characteristics of laser pulses. One is a pure electronic method, such as photodiodes, high-speed oscilloscope[8] and high-speed streak camera[9]. The other is an all-optical method, such as autocorrelation[10–13], cross-correlation[14–16], Frequency Resolved Optical Gating (FROG)[17–21],

Spectral Interferometry (SI)[22], Spectral Phase Interferometry for Direct Electric-field Reconstruction (SPIDER)[23–27], and Pump-Probe technology[6,28,29]. In the above methods, photodiodes and high-speed streak camera are only suitable for measuring the pulse width of hundreds femtosecond due to the effect of measurement resolution, which are not suitable for measuring the pulse width less than 100 fs. FROG and SPIDER have proven capable of measuring the temporal and phase characteristics of a given pulses accurately, but it is need to assume uniform transverse spatial distribution. FROG is needed complex iterative algorithm to retrieve the pulse shape of premeasured pulse in time domain, which only gives approximate information. SPIDER is particularly suited for measuring the spectral phase of a pulse, which has an advantageous for tracking the influence of dispersion on an ultrashort pulse. SPIDER neither moves components nor requires iterative algorithm, but it does not give the pulse width information directly. It needs the multiplied result of its measurement spectrum and phase, and then reconstructs the pulse shape and width by Fourier Transform. Compared with other methods, FROG and SPIDER are more complex in experimental operation. The intensity autocorrelation method is simple operation and no need complex calculation, but it is only suitable for measuring the pulse width information and need to assume the shape of premeasured pulse during the measurement process. While the coherent intensity autocorrelation method can provide some phase information, the accurate phase information is not given directly.

The intensity cross-correlation method is also simple operation and no need complex calculation, whose measurement resolution is associated with the pulse width of a probe pulse. When the probe pulse is very clean in time domain and its pulse width is very short, the measurement resolution is higher. The cross-correlation curve characterizes the temporal fine information of pre-measured pulse directly when the pulse width of a probe pulse is very short.

In this paper, we propose a method for precision measuring the spatiotemporal evolutions of a long laser pulse by synchronized ultrashort pulse according the principle of intensity cross-correlation. And we set up an experimental platform to measure the spatiotemporal evolutions of a picosecond laser pulse after propagating in CS_2 nonlinear media. This paper is organized as following. In Sec. 2 we mainly introduce the experimental setup. In Sec. 3 we analyze the experimental results in detail. Conclusions are presented in Sec. 4.

2 EXPERIMENTAL SETUP

The regenerative amplifier systems of the femtosecond laser and picosecond laser are adjusted to synchronize before doing the experiment. The experimental setup is shown in Figure 1. The femtosecond laser (Coherent Libra) generates a probe pulse, whose main parameters are as following: 800 nm central wavelength, pulse width ~100 fs,

1 KHz repetition. The picosecond laser (High Q) generates a pre-measured pulse, whose main parameters are as following: 1054 nm central wavelength, pulse width ~75 ps, 1 KHz repetition. The femtosecond probe pulse passes through the M1 mirror, delay line, telescopes, M4 mirror, and injects the BBO crystal with a thickness of 0.5 mm. The sum-frequency signal with a wavelength of 455 nm is generated in the BBO crystal by a small angle nonlinear sum-frequency interaction between the femtosecond probe pulse and the pre-measured picosecond pulse. Femtosecond pulse scans the picosecond pulse completely by adjusting the delay line. The cross-correlation curve is obtained by probing the sum-frequency signal light with an oscilloscope and Photoelectric Detector (PD). Therefore the initial fine structure of the picosecond pulse in time domain and its temporal evolutions after CS_2 nonlinear media are obtained. The charge-coupled device CCD (Coherent Laser Cam-HR, pixel: 1280×1024, resolution: 6.7 µm × 6.7µm) is used to measure the spatial evolution of the picosecond laser passing through CS_2. So the spatiotemporal evolutions of picosecond laser pulse are obtained by getting the measurement results of the PD and CCD camera. Because the picosecond laser beam spot is smaller than the femtosecond laser, in order to make their beam spots matching, the femtosecond pulse beam spot should be shrunk by using a telescope.

3 EXPERIMENTAL RESULTS AND ANALYSIS

Figure 2 (a–c) shows the spatial intensity evolutions when the picosecond laser propagates in different length of CS_2 nonlinear media. In the experiment, the input energy of picoscond laser is about 2 mJ, whose corresponding peak power is 26.68 kW. The self-focusing critical power of CS_2 media is 1.9 kW, it is easy to see that the input peak power is lager than the self-focusing critical power. So the self-focusing effect is generated when picosecond laser passes through the CS_2 nonlinear media. Although the initial spatial intensity of picosecond laser has lots of random noise modulation, the growth of spatial noise modulation is not obviously. The small-scale self-focusing effect is not obviously.

In order to compare the evolutions of the spatial modulation intensities of the picosecond laser after propagating in a nonlinear media with different length, the spatial intensities profiles at the laser central position are shown in Figure 2 (d). The normalized Gaussian fitting curve is identical in the condition of three different propagation distances from Figure 2 (d),

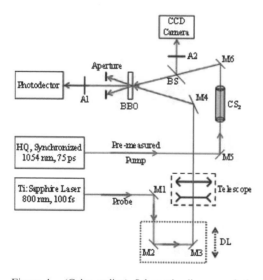

Figure 1. (Color online) Schematic diagram of the experimental setup: M1-M6, silver-coated plane mirror; BS, beam splitter; DL, Delay Line; BBO, β-barium borate crystal; A1 and A2, adjustable neutral density attenuator.

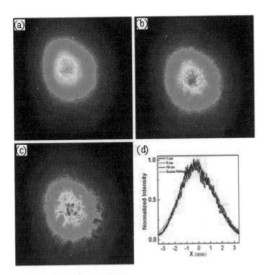

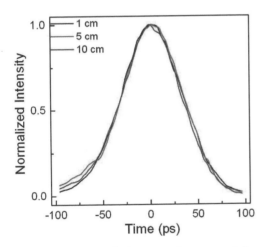

Figure 2. (Color online) (a–c) Variation of spatial intensity distributions of the picosecond laser pulses with the length of CS$_2$: (a) 1 cm, (b) 5 cm, (c) 10 cm, respectively. (d) Spatial intensity profile distributions of the picosecond laser pulses after propagating in different length of CS$_2$ nonlinear media. The green curve is Gaussian fitting result.

Figure 3. (Color online) measured cross-correlation curves as functions of a length of CS$_2$ nonlinear media.

which shows that the whole-beam self-focusing effect is not generated.

The temporal evolutions of picosecond laser pulse are measured by the experimental setup [Fig. 1] when the picosecond laser pulse propagates in nonlinear media with different lengths, which are presented in Figure 3. The Full Width At Half Maximum (FWHM) of the cross-correlation curve is about 75 ps when the length of CS$_2$

is 1 cm, which is the same as the result of no CS$_2$ [Fig. 3]. The cross-correlation curve also shows that the effect of self-focusing is not obviously. The cross-correlation curves become narrower slightly when the CS$_2$ length is increased, which shows that the slight self-focusing effect is generated. The self-focusing effect pushes the energy away from the peak position of a beam, thus leading the temporal compression of a laser pulse.

4 CONCLUSIONS

Ultrashort pulse laser technology has a broad application prospects in optical communication, optical switch, optical storage, laser-plasma interaction, laser-atom molecule interaction, and pump-probe spectroscopy. According to intensity cross-correlation principle, we propose a method of measuring the spatiotemporal evolutions of a long laser pulse after nonlinear propagation by a synchronized ultrashort pulse. This method has advantages of simple operation and high resolution, which can measure the temporal shape of a complex picosecond laser pulse. The spatiotemporal evolutions of a picosecond Nd: YLF laser pulse are characterized by a synchronized femtosecond pulse experimentally. We find that the slight self-focusing effect is generated in space of the picosecond laser pulse when the CS$_2$ length is increased. The temporal shape of the picosecond laser pulse appears narrow phenomenon slightly due to the effect of self-focusing. If there is a proper CCD camera, we believe that this method is also suitable for measuring the spatiotemporal evolutions of a mid-IR laser pulse during nonlinear propagation.

ACKNOWLEDGEMENTS

This work is partially supported by the Department of Science and Technology of Hunan Province (2012FJ3025), Hunan Provincial Natural Science Foundation of China (14JJ6043), and the Department of Science and Technology of Yiyang City (2013JZ08).

REFERENCES

[1] Wegener, M. 2005. *Extreme nonlinear optics*. Berlin: Springer.
[2] Baker, S. 2011. Femtosecond to attosecond light pulses from a molecular modulator. *Nature Photonics* 5(20):664–671.
[3] Levis, R.J. 2001. Selective bond dissociation and rearrangement with optimally tailored, strong-filed laser pulses. *Science* 292(5517):709–713.

[4] Dudovich, N. 2002. Single-pulse coherently controlled nonlinear Raman spectroscopy and microscopy. *Nature* 418:512–514.

[5] Kruer, W.L. 2000. Interaction of plasmas with intense lasers. *Physics of Plasmas* 7(6):2270–2278.

[6] Polli, D. 2007. High-time-resolution pump-probe system with broadband detection for the study of time-domain vibrational dynamics. *Review of Scientific Instruments* 78(10):103108.

[7] Polli, D. 2010. Effective temporal resolution in pump-probe spectroscopy with strongly chirped pulses. *Physical Review A* 82(5):053809.

[8] Rullière, C. 2003. *Femtosecond Laser Pulses: Principles and Experiments.* Berlin: Springer, Second Edition.

[9] Tsuchiya, Y. 1984. Advances in streak camera instrumentation for the study of biological and physical processes. *IEEE Journal of Quantum Electronics* 20(12):1516–1528.

[10] Nikolopoulos, L.A.A. 2005. Second order autocorrelation of an XUV attosecond pulse train. *Physical Review Letters* 94(11):113905.

[11] Luan, S. 1993. High dynamic range third-order autocorrelation measurement of picosecond laser pulse shapes. *Measurement Science Technology* 4(12):1426–1429.

[12] Sacks, Z. 2001. Adjusting pulse-front tilt and pulse duration by use of a single-shot autocorrelator. *Optics Letters* 26(7):462–464.

[13] Mashiko, H. 2003. All-reflective interferometric autocorrelator for the measurement of ultrashort optical pulses. *Applied Physics B* 76(5): 525–530.

[14] Träger, G. 2007. *Handbook of lasers and optics.* Berlin: Springer.

[15] Ma, J.G. 2011. Single-shot cross-correlator using a long-wavelength sampling pulse. *Optics Letters* 36(6):978–980.

[16] Deng, Y.B. 2011. Experimental research on measuring the fine structure of long pulses in time domain by synchronized ultrashort pulse. *Optics Communications* 284(3):847–851.

[17] Kane, D.J. 1999. Characterization of arbitrary femtosecond pulses using frequency-resolved optical gating. *IEEE Journal of Quantum Electronics* 29(2):571–579.

[18] Trebino, R. 1993. Using phase retrieval measure the intensity and phase of ultrashort pulses: frequency-resolved optical gating. *Journal of the Optical Society of America A* 10(5):1101–1111.

[19] Kane, D.J. 1993. Single-shot measurement of the intensity and phase of an arbitrary ultrashort pulse by using frequency-resolved optical gating. *Optics Letter* 18(10):823–825.

[20] DeLong, K.W. 1994. Frequency-resolved optical gating with the use of second-harmonic generation. *Journal of the Optical Society of America B* 11(11):2206–2215.

[21] DeLong, K.W. 1994. Pulse retrieval in frequency-resolved optical gating based on the method of generalized projections. *Optics Letters* 19(24):2152–2154.

[22] Lepetit, L. 1995. Linear techniques of phase measurement by femtosecond spectral interferometry for applications in spectroscopy. *Journal of the Optical Society of America B* 12(12):2467–2474.

[23] Iaconis, C. 1999. Self-referencing spectral interferometry for measuring ultrashort optical pulses. *IEEE Journal of Quantum Electronics* 35(4):501–509.

[24] Gallmann, L. 1999. Characterization of sub-6-fs optical pulses with spectral phase interferometry for direct electric-field reconstruction. *Optics Letter* 24(18):1314–1316.

[25] Hirasawa, M. 2002. Sensitivity improvement of spectral phase interferometry for direct electric-filed reconstruction for the characterization of low-intensity femtosecond pulses. *Applied Physics B* 74(1):s225–s229.

[26] Kornelis, W. 2003. Single-shot kilohertz characterization of ultrashort pulses by spectral phase interferometry for direct electric-field reconstruction. *Optics Letter* 28(4):281–283,.

[27] Supradeepa, V.R. 2009. Optical arbitrary waveform characterization via dual-quadrature spectral interferometry. *Optics Express* 17(1):25–33.

[28] Manzoni, C. 2006. Two-color pump-probe system broadly tunable over the visible and the near infrared with sub-30 fs temporal resolution. *Review of Scientific Instruments* 77(2):023103.

[29] Polli, D. 2010. Effective temporal resolution in pump-probe spectroscopy with strongly chirped pulses. *Physical Review A* 82(5):053809.

Computer, Intelligent Computing and Education Technology – Liu, Sung & Yao (Eds)
© *2014 Taylor & Francis Group, London, ISBN 978-1-138-02469-4*

The research on reliability optimization of software system

W.J. Gu, Y.X. Qian & Y.L. Wang
Changzhou Institute of Mechatronic Technology, China

ABSTRACT: To deal with the problem of low efficiency and low convergence speed in searching the global optimum, Niche Genetic Algorithm was used in reliability optimization of software system. Linear programming works with multi-variable and multi-constraint were solved successfully. And also, the searching performance of the genetic algorithms was improved by introducing the stochastic tournament model, the uniform schema crossover operator and the non-uniform mutation in the genetic algorithm. The simulation results show that the Niche Genetic Algorithm can resolve the multi-module complex software system's reliability allocation effectively, which can improve the computing speed and the resolution quality effectively.

Keywords: genetic algorithm; niche genetic algorithm; software reliability

1   INTRODUCTION

The original of the Genetic Algorithm is the computer simulation research on biological systems. It was put forward by professor J.H. Holland in the university of Michigan in 1960s [1]. Genetic Algorithm is a random search technique based on imitating the natural selection, species evolution and population genetics. And it is particularly suitable for getting the optimal solution of combinatorial optimization problems [2]. In recent years, Genetic algorithm has been applied in many fields and has become an important method of researching artificial intelligence and information processing technology [3]. The reliability optimization of software system, which is also called reliability allocation problem of software system, is to find an optimal reliability allocation scheme of software system under the conditions of a certain resource constraints. It makes the system obtain the highest reliability. Generally speaking, there are a large number of local extreme points. It is difficult to solve the global optimal solution accurately. Many scholars have achieved good results in solving the combinatorial optimization problem with intelligent optimization algorithms. But it is still rare to see the research on reliability allocation problem of software system with Niche Genetic Algorithm [4].

The reliability optimization of software system was researched based on Niche Genetic Algorithm in this paper. And it was compared with other heuristic optimization algorithms. The theoretical analysis and simulation results show that Niche

Genetic Algorithm is suitable for solving reliability allocation problem of software system. And also the operating efficiency and the solution quality are improved.

2   THE ANALYSIS OF NICHE GENETIC ALGORITHM

In biology, a niche refers to the organizational function or role in a specific environment. Species refer to the common features of organization. The organisms tend to live with each other with similar features and shapes [5]. The individual process of evolution is put in the same population repeatedly in traditional genetic algorithm. With the smoothly genetic exchanging, it is difficult for respective developing of the individual. So the diversity of population is reduced. To solve the problem, the individuals in the initial population are sorted by fitness value firstly. And the similar individuals evolve independently in the niche. The scale of sub-population is changing with parent population. Let N be the scale of parent population, K be the scale of sub-population, we must have $K = N(D)$, K is a function of D. It can be set firstly according to the characteristics of the problem. D is the variance of the individuals in a population while σ is a constant. When the diversity decreases, D decreases. When D is less than a threshold σ, the sub-population size will reduce to the minimum value 2 in order to stimulate the improvement of the diversity of the population.

3 THE RELIABILITY ALLOCATION MODEL OF SOFTWARE SYSTEM BASED ON THE MODULE SUBSYSTEM

The reliability can be represented as formula 1 for a software system which has n modules and m operations.

$$R(\lambda_1, \lambda_2, ..., \lambda_n; \tau) = \exp\left(-\sum_{j=1}^{n}\sum_{i=1}^{m} p_i q_{ij} \lambda_j \tau\right) \quad (1)$$

In the formula, n stands for the number of module. The m stands for the number of operations. τ stands for the running time. λ_j stands for the failure rate of module j. p_i stands for the probability of operation. q_{ij} stands for the running time proportion of module j in operation i.

The running time proportion of module j in the total task can be defined as formula 2.

$$\phi_j = \sum_{i=1}^{m} p_i q_{ij} \quad (2)$$

ϕ_j stands for occupied time of module j in the total task. Then we can get the reliability of module j in the time of ϕ_j. As shown in formula 3.

$$R(\lambda_i; \phi_j \tau) = \exp\left(-\sum_{i=1}^{m} p_i q_{ij} \lambda_j \tau\right) = \exp(-\phi_j \lambda_j \tau) \quad (3)$$

Then, the reliability of module j in the time τ can be represented as formula 4.

$$R(\lambda_i; \tau) = \exp(-\lambda_j \tau) = R(\lambda_j; \phi_j \tau)^{1/\phi_j} \quad (4)$$

Then, the reliability of the software system which has n modules can be represented as formula 5.

$$R(\lambda_1, \lambda_2, ..., \lambda_n; \tau) = \prod_{j=1}^{n} \exp(-\phi_j \lambda_j \tau) \quad (5)$$

So the cost of software development can be got as formula 6.

$$TC(\lambda_1, \lambda_2, ..., \lambda_n) = \sum_{j=1}^{n} C(\lambda_j) \quad (6)$$

The reliability of the software system can be got to the expression as formula 7.

$$R(\lambda_1, \lambda_2, ..., \lambda_n; \tau) \geq \rho \quad (7)$$

In the formula, ρ stands for the reliability target of the software system with n modules and m operations. That is a combinatorial optimization problem with a linear function and multiple constraints. So Niche Genetic Algorithm is imported to solve the engineering problem.

4 RELIABILITY OPTIMIZATION OF SOFTWARE SYSTEM BASED ON NICHE GENETIC ALGORITHM

The genetic algorithm which simulates biological niche genetic is produced by using the concept of niche genetic. The purpose of the algorithm is to form and maintain a variety of sub-populations and do parallel search in the search space. It is often used to solve multimodal function, multi-objective optimization and simulation of complex systems [6]. Niche Genetic Algorithm simulates the fittest principle of biological evolution by maintaining a group of individuals. Repeated selection, crossover and mutation of the individuals are carried out until the global optimal solution is obtained.

4.1 The coding and the generation of initial population

The primary task of an algorithm is the encoding method. It affects not only the design method of crossover operator, mutation operator, but also the convergence speed of the algorithm. The genetic algorithm which is based on real-coded is the actual description of the continuous parameter optimization problem. There is no binary encoding and decoding process which can greatly increase the efficiency of the algorithm.

Individual chromosomes are real-coded in genetic algorithm. Each chromosome is represented by feasible solution vector $\lambda = (\lambda_1, \lambda_2, ..., \lambda_n)$. At the same time, the upper and lower limits can be determined by the given constrains. That is the search space. The reliability allocation value can be obtained using formula 4 after getting the value of $(\lambda_1, \lambda_2 ..., \lambda_n)$. And we can calculate the reliability index of the whole modules by using formula 4 and formula 5 repeated.

Cell generation is used in order to make the initial population distribute throughout the solution space. First, the whole solution space is divided into N small intervals. M individuals in each small interval are generated randomly. Then, an $N \times M$ population is generated. The initial population is evenly distributed throughout the solution space by this method. Each individual has a greater probability to participate in the algorithm because of the significantly difference between each individual. The system's reliability goals can be tested by formula 7. New individuals can be generated until it meets the given constraints. That is to say, the cost of the software should be within the specific range and the reliability of the system should achieve the given goal.

4.2 Selection operating

We use the (μ + λ) selection strategy in the niche technology. It is considered to be the highest kind of selection pressure in evolutionary algorithm between several popular selection mechanisms. The (μ + λ) selection mechanism can produce the fastest local convergence rate when the crossover operator paired in the population. The (μ + λ) selection strategy is to select the μ best individuals in the μ parent individuals and μ an individual cross λ tall individual.

Stochastic Tournament Model is selected in this paper. The winners become the next generation of individuals by the method of competing. In each generation of groups, K individuals are selected to constitute a small group randomly. And then, the fittest individuals are copied to next generation among the K individuals. The copy of the individual still returns to the parent groups and participate in the next random selection. This kind of selection will repeat M times and produce M next generation of individuals. In the method, we usually set K = 2.

The basic operation is as follows:

1. K individuals are selected randomly between the individuals of generation T.
2. The fittest individual will enter the generation T+L by comparing the fitness between K individuals. And the copy individual will remains in the generation T.
3. M individuals can be got by repeating the above two steps M times.

4.3 Crossover operating

The purpose of crossover operating is to do global searching in genetic algorithms. The emergence of new excellent genetic model can promote the population and improve the accuracy of reconciliation.

Uniform Schema Crossover Operator is used in this paper. A random template is produced before the crossover operating. The crossover operating will carried out if the gene position of individual is 1. Compared to the single point crossover in traditional genetic algorithm, it has greater variation of the area and random mutation probability. And thus the search space is more effective and the local search ability is improved.

The uniform crossover operation is as follows:

1. A long and individual encoded string $w = \omega_1 \omega_2 \dots \omega_i \dots \omega_L$ is generated randomly. L is the individual coding string length.

2. Two new offspring A' and B' will be produced from A and B generations following the rules.

If $\omega_i = 0$, then the gene value in position I of A' inherits the value of A while the gene value in position I of B' inherits the value of B.

If $\omega_i = 1$, then the gene value in position I of A' inherits the value of B' while the gene value in position I of B' inherits the value of A.

4.4 The mutation operating

Mutation operation in genetic algorithm means the gene value of certain genes in the individual is replaced by other gene value. The local search ability of genetic algorithm is improved by mutation operation. The diversity is maintained and the premature phenomenon is prevented.

A Nun-Uniform Mutation is used in this paper. It refers to a random perturbation of the original genetic value. The new gene value is the result of the disturbance. A slight change in the solution space is made for each mutation operation.

Set that the mutation operation is from $X = x_1 x_2 \dots x_k \dots x_L$ to $X' = x_1 x_2 \dots x_k' \dots x_L$. The range of x_k is $x_k \in [x_{min}^k, x_{max}^k]$. Then x_k' is determined by Formula 8.

$$x_k' = \begin{cases} x_k + \Delta(t, x_{max}^k - x_k), & if \quad random(0,1) = 0 \\ x_k - \Delta(t, x_k - x_{min}^k), & if \quad random(0,1) = 1 \end{cases}$$

(8)

In the formula, $\Delta(t,y)$ is a random function in the range of [0,y]. $y = x_{max}^k - x_k$ or $y = x_k - x_{min}^k$.

5 THE ANALYSIS OF SIMULATION RESULTS

The Niche Genetic Algorithm is used to solve the problem of three-module software system reliability. The cost function of its software system takes the number of exponential cost model. We can get the function as follow.

$$C(\lambda_1) = -126 \ln(1 - \exp(-\lambda_1))$$
$$C(\lambda_2) = -315 \ln(1 - \exp(-\lambda_2)) \qquad (9)$$
$$C(\lambda_3) = -238 \ln(1 - \exp(-\lambda_3))$$

The total cost of the development $TC(\lambda_1, \lambda_2, \lambda_3)$ can be got by Formula 6.

The development and investment of the software system is 186,000 yuan and the profit is 48%. Other parameters are as follow: $\phi_1 = 0.21, \phi_2 = 0.48, \phi_3 = 0.31, \rho = 0.975$. The lower limit value of each module is as follow by the analysis of fault trees and the division of the importance of the modules. $(I_1 \ I_2 \ I_3) = (0.921 \ 0.978 \ 0.965)$.

Table 1. Comparison of niche genetic algorithm and simple genetic algorithm.

Software system	Algorithm	The number of precocity	The number of finding optimal solution	Success rate
Three-module	SGA	156	324	63.5%
	NGA	18	487	87.9%
Five-module	SGA	267	308	52.3%
	NGA	89	415	83.4%

$(w_1 \; w_2 \; w_3) = (0.212 \; 0.487 \; 0.311)$. The reliability allocation model can be got as follow.

The objective function:

$$Min \left\{ f = -126ln(1 - exp(-\lambda_1)) \right.$$
$$\left. -315ln(1 - exp(-\lambda_2)) - 238ln(1 - exp(-\lambda_3)) \right\}$$

The constraints are as follow:

$$\begin{cases} e^{-(0.21\lambda_1 + 0.48\lambda_2 + 0.31\lambda_3)} \geq 0.975 \\ \lambda_i \geq 0 \qquad (i = 1,2,3) \\ e^{-0.21\lambda_1} \geq 0.921 \\ e^{-0.48\lambda_2} \geq 0.978 \\ e^{-0.31\lambda_3} \geq 0.9756 \qquad (10) \\ 24 + 15e^{-0.21\lambda_1} \leq 0.52 \times 74.5 \\ 20 + 71e^{-0.48\lambda_2} \leq 0.52 \times 175 \\ 26 + 32e^{-0.31\lambda_3} \leq 0.52 \times 111.5 \\ 70 + 15e^{-0.21\lambda_1} + 71e^{-0.48\lambda_2} + 32e^{-0.31\lambda_3} \leq 186 \\ (unit : 1000 \, yuan) \end{cases}$$

It is a combinational optimization problem with one linear objective function and 3n+2 linear constraints. N means the number of modules. $\lambda_i(i = 1,2,3)$ is the failure rate parameter in the modules. That is to say, the cost of the software should be minimized in a certain task time. And the reliability of the software should be greater than 97.5%.

The Niche Genetic Algorithm is used in the paper to solve the reliability of the three modules. And it is compared with the simple genetic algorithm as shown in Table 1. In the simulation, the scale of the population is 150. The maximum number of the generations is 500. The crossover probability is 0.98 and the mutation rate is 0.01. The approximate optimal solution is: (R1 R2 R3) = (0.96879 0.98176 0.97965), RS = 0.97642. That is the maximum reliability of the software.

From Table 1, we can see that the precocity phenomenon is inhibited effectively. And the global optimal solution is found quickly.

6 CONCLUSIONS

Linear programming works with multi-variable and multi-constraint were solved successfully by using Niche genetic algorithm in multi-module software system. At the same time, the search ability of genetic algorithm was improved by using Stochastic Tournament Model, Uniform Schema Crossover Operator and Non-Uniform Mutation. The simulation results show that Niche Genetic Algorithm in solving the multiple modules of complex software systems reliability allocation problem was efficient and effective. The next step, we will do some research on improving encoding, genetic operators and selection strategies. In short, the reliability of software systems based on genetic algorithm optimization problem worthy of further research.

ACKNOWLEDGMENT

This work is supported by the 2013 Changzhou Science and Technology Program (CJ20130007) and sponsored by Qing Lan Project.

REFERENCES

[1] X.G. Mao, Y.J. Deng. A general model for component-based software reliability [J]. Journal of Software, 2012,20(1):27–32.
[2] Kapur P.K., Goswami D.N., Gupta A. A software reliability growth model with testing effort dependent learning function for distributed systems [J]. Journal of Reliability, Quality and Safety Engineering, 2011,17(4):365–377.
[3] Lu Qing, Liang Chang-Yong. An Adaptive Niche Genetic Algorithm for Multimodal Function Optimization [J]. Pattern Recognition and Artificial Intelligence, 2009,22(1):91–100
[4] Huang Cong-ming, Chen Xiang-xiu. Improvements on Niche Genetic Algorithm [J]. Journal of Beijing Institute of Technology, 2011,31(8):675–678.
[5] Feng Yi, Li Li, Gao Yan-ming. A Niching Hybrid Genetic Simulated Annealing Algorithm [J]. Mechanical Science and Technology, 2004, 23(12):1494–1498.
[6] Xi Hong-lei, Xing Xiao-Shuai, Zhang Qing-quan. Adaptive Niche Genetic Algorithm Based on Gradi-optimization [J]. Computer Engineering, 2012, 34(11):186–188.

Computer, Intelligent Computing and Education Technology – Liu, Sung & Yao (Eds)
© 2014 Taylor & Francis Group, London, ISBN 978-1-138-02469-4

Enhancing IP anycast with location redirection for stateful communication

J. Jiang
Department of Computer Science and Technology, Tsinghua University, Beijing, P.R. China

ABSTRACT: IP anycast has several distinct properties such as server selection, load balancing, server fail-over, and DDoS migration. Unfortunately, its incompatibility with stateful communications limits its adoption to a few stateless services such DNS. This paper explores possible enhancements of the current TCP/IP stack to eliminate this limitation. We propose two alternative approaches to accomplish network location redirection, an essential primitive to compose anycast with stateful communications. We further discuss their implications for various aspects such as routing scalability and security.

Keywords: network architecture; anycast; stateful communication; location redirection

1 INTRODUCTION

IP anycast is one of the several communication paradigms supported by the Internet. In anycast, a group of servers share a same IP address, and independently announce the prefix into the global routing table. Clients trying to contact the anycast address then are routed to the nearest server in terms of routing distance [21]. Figure 1 illustrates an example.

Anycast has several distinct properties such as server selection, load balancing, server fail-over, and DDoS migration [5]; all of these properties are indispensable in building a highly scalable, reliable, and robust distrusted service. Indeed, anycast has been extensively deployed in DNS, one of the most important services of the Internet [1]. Now, anycast has been widely recognized as the key of the scalability and robustness of DNS [7, 9, 18].

Despite of its various advantages, the current form of anycast has a significant limitation: it cannot work with stateful protocols as the Internet routing process it depends on is inherently unstable. This limitation unfortunately causes anycast not applicable for most of Internet applications, which are base on TCP, a connection-oriented thus stateful transport protocol.

This paper explores possible enhancements of the current TCP/IP stack to compose anycast with stateful communications. Our observation is that the conflict between anycast and stateful communication is caused by lack of a network redirection primitive in the current TCP/IP stack. Once such a primitive is provided, the limitation of anycast can be eliminated, as a client could initiate a conversation using an unstable anycast address, then be redirected to a stable unicast address for subsequent communications. We propose two location redirection mechanisms: one is in network layer, using a new ICMP message; the other is in transport layer, leveraging a new TCP option. We compare the two mechanisms; further discuss their implications on the inherent properties of anycast such as server fail-over and DDoS migration, as well as other aspects such as routing scalability and security.

2 BACKGROUND

The first formal document of anycast is RFC 1546 [21], in which Partridge et al. described the expected form of IP anycast, as illustrated in Figure 1. They also discussed several possible architectural issues of this communication paradigm, such as addressing, applications on UDP and TCP, comparisons with IP multicast.

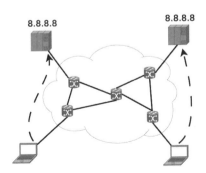

Figure 1.   An illustration of IP anycast.

In RFC 1546 [21], Partridge et al. considered the advantages and disadvantages of distinguishing anycast address space and operating semantics from unicast. A few subsequent documents stated that there should be some semantic differences between anycast addresses and others. For example, in RFC 2101 [8], Carpenter et al. stated that "there is no way such an address can be anything but a locator; it can never serve as an identifier"; and the IPv6 addressing architecture originally explicitly restricted that an anycast address must not be appeared as a source address, neither be assigned to an IPv6 host [14]. However, these suggested semantic differences are never adopted in implementation and operation. The IPv6 standard was finally refined to remove the restrictions on IPv6 anycast address [15, 23]. Currently, an anycast address is nothing different with an unicast address except that it is assigned to multiple hosts at different locations.

From architectural perspective, although anycast enables several distinct and desirable features such as network layer server selection, load balancing, server fail-over and DDoS protection; it is limited for stateless service as it depends on IP routing to find a service point of a ongoing session, which is inherently unstable; it also has negative effect on routing scalability as the global routing table size grows with the number of anycast groups. From operational perspective, anycast eases the configuration of a global service to be highly available and reliable; on the other hand, it also brings subtleties in other operational respects such as fault diagnosis and fine-grained control [6].

Anycast was not deployed at scale until 2002, where Hardie introduced their experience of adopting anycast for authoritative name servers (they used the term "shared unicast addresses" rather than anycast) [13]. DNS is a stateless service with extremely high traffic volume and reliability requirements, a natural fit of anycast. Since then, anycast has been extensively deployed in DNS, especially top level DNS servers and some popular DNS resolvers [22, 18, 1, 3]. Subsequently, a number of documents on anycast operations and architectural considerations have also been developed [20, 2, 25, 19].

3 IP ANYCAST AND STATEFUL SERVICE: AN ARCHITECTURAL VIEW

Anycast is only applicable for stateless services; this is largely limited its adoption, as most of Internet applications are based on TCP, a connection-oriented transport protocol. A common view of this limitation is that the underlying IP routing is unstable so that packets with anycast destination might go to different servers, resulting broken states of stateful sessions.

We take a different angle to view the limitation of anycast. Our observation is that anycast and stateful communication are not necessarily incompatible. The conflict is caused by the tightly-coupled communication phrases in the current TCP/IP stack. In essence, there are two phases of a communication between a client and a server. The first phase is for the client to locate the server, and then the second phase is for the two to start talking. The problem is that, in some scenarios, the two phrases might not happen at same place. For example, consider the client Alice finds the server Bob at his home, then Bob says let us talk at a cafe. Stateful communication with anycast is essentially such a case: a unstable anycast address should be only used by the client to locate the server, then the second phase should be redirected to a stable unicast address. However, the current TCP/IP stack does not provide network level primitives to express such location redirection behavior to decouple the two phases. Therefore the conflict occurs.

It is worth to clarify the connection between this problem and the well-known locator/identifier split concept [24, 11], which suggests to separate "identifier" used by upper level communications from "locator" used by routing. To some extent, the problem here could be more apparently observed under the locator/identifier split context, as separating identifier from locator naturally draws a line between the aforementioned two communication phases: phase one is between locators; phase two is between identifiers. However, a locator/identifier separation protocol itself is not sufficient to compose anycast with stateful communication; a location redirection primitive is still needed to proactively redirect an unstable anycast locator to a stable unicast one, though the process might be easier to implement with locator/identifier separation architecture than with the current TCP/IP stack.

4 PROPOSED ENHANCEMENTS

In this section, we explore how to add a location redirection primitive in the current TCP/IP stack. In fact, the original document of IP anycast, RFC 1546, has briefly mentioned how anycast could work with TCP [21]. Here we propose two detailed designs, one works in network layer and the other works in transport layer.

4.1 *Network layer redirection*

As location redirection is essentially a network layer primitive, we first consider putting it in

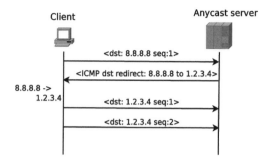

Figure 2. Network layer location redirection via ICMP.

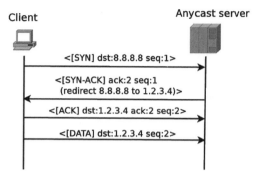

Figure 3. Location redirection via TCP option.

network layer. We proposal a new ICMP message named "ICMP destination redirect" to accomplish this functionality. Figure 2 illustrates how our proposal works:

1. A client sends a packet to an anycast address 8.8.8.8;
2. the anycast interface on the server receives the packet, then responses a ICMP destination redirect telling the client that 8.8.8.8 has been mapped to another (unicast) address 1.2.3.4; the payload of the previous packet is also sent along;
3. upon receiving the ICMP message, the client maintains the mapping as a kernel state; then resend the first packet to 1.2.3.4;
4. as long as the mapping state is valid, the client sends subsequent packets to 1.2.3.4 as well.

The timeout period of the mapping state could be measured empirically, say 5 minutes. In addition, the socket interfaces need to be extended so that a user-space program can explicitly query a mapping, or clear a mapping in case the mapped address fails.

4.2 Transport layer redirection

Although implementing location redirection via ICMP is suitable from the viewpoint of layering, the cost is rather high. It potentially causes an extra round-trip to establish a connection, as well as considerable complexity to the current TCP/IP stack. A more pragmatic approach is to implement location redirection on top of TCP. In fact, a slight extension of the TCP three-way handshake is sufficient to accomplish this goal, as shown in Figure 3:

1. a client sends a TCP SYN to an anycast address 8.8.8.8;
2. the anycast interface on the server receives the packet, then responses a normal SYN/ACK, along with a new TCP direct option telling the

client that 8.8.8.8 has been mapped to another (unicast) address 1.2.3.4;
3. upon receiving the SYN/ACK, the client sends ACK to 1.2.3.4 to finish the three-way handshake;
4. the client sends subsequent packets of this connection to 1.2.3.4

Compared with the network layer approach, this approach does not require any extra state maintained by kernel. It is also transparent to legacy user-space programs (a few socket interfaces, such as *getpeername*, might need to be modified).

5 DISCUSSIONS ON IMPLICATIONS

The proposed location redirection mechanisms could have some side effects on several aspects. We discuss in detail below.

Server selection, Load Balancing and Fail-over: Apparently, both of the two mechanisms preserve the properties of server selection, load balancing and fail-over. A small side effect of the network layer location redirection is that an anycast instance might fail while its mapping state is valid on a client. The client either suffer a temporary service outage until the mapping state expires; or clear the state once observing a connection time-out, which requires more programming efforts.

DDoS Migration: The original anycast has a nice property of migrating DDoS attacks to some extent. Because an attacker cannot control his attacking traffic to converge on an anycast instance. However, with the enhancement of location redirection, this property does not exist anymore, because the process of location redirection exposes unicast addresses of anycast instances, which then can be specifically targeted.

Routing Scalability: Since the proposed enhancements enable anycast to work with stateful services. Once being adopted, more Internet services

65

might go to anycast because of its many desirable properties, which is a potential issue if the anycast community becomes crowded. However, we believe this is should not be a practical matter. Since deployment of anycast requires the ability of announcing prefixes globally from multiple sites, which most of service providers do not have.

Security: The proposed mechanisms have subtle side effects on security. Specifically, the proposed mechanisms to some extent increase the ability of on-path or blind attackers. Previously, the attackers can send spoofed packets to disrupt a connection in case they can intercept the connection or make a good guess; with the location mechanisms, the attackers could hijack an address entirely once a spoofed response with redirection is accepted. However, we believe the practical impact is acceptable. Because neither on-path nor blind attackers cannot suppress a legitimate response being received by client, which then could serve as an indicator of anomaly to interrupt the spoofed redirection.

6 RELATED WORK

Architectural Designs: We only recognize a few studies that aimed to enhance IP anycast in current TCP/IP context. Katabi et al. proposed GIA [16] that separates anycast routing from unicast to improve the scalability of anycast. Ballani et al. designed PIAS [4], which adds a new component named anycast proxy; an anycast proxy is that essentially a NAT device which enables reuse of one anycast address for multiple services to improve the scalability as well as other properties of anycast. Besides the above work, a number of researches [27, 12] have been conducted to design application layer anycast services. Although these systems were named as "anycast" and have similar goals, they are fundamentally different with IP anycast. Because working on different layers brings significant differences in their technical properties and challenges.

Measurement Studies: Anycast has attracted lots of measurement efforts. A number of studies [7, 9, 18] investigated the behaviors of anycast of DNS root servers by examining server-side query log. Some studies on the other hand, evaluated anycast by active probing. Sarat et al. [22] evaluated the effectiveness of anycast in DNS by active probing from PlanetLab nodes; Liang et al. [17] measured query latencies of DNS root servers and a few TLDs from a large number of open resolvers; Ballani et al. [6] designed dedicated experiments by leveraging a large number of client to actively probe several anycast groups to study several properties of anycast such as proximity, fail-over time, affinity and client load distribution. Overall, these measurement studies confirmed the effectiveness of anycast in increasing performance and reliability. However, these studies, especially the one conducted by Ballani et al. also revealed subtle behaviors of anycast caused by complicated interactions of network topologies and routing policies.

Ye et al. [26] and Xun [10] developed techniques utilizing specific DNS queries and heuristic inference to reverse engineering anycast the number and placements of anycast instances in DNS.

7 CONCLUSION

We have presented two alternative enhancements of the current TCP/IP stack to accomplish network location redirection, which is essential to compose anycast with stateful communications. We have also discussed their implications for various aspects.

Although the proposed enhancements require changing the semantics of the current TCP/IP stack, a great obstacle of their deployability. We believe some vendors such as CDN providers would like to have such features because of the attractive benefits of anycast to their services. Future work includes complete implementation of the proposals and detailed evaluation of their overhead and compatibility with legacy applications.

REFERENCES

[1] Root Server Location, http://www.root-servers.org/.

[2] J. Abley and K.E. Lindqvist. RFC 4786: Operation of Anycast Services. 2006.

[3] B. Ager, W. Mühlbauer, G. Smaragdakis, and S. Uhlig. Comparing dns resolvers in the wild. In IMC 2010.

[4] H. Ballani and P. Francis. Towards a global ip anycast service. In ACM CCR, volume 35, pages 301–312, 2005.

[5] H. Ballani and P. Francis. Mitigating dns dos attacks. In CCS 2008.

[6] H. Ballani, P. Francis, and S. Ratnasamy. A measurement-based deployment proposal for ip anycast. In IMC 2006.

[7] P. Barber, M. Larson, M. Kosters, and P. Toscano. Life and Times of J-Root. http://www.nanog.org/meetings/nanog32/presentations/kosters.pdf, 2004.

[8] B. Carpenter, J. Crowcroft, and Y. Rekhter. RFC 2101: IPv4 Address Behaviour Today. 1997.

[9] L. Colitti, E. Romijn, H. Uijterwaal, and A. Robachevsky. Evaluating the effects of anycast on dns root name servers. RIPE document RIPE-393, 2006.

[10] X. Fan, J. Heidemann, and R. Govindan. Evaluating Anycast in the Domain Name System. 2013.

[11] D. Farinacci, D. Lewis, D. Meyer, and V. Fuller. RFC 6830: The Locator/ID Separation Protocol (LISP). 2013.

[12] M.J. Freedman, K. Lakshminarayanan, and D. Mazi`eres. Oasis: anycast for any service. In NSDI 2006

[13] T. Hardie. RFC 3258: Distributing Authoritative Name Servers via Shared Unicast Addresses. 2002.

[14] R. Hinden and S. Deering. RFC 3513: Internet Protocol Version 6 (IPv6) Addressing Architecture. 2003.

[15] R.M. Hinden and S.E. Deering. RFC 4291: IP version 6 addressing architecture. 2006.

[16] D. Katabi and J. Wroclawski. A framework for scalable global ip-anycast (gia). In ACM CCR, volume 30, pages 3–15. 2000.

[17] J. Liang, J. Jiang, H. Duan, K. Li, and J. Wu. Measuring query latency of top level dns servers. In PAM 2013.

[18] Z. Liu, B. Huffaker, M. Fomenkov, N. Brownlee, et al. Two days in the life of the dns anycast root servers. In PAM 2007.

[19] D. McPherson, E. Osterweil, D. Oran, and D. Thaler. Architectural considerations of ip anycast. 2013.

[20] K. Miller. Deploying IP Anycast. http://www.nanon.org/meetings/nanog29/presentations/miller.pdf, 2003.

[21] C. Partridge, T. Mendez, and W. Milliken. RFC 1546: Host Anycasting Service. 1993.

[22] S. Sarat, V. Pappas, and A. Terzis. On the use of anycast in DNS. In ICCCN 2006.

[23] P. Savola, S. Krishnan, and E.B. Davies. RFC 4942: IPv6 Transition/Co-existence Security Considerations. 2007.

[24] D. Thaler. Why do we really want an id/locator split anyway? http://www6.ietf.org/proceedings/79/slides/nbs-0.pdf, 2008.

[25] F. Weiden and P. Frost. Anycast as a load balancing feature. In LISA 2010.

[26] Y. Yu, J. Cai, E. Osterweil, and L. Zhang. Measuring the placement of dns servers in top-level-domain.

[27] E.W. Zegura, M.H. Ammar, Z. Fei, and S. Bhattacharjee. Application-layer anycasting: a server selection architecture and use in a replicated web service.,IEEE/ACM Transactions on Networking, 8(4):455–466, 2000.

Computer, Intelligent Computing and Education Technology – Liu, Sung & Yao (Eds)
© 2014 Taylor & Francis Group, London, ISBN 978-1-138-02469-4

On adaptability of web-based learning for science and engineering students

Meng Zhang & Cai-Xing Zheng
School of Physics and Microelectronic Science, Hunan University, Changsha, Hunan, China

Jing Peng
School of Education, Hunan Agricultural University, Changsha, Hunan, China

ABSTRACT: In the higher education information environment, various factors have different influence on web-based learning. In order to improve the learners' web-based learning performance, we provide web-based learning adaptability questionnaires in accordance with the science and engineering students' characteristics and their learning status while studying the basic course University Physics online. Using factor analysis method to extract 11 common factors, which is the potential impact of web-based learning adaptability determinants, we gain the statistical model of web-based learning adaptability. According to the 11 common factors, strategies of intervention are then proposed to improve the low performance problems of web-based learning.

Keywords: science and engineering; web-based learning adaptability; SPSS; factor analysis; University Physics

1 INTRODUCTION

Web-based learning field is an open and self-organizing system. Not only the individual learners have many differences, but also multi-dimensional objective and subjective factors have an effect on it. Science and engineering students' habits are formed during the basic courses learning, so we can do empirical research on the basic courses to obtain statistical regularity. As a science and basic science course and a scientific quality education course, University Physics is the basis of other scientific and technical courses and one of the important courses for logical, exploratory and innovative high-quality personnel training. Therefore, web-based learning adaptability questionnaires are provided. The students of science and engineering in HNU are the objects of this survey and University Physics being the course in this study. Using the physics paradigm, we abandon secondary factors, highlight main factors and make the cluster analysis as well as dimensionality reduction on the multidimensional variables, thereby gaining the statistical model of web-based learning adaptability, go into the "quantity" research level of soft science emphasized. On this basis, we study web-based learning intervention strategies.

2 RESEARCH METHODS

This study uses methods of questionnaires and factor analysis by SPSS19.0. Based on the summary of impact factors of web-based learning adaptability at home and abroad, we determine the formal questionnaire dimensions. There are 8 first-order factors which named A, B … H respectively, including learning attitude, motivation, methods, environment, information literacy, physical and psychological health, interpersonal communication and teachers' assistance. The 8 first-order factors consist of 20 second-order factors. Learning attitude includes learning concept and learning situation. Motivation includes internal motivation and external motivation. Methods include learning skills and habits. Environment includes network environment, school environment and social environment. Information literacy includes information knowledge, skills and consciousness. Physical and psychological health includes autonomy, attention, adaptability and physical function. Interpersonal communication includes teacher-student relationship and students' relationship. Teachers' assistance includes shared resources provision and organization and guide of activities. According to the first-order factors' capitals, the second-order factors use digital subscript in turn to represent, such as

A_1 represents learning concept and A_2 represents learning situation. In the end, the Richter 5-point method is adopted to establish 41 subjects.

Before questionnaire testing, we have carried on the mobilization work. The questionnaire has been uploaded to the HNU curriculum center website in the form of electronic version, so that students can download and fill forms freely. And we have told them the E-mail to send back completed questionnaires. Finally, 330 questionnaires have been recovered, including 115 girls and 205 boys, excluding 10 blank or invalid questionnaires. The effective rate is 97%. 33 majors cover all science and engineering colleges of HNU, belonging to four grades, giving priority to freshman.

3 FACTOR ANALYSIS

3.1 Reliability, KMO and Bartlett test of sphericity

According to the analysis of reliability, the cronbach's alpha is 0.914. It is greater than 0.6 and close to 1. It shows that the questionnaire has good reliability.

The sample's KMO value is 0.880. On the basis of KMO measures given by Kaiser, they are suitable for factor analysis. The concomitant probability value got from Bartlett test of sphericity is 0.000 which is less than 0.05. The questionnaire is considered suitable for factor analysis as well. (Yang. 2004).

3.2 Extract common factors

Seen from Table 1, the cumulated variance contribution ratio of the 11 common factors is 83.363%. Variance contribution rate is an indicator to measure common factors of the relative importance. The common factors can contribute more with greater value. 11 common factors reflect 83.363% of the original information and they have reached the standard of most information interpretation.

3.3 Common factors constitution

Many variables in component matrix are high or similar. Nevertheless, the rotated component matrix can make structure simplified and meaning clear. Seen from Table 2, factor 1 contains B_1, B_2. Factor 2 contains A_2, F_2 and F_4. Factor 3 contains H_1, H_2. Factor 4 contains G_2. Factor 5 contains E_3. Factor 6 contains E_1. Factor 7 contains A_1. Factor 8 contains F_1. Factor 9 contains D_2. Factor 10 contains G_1. Factor 11 contains D_3. According to the contribution ratio of the factors displayed in Table 1, we can see that whichever factor comes before the other in the sequence certainly contributes more. In view of the larger contribution factors, we can intervene the

Table 1. Total variance explained.

Component	Initial eigenvalues			Rotation sums of squared loadings		
	Total	% of variance	Cumulative %	Total	% of variance	Cumulative %
1	6.670	33.349	33.349	2.574	12.870	12.870
2	1.893	9.465	42.814	2.386	11.930	24.800
3	1.566	7.832	50.646	1.896	9.481	34.281
4	1.149	5.744	56.391	1.618	8.089	42.370
5	1.016	5.078	61.469	1.284	6.418	48.788
6	0.913	4.565	66.035	1.244	6.219	55.008
7	0.840	4.202	70.236	1.221	6.103	61.110
8	0.723	3.616	73.852	1.193	5.966	67.076
9	0.653	3.266	77.118	1.094	5.472	72.548
10	0.640	3.200	80.318	1.082	5.410	77.958
11	0.609	3.045	83.363	1.081	5.404	83.363
12	0.549	2.747	86.109			
13	0.485	2.426	88.536			
14	0.432	2.159	90.695			
15	0.409	2.043	92.738			
16	0.367	1.834	94.572			
17	0.341	1.703	96.275			
18	0.279	1.396	97.671			
19	0.248	1.239	98.910			
20	0.218	1.090	100.000			

Table 2. Rotated component matrix.

	Component										
	1	2	3	4	5	6	7	8	9	10	11
A_1	0.347	0.158	0.257	0.019	0.166	0.119	0.746	0.048	−0.052	0.040	0.207
A_2	0.316	0.724	0.271	0.056	0.014	0.046	−0.012	0.093	−0.099	−0.071	0.003
B_1	0.729	0.212	0.256	0.156	0.031	0.097	0.065	0.238	0.009	−0.003	0.015
B_2	0.732	0.201	0.163	0.176	0.137	0.058	0.298	0.051	0.093	0.021	0.082
C_1	0.125	0.020	0.166	0.532	−0.154	−0.030	0.485	0.364	0.288	0.062	−0.041
C_2	0.528	0.202	0.228	0.578	0.149	0.094	0.098	0.229	0.048	0.138	0.110
D_1	0.614	0.204	0.095	−0.006	0.129	0.146	0.118	−0.032	0.276	0.325	0.295
D_2	0.145	0.061	0.268	0.117	0.021	0.022	0.024	0.031	0.879	0.027	0.166
D_3	0.125	−0.003	0.081	0.173	0.041	0.026	0.100	0.100	0.148	0.065	0.913
E_1	0.098	0.141	0.101	0.074	0.031	0.921	0.120	0.078	0.018	0.119	0.052
E_2	0.327	0.034	0.065	0.094	0.526	0.508	−0.137	0.269	0.036	0.101	−0.070
E_3	0.095	0.121	0.135	−0.001	0.908	0.023	0.125	0.025	0.013	0.144	0.067
F_1	0.163	0.113	0.069	−0.035	0.086	0.126	0.071	0.904	0.018	0.026	0.101
F_2	−0.027	0.890	−0.083	−0.035	0.066	0.055	0.040	0.041	0.015	0.044	0.069
F_3	0.452	0.480	0.054	0.206	0.065	0.117	0.429	0.053	0.186	0.100	−0.050
F_4	0.339	0.766	0.002	0.114	0.088	0.088	0.149	0.038	0.159	0.103	−0.063
G_1	0.105	0.053	0.209	0.009	0.167	0.138	0.044	0.037	0.024	0.917	0.063
G_2	0.132	0.035	0.058	0.900	0.019	0.081	0.008	−0.128	0.054	−0.040	0.155
H_1	0.102	0.039	0.837	0.096	0.116	0.074	0.187	0.045	0.207	0.122	0.017
H_2	0.258	0.037	0.838	0.082	0.064	0.064	0.050	0.061	0.094	0.123	0.088

Table 3. Component score coefficient matrix.

	Component										
	1	2	3	4	5	6	7	8	9	10	11
A_1	−0.033	−0.073	0.033	−0.176	0.071	0.066	0.801	−0.120	−0.220	−0.129	0.133
A_2	0.020	0.379	0.249	−0.010	−0.091	−0.051	−0.238	0.013	−0.231	−0.150	0.058
B_1	0.518	−0.084	0.047	−0.071	−0.140	−0.058	−0.224	0.083	−0.128	−0.096	−0.067
B_2	0.476	−0.124	−0.092	−0.084	0.006	−0.073	0.100	−0.127	−0.022	−0.105	−0.045
C_1	−0.235	−0.059	−0.070	0.321	−0.123	−0.103	0.450	0.321	0.190	0.114	−0.235
C_2	0.159	−0.016	−0.002	0.361	0.029	−0.109	−0.184	0.108	−0.153	0.090	−0.017
D_1	0.419	−0.072	−0.176	−0.217	−0.085	0.005	−0.100	−0.177	0.188	0.220	0.171
D_2	−0.048	−0.004	−0.020	−0.100	0.048	0.021	−0.131	−0.025	0.966	−0.132	−0.041
D_3	−0.096	0.023	−0.023	−0.001	−0.029	−0.009	−0.053	0.046	−0.089	−0.063	0.953
E_1	−0.166	−0.003	0.013	−0.031	−0.192	0.945	0.119	−0.118	−0.009	−0.086	0.038
E_2	0.121	−0.115	−0.084	0.038	0.372	0.329	−0.268	0.128	0.078	−0.113	−0.150
E_3	−0.195	0.013	−0.018	0.044	0.897	−0.193	0.128	−0.041	0.029	−0.097	−0.008
F_1	−0.092	0.008	−0.041	−0.097	−0.016	−0.072	−0.056	0.885	−0.025	−0.001	0.074
F_2	−0.328	0.552	−0.019	0.006	0.025	−0.014	−0.036	0.033	0.001	0.027	0.138
F_3	0.085	0.100	−0.159	0.009	−0.025	0.013	0.337	−0.085	0.137	0.038	−0.190
F_4	−0.003	0.341	−0.104	0.015	−0.003	−0.035	−0.006	−0.048	0.142	0.063	−0.127
G_1	−0.082	−0.002	−0.027	0.047	−0.120	−0.104	−0.047	0.031	−0.120	1.034	−0.061
G_2	−0.130	0.023	−0.019	0.731	0.070	0.043	−0.156	−0.188	−0.123	−0.042	0.073
H_1	−0.220	0.024	0.578	−0.021	0.025	0.012	0.058	−0.046	0.028	−0.061	−0.075
H_2	−0.006	0.002	0.599	−0.050	−0.082	−0.022	−0.171	−0.040	−0.138	−0.045	0.035

influence factors of high factor weight to improve web-based learning adaptability.

3.4 Component score coefficient matrix

Table 3 called component score coefficient matrix expresses the linear relationship between common factors and original variables. We can calculate 11 factors' score of 320 samples by taking advantage of component score coefficient matrix. The formulas are as follows:

$$F_1 = -0.033 \times x_1 + 0.020 \times x_2 \ldots -0.006 \times x_{20}$$
$$F_2 = -0.073 \times x_1 + 0.379 \times x_2 \ldots +0.002 \times x_{20}$$
$$\ldots$$
$$F_{11} = 0.133 \times x_1 + 0.058 \times x_2 \ldots +0.035 \times x_{20}$$

$$(1)$$

where F = factor score; x = original variable.

At the same time, in accordance with 11 common factors' scores, we can use eigenvalue as the weight and calculate the composite score E. That is to say, we get the mathematical expression of factor analysis statistical model. Thereby, web-based learning adaptability is quantified.

$$E = 2.574 \times F_1 + 2.386 \times F_2 \ldots +1.081 \times F_{11} \quad (2)$$

Using the formulas, we can evaluate web-based learning adaptability ability of learners. Afterwards, we finished the dimension reduction of 20 original variables. The new common factors have been given the new meanings.

3.5 Verification

In order to verify the effectiveness of this study, we conduct the single-sample K-S test for composite scores and compare with normal distribution. The results show that the average of composite score is 0.000, the standard deviation is 5.30826, the Z statistic of K-S is 0.627, and the corresponding concomitant probability value is 0.826 which is greater than significance level 0.05. Thus, it shows that the 320 students' composite scores of web-based learning adaptability are in line with normal distribution. Meanwhile, according to the statistics of 2530 science and engineering students' University Physics final grade in HNU, it can be seen that the grade correspond to normal distribution as well from Figure 1. Consequently, the study is consistent with the overall learning situation in HNU.

4 DISCUSSION

The above is the factor analysis of web-based learning adaptability research for science and engineering students in HNU. In accordance with classification and summary of contribution ratio and original dimensions for 11 common factors, they can be named in turn as follows. Learning motivation comprehends common factor 1. Learning personality covers common factor 2, 7 and 8. Teachers' assistance contains common factor 3. Interpersonal communication includes common factor 4 and 10. Information literacy includes common factor 5 and 6. Learning environment is constitutive of common factor 9 and 11. In view of the importance of common factors for web-based learning adaptability, we put forward the following several aspects of the intervention strategies for reference.

4.1 Learning motivation

The constitution of web-based learning tasks should be slightly improved within the scope of the learners' ability, so that learners can get emotional experience of success and challenges. Next, we can adopt reasonable competition methods to stimulate external motivation. However, teachers need to make the right guidance of appraisal methods, avoid negative impact brought by the competition, pay attention to students' task completion at any time and give timely encouragement.

4.2 Learning personality

The survey shows that even the subjects which students are interested in, the time of efficient concentration is only 15 to 20 minutes. So the web-based learning content should be rational planned to make sure that learners can finish them in short time. On the teachers' side, they should supervise and guide students to reasonable planning time.

4.3 Teachers' assistance

Teachers should provide reasonable web-based learning resources, create problem situation to lead to knowledge and set up good navigation mechanism

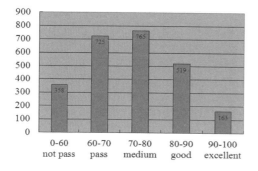

Figure 1. University Physics final grade histogram.

for learners. In addition, teachers should organize web-based learning activities to accomplish specific tasks for the target and promote healthy competition and teamwork. In the meantime, guiding students to correct attribution is necessary.

4.4 *Interpersonal communication*

Virtual learning community can be organized and built by teachers to strengthen the collective sense of belonging in the web-based learning process. It is also necessary to establish rules and guide rational group division.(Wu. 2012) In order to promote the emotional interaction between teachers and students, teachers should actively participate in students' online discussion activities and fully play the role of good guiders and organizers.

4.5 *Information literacy*

Before the network teaching, we can consider to set up dedicated information technology courses to standard students' information consciousness, guide the correct learning concept and introduce information knowledge of search engine and pictures download. We should provide teachers' training of instructional design and network teaching theory and application in order to assist students' efficient web-based learning. (Qiu. 2009).

4.6 *Learning environment*

On the basis of ensure software and hardware facilities, schools can establish personal file for each student to track students' progress and help teachers to develop targeted solutions. And society should standardize the public opinion direction. Relevant government departments should take measures to guide the healthy development of web-based learning and promote the establishment of a learning society.

5 CONCLUSIONS

At present, the research of web-based learning adaptability at home and abroad has a great space for development. It is limited to treat science and engineering students in HNU as the objects of this study. We hope to throw out a minnow to catch a whale and provide reference for a wide range of higher education informatization practice.

REFERENCES

Qiu, H.Q. 2009. *The exploratory of the model for integrated intervention on college student's E-learning adaptability*. Master thesis: Hunan University.
Wu, B. 2012. *Design of web learning activities for mental activity model*. China Educational Technology (309):37–41.
Yang, X.M. (ed.) 2004. *The application of SPSS in education statistics*. Beijing: Higher Education Press.

Computer, Intelligent Computing and Education Technology – Liu, Sung & Yao (Eds)
© 2014 Taylor & Francis Group, London, ISBN 978-1-138-02469-4

A novel method for optimal capacitor placement in radial distribution system

Xiang-Chun Xiao
Huaihua Design Institute of Water Conservancy and Electric Power, Huaihua, Hunan, China

Bai-Yang Liu & Qing-Yue Luo
Department of Electrical Engineering, Shaoyang College, Shaoyang, Hunan, China

ABSTRACT: In this paper, a new approach based on improved Particle Swarm Optimization (PSO) algorithm is proposed in radial distribution system. The improved PSO can find optimal location and sizes of capacitors in the system by dividing reasonable search field. Finally the proposed method is implemented on the IEEE33 standard bus system. The obtained results are then compared with accurate moment method to validate its effectiveness.

Keywords: PSO; radial distribution system; optimal power flow; capacitor placement

1 NOMENCLATURE

Ke	Line loss cost factor
P_{Li}	Line loss
N	Number of bus bar
Km	Capacitor installation cost
M	Amount of installation place
Kc	Capacitor cost
Qci	Size of capacitor
Kv	Voltage penalty factor
dU	Deviation of voltage
$Rand()$	Random function
V	Particle velocity
x	Particle location
ϖ	Inertia weight

2 INTRODUCTION

Optimal distribution system planning plays a very important role in the growth of the distribution system network and in the effective use of the distribution system. With the continuing increase in load demand, the future expansion of the network depends on the study of the load flow of the distribution system network and this is one of the most important research fields in electrical engineering. With the growing effort to reduce system losses and to increase the efficiency of the system and proper voltage profile, research on optimal distribution system planning has been conducted[1].

The shunt capacitors installation on radial distribution is commonly used to improve power flow control, system stability enhancement and power factor correction, managing voltage profile, and reducing active power and energy loss in distribution network. The method using Genetic Algorithm (GA) in [2] can compute the (near) global solution with a lower probability of getting stuck at a local optimum and weak dependency on initial conditions, while avoiding numerical problems in large system. A combined Power Loss Sensitivity (PLS) index-based approach is proposed in [3] to determine the optimal location of the capacitors in the Radial Distribution System (RDS) based on the real and reactive combined loss sensitivity index. Besides, [4] uses a sensitivity analysis based method to select the candidate locations for the capacitors. A new optimization method using a Genetic Algorithm is proposed to determine the optimal selection of capacitors.

The other methods based on intelligent algorithm are researched, such as an Improved Harmony Search (IHS) algorithm is applied to solve the optimal capacitor placement problem[5]; a general solution algorithm based on simulated annealing for optimal capacitor placements in distribution systems is proposed and analyzed in[6];[7] shows a fuzzy decision making which using a new evolutionary method known as Bacteria Foraging Algorithm (BFA). Besides, the methods perform efficiently that a loop-analysis based analytic algorithm is developed in[8] to efficiently calculate the optimal settings of capacitor with time-varying load and that an approach based on dynamic programming is presented to reach such an optimal schedule such that the total feeder loss in a day is minimized[9–10].

The advantages with the addition of shunt capacitors banks are to improve the power factor, feeder voltage profile, power loss reduction and increases available capacity of feeders. Therefore it is important to find optimal location and sizes of capacitors in the system to achieve the objectives[11–12].

In this paper, The improved PSO algorithm is discussed firstly and divided search field is introduced. Finally this method is implemented on the IEEE33 standard bus system for optimal capacitor placement. The results compared with the accurate moment method validate that the proposed method needs to take a little more time but it is more effective to search optimal solutions than accurate moment method.

3 PROBLEM FORMULATION

For finding the best shunt capacitor size and location in the radial distribution system to minimize the costs incurred due to power loss and capacitor installation, considering the voltage profile, the following objective function is designed:

$$min\,F = k_e \sum_{i=1}^{n} P_{Li} + k_M M + k_c \sum_{i=1}^{M} Q_{ci} + k_v \sum_{i=1}^{n} (dU_i)^2 \tag{1}$$

Subject to:

$$\begin{cases} P_i = U_i \sum_{j=1}^{N} U_j (G_{ij} \cos\theta + B_{ij} \sin\theta) \\ Q_i = U_i \sum_{j=1}^{N} U_j (G_{ij} \sin\theta - B_{ij} \cos\theta) \end{cases} \tag{2}$$

$$\begin{cases} V_{min} < V < V_{max} \\ Q_{ci} > 0 \end{cases} \tag{3}$$

The deviation of voltage is defined by:

$$dU = \begin{cases} V_{min} - V & (V < V_{min}) \\ 0 & (V_{min} < V < V_{max}) \\ V - V_{max} & (V > V_{max}) \end{cases} \tag{4}$$

To find the optimal capacitor location and sizing in radial distribution network, backward/forward sweep power flow is used to compute power loss and voltage.

4 IMPROVED PSO ALGORITHM

Figure 1 shows the principle of PSO algorithm. A group of random particles (solutions) are initialized. In every iteration, each particle is updated

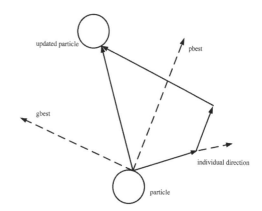

Figure 1. The principle of PSO algorithm.

by following two "best" values. The one, called pbest, is the best solution (fitness) which has been searched so far and also stored by a particle. The other one, called gbest (global best), is the best solution (fitness) which has been searched so far and also stored by particle swarm. The PSO algorithm is expressed as follows (5–6):

$$v_{t+1,i} = \omega v_{t,i} + c_1 rand()(pbest_{t,i} - x_{t,i}) + c_2 rand()(gbest_t - x_{t,i}) \tag{5}$$

$$x_{t+1,i} = x_{t,i} + v_{t+1,i} \,(1 \le i \le m, \quad 1 \le d \le D) \tag{6}$$

In radial distribution network, lower voltage always occurs at the end of branches of system. Such that the further distance from the root node, the larger amount of reactive power is needed. But nodes which feed large load also need more reactive power. So accurate moment is defined as follows:

$$T_q^2(i) = R_{di} \left(\frac{Q_{bi}^2}{U_i^2} - \sum_{j \in i} \frac{Q_{bj}^2}{U_j^2} \right) \tag{7}$$

According to accurate moment, bus bar numbers can be reorder by descending order. So optimal capacitor location(s) can be found.

The classical PSO algorithm can not slove problem of reactive power optimization in distribution network with discrete variables, called mixed-integer nonlinear programming problem. So PSO algorithm needs to be improved. Figure 2 shows that search field, a set of discrete variables (capacitor location), is divided into n sections by accurate moment. So a new location vector is defined by:

$$y = (y_1, y_2, \ldots, y_n)^T \tag{8}$$

where yi = any value from number i section.

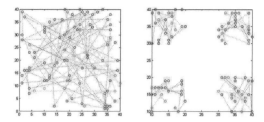

Figure 2. The search field is divided into 4 sections ($n = 4$).

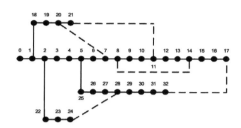

Figure 4. IEEE33 standard bus system.

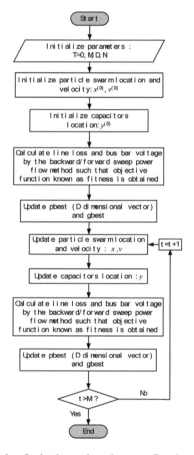

Figure 3. Optimal capacitor placement flowchart.

Now an augmented vector is described as follows:

$$\bar{x} = \begin{pmatrix} x \\ \cdots \\ y \end{pmatrix} \tag{9}$$

where x = sizing of capacitor.

Table 1. Loads and lines data of the IEEE33 standard system.

i	j	Impedance (Z_{ij}) p.u.	Load (Q_j) KVA
0	1	0.0922 + j0.047	100 + j60
1	2	0.4930 + j0.2511	90 + j40
2	3	0.3660 + j0.1864	120 + j80
3	4	0.3811 + j0.1941	60 + j30
4	5	0.8190 + j0.7070	60 + j20
5	6	0.1872 + j0.6188	200 + j100
6	7	0.7114 + j0.2351	200 + j100
7	8	1.0300 + j0.7400	60 + j20
8	9	1.0440 + j0.7400	60 + j20
9	10	0.1966 + j0.0650	45 + j30
10	11	0.3744 + j0.1238	60 + j35
11	12	1.4680 + j1.1550	60 + j35
12	13	0.5416 + j0.7129	120 + j80
13	14	0.5910 + j0.5260	60 + j10
14	15	0.7463 + j0.5450	60 + j20
15	16	1.2890 + j1.7210	60 + j20
16	17	0.3720 + j0.5740	90 + j40
17	18	0.1640 + j0.1565	90 + j40
18	19	1.5042 + j1.3554	90 + j40
19	20	0.4095 + j0.4784	90 + j40
20	21	0.7089 + j0.9373	90 + j40
2	22	0.4512 + j0.3083	90 + j50
22	23	0.8980 + j0.7091	420 + j200
23	24	0.8960 + j0.7011	420 + j200
5	25	0.2030 + j0.1034	60 + j25
25	26	0.2842 + j0.1447	60 + j25
26	27	1.0590 + j0.9337	60 + j20
27	28	0.8042 + j0.7006	120 + j70
28	29	0.5075 + j0.2585	200 + j600
29	30	0.9744 + j0.9630	150 + j70
30	31	0.3105 + j0.3619	210 + j100
31	32	0.3410 + j0.5362	60 + j40
7	20	2 + j2	Tie switches
8	14	2 + j2	
11	21	2 + j2	
17	32	0.5 + j0.5	
24	28	0.5 + j0.5	

77

5 APPLICATION IN SOLVING THE OPTIMAL CAPACITOR PLACEMENT

Figure 3 shows a flowchart which describes optimal capacitor placement procedure involved in improved PSO algorithm.

6 TEST RESULTS

For optimizing capacitor placement and validating its effectiveness the improved PSO algorithm is applied on the IEEE33 standard bus distribution system shown in Figure 4.

Loads and lines data of the IEEE33 standard bus system are shown in Table 1. Table 2 and Table 3 show the results of the test. The results including optimal solutions, fitness and time are obtained in 2 cases ($n = 2$ and $n = 3$) and in Tables 2 and 3 results compare improved PSO with accurate moment.

Figures 5 and 6 describe a histogram that visually demonstrates the fitness (or time) of improved

Table 2. Optimal capacitor placement (n = 2).

Method	Location	Size (kVar)	Fitness (¥)	Time (s)
Improved PSO	14	359	919606	81.864
	29	1032		
Accurate moment method	30	737	947819	75.654
	6	820		

Table 3. Optimal capacitor placement (n = 3).

Method	Location	Size (kVar)	Fitness (¥)	Time (s)
Improved PSO	11	298	916306	82.432
	29	1266		
	1	1337		
Accurate moment method	30	605	1041105	76.959
	6	988		
	3	534		

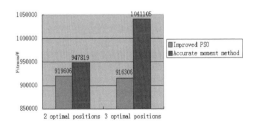

Figure 5.   Fitness of 2 methods in 2 cases.

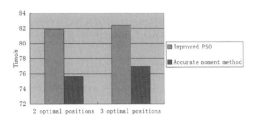

Figure 6.   Time of 2 methods in 2 cases.

PSO compared with accurate moment method in 2 cases respectively.

7 CONCLUSION

The application of improved PSO algorithm in determining the optimal location(s) and sizing of shunt capacitors in IEEE33 standard bus system has been presented. Improved PSO algorithm can find optimal location(s) of shunt capacitors by dividing some special sections according to accurate moment method.

The obtained results validate that the proposed method is more effective in searching optimal solution(s) than accurate moment. The improved PSO gives less total costs than accurate moment method. Moreover in cases (n = 3 or more) the proposed method is better than accurate moment method in optimal location(s) of shunt capacitors. So the proposed method can optimize capacitor placement in radial distribution network system effectively and is better in optimal location(s) of shunt capacitors than accurate moment method except for taking a little more time.

REFERENCES

[1] Sallam, A.A. & Malik, O.P. 2011. *Electric Distribution Systems*. New Jersey: John Wiley and Sons.
[2] Abbas, T.S., Mohammad, H. & Ali, K. 2011. A novel method for optimal capacitor placement and sizing in distribution systems with nonlinear loads and DG using GA. *Communications in Nonlinear Science and Numerical Simulation* 16(2):851–862.
[3] Murty, V.V.S.N. & Kumar, A. 2013. Comparison of optimal capacitor placement methods in radial distribution system with load growth and ZIP load model. *Frontiers in Energy* 7(2):197–213.
[4] Sundhararajan, S. & Pahwa, A. 1994. Optimal Selection Of Capacitors For Radial Distributions Systems Using a Genetic Algorithm. *IEEE Transactions On Power Systems* 9(3):1499–1507.
[5] Sirjani, R., Mohamed, A. & Shareef, H. 2011. Optimal Capacitor Placement in Three-Phase Distribution Systems Using Improved Harmony Search Algorithm. *International Review of Electrical Engineering—IREE* 6(4):1783–1793.

[6] Chiang, H.D. et al. 1990. Optimal capacitor placements in distribution systems. II. Solutionalgorithms and numerical results. *IEEE Transactions on Power Delivery* 5(2):643–649.

[7] Tabatabaei, S.M. & Vahidi, B. 2011. Bacterial foraging solution based fuzzy logic decision for optimal capacitor allocation in radial distribution system. *Electric Power Systems Research* 81(4):1045–1050.

[8] Wu, W.C., Zhang, B.M. & Lo, K.L. 2010. Capacitors dispatch for quasi minimum energy loss in distribution systems using a loop-analysis based method. *International Journal of Electrical Power and Energy Systems* 32(6):543–550.

[9] Hsu, Y.Y. & Kuo, H.C. 1993. Dispatch of capacitors on distribution system using dynamic programming. *IEE Proceedings. Part C: Generation, Transmission and Distribution* 140(6):433–438.

[10] Liang, R.H. & Cheng, C.K. 2001. Dispatch of main transformer ULTC and capacitors in a distribution system. *IEEE Transactions on Power Delivery* 16(4):625–630.

[11] Rao, R.S., Narasimham, S.V.L. & Ramalingaraju, M. 2011. Optimal capacitor placement in a radial distribution system using plant growth simulation algorithm. *International Journal of Electrical Power & Energy Systems* 33(5):1133–1139.

[12] Taher, S.A. & Bagherpour, R. 2013. A new approach for optimal capacitor placement and sizing in unbalanced distorted distribution systems using hybrid honey bee colony algorithm. *International Journal of Electrical Power & Energy Systems* 49:430–448.

Computer, Intelligent Computing and Education Technology – Liu, Sung & Yao (Eds)
© 2014 Taylor & Francis Group, London, ISBN 978-1-138-02469-4

Design and construction of the government external access network based on EPON

Z.Y. Hu
Oriental Cable Network Co. Ltd., Shanghai, China

ABSTRACT: The Shanghai government external network is a metropolitan area network that serves the bureaus. The access nodes of the bureau are widely distributed in the city. The ethernet access network link has been built, but it has many problems such as the powerless access network switch, loops in the network, broadcast storm. With the development of the network, the demands of network bandwidth and QOS are increasing. EPON is a technology with the advantages of the low-price equipments and passive optical network, high bandwidth. It becomes the best choice of the access network. In this paper, it introduces the principle of EPON and the scheme of the Shanghai government external access network (EPON). According to implementation of the scheme, it will provide a high bandwidth, scalable, stable, uniform access network. This scheme also meets the construction principle and target of the national government external network.

Keywords: Ethernet Passive Optical Network (EPON); government external access network

1 INTRODUCTION

1.1 Background

1.1.1 Market background

The access network is the basement of the next generation national informatization infrastructure. It is also the basement of the intelligent channel control. The next access network must use the IP protocol as the network carrying protocol. Constructing the intelligent channel with high bandwidth and efficiency is a target. Through speed up the development of the network technology, space extension, optimize network architecture and increase intelligent level, the company can achieve some targets such as high access network, full IP carrying network, controlled network resource, convergence network service. If the company builds a good access network, the company will have an uniform and convergent carrying platform for the service and application.

1.1.2 Trade and technical background

Shanghai government external network has almost 1200 customers. As the network contractor, Oriental Cable Network Co. Ltd actively participates in the progress of the social informatization. The company assists the sustainable development of the Shanghai economy in the aspects of the network infrastructure and digital television. The company is an innovative and energetic internet service provider. It has built a sustainable

development model that meets the requirements of the information and communication services with the economic development.

Shanghai government external network is built by Oriental Cable Network Co. Ltd. As a Shanghai local high IP network, it has finished the construction of the backbone network and access network by the several previous projects. It has provided the MPLS VPN capability of the whole network. The whole Shanghai government external network services are in operation by this network.

Oriental Cable Network Co. Ltd recognizes the optimized network service quality and a variety of application services as the key point of the value for the customers.

1.2 Target

The target is building a 1000Mbps Ethernet Passive Optical Network link for Shanghai government external network. The EPON link will be satisfied with the Shanghai government external network services three years. The specific content is as follows.

In the city, every core room will increase an OLT, every access room will increase an OBD, every customer room will increase an ONU.

In the suburban district, every core room will increase an OLT, every access room will increase an OBD, every customer room will increase an ONU, some remote access rooms will increase an

OLT and an OBD, some core rooms will increase a convergence switch that connects the PE in the core room.

2 EPON TECHNOLOGY

2.1 *Principle*

EPON stands for Ethernet Passive Optical Network. The topology of EPON is a point-to-multipoint network topology. The target of EPON provides a data, voice and video service access network.

The network structure of EPON is shown in Figure 1. It consists of the OLT, ONU, OBD. OLT stands for Optical Line Terminal. ONU stands for Optical Network Unit. OBD stands for Optical Branching Device. OLT (Optical Line Terminal) is placed in the core room. ONU (Optical Network Unit) is placed in the customer room. OBD (Optical Branching Device) is placed in the access room.

EPON belongs to the IEEE802.3 protocol family. EPON can transport 1518 bytes (maximum). The uplink and downlink transport technology of EPON is difference. The downlink transport technology of EPON is shown in Figure 2.

The downlink transport technology of EPON uses TDM technology. The wavelength of downlink is 1490 nm. TDM stands for Time Division Multiplexing. According to the IEEE 802.3ah protocol, each frame header contains a special ONU logical link identifier, this is allocated when the ONU registers. The identifier indicates that this frame is transmitted to a special ONU. As shown in the Figure 2, the OLT transmits several frames to the OBD through the broadcast way. These frames are copied three times, every copy contains whole frames. When the copy comes into the ONU, the ONU will receive and transmit matched frames, drop the unmatched frames according to compare the frame logical link identifier with the ONU logical link identifier. For example, in the ONU1 the frame one is transmitted, the frame two and frame three are dropped, the frames are transmitted in chronological sequence.

The uplink transport technology of EPON is shown in Figure 3.

The uplink transport technology of EPON uses TDMA technology. The wavelength of uplink is 1310 nm. TDMA stands for Time Division Multiplexing Access. The network bandwidth of EPON is the quantity of the basic time slot for transmission of data. A basic time slot is 16ns. The time of the PON interface between the OLT and the ONU is strictly synchronous. The OLT assigns a certain quantity of basic time slots for every ONU. The OLT sets the time when starts transmission. Every ONU only can transfer data frames to the OLT in the assigned time by the OLT. The time slot assignment and time delay compensation can ensure the uplink data frames without conflict, when the uplink data frames of several ONUs use an optical fiber for transporting data to the OLT. The data frames are transported through the OBD.

2.2 *Network architecture*

According to the different placement of the ONU, the architecture of EPON generally can be divided into several patterns: FTTH/FTTO, FTTB and so on.

FTTH stands for Fiber to the Home. FTTO stands for Fiber to the Office. The architecture of FTTH/FTTO is uniform. As shown in the Figure 4, OLT (Optical Line Terminal) is placed in the core

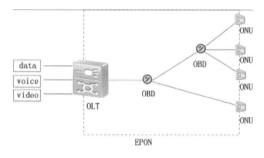

Figure 1. The network structure of EPON.

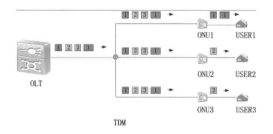

Figure 2. The downlink transport technology of EPON.

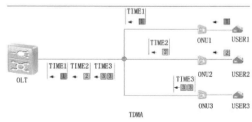

Figure 3. The uplink transport technology of EPON.

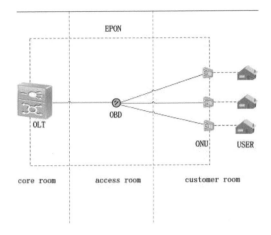

Figure 4. The architecture of FTTH/FTTO.

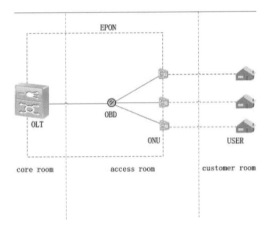

Figure 5. The architecture of FTTB.

room, OBD (Optical Branching Device) is placed in the access room, ONU (Optical Network Unit) is placed in the customer room.

FTTB stands for Fiber to the Building. As shown in the Figure 5, OLT (Optical Line Terminal) is placed in the core room, OBD (Optical Branching Device) and ONU (Optical Network Unit) are placed in the access room. The connect between the ONU and customers can use several cables such as telephone line, twisted pair cable, coaxial cable and so on.

2.3 *Advantage*

The advantage of EPON is mainly shown in the following aspects:

1. EPON can provide the 1.25 Gbps symmetrical bandwidth of the uplink and downlink. In the feature GPON can support to provide 2.5 Gbps symmetrical bandwidth.

2. The topology of EPON is a point-to-multipoint network topology. EPON can cover a lot of territory.

   Each OLT can insert several pon interface cards.

   Each pon interface card assembles many pon interfaces. Each pon interface can connect 64 ONUs at most. So each OLT can connect a lot of customers.

3. The EPON link between the OLT and ONU only has passive equipment. This network architecture can reduce the costs of operation, administration, maintenance and construction.

4. Because the modularization of EPON is a high level and has strong expansibility, EPON can protect the prophase investment well.

3 SCHEME

3.1 *Present condition*

As shown in the Figure 6. Shanghai government external access network (ETHERNET) contains core room, access room, customer room. The equipments of core room contain a core PE, two transparent firewalls, a core convergence network switch. The equipment of access room contains an access network switch. The equipment of customer room contains a customer network switch.

Shanghai government external network contains almost 40 core rooms, 200 access rooms now.

3.2 *Scheme*

In the city, the OLT is placed in the core room. The OLT connects the PE and OBD. The 1:8 OBD is placed in the access room. The OBD connects

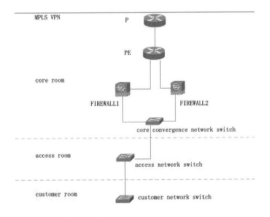

Figure 6. The architecture of access network.

the OLT and ONU. The ONU is placed in the customer room. As shown in the Figure 7.

In the suburban district, some OLTs are placed in the access room because the distance between core room and customer room exceeds 20 KM. So it should increase the core convergence network switch. The switch is placed in the core room. The switch connects the PE and OLT. So there are two network architectures. As shown in the Figure 8.

1. The OLT that is placed in the core room connects the core convergence network switch and OBD. The 1:4 OBD is placed in the access room.

   The OBD connects the OLT and ONU. The ONU is placed in the customer room.
2. The OLT that is placed in the access room connects the core convergence network switch and OBD. The 1:4 OBD is placed in the access room. The OBD connects the OLT and ONU. The ONU is placed in the customer room.

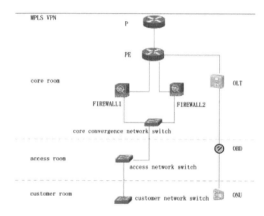

Figure 7.   The architecture of central EPON network.

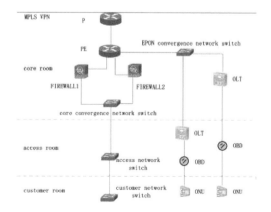

Figure 8.   The architecture of suburban EPON network.

3.3 Resources plan

3.3.1 VLAN

The plan of VLAN is shown in Table 1.

3.3.2 Management

1. The 37 C IP address segments are allocated to EPON management.
2. The management IP address segment is 10.X.238.0/24. VLAN is X+10.
3. The management address is configured in the PE. It notifies under the ISIS protocol.
4. The management IP address of OLT is 10.X.238.2. The management IP address of PE is 10.X.238.1. The management IP address of ONU is 10.X.238.10–254.
   * X is room number.

3.3.3 Olt interface

The OLT must configure uniformly. The configuration rule of the OLT interface is planned according to the Oriental Cable Network IP and interface rule.

1. The number 1 PON interface starts to use for the downlink PON interface. The number 11 and 12 interface are reservation PON interface.
2. The patterns of uplink ethernet interface and downlink PON interface are trunk.
3. The PON interface configures the registration pattern of ONU.

3.3.4 Onu interface

The ONU must configure uniformly. The configuration rule of the ONU interface is planned according to the Oriental Cable Network IP and interface rule.

1. The video service uses number 1 ethernet interface. The vdi service uses number 2 ethernet interface. The gov backup service uses number 3 ethernet interface. The internet backup service uses number 4 ethernet interface. The number 7 and 8 interface are reservation ethernet interface.
2. The pattern of uplink PON interface is trunk.

Table 1.   The plan of VLAN.

Service	ONU (CVLAN)	OLT (SVLAN)
Video	1501–2000	1501–2000
Vdi	2001–2500	2001–2500
Backup	Used VLAN	Used VLAN
Management	Allocated VLAN	Allocated VLAN
Reserve	1–200	1–200

3. The pattern of downlink ethernet interface is access and nonegotiation.

4 CONCLUSION

Oriental Cable Network Co. Ltd will increase the development of the Shanghai government external network. The EPON link will provide a redundancy backup network link for the government external network.

The EPON link will enlarge the government external access network. The EPON link will carry more government external network service. We can avoid some network problems and carry more services through building the EPON link:

1. The access room powerless or damaged access network switch.
2. Video network service.
3. Vdi service.
4. Backup network link.

REFERENCE

Haoran Huang, Ling Gong. 2004. The ip address and interface plan of Oriental Cable Network.

Computer, Intelligent Computing and Education Technology – Liu, Sung & Yao (Eds)
© 2014 Taylor & Francis Group, London, ISBN 978-1-138-02469-4

The study of CFD on aerodynamic characteristics of freestyle skiing athletes in the curve slideway period

Xin Wang
School of Exercise Human Science, Shenyang Sport University, Shenyang, Liaoning, China

ABSTRACT: In order to explore the aerodynamic characteristics of athletes in the aerials event of freestyle skiing sliding on the platform, to provide aerodynamic parameters for the calculation on leaving platform speed, the essay makes use of the CFD method to study on aerodynamic characteristics of Chinese freestyle skier Mengtao Xu in the curve slideway period. The results show that: The lift of athletes in the curve slideway period can be neglected, and the resistance can't be neglected because it is relatively large. With the common superposition of resistance and own gravitational tangential component, the athletes sliding speed will decay rapidly. In addition, to improve the stability of athletes' movements on leaving platform, athletes should try to keep away from the eddy zone formed by the slope on leaving platform and the angle area of the vertical wall.

Keywords: freestyle skiing aerials; curve slideway; lift; resistance; CFD

1 GENERAL INTRODUCTION

Aerials of freestyle skiing is the Winter Olympics standing event. Xiaopeng Han, Chinese athlete won the gold medal of the event in the 20th Turin Winter Olympics and achieve the gold medal zero breakthrough about snow events in history of the Winter Olympics. Aerial of freestyle skiing is composed of slipping, taking off, launching turn and falling to the ground. In the game, athletes take off from the height of about 4 m platform and complete a series of turn in falling process after launching the height of about 15 m and finally land in 37° slope stably. The granding of freestyle skiing aerials is mainly based on the completed quality of launching turn and landing phase. So the related research both here and abroad more concentrated upon the launching turn and landing phase and there is little attention to slipping and taking off phase. A perfect taking off can provide enough launching height and stability for completing launching and turn and slipping stage is the key to guarantee the perfect taking off. In slipping stage, athletes will shift their position from stances like horse riding step to jumping position, straighted up arms and the body upright. As shown in Figure 1 (in the curve slideway, athletes basically keep the position shown in Fig. 2). It plays an important role in completion a high-quality taking off to control slipping phase, especially the aerodynamic characteristics in the curve slideway period. There is not detailed study reports here and abroad because of the bad environment, experimental means and testing technology limited. With the

rapid development of computer hardware and software technology, CFD has become comeplex fluid flows, even the main methods and means of study on the fliud-structure heat and mass transfer. In this essay, adopt the concepts and methods of CFD to study the aerodynamic characteristics of

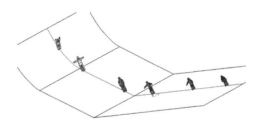

Figure 1. Athletes posture slideway evolution diagram.

Figure 2. Athletes physical model.

Chinese freestyle skiing aerials athletes in the curve slideway period, so it will reach a basis for simulating of motion process of athletes slipping stage.

2 ATHLETES THREE-DIMENSIONAL ENTITY MODEL AND CFD MODEL

Athletes' materialization model has been restricting the freestyle skiing slip stage the bottleneck of the aerodynamic characteristics for CFD study. According to the theory of reverse modeling, the Application of Laser Scanning Technology Mengtao Xu in the Three-dimensional Human Body Model in our country (the windward surface projection area of athletes is 0.676935 m²), get up to more than 20 points of point cloud data, In the 3D design software integrated by small plane modeling, to repair the broken surface and materialization process set up the three-dimensional entity model of the athletes (Athletes surface is divided into 87 seamless connection surface). As shown in Figure 2.

The freestyle skiing slope is consisted by plummeting, straight and curve segments. The curve equation of curve segment is little detailed reported in the literature at home and abroad. According to the measured results by polynomial fitting to get the help of ramp curve equation for the curve segment:

$$y = a_1 + a_2x + a_3x^2 + a_4x^3 + a_5x^4 + a_6x^5$$

Type in:

$$a_1 = 0;\ a_2 = 4.4 \times 10^{-2};\ a_3 = 1.3 \times 10^{-5};$$

$$a_4 = 5.4 \times 10^{-8};\ a_5 = -1.6 \times 10^{-11};\ a_6 = 1.6 \times 10^{-15}$$

Finally, using 3D design of insert/merge and inheritance function module, the space model of athletes about the flow field around was established (for save computational cost, in addition to the ways of plummeting). Seen from Figure 3, slide for the athletes to the section curve of 6.752 m at

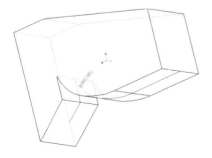

Figure 3.   CFD computing model.

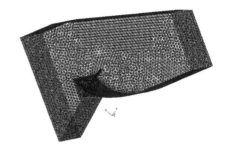

Figure 4.   Schematic diagram of grid division.

the time of the flow field around the space model (point of curvature radius of 3.09 m, at that point slide tangent plane and horizontal plane Angle is 117.291°).

3 CFD SIMULATION RESEARCH

The air power is applied to the pressure and friction force of athletes, the resultant force can be obtained by solving the flow field around a athletes. Because of the complicated shape and large athletes sliding speed, so the flow field around the athletes will be for the turbulent flow field. In a variety of turbulence model chose k—ωSST turbulence model, the finite element method to solve the turbulence model equations. Seen from Figure 3 and Figure 4, the flow field around a space model of meshing (more than 320000 is divided into four nodes tetrahedron element) after the meshing diagram. Considering the close to the player within the boundary layer on the surface of the larger velocity gradient and the uneven surface of the athletes, meshing specially in athletes encryption on the surface of the grid. Athletes in the program and ski slopes were defined as not penetrate the surface of the wall (including athletes for mobile wall surface), the rest of the surface is the surface of the open (consistent with the actual). Assumes that the environment temperature is −20°, the air density and dynamic viscosity were 1.395 kg/m³, 1.62 × 10⁻⁵ Pa·s. And the difference of linear slide athletes in the translation is that in the curve track athletes are turning around its instantaneous center. The instantaneous center is changing the curvature of the curve track centre.

4 RESULTS AND ANALYSIS

The circle flow field around an athlete was calculated at the angular velocity of 6, 7, 8, 9, 10, 11, 12 degrees/sec. Figure 5 shows the number of longitudinal profile velocity distribution when the

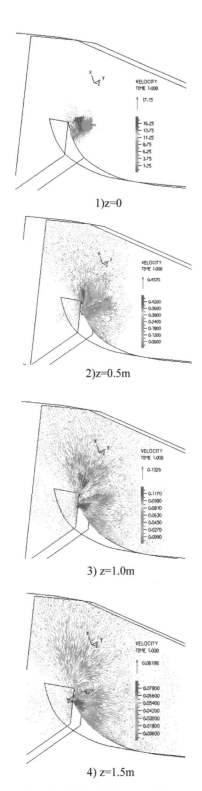

1)z=0

2)z=0.5m

3) z=1.0m

4) z=1.5m

Figure 5. Longitudinal velocity vector diagram.

angular speed of 8 degrees/sec (where the longitudinal profile of $z = 0$ and athletes' median coincide plane sagittally).

Seen from Figure 5, velocity distribution in each longitudinal profile showed a non-uniform characteristics, although athletes' sliding speed is large, the walls except snow road are open, so that the air volume flow rate that the athletes taking around are minimal in terms of sliding speed. When the athletes near the end of the chute, influenced by player driven, it will form air flowing in the same direction with athletes' sliding speed in the region of a space that athletes will participate in and form eddy current in the upcoming slopes and Angular domain vertical walls.

Figure 6 and Figure 7 shows the curves equations which are about the relationship between athletes lift and drag obtained by polynomial fitting and the sliding speed.

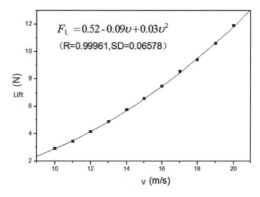

$$F_L = 0.52 - 0.09\upsilon + 0.03\upsilon^2$$

$$(R=0.99961, SD=0.06578)$$

Figure 6. Curve and equation between lift and sliding velocity.

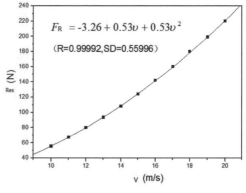

$$F_R = -3.26 + 0.53\upsilon + 0.53\upsilon^2$$

$$(R=0.99992, SD=0.55996)$$

Figure 7. Curve and equation between resistance and sliding velocity.
(Note: Figures 6 and 7 in the R correlation coefficient, SD as the standard deviation of the fit).

Seen from Figures 6 and 7, both lift and drag sliding velocity increases as the athletes and non-linearly increases, the curve is concave, and therefore with the sliding speed increases athlete, increased lift and drag, the faster the lift resistance is concerned than an order of magnitude smaller. athletes slide to the area, if the sliding speed of 20 m/s, from Figures 6 and 7 shows, drag and lift of approximately 220 N and 12 N, at which point its own gravity (with the securing fitting) of the tangential and normal components of approximately 548 N and 283.07 N. Visible, lift compared to the component itself in terms of gravity was much smaller, so that the lift can be ignored. The friction between the skis and the slide is mainly due to the component of gravity and centrifugal force caused. Resistance is the tangential component of gravity rather, a strong air resistance and gravity tangential component of the double effects, athletes tangential acceleration up −12.2 m/s, so athletes slide sliding speed at the end of the curve will decreased rapidly.

5 CONCLUSION

According to the theory of the reverse modeling, based on the created entity model of freestyle skiing aerials in the curve slideway period, we have created the space model of flow field within 3D virtual design software and simulated the there were effectives in study on the aerodynamic characteristics of freestyle skiing aerials slipping phase with CFD. The results show that: Athletes should try to keep away from the eddy zone formed by the slope on leaving platform and the angle area of the vertical wall and made against the satability of athletes' movements on leaving platform. At the end of the curve slideway, the influence of friction between skateboard and slideway by lift could be neglected. The air resistance is similar to own gravitational tangential component, so it will have a large tangential acceleration and sliding speed will decay rapidly. If athletes want an enough leaving platform speed, besides raising the starting height properly, still need to try to reduce own weight and frount face area.

REFERENCES

[1] Dan Liu, Fengxin Chen. Application of CFD in the calculation of performance for propeller openingwter[J]. Modern Manufacturing Engineering, 2010(4): 18–20.
[2] Huawei Lai, Yueqin Liu, Jiaming Wu. Calculation and analysis the performance of propeller based on CFD method[J]. Ship and Ocean Engineering, 2009, 38(4): 131–135.
[3] Jian Hu, Sheng Huang, Peisheng Wang. Numerical prediction method of propeller hydrodynamic performance[J]. Journal of Jiangsu University of Science and Technology, 2008, 22(1): 1–6.
[4] Yansheng Lei, Zhenggui Zhou. Wind turbine oscillating airfoil dynamic stall CFD research[J]. Journal of Solar Energy, Vol. 31, No. 3 (2010.3): 367–372.
[5] Yu Zhou, Weiqi Qian, Youqi Deng, Ming Ma. A preliminary analysis of parameters of k—ωSST two equation turbulence model effect[J]. Air power journal, Vol. 28, No. 2 (2010.4): 213–217.
[6] Benzhao Zhang, Jian'an Yin, Hongji Zhang. Numerical methods for fluid dynamics[M]. Machinery Industry Press, 2003 June: 1–246.

Computer, Intelligent Computing and Education Technology – Liu, Sung & Yao (Eds)
© 2014 Taylor & Francis Group, London, ISBN 978-1-138-02469-4

Kinematic comparative study of technical actions of backhand chop of table tennis and tennis

Bo Zhang & Ke-Fei Wei
First Author School of Exercise Human Science, Shenyang Sport University, Shenyang, Liaoning, China
Physical Teaching and Research Department, Hebei University, Hebei, China

ABSTRACT: In order to specify the kinematical characteristics of backhand chop in table tennis and tennis and to provide a large number of quantitative scientific basis for teaching and training, this paper tries to use the three-dimensional photography analytical method to get the kinematic parameters of high-pressure tennis action and deals with these data statistically. The study shows: table tennis backhand chop has to overcome small resistance. The action is reflexible with rapid immobilization while tennis backhand chop has to overcome greater resistance. Improving the speed of backhand chop is realized by increasing the turning radius and thereby increasing the distance of the acting, in another word "hitting by borrowing power". The action is relatively fixed because of the slow joint movement.

Keywords: table tennis; tennis; backhand chop skill; kinematics

1 INTRODUCTION

Technology of backhand chop is one of the attacking skills which has the characteristics of great power, fast speed and requiring a short period of landing.[1,2] Good Technology o backhand chop will help to gain the most effective scores and to win the match. Most of the researches are centered on the summary of experience. They have no quantified scientific description.[3–6] In recent years, with the application of the high speed video analysis technology in analyzing sport skills,[8] it provides a scientific method for the quantified analysis of tennis skills.[9] This study can help the teachers in comprehensive universities and colleges and students who participate in sports understand more about the action of backhand chop, and help teachers to guide correctly in the teaching practice. In the teaching practice, the students have basic knowledge about one of the event knowing what they can share and how to treat them differently in practising anther event, which can promote the rapid development of sports teaching practice.

2 RESEARCH SUBJECT AND METHODS

2.1 Research subject

The thesis focuses on ten elite professional athletes of table tennis and tennis in provincial team whose athletic careers are of at least two or more years. The athletes all hold the rackets by right hand and all the research targets are centered on the joints of the right hands.

2.2 Research methods

The researching equipments include two Sony video-cameras with the same standard and the shooting frequency of 125 Hz/s, a three-dimensional DLT radiate frame, two photography lights and two personal computers. The two video-cameras are placed respectively to the left side of the athlete in front and the horizontal front for the purpose of recording the overall movements completely. The main axis of the two cameras is of 90 degree. The data obtained from the SPAS system will be dealt with Excel, and the kinematic data of backhand chop of table tennis player and tennis player provide evidence for the future theory analysis.

3 RESULTS AND ANALYSIS

3.1 Analysis of the lower limbs' movements

3.1.1 Hip joint movement

As is shown in Figure 1, compared with tennis player, hip joint speed of table tennis player is small with great changes; On the comparison of the angle of hip joint, there is small change in both table tennis and tennis. The hip joint angles of table tennis and tennis decrease in the stage of forward swing, but from the stage of swinging racket to

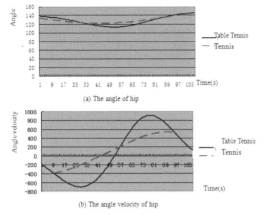

(a) The angle of hip

(b) The angle velocity of hip

Figure 1.　The curve change of each hip joint variable.

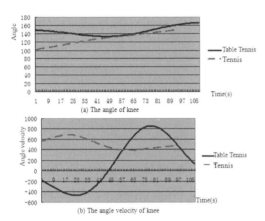

(a) The angle of knee

(b) The angle velocity of knee

Figure 2.　The curve change of each knee variable.

meet the ball to the stage of touching the ball with the racket, the hip joint angle of table tennis are more changeable than tennis. During this stage, the decrease of hip joint angle may make the ball hit more stable. However, because tennis players have to overcome relatively greater resistance, the angle of hip joint is not easy to change.

3.1.2　Knee movement

From Figure 2 we know that there are changes in each variable of knee and the change of knee angle is smallest in the process of backhand chop of table tennis and tennis. According to this research, when the scope of knee angle is from 75 ° to 150 °, the kicking strength of knee increases with the increase of the knee angle; When knee angle is greater than 150 °, the kicking strength of knee decreases with the increase of the angle. When table tennis and tennis players take the action of backhand chop, the knee angle is always less than 150 °. The knee angle

is more than 150 ° only in the stage of swinging the racket to hit the ball, which indicates that the knee is within the best range of kicking strength of knee when table tennis and tennis players take the action of backhand chop.

3.1.3　Ankle movement

Figure 3 shows that there are great changes of each ankle variable in the process of table tennis and tennis backhand chop, in which the change of ankle joint angle is smallest. In the whole process of hitting balls, the change of the curve of ankle angle in playing table tennis and tennis is consistent within a range of about 10 °, which shows that the ankle is relatively fixed. In the entire process of the movement, the ankle angle of table tennis is obviously greater than the ankle angle of tennis, and the change of ankle angular velocity in table tennis is more obvious than tennis's, which indicates that in the process of backhand chop of table tennis and tennis, the movement radius of ankle of table tennis is larger than tennis's.

3.2　Analysis of upper limbs' movements

3.2.1　Shoulder movement

From Figure 4 we know that in the process of backhand chop, the initial speed of shoulder joint in tennis was significantly greater than the initial speed of shoulder in table tennis. The decline rate of the speed of shoulder in tennis is slow and relatively stable, but the speed of shoulder in table tennis has large fluctuations in the whole downward trend. The changes of the shoulder angle in table tennis and tennis are similar. The shoulder angle of tennis is smaller than table tennis's with a small variation range. There are large fluctuations in the whole hitting process, while the angular velocity of

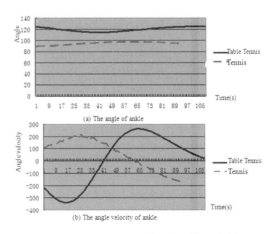

(a) The angle of ankle

(b) The angle velocity of ankle

Figure 3.　The curve change of each ankle variable.

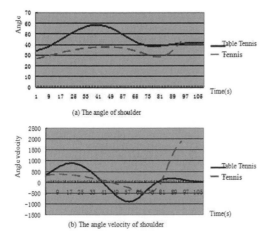

(a) The angle of shoulder

(b) The angle velocity of shoulder

Figure 4. The curve change of each shoulder joint variable.

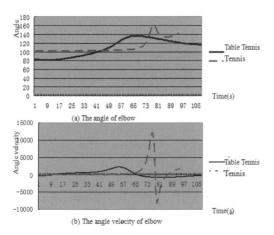

(a) The angle of elbow

(b) The angle velocity of elbow

Figure 5. The curve change of each elbow variable.

shoulder joint in tennis increases rapidly after the racket contact the ball.

3.2.2 Elbow movement

From Figure 5 we know in the stage of forward swing in table tennis and tennis backhand chop, there are changes in the speed of table tennis athlete's elbow. The angle increases but the angular velocity of the elbow remains relatively stable. From the stage of forward swing to meet ball to the stage of touching the ball with the racket, the elbow speed increases from a low point rapidly, while the angle and the angular velocity increase. In the stage of backswing, the speed of the elbow rapidly decreases to the lowest point, while the angle has a slight decrease and the angular velocity

gradually returns to the previous state. While in the stage of forward swing, there is almost no change in the tennis player's elbow speed as well as angle and angular velocity. From the stage of swingnig the racket to meet the ball to the stage of touching the ball with the racket, the speed of the elbow increases gradually. The angle remains the same, but increases rapidly at the moment of hitting the ball, and the angular velocity increases at the moment. During the stage of backswing, elbow speed increases slowly and the angle decreases together with the gradual return of angular velocity to the state of the stage of forward swing. The differences of curve changes during the stage of foreward swing are the results of the different intensity of force from shoulder joint in these two sports events. So table tennis player's elbow varies a lot with a relative flexibility. while at this stage tennis player is accumulating energy, and the elbow is relatively stable. During this stage, the increase of the speed of tennis player's elbow is less faster than that of the table tennis's, which indicates the elbow in tennis backhand chop is less flexible than that of the table tennis's. Due to the different force intensity from shoulder joint in these two sports events, the elbow speed, angle and angular velocity of table tennis player decrease rapidly after contacting the ball in the backswing, and return to the previous state immediately. However, the angle and strength of arm swinging after contacting the ball will decrease gradually by moving with the shoulder for a while.

3.2.3 Wrist movement

Figure 6 shows that in the stage of forward swing of table tennis backhand chop, there exists variation of athlete's wrist speed. The angle decreases and the angular velocity remains relatively stable.

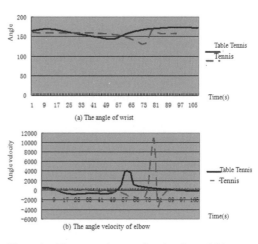

(a) The angle of wrist

(b) The angle velocity of elbow

Figure 6. The curve change of each twist variable.

In the stage of swinging the racket to contact the ball with the racket, wrist speed rapidly increases from the low point, while the angle increases slightly and angular velocity reaches the peak. In the stage of swinging the racket after hitting a ball, the speed of the wrist decreases quickly to the lowest, while angular decreases lightly and angular velocity gradually returns to the state of the stage of forward swing. Tennis player's wrist does not change in the stage of forward swing, which remains at a relative low level and angle and angular velocity almost have no change. In the stage of swinging the racket to contact the ball with the racket, the speed of the wrist increases gradually, and the angle decreases. However, the angle increases rapidly in the moment of touching the ball and the angular velocity also increases rapidly at the same time. In the stage of swinging the racket after hitting a ball, wrist speed increases slowly, while the angle decreases and the angular velocity gradually returns to the state of the stage of forward swing.

4 CONCLUSION AND SUGGESTIONS

4.1 *Conclusion*

From the stage of foreward swing to the stage of swinging the racket, the resistance of table tennis backhand chop is small, while the action is flexible and the immobilization of joint is rapid. Therefore, players have to produce force by coordinating each joint in the hitting process.

Because the resistance in the process of hitting tennis is large, improving shotting speed of tennis backhand chop is achieved by increasing the turning radius and thereby increasing the distance of the acting, namely "hitting by borrowing power". The action is relatively fixed because the movement of joints is slow.

In the process of backhand chop in table tennis and tennis, the angle of the knee joint is always less than 150 °, which is within the best range of kicking strength; The ankle angle curve variation is consistent in the process of backhand chop of table tennis and tennis within a range of about 10 °.

For the sense of keeping gravity, backhand chop of table tennis can only consider the relative contents about hitting rate, without haing to consider the effects from the racket to the ball and effects from the player's body to the ball; However, tennis backhand chop must take the processing of the ball momentum into account, and in the process of tennis backhand chop we must "first withstand and then turn body", that's to say, turning our body after withstanding the momentum from the ball.

4.2 *Suggestions*

In teaching and training technical actions of table tennis backhand chop, we should emphasize and strengthen the strength training of all aspects of body muscle and the ability of coordinating each joint of our body.

In teaching and training technical actions of tennis backhand chop, based on the conventional action essentials, all joints are relatively fixed, and improving the ball's hitting quality is achieved by increasing the turning radius.

In teaching and training table tennis and tennis, we have to strengthen the strength training of players' joints and their coordination so as to increase energy transferring effects. In tennis teaching and training, we should improve the processing of the momentum from the ball and avoid the overlapping of teaching and trainning both table tennis and tennis before have an intimate knowledge of one of the two sports events.

REFERENCES

[1] Tan Maijiu. *Sports Coaching* [M]. Beijing: Higher Education Press, 2006.
[2] Jiang Fusheng. *Tennis Tutorial* [M]. Beijing: People's Sports Press, 2007.
[3] Tracking Method Based on H∞ Filtering", JCIT, Vol. 6, No. 10, pp. 251.
[4] Yan Botao et al. Biomechanical Analysis of the Serve Techniques in Tennis [J]. *Sports Science*, 2000, 20 (4): 80–85.
[5] Liu Hui. Sports Biomechanical Principles of Power Serve Technique in Tennis [J]. *Journal of Beijing Sport University*, 2000, 23(2): 173–180.
[6] Zhijun Song, Changle Zhou, Kunhui Lin, "IK and Biomechanical Model of Human Skeleton for Motion Simulation", AISS, Vol. 3, No. 7, pp. 302–310, 2011259, 2011.
[7] Pan Sheng, Zhang Hongcheng. Characteristics and Comparison—Two Kinds of Baseline Drives [J]. *Journal of Suzhou University*, 2002(4): 102–105.
[8] Peng Chengji. Biomechanical Analysis of Delivering the Ball in Tennis [J]. *Journal of Beijing Sport University*, 2000, 23(2): 181–184.
[9] Zhang Hui, Dai Jinbiao. Research on Technical & Tactical Characteristics of Racket Games [J]. *Journal of Shanghai Sport University*, 2007, 31 (4): 65–69.

Computer, Intelligent Computing and Education Technology – Liu, Sung & Yao (Eds)
© *2014 Taylor & Francis Group, London, ISBN 978-1-138-02469-4*

The kinematics analysis on throwing ability of 2–6 years old healthy infants

Xin Guan & Xin Wang
Department of Physical Education, Shenyang Agricultural University, Shenyang, Liaoning, China
School of Exercise Human Science, Shenyang Sport University, Shenyang, Liaoning, China

ABSTRACT: By 2-d camera and video analytical method, 3 to 5 years old healthy children throwing action feature points age, points are analyzed, and compared gender six months after its action characteristic changing circumstances. Through the analysis in the process of throwing mastery of upper limb movement structures and the Angle of each joint of each phase of change and finish the time needed for changes, and points out that the healthy children throwing movement characteristics and development law, as a child in the growth process of development and promote cheeper action to provide theoretical basis for healthy growth.

Keywords: children; throwing; biomechanics; kinematics analysis

1 GENERAL INTRODUCTION

Throwing is a very difficult action which needs the coordination of many parts of the body. Throwing ability is of great value in infants' daily life, work and physical activities. So it is significant to observe infants' development in throwing action as well as its development patterns.[1–3] Research on human's throwing action by far for the purpose of improving competitive sport performance such as shout put, hammer throw and javelin. Other research concerning average healthy infants focused on the value of games to the development of infants' throwing ability.[4–6] Rarely is there any research or documents monitoring infants' structure of throwing action, changes of joint angle of different phase and the maturity of action from the aspect of sport biomechanics. This paper is based on sport biomechanics and conducts technical analysis on infants' throwing action by means of video analysis. The study focuses on the feature difference and development pattern of body movement of different age and gender, so as to lay a foundation for the evaluation of the development level of infants and provide proper guide and method for the development of infants' throwing ability.

2 RESEARCH SUBJECTS AND METHODS

2.1 Research subject

From Dec 2010 to Feb 2011, Video clips were captured among children aged 1–6 in Donghu Kindergarten, Kindergarten attached to Liaoning Provincial Committee and Montessori Early Education Center. Children were grouped with the age gap of half a year and there are about 50 members in each group. According to the age feature of the development of children's big movement, children aged from 2 to 6 were videotaped their throwing in 8 groups, see Table 1.

2.2 Research method

Sony video cameras (50 Hz sample rate) were used to shoot infants' throwing a tennis ball from the side. A one-meter square scale was used for camera calibration. Camera at the side divides the action

Table 1. Groups of subjects.

Age group (year)	Group 1 2.0–2.5	Group 2 2.5–3.0	Group 3 3.0–3.5	Group 4 3.5–4	Group 5 4.0–4.5	Group 6 4.5–4	Group 7 5.0–5.5	Group 8 5.5–6
N (person)	20	27	50	50	50	50	50	50
Av. height (cm)	89.34	95.62	100.02	103.37	106.98	110.59	113.90	116.03
SD (cm)	6.02	5.02	5.02	4.20	4.76	5.28	5.34	4.90

into phases and obtains indices of joint angle change of the subjects with a calibration error less than 0.5 mm. DV tracker was employed to analyze these videos and configure physical quantity to be analyzed. Matsui Hideji's 15-link model was adopted and 21 tracking points were used to calculate human gravity center. The measured data were processed with five-spot e smoothing method. Spss13.0 was used to process data, and the data were presented with ($\bar{x} \pm s$), Independent Samples T-test was employed to compare the two groups, $P < 0.05$ means significant difference and $P < 0.01$ indicates rather significant difference.

3 RESEARCH RESULT AND ANALYSIS

3.1 *Phases of throwing action*

As one of the basic physical movements of healthy people, throwing action can be seen both in daily life and sport activities. The completion of the movement needs the coordinative cooperation of upper body, trunk and lower body. A standard throwing action can be divided into initial posture phase, rotation and arm-raising phase, final pitch phase and buffer phase[7] as follows:

Initial Posture Phase: Spread fingers naturally, put the ball on the root of fore finger, middle finger and ring finger, with sum and small finger holding the ball to prevent sliding as well as to control the ball. The palm does not contact the ball. When this is done, the left side body faces the direction of throwing, with two feet separating a little wider than shoulder, left toe tip pointing oblique front and being on the same line with right foot arch.

Rotation and Arm-Raising Phrase: Bend right knee, trunk and shoulder lean and rotate to right,

gravity center rests on right leg; bend left arm lightly to chest and thus the ball's vertical point falls outside tight foot to extend pitch distance and tighten muscle on the left.

Final Pitch Phrase: Kick the ground forcefully with right foot, raise heel, turn right knee inward, push right hip forward, raise the upper body to the left and rotate to the pitch direction. When the left body is close to be vertical to the ground, straighten right leg with left shoulder as an axis, body turns to throwing direction, raise head and chest with right shoulder pushing forward forcibly, right arm straighten quickly and push the ball forward with angle of 40–42 degrees. Snap wrist when the ball leaves hand and push the ball with hand. In the meantime, straighten left leg upward to push the ball upward and forward.

Buffer Phase: Right leg switches quickly with left foot after the ball leaves, left leg moves backward to lower gravity center and buffer the momentum forward and keeps balance.

Children's body is not well developed, their muscles are less coordinative and what's more, they are not professionally trained, so they take a natural posture of throwing. In the beginning their postures are not standard, they just split their feet sideways. There are not obvious trunk rotation and buffer phases or there are none at all. So the research mainly focuses on the joint angle and development pattern of arm-raising and final pitch phase as well as the rotation of children and the time of action completion.

3.2 *Kinematics analysis on throwing action*

From Table 2 we can see that there is no significant difference among children of different genders. It is found during data processing that the difference

Table 2. Angular change of shoulder and elbow joints of different age groups after arm-raising.

Subject	Angular change of shoulder joint (degree)		Angular change of elbow joint (degree)	
	Male	Female	Male	Female
Group 1	118.20 ± 11.38	123.60 ± 9.09	61.96 ± 10.81	58.74 ± 32.31
Group 2	120.11 ± 13.85	125.37 ± 32.57	63.89 ± 36.68	60.66 ± 27.88
Group 3	121.84 ± 29.72	126.46 ± 24.99	64.91 ± 5.62	61.48 ± 37.83
Group 4	127.36 ± 24.68	131.84 ± 23.67	66.95 ± 41.99	62.05 ± 31.72
Group 5	132.66 ± 13.91	135.29 ± 21.98	70.96 ± 39.83	64.63 ± 23.10
Group 6	$144.15 \pm 25.41^*$	$143.03 \pm 20.13^*$	$87.09 \pm 43.07^*$	$80.65 \pm 22.83^*$
Group 7	148.16 ± 32.01	$155.57 \pm 27.26^*$	$88.65 \pm 30.00^*$	$91.43 \pm 36.70^{**}$
Group 8	$156. \pm 24.27^*$	$162.03 \pm 18.85^*$	$111.54 \pm 22.41^*$	$110.48 \pm 32.43^*$

Note: Data is presented as Average value ± SD, *: means the difference is significant at 0.05, **: means the difference is significant at 0.01, the same below.

in writ angle is statistically insignificant, whereas the difference between shoulder and elbow joints is statistically significant. So the research mainly studies the change of shoulder and elbow joints during final pitch and the time needed among different age groups.

3.2.1 Angular change of shoulder and elbow joints in arm-raising phrase

Spss was used to conduct an One-way ANOVA of the data which shows that there is no significant difference of shoulder and elbow joint angle during arm-raising for children of 3–4 years old. Difference of shoulder and elbow joint angle during arm-raising for children of 4–5 years old begins to be significant and the angle is obviously larger. Analysis shows that the shoulder and elbow joint angle increases as age grows, the older, the larger increase of the angle. This is an indication of body maturity. The wider spreading of shoulder and elbow help increase the distance of power exerting, the longer the muscles stretch, the more elasticity produced, and is released in final pitch. This increases body's work on the object and increase the object's speed when leaving the hand.[7]

3.2.2 Angular change of shoulder and elbow joints in final pitch phase

One-way ANOVA was conducted and results shows that significant difference of shoulder and elbow joint angle during final pitch for children of 3–4 years old. Difference of shoulder and elbow joint angle in final pitch phase for children of 4–5 years old begins to be significant and the angle is obviously larger. Analysis shows that the shoulder and elbow joint angle increases as age grows, the older, the larger increase of the angle. This is an again the indication of body maturity. Larger shoulder and elbow joint angle can increase the distance of the object away from the body and increase pitch distance.[7] In addition, it can increase the time that muscles work on the object and increase the object's kinetic energy.

3.2.3 Wrist angle when object leaves the hand

Seen from Table 4, children' wrist angle is obviously less than 180 degree when the object leaves the hand. This means children unconsciously turn their wrists downward. This reduces the flight height and time of the object and shortens the pitch distance of the object. The degree of turning wrist downward reduces as age grows, the throwing

Table 3. Angular change of shoulder and elbow joints in final pitch phase.

Subject	Angular change of shoulder joint (degree)		Angular change of elbow joint (degree)	
	Male	Female	Male	Female
Group 1	113.32 ± 29.22	116.09 ± 22.01	138.71 ± 13.25	128.91 ± 9.67
Group 2	116.35 ± 20.38	114.63 ± 11.64	138.99 ± 13.67	131.84 ± 31.61
Group 3	121.71 ± 23.45	118.99 ± 36.82	145.26 ± 20.49	147.15 ± 23.72
Group 4	120.11 ± 22.07	121.38 ± 31.67	149.06 ± 25.37	150.43 ± 23.2
Group 5	116.02 ± 17.92	127.16 ± 34.86	151.73 ± 39.83	143.94 ± 23.10
Group 6	128.40 ± 14.38**	138.42 ± 20.62*	159.21 ± 25.71	152.38 ± 21.86*
Group 7	137.58 ± 34.73**	135.58 ± 19.10	150.39 ± 14.5*	157.03 ± 17.07
Group 8	149 ± 15.74*	148.54 ± 19.23*	164.58 ± 11.06*	168.60 ± 13.23**

Table 4. Wrist angle when object leaves the hand.

Subject	Male	Female
Group 1	164.67 ± 9.86	155.78 ± 4.34
Group 2	155.42 ± 9.51	156.09 ± 26.79
Group 3	157.96 ± 14.25	156.82 ± 19.95
Group 4	159.81 ± 12.51	165.96 ± 7.90
Group 5	159.46 ± 12.36	156.47 ± 18.85
Group 6	164.22 ± 12.11	160.89 ± 8.45
Group 7	165.98 ± 11.14	166.28 ± 13.27
Group 8	162.94 ± 16.52	168.69 ± 21.57

Table 5. Time needed for throw action.

Subject	Male	Female
Group 1	0.136 ± 0.028	0.143 ± 0.022
Group 2	0.134 ± 0.017	0.143 ± 0.032
Group 3	0.134 ± 0.025	0.142 ± 0.024
Group 4	0.120 ± 0.027*	0.132 ± 0.030*
Group 5	0.122 ± 0.028	0.129 ± 0.040
Group 6	0.112 ± 0.018*	0.127 ± 0.027
Group 7	0.116 ± 0.032	0.113 ± 0.024*
Group 8	0.110 ± 0.024	0.112 ± 0.022

Table 6. Rotation percentage of different age groups.

Subjects	Cases of body rotation		Sample amount		Percentage of body rotation	
	Male	Female	Male	Female	Male	Female
Group 1	0	0	20	25	0%	0%
Group 2	0	0	27	22	0%	0%
Group 3	0	0	28	25	0%	0%
Group 4	2	2	31	32	6.5%	6.3%
Group 5	5	3	28	20	17.9%	15%
Group 6	8	7	35	34	22.9%	20.6%
Group 7	11	10	27	28	40.7%	35.7%
Group 8	14	14	24	33	58.3%	42.4%

action tends to be perfect and the pitch distance increases.

3.2.4 *Time needed for throw action*

Seen from Table 5, the time needed for throwing action reduces when children grow older. Stretching muscles tend to lose power as time extends, the tension power of muscles reduces when stretching a longer time. So the shorter the time needed, the higher efficiency of elasticity, and vice versa.[8] So the shortening of time is also a sign of perfect action performance as well as a sign of the improvement of body coordination.

3.2.5 *Development of body rotation*

There is no body rotation phase for children under 3 years old. The rotation of the trunk appears among children over 4 years old. The leaning back and rotation of the trunk increase the distance of power exerting and increase body's work on the object. The rotation of body also can stretch wait muscles and create elasticity which will work on the object in the final pitch and add more work to the object. From Table 6 we can also see that the ratio of rotation grows with the growth of age. There is no significant difference between male and female children with body rotation phrase, but the ratio of male children is obviously higher than female children when they are over five years old.

4 CONCLUSION

There is no significant difference between development of throwing action of children aged 3–5.

As children grow older, there is the tendency of the increase of arm raising, joint angle of both shoulder and elbow. This is especially obvious in angle increase of back joint of children over 4 years old. The wider spreading of shoulder and elbow help strengthen the elasticity of the upper limb and increase the speed of the thrown object.

There is apparent wrist bending when the object leaves hand, and this bending decrease as age grows. This change can make the parabola cover larger distance and height, and thus the object is thrown further.

As age grows, children need shorter time to finish throwing action. The shortening of the time of muscle stretch reduces consumption of tension makes elasticity transform into kinetic energy more effectively.

ACKNOWLEDGEMENTS

This work was financially supported by the Liaoning Natural Science Foundation (20102210) and the outstanding young growth plan of colleges and universities of Liaoning Province.

REFERENCES

[1] Yan Hongguang, Wang Xin. Principles and Analysis of Basic Sport Movements [M]. Shenyang, Dean's Office of Shenyang Sport University, 2007.
[2] Qian Jingguang, Song Yawei et al. Sports Rehabilitation Biomechanics, [M]. Beijing: People's Sport University, 2008.
[3] Naodoyagura Mak I, Tasukukimura. Acquirement of stability and mobility infant gait [J]. Gait Posture, 2002, 16:69–77.
[4] Wang Xin, Zheng Ximing, Biomechanical Analysis on Infants' Running Ability [J]. Journal of Shenyang Sport University, 2010,4:81–83.
[5] Qian Jingguang, Song Yawei, Ye Qiang, Biomechanical Principle and Analysis on Walking [J]. Journal of Nanjing Sport Institute, 2006,4:1–7.
[6] Liu Hui, A Biomechanical Study on the Principle of Upper Limb Whipping [J]. Beijing: Sport Science, 2004,24(11):7–13.
[7] Fan Jiangbo, Ren Aijun, Liu Huifang. A Study on the Development of 3–11 Years Old Children's Throwing Ability, [J]. China School Sport, 2010,28(12): 12–17.

Computer, Intelligent Computing and Education Technology – Liu, Sung & Yao (Eds)
© 2014 Taylor & Francis Group, London, ISBN 978-1-138-02469-4

Discussion on the improvement of the effect of 2/3 court zone press defense through court awareness

Yao Fan & Wei-Feng Kang

Institute of Physical Education, Northeast Normal University, Changchun, Jilin, China

ABSTRACT: The tactics of 2/3 court zone press defense is a kind of transformation of the tactics of full-court zone press defense. Inheriting the core content of full-court zone press defense—midcourt attack and positive steals, it is a kind of basketball defensive tactics with aggressive, destructive and strategic nature and relatively good practical application effect. The introduction of court awareness to the tactics of 2/3 court zone press defense can improve the defense effect effectively.

Keywords: court awareness; 2/3 court; zone press; effect

1 PRESENTATION OF QUESTION

As a defensive means commonly used in modern basketball sports, zone press shows the development trend of modern basketball defense. It mainly includes full-court zone press, 3/4 court zone press, 2/3 court zone press and half-court zone press. 2/3 court zone press exists as a kind of middle type defensive means between 3/4 court zone press and half-court zone press. In spite of its conspicuous advantage and reasonableness, as far as court division is concerned, 2/3 court zone press is relatively vague in court concept compared to zone press of other forms. What can make athletes have specific court concept at the court and improve court utilization accordingly? The author holds that it should be court awareness of athletes. Then how can court awareness improve the defense effect of 2/3 court zone press? In view of this, the article makes an in-depth discussion for the purpose of providing reference for theory and application of basketball teaching and training.

2 COURT AWARENESS

2.1 *Concept about court awareness*

Modern basketball coaches attach great importance to "awareness". Here awareness refers to "basketball awareness", "field awareness", "court awareness" and etc. This is individual experience and outward manifestation of athletes' inherent quality through training about modern basketball theory, skills, tactics, psychology and etc. The basketball coach Bremner of University of Nebraska presented the viewpoint about "Court Awareness and Utilization" in his article Twelve Daily Shooting Practice first, which further exposed the relevance between athletes' reasonable application of skills and tactics and court area. Professor Jiang Lijia, Professor Zhang Qiang and Associate Professor Cheng Dongmei of Northeast Normal University published the article "On 'Court Awareness' and Cultivation of Basketball Players" in China Sport Science and Technology in 1996. This was the discussion on the viewpoint about "court awareness" in China for the first time, in which explanation was made in terms of the concept, mechanism, training method and approach of court awareness. From this, it can be seen that court awareness really exists, and plays a significant role which can't be neglected in athletes' reasonable application of skills and tactics.

"Court awareness" refers to the sum of psychological process of athletes to make right judgment and utilization of the object basketball court through vision and thinking. Specifically, it means that athletes can realize what position they are on the ground at any time and anywhere in training or competition, and make responsive reaction according to the condition about attack and defense with their own position into consideration.[1]

2.2 *Formation of court awareness*

Such kind of responsive reaction is a kind of players' reaction based on the object, court through vision, and then imaging is formed on retina, information is conveyed to cerebral cortex through optic nerve passage, and contact is established with motor nerve center through analysis and arrangement, and locomotive organ is governed to make action.[1] Its formation process (e.g. Fig. 1) is that athletes form reactive stimulation towards some

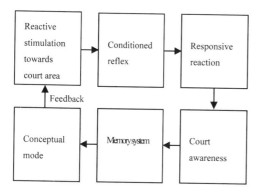

Figure 1. Diagram about the mode of the formation process of court awareness.

court area, establish conditioned reflex, and make responsive reaction, finally a kind of conceptual mode is established and stored in memory system. The revelation of the mechanism and formation process of "court awareness" makes us further know that "court awareness" must be intensified repetitively in training and competition, effective conditioned reflex shall be established, so that our skills and tactical operation more effective and aggressive.

3 TACTICS OF 2/3 COURT ZONE PRESS DEFENSE

The tactics of 2/3 court zone press defense refers to a kind of strongly aggressive and destructive defensive tactics in which all the team members choose 2/3 court area to stand according to certain formation when the situation turns to defense from attack, every team member is responsible for defending certain area, and the attack of the other party is broken through individual active defense and coordination and cooperation of all the team members. Since such kind of tactics features wide moving plane in defense, fierce fight, fast speed, great intensity, and high demand on coordination consciousness, it can bring the strong points of team members into full play and restrict activities of the other party effectively, disturb the deployment and usual practice of the other party, cause mental tension and technical error of the other party, and win over initiative in the competition. It owns four advantages that retreat and defense are fast, formation is concealed; physical strength is saved, fouls are reduced; labor division is specified, blind action is reduced; method is simple, effect is obviously seen and etc. The tactics of 2/3 court zone press defense is a kind of transformation of the full-court zone press defense.

Inheriting the core content of full-court zone press defense—midcourt attack and positive steals, it is a kind of basketball defensive tactics with aggressive, destructive and strategic nature and relatively good practical application effect.

4 INTENSIFY COURT AWARENESS, IMPROVE THE EFFECT OF 2/3 COURT ZONE PRESS DEFENSE

4.1 *Improve the understanding about court awareness, specify the guiding significance of court awareness in the tactics of 2/3 court zone press defense*

Although court awareness cannot be seen or touched, it really exists. The correct application of every skill and tactics made by team members in competition is associated with court more or less, and contains the content about court awareness. In time of defense, players also tend to depend on court awareness to make correct judgment towards people, basketball and basket as well as the spatial relations among them, take corresponding and reasonable skills and tactics through timely conceptual work in order to bring their own strong points into full play and defeat opponents more effectively. In 2/3 court zone press defense of such special form, it especially needs to apply court awareness to make reasonable division of court, make full use of court to dominate and guide defense action of athletes. Therefore, we should pay sufficient attention to court awareness, for it has guiding significance towards the tactics of 2/3 court zone press defense.

4.2 *To intensify court awareness can make athletes establish the concept about court and deepen their understanding about tactics*

Basketball awareness can be divided into the perceptual stage, the practical stage and the rational stage.[2] This is also the case with court awareness. Its formation process is started when offensive players enter perception of certain area. Through personal experience of practical exercise and practical application in competition, and then through rational comprehensive analysis, players grasp the basic rules for defense at different distance, different position and in different direction, make application and summary repeatedly in practice, form their own court awareness, and play with high proficiency in competition and fight at limited basketball court.

In the cognitive structure, as the foundation of tactical awareness, court awareness of athletes plays a very important role in correct understanding of court form, guiding thinking and the implementation of tactical operation, and exerts direct impact on the state of consciousness of subject. On the one hand, the application of tactics made by athletes depends on their ability to make subtle differentiation of court area; on the other hand, it depends on their court awareness formed in the process of teaching training and competition as well as their ability to differentiate the understanding of tactical operation, so that athletes can make proper defense action quickly and accurately in the complicated attack and defense system they have grasped. Athletes with certain court awareness can differentiate zone position at the court easily, and implement proper tactics according to their position. Therefore, to intensify athletes' court awareness can deepen their understanding of tactics.

4.3 To intensify court awareness can bring the signal reflex action of athletes towards court into full play and improve the integrity of team defense

The formation of court awareness is a kind of conditioned reflex mechanism, while the condition to form such kind of stimulation is court. Court here is equivalent to signal. Therefore, to intensify court awareness can bring the signal reflex action of athletes towards court into full play. In the whole process of 2/3 court zone press defense, court awareness impels athletes to form conditioned reflex towards the object, court, take reasonable and effective action to change once signal is sent out or according to the condition at the court, and make defense actively and effectively.

4.4 To intensify court awareness can make athletes make full use of court and take position and labor division in a reasonable way

The leading point in court awareness is court division and utilization. This is also one problem that must be solved in 2/3 court zone press. Only with good court awareness, can athletes take reasonable position and labor division and get more aware of their own responsibility based on sufficient utilization of court. Take the 2/3 court 1-2-2 zone press defense for example (Fig. 2), Every time when attack comes to an end, all the team members are requested to take their position quickly according to 2/3 court 1-2-2 formation. We can see that different positions are set for different tasks, while different positions can have different defense effect. Therefore, court awareness seems to be especially important as the key to reasonable defense.

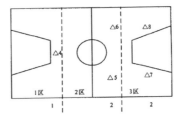

Figure 2. 2/3 court 1-2-2.

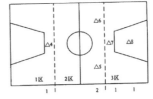

Figure 3. 2/3 court 1-2-1-1.

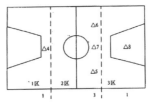

Figure 4. 2/3 court 1-3-1.

4.5 To intensify court awareness can make athletes change the defense formation of the team properly and improve the defense effect

In basketball match, the fixed defense formation can't make full use of court. Instead, it is requested to make flexible and variable application according to the characteristics of attack made by the other party, the position of offensive players and actual demand in competition. To intensify court awareness can make athletes have a clear awareness of their position and the position form of the team at the court, change the team defense formation properly mainly according to the position of opponent team members in order to strengthen defense effect. For example, based on the 2/3 court 1-2-2 zone press defense, several kinds of formation transformation as follows can be realized through court awareness of athletes: 1-2-1-1 (Fig. 3); 1-3-1 (Fig. 4); 2-2-1 (Fig. 5), and the defense effect of the 2/3 court zone press is strengthened accordingly. Certainly, the mutual transformation of several formations listed above is guided by defense strategy, so that the offensive intention and the weak link of the offensive party

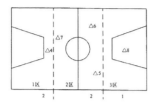

Figure 5.   2/3 court 2-2-1.

can be specified. However, the specific change of the position of team members is still dominated through court awareness.

Through discussion, it is not hard for us to find that the existence of court awareness in basketball awareness is the most fundamental awareness. It is not unfathomable. We should attach importance to the cultivation of court awareness of team members in teaching and training at ordinary times. Court awareness plays an active promoting role in 2/3 court zone press defense. To intensify court awareness can make athletes deepen the understanding of tactics, improve the integrity of defense of the whole team, and enhance defense effect.

REFERENCES

[1] Zhang Qiang, Cheng Dongmei, Jiang Lijia, On "Court Awareness" and Cultivation of Basketball Players [J], China Sport Science and Technology, 1996, (10).
[2] Wang Shouheng, Zhang Quanning, Discussion on the Theory about "Basketball Awareness [J], Journal of Beijing Sport Normal College, 1999, (1).
[3] Tian Hong, Conceptual Mode of Basketball Defense Awareness [J], Journal of Chengdu Sport University, 1999, (1).
[4] Guo Jianhui, Analysis about the Tactics of 2/3 Court 1-2-2 Zone Press Defense [J], Journal of Henan Education Institute, the Edition of Natural Science, 2006, (2).
[5] Mo Chaoqun, Operation Principle and Method of the Zone Press Defense Tactics in Basketball [J], Journal of Hunan Institute of Humanities, Science and Technology, 2006, (3).
[6] Chen Zhangyun, Study on Basketball Awareness (Summary) [J], Journal of Beijing Sport University, 1996, (3).

Computer, Intelligent Computing and Education Technology – Liu, Sung & Yao (Eds)
© 2014 Taylor & Francis Group, London, ISBN 978-1-138-02469-4

Chinese taekwondo environment analysis and development strategy

Z. Zhang & F. Yi
Guangxi Normal University, College of Physical Education, Guilin, Guangxi, China

ABSTRACT: In order to popularize taekwondo, enhance the understanding of sport taekwondo and increase participation of the general public, this paper analyses the development environment for Chinese taekwondo by using the literature method, expert interview method, comprehensive logical analysis and SWOT analytical method so as to adapt to the development trend of world taekwondo, increase the number of people teaching and learning taekwondo in China and reveal a strategy for popularizing Chinese taekwondo, thus providing theoretical and practical basis for its further development.

Keywords: taekwondo; environment analysis; development strategy

1 INTRODUCTION

Taekwondo as a traditional Japanese martial art originated in South Korea. As an oriental martial art that differs from western sports, it is of special inherent significance, characteristics and value in the modern world, being a very good popular sport. In the modern world, taekwondo as a popular sport has positive influence on the body and mind of small children, primary school students, middle school students, youngsters, adults and the elderly.[1] It has developed into a great popular sport in the world participated by over 80 million people and 205 member states.[2] China has made substantial achievements in the development of taekwondo, especially in respect of competition. However, due to the insufficient understanding of taekwondo by the people, taekwondo is not developing in a balanced manner with unsatisfactory teaching and learning condition and the instructors are not competent enough, resulting in the low level of popularization of taekwondo in China.[3] Therefore, it has become a matter of first importance for the development of Chinese taekwondo to popularize taekwondo, enhance the understanding of sport taekwondo and increase participation by the general public.

This paper conducts a comprehensive analysis of the development environment for taekwondo in China by using the literature method, expert interview method, comprehensive logical analysis and SWOT analytical method so as to adapt to the development trend of world taekwondo, increase the number of people teaching and learning taekwondo in China, promote popularization projects and reveal a strategy for popularizing taekwondo in China, thus providing theoretical and practical basis for its further development.

2 DEVELOPMENT OF CHINESE TAEKWONDO

China has made relevantly good results in competitive taekwondo despite its short development time. Up to now, athletes of the country have won six Olympic gold medals in individual events (including two gold medals of Taipei, China) and dozens of world (intercontinental) medals in major international competitions such as the Olympic Games, World Championship, World Cup and the Asian Games, showing substantial competitive capacity of our athletes as well as problems such as women athletes performing better than men athletes and insufficient development in the cultivation of reserve young talents and echelon construction. With the taekwondo event entering China in 1992, popular taekwondo stepped onto the stage of history. And with the social development, the sports awareness of the general public has been through constant changes and sports and fitness are more and more valued by the people. Popular taekwondo has hence experienced rapid development in China and taekwondo dojo and clubs of various sizes have opened here and there like bamboo shoots after a spring rain. Based on incomplete statistics, participants in China have presently exceeded 5 million and taekwondo clubs of various sizes over 3000.4 However, generally speaking, the popularization of taekwondo in China is still not well developed and there are a number of problems to be solved.

3 SWOT ANALYSIS OF THE ENVIRONMENT FOR DEVELOPMENT OF CHINESE TAEKWONDO

3.1 Advantages of Chinese taekwondo in terms of the development environment

Up to now, the taekwondo event has 202 member states included in the World Taekwondo Federation, becoming the eighth major international sports federation event and being formally accepted as a competition event in the Olympic Games of 2000. Now, it has evolved into a world sport involving huge numbers of participants. And in China, Chinese Taekwondo Association has taken the initiative and set up various management bodies and organizes competitions and events of various forms, forming a management system of a certain kind and attracting huge numbers of taekwondo lovers. In addition, due to the harmonious integration of taekwondo as an oriental Korean martial art with traditional Chinese culture, its rich philosophic thinking, unique spiritual value and exercise value as well as a unified, definite and regulated level management system, taekwondo enjoys remarkable advantages as a good physical exercise in its popularization.

3.2 Disadvantages of Chinese taekwondo in terms of the development environment

The deviation of the Chinese government and sports management department, etc. in the understanding of the substantive characteristics of taekwondo has led to its imbalanced development in China and other problems in the popularization of Chinese taekwondo include: low level of the taekwondo association in its scientific and systematic organization and management and inefficiency, small scale, inadequate cultivation of taekwondo talents of various kinds, low level of education, theoretical and scientific studies relating to taekwondo and development of information channels such as various types of modern techniques, publicity media and internet.

3.3 Opportunities of Chinese taekwondo in terms of the development environment

At the current stage, the sports policy of China has placed its emphasis on popular sports and national fitness and the country and government pay much attention to the people's livelihood and the health of the body and soul. With the rapid social and economic development of China, the people have more and more realized that they should achieve mental health through leisure sports, rich spare-time life and social welfare development.

Shift of the people in the modern world to healthy mental and physical entertainment and emphasis has promoted the change in their understanding of the value of the most representative Japanese sport and the fitness effect of life sports, which provides a great environment opportunity for the popularization of taekwondo in china.

3.4 Threats of Chinese taekwondo in terms of the development environment

Presently China still has its emphasis placed on the pursuit of gold medals due to the national sports system which values competitive sports and neglects rational thinking on popular taekwondo resulting in insufficient understanding of the nature, connotation and value of taekwondo, especially in respect of the popularization of sport taekwondo. In addition, the imbalanced development of regions, culture and economy, development difference between various regions, provinces and cities, difference in local customs and practices between nationalities and regions as China is a country with a large population and a number of nationalities, especially the fiercely competition for market share proportion among various national sports, civilian sports and folk sports, have become a thread for further popularization of taekwondo in China.

4 STRATEGY FOR THE POPULARIZATION OF CHINESE TAEKWONDO

Based on analysis of the environment for the development of Chinese taekwondo using the SWOT method, the following strategic guidelines for popularization of Chinese taekwondo is proposed: according to national policies and trend of social economy and people's demand, give play to the nature characteristics and advantages of the taekwondo event, strengthen organizational management standard, enhance the understanding of taekwondo of various groups of people, conduct propaganda and promotion activities of various forms, carry out promotion of taekwondo extensively to give an impetus to further popularization of taekwondo. Specific strategies include.

4.1 The country and government should further transform thoughts and emphasize the popularization of taekwondo

The country, government and management authorities should further change their understanding of the taekwondo event, realizing that the focus for the development of taekwondo is not on the development of competitive sports but on popular sports and that development of popular taekwondo will drive the development of competitive taekwondo. Taekwondo will have a development basis only when the taekwondo event is effectively carried out and popularized in popular sports, thus meeting the demand of people in the modern world for healthy life sports while promoting the standard of competitive taekwondo. More manpower, materials and financial resources should be invested in taekwondo so that various tasks can be implemented more effectively to promote the sound development of taekwondo.

4.2 Strengthening and improvement of functions of organization and management bodies such as Chinese Taekwondo Association

The Chinese Taekwondo Association should take the lead to strengthen the construction and management of various local associations, special societies, dojo, clubs and organizations. Relevant bodies shall be established at various provinces, cities and regions to manage and promote taekwondo. And relevant associations and organizations should be established in various industries and units in various forms so as to form a systematic organizational network to promote taekwondo in the country. Duties of departments at various levels and management systems should be improved to regularize the approval, setup, standards of associations and dojo at various levels, form various levels of systems related to trainers, instructors and referees, enhance the quality of personnel involved in the industry to form a good development order for organizations such as associations and dojo and to regularize and promote the taekwondo competition system to organize amateur and popular taekwondo competitions of various kinds.

4.3 Intensifying the cultivation of taekwondo talents

Supported mainly by government investment, cultivation of relevant special talents should be strengthened including trainers, referees, instructors and social sport instructors. Trainers and instructors should be further trained regarding theoretical knowledge such as taekwondo connotation and value awareness so as to enhance their understanding of the nature of the taekwondo event and master taekwondo knowledge in a better manner, providing a correct and scientific theoretical basis for the application of more effective teaching and training methods. The taekwondo subject and research institutes should be established at national institutions of higher learning with relevant public, specialized and selective courses and subjects related to taekwondo established to

cultivate special taekwondo talents and guarantee the supply of human resources for the popularization of taekwondo.

4.4 Strengthening the development of theories and scientific research related to taekwondo

The Chinese Taekwondo Association should take the lead to establish special organizations and departments for theoretical research of taekwondo; sort out theories related to the nature, significance and value of taekwondo in a scientific manner; organize training classes for referees, trainers and instructors in a regular and irregular manner to improve their theoretical level with regard to taekwondo; carry out theoretical sorting and scientific research regarding the value of taekwondo as a modern life sport to find a way suitable to the characteristics of Chinese people and the development environment of China; establish special organizations related to taekwondo such as relevant academic societies and establish theory communication platforms such as society logs, various periodicals and magazines; stimulate the initiative of special personnel involved in the taekwondo event and taekwondo lovers in taekwondo theoretical research.

4.5 Intensifying publicity to increase the number of people teaching and learning taekwondo

Publicity should be intensified through media, newspapers, magazines and the internet to make more people know about taekwondo, understand taekwondo and promote taekwondo so that the audiences of the taekwondo event as a good modern life sport can be increased to enable people to experience the value of the martial art in routine life. Teaching should be made for taekwondo trainers, learners and taekwondo lovers in respect of techniques, body and soul, thoughts, etc. with teaching contents covering theories, basic movements, leg techniques, patterns, pair work, demonstration and defense techniques. The teaching plan should increase the proportion of taekwondo spirit. Education and publicity should be made to strengthen the correct understanding of taekwondo so as to provide theoretical development conditions and environment to increase taekwondo participants and enhance competitive level.

4.6 Further popularizing and promoting taekwondo effectively

Various levels of social dojo should promote the special quality of the managerial staff and instructors while perfecting facilities and education plans, updating education contents, improving education methods to form education plans suitable for different groups of people and should attract more participants through advanced conditions, effective education plans and positive publicity methods. Popularization efforts should be intensified in groups such as enterprises and major communities to strengthen their understanding of the taekwondo connotation and value, attracting more people to take part in the taekwondo event. In addition, taekwondo should be promoted and popularized as a life sport in primary and middle schools and colleges and universities. Special cultivation of taekwondo teachers and trainers should be intensified to enable them to teach correct taekwondo knowledge. Taekwondo teaching and evaluation system should be improved and taekwondo should be properly applied to various kinds of entrance exams and physical education specialty exams so as to promote it as a school sport.

5 CONCLUSION

During the fast development of Chinese taekwondo in a short time, competitive taekwondo has made remarkable achievements but life sport taekwondo has encountered a number of problems in its popularization such as insufficient understanding of taekwondo, poor promotion result and imbalanced development. Taekwondo as an important part of the Korean fad is being developed in combination with traditional Chinese culture and people are gradually accepting the value, thought, spirit and essence of taekwondo. In China, taekwondo as a life sport has huge potential for development and there are a number of issues that require follow-up attention and research such as how to make taekwondo more popular with the people and acquire more audience markets and how to optimize and boost the essence of taekwondo to make it a sport with Chinese characteristics.

REFERENCES

1. World Taekwondo Federation official website http://www.wtf.drg/.2013.
2. Wang Weiyue, Research on 20 years of Development of Taekwondo in China and its Future Direction of Development, South Korean Martial Art Society Logs, 2010, 12(1), 29–38.
3. Chinese Taekwondo Association official website http://www.chntkd.or.cn/.2013.

Computer, Intelligent Computing and Education Technology – Liu, Sung & Yao (Eds)
© 2014 Taylor & Francis Group, London, ISBN 978-1-138-02469-4

Key technology research of personalized virtual learning community

Yan-Fei Ren & Chuan-Wei Qi
Puyang Vocational and Technical College, Puyang, China

ABSTRACT: The construction of the key technologies of personalized virtual learning community is the use of virtual reality technology to build an immersive virtual learning platform situational digital; utilize portal technology to customize individual learning portals; utilize web crawler digging integrate online learning resources, and ultimately learn by personalized self-learning.

Keywords: personalized learning; virtual learning communities; web crawler; portal technology

1 INTRODUCTION

National long-term Education Reform and Development Plan (2010–2020) states: vigorously develop modern distance education, and other building to satellite television and the Internet as the carrier continues to open and distance education and public service platform to provide convenience for the learner, flexible personalized learning conditions to meet the individual needs of a variety of learning and development. Personalized virtual learning community for its autonomy, individuality, without the constraints of time and other characteristics, to provide learners with an easy-to-use, personalized learning platform to meet the learners' personalized learning, independent learning, immersive learning situations demand, thus greatly improving the learning efficiency of learners, promote the development of modern distance education.[1]

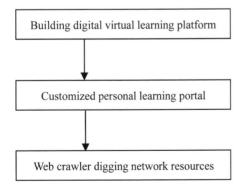

Figure 1. Build personalized virtual learning communities Technology Roadmap.

2 TECHNOLOGY ROADMAP OF PERSONALIZED VIRTUAL LEARNING COMMUNITY

First, the use of virtual reality technology to build an immersive virtual learning contexts digital platform, and then use the portal technology to customize individual learning portals, web crawler digging. Finally, the integration of online teaching resources needed to achieve personalized learning self-learning. Build personalized virtual learning community technology roadmap shown in Figure 1.

3 KEY TECHNOLOGY OF PERSONALIZED VIRTUAL LEARNING COMMUNITY

3.1 *The use of virtual reality technology to build immersive virtual learning contexts digital platforms*

In order to increase interest in learning and immersion learners, introducing network game developers to construct the diversity of situations, role playing, realistic and teamwork and other ideas, integrated use of Web 2.0, Web3D and Web GIS technology, based on virtual reality technology to build immersive virtual learning contexts digital platforms. Learners in immersive virtual learning contexts digital platforms, not only can learn individually, you can also team up to play relevant roles by way of immersive, be independent, personalized, diversified and efficient learning. The digital virtual learning platform of "learner-centered as the main body, for all learners service" construct. Learners use the digital virtual learning platform, combined with their own situation, the use of virtual reality technology with interactive, immersive, simulation and other features, according to their own interests and hobbies, learning content discretion, change from passive learning to active learning; improve teamwork capacity, improve emotional loss and loneliness caused by separation because of time and space. Immersive virtual learning platform situational figures provide learners with a smooth interactive platform, creating a personalized learning, personalized learning environment, greatly mobilized the learner initiative, enthusiasm, greatly improving the learning efficiency and quality.

3.2 Use of portal technology, customized personal learning portal to meet the individual needs of diverse learners

Portal technology for different user content aggregation, customizable user interface, personalized learning. Learners through a unified identity authentication login after a virtual learning community, learning content can be selected according to their needs and customize learning and progress, change only accept the monotony of learning content in the passive situation, improve the autonomy and motivation to learn. Personalized information platform virtual learning community, through the Path of learners can determine learner preferences and formulate recommended learning path to help learners to content aggregation based on study habits, differences in the level of knowledge and different learning styles, and create their own user interface, accurate positioning of content of interest to learn learner, self-determined learning progress and improve the service levels of personalized learning.[2]

The use of virtual learning community portal technology has the following advantages:

1. Autonomy

Autonomy refers to learners from passive learning to active learning. Learners according to their interests, learning styles and even learning objective is to actively select learning content, learning partners, teachers, teaching resources, learning, evaluation methods. Personalized Virtual Learning Community support learners according to their own ideas ideas custom assembled personal portal to add learning resources they need, the team members to their community portal being, and can be adjusted at any time on demand, dynamically updated.[3]

2. Personalized

Personalization is reflected in their learning characteristics of learners. Registered members after learners can enter into a customized and personalized learning portal, select the desired combination of their actual curriculum, customized relevant learning resources to achieve one's

individualized education. Personalized include: learning time and place of personalized; learning content and schedule personalized; learning personalized and individualized learning assessment methods. Personalized virtual learning, the learner is the real owner of the personal learning portal, it can be self-management, you can get a great sense of belonging and identity, improve the learning initiative and enthusiasm.

3. Accuracy

Because learning resources are customized according to user needs, precise practicality resources has been a reliable guarantee to improve the learning efficiency. As the master learners learning path, the portal can be based on the interests of learners hobbies, learning resources, learners can push the required precision to ensure the dynamic update of resources.

3.3 The use of customized web crawler digging optimize network resources for education

Online education resource library is a necessary foundation for learners online learning, otherwise it would become "bricks without straw", so to develop a content-rich, convenient and practical and safe use of online education resource library;[4] We must also realize, again abundant local resources, it is also limited, so be sure to take advantage of the rich network resources, such as: Baidu Encyclopedia, Wikipedia, professional forums, national excellent course websites. However, it is precisely because of too rich network resources, learners but feel no choice, dazed confusion, which is on the need for massive screening network resources, integration, optimization and customized to achieve the target learners use. Then we must develop a customized Web crawler to digging, optimization, integration and customization of network resources. Web crawler design principles are as follows:

1. Basic concept

Web crawler is an automated program to collect information on the Internet. Not only for the search engine crawlers collect network information through the network, and can be used as directional information collection, directional collect specific information about some website. The system is mainly collected Baidu Encyclopedia, Wikipedia, professional forums, websites and other related national fine lesson about computer technology.

2. Works

Select seed URL to be crawled into the URL queue, and then get the host for DNS resolution IP, based on the URL to download the corresponding page and in the database, the last of these URL into the URL queue crawled its storage.

3. Customization

Customized web crawler is to make good rule in accordance with pre-customized strategies purposefully active grab the necessary resources. Specific, you can use qualified domain name, IP strategy and defining the rules defining keywords and other forms. The system of domain names and IP will be mainly limited to the Baidu Encyclopedia, Wikipedia, professional forums, such as the National Quality Course Web sites, mainly limited to the words "computer" aspect.

4. Information storage

After digging a custom resource web crawler digging cleaning convert stored in the local database for learners.

4 CONCLUSION

The personalized virtual learning communities can be used as a public service platform of modern distance education, the project successfully resolved at this stage due to the use of distance education in the backward mode of teaching can not effectively exist, such as personalized learning, independent learning a lot of problems to be solved issues through the implementation of the project, can greatly improve the efficiency and quality of distance education level, can bring significant economic and social benefits, thus promoting sustainability leapfrog development of modern distance education, while the construction of universal learning, lifelong learning learning society also has some positive significance.

REFERENCES

[1] Ren Yanfei applied research. Based 3D virtual campus on VRML [J]. Computer CD-ROM software and applications, 2013,4.

[2] QI Chuan Wei, Ren Yanfei based design and research of virtual reality technology distance education platform [J]. Puyang Vocational and Technical College, 2013,2.

[3] Zhang Ying. Web3.0: personalized learning new platform [J] Chinese education technology and equipment, 2012,27.

[4] Liao Weiwei Professional Design and Application of Virtual Community [J] learning. Chinese distance education, 2012,12.

Computer, Intelligent Computing and Education Technology – Liu, Sung & Yao (Eds)
© *2014 Taylor & Francis Group, London, ISBN 978-1-138-02469-4*

Development of standard connector library system based on UG software

Xuan-Jun Dai
Guangxi Scientific Experiment Center of Mining, Metallurgy and Environment, Guilin, China
College of Mechanical and Control Engineering, Guilin University of Technology, Guilin, China

Xiao-Yong Chen
College of Mechanical and Electrical Engineering, Guilin University of Electronic Technology, Guilin, China

ABSTRACT: The standard connector library system has vital significance to the fast manufacturing of e-machine equipment model. This paper aims at the problems of standard connector model which is vital to routing. First the characteristics of connector library and the current methods are analyzed. Then some key technologies of establishing standard connector library are studied. Finally based on UG secondary development and interface technology, parametric 3D connectors' library was developed. This standard connector library has improved the design efficiency greatly by application.

Keywords: secondary development; connectors library; 3D modeling; interface technology

1 INTRODUCTION

E-machine communications, as the main products, are now widely used in various communications. With the rapid development of science and technology, both in the field of civil and military field, the demand of electronic machine are increasingly growing. Computer aided design technology can be used to quickly and accurately complete the three-dimensional design of digital electronic machine.[1] While large quantity connectors with shape complexity are used in electronic machine, so a standard connector library of three-dimensional model should be created to reduce the machine design time, which is a great significance for the design, manufacture and assembly.

This paper studied the integration of Visual C + +6.0 development environment, by the UG secondary development to establish standard connector library. Firstly the technology of UG interface combined with the MFC and parametric modeling technology is discussed. Then based on ADO (Active Date Object) and UG/OPEN API technology a parameterized three-dimensional library is established. The method is a highly reusable code that can effectively improve the design efficiency of connector modeling and routing.

2 MODELING METHOD OF STANDARD CONNECTOR LIBRARY

The standard connector modeling has vital significance to the fast manufacturing of three-dimensional electronic machine. There are two main methods of modelling:[2] One is the static model, namely the approach of library establishment is to establish solid CAD model respectively, then a fully three-dimensional model of the standard connector is obtained which contains a number of three-ding a database workload, share a large space, and it is not parameterized in the form, not carrying the ways by changing the parameters to change the three-dimensional model of standard parts. Therefore, it is difficult to maintain and extend the standard library; another is the dynamic programming model, that is, parametric feature-based three-dimensional modeling approach. By this way, all standard parts library of standard parts has its own characteristics and parameter control. This method has strong point of small space consume, easy to add or delete and modify. The key technology of this method is the standard connector parameters feature analysis and database access.

UG software commonly used in building a database of standard parts library methods, such as expression method, User Defined Features (UDF) method, spreadsheet method and programming method. All these methods have the feature of the establishment of a three-dimensional model of standard parts manually or procedurally, and then using different methods to modify the parameters to meet the requirements. The expression method has the characteristic of easily creating and conveniently modifying, but users need to find standard parts manually to modify the parameters, which are inefficient and complex. The user-defined feature method, which can create links between features, is easier to define feature of the variable. It can set the default values, prompt for a key value, restore and edit the value easily. Each call requires a new part to enter the user defined features, with the feature of low degree of automation. Spreadsheet method provides a three-dimensional physical format defined by UG standard parts library system, which is created an intuitive easily, and transferred through an intuitive graphical interface assembly. Standard parts have a sub-assembly capability, and can be encapsulated in UG software, and that is the general method of establishing standard parts library. However, it need to detailed classification of parts. Management and using of this library are cumbersome and not intuitive. Higher level of secondary development application is applied to establish a standard parts library with easy, simple, user interface, but it has the feature of programming workload, complexity of implementation technology.

In this paper, the way of data-driven template part is used to generate a new three-dimensional model of the standard connector. Firstly the connector template part has been established, which include the standard connector geometry and non-geometric information, and is stored in the parameter database. Then the standard connectors library was designed combined the Visual C + +6.0 MFC with the user interface of UG/OPEN API. Generally, the user can get standard connector modeling directly by using the driver parameters on UG platform.

3 KEY TECHNOLOGIES OF DEVELOPMENT

3.1 Interface technology

Three kinds of engineering application wizard provided in the Visual C + + 6.0 environment, Only the DLL file generated by UG/Open AppWizard can be directly called by UG.[3] However, UG/Open AppWizard does not support MFC, which can not directly call the MFC application to achieve communication with the MFC. Especially, the database can not connect with the MFC application. Therefore, we must resolve the interface problems. Figure 1 showed the interface realization

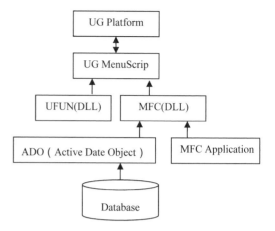

Figure 1.   Interface realization technology.

technology on the UG platform by Secondary development toolkit.

UG/Open AppWizard can not only be as Dynamic-Link Library (DLL) to achieve UG graphical interface within the system and internal communication, but also through the Dynamic Link Library (DLL) implementation of the way fast, a way through the embedded DLL to achieve communication between UG and the MFC are proposed. Figure 1 shows the interface program.[4] The first step is to create an MFC AppWizard (DLL) project, then set the engineering environment, and join the UG/Open API entry function. So the aim of communication database would be achieved, and the program could be generated by MFC.

3.2 Development of standard connector library

The main features of the connector library are: 1) Connector types have many kinds which could be divided into round, rectangular and special types. The same type of connector has similar shapes, but the number of ports is different, all we need is to change the parameters to generate the model. 2) Connector model serves mainly as a whole wiring assistance, which could simplify the independent of the characteristics, and the related need for accurate feature set, such as port properties location and multi-port properties. 3) Connector is usually used in pairs with the mother and child piece parts, the two are connected by tight fit, some features are related.

Application of relational expression method, user defined features methods and spreadsheet method would be difficult to complete the connector library building, while it can be achieved by programming method. Development process is as follows: First, classifying the connectors by their shape features. Then, according to the special shape of model and needs for wiring, simplifying the models. The simplified model is decomposed into a primary and secondary characteristic and to extract the small size of the main parameters determine the model. UG secondary development language development using three-dimensional model to establish procedures for all of its features to be used for parametric modeling and can be changed according to the number of multi-port port location. Finally, the MFC was developed to interface the same time. According to standard parts of the main parameters, the main parameters of standard parts should be found out, and transfer interface between the main parameter database and application would be established. Finally, system menu and dialog boxes were created. Figure 2 shows the system menu of tools for developers to achieve seamless MFC connection with UG software.

3.3 Database access

By using feature modeling technology and topology constraints, three-dimensional parametric standard connector library was established. The goal of database design is to provide a highly efficient operating environment for the users' applications for. Database system and its interface formed the parameter library that enables the connector to store and access main parameters, and assign the appropriate connector model parameters. Connector model structure is complicated and has many feature parameters. Therefore, the main parameters of models should be determined; this method can effectively reduce the connector model parameters.

Standard connectors used entity relationship model is ER model. It is established, managed and maintained by Visual C + +6.0 development tools and MFC functions, and ADO access databases. Figure 3 shows the connector parameter database management systems interface. First obtain permission to connect to the connector parameter library to access and modify the main parameters, then other parameters corresponding will change with the main parameters. The connector modeling was updated accordingly with the parameters.

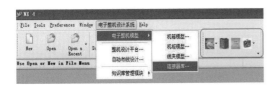

Figure 2. Interface system menu of tools for developers.

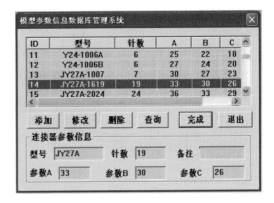

Figure 3. Database management interface.

4 SOFTWARE IMPLEMENTATION

Standard connector model include interface, database, and a variety of qualify part. Interface can be used to human-computer interact, database store a simplified model of the main features of the connector parameters, through a variety of database access interface, standard parts required for the current parameter value can output to the dialog box interface. Parameters in the dialog box that is assigned one by one the corresponding model generation program Variable. It can also be modified in the database information.

Figure 4 shows the standard connector main user interface library. The left side of the connector interface is the type of tree navigation. According to the characteristics of shape, connector type can be divided into rectangular connectors, circular connectors and special connectors. While the standard connector model is created, through the left navigation tree a standard connector will be selected, the right window will also show the standard connector type and the geometric parameters of the main information. By choosing the required connector, the system can display all the main parameters of the connector information automatically. All the main parameters of the connector information are stored in the database, and the remaining parameters are associated with the main parameters. According to the main parameter information the appropriate template file type connector can be called to generate connector model.

Figure 5 shows the connector model. Qualify part allows users to add routing specific intelligence to a part file. This intelligence dictates how the part is placed into a routing assembly, how it relates to other part in the routing assembly, and how it behaves during routing operations. In addition, it manages the electrical connectivity information as well as mechanical connectiv-

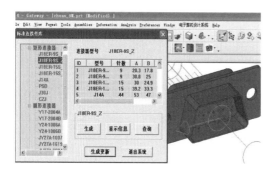

Figure 4. Connector library application program interface.

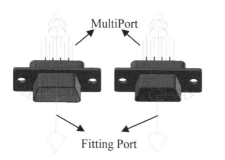

Figure 5. Qualify connectors.

ity information. Qualify connector provides the exclusive interface for creating routing specific objects in a part file that carry this intelligence. Port property generally includes multiport and fitting ports. Fitting ports are used for connecting devices and connectors. Multiport are used for port to port mating, if lock engagement is selected. Multiport are created to multiple logical connections using a single connection object. The multiport represents a collection of logical connections by maintaining a list of unique identifiers. So the process in the wiring system can accurately locate a specific multiport.

5 SUMMARY

Based on the interface technology of UG secondary development and the characteristics of the standard connector model, combined UG/Open API interface with the secondary development and MFC Application Wizard, realized the UG interface entry function problem, this paper achieve the secondary development of database applications with UG (MFC DLL development program) Integrated.

The standard connection established library system has intuitive interface, easy operation, functional. Users can easily and quickly generate the required connector model, greatly reducing the routing time before create the e-machine model, which is effectively improving the efficiency of electronic machine layout design.

ACKNOWLEDGMENTS

This research is sponsored by the Director Project Found of Guangxi Key Laboratory of Guangxi Scientific Experiment Center of Mining, Metallurgy and Environment (Grant No. KH2012ZD006).

REFERENCES

[1] Wu Zhaohua, Zhou Dejian and Wu Yinfen. Research of 3D routing system of electronic equipment[J]. Proceedings of the Electronic Packaging Technology Conference, EPTC. 2007.

[2] WAN Jiutuan, Huang Xiang. The Establishment of 3D Parameterized Standard Parts Library Based on UG[J]. Machinery Manufacturing and Automation. 2003,(1):82–84 (In Chinese).

[3] Zhenwei Dong, Lizhong Tian and Yili Fu. UG/OPEN API Program foundation[M]. Tsinghua University Press. 2002.

[4] Chen Xiaoyong, Zhou Dejian and Wu Zhaohua. The Research of Interface Technology Based on UG[J]. Machine Tool and Hydraulics. 2009, 37(7):196–198 (In Chinese).

Computer, Intelligent Computing and Education Technology – Liu, Sung & Yao (Eds)
© 2014 Taylor & Francis Group, London, ISBN 978-1-138-02469-4

A further study on semantics demonstrativeness' control on the transformation from "NPL + have (you) + Num-Classifier-Noun phrases" sentence pattern to "on (zai)" sentence pattern

Y. Xu & H. Xiao
College of Chinese Language and Literature, Wuhan University, Wuhan, Hubei, China

ABSTRACT: Because of the transformation of the situation of referential expression, the indefinite numeral "one (yi)" in "NPL + have (you) + ncp-np" sentence pattern should be shifted into definite article "the(na)" in "on (zai)" sentence pattern. Therefore, the strength and weakness of semantics demonstrativeness controls the transformation from "NPL + have (you) + Num-Classifier-Noun Phrases" sentence pattern to "on (zai)" sentence pattern.

Keywords: semantics; demonstrativeness; accessibility; NLP

1 INTRODUCTION

In recent years, some scholars have already noticed the significance of lexical-semantics in the study of grammar. Lu (2004) proposed that sentences or even the whole passage, to some extent, can be regarded as a conceptual network. First of all, people should pay attention to the analysis and understanding of the meaning of each word in the sentence if they want to analyze or understand a sentence or a whole passage. At the same time, Zhao (2008) proposed that semantics is the basis of syntax. Semantic meaning set the syntax pattern. The meaning of the words set the frame of semantic meaning expression (that means how many semantic roles comprised and what kind of semantic role can be matched). The frame of semantic meaning expression set its basic syntax pattern (that means some basic syntactic component co-occurrence, the basic organized model of syntactic component). According to the two viewpoints above, semantic meaning has the decisive effect on the understanding of the meaning of sentence and grammar. These two scholars have stated the effect of semantic meaning towards the grammar; this thesis will discuss on semantic demonstrativeness' control on the transformation from "NPL + have (you) +Num-Classifier-Noun Phrases" Sentence Pattern to "on (zai)" Sentence Pattern.

2 DEMONSTRATIVENESS AND ACCESSIBILITY

Referential expressions have a certain form and semantic feature, which have the syntax function.

The basic presupposition of the identification Principle is the corresponding relationship between accessibility and the language expression. For example, in the discourse, the shorter form reflects the higher accessibility ability (such as zero forms, pronouns, etc.). On the contrary, it has lower accessibility ability (such as noun, etc), the longer language form reflects a lower accessibility ability (Xu 2004). Chafe (1987) holds that people's memory states are the main cause to decide the distribution of referential expressions in the discourse. The basic assumption is that there is a certain corresponding relationship between memory state and language form. He divided the activation which showed human beings' mind state into three types: active, semi-active and inactive. Activation is the important factor of markup language expression; it decides the distribution of referential expression in the discourse. In Chafe's model, the activation has two different dimensions: the activation and the length of time. The longer the time, the lower the activation is. On the contrary, the activation will be higher.

Ariel has established the accessibility theory to explain the distribution of referential expressions. The basic understanding of the theory is that the selection of referential expressions and the accessibility of referential object in the memory have a corresponding relationship. Language expressions carry different degrees of accessibility. The degree of accessibility of referential expressions is decided by four factors: distance; the competition of referential expressions; salient and consistent. According to accessibility, Ariel (1988) categorized referential expressions and he thought that the choice of referential expressions relied on accessibility. The basic assumption on this theory was the amount of referential expression can carry demonstrativeness was the main cause of the choice of referential expressions. Shen Jiaxuan came up with the concept of lexical-semantics demonstrativeness and accessibility. Demonstrativeness means the speakers' referential expressions indicate the listeners searching information from their mind or surroundings to find the target object or the complexity of the events (Shen 2011). If the events have high demonstrativeness, they have got high referential degree and if the events have low demonstrativeness, they have got low referential degree. Accessibility means speakers suppose that after listeners hear a referential expression, they will search information from their mind or surroundings to find the target object or the complexity of the events. The referents which can be found easily have high accessibility, and which are difficult to be found have low accessibility. According to the views of Shen, if the lexical-semantics have high demonstrativeness, the target object has got low accessibility and vise verse.

3 USING THE THEORY OF THE STRENGTH AND WEAKNESS OF SEMANTICS DEMO-NSTRATIVENESS TO EXPLAIN THE TRANSFORMATION FROM "NPL + HAVE (YOU) + NCP-NP" SENTENCE PATTERN TO "ON (ZAI)" SENTENCE PATTERN

"Have" (you) sentence is one of the special sentence patterns in modern Chinese. This kind of construction is a typical existential sentence in Chinese which is frequently used. "Have" (you) sentence are listed in the low level grammar in the universally used Chinese textbook. However, the error rates are still very high in the actual learning. According to the statistics from *Beijing Language and Culture University HSK composition corpus*, the accuracy is low in Chinese grammar, and the error rate for the South Korean students is particularly high. Because there is no difference between the meaning of "have" (you) and "in" (zai). The students are affected by negative transfer of their mother tongue and the grammar generalization of the target language. For example,

1. 교사의? Is the teacher in here?
2. 교사는 어떻게? Is there a teacher here?

Both of the two sentences mean: "is the teacher here or not". The example (2) "Is there a teacher here" is a kind of existential construction, but it doesn't make any sense in Chinese because "have"

(you) here is a subordinative meaning but not the existential meaning. However, there is no difference between "have" and "in" in Korean, both of the two expressions can be used. Therefore, when learned Chinese as a foreign language, South Korean students often make mistakes between the use of "have" and "in". For example:

3. There is a bottle of water on the table.
4. There is a basin on the ground.
5. *That bottle of water is on the table.
6. *That basin is on the ground.
7. That bottle of water is on the table.
8. That basin is on the ground.
9. *A bottle of water is on the table.
10. *A basin is on the ground.

The sentences with the symbol* are not often used in Chinese, we can explain that sentence (3), (4) and (7) and (8) are right through the old and new theory: generally speaking, the new information appears in the end and the known information appears at the beginning of the sentence. That sentence (5), (6) and (9), (10) are not right is because that the known information will not appear at the end of the sentence and the new information will not appear at the beginning of the sentence. The numeral word of "a" in the sentence "A bottle of water" is uncertain, it's the new information. However, the demonstrative pronoun of "that" in the sentence "that bottle of water" is certain, it's the old information.

Generally speaking, the new information and the old information are different from people to people. Students didn't pay much attention to it and they can't grasp the difference between them. Under such kind of circumstances, how should we explain it? Shen Jiaxuan's theory of lexical-semantics demonstrativeness can explain it. Generally speaking, whether the demonstrativeness is high or low is decided by the objective state of referential expressions. For example, the demonstrativeness in a sentence with an indicator is higher than the sentence without an indicator, the demonstrativeness of personal pronoun is higher than the demonstrativeness of general nouns. Sentences with more determiners have higher demonstrativeness than sentences without many determiners. The stressed sentences have higher demonstrativeness than non-stressed sentences.

So what's the function of "there" (na)? It is to improve the demonstrativeness of the referential expression, that is to say, to improve the accessibility of the referent. The referents which can be found easily have high accessibility, and which are difficult to be found have low accessibility.

In example (3) "bottle of water" and in example (4) "a basin" both have low demonstrativeness. According to the assumption of the speaker, after the listener heard the referents of "a bottle of water" and "basin", they searched information in their memory or the surroundings; if the listener is not difficult to find the target object "water" and "basin" which are given the definite characteristics, the strength of the speaker's referential expression's demonstrativeness is low. So in example (3) and (4), to the speaker, It is obvious for the listener that "a bottle of water" and "a basin" have high accessibility, that's why he uses low demonstrativeness "a bottle of water" and "a basin".

Shi (2004) thought that typical quantitative phrases have no fixed semantic characteristics and they should not be put at the beginning of the sentences at will. Go in seriously, it is that quantitative phrases have low demonstrativeness. So example (9) and (10) can also be explained by semantic demonstrativeness and accessibility: to the speaker, "a bottle of water" and "a basin" are explicit, unfixed, with low accessibility, so he uses low demonstrativeness "a bottle of water" and "a basin", but these expressions make people confused and can't appear at the beginning of a sentence at will, it is also hardly use in our oral expressions.

However, In example (7) and (8), "that bottle of water" and "that basin", according to the assumption of the speaker, after the listener heard the referential expressions, they searched from their memories and surroundings, it is hard to find the target object "water" and "basin", so they add fixed words "that" to make them fixed and have high demonstrativeness. Therefore, in example (7) and (8), the speaker thought that objects are implicit to the listener and have low accessibility, so he uses high accessibility referential "that"; but in example (5) and (6), to the speaker, the objects are explicit and have high accessibility, so they should not be "that bottle of water" or "that basin". Such kinds of sentences are rare in Chinese.

4 IN SPECIAL CONTEXT, THE STRENGTH AND WEAKNESS OF SEMANTICS DEMONSTRATIVENESS TO EXPLAIN THE TRANSFORMATION FROM "NPL + HAVE (YOU) + NCP-NP" SENTENCE PATTERN TO "ON (ZAI)" SENTENCE PATTERN

If we add particular context to example (5), (6), (7), (8), it seems that they can still be understood, for example:

5. *That bottle is on the table. → I drank this bottle of water, that bottle of water is on the table.
6. *That basin is on the ground. → I used this basin, that basin is on the ground.

9. *A bottle of water is on the table. → A bottle of water was on the ground; a bottle of water is on the table.
10. *A basin is on the ground. → A basin is on the frame, a basin is on the ground.

How to explain this kind of phenomenon? In example (11) and (12), to the speaker, he thought that "that bottle of water" and "that basin" are implicit to the listener, they have low accessibility, so he added particular context, " I drank this bottle of water" and "I used this basin". "this" and "that" appeared together to improve the accessibility of "that bottle of water" and "that basin", so it is appropriate to use "that bottle of water" and "that basin" in this context. In example (13) and (14), to the speaker, "a bottle of water" and "a basin" are implicit to the listener and have low accessibility, so he added particular context and use comparison "a bottle of water is on the ground" and "a basin is on the frame" to make "a bottle of water" and "a basin" have high accessibility, so example (13) and (14) are appropriate in this context.

15. That tobacco pouch is on the table. Conan Doyle, *the return of Sherlock Holmes*, Black Peter
16. However, they in here, one was dead and the other has been abroad. Liu Zhanqiu, *A Fashion for the Men of Letters to Auct the Privacy, Different Views on the Phenomenon of LIU Zhanqiu, by Zhao Guoming.*

Example (15) and (16) are found in CCL corpus in Beijing University, example (15) is the only sentence which match "NPL + have (you) + nip-up" sentence pattern. This sentence pattern appeared in the conversation between Holmes and Hopkins. "Tobacco pouch" has low accessibility and demonstrativeness, so the author used referential expression "that (na)" to improve the demonstrativeness of the referential object, so "that Tobacco pouch" became the common knowledge of the two persons. To the speaker Hopkins, "that Tobacco pouch" had high demonstrativeness, that's because to the listener Holmes "tobacco pouch" had low accessibility; therefore, demonstrative pronoun "that (na)" was appropriate to be used here. Example (16) has similar sentence pattern to example (13), just example (16) omitted noun "person (ren)"; "one (yi)" here meant one of "them (ta men)", so the accessibility can be relatively high, in this sentence, two "one (yi)" were also appropriate to be used here. If we use new-old information theory to explain example (15) and (16), it is contradictory. It seemed that we can use lexical-semantic theory to explain the phenomenon.

Shen (2011) said that distinguishing accessibility and demonstrativeness is to differentiate the speaker and listener: accessibility relates to the listener and demonstrativeness relates to the speaker; accessibility is in terms of alleged target and demonstrativeness is in terms of referential expression. This also pointed out on the other way there is little grammar when it is separated from semantics and pragmatics.

5 CONCLUSION

Referential expression "that (na)" is just like a hand to improve demonstrativeness, so the referential lexical meaning of "that(na)" improve the lexical demonstrativeness. In the process of NPL + have (you) + nip-up sentences transform to "on (zai)" sentences, for the place of the referential expression changes, so the indefinite quantifier "one (yi)" has to change to "that (na)" and the sentence change into "na +quantifier +noun+on + NPL" pattern, it can finally transformed successfully. In special context, referential things are the common knowledge of both speaker and listener, which have high demonstrativeness, we can also use "NPL + have (you) +Num-Classifier-Noun Phrases" Sentence

Pattern; though the things are not specific references but only referred together and has high accessibility, we also use "Yi+ quantifier + on + NPL" sentence pattern.

REFERENCES

Ariel, M. 1988. Referring and accessibility [J]. Journal of Linguistics, (24): 65–87.

Chafe, W. 1987. Cognitive Constraints on Information Flow [A]. In R. Tomlin (ed.). Coherence and Grounding in Discourse [C]. Amsterdam: JohnBenjamins.

Lu, J.M. 2004. The influences of the concrete meaning of words towards the understanding of sentences [J], Journal of Chinese Learning, (2).

Shen, J.X. 2011. The Six lectures of Grammar [M] Beijing: The commercial press, December:57.

Xu, Y.l. 2004. The Pragmatic Study of the Function of Discourse Anaphora [M], Shanghai: Shanghai foreign Language Teaching Press:248.

Zhao, SH.J. 2008. The decisive function of lexical-semantics to grammar [J], Journal of Wuhan University, (2).

Computer, Intelligent Computing and Education Technology – Liu, Sung & Yao (Eds)
© 2014 Taylor & Francis Group, London, ISBN 978-1-138-02469-4

Sensitivity analysis on transient responses of coupled transmission lines in the time domain

X.-K. Chen & Y.J. Zhao
Electric Power Research Institute of Guangdong Power Grid Corporation, Guangzhou, China

J.-Q. Zhao & N.J. Fan
School of Electrical Engineering, Xi'an Jiao Tong University, Xi'an, China

X.X. Guo
Jiangsu Electric Power Company Research Institute, Jiangsu, China

ABSTRACT: A new method based on the precise integration is presented in this paper, which is used to analyze the sensitivity of the transient responses of the coupled transmission lines. In this method, the telegrapher's equations of coupled transmission lines in the time domain are firstly differenced and discretized in spatial domain, and then the first-order differential equations of the sensitivity of transient responses of the transmission lines with respect to time are established. By this method, the sensitivity analysis on the transient responses of the coupled transmission lines is transformed into solving the transient responses of transmission lines and the first-order differential equations. This method can be applied to analyze the uniform and non-uniform transmission lines and the arbitrary loads. Example given shows the validity and consistency of the suggested method.

Keywords: coupled transmission lines; sensitivity analysis; transient responses

1 INTRODUCTION

With the rapid increase of the signal frequency and the decrease of the size, the analysis and design of the interconnections become more important in the high-speed Very Large Scale Integration (VLSI) chip and the printed circuit boards. Improper design could result in signal delay, reflection, crosstalk and false switching,[1] etc., seriously the circuit cannot work. Therefore, the transmission line effects have become a bottleneck in the development of high-speed VLSI and it is necessary to find the key factors that influence transmission line effects and provide the basis for the design of VLSI.

The sensitivity analysis on transient responses of transmission lines has two methods, the time-domain method and the frequency-domain method. The frequency-domain method include the numerical inversion of Laplace transform[1–3] and the adjoint network,[4,5] etc, which is often used but complex to compute and difficult to analyze the nonlinear load problem. The time-domain method is of simplicity, but the stability and precision of the algorithm is hard to guarantee because of the effects of the time step and space step.

In this paper, the method based on precise integration of sensitivity analysis on transient responses of the coupled transmission lines in the time-domain is presented, in which the telegrapher's equations of the coupled transmission lines in time domain is differenced and discretized in spatial domain, then the first-order constant coefficient differential equations about the sensitivity of the transmission lines transient responses with respect to time is established. Through this method, the sensitivity analysis on transient responses of the coupled transmission lines is transformed into solving the first-order differential equations and the transient responses of transmission lines. This method is stable and simple, can analyze any types of uniform and non-uniform transmission lines and loads. The examples as given below illustrate the reliability and validity of the method presented in this paper.

2 SENSITIVITY OF THE TRANSIENT RESPONSES OF COUPLED TRANSMISSION LINES

Under the TEM wave approximation, the voltage and current of multi-conductor transmission lines satisfy the telegrapher's equations.

$$-\frac{\partial \mathbf{v}(x,t)}{\partial x} = \mathbf{R}\mathbf{i}(x,t) + \mathbf{L}\frac{\partial \mathbf{i}(x,t)}{\partial t}$$
$$-\frac{\partial \mathbf{i}(x,t)}{\partial x} = \mathbf{G}\mathbf{v}(x,t) + \mathbf{C}\frac{\partial \mathbf{v}(x,t)}{\partial t} \qquad 0 \le x \le 1 \tag{1}$$

where l is the length of the transmission lines, and

$$\mathbf{v}(x,t) = \left[v_1(x,t), v_2(x,t), \ldots, v_N(x,t) \right]^T$$
$$\mathbf{i}(x,t) = \left[i_1(x,t), i_2(x,t), \ldots, i_N(x,t) \right]^T$$

are the voltage and the current matrix of the transmission lines respectively. N is the number of multi-conductor transmission lines.

$$\mathbf{R} = \begin{bmatrix} R_{11} & R_{12} & \cdots & R_{1N} \\ R_{21} & R_{22} & \cdots & R_{2N} \\ \vdots & \vdots & \ddots & \vdots \\ R_{N1} & R_{N2} & \cdots & R_{NN} \end{bmatrix},$$

$$\mathbf{L} = \begin{bmatrix} L_{11} & L_{12} & \cdots & L_{1N} \\ L_{21} & L_{22} & \cdots & L_{2N} \\ \vdots & \vdots & \ddots & \vdots \\ L_{N1} & L_{N2} & \cdots & L_{NN} \end{bmatrix},$$

$$\mathbf{G} = \begin{bmatrix} G_{11} & G_{12} & \cdots & G_{1N} \\ G_{21} & G_{22} & \cdots & G_{2N} \\ \vdots & \vdots & \ddots & \vdots \\ G_{N1} & G_{N2} & \cdots & G_{NN} \end{bmatrix},$$

$$\mathbf{C} = \begin{bmatrix} C_{11} & C_{12} & \cdots & C_{1N} \\ C_{21} & C_{22} & \cdots & C_{2N} \\ \vdots & \vdots & \ddots & \vdots \\ C_{N1} & C_{N2} & \cdots & C_{NN} \end{bmatrix}$$

are the transmission lines' resistance, inductance, conductance and capacitance respectively per unit length.

Making the transmission lines divided into M equal segments and equation (2) differenced and discredited in spatial domain

$$\frac{dv_k(t)}{dt} = \mathbf{C}^{-1}\frac{i_k(t) - i_{k+1}(t)}{\Delta x} - \mathbf{C}^{-1}\mathbf{G}v_k(t)$$
$$\frac{di_{k+1}(t)}{dt} = \mathbf{L}^{-1}\frac{v_k(t) - v_{k+1}(t)}{\Delta x} - \mathbf{L}^{-1}\mathbf{R}i_{k+1}(t) \tag{2}$$

where $\Delta x = l/M$, $v_k(t) = v_k(k\Delta x, t)$, $i_k(t) = i_k(k\Delta x, t)$, $k = 0, 1, \ldots, M$.

Equation (2) can be written as

$$\frac{d\mathbf{X}}{dt} = \mathbf{H}\mathbf{X} + \mathbf{F} \tag{3}$$

in which

$$\mathbf{X} = \left(v_0\ v_1\ \cdots\ v_{M-1}\ i_1\ i_2\ \cdots\ i_M \right)^T$$
$$\mathbf{F} = \left(\mathbf{C}^{-1}\frac{i_0}{\Delta x}\ \cdots\ 0\ 0\ 0\ 0\ \cdots\ -\mathbf{L}^{-1}\frac{v_M}{\Delta x} \right)^T$$

$$\mathbf{H} = \begin{bmatrix} -\mathbf{C}^{-1}\mathbf{G} & & 0 & & \mathbf{C}^{-1}\frac{1}{\Delta x} & -\mathbf{C}^{-1}\frac{1}{\Delta x} & & 0 \\ & \ddots & & & & & \ddots & \\ & & \ddots & & & & & -\mathbf{C}^{-1}\frac{1}{\Delta x} \\ 0 & & -\mathbf{C}^{-1}\mathbf{G} & 0 & & & & \mathbf{C}^{-1}\frac{1}{\Delta x} \\ -\mathbf{L}^{-1}\frac{1}{\Delta x} & & 0 & -\mathbf{L}^{-1}\mathbf{R} & & & & 0 \\ \mathbf{L}^{-1}\frac{1}{\Delta x} & \ddots & & & \ddots & & & \\ & \ddots & \ddots & & & \ddots & & \\ 0 & \mathbf{L}^{-1}\frac{1}{\Delta x} & -\mathbf{L}^{-1}\frac{1}{\Delta x} & 0 & & & & -\mathbf{L}^{-1}\mathbf{R} \end{bmatrix}$$

Let p be the transmission lines parameters or the terminal load parameters and the partial differentiation of (3) with respect to p yields

$$\frac{\partial^2 \mathbf{X}}{\partial t \partial p} = \frac{\partial \mathbf{H}}{\partial p}\mathbf{X} + \mathbf{H}\frac{\partial \mathbf{X}}{\partial p} + \frac{\partial \mathbf{F}}{\partial p} \tag{4}$$

Let $\mathbf{X}_p = \partial \mathbf{X}/\partial p$, (4) becomes

$$\frac{\partial \mathbf{X}_p}{\partial t} = \mathbf{H}\mathbf{X}_p + \frac{\partial \mathbf{H}}{\partial p}\mathbf{X} + \frac{\partial \mathbf{F}}{\partial p} \tag{5}$$

The solution of equation (4) is

$$\mathbf{X}_p(t) = \exp(\mathbf{H}t)\int_{-\infty}^{t} \exp(-\mathbf{H}\zeta)\left[\frac{\partial \mathbf{H}}{\partial p}\mathbf{X}(\zeta) + \frac{\partial \mathbf{F}(\zeta)}{\partial p} \right]d\zeta$$
$$= \exp(\mathbf{H}t)\left\{ \int_{-\infty}^{0} \exp(-\mathbf{H}\zeta)\left[\frac{\partial \mathbf{H}}{\partial p}\mathbf{X}(\zeta) + \frac{\partial \mathbf{F}(\zeta)}{\partial p} \right]d\zeta \right.$$
$$\left. + \int_{0}^{t} \exp(-\mathbf{H}\zeta)\left[\frac{\partial \mathbf{H}}{\partial p}\mathbf{X}(\zeta) + \frac{\partial \mathbf{F}(\zeta)}{\partial p} \right]d\zeta \right\}$$
$$= \exp(\mathbf{H}t)\mathbf{X}_p(0) + \int_{0}^{t} \exp[(\mathbf{H}(t-\zeta)]$$
$$\times \left[\frac{\partial \mathbf{H}}{\partial p}\mathbf{X}(\zeta) + \frac{\partial \mathbf{F}(\zeta)}{\partial p} \right]d\zeta$$

Let $t_j = j\Delta t$, $\mathbf{X}_p^j = \mathbf{X}_p(t_j)$, $j = 0, 1, 2, \cdots$, Δt is time step, have

120

$$X_p^{j+1} = \exp\left(Ht_{j+1}\right)X_p^0 + \int_0^{t_{j+1}} \exp\left[(H(t_{j+1}-\zeta)\right]$$

$$\times \left[\frac{\partial H}{\partial p}X(\zeta) + \frac{\partial F(\zeta)}{\partial p}\right]d\zeta$$

$$= \exp\left(H\Delta t\right)X_p^j + \int_{t_j}^{t_{j+1}} \exp\left[H\left(t_{j+1}-\zeta\right)\right]$$

$$\times \left[\frac{\partial H}{\partial p}X(\zeta) + \frac{\partial F(\zeta)}{\partial p}\right]d\zeta$$

$$= \exp\left(H\Delta t\right)X_p^j + \int_0^{\Delta t} \exp\left(H\zeta\right)$$

$$\times \left[\frac{\partial H}{\partial p}X(t_{j+1}-\zeta) + \frac{\partial F(t_{j+1}-\zeta)}{\partial p}\right]d\zeta$$

$$= \exp(H\Delta t)X_p^j + H^{-1}\left[I - \exp(H\Delta t)\right]$$

$$\times \left[\frac{\partial H}{\partial p}\frac{X^{j+1}+X^j}{2} + \frac{\frac{\partial F(t_{j+1})}{\partial p} + \frac{\partial F(t_j)}{\partial p}}{2}\right] \quad (6)$$

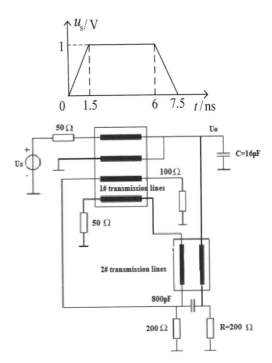

Figure 1. Transmission line system in the example. a) Waveform of the driven. b) Circuit of transmission line system.

It is obvious that the method proposed in this paper did not analyze the sensitivity of the transient responses of the coupled transmission lines directly in equation (6), but transformed it into solving the transient responses of the coupled transmission lines. The study shows that the method used to analyze the sensitivity of the transient responses of the coupled transmission lines based on precise integration is simple and efficient in the time domain [6]. Therefore, the method in this paper greatly simplifies the sensitivity analysis on transient responses of the coupled transmission lines, is a simple method to analyze the sensitivity of transient responses of the coupled transmission lines.

From the above analysis process we can see, this method proceeded in the time domain directly, time step and space step have no effect on the stability of the algorithm, only a certain impact on the precision of the algorithm, the smaller the step length, the higher the calculation precision. Meanwhile, the method proposed in this paper doesn't require decoupling of the coupled transmission lines and a large number of conversions between the frequency domain and the time domain, can be applied to analyze uniform, non-uniform lossy coupled transmission lines and any kinds of loads, is a novel, all-purpose method to analyze the sensitivity of transient responses of the coupled transmission lines.

3 EXAMPLE

Examples taken from literature[1] and the circuit as shown in Figure 1.The length of the transmission

lines, 1# and 2#, are 0.3 m and 0.4 m respectively. The parameters of 1# are R = 0, G = 0.

$$L = \begin{bmatrix} 1.5 & 0.18 & 0 & 0 \\ 0.18 & 1.5 & 0.18 & 0 \\ 0 & 0.18 & 1.5 & 0.18 \\ 0 & 0 & 0.18 & 1.5 \end{bmatrix} \mu H/m$$

$$C = \begin{bmatrix} 0.266 & -0.02 & 0 & 0 \\ -0.02 & 0.266 & -0.02 & 0 \\ 0 & -0.02 & 0.266 & -0.02 \\ 0 & 0 & -0.02 & 0.266 \end{bmatrix} nF/m$$

The parameters of 2# are R = 0, G = 0

$$L = \begin{bmatrix} 750 & 95 \\ 95 & 750 \end{bmatrix} nH/m,$$

$$C = \begin{bmatrix} 0.133 & -0.009 \\ -0.009 & 0.133 \end{bmatrix} nF/m$$

Take M = 50, Δt = 50 ns, Figure 2, 3 show the part of the analysis results of the method in this paper and literature [1] respectively. As the figures shown, the parameters, such as amplitude, delay

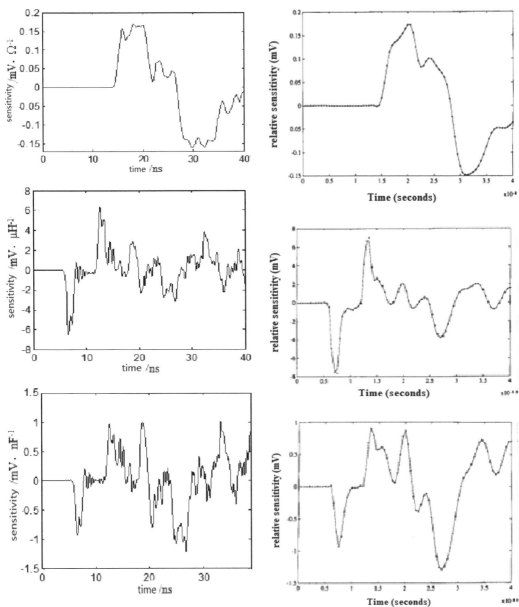

Figure 2.   Results of the proposed method. a) Sensitivity of u_o with respect to R. b) Sensitivity of u_o with respect to L_{11} (1.5 µH/m) of $1^\#$. c) Sensitivity of u_o with respect to C.

Figure 3.   The results of literature [1]. a) Sensitivity of u_o with respect to R. b) Sensitivity of u_o with respect to L_{11} (1.5 µH/m) of $1^\#$. c) Sensitivity of u_o with respect to C.

time, shape, etc., of the sensitivity waveform of these two methods are almost consistent. The sensitivity waveforms have some glitch with the method proposed in this paper, which is due to the smaller M and the larger time step Δt. In order to ensure the authentic results, the method in this paper did not conduct data fitting. Running time turned out to be less than 100 s at M = 100, so the method proposed in this paper have a high computational efficiency. The result shows the consistency of the proposed method with the literature [1].

122

4 CONCLUSION

Based on the precise integration of sensitivity analysis on transient responses of the coupled transmission lines in the time-domain, the telegrapher's equations of the coupled transmission lines are differenced and discredited in spatial domain and the first order differential equations of the sensitivity of the transient responses of the transmission lines are established, then transform the sensitivity problem into solving the transient responses and the first-order differential equations. The results of the example demonstrate that this method is correct and stable, with efficient and accurate results. This method is easy to compute, and can be applied to analyze the sensitivity of uniform and non-uniform of transmission lines and the arbitrary loads.

REFERENCES

[1] Lum S, Nakhla M, Zhang Q.J, "Sensitivity analysis on lossy coupled transmission line with nonlinear terminations," IEEE Trans on Microwave Theory and Techniques. vol. 42, 1994, pp. 607–625.

[2] Jinquan Zhao, Danyang Zhang, Helong Li, Wenwen Cao, "Sensitivity analysis for transient responses of nonuniform coupled transmission lines," Journal of Xi'an Jiaotong University. vol. 46, 2012, pp. 53–57.

[3] Danyang Zhang, "Sensitivity Analysis on Transient Responses of the transmission lines with precise integration method," Xi'an Jiaotong University, 2011.

[4] Stephen Lum, Michel S. Nakhla, Qi-Jun Zhang,"Sensitivity Analysis on Lossy Coupled transmission Lines," IEEE Trans on Microwave Theory and Techniques. vol. 39, 1991, pp. 2089–2099.

[5] Natalie Nakhla, Michel Nakhla, Ramachandra Achar., "A General Approach for Sensitivity Analysis on Distributed Interconnects in the Time Domain," IEEE Trans on Microwave Theory and Techniques. vol. 59, 2011, pp. 46–55.

[6] Liang Guishu, Wang Yong, Dong Huaying, "Research on frequency-domain sensitivity of lossless exponential transmission line network," Journal of North China Electric Power University. vol. 33, 2006, pp. 7–9.

[7] J.I. Chang hu, DONG Huaying, LIANG Guishu, "Adjoint network method of time-domain sensitivity of the networks containing nonuniform transmission lines," Power System Technology, vol. 31, 2007, pp. 41–45.

[8] Jinquan Zhao, Xikui Ma, Jing Xue, Guanyuan Qiu, "Transient analysis on nonuniform transmission lines with nonlinear terminal networks," Journal of electronics. vol. 23, 2006, pp. 428–432.

[9] Cheng Jiao, Andreas C. Cangellaris, Abdul M. Yaghmour, and John L. Prince, "Sensitivity Analysis on Multiconductor Transmission Lines and Optimization for High-Speed Interconnect Circuit Design," IEEE Trans on Advanced packaging. vol. 23, 2000, pp. 132–141.

[10] Kambiz Afrooz, Abdolali Abdipour, "Efficient Method for Time-Domain Analysis on Lossy Nonuniform Multiconductor Transmission Line Driven by a Modulated Signal Using FDTD Technique," IEEE Trans on Electromagnetic Compatibility. vol. 50, 2011, pp. 2233–2246.

[11] Gad E, Nakhla M, "An efficient algorithm for sensitivity analysis on nonuniform transmission line," IEEE Trans on Advanced Packaging. vol. 28, 2005, pp. 197–208.

[12] Gad E, Nakhla M, "Simulation and sensitivity analysis on nonuniform transmission line using integrated congruence transform," IEEE Trans on Advanced Packaging. vol. 28, 2005, pp. 32–44.

[13] Qinwei Xu, Pinaki Mazumder, "Accurate Modeling of Lossy Nonuniform Transmission Lines by Using Differential Quadrature Methods," IEEE Trans on Microwave Theory and Techniques. vol. 50, 2002, pp. 2233–2246.

Computer, Intelligent Computing and Education Technology – Liu, Sung & Yao (Eds)
© 2014 Taylor & Francis Group, London, ISBN 978-1-138-02469-4

Study on the measurement method of power frequency impedance parameters of multiple-circuit transmission lines on the same tower

W.G. Gu & Y.J. Zhao
Electric Power Research Institute of Guangdong Power Grid Corporation, Guangzhou, China

J.-H. Yin
CSG Electric Power Research Institute, Guangzhou, China

J.-Q. Zhao & N.J. Fan
School of Electrical Engineering, Xi'an Jiao Tong University, Xi'an, China

X.X. Guo
Jiangsu Electric Power Company Research Institute, Jiangsu, China

ABSTRACT: A new measurement method of the multiple-circuit transmission lines' power frequency impedance parameters on the same tower is proposed in this paper based on the assumption of the three-phase unbalance and induced voltage is constant in a short time. By applying a single-phase AC supply and multiple measurements, the mathematical model of the double-circuit transmission lines' power frequency impedance parameters based on the measured voltage and current is established, and then the sequence impedances and sequence coupled impedances can be resolved. This method is simple, accurate and without the influence of three-phase unbalance on the measurement of transmission line parameters. The simulation results show the validity of the proposed method.

Keywords: multiple-circuit transmission lines; three-phase unbalance; impedance parameters; anti-high induced voltage; measurement method

1 INTRODUCTION

The parameters of transmission lines, as the basic parameters of power system, have an important role in the calculation, analysis and protection of power system. Due to the variability and complexity of the lines construction field and the geographical environment, it is almost impossible to calculate transmission lines' parameters precisely. therefore, the domestic regulations required that positive and zero sequence impedances of transmission lines must be measured actually.

With the rapid development of power grid and the urban construction, land resources become more and more valuable. To save line corridors and construction costs, double or even more transmission lines on the same tower have been widely used in the grid recently. However, due to the strong electromagnetic coupling between transmission lines on the same tower, induced voltage can reach several hundreds volts and the short-circuit current reach more than 100 A, which make the application of traditional methods for parameters of transmission lines more and more difficult, even

impossible. Therefore, how to measure the parameters of transmission lines simply and precisely under the strong electromagnetic interference environment has become an urgent problem to be solved.

In the traditional method, for the single-circuit transmission lines, when a sequence symmetrical current flows through the three phase circuit, only produce its sequence voltage without coupling with other sequences under the assumption that the parameters of transmission lines are symmetrical. For the parallel double-circuit, assumed that the geometry mean distance is far less than the distance between double circuits with electromagnetic coupling, the mutual inductances of the double circuits are equal. In fact, for the single-circuit transmission lines, especially the not transposed one, the space between the lines are asymmetrical; for the multi-circuit transmission lines, distance between one phase of the circuit and the three phases of the other circuit are not equal, thus lead to the asymmetry of the parameters of three phases and the coupling between the each sequence. The positive sequence impedances, zero sequence self-impedances and zero sequence mutual imped-ances are main parameters to be measured, while the coupling parameters of each sequence are rarely mentioned in traditional methods.

This paper proposed a new measurement method of the multiple-circuit transmission lines' power frequency impedance parameters on the same tower. By applying a single-phase AC supply to the different measurement terminals to get the voltage and current of each phase under the differ-ent circumstance, establish the mathematical model of the transmission lines' power frequency imped-ance parameters to get the parameters of transmis-sion lines, including each sequence impedances, the coupling impedance between each sequence and the quantitative evaluation of the asymmetry degree of the transmission lines. This method is simple and accurate. The simulation results show the validity of the proposed method.

2 MEASUREMENT CIRCUIT MODEL OF THE DOUBLE-CIRCUIT TRANSMISSION LINES' IMPEDANCE PARAMETERS

Considering the asymmetric parameters of trans-mission lines, induced voltage and the earth impedance, the impedance parameters measure-ment circuit model of the double-circuit transmis-sion lines is established as shown in Figure 1. In the figure, Z_{aa}, Z_{bb}, Z_{cc}, $Z_{a'a'}$, $Z_{b'b'}$, $Z_{c'c'}$ are the self-impedance of each phase, Z_{ab}, Z_{bc}, Z_{ac}, $Z_{a'b'}$, $Z_{b'c'}$, $Z_{a'c'}$ are the mutual impedance of each phase in the single-circuit transmission lines. Z_{12} is the mutual impedance of each phase in the double-circuit transmission lines, such as $Z_{aa'}$, $Z_{ab'}$, $Z_{ac'}$, $Z_{ba'}$, $Z_{bb'}$, $Z_{bc'}$, $Z_{ca'}$, $Z_{cb'}$, $Z_{cc'}$. Zg is the impedance between the two substations, U_A, U_B, U_C, I_A, I_B, I_C, $U_{A'}$, $U_{B'}$, $U_{C'}$, $I_{A'}$, $I_{B'}$, $I_{C'}$ are the voltage and current of each phase, and E_A, E_B, E_C, $E_{A'}$, $E_{B'}$, $E_{C'}$ are the interfere voltage of each phase.

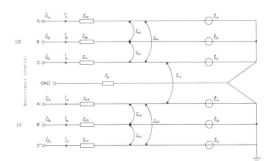

Figure 1. Measurement circuit model of the double-circuit transmission lines' impedance parameters.

3 MEASUREMENT PRINCIPLE OF THE DOUBLE-CIRCUIT TRANSMISSION LINES' IMPEDANCE PARAMETERS

Apply the test supply $\dot{U}_{S1}$ between phase A and B, the voltages of each phase are

$$
\begin{cases}
\dot{U}'_A = \dot{I}'_A Z_{aa} + \dot{I}'_B Z_{ab} + \dot{I}'_C Z_{ac} + \dot{I}'_{A'} Z_{aa'} + \dot{I}'_{B'} Z_{ab'} \\
\quad + \dot{I}'_{C'} Z_{ac'} + \dot{I}'_g Z_g + \dot{E}'_A \\
\dot{U}'_B = \dot{I}'_A Z_{ab} + \dot{I}'_B Z_{bb} + \dot{I}'_C Z_{bc} + \dot{I}'_{A'} Z_{ba'} + \dot{I}'_{B'} Z_{bb'} \\
\quad + \dot{I}'_{C'} Z_{bc'} + \dot{I}'_g Z_g + \dot{E}'_B \\
\dot{U}'_C = \dot{I}'_A Z_{ac} + \dot{I}'_B Z_{bc} + \dot{I}'_C Z_{cc} + \dot{I}'_{A'} Z_{ca'} + \dot{I}'_{B'} Z_{cb'} \\
\quad + \dot{I}'_{C'} Z_{cc'} + \dot{I}'_g Z_g + \dot{E}'_C \\
\dot{U}'_{A'} = \dot{I}'_A Z_{aa'} + \dot{I}'_B Z_{ba'} + \dot{I}'_C Z_{ca'} + \dot{I}'_{A'} Z_{a'a'} \\
\quad + \dot{I}'_{B'} Z_{a'b'} + \dot{I}'_{C'} Z_{a'c'} + \dot{I}'_g Z_g + \dot{E}'_{A'} \\
\dot{U}'_{B'} = \dot{I}'_A Z_{ab'} + \dot{I}'_B Z_{bb'} + \dot{I}'_C Z_{cb'} + \dot{I}'_{A'} Z_{a'b'} \\
\quad + \dot{I}'_{B'} Z_{b'b'} + \dot{I}'_{C'} Z_{b'c'} + \dot{I}'_g Z_g + \dot{E}'_{B'} \\
\dot{U}'_{C'} = \dot{I}'_A Z_{ac'} + \dot{I}'_B Z_{bc'} + \dot{I}'_C Z_{cc'} + \dot{I}'_{A'} Z_{a'c'} \\
\quad + \dot{I}'_{B'} Z_{b'c'} + \dot{I}'_{C'} Z_{c'c'} + \dot{I}'_g Z_g + \dot{E}'_{C'} \\
\dot{I}'_g = \dot{I}'_A + \dot{I}'_B + \dot{I}'_C + \dot{I}'_{A'} + \dot{I}'_{B'} + \dot{I}'_{C'}
\end{cases}
$$

Change the voltage of the test supply, have

$$
\begin{cases}
\dot{U}''_A = \dot{I}''_A Z_{aa} + \dot{I}''_B Z_{ab} + \dot{I}''_C Z_{ac} + \dot{I}''_{A'} Z_{aa'} \\
\quad + \dot{I}''_{B'} Z_{ab'} + \dot{I}''_{C'} Z_{ac'} + \dot{I}''_g Z_g + \dot{E}''_A \\
\dot{U}''_B = \dot{I}''_A Z_{ab} + \dot{I}''_B Z_{bb} + \dot{I}''_C Z_{bc} + \dot{I}''_{A'} Z_{ba'} \\
\quad + \dot{I}''_{B'} Z_{bb'} + \dot{I}''_{C'} Z_{bc'} + \dot{I}''_g Z_g + \dot{E}''_B \\
\dot{U}''_C = \dot{I}''_A Z_{ac} + \dot{I}''_B Z_{bc} + \dot{I}''_C Z_{cc} + \dot{I}''_{A'} Z_{ca'} \\
\quad + \dot{I}''_{B'} Z_{cb'} + \dot{I}''_{C'} Z_{cc'} + \dot{I}''_g Z_g + \dot{E}''_C \\
\dot{U}''_{A'} = \dot{I}''_A Z_{aa'} + \dot{I}''_B Z_{ba'} + \dot{I}''_C Z_{ca'} + \dot{I}''_{A'} Z_{a'a'} \\
\quad + \dot{I}''_{B'} Z_{a'b'} + \dot{I}''_{C'} Z_{a'c'} + \dot{I}''_g Z_g + \dot{E}''_{A'} \\
\dot{U}''_{B'} = \dot{I}''_A Z_{ab'} + \dot{I}''_B Z_{bb'} + \dot{I}''_C Z_{cb'} + \dot{I}''_{A'} Z_{a'b'} \\
\quad + \dot{I}''_{B'} Z_{b'b'} + \dot{I}''_{C'} Z_{b'c'} + \dot{I}''_g Z_g + \dot{E}''_{B'} \\
\dot{U}''_{C'} = \dot{I}''_A Z_{ac'} + \dot{I}''_B Z_{bc'} + \dot{I}''_C Z_{cc'} + \dot{I}''_{A'} Z_{a'c'} \\
\quad + \dot{I}''_{B'} Z_{b'c'} + \dot{I}''_{C'} Z_{c'c'} + \dot{I}''_g Z_g + \dot{E}''_{C'} \\
\dot{I}''_g = \dot{I}''_A + \dot{I}''_B + \dot{I}''_C + \dot{I}''_{A'} + \dot{I}''_{B'} + \dot{I}''_{C'}
\end{cases}
$$

Literature [2] pointed out that the load and oper-ation mode of power system are rarely changed within a few seconds, and the induced voltage will not frequently change significantly. Based on this thought, assumed that the interference voltage of the transmission lines is constant between two tests. Then (1) minus (2), have

$$
\begin{cases}
\dot{U}_A^{(1)} = \dot{I}_A^{(1)}Z_{aa} + \dot{I}_B^{(1)}Z_{ab} + \dot{I}_C^{(1)}Z_{ac} + \dot{I}_{A'}^{(1)}Z_{aa'} \\
\qquad + \dot{I}_{B'}^{(1)}Z_{ab'} + \dot{I}_{C'}^{(1)}Z_{ac'} + \dot{I}_g^{(1)}Z_g \\[4pt]
\dot{U}_B^{(1)} = \dot{I}_A^{(1)}Z_{ab} + \dot{I}_B^{(1)}Z_{bb} + \dot{I}_C^{(1)}Z_{bc} + \dot{I}_{A'}^{(1)}Z_{ba'} \\
\qquad + \dot{I}_{B'}^{(1)}Z_{bb'} + \dot{I}_{C'}^{(1)}Z_{bc'} + \dot{I}_g^{(1)}Z_g \\[4pt]
\dot{U}_C^{(1)} = \dot{I}_A^{(1)}Z_{ac} + \dot{I}_B^{(1)}Z_{bc} + \dot{I}_C^{(1)}Z_{cc} + \dot{I}_{A'}^{(1)}Z_{ca'} \\
\qquad + \dot{I}_{B'}^{(1)}Z_{cb'} + \dot{I}_{C'}^{(1)}Z_{cc'} + \dot{I}_g^{(1)}Z_g \\[4pt]
\dot{U}_{A'}^{(1)} = \dot{I}_A^{(1)}Z_{aa'} + \dot{I}_B^{(1)}Z_{ba'} + \dot{I}_C^{(1)}Z_{ca'} + \dot{I}_{A'}^{(1)}Z_{a'a'} \\
\qquad + \dot{I}_{B'}^{(1)}Z_{a'b'} + \dot{I}_{C'}^{(1)}Z_{a'c'} + \dot{I}_g^{(1)}Z_g \\[4pt]
\dot{U}_{B'}^{(1)} = \dot{I}_A^{(1)}Z_{ab'} + \dot{I}_B^{(1)}Z_{bb'} + \dot{I}_C^{(1)}Z_{cb'} + \dot{I}_{A'}^{(1)}Z_{a'b'} \\
\qquad + \dot{I}_{B'}^{(1)}Z_{b'b'} + \dot{I}_{C'}^{(1)}Z_{b'c'} + \dot{I}_g^{(1)}Z_g \\[4pt]
\dot{U}_{C'}^{(1)} = \dot{I}_A^{(1)}Z_{ac'} + \dot{I}_B^{(1)}Z_{bc'} + \dot{I}_C^{(1)}Z_{cc'} + \dot{I}_{A'}^{(1)}Z_{a'c'} \\
\qquad + \dot{I}_{B'}^{(1)}Z_{b'c'} + \dot{I}_{C'}^{(1)}Z_{c'c'} + \dot{I}_g^{(1)}Z_g \\[4pt]
\dot{I}_g^{(1)} = \dot{I}_A^{(1)} + \dot{I}_B^{(1)} + \dot{I}_C^{(1)} + \dot{I}_{A'}^{(1)} + \dot{I}_{B'}^{(1)} + \dot{I}_{C'}^{(1)}
\end{cases}
$$

where $\dot{U}_A^{(1)} = \dot{U}_A' - \dot{U}_A''$, $\dot{U}_B^{(1)}$, $\dot{U}_C^{(1)}$, $\dot{U}_{A'}^{(1)}$, $\dot{U}_{B'}^{(1)}$, $\dot{U}_{C'}^{(1)}$, $\dot{I}_A^{(1)}$, $\dot{I}_B^{(1)}$, $\dot{I}_C^{(1)}$, $\dot{I}_{A'}^{(1)}$, $\dot{I}_{B'}^{(1)}$, $\dot{I}_{C'}^{(1)}$ have the same meaning with $\dot{U}_A^{(1)}$.

Visible, (3) is independent of the interference voltage, eliminating the influence of the interference voltage.

In the same way, apply the test supply to phase B and C, phase A' and B', phase B' and C', phase A, B, C, A', B', C' and earth respectively to get $U_A^{(k)}$, $U_B^{(k)}$, $U_C^{(k)}$, $U_{A'}^{(k)}$, $U_{B'}^{(k)}$, $U_{C'}^{(k)}$, $I_A^{(k)}$, $I_B^{(k)}$, $I_C^{(k)}$, $I_{A'}^{(k)}$, $I_{B'}^{(k)}$, $I_{C'}^{(k)}$, $k = 2, 3, \dots$.

The relation equation of voltage, current and impedance can be written as

$$\dot{U} = \dot{I}Z \tag{4}$$

where

$$
\dot{U} = \begin{bmatrix} \dot{U}_A^{(1)} & \dot{U}_B^{(1)} & \dot{U}_C^{(1)} & \dot{U}_{A'}^{(1)} & \dot{U}_{B'}^{(1)} & \dot{U}_{C'}^{(1)} & \cdots & \dot{U}_A^{(n)} \\ \dot{U}_B^{(n)} & \dot{U}_C^{(n)} & \dot{U}_{A'}^{(n)} & \dot{U}_{B'}^{(n)} & \dot{U}_{C'}^{(n)} \end{bmatrix}^T
$$

$$Z = \begin{bmatrix} Z_I & Z_{I-II} & Z_{II} & Z_g \end{bmatrix}^T$$

$$Z_I = \begin{bmatrix} Z_{aa} & Z_{ab} & Z_{ac} & Z_{bb} & Z_{bc} & Z_{cc} \end{bmatrix}^T$$

$$Z_{II} = \begin{bmatrix} Z_{a'a'} & Z_{a'b'} & Z_{a'c'} & Z_{b'b'} & Z_{b'c'} & Z_{c'c'} \end{bmatrix}^T$$

$$Z_{I-II} = \begin{bmatrix} Z_{aa'} & Z_{ab'} & Z_{ac'} & Z_{ba'} & Z_{bb'} & Z_{bc'} & Z_{ca'} & Z_{cb'} & Z_{cc'} \end{bmatrix}^T$$

$$
\dot{I} = \begin{bmatrix}
\mathbf{i}_n^{(1)} & \mathbf{i}_n^{(1)} & \mathbf{i}_n^{(1)} & \mathbf{i}_n^{(1)} & \mathbf{O} & \mathbf{i}_{g'}^{(1)} \\
\mathbf{O} & \mathbf{i}_{n'}^{(1)} & \mathbf{i}_{n'}^{(1)} & \mathbf{i}_{n'}^{(1)} & \mathbf{i}_{n'}^{(1)} & \mathbf{i}_{g'}^{(1)} \\
\mathbf{i}_n^{(2)} & \mathbf{i}_n^{(2)} & \mathbf{i}_n^{(2)} & \mathbf{i}_n^{(2)} & \mathbf{O} & \mathbf{i}_{g'}^{(2)} \\
\mathbf{O} & \mathbf{i}_{n'}^{(2)} & \mathbf{i}_{n'}^{(2)} & \mathbf{i}_{n'}^{(2)} & \mathbf{i}_{n'}^{(2)} & \mathbf{i}_{g'}^{(2)} \\
\vdots & \vdots & \vdots & \vdots & \vdots & \vdots \\
\mathbf{i}_n^{(n)} & \mathbf{i}_n^{(n)} & \mathbf{i}_n^{(n)} & \mathbf{i}_n^{(n)} & \mathbf{O} & \mathbf{i}_{g'}^{(n)} \\
\mathbf{O} & \mathbf{i}_{n'}^{(n)} & \mathbf{i}_{n'}^{(n)} & \mathbf{i}_{n'}^{(n)} & \mathbf{i}_{n'}^{(n)} & \mathbf{i}_{g'}^{(n)}
\end{bmatrix}
$$

In the matrix I:

$$
\mathbf{i}_n^{(i)} = \begin{bmatrix}
\mathbf{i}_A^{(i)} & \mathbf{i}_B^{(i)} & \mathbf{i}_C^{(i)} & 0 & 0 & 0 \\
0 & \mathbf{i}_A^{(i)} & 0 & \mathbf{i}_B^{(i)} & \mathbf{i}_C^{(i)} & 0 \\
0 & 0 & \mathbf{i}_A^{(i)} & 0 & \mathbf{i}_B^{(i)} & \mathbf{i}_C^{(i)}
\end{bmatrix},
$$

$$
\mathbf{i}_{n'}^{(i)} = \begin{bmatrix}
\mathbf{i}_{A'}^{(i)} & \mathbf{i}_{B'}^{(i)} & \mathbf{i}_{C'}^{(i)} & 0 & 0 & 0 \\
0 & \mathbf{i}_{A'}^{(i)} & 0 & \mathbf{i}_{B'}^{(i)} & \mathbf{i}_{C'}^{(i)} & 0 \\
0 & 0 & \mathbf{i}_{A'}^{(i)} & 0 & \mathbf{i}_{B'}^{(i)} & \mathbf{i}_{C'}^{(i)}
\end{bmatrix},
$$

$$
\mathbf{i}_n^{(i)} = \begin{bmatrix}
\mathbf{i}_{A'}^{(i)} & \mathbf{i}_{B'}^{(i)} & \mathbf{i}_{C'}^{(i)} \\
0 & 0 & 0 \\
0 & 0 & 0
\end{bmatrix}, \quad
\mathbf{i}_{n'}^{(i)} = \begin{bmatrix}
\mathbf{i}_{A'}^{(i)} & 0 & 0 \\
0 & \mathbf{i}_{A'}^{(i)} & 0 \\
0 & 0 & \mathbf{i}_{A'}^{(i)}
\end{bmatrix},
$$

$$
\mathbf{i}_n^{(i)} = \begin{bmatrix}
0 & 0 & 0 \\
\mathbf{i}_{A'}^{(i)} & \mathbf{i}_{B'}^{(i)} & \mathbf{i}_{C'}^{(i)} \\
0 & 0 & 0
\end{bmatrix}, \quad
\mathbf{i}_{n'}^{(i)} = \begin{bmatrix}
\mathbf{i}_{B'}^{(i)} & 0 & 0 \\
0 & \mathbf{i}_{B'}^{(i)} & 0 \\
0 & 0 & \mathbf{i}_{B'}^{(i)}
\end{bmatrix},
$$

$$
\mathbf{i}_n^{(i)} = \begin{bmatrix}
0 & 0 & 0 \\
0 & 0 & 0 \\
\mathbf{i}_{A'}^{(i)} & \mathbf{i}_{B'}^{(i)} & \mathbf{i}_{C'}^{(i)}
\end{bmatrix}, \quad
\mathbf{i}_{n'}^{(i)} = \begin{bmatrix}
\mathbf{i}_{C'}^{(i)} & 0 & 0 \\
0 & \mathbf{i}_{C'}^{(i)} & 0 \\
0 & 0 & \mathbf{i}_{C'}^{(i)}
\end{bmatrix},
$$

$$\mathbf{i}_g^{(i)} = \begin{bmatrix} \mathbf{i}_g^{(i)} & \mathbf{i}_g^{(i)} & \mathbf{i}_g^{(i)} \end{bmatrix}^T,$$

$$\mathbf{i}_g^{(i)} = \begin{bmatrix} \mathbf{i}_A^{(i)} + \mathbf{i}_B^{(i)} + \mathbf{i}_C^{(i)} + \mathbf{i}_{A'}^{(i)} + \mathbf{i}_{B'}^{(i)} + \mathbf{i}_{C'}^{(i)} \end{bmatrix},$$

$i = 1, 2, \dots, n$, $\mathbf{O}$ is a zero matrix of three lines and six columns.

(4) is an over determined equations, use the least square method based on the literature [5], the solution of (4) is

$$Z = (\dot{I}^T \dot{I})^{-1} (\dot{I}^T \dot{U}) \tag{5}$$

4 SOLUTION OF THE SEQUENCE IMPEDANCE

Let $T = \text{diag}\{A, A\}$, $A = \begin{bmatrix} 1 & 1 & 1 \\ \alpha^2 & \alpha & 1 \\ \alpha & \alpha^2 & 1 \end{bmatrix}$, $\alpha = e^{j120°} = -\frac{1}{2} + j\frac{\sqrt{3}}{2}$ The matrix of sequence impedance is:

$$Z_{120} = T^{-1}ZT \qquad (6)$$

We can not only get the positive sequence, negative sequence and zero sequence impedances, but also the mutual impedance of each sequence. The coupling impedance reflects the degree of the asymmetry of the transmission lines.

5 MEASUREMENT OF THE DOUBLE-CIRCUIT TRANSMISSION LINES IMPEDANCE PARAMETERS

The parameter measurement instrument of multiple-circuit transmission lines developed based on the measurement principle proposed in this paper is used to measure the parameters of 220 kV

Guanshui Jiayi lines of Dongguan power bureau. 220 kV Guanshui Jiayi lines and 500 kV Shuiguan Jiayi lines composed the double-circuit transmission lines on the same tower. 500 kV Shuiguan Jiayi lines is 37.6 km in length, using the lines of $4 \times$ LGJ-630/45; 220 kV Guanshui Jiayi lines is 37.9 km in length, using the line of $2 \times$ LGJ-630/45.

Test place: 500 kV Shui xiang substation in Dong guan;

Weather: Light rain turn cloudy;

Temperature: 18.0 °C; Relative humidity: 81.5%.

The measurement results are shown in Table 1. In the table, Z_{I1}, Z_{I2}, Z_{I0}, Z_{II1}, Z_{II2}, Z_{II0} are the positive sequence, negative sequence and zero sequence impedance of 220 kV Guanshui Jiayi lines respectively.

YTLP-B is an instrument of measuring transmission lines' impedance parameters based on the principle of frequency conversion, which can measure the positive sequence and zero sequence impedance parameters of single-circuit transmission lines, the measurement results of YTLP-B are shown in Tables 2 and 3.

The results shown in Table 2~3 illustrate that the results of positive sequence impedance parameter is relatively fine, while the zero sequence impedance

Table 1. Measurement results of 220 kV Guanshui Jiayi lines' impedance parameters Z120 (Ω).

	Z_{I1}	Z_{I2}	Z_{I0}
Z_{I1}	11.5008∠84.9962	0.5453∠163.5803	0.3501∠−173.1717
Z_{I2}	0.5678∠13.2919	11.5008∠84.9962	0.3434∠−9.1300
Z_{I0}	0.3434∠−9.1300	0.3501∠−173.1717	37.2943∠79.8306
Z_{II1}	0.2808∠88.6961	0.1099∠−172.7307	0.6267∠−116.2935
Z_{II2}	0.1087∠−7.4387	0.2787∠88.9559°	0.6195∠−66.8513
Z_{II0}	0.6453∠−66.9286	0.6596∠−117.3144	19.9828∠73.9557

	Z_{II1}	Z_{II2}	Z_{II0}
Z_{I1}	0.2787∠88.9559	0.1099∠−172.7307	0.6596∠−117.3144
Z_{I2}	0.1087∠−7.4387	0.2808∠88.6961	0.6453∠−66.9286
Z_{I0}	0.6195∠−66.8513	0.6267∠−116.2935	19.9828∠73.9557
Z_{II1}	11.5374∠84.9879	0.5747∠163.7336	0.3736∠−173.8624
Z_{II2}	0.5562∠14.1196	11.5374∠84.9879	0.2972∠−5.5820
Z_{II0}	0.2972∠−5.5820	0.3736∠−173.8624	37.8596∠79.9869

Table 2. Measurement results of 500 kV Shuiguan Jia lines.

No.	Sequence parameter	
	Z1	Z0
1	10.237∠86.956	26.711∠78.423
2	10.263∠86.715	28.156∠77.873

Table 3. Measurement results of 500 kV Shuiguan Yi lines.

No.	Sequence parameter	
	Z1	Z0
1	10.224∠86.917	20.824∠84.590
2	10.219∠86.993	24.737∠80.513
3	10.239∠85.859	28.113∠77.941

parameter is very poor. Besides, YTLP-B can not measure the impedance parameters of double-circuit transmission lines and the coupling impedance parameters between each sequence. The instrument developed based on the method proposed in this paper not only can measure each sequence impedance parameters and the coupling impedance parameters of double-circuit transmission lines at the same time, but also have a good stability.

6 CONCLUSION

The measurement method of the multiple-circuit transmission lines' impedance parameters proposed in this paper does not require the symmetrical three phase power supply, just one ordinary single phase test power, can not only obtain actual parameters of transmission lines, but also get positive sequence, negative sequence, zero sequence impedance parameters and the coupling impedance parameters. The experimental results show that the proposed method can overcome the influence of the induced voltage and the asymmetry parameters of transmission lines. The proposed method is simple, high precise and effective.

REFERENCES

[1] Mao, P. & Zhang C.X. etc. 2010. Capacitance compensation algorithm of zero sequence parameter under operation of transmission line. Automation of electric power systems, 34(17):55~58.
[2] Yang, J.C. & Yin, X.G. etc. 2008. Measurement of power frequency parameters of transmission lines in an intensive interference environment. Automation of electric power systems, 2(18):67~70.
[3] Zhu, Y.C. & Fan, Y.P. & Tang, C. 2009. Calculation and measurement of sequence impedance parameters of asymmetry transmission line with mutual inductance. Guangxi electric power, 6:7~13.
[4] Yuan, L.R. & Liu, Z.Y. & Zhang, C. 2006. Study on a new way to measure power frequency parameters of transmission lines. Guandong electric power, 19(10):6~10.
[5] Gu, X.Q. & Kang, H.W. & Cao, H.X. 2006. Least Square Method in the complex domain. Progress in Natural Science, 16(1):49~54.
[6] Hu, Z.J. & Cheng, X.M. 2010. Measurement methods of zero-sequence impedance parameters for transmission lines.Journal of electric power science and technology, 25(3):25~31.

Computer, Intelligent Computing and Education Technology – Liu, Sung & Yao (Eds)
© 2014 Taylor & Francis Group, London, ISBN 978-1-138-02469-4

Software security concerns modeling method based on UML extension

Wen-Juan Li, Kai Zhao, Lin-Lin Zhang, Chun-Xia Wei, Jie Wang & She-Hui Xu
College of Information Science and Engineering, Xinjiang University, Urumqi, China

ABSTRACT: Software security has an enormous impact on almost all areas ranging from general software systems to security critical systems. The traditional measures such as firewalls cannot fundamentally solve the problem of software security. The major focus of software security has transferred to highly secure design of software systems. A number of modeling methodologies have been proposed to address the problem of software security. These approaches improve the security of software but to some extent increase the complexity of system. Security concerns as stakeholder's interests can be used to resolve this problem. This paper presents a modeling approach for security concerns and their relationships. This method extends UML to support aspect-oriented modeling and considers security concerns as aspects. It also describes the association analysis among security concerns used by UML stereotypes.

Keywords: software security concerns; UML; modeling

1 INTRODUCTION

Software security has an enormous impact on almost all areas ranging from general software systems to critical systems. Gary McGraw points out that software security is an engineering idea that the software can continue to function correctly under malicious attack[6]. While the statistics from the National Vulnerability Database (NVD) show that more than 5500 new vulnerability instances were reported and registered by NVD in 2008[15]. The number of security incidents reported to the Computer Emergency Readiness Team Coordination Center (CERT/CC) involve from one to thousands of sites, result from software vulnerabilities[5]. Therefore, it was soon realized that external protections in the form of firewalls, network level control and operating systems level controls were not much enough to secure software[12].

More consideration is required to address security issues of software systems[18], especially in the early development phases of software projects, such as requirements and architecture. But as claimed by Firesmith[3], most software engineers do not have a proper training in security. That's to say, software developers lacks of the knowledge of software security. Similarly, For security experts, software development is also quiet difficult because they have less experience for practices of development. Consequently, it is needed to bridge the gap between software developers and security experts to achieve software's security goals. The modeling of Software security concerns (e.g., stakeholders' interests) is a good approach to resolve this problem. Security concerns are aspectual or cross-cutting and it is difficulty to be encapsulated into one part of the design. Aspect-Oriented Software Development (AOSD)[10] has been considered as a suitable solution to address the design of cross-cutting concerns.

In this work, we focus on modeling and analyzing security concerns to bridge the gap between software developers and security experts to construct optimized security software. The approaches for modeling software security concerns mainly include use cases[8], misuse cases and attack trees[15] and Petri net[11] and so on. Besides, UML as a kind of industry standard modeling language was employed to model security concerns, such as MAC-UML[4], SecureUML[1] and UMLsec[9], et al. In this work, we select UML and its extending mechanism to model security concerns as aspects. What's more, we find that a system may require multiple security concerns and each security concerns can be achieved by many security solutions. So the modeling of associations among security concerns is needed for software architects, which can reduce the complexity due to the adding of security.

In this paper, there are two contributions, firstly, we extended UML to support the modeling of security concerns and made developers considered security in the early-stage software development. Secondly, we analyzed the associations among security concerns.

2 RELATED WORK

Given the important role of software security in the software development process, in recent years, researchers have proposed different methods to modeling security of the software in the development of software. This session will discuss the security modeling approach on UML extension and aspect-oriented.

The research shows that the modeling methods of software security concerns mainly include: The MAC-UML Framework addresses the issue that UML lacks of support to security requirements of incorporating Mandatory Access Control (MAC) into UML design artifacts, including use cases, class diagram, and sequence diagram, providing the clearance definition and classification about the related UML elements. At last it proposes the security framework[4]. David Basin et al. defined a security model-driven modeling language said Secure UML based on the UML distributed system. This method is established on the role based access control model, besides, it also support specification authorization restriction[1]. Hassan Gomaa et al. propose security concerns modeling technique, adopting use case to modeling security concerns and enhancing the system reusability[8]. UMLsec[9] is an extension of UML, which is used to specify security requirements. It adopts stereotypes, tags and constraints, class diagram, sequence diagram and so on to model security into the system components. SMASC[7] (Separating Modeling of Application and Security Concerns) is put forward, modeling the functional requirement by the UML use cases, class and object collaboration diagram and capturing the security concerns by security case and security object. It presents software security Petri nets, which have designed and implemented automation modeling of software security requirements[11]. These methods above enhance the software security performance, but the security is still mixed in the whole system, increasing the system complexity.

In allusion to the problems mentioned above, aspect-oriented modeling methods based on the UML extension had emerged, which provide new ideas on the study of security modeling methods. Crosscutting threat adopt aspect-oriented method, using the use case to modeling security threat, and these methods need security engineers to determine the security threat requirements[17]. [14] As the security integration at the early stage of the software development generate the problems of security scattered and tangled in the system, it propose the aspect-oriented modeling method to specify and integrate the security solutions in the UML design model. Ref.[13] proposes security design weaving method, establishing the UML profile to specify security concern and weaving the security concern of

the design layer to the basic model. Ref.[2] presents a mapping mechanism, mapping the security components of software architecture to the codes of implementation using security concerns model. These methods above decrease the system complexity and lay the foundation of the software security, but they lack the modeling of the security's properties and the analyses among security concerns. Ref. [16] exploits aspect-oriented Petri nets as a unified formalism to specify the intended functions, security threats, and threat mitigations of a security design. Intended functions and security threats are modeled by Petri nets, whereas threat mitigations are modeled by Petri net-based aspects. This approach can make software design provably secured from anticipated security threats and reduce significant design-level vulnerabilities. Consequently, this paper uses the UML extension mechanism to build the security concerns model and analyze corresponding relationships among them.

3 MODELING SOFTWARE SECURITY CONCERNS USING EXTENSIONAL UML

3.1 *Software security concerns*

As an important conception in software engineering, concerns are the matters that are interested in the process of system development, and its implementation is critical to one or more stakeholders. So far, the concerns have not form a unified definition, such as in object-oriented development approach, the concern has modeled as a class or object. In structured approach, the concerns have been expressed as process. In aspect-oriented programming, the concerns have been extended to the crosscutting attributes (such as synchronization, memory management, or persistence).

The software security concerns serve as a subset of concerns that contain the whole security matters of system and mainly highlight the system security. They can be the quality attributes of software like security audit, access control, confidentiality, integrity, non-repudiation and so on. And they also can be the potential threats of system or System's vulnerability that due to insufficient design for software. These concerns in the system are not independent modules and often scattering in system modules, Such as log audit needs to exist in each module of system. In the process of software development, the reasonably use of software security concerns can improve the defense capability of the software.

3.2 *UML extending mechanism*

UML usually represents the function properties of the system in the software developing process, and security concerns are represented via annotations or labels, in this way that can't reflect the importance of security in software. But UML well extension mechanism is able to provide a solution to resolve the problem.

In the UML extension mechanism, the general method is extending the modeling capabilities of UML by adding some stereotypes, the tagged value and constraint for the model element and it usually build on the basis of not modifying the existing metamodels. Stereotypes are based on an existing model element to define a new kind of model elements. Stereotype generally signed by the string in the double Angle brackets "<< >>". Tag values are the explicit definition of a feature and it is a kind of mechanism used to specify the model element properties. Constraint is the semantics conditions or restrictions that applied to one or more elements and expresses by the string expression in the braces. In this paper, we use structure of UML extensions.

Above we have pointed out that security concerns are the concerns distributed in various modules with crosscutting attributes. So the Aspect-Oriented Programming (AOP) technology is the best choice for modeling security concerns. Using AOP technology can be modular to security concerns and reduce the complexity of the system due to security. Therefore, it's important to extend UML to describe, visualize, construct and document the elements in AOP. Following we will implement the aspect-oriented modeling with the UML metamodel and framework extension mechanism of UML extension.

3.3 Modeling approach

We are going to the elements in the AOP are collectively referred to as crosscutting elements. The aspect-oriented elements based on extended UML included Crosscutting Relationship, Aspect, CrosscuttingInterface and Crosscutting Feature. The extended framework is shown in Figure 1. It represents that the CoreElements crosscut by the CrosscuttingElements, and the CrosscuttingRelationaship describes the structure and behavior which CrosscuttingElements localized into system CoreElements. CrosscuttingInterface is a describtion approach for a set of aspect-oriented objects. It separated the objects related to aspect-oriented from all objects of the system. CrosscuttingInterface can be the attributes and operations which aspects were introduced to the system, and also the aspect operations. CrosscuttingFeature describes features that combined to several base elements. Each crosscutting feature has the functions of defining extension types and crosscutting types. Aspect implemented the encapsulation of

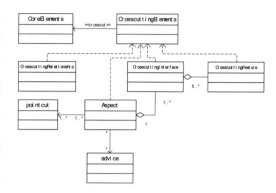

Figure 1. The extended UML model framework.

the pointcut, advice and many other crosscutting elements.

The above we have designed the aspect-oriented modeling framework which was supported by the extended UML. On this basis we employ UML extension mechanism to express security concerns, the association between security concerns and core concerns, as well as the relationships among the security concerns.

Firstly, according to the characteristics of the security concerns, we extended <<SecurityConcern>> stereotype based on UML elements and it encapsulated security concerns as aspects, which make sure the structure and behavior of security concerns are the same as the class instances. Security concerns model is shown in Figure 2, it is isolated from the core class and is executed after the operation.

Secondly, we analyzed the association about security concerns in a system. There are two parts: one is the relationship between security concerns and core classes. The other is associations among security concerns. The whole construct is shown in Figure 3. The main purpose of security concerns is crosscutting core classes, so we can extend <<crosscut>> stereotype to represent the relationship between security concerns and core classes with the aid of association in UML model elements. We find that one security concern can be resolved by many solutions, for example, If we employed digital signature to implement data authentication, RSA, DSA and ECDSA are optional solutions to developers. On condition that you want a signature process faster, the choice of the DSA algorithm; If you want to choose one which validation process is faster, then the RSA algorithm is better; If it is to hope that under the same degree of security use of shorter key and then select ECDSA. Therefore, The stereotype <<optional>> is added for the relationship between Coreclass and security concerns. And one

Figure 2.   Security concerns model.

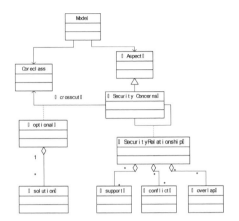

Figure 3.   Association of security concerns.

aspect must be chosen among the optional aspects which can implement the same feature.

What's more, a software system could be cross-cut by one or more security concerns. There is also a corresponding relationship between these concerns: firstly, one security concern serves as a supporting of another security concern, such as the security concern used to decrypt can support the encryption security concern. Secondly, due to the limitation of time or system interoperability and so on, there is also a conflict between security concerns. Thirdly, Security concerns can be implemented by one or more solutions, and it is possible that many different security concerns can be realized by the same solution, so there are overlap relationship between security concerns. For example, the concerns of security strategy can support the mitigation of security threats concerns. In a word, we will extend relationships among security concerns to three categories: support, conflict and overlap. With the help of association model elements in UML, <<SecurityRelationship>> stereotype have been extended to represent the relationship among security concerns and <<support>>, <<conflict>>and<<overlap>> have become its subclasses. As shown in Figure 3.

4   CONCLUSIONS AND FUTURE WORK

With the rapid growth of Internet, the scope of software is increasing, at the same time, the security of software system also becomes more and more important. Thus the research works that makes software far away from the threats through modeling software security concerns is one of the research hotspots in the field of software development. In terms of the existing research results lacking modeling methods of security concerns and the analysis for the security concerns relationship, this paper presents a software security concerns modeling method based on UML extension. Firstly, we extend UML elements, allowing the UML to describe aspect-oriented elements. Secondly, on the basis of extended UML, we model security concerns and finally analyze the relationships among security concerns. This method can assist software architects to build more secure software. There are several directions for the future work of the approach: One direction is how to weave the extended security concerns to the whole system model using UML. Another direction is to analyze the security concerns' impact to other non-functional attributes and so on.

ACKNOWLEDGMENT

This work is supported by National Science Foundation of China (No. 61100017 and 61262023), Xinjiang Uygur Autonomous University Research Foundation (No. XJEDU2011S24), Xinjiang University Doctoral Graduate research startup foundation (BS120126).

REFERENCES

[1] Basin D., Clavel M., Egea M. A decade of model-driven security[C], Proceedings of the 16th ACM Symposium on Access Control Models And Technologies (SACMAT 11). ACM press, 2011, pp: 1–10.
[2] Chase Baker, Michael Shin. Mapping of Security Concerns in Design to Security Aspects in Code[C], Proceedings of IEEE 6th International Conference on Software Security and Reliability Companion (SERE-C12). IEEE press, 2012, pp: 102–110.
[3] D. Firesmith, Engineering security requirements[J], Journal of Object Technology, 2003, Vol. 2, No. 1, pp: 53–68.
[4] Doan T., Demurjian S., Ting T.C., Ketterl A. MAC and UML for secure software design[C], Proceedings of the 2004 ACM workshop on Formal Methods in Security Engineering (FMSE'04). ACM press, 2004, pp: 75–85.
[5] Dai L., Cooper K., Using FDAF to bridge the gap between enterprise and software architectures for security[J]. Science of Computer Programming, 2007, Vol. 66, No. 1, pp: 87–102.
[6] Gary McGraw. "Software Security," security & privacy, IEEE press, vol. 2, no. 2, 2004, pp: 80–83.

[7] Gomaa H., Eonsuk Shin M., Modeling complex systems by separating application and security concerns[C], Proceedings of the 9th IEEE International Conference on Engineering Complex Computer Systems (ICECCS 09), IEEE press, 2004, pp: 19–28.

[8] Hassan Gomaa, Michael E. Shin. Separating Application and Security Concerns in Use Case Models[C], Proceedings of the 15th workshop on early aspects (EA 09), ACM press, March 3, 2009, pp: 1–5.

[9] Hussain S., Rasool G., Atef M. and Shahid A.K. A Review of Approaches to Model Security into Software Systems[J], Journal of Basic and Applied Scientific Research. 2013, Vol. 3, No. 4, pp: 642–647.

[10] Losavio F, Matteo A., Morantes P. UML Extensions for Aspect Oriented Software Development[J]. Journal of Object Technology, 2009, Vol. 8, No. 5, pp: 85–131.

[11] Li Zhen, Liu Bin, Miao Hong, et al. Formalization verification of requirements based on partition of software safety Petri net [J]. Systems Engineering and Electronics, 2012, Vol. 34, No. 9, pp: 1966–1972.

[12] Muniraman, C. & Damodaran, M., A practical approach to include security in software development[J]. Issues in Information Systems, 2007, Vol. 2, No. 2, pp: 193–199.

[13] Mouheb D, Talhi C, Lima V, et al. Weaving Security Aspects into UML 2.0 Design Models[C], Proceedings of the 13th Aspect-Oriented Modeling Workshop (AOM 09). ACM press, 2009, March 2, pp: 7–11.

[14] Mouheb D., Talhi C., Nouh M. Aspect-oriented modeling for representing and integrating security concerns in UML, Software Engineering Research[J], Management and Applications. Springer Berlin Heidelberg, 2010, pp: 197–213.

[15] Tndel I.A., Jensen J., Rstad L., Combining misuse cases with attack trees and security activity models. Proceedings of the 5th International Conference on Availability, Reliability and Security (ARES 10). Feb. 2010, pp: 438–445. Doi: 10.1109/ARES.2010.101.

[16] Xu D., Nygard K.E., Threat-driven modeling and verification of secure software using aspect-oriented Petri nets[J]. IEEE Transactions on Software Engineering, 2006, Vol. 32, No. 4, pp: 265–278.

[17] Xu D., Goel V., Nygard K.E. and Eric Wong, W. Aspect-oriented specification of threat-driven security requirements[J], International Journal of Computer Applications in Technology, Vol. 31, No. 1, 2008, pp: 131–140.

[18] Zulkernine, M. & Ahamed, S., Software security engineering: Toward unifying software engineering and security engineering[J]. Enterprise Information Systems Assurance and Systems Security: Managerial and Technical Issues, M. Warkentin & R. Vaughn, 2006, pp: 215–232.

Computer, Intelligent Computing and Education Technology – Liu, Sung & Yao (Eds)
© 2014 Taylor & Francis Group, London, ISBN 978-1-138-02469-4

Video semantic feature extraction model

X. Zhong
College of Computer Science, South-Central University for Nationalities, China

L. Li
School of Computer Science and Technology, Wuhan University of Technology, China

ABSTRACT: Video semantic feature extraction methods are studied in this paper. A novel video semantic feature extraction framework is proposed to realize automatic annotation and extraction for the concept ontology of video semantic features, which focuses on time and space structure combined with conditional random model.

Keywords: video; semantic feature; CRF; ontology

1 INTRODUCTION

Video semantic feature extraction is the basis of video semantic retrieval technology, good video semantic feature extraction model is implemented high quality, high efficiency of video semantic retrieval technology. Due to the Ontology has the strong Ability of semantic differential, namely different large differences between the concept of Ontology, and has the invariance, therefore this paper mainly uses the concept of Ontology to characterize the semantic characteristics of videos. The current domestic and foreign about the extraction of video semantic feature model, can be mainly classified into four categories.[1,2]

This paper puts forward a video semantic feature extraction framework, its research content based on conditional Random Field[3–5] model and the related knowledge of probability statistics, exploring the use machine automatic labeling (extraction) video semantic feature concept ontology model.

2 VIDEO SEMANTIC FEATURE EXTRACTION FRAMEWORK

From the Angle of human cognitive video semantic classification, its semantic concepts including objects, scenes and three types of events.[19] In view of these three kinds of semantic concepts in Video semantic differences and the difficulty of feature extraction methods, this chapter focuses on Video semantic Video Object extraction method, in which Video objects refers to the entities which are subjects of physical performance, and is keeping

semantic Video scenes and events for further discussion.

Conditional random field[120] is very suitable for time series labeling problem of random variables, datat Therefore, our research work is mainly based on the conditional random field to build video semantic feature extraction method.

Figure 1 shows the video semantic feature extraction framework based on conditional random field. The framework of the concrete

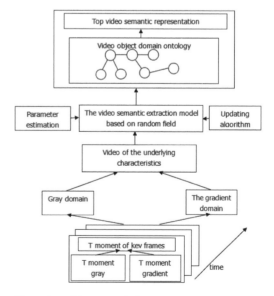

Figure 1. Video semantic feature extraction framework diagram.

implementation is made up of several related probability submodel, including video low-level features model, video lower likelihood model and high-level semantic video object extraction model, and high-level semantic video object model.

2.1 Define 5-1 video key frame sequence

Given a key frame extraction of the video data and combination extraction in chronological order to get a collection of key frame sequence, called video key frame sequence, it said $\{K_t \mid t \in N\}$. Here, the variable t defined as the time scale of video key frame sequence.

2.2 Define 5-2 video object ontology field

Given a video there are physical entity semantic objects of a Random field, referred to as a semantic video object domain. Because this article is based on a semantic description of real objects in video concept Ontology to represent, and thus also known as video semantic video object domain object domain Ontology, namely high-level semantic annotation object domain Ontology, it said for collection $O = \{O_i \mid i \in N\}$, which said the Ontology is domain specific elements, such as "car", "people" concept. If s is the video key frames on a number of space of adjacent pixels of physical object area at t moment, which corresponding domain ontology can be labeled as $O_t(s)$. In the actual calculation, the element in video object domain ontology will be quantitative vector-valued for concrete.

2.3 Define 5-3 video low-level feature field

Given a period of video, the low-level pixel of image characteristics related to a random field, known as the video low-level feature domain, also known as the video key frames domain, it said to F. For example, the low-level features of domain of the video key frames at t moment can be expressed as F_t, which specific to the key frames on a certain pixel x of the low-level features can be represented as random vector $F_t(x)$.

2.4 Define 5-4 video image pixel field

Given a video sequence, a key frames at a certain moment constitutes a collection of all pixels, known as the video image pixel Domain, it is also the moment video key frames in space Domain, expressed as X. For example, the pixel set of video key frames at t moment can be expressed as X_t.

2.5 Video low-level features and likelihood model

According to the given earlier video semantic feature extraction framework, the low-level video key frames in a sequence of each pixel point is mapped as the object of high-level semantics, and in the form of object concept ontology representation. For example, assuming that x is a video sequence in the t time domain F_t key frame of a pixel point, it will be based on semantic mapping video semantic extraction model, labeled as high specific object $O_t(x)$. Also, if the x in the present moment for the video key frame semantic concept "car" low-level pixel, $O_t(x)$ be quantified as the concept of "auto" ontology vector $O_{车}$.

3 VIDEO LOW-LEVEL FEATURE MODEL

Video low-level features are specifications into the video key frames on the pixel gray level and Gradient two kinds of information of random field F_t. In the video sequence in $\{K_t\}$ any pixel x protocol as a random vector, expressed as $F_t(x) = (I_t(x), G_t(x))$.

3.1 Gray domain

At time t, video key frame pixel gray level information on x mathematics expressed as pixel x coordinates (x_x, y_x) corresponds to a function, that is $I_t(x) = f(x_x, y_x)$. At the same time, for the convenience of calculation, and according to the principle of gaussian mixture model, it is assumed that video key frames the gray level information of each pixel in the approximate gaussian model is subject to different $N(\mu_{O_i,t}, \sigma_{O_i,t})$, and these different gaussian model respectively corresponding to the video key frames pixels belonging to several classes of objects by ontology.

Then, the gray model at time t video key frame pixel point on X can be expressed as follows:

$$I_t(x) = \lambda_{O_1} I_{O_1,t}(x) + \lambda_{O_2} I_{O_2,t}(x) + \cdots + \lambda_{O_k} I_{O_k,t}(x)$$
$$= \sum_{i=1}^{k} \lambda_{O_i} I_{O_i,t}(x)$$
$$= \sum_{i=1}^{k} \lambda_{O_i} (u_{O_i,t}(x) + n_{O_i,t}(x)) \qquad (1)$$

In the model:

1. The λ_{O_i} representation for video key frame at time t, all the semantic annotation of $N(\mu_{O_i,t}, \sigma_{O_i,t})$ obeys Gauss distribution for the pixel i object O_i in the gray model weights, and satisfy the $\sum_{i=1}^{k} \lambda_{O_i} = 1$ and $0 \leq \lambda_{O_i} \leq 1$, where $i \in N$.
2. $I_{O_i,t}(x) = u_{O_i,t}(x) + n_{O_i,t}(x)$. Among them, $u_{O_i,t}(x)$ said for all semantic belongs to the first

138

i object ontology O_i pixels gaussian distribution model of average, $n_{O_i,t}(x)$ is expressed as their corresponding noise variance $\sigma_{o_i,t}$.

Thus, t time video key frames of gray domain for I_t.

3.2 The gradient domain

At time t, video key frame pixel gradient information on x mathematics expressed as pixel x coordinates (x_x, y_x) corresponds to an operator, a vector is defined as the following:

$$G_t(x) = \nabla f(x_x, y_x) = [G_x, G_y]^T = \left[\frac{\partial f}{\partial x}, \frac{\partial f}{\partial y}\right]^T \quad (2)$$

For convenience of calculation, using video key frames here in adjacent pixel gray level difference to specific statute gradient information. So, video key frames in t time pixel gradient model x can be expressed as follows:

$$G_t(x) = \nabla f(x_x, y_x) = [I_t(x + \Delta x)$$
$$- I_t(x), I_t(x + \Delta y) - I_t(x)]^T \quad (3)$$

In the model:

1. the Δx, Δy, respectively for the pixel x in key frames the increment of the unit on the transverse and longitudinal axis.
2. the gradient model $G_t(x)$ approximately obey Gauss distribution $N(\mu_{G,t}, \Sigma_{G,t})$.

3.3 Video low-level feature likelihood model

Low-level video features likelihood model $p(F_t | O_t)$, is in a given high-level object semantic annotation ontology domain conditional probability model based on O_t, it is the final statistical derivation of high-level object semantic annotation model data premise.

Here, the first hypothesis when given high-level object semantic annotation ontology domain O_t, low-level video features random fields F_t in video spatial domain satisfy the conditional independence, thus, low-level video features likelihood model factor decomposition as follows:

$$p(F_t | O_t) = \prod_{x \in X} p(F_t(x) | O_t(x)) \quad (4)$$

At the same time, assuming that video low-level features in the random field F_t gray level and gradient domains also meet the conditions for independence, then the likelihood model and factorization is:

$$p(F_t | O_t) = p(I_t, G_t | O_t) = p(I_t | O_t) p(G_t | O_t) \quad (5)$$

4 VIDEO HIGH-LEVEL OBJECT SEMANTICS EXTRACTION MODEL

The previous section gives the low-level video features likelihood model of P, however, the model only focuses on each pixel video key frame in its influence on the extraction of video object semantics, and never consider the pixel correlation information between each of the points in video sequences. This section from the spatial and temporal information analysis and statistics of the pixels of the video semantic feature extraction framework, for the further construction of high-level object semantics extraction model, which helps to enhance the accuracy of video semantic extraction.

4.1 Spatial information analysis and modeling

Same key frames in video sequences there are interaction relationship between the pixel, reasonable use of this information is helpful to improve the quality of video semantic extraction. Here, We mainly focus on the correlation between the same pixels in x key frame in the spatial domain directly adjacent to the up and down about four pixels x_u x_d, x_l, x_r, let $N_x = \{x_u, x_d, x_l, x_r\}$, thus assuming the same key frames of pixels between each other to satisfy markov properties, namely:

$$p(r(x) | r', r(y), y \neq x) = p(r(x) | r', r(y), y \in N_x) \quad (6)$$

The r and r' are two random domain video sequence on the key frame.

Thus, through the analysis of key frames in video sequences of spatial information in time t, high-level semantic video object extraction model can be modeled as a conditional random fields model, namely $p(O_t | F_{1...t})$.

Then, according to the law of Hamersley–Clifford, the model can factor into the model corresponds to the probability of undirected graph in several product of maximal clique of potential function, namely:

$$p(O_t | F_{1...t}) = \frac{1}{Z(O_t | F_{1...t})} \prod_C \Psi_C(O_t | F_{1...t}) \quad (7)$$

In the model:

1. $Z(O_t | F_{1...t})$ is normalized Factor (Normalization Factor), which is:

$$Z(O_t | F_{1...t}) = \sum_{O_t} \prod_C \Psi_C(O_t | F_{1...t}) \quad (8)$$

2. C is the probability corresponding model of undirected clique in the graph, the key frames

of video sequence pixels x satisfy the spatial neighborhood pixels of markov property set.

3. $\Psi_C(O_t\,|\,F_{1...t})$ for a Potential on the biggest group C.

Then, according to the spatial information of key frames in a video sequence, expression of potential function model can be further specific for the potential and the gradient of pixel gray of the potential and, that is:

$$\Psi_C(O_t\,|\,F_{1...t}) = \exp(-E_C(O_t\,|\,F_{1...t}))$$
$$= \exp(-\sum_{x\in C}(\Psi_{I_t(x)}(O_t(x)\,|\,F_{1...t}(x))$$
$$+ \sum_{y\in N_x}\Psi_{G_t(x)}(O_t(x),O_t(y)))) \qquad (9)$$

Among them, $\Psi_{I_t(x)}(O_t(x)\,|\,F_{1...t}(x))$ is a key frames in video sequences pixels x potential of gray, it can be made of video low-level feature model of the gray model $I_t(x)$ provide data; $\Psi_{G_t(x)}(O_t(x),O_t(y))$ is a key frames in video sequences pixels x potential gradient, it can be provided by the video lower characteristic model of the gradient model $\Psi_{G_t(x)}(O_t(x),O_t(y))$ data.

4.2 The time-domain analysis and modeling

In video sequences, the same position on the adjacent key frames of image frames also exist between the pixels of interdependent relationship, rational use of this kind of video sequence of temporal information, also help improve the quality of video semantic extraction. Here, we focus on the two adjacent key frame, such as K_t and K_{t+1}, the same position between x_t pixels and pixel x_{t+1} time domain information relevance in a video sequence, $M_{x_t}=\{x_t,x_{t+1}\}$. Therefore, also assume that the pixels to satisfy markov property of video sequences on the time domain:

$$p(r(x_t)\,|\,r',r(y),y\neq x_t)=p(r(x_t)\,|\,r',r(y),y\in M_{x_t})$$
$$\qquad (10)$$

The r and r' are two random domain video sequence on the key frame in a video sequence, y is in the video sequence with pixel x at the same location on another pixels.

Thus, high-level semantic video object extraction time domain model in video sequences, can be modeled as a Linear Conditional Random Fields[5] (LCRF) model, namely:

$$p(O_{t+1}\,|\,O_t)=\frac{1}{Z(O_{t+1}\,|\,O_t)}\prod_C\Psi_C(O_{t+1}\,|\,O_t)$$
$$=\frac{1}{Z(O_{t+1}\,|\,O_t)}\exp\left(\sum_{x\in X,t}\alpha_t\omega_t(x_t,x_{t+1})\right.$$
$$\left.+\sum_{y\in N_{x(t+1),t}}\beta_t\gamma_t(x_{t+1},y))\right) \qquad (11)$$

In the model:

1. $Z(O_{t+1}\,|\,O_t)$ is normalized Factor (Normalization Factor), which is:

$$Z(O_{t+1}\,|\,O_t)=\sum_{O_{t+1}}\prod_C\Psi_C(O_{t+1}\,|\,O_t) \qquad (12)$$

2. C probability corresponding to the model of undirected clique in the graph, is a set of two pixels in adjacent time domain of the video sequence.

3. $\Psi_C(O_{t+1}\,|\,O_t)$ as a potential maximal clique on C (Potential), all of its potential is the product of an exponential function.

In addition, the exponential function in the $\exp\left(\sum_{x\in X,t}\alpha_t\omega_t(x_t,x_{t+1})+\sum_{y\in N_{x(t+1),t}}\beta_t\gamma_t(x_{t+1},y)\right)$:

1. Function $\omega_t(x_t,x_{t+1})$ refers to time t key frames of video sequence in time domain pixel point x_t and x_{t+1} semantic extraction of the potential of this point, it can through the video low-level feature model of the gray model $I_t(x)$ provide data; Function $\gamma_t(x_{t+1},y)$ refer to time t key frames of video sequence in time domain pixel x_t corresponding pixels in the next frame potential gradient effect, it can be made of video low-level features provide data model of the gradient $G_t(x)$.

2. the parameters α_t and β_t corresponding function $\omega_t(x_t,x_{t+1})$ and $\gamma_t(x_{t+1},y)$ to potential weight, it can be through the front of the model parameter estimation algorithm is used to estimate sample.

5 CONCLUSIONS

This paperr is to study the extraction method for video semantic features, the first introduced the video semantic features and significance of extraction method in the research of the status, and a brief description of the contents of this chapter focus of research; and then analyzes the related work at home and abroad on video semantic extraction at present; then, from the video of the time and the spatial structure features, and combining with the condition and the domain model, propose a semantic feature extraction framework, automatic annotation and extraction of concept ontology to realize semantic feature; finally an example test, validate the rationality and validity of the research method, and the availability of relevant algorithms in this chapter.

ACKNOWLEDGEMENTS

The research is supported by Wuhan Science & Technology Bureau, Innovation Team

Project (2013070204005) and National Science & Technology Pillar Program under Grant No. 2012BAH33F03.

REFERENCES

[1] Wei Wei, Jing You, Fengyu Liu. A survey on semantic retrieval [J]. Computer Science (Chinese), 2006, 33(2): 1–8.

[2] Zhou H, Sadka A.H, Swash M.R, et al. Feature extraction and clustering for dynamic video summarisation [J]. Neurocomputing, 2010, 73(10): 1718–1729.

[3] Smeulders A.W.M., Worring M., Santini S., et al. Content-based image retrieval at the end of the early years [J]. IEEE Transactions on Pattern Analysis and Machine Intelligence, 2000, 22(12):1349–1380.

[4] Kollar D, Friedman N. Probabilistic graphical models: principles and techniques [M]. Cambridge: The MIT Press, 2009.

[5] Li S.Z. Markov random field modeling in image analysis [M]. Springer, 2009.

Computer, Intelligent Computing and Education Technology – Liu, Sung & Yao (Eds)
© *2014 Taylor & Francis Group, London, ISBN 978-1-138-02469-4*

Application of multi-population genetic algorithm in economic dispatch of power systems

Kai Wang
Department of Economics and Management, North China Electric Power University, Baoding, China

ABSTRACT: Aiming at the characteristics of economic dispatch of power systems, Multi-population genetic algorithm is proposed to solve this problem. Through different parameters of population, immigration operator, elite population retention strategy, the algorithm solves the problems of conventional SGA "premature" and hard to maintain population diversity in the later evolution etc, and effectively improves the searching speed and the global optimal searching capability of genetic algorithm. Through simulation examples, and compared with other optimization algorithm, the results verify the validity of the proposed method.

Keywords: power system; economic dispatch; multi-population genetic algorithm

1 INTRODUCTION

Economic Load Dispatch (ED) is to minimize the cost of power generation under the premise of the load and operating constraints, which will be of great significance for the reliability and economy of power system operation [1]. As the constraint of the valve point effect in thermal power generating units, the limits of operational capacity and stability of the system, lead to problem solving is the essence of a optimization problem with high dimension of non-convex, nonlinear, non-differentiable.

At present, genetic algorithm has been successfully applied to various optimization problems with its good global searching ability and the strong adaptability [2]. But there are still "premature" and hard to maintain population diversity in the later evolution etc.

Aiming at these problems, this paper proposes a multi-population genetic algorithm to solve the ED problem. By using the structure of multi-group parallel evolution and immigration operator, the algorithm maintains the link between populations, and promotes information exchange among populations of individuals in order to enhance the diversity of population, and to avoid the "premature" phenomenon of population. Meanwhile, the introduction of the elite retention policy which protects the best individual in the population, improves the convergence speed and computing precision of algorithm.

2 ECONOMIC DISPATCH OF POWER SYSTEMS PROBLEM

2.1 Objective functions

The ED problem is to optimize the output of generating unit in the system under meeting the operating constraints, and to bring the total system power consumption to a minimum, that is to minimize the cost of power generation, the objective function is:

$$\min F = \min \left\{ \sum_{i=1}^{Ng} F_i(P_i) \right\} \qquad (1)$$

where F = the total generation costs; N_g = the total system generator; P_i represents the i-th generator active power; $F_i(P_i)$ = the amount of consumption characteristics of the i-th generator, generally available approximated by a quadratic function:

$$F_i(P_i) = \alpha_i P_i^2 + \beta_i P_i + \gamma_i \qquad (2)$$

where $\alpha_i, \beta_i, \gamma_i$ is the i-th generator consumption characteristic constant.

Roberts's phenomenon appeared in the turbine inlet valve opens suddenly makes generating unit consumption characteristics produce the valve point effect. Ignore valve point effect will significantly affect the solution accuracy [3].

The consumption characteristic change caused by the valve point effect is:

$$E_i = \left| g_i \sin\left[h_i(P_i - P_{\min,i}) \right] \right| \qquad (3)$$

where g_i, h_i are the parameters; $P_{min,i}$ = the lower limit of the i-th generator active power.

Therefore, the total cost objective function meeting the valve point effect is:

$$\min F = \sum_{i=1}^{Ng} F_i(P_i) + \sum_{i=1}^{Ng} E_i \qquad (4)$$

2.2   Constraint conditions

1. Due to the limit of generator power, the constraint for the generator operation is:

$$P_{min,i} \le P_i \le P_{max,i} \ (i = 1, 2, ..., Ng) \qquad (5)$$

where $P_{min,i}$, $P_{max,i}$ respectively, as the i-th units of the power of upper and lower limits.

2. Power balance refers to it that the sum of the generator active power is equal to total system net loss and total load of the system. But network losses can be ignored when the power system network covers densely [4], so the power balance constraint can be simplified as:

$$P_D = \sum_{i=1}^{Ng} P_i \qquad (6)$$

where P_D = the total load.

3   MULTI-POPULATION GENETIC ALGORITHM

Considering the essence of solving ED problem is a class of the optimization problems with high dimension, nonlinear, non-differentiable and non-convex. While genetic algorithm is an algorithm that does not rely on gradient information and does not require a continuous and differentiable objective function, and has the great advantage in dealing with large scale, nonlinear combinatorial optimization problem. But it still has many problems such as "premature", species diversity is difficult to remain in the late evolution. This paper proposes a multi-population genetic algorithm to solve these problems. The characteristics of the model are as follows.

3.1   Populations with different parameters

Evolutionary mechanisms of population $1 \sim N$ are conventional SGA. While various groups

by selecting different crossover probability Pc, deciding algorithm global search capability, and mutation probability Pm, determining the local searching ability of the algorithm, accomplish evolving independently, to improve the diversity of the population.

3.2   Immigration operator

Between the various groups are independent of each other, through the immigration operator contact. It will introduce the best individual arising in the evolutionary process from various groups into other population regularly, realizing the information exchange between populations of individuals, and promoting co-evolution between populations.

3.3   The elite reservation

In every generation of the evolution, we save other species of the best individual in the elite group through artificial selection. In order to ensure the best individual arising in the evolutionary process from various groups is not damaged and lost, elite population do not select, crossover and mutation. Meanwhile, elite population takes optimal individual reaching stay algebra for at least as the basis of algorithm terminates.

4   ALGORITHM STEPS

Using multi-population genetic algorithm to solve the ED problem, the specific steps are as follows:

1. Assign initial values for various parameters randomly, to create the initial population;
2. Calculate the objective function value of the individuals of the initial population;
3. Do selection, crossover, mutation, and reinsert operation for each of the individual populations;
4. Replace the worst individual in target population for the best individual from the original population successively through immigration operator;
5. Preserve the best individual from the various groups in the elite population at the frequency of artificial operator set;
6. Take the best individual from elite populations, judge whether the current optimization value is always the same value as the previous optimization when reaching the preset number of iterations;
7. If so then the algorithm converges, reaching the optimal value; If not, update the optimal value

according to the situation, and turn to step 3), recalculate the number of iterations;
8. Output global optimal solution, terminate optimization.

5 ANALYSES OF CASES AND COMPARISON

This paper takes IEEE3 machine 9 nodes standard test system for example, and multi-population genetic algorithm is adopted to test, IEEE3 machine 9 nodes generator specific characteristic parameters see literature [5]. The total load of the system is 500 MW.

Do optimization in two different conditions:

1. Regardless of the valve point effect, so that $g = 0$, $h = 0$, meet the total load system. The optimization results are as follows in Figure 1.
   Comparing with the literature [6–7], the results are as follows in Table 1.
2. Considering the valve point effect, meet the overall system load, the optimization results are as follows in Figure 2.
   Comparing with the literature [6–7], the results are as follows in Table 2.

Tables 1 and 2 shows, the fuel costs optimized by the algorithm proposed in this paper is below the literature [6], higher than the literature [7].

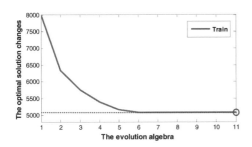

Figure 1. The evolutionary process without considering the valve point effect.

Table 1. Value comparison of different algorithms for the first case.

Algorithm	P1 /MW	P2 /MW	P3 /MW	The total load/MW	Costs /($/h)
This algorithm	236.75	203.25	60.00	500.00	5082.71
Literature [6]	237.73	187.58	74.69	500.00	5083.04
Literature [7]	228.64	202.13	68.80	499.57	5080.50

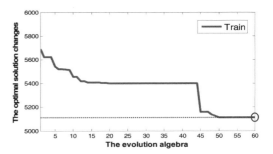

Figure 2. The evolutionary process considering the valve point effect.

Table 2. Value comparison of different algorithms for the second case.

Algorithm	P1 /MW	P2 /MW	P3 /MW	The total load/MW	Costs /($/h)
This algorithm	200.03	249.19	50.77	499.99	5111.57
Literature [6]	299.41	100.70	99.90	500.01	5121.47
Literature [7]	199.73	250.18	50.00	499.91	5094.70

But on the power balance in the system, the results in this paper basic strictly meet the demand. And the evolution algebra is smaller, convergence speed is fast, so this algorithm has a better optimization performance.

6 CONCLUSIONS

This paper breakthrough SGA only rely on the framework of a single population optimization, by using multi-swarm with different parameters at the same time to search for the optimal, and exchanging genetic information in a variety of populations through immigration operator, achieve a variety of group co-evolution; Through artificial selection operator select the best individual in elite population, ensure the accuracy and efficiency of the algorithm.

From the comparison analysis of examples can be seen, multi-population genetic algorithm can achieve the optimal economic dispatch of power system load with less evolutionary generation under the premise of the load and operating constraints, which has an important significance for economic dispatch of power system research. At the same time, it also provides a new way to solve the optimization problem of high dimensional non-convex, nonlinear, non-differentiable.

REFERENCES

[1] Hou Yunhe, Lu Lijuan, Xiong Xingen, et al. Improved particle swarm optimization algorithm and its application in economic dispatch of power systems [J]. Proceedings of the CSEE, 2004, 24(7):95–100.

[2] Ge Jike, Qiu Yuhui, Wu Chunming, et al. Summary of genetic algorithms research [J]. Application Research of Computers, 2008, 25(10):2911–2916.

[3] David C. Walters. Gerald B. Sheble. Genetic algorithm solution of economic dispatch with valve point loading [J]. IEEE Trans on PS. 1993, 8(3):1325–1332.

[4] Zhang Youhua, Wang Lianguo. Economic dispatch of power systems based on shuffled frog leaping algorithm [J]. Transducer and Microsystem Technologies, 2012, 31(6):58–61.

[5] Tang Wei, Li Dianpu. Chaotic optimization for economic dispatch of power systems [J]. Proceedings of the CSEE, 2000, 20(10):36–40.

[6] Tang Wei, Li Dianpu. Chaotic optimization for economic dispatch of power systems [J]. Proceedings of the CSEE, 2000, 20(10):36–40.

[7] Han Fang, Wang Shuangxin, Guo Xiaobao. Study of chaotic optimization method for power system economic load dispatch [J]. Chinese Journal of Scientific Instrument, 2005, 26(8):772–777.

Computer, Intelligent Computing and Education Technology – Liu, Sung & Yao (Eds)
© 2014 Taylor & Francis Group, London, ISBN 978-1-138-02469-4

The enlightenment of space teaching for the talent nurturing mode at the information age

N. Zhu, G. Ding & Y. Shen
Academic Affairs Office, Harbin Institute of Technology, Harbin, China

ABSTRACT: The activity of teaching in space shows the strong confidence of our government in forwarding the education innovation and development, and demonstrate the fact that the information technology is ready to be integrated with education deeply and thoroughly. The best case to show this integration is the emergence of the teaching mode MOOCs (massive open online courses) in America in the past two years. This paper analyzes the problems of talent nurturing in higher education in China, and approaches the possibility of MOOCs-based talent nurturing mode with the support of information technology.

Keywords: space lessons; information technology; MOOC (massive open online course); talent nurturing mode

1 REFLECTIONS ON SPACE COURSE

The complete success of manned spacecraft Shenzhou 10 and the first space teaching mission is the embodiment of innovation strength of science and technology and of China's national competitiveness. This also is a major historic breakthrough in education, especially in the educational informatization since National medium and long-term education reform and development plan outline (2010–2020) and Ten-Year Development Plan of Education Informatization (2011–2020) were issued, which is destined to exert impact on the higher education, especially the innovation of the mode of talent cultivation in Higher Education.

First take a look at China's first space lesson, its implementation process and characteristics. The manned spacecraft Shenzhou 10 has been successfully launched on June 11, 2013, and landed on June 26, 2013, successfully orbiting for 15 days. Among them, China's first female astronaut, Wang Yaping, gave a space lesson on June 20, 2013 from 10:04 to 10:55 to demonstrate 5 physical experiments at weightless environment for 80000 schools and 80000 young students. Learners from all over the world have participated in this space lessons through TV or Internet. This space teaching project is jointly hosted by CMSEO (China Manned Space Engineering Office), MOE (Ministry of Education of the People's Republic of China), and CAST (China Association for Science and Technology). The characteristics of space lessons are as follows:

1. From the viewpoint of teaching concept, the space teaching emphasizes orienting students as its mission, and instructs students a self-regulated learning mode by stimulating the students' interest. Concretely, this space lesson is first educational task in China's manned space flight missions, which embodies the direct service function of manned space engineering for national education, and also will further inspire the teenagers' enthusiasm and dream of loving the motherland, advocating science, and exploring the unknown.
2. From the viewpoint of teaching design, the space teaching put greater emphasis on the ways to carry on the teaching design based on the characteristics of learning, which is different from traditional cramming teaching method. Before the space mission, the teaching design must have been thoroughly prepared and rehearsed on the ground. The teaching design for space lesson will consider the practical requirements before the class, during the class, and after the class. For example, the aim, the principles, and the basic procedure of the experiment should be known before experiments through self-learning; during the class, the consideration of how to instruct students to observe the whole experiment process and grasp the abstract experimental principles through the teacher's explanation and the interaction between teachers and students, to deepen the students' understanding of knowledge and improve their ability of problems-solving and make innovation through the homework or

assignments after class. It can be said that teaching design, either for classroom teaching, or for space teaching, always plays an important role in improving study quality of learners.

3. From the viewpoint of teaching organization, the astronauts have clear division of labor. Wang Yaping gives the lectures, the commander Nie Haisheng is the teaching assistant, and Zhang Xiaoguang is in charge of the video camera.

4. The teacher-student interaction has been realized by means of sky chain between Shenzhou 10 and ground classroom in the type video conversation. It can be seen from that this teaching design is perfect because this in-time interaction is beneficial for students to understand knowledge better than the traditional cramming teaching in the classroom in which the teacher is the center of whole teaching activity.

5. As the teaching scale is considered, the space teaching activity involves not only 60 millions young people in China, but hundreds of millions of other learners with various ages, from various countries and areas. The scale of audience is tremendous, obviously. This shows that in the information age, the approaches of acquiring knowledge have earth-shaking changes than before. Finding ways to use limited good educational resources to benefit more people in an open sharing way has become a hot issue for higher education in the information age.

Generally speaking, the space teaching brought enlightenment to high education, especially the higher education informatization as follows:

1. It is pointed out in National Medium and Long-Term Education Reform and Development Plan Outline (2010–2020) that "information technology has revolutionary influence on education development which must be taken into account seriously". The Ten-Year Development Plan of Education Informatization (2011–2020) has also considered the educational informatization in a national strategic level. In order to push forward the educational informatization and realize the integration of information technology and higher education, is the new technology such as information technology, or high-grade, high-precision, advanced technology ready to face this challenge? We can get the answer from the space teaching. It is no doubt that the information technology has wrought major changes in manufacturing, living and studying styles in our society. Currently, it is necessary to find a good talent cultivating mode to satisfy the study requirements of learners. It is important to use information technology to solve this problem and realize the strategies of national innovation driving development and building a strong country.

2. It can be seen from the scale of space teaching that people have strong requirement for high quality educational resources. To accelerate the development and construction of high-quality educational resources and realize open and sharing is critical in the promotion of educational equality. In our country, a series of activities related to higher education have been adopted recently, such as Resource-Sharing Courses in China Universities, Open Video Courses, ICourses internet platform, etc. These endeavors have gained certain achievements, but they have not fully achieved the desired effect in promoting the educational equality. Massive Open Online Courses, briefly named MOOCs, arisen in USA in 2012, have highlighted the potential for promoting the educational resources sharing and making educational equity. For instance, many courses in the famous edX and Courser have attracted interests of thousands, even more than 100 thousands of learners from all over the world. It is important to refer to the experience of other countries, and to accelerate the construct, open, share and spread of high quality educational resources based on actual conditions in China, which are beneficial to the improvement of the education quality and equality.

2 MAIN PROBLEMS IN CURRENT TALENT NURTURING MODE OF HIGHER EDUATION

It can be seen from the analysis above that the critical issue for China's education development, especially the connotative development of higher education, is the close integration of information technology and education. The activity of space teaching tells us that the current information technology and other advanced techniques are able to satisfy the requirement of educational informatization-based innovation talent nurturing mode. The national demand for educational informatization is great. The information technology-based educational revolution, especially the innovation talent nurturing mode revolution, is urgent (Aguaded-Gomez, J.I. 2013). Therefore, it is necessary for us to make a review and reflection of the current talent nurturing mode in higher education. From the micro perspective, the problems are as follows:

1. From the perspective of teaching principle, the current talent nurturing mode is centered on teachers. At the information age, the ways that learners obtain the knowledge are changing from pure acceptance of teachers' presentation

to multi-channel access. This breaks the monopoly of knowledge control of teachers and the asymmetry of information control. Under this new situation, if teachers cannot delve into the learners' learning characteristics, and cater to their diversified needs and levels of knowledge of different levels, and are lack of a comprehensive reflection of teaching design, and reconstruction of the whole teaching steps, it will be difficult to continue to attract students to participate in classroom learning, let alone improving the quality of personnel training.

2. From a viewpoint of teaching methodology, in our current class teaching, the cramming method has been commonly used. Although facilitation of interactive teaching approaches has been advocated in many universities, the effect of classroom teaching is generally not good because most teachers have not taken the student–centered educational principle. The research results show statistically that the efficiency of students who participate in the lectures through audio, visual, or oral channel is 13%, 18% and 31%, respectively, while the combination of the three channels can increase the efficiency up to 52% and with an additional channel of hands-on participation, the efficiency increases up to 72%. Naturally, the efficiency of cramming or lecturing approaches is lower than or equals to 50%. Therefore, students often feel tired and tend to lose interests in study. This is one of reasons that the attendance rate has continued to decline in China's universities.

3. With regards to educational resources, the main resources in classroom teaching in universities include: textbook, reference books, lecture notes, teaching courseware, videos, teaching equipment and software, etc. Most of these resources are made by teachers themselves, and the rest are bought by universities. The current problem of the usage of these resources lie in slow update, extensive management, poor openness, poor sharing, and low utilization. This situation is conflictive with the huge open and sharing demand of high quality educational resources so that it is difficult to promote educational equalty by using these resources.

4. Viewed from the teacher-student interactivity, the main communication between teachers and students are after-class face-to-face interaction. This kind of communication is good to help the students to precisely understand knowledge, but sometimes not good because of the limitation of space and time. In recent years, emails, microblog, instant message software, such as QQ and Wechat, or SMS, have been increasingly used in communication. These ways are not limited by time and space so that student can communicate

with teachers anytime and anywhere. But they still can cause a breakdown in communication because the lack of face to face conversation.

5. As far as the assessment evaluation is concerned, the universities in our country pay attention to the appraisal of students learning results, not the learning process, emphasize the appraisal of students learning and overlook the comprehensive evaluation of ability. In the long run, the scores will become the baton of students for their study. It may result in the loss of interest in learning, or utilitarian learning.

Influenced by factors discussed above and other factors such as teachers' sense of responsibility, the contradiction between personnel training mode and learners' demand has become increasingly prominent at present stage in the most of the colleges and universities in our country. This has become a bottleneck problem restricting the quality of higher education talent nurturing in our country.

3 MOOC-BASED INNOVATION TALENT CULTURING MODE

It is the requirement and trend to improve the education quality and efficiency, build a platform for education with the advance of times, provide new teaching resources and change the teaching mode with the time. To thoroughly integrate the information technology, represented by mobile internet, artificial intelligence, massive data analysis, cloud computing, with higher education, is not only the enlightenment of space teaching, but also the practical implementation of gist of MOOCs. MOOCs have been followed with great enthusiasm by worldwide education organizations and learners for its openness and sharing. MOOCs provide possibility of changing the talent nurturing mode in higher education. The characteristics of MOOCs are briefly analyzed as follows:

1. Individualized learning. Learners use mobile internet and MOOC platform to break the limits of time and space anymore. The courses in MOOC platform are organized with many knowledge points which are explained through video resources in several minutes. By the organization and management of fragmentation of knowledge points, MOOCs provide possibility for students to begin study by following their own personalized pace.

2. Social interaction. As for massive learners in the course, for example, more than 100 thousands of people registered the course "Machine Learning" instructed by Professor Andrew in Coursera, the teacher for this course seldom encourages

learners to send email to him. Students have a virtual community on the internet which makes communication among students and teachers, or among students much more convenient and fast. Furthermore, learners may get answers of questions they have published from other learners in a very short time. There is no need for lecturers or teaching assistants to answer each question by themselves. This makes study and communication more less tiresome.

3. Diverse Evaluation. MOOCs provide many evaluation ways for learners. For instance, a learner may be quizzed randomly during a course by which the learner's participation and his study efficiency can be evaluated. In addition, an advanced type of evaluation may be adopted in which the learner cannot continue learning if he gives a wrong answer to the question. For the learners who have finished the whole course study, they will get the certificate for this course from the organization edX or Coursera. This may encourage learners to continue their study in MOOC platform.

4. Intelligent learning situation analysis. The number of learner engaged in MOOC courses is very large. Teachers can keep track of each student's learning situation and can provide timely feedback to guide and learning resources through in-depth analysis of various aspects of learning process for each student using big data. Furthermore, we can summarize law of education from the large data, which provide a way to improve the course content and teaching design.

Through tracking and mastering the characteristics of learners, their learning behavior, learning process using big data analysis techniques, instructors can design innovative teaching, targeted teaching, and can evaluate students more accurately and improve the quality and efficiency of learning process. As a result, it will promote the cultivation of personalized talents.

With the support of MOOC platform and MOOC curriculum resources, universities can adopt a variety of teaching modes, such as Blended Learning and Flipped Class Model. In fact, China's first space lectures can be seen as a success story of Flipped Class Model.

Through introducing MOOC into the classroom teaching on campus and remodeling university education, we then can change the routine from "teacher-centered" to "student-centered" teaching, thus to complete the core institutions of higher learning task—improving the talent training quality.

Therefore, we should conduct an all-round thinking on educational philosophy, instructional design, construction and open sharing of teaching resources, the reform of teaching methods with the reference of MOOC and the support of information technology. Creation of new training model in institutions of higher education is critical to the completion of the strategic objectives proposed by "Long-term Education Reform and development Plan (2010–2020)" and the "decade of Education information development Plan (2011–2020)". In addition, through these changes, it will greatly promote the equality of China's education, which is also crucial to the improvement of the comprehensive quality of citizens and build a learning society.

4 SUMMARY

China's first space teaching brings the world great impact, and also gives us inspiration that the integration of the information technology and education, especially the higher education, has been beady. MOOC has deeply impacted the education world and the educational informatization has become urgent for us. How to cultivate innovative talents by using information technology depends on the change of educational idea, richness of teaching resources and fundamental change of teaching methods. It is the only way to promote the national development strategy innovation and realize the smooth implementation of the education strategy by continuously improving the quality of personnel training.

REFERENCES

Aguaded-Gomez, J.I. 2013. The MOOC Revolution: A new form of education from the technological paradigm? *Comunicar* 41:7-8[14]C *instead of* C[14]/C-14 *and* BP/BC/AD *instead of* B.P./B.C./A.D.

Cooper, S. & Sahami, M. 2013. Education reflections on stanford's MOOCs. *Communications of the ACM* 56(2): 28–30.

Grünewald, F. et al. 2013. Designing MOOCs for the support of multiple learning styles. *Lecture Notes in Computer Science* 8095:371–382.

Kay, J. et al. 2013. MOOCs: So many learners, so much potential. *IEEE Intelligent Systems* 28(3): 70–77.

Rice, J. 2013. What I Learned in MOOC. *College Composition and Communication* 64(4): 695–703.

Computer, Intelligent Computing and Education Technology – Liu, Sung & Yao (Eds)
© 2014 Taylor & Francis Group, London, ISBN 978-1-138-02469-4

Hierarchical model for digital image processing and practice

Z.S. Li, T.C. Wang, B. Xie & J.J. Liu
Department of Information Engineering, Shaoyang University, Shaoyang, Hunan, China

ABSTRACT: "Digital image processing" course is very integrative. In order to let the students know the how and know the why, a hierarchical model of digital image processing is built with the Internet of things as background. Teaching purpose is cleared, knowledge chain being introduced, and content selection, teaching method and teaching means are normalized with the hierarchical model. The teaching results showed the proposed model is effective.

Keywords: digital image processing; hierarchical model; teaching approach; knowledge chain

1 INTRODUCTION

The technology of digital image processing has been applying widely and it has been becoming one of the new branches of science, drawing work from areas including pattern recognition, statistics, computer vision, communication and multimedia (Hu et al. 2011). In addition, automation in industrial production and the need for image information handling and retrieval are becoming increasingly important, which in turn set new demands for further theoretical and experimental developments. Then, there are at least three attributes for digital image processing technology: extensive application, comprehensiveness and development.

The comprehensiveness and development of digital image processing technology is issuing its challenge to the teaching of digital image processing course, while the extensive application is driving the establishment of a course in digital image processing technology at a university. For the chanllenge, strategies have been proposed by some researchers (McAndrew et al. 2005, Ning et al. 2010), but they only involve the teaching of the digital image processing course without taking the background, Internet of things (Li et al. 2013) into account, which is disadvantage to the training of practical ability for students. With the background of Internet of things which is in rapid development, here a hierarchical model for digital image procesing is poposed through the overall analyses of the digital image processing technology.

2 HIERARCHICAL MODEL

A good reason for students feeling it difficult to understand teching content is that they know that the teaching content is so but not why it is so, which is found by teachers during a long period of teaching process. In order for the students to clarify their mind and know "why it is so", a hierarchical model for teaching is constructed for digital image processing course (Fig. 1).

The hierarchical structure showed in Figure 1 is very much like the architecture of Internet of things. Or it can be said that the hierarchical structure is an object of Internet of things if the abstract hierarchical structure of Internet of things is viewed as a class. The object macroscopically provides an approach for students to know "why it is so" because it has a good progressive structure and teaching content is easy to find its source with it. On the other hand, from the micro-aspect, or from the view of the correspondence between the hierarchical model and the details of teaching content, teching experience has proved that the hierarchical model covers all the details.

Images must be sampled and quantized before they can be processed by computers. Then the first layer of the hierarchical model, "sampling and quantization of image data" is regarded as physical

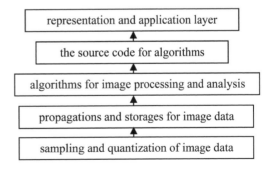

Figure 1. Hierarchical model.

layer, involving a variety of image acquisition equipment which is produced with modern techniques in optics and electronics. The second layer is "propagations and storages for image data". The most direct method to save storage space and increase the speed of transmission is to compress data. Before high-efficiency compressed data are obtained, images should be reformed with such as fourier transform, discrete cosine transform, K-L transform and wavelet transform. The third layer is "algorithms for image processing and analysis". The algorithms for image processing include image enhancement, image restoration, dither technique, pseudo-color encoding and processing, mathematical morphology, and so on. The algorithms for image analysis cover image segmentation, salient object extraction, automatic image annotation, image retrieval, etc. Both the algorithms for image processing and the algorithms for image analysis generally take the results of the second layer as their inputs. The fourth layer is "the source code for algorithms". The algorithms for image processing and analysis are described as mathematical formulae which can't be accepted by computers directly, so before the algorithms are coded, the mathematical formulae should be transformed with mathematical theory—numerical analysis for example. The fifth layer is "representation and application layer". It is an interface which shows results achieved by the algorithms for image processing and analysis, such as regions of image segmentation, objects from salient object extraction, return results from image retrieval based on content, and so on.

In a word, the hierarchical model covers whole course of digital image processing from begin to end, and can adapt to all types of teaching materials for digital image processing. That is to say, the hierarchical model is universal in teaching practice, which are fit of various teaching materials for digital image processing, no matter when the books are published.

3 TEACHING PRACTICE

Teaching practice are launched according to the hierarchical model by four steps: mobilization of students, selection of content, formulation of teching method and choice of teaching means.

Mobilization of students. There are two participants in the course of teaching and learning—teachers and students, and students are centered. The service quality of teching activities is decided by the achievements of students. So it is very important to mobile students and make them active participants. Before students are mobilized, they must obtained two aspects of information about the

course—useful and easy to learn. In order to make students feel the course of digital image processing useful, we can relate the hierarchical model to Internet of things. Internet of things is developing by leaps and bounds and produces numerous employment opportunities, which can encourage students be active and enthusiasm. The hierarchical model of digital image processing implies that digital image processing techniques are a subset of Internet of things. One can find his position in enterprises of Internet of things if he has done better work in digital image processing course.

Selection of content. It is the foundation of making students feel a course easy-to-earn to choose proper content. The content of digital image processing techniques accumulates at surprising rapidity with many researchers and is like the sea of knowledge. How to surf on the sea without missing one's way? Navigation marks are needed, and all the Navigation marks should compose a route which covers all the sights on the sea. The hierarchical model is such a kind of route on the endless sea of digital image processing techniques. According to the hierarchical model, teching content is chosed in the order of sampling, quantifying, transforming, processing and analyzing, on the principles of macro-control, Clarifying the context, stripping the knowledge of all irrelevancies and keeping in step with the times. For example, we keep items of image processing such as related concepts, properties and applications of gray scale histogram, image enhancement, image reconstruction, and so on, in the area of Special image processing, and in the area of the generalized image processing, items such as edge detection, region segmentation, gray level cooccurrence matrix, template matching, etc, are kept. And more, advanced knowledge is considered, such as fractal analysis, multiresolution algorithm, and so forth. When credit hours are limited, some theories difficult to understand are studied by interested students themselves, such as markov random field, neural network, etc. To stimulate students, we emphasize the introudction of up-to-date and advanced discipline knowledge, especially some fresh achievements with high value in practice.

Teaching method. The feeling of students, "easy to learn", can be deepened with proper teaching methods. With the hierarchical model as bone and course content as meat, the teaching method can be formed as follows: advancing step by step, from simple to complex and from the shallower to the deeper. Acquisition, quantification, storage, transmission, processing and analysis algorithms, code implementation, final interface, all these contents of image processing appear one by one, and there is a strong correlations between before and after. Based on the correlations, the teaching contents are organized so that students can understand new contents on the basis of what they have learned. For example, in terms of image coding, we have the following knowledge chain: image acquisition, image quantization matrix, linear transform, discrete cosine transform, image coding. There are five nodes before image coding. The five nodes have been told when image coding is coming, then we can only extend the knowledge chain forward. A further example, in terms of discrete cosine transform, the knowledge chain can be constructed as following: unit impulse function, linear shift invariant system, Fourier transform, discrete cosine transform. Before digital image processing course begins, we clarify knowledge chains according to the hierarchical model, which will make all knowledge points have roots, and let students find them "easy to learn".

Teaching means. Effective teaching means, can let the feeling of students, "easy to learn" into reality. Each part of "Digital image processing" has a strong correlation with its neighbour and can be connected in series to form chain. To show the chain in front of students, we design the following two kinds of teaching means: visualization of knowledge chain; knowledge layer penetration and multi-layer fusion. Knowledge chain visualization can be achieved with the help of animation which can be played back and forth.

For the realization of "knowledge layer penetration, multi-layer fusion", using VC and OpenCV development environment, demonstrations for each layer of the digital image processing hierarchy model are given. All demonstrations form a demo system. In order to enhance the students' sense of participation, they can change to the demo program in scene, and observe the effect. As an example here show the penetration and fusion among three layers, "algorithms for image processing and analysis", "the source code for algorithms" and "representation and application layer". There are three aspects and an interface in this example: results, algorithm implementation process and key code. Students can modify the code with the interface. Figure 2 is the result demonstration for edge extraction using Canny operator. We mark corresponding edge in the original image position with yellow color for comparison. The corresponding algorithm implementation process is demonstrated with animation.

Table 1. Comparison of teaching effect.

Year	Excellent	Good	Medium	Pass	Fail
13	10.9%	37.5%	32.8%	17.2%	1.6%
12	1.2%	25.9%	32.1%	28.4%	12.4%
11	2.1%	26.7%	31.5%	29.6%	10.1%

The principle of the Canny operator is presented in the animation, especially the effect of the upper and lower limits. Then the demonstration is started. The edges corresponding to different upper and lower limits are given, and will automatically be written into the original edge for verification.

The key code corresponding to the results are showed as follows, in this case:

cvCanny (gray, edge, LOW, HIGH, 3).

The parameters are the source image, the target image, the floor, the ceiling and aperture, corresponding to the previously explained algorithm. When the key code has been learned, the algorithm is runned in limited speed so that further analysis can be done.

The three parts mentioned above can freely be switched, for example, clicking result demo interfaces, then the corresponding key code coming, vice versa, which helps students to understand the strong relationship between codes and results.

4 PRACTICE EFFECT

Table 1 gives the score distribution over the past three years of "digital image processing" course. The teacher in three years is the identical one, and papers of the three years are equivalent. Conventional PPT teching means are used in year 11 and 12, and the hierarchical model based in 13. From the distribution of achievement, the excellent rate in 13 is 5 times of that in 11 and 12. The good rate in 13 is 10% more than in 11 and 12. Medium rates are close. The pass rate in 13 is over 10% lower than in 11 and 12. The fail rate in 13 is just less than one fifth of that in 11 and 12. The effect of the proposed hierarchical model is showed.

5 CONCLUSION

The hierarchical model of "digital image processing" is presented, taking the Internet of things as background and combining with the characteristics of "digital image processing" course. The model reinforces classroom interaction between teaching and learning and can help the students know why about the teching content, which has been proved by practice.

Figure 2. Results.

ACKNOWLEDGMENT

This research is supported by the natural science foundation of Hunan Province China, (No. 13JJ6078) and the 2013 Educational Reform Project of Shangyang University China (No. 2013JG28).

REFERENCES

Hu, F.Y., Wang, J., Xiao, J.Q. & Wu H.J. 2011. Experimental teaching reform of "digital image processing". *Circuits, Communications and System (PACCS), 2011 Third Pacific-Asia Conference*, pp: 1–3.

Li Z.S., Huang T.C., Xie B. et al. 2013. Concrete practice of visualization teaching mode for digital image processing, *Kaoshi Zhoukan,* 1(67): 136–138 (in Chinese).

McAndrew, A. & Venables, A. 2005. "A 'secondary' look at digital image processing," *Proceedings of the 36th SIGCSE Technical Symposium on Computer Science Education*, pp. 337–341, St. Louis, Missouri, USA.

Ning Y., Huang R.L., Tan X. Tan Wei X.J. 2010. "Research on the teaching reform of digital image processing course", *2010 International Conference on Educational and Information Technology (ICEIT)*, pp. V2-457–V2-459.

Computer, Intelligent Computing and Education Technology – Liu, Sung & Yao (Eds)
© 2014 Taylor & Francis Group, London, ISBN 978-1-138-02469-4

Empirical analysis for virtual reality telepresence

F.Y. Wu
College of Chemical Engineering and Life Sciences, Chaohu University, Hefei, China

H. Wang
Foreign Languages Department, Chaohu University, Hefei, China

ABSTRACT: The characters of Virtual Reality telepresence were investigated with an empirical analysis. Students' learning was assessed in the light of students' perceived learning performance. Correlations between Virtual Reality telepresence and learning performance were analyzed. The result shows that the construct characters of Virtual Reality telepresence include four factors: third dimension, interactivity, immersive, Multi-sensitive. Every Virtual Reality telepresence factor is positively related to perceived learning achievement.

Keywords: virtual reality; telepresence; learning performance

1 INTRODUCTION

Virtual Reality (VR) is a type of 3-D reality that is implemented by use of a series of sensing-assisted equipment like HMD and data gloves. People input all kinds of action information into computers in a natural way (for example, the rotation of head, the movement of hands) by virtue of this equipment and make their sensory organs feel the world through seeing, hearing and touching equipment. People's feelings change along with their various actions.

There are many examples of VR-based learning environments in the field of engineering education, including online science education laboratories (Shin, 2002) and virtual engineering laboratories (Bresciani, Morsi, Tucker, Siprut, Stewart, & Duncan, 2010). There are also specific examples in the fields of mining engineering (Stothard et al., 2008), construction engineering (Messner, Yerrapathruni, Baratta,& Whisker, 2003), and manufacturing (Fernandes, Raja, & Eyre, 2003, Mujber, Szecsi, & Hashmi, 2004). Of particular interest is the Pharmatopia project run by the Faculty of Pharmacy and Pharmaceutical Sciences at Monash University in Australia, in which students undertake simulated tasks in a virtual tablet manufacturing plant within the online VR-based environment of Second Life (see Monash University, 2011).

Compared to the amount of discussions and reach on the application of VR from the perspectives of technology and practice, discussions the application of VR from the perspectives of theory in chemical engineering education have been limited and scattered.

From a review of literatures, The study of students' telepresence at VR education setting remains limited with "social presence" theory. The concept of "social presence" was originally developed in order to differentiate Communications media according to their capabilities for conveying media users' sense of engagement with other users in a different time and space (Short et al., 1976). Later, the term of "social presence" is used to study a mediated communication situation where "people" (students and teachers) deal with a certain "task" (learning and teaching) through communication media (instructional media) by educational researchers.

This thesis explored the construct characters of VR telepresence at education setting with empirical analysis. Correlations between telepresence at VR education setting and learning performance were analyzed.

2 METHOD

2.1 *The study participants*

A sample of students was selected among those who attended compulsory chemical equipment and machinery course at VR education setting. One hundred twenty four survey questionnaires were distributed over a period of 3 days in the middle of November 2012, when the fall semester was about to end. One hundred twenty copies were collected and used for analysis. Students were junior from chemical engineering class Chao Hu College. The gender ratio was skewed towards male students (74.16%).

2.2 *The instrument for measuring VR telepresence*

Given the initial nature of the study, it was necessary to develop a scale of measurement that could assess individual students' perceptions of VR telepresence at education setting. For this, Witmer and Singer's (1998) Measuring Presence in Virtual Environments: *a presence questionnaire* was

Table 1. The items of VR telepresence questionnaire.

Dependent variable	Items
Interactivity	1. I can quickly obtain the corresponding the knowledge from the VR system.
	2. Learning contents are random rendered according to students' needing.
	3. Learning feedback are random rendered by the VR system.
	4. Students can control the VR system and learn knowledge at their own pace.
	5. Evaluation for students is made by the VR system anytime.
Immersive	1. I'm drawn to the course when using the VR system.
	2. I forget time when using the VR system.
	3. I feel sense of self existence disappears when using the VR system.
	4. I feel a strong sense of fulfillment when using the VR system.
	5. My learning spirit can be stimulated when using the VR system.
Third dimension	1. The scene and devices, stereo sense in the VR system involved is strong clear and real, as in the reality.
	2. I feel like in a real-world scenario when using the VR system.
	3. Operating the VR system can get appropriate responses.
	4. The connection and interaction of the VR system conforms to general cognitive laws.
	5. The response of operating the VR system conforms to natural objective laws.
Multi-sensitive	1. I feel a realistic auditory perception when using the VR system.
	2. I feel a vivid sense perception when using the VR system.
	3. I feel a realistic haptic perception when using the VR system.
	4. I feel a realistic motion perception when using the VR system.
	5. I feel a realistic taste perception and sense of smell when using the VR system.

the main reference; and the major tasks involved were item writing, a panel-of-experts review, and a pilot survey. A 5-point Likert scale was used in the survey in which "1" indicated strong disagreement with a statement and "5" indicated strong agreement. The final instrument, the "VR telepresence Questionnaire" included four scales of measurement: third dimension, interactivity, immersive, multi-sensitive. (See Table 1).

2.3 *The instrument for measuring learning performance*

As was proposed in the research hypothesis, learning performance was the criterion of assessing students. According to Wang zhaojun's measuring satisfaction of net—based learning environment, learning performance was grouped into three scales of measurement: learning achievement, learning satisfaction, and Learning persistence. Learning achievement was assessed by students' self-report on Grade Point Average (GPA) scores of the previous semester as well as their own perceived achievement. The perceived learning achievement was indicated on a 1–5 scale under the question of "My professional knowledge and skills are improved." ("1" meant strong disagreement and "5" meant strong agreement).

Learning satisfaction was defined as the degree to which a student feels a positive association with his or her own educational experience. Learning persistence was operationalized as a student's "intent-to-persist" with their current study. The items constituting the achievement, satisfaction and persistence scale are listed respectively Table 2.

Table 2. The items of questionnaire of learning performance.

Dependent variable	Items
Learning achievement	1. My professional knowledge and skills are improved.
	2. Operation computer skill is improved.
	3. Academic record is improved.
Learning satisfaction	1. Learning motivation and enthusiasm are inspired.
	2. I like studying at VR education setting.
	3. I feel happy to share information with other participants.
Learning persistence	1. This learning experience is important to me.
	2. I am willing to complete the course at the VR education setting.
	3. I am confident that I can overcome obstacles encountered in the course of studying.

3 DATA ANALYSIS AND DISCUSSION

3.1 Validity of questionnaire of telepresence at VR education setting

For ensuring content and construct validity of the survey instrument, the instrument was pilot-tested with 35 voluntary students involved in VR education setting. The content of the instrument was further validated by consulting a panel of experts, which included: three authors who had published articles related to the theme of the present study; four faculty members who have been engaged in the virtual reality research in China, Hong Kong, and South Korea. Communication between the researcher and the panel was by e-mail. The panel was asked to judge in an evaluation sheet provided whether or not each item could shed light on the definition of the construct that it was purported to measure, and the result was tallied item by item. Only items on which there was over 80% agreement were included in the final questionnaire. The Statistical Package for Social Sciences (SPSS) was used for the analysis of these data. Factor analysis was used to examine the telepresence at VR education setting scale's construct validity (see Table 3).

The result of statistical analysis shows that the value of KMO is 0.808 and greater than 0.8. The questionnaire has good structure validity.

3.2 Reliability of VR telepresence questionnaire

The reliability of each scale was checked with Cronbach's alpha coefficient, which indicates the extent of internal consistency among the items in eliciting responses from survey respondents. The result of reliability analysis showed acceptable levels of Alpha coefficient for each scale, ranging from 0.8124 to 0.8941 (see Table 4).

Table 3. KMO and Bartlett's test.

Sampling enough of Kaiser—Meyer—Olkin measurements		0.808
Bartlett sphericity test	The approximate chi-square	930.039
	df	112
	Sig.	0.000

3.3 Principal component analyses of telepresence at VR education setting

A series of Principal Component Analyses were run on the item clusters defining VR telepresence at education setting, with an eigenvalue greater than one as criterion for number of factors. Overall, a consistent and clear pattern was observed from the analysis (See Table 5).

The first four common factors reflect 89.869% information of the all things. Hence, The characters of VR telepresence at education setting can be described by The first four common factors: third dimension, interactivity, immersive, multisensitive. Third dimension is defined that students feel degree of authenticity in the virtual reality environment as main body exists. Interactivity is defined that Learners interact with things at virtual environment. Immersive is defined that learners feel that they are part of a virtual world to immerse and participate in the virtual world. Multi-sensitive is defined that VR media give learners a "perception of presence", the "perception of presence" include visual perception, auditory perception, perception, tactile perception, motion perception, and even taste perception and olfactory perception, etc.

3.4 Learning performance and VR telepresence correlation analyses

The data were analyzed by means of a series of Multiple Regression and Correlation analyses (MRC) (Licht, 1997). Multiple independent variables of third dimension, interactivity, immersive, multi-sensitive was entered into a regression model with a respective criterion variable of learning achievement, learning satisfaction, and Learning persistence.

Each regression was run using a stepwise backward elimination method, which included all the hypothesized predictors in the first step of the series of MRC analyses and terminated when the elimination of any variable significantly reduced the equation model's explanation power, or $R2$ (Licht, 1997). The alpha level for a significant test was set at the p value of 0.05.

One of the notable findings of this investigation is the pervasive influence of the variables of VR telepresence on learning performance: students' perceived learning achievement, satisfaction, and Learning persistence. Constructivist emphasize

Table 4. Questionnaire reliability index.

Reliability index	Interactivity	Immersive	Third dimension	Multi-sensitive	Total questionnaire
Cronbach's alpha coefficient	0.894	0.856	0.823	0.812	0.893

157

Table 5. Common factors of VR telepresence.

Factor	Initial ergenvalues	Of variance %	Cumulative %
1	4.594	38.283	38.283
2	2.893	24.108	62.392
3	1.889	15.745	78.137
4	1.408	11.732	89.869

Extraction method: Principal Component Analyses.

Table 6. Inter-correlations of the variables.

	Learning achievement	Learning satisfaction	Learning persistence
Third dimension	0.753**	0.412*	0.354*
Interactivity	0.632**	0.417*	0.318*
Multi-sensitive	0.718**	0.311*	0.434**
Immersive	0.627**	0.359*	0.432*

*Correlation is significant at the 0.05 level (two-tailed);
**Correlation is significant at the 0.01 level (two-tailed).

that students can't gain knowledge simply from the teachers or other people but by making a construction of knowledge based on what they have owned. The study Theory of Constructivism holds that context, cooperation, conversation and meaning construction are important factors of learning environment. Compared to traditional education setting, it is more beneficial for students to promote meaning construction at VR education setting. Hence, the relatively high correlation found in the data analysis between learning achievement and the variables of VR telepresence confirms this observation.

Compared to the relatively high correlation between the variables of VR telepresence and learning performance, the effect of VR telepresence is limited to the perceived learning satisfaction and persistence.

However, the unsupported relationship between the variables of VR telepresence and learning satisfaction and persistence variables should be interpreted with some caution. On the one hand, learning satisfaction and persistence is associated with a complex psychological mechanism. Learning satisfaction and persistence may be affected by other factors, such as personal psychological status, etc.

On the other hand, MRC analysis deals with inter-correlations among multiple independent variables and the correlations between each independent variable and a dependent variable at the same time, when inter-correlations among independent variables are high—the status of so-called multi-collinearity—it can suppress the effect of a certain independent variable despite its actual high correlation with a dependent variable (Licht, 1997). Indeed, the three learning performance variables put in the regression model are inter-correlated to a certain extent. Thus, rather than totally dismissing the effect of VR telepresence on satisfaction and persistence variables, it would be reasonable to view there is to some extent the effect of telepresence VR on satisfaction and persistence variables.

4 IMPLICATION AND RECOMMENDATIONS

What may be learnt from this study is not so much the relative importance among the characters of VR telepresence as the idea that this kind of information can help teachers and instructional designers make decisions about teaching, design course by VR technology. In addition, this study should encourage researchers to further investigate the notion of VR telepresence at education setting. As a factor, whether it is appropriate to mirror students' learning performance needs to be examined. It would be desirable for further research to take an in-depth, micro-level approach to reveal what notions of presence students at VR education setting hold with respect to each party. Furthermore, researchers interested in individual differences may wish to investigate the elements of individual student characteristics contributing to varying degrees of perceived students at VR education setting.

ACKNOWLEDGEMENTS

The author gratefully acknowledge Yun X. Wang and Ling Z. Fang. Thanks are also given to students form chemical engineering class Chao Hu College. This project was supported by teaching-research Anhui Province, China (Grant No: 2012jyxm493).

REFERENCES

Bresciani, M.J., Morsi, K., Tucker, M., Siprut, M., Stewart, K., & Duncan, A. 2010. Designing and implementing an assessment plan for a virtual engineering lab. *Eludamos: Journal for Computer Game Culture,* 4(2), 277–285.

Fernandes, K.J., Raja, V.H., & Eyre, J. 2003. Immersive learning system for manufacturing industries. *Computers in Industry*, 51(1), 31–40.

Licht, M.H. 1997. Multiple regression and correlation. In L.G. Grimm & P.R. Yarnold (Eds.), *Reading and understanding multivariate statistics (pp. 19–64).* Washington, DC: American Psychological Association.

Messner, J.I., Yerrapathruni, S.C.M., Baratta, A.J., & Whisker, V.E. 2003. Using virtual reality to improve construction engineering education. *In Proceedings of the 2003 American Society for Engineering Education (ASEE) Annual Conference & Exposition.* Washington, DC: American Society for Engineering Education.

Mujber, T.S., Szecsi, T., & Hashmi, M.S.J. 2004. Virtual reality applications in manufacturing process simulation. *Journal of Materials Processing Technology*, 155–156, 1834–1838.

Shin, Y.-S. 2002. Virtual reality simulations in web-based science education. *Computer Applications in Engineering Education*, 10(1), 18–25.

Short, J., Williams, E., & Christie, B. 1976. *The social psychology of telecommunication.* New York: John Wiley.

Stothard, P., Squelch, A., van Wyk, E., Schofield, D., Fowle, K., Caris, C. … Schmidt, M. 2008. Taxonomy of interactive computer-based visualisation systems and content for the mining industry: Part One. In S. Saydam (Ed.), *Proceedings of the First International Future Mining Conference and Exhibition 2008 (pp. 201–210).* Melbourne, Australia: The Australasian Institute of Mining and Metallurgy.

Computer, Intelligent Computing and Education Technology – Liu, Sung & Yao (Eds)
© 2014 Taylor & Francis Group, London, ISBN 978-1-138-02469-4

Example-based image denoising in technology enhanced learning

D. Fu
Yunnan University of Nationalities, Kunming, P.R. China

ABSTRACT: A novel example-based image denoising algorithm is proposed by using matrix-value operator regression. Different from the traditional example-based image denoising algorithms, all training image pairs are understood as the matrix-value operators in the proposed algorithm for benefitting from the structure information of training images themselves. Experimental results have shown that the information of training image pairs is well represented by these matrix-value operators, and the performance of the novel matrix-value operator based denoising algorithm is competitive to some known example based denoising algorithms.

Keywords: technology enhanced learning; image denoising; example-based image processing

1 INTRODUCTION

Image denoising is a core issue in the field of image processing. For the historic problem, many efforts have been paid, for example, the local smoothing methods [1, 2] and the frequency domain filters [3, 4]. However, these denoising methods reported in these references focus either on a noise reduction or on a reconstruction of the main geometrical structures. The details and texture of an image are always destroyed during the process of denoising. Therefore, it is a challenge in the field of image denoising to preserve enough details of a noised image as well as to remove most of noise.

Notice that the details of a noised image are always smoothed out for the similarity between these details and the noise. One of the methods to preserve details of a noised image during the process of denoising is to consider the geometrical information of an image patch during the process of denoising. For example, in Nonlocal Means Algorithm (NLM) [5], the similarity between two pixels is defined by the Euclidean distance between two image patches whose centers are interested pixels respectively. Similarly, more sensitive information about the geometry of an image patch defined by a steering kernel [6] is used in K-LLD [7].

Example-based method motivated by the success of machine learning in image processing is also an attractive option. For example, many example-based algorithms for super-resolution [8, 9, 10] have shown the power of example-based method in restoring the details of an high-resolution image. In example-based super-resolution algorithms, a training set is used to define a relationship between low- and high-resolution image patches. The details of a high-resolution image patch can be restored by combining the details of high-resolution training image patches.

Following the idea, example-based method is introduced into image denoising, such as [11, 12, 13, 14]. Different from the example-based algorithms for super-resolution, the training set employed in denoising algorithms is used to model the relationship between noised and noise-free image patches.

In this paper, we propose a novel example-based algorithm for denoising. Different from most of example-based algorithms for denoising, all training image pairs are understood as matrix-value operators for obtaining directly the information of image patches. In our algorithm, the neighbors of a noised image patch are chosen from a set of noised and noise-free training image pairs according to the geometry-based similarity between noised test image patches and noised training image patches. By using these noise-free neighbors, a matrix-value operator could be generated by the weighted averaging of neighbor matrix-value operators defined by neighbor training image pairs. To determine the coefficients used in averaging, a weighted nearest neighbor embedding technique motivated by LLE [15] is used where the geometry-based information of noised image patch is considered. The weighted matrix-value operator will map the noised test image into a noise removing estimation. Meanwhile, the geometry-based information is used in estimating the denoised image patch, which makes more meaningful details of noised image patch be preserved.

The rest of the paper is organized as follows. In Section 2, training image pairs are represented as matrix-value operators, and a novel operator based denoising algorithm is introduced by employing geometry-based nearest neighbor embedding of these matrix-value operators. In Section 3, some preliminary experiments are reported.

2 MAIN ALGORITHM

2.1 *Matrix-value operator based training information*

The information of training image pairs which consists of noised and noise-free training images is the base of example-based denoising algorithms. Traditionally, these training image pairs are directly used based on different similarity measure. For example, it is a popular way to search a best matched training image pair according to the similarity between noised training and test image patches, and then the noise-free training image patch is used to replace the noised test image patch. However, it is inefficient in using these training image pairs because the training image pairs are always limited, but the noised image patches are various.

To improving the efficiency of using these limited training image pairs, we introduce a novel operator based method to represent the information of these training image pairs. It should be noted that all training image pairs are transformed into the matrix-value operators which could be used to map any noised image patch into another image patch. In other words, the information of a pair of training images could be used to any test image patch. Therefore, the matrix-value operators generated from training image pairs could offer more useful information of training image pairs.

Let X, Y $\subseteq R^{n \times n}$ be the image patch sets where X denotes noised training image patches, and Y noise-free image patches. Here, n denotes the size of an image patch. For any pair of training image patch $z_i = (x_i, y_i)$, the matrix-value operator

$$P_{z_i} = y_i x_i^{-1},$$

is used to represent the information of the training image pair z_i, where x_i^{-1} means the invers matrix of x_i.

It is clear that the matrix-value operator P_{z_i} will map the noised image patch x_i to the its exact noise-free image patch y_i. Moreover, for any different test image patch x_j, the difference between both noised image patches will preserved in the noise-free estimation by using the matrix-value operator P_{z_i}. Therefore, it could be expected that the information of limited training image pairs could be used more efficiently by employing these matrix-operators.

2.2 *Geometry-based nearest neighbor embedding*

Given a noised test image patch, the matrix-value operator used to denoise the test image patch is generated by nearest neighbor embedding of the matrix-value operators defined by K-nearest neighbor training image pairs. The K-nearest neighbor training image pairs are selected according to the geometry-based similarity measure between noised image patches.

In this paper, the geometry-based feature of an image is defined by a steering kernel [7]. According to [7], steering kernel can be defined as

$$w_{ij} = \frac{\sqrt{\det(c_j)}}{2\pi h^2} \exp\left(-\frac{(p_i - p_j)'c_j(p_i - p_j)}{2h^2}\right),$$

where p_i and p_j are the i-th and j-th pixels of an image patch respectively, C_j is the symmetric gradient covariance matrix for the estimated image in the direction of vertical and horizontal gradients of the p_j, and h a global smoothing parameter. For any image patch x, the corresponding geometry-based feature defined by steering kernel is denoted as $w(x)$.

Taking advantage of steering kernel, K best matched training image pairs are selected from all training image pairs. By using the method introduced in Subsection 2.1, these neighbor training image patches are transformed into matrix-value operators. Following the idea of LLE [15], the matrix-value operator used for denoising the test image patch is generated by minimizing the optimization problem

$$R(\alpha) = \left\| \hat{x}_j - \sum_{i=1}^{K} \alpha_i x_i^j \right\|_F^2,$$

where $\hat{x}_j$ is the j-th test image patch, x_i^j is the i-th neighbor of $\hat{x}_j$. Similar to LLE, α is restricted by $\Sigma_{i=1}^{K}\alpha_i = 1$, $\alpha_i \geq 0$.

Denote $u_i^j = \hat{x}_j - x_i^j$ and $U^j = (u_i^j)_{i=1}^{K}$. The restricted optimization problem is equivalent to the problem of

$$\alpha^j = \arg\min R(\alpha) - \tau \left(\sum_{i=1}^{K} \alpha_i - 1 \right),$$

where $\tau > 0$ is a Lagrange multiplier. Moreover, α_j can be represented as

$$\alpha_j = \frac{(G^j)^{-1}1}{1'(G^j)1},$$

where $G^j = U^j w(\hat{x}_j)(U^j)'$.

162

Taking advantage of α, a weighted matrix-value operator could be defined as

$$\hat{P}_{\hat{x}_j} = \sum_{i=1}^{K} \alpha_i P_{z_i^j},$$

where z_i^j is the i-th neighbor image pair of $\hat{x}_j$.

3 EXPERIMENT

3.1 Experiments settings

All training images which used in all experiments are shown in Figure 1. The test images which includes *Parrot* and *Cameraman* are shown in Figure 2. Gaussian noise whose standard deviation is 25 is added to the test images and training images for generating noised images. These noised and noise-free images are transformed into a set of image patches with the patch size of 7×7. The noised and noise-free image patches generated from training images serve as a training set. To comparing the performance of our algorithm, the median filter is employed as a baseline algorithm. Meanwhile, Mean Square Error (MSE) is used to measure the performance of both algorithms quantitatively.

3.2 Experiments results

All denoised images are shown in Figures 3 and 4. And the MSE curves corresponding to both test

Figure 1. Samples of training images.

Figure 2. Samples of test images.

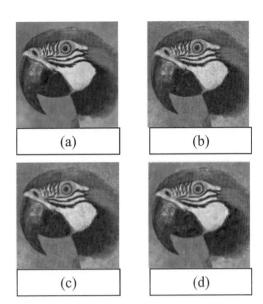

Figure 3. Parrot: (a) noise-free image; (b) noised image; (c) result of median filter; (d) result of our algorithm.

Figure 4. Cameraman: (a) noise-free image; (b) noised image; (c) result of median filter; (d) result of our algorithm.

images are shown in Figures 5 and 6. In both figures, the relation between the MSEs and the number of neighbors is shown. It is clear that more neighbors will enhance the performance of our algorithm which shows more training information is gained because more training samples are used.

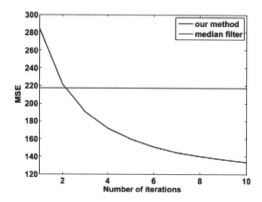

Figure 5. Parrot: Relations between MSE and the number of neighbor samples K.

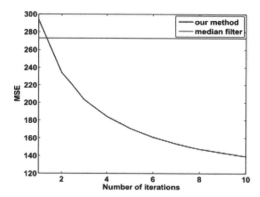

Figure 6. Cameraman: Relations between MSE and the number of neighbor samples K.

REFERENCES

[1] M. Lindenbaum, M. Fischer, and A. Bruckstein, "On ga-bor contribution to image enhancement," Pattern Recognition, vol. 27, pp. 1–8, 1994.

[2] L. Rudin, S. Osher, and E. Fatemi, "Nonlinear total variation based noise removal algorithms," Physica D, vol. 60, pp. 259–268, 1992.

[3] D. Donoho, "De-noising by soft-thresholding," IEEE Transactions on Information Theory, vol. 41, pp. 613–627, 1995.

[4] K. Dabov, A. Foi, V. Katkovnik, and K.O. Egiazarian, "Image denoising by sparse 3-d transform-domain collaborative filtering," IEEE Transactions on Image Processing, vol. 16, no. 8, pp. 2080–2095, Aug. 2007.

[5] A. Buades, B. Coll, and J.-M. Morel, "A non-local algorithm for image denoising," IEEE.

[6] H. Takeda, S. Farsiu, and P. Milanfar, "Kernel regression for image processing and reconstruction," IEEE Transactions on Image Processing, vol. 16, no. 2, pp. 349–366, Feb. 2007.

[7] P. Chatterjee and P. Milanfar, "Clustering-based denoising with locally learned dictionaries," IEEE Transactions on Image Processing, vol. 18, no. 7, pp. 1438–1451, July 2009.

[8] H. Chang, D. Yeung, and Y. Xiong, "Super-resolution through neighbor embedding," in Proc. IEEE CVPR'04, 2004, vol. 1, pp. 275–282.

[9] K. Kim and Y. Kwon, "Single-image super-resolution using sparse regression and natural image prior," IEEE Transactions on Pattern Analysis and Machine Intelligence, vol. 32, no. 6, pp. 1127–1133, 2010.

[10] J. Yang, J. Wright, T. Huang, and Y. Ma, "Image super-resolution as sparse representation of raw image patches," in Proc. IEEE CVPR'08, Aug. 2008, pp. 1–8.

[11] D. Li, S. Simske, and R. Merserau, "Image denoising through support vector regression," in Proc. IEEE ICIP'07, 2007, pp. IV-425-IV-428.

[12] M. Aharon, M. Elad, and A. Bruckstein, "K-svd: An algorithm for designing overcomplete dictionaries for sparse representation," IEEE Transactions on Signal Processing, vol. 54, no. 11, pp. 4311–4322, Nov. 2006.

[13] V. Laparra, Juan Gutiérrez, G. Camps-Valls, and J. Malo, "Image denoising with kernels based on natural image relations," Journal of Machine Learning Research, vol. 11, pp. 873–903, 2010.

[14] P. Bouboulis, K. Slavakis, and S. Theodoridis, "Adaptive kernel-based image denoising employing semi-parametric regularization," IEEE Transactions on Image Processing, vol. 19, no. 6, pp. 1465–1479, 2010.

[15] S. Roweis and L. Saul, "Nonlinear dimensionality reduction by locally linear embedding," Science, vol. 290, no. 5500, pp. 2323–2326, 2000.

Research and application of high-speed railway passenger query system base on flex

W.Q. Zhu, T.Y. Shi, L. Jiang & Y.X. Liu
Institute of Computing Technologies, China Academy of Railway Sciences, Beijing, P.R. China

ABSTRACT: To meet the status and existing problems of high-speed railway passenger query system, based on discussing the business requirements, a new type of high-speed railway passenger query system based on the technology of Flex is studied and designed, software structure of the system, including hardware/network layer, application support layer, application layer and the user access layer, is designed; system data transmission mode and two level network structure of railway board and station are given. Finally, main functions are discussed in details. At present the system has found successful application in Shijiazhuang-Wuhan passenger dedicated line, and the key technologies are verified.

Keywords: intelligent transportation; passenger query system; rich internet applications; flex; application

1 INTRODUCTION

As the development of China Railway, the passengers want better station service. The passenger query system, as one of the key platform of passenger service, need to meet the passenger travel service requirement [1, 2]. At the same time, with the widespread use of interactive technology (i.e. the touch screen, animation), the passengers put forward higher requirements on player interactive experience, information query efficiency. But the traditional business applications of the C/S (Client/Server) mode and the B/S (Browser/Server) mode, due to technical characteristics of their own, can't adapt to new requirements.

At present, the passenger query system has some problems: (1) information display mode is single, the player interactive experience is poor; (2) the response to real-time information query is slow; (3) the query content is not intuitive, and interactive ability is weak; (4) because of the ability of data synchronous update and the offline processing are poor, the passengers will not query some information when the network is abnormal.

In view of the above problems, we use the Rich Internet Application (RIA) technology, which can solve complex application requirements, improve the user interaction ability, and enhance the user experience ability [3]. Flex is the main application framework technology in the client development of RIA.

2 SYSTEM ARCHITECTURE DESIGN

2.1 Software architecture

In the multi-tier architecture model, Flex technology belongs to the view layer technology, it requires a combination of server-side technology to play its client advantages; we adopt JavaEE+Flex multi-layer architecture as a solution system.

Based on the user requirement analysis, according to the system design principles, the software architecture of high-speed railway passenger query system can be divided into hardware/network layer, application support layer, application layer and user access layer (see Fig. 1) [4].

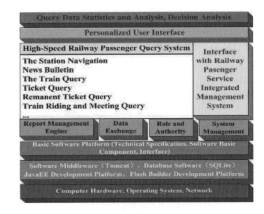

Figure 1. The overall structure of the system.

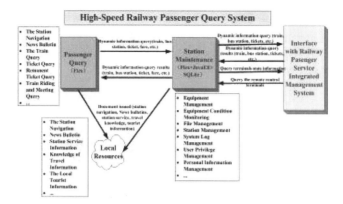

Figure 2. System data transmission mode of high-speed railway passenger query system.

The hardware/network layer consists of computer hardware, operating system and network, which is the basis of the information system and realize the information system application service by the railway passenger service LAN.

The application support layer is the key core of system design, which composed of application software, middleware, database software development platform and basic software platform. We use SQLite database, Tomcat application server, JaveEE development platform and Flash Builder development platform. Through the design and application support layer, system can realize the data sharing, software reuse, process and message reuse, improve the scalability and robustness of system.

The application layer includes the application software function modules and data interfaces, and achieves a comprehensive data sharing between systems. The user access layer consists of customized user pages, statistics and analysis of query data, and etc.

2.2 Data transmission

Data transmission between each subsystem and the system interfaces is a representation of the system dataflow (see Fig. 2). On the one hand, the station maintenance subsystem compiles "static" query information (i.e. the station navigation, news bulletins, station service information and travel information) into readable SWF files and sends them to local resources of query terminals. On the other hand, query terminals realize the interface management with integrated management platform system, and realize the real-time dynamic information request response by calling JavaEE program.

2.3 System network design

The system network of high-speed railway passenger query system relates to railway bureau and

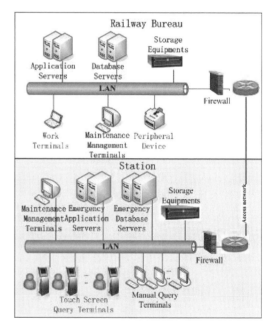

Figure 3. Network structure of high-speed railway passenger query system.

stations (see Fig. 3). We set up centralized control application servers, database servers, storage equipments and maintenance management terminals in railway bureau, which can manage the passenger query system in stations of railway bureau. We set up emergency application servers, database servers, storage devices, maintenance management terminals, touch screen query terminals, manual query terminals and networking equipments in the station. When network between the railway bureau and the railway station is abnormal, the station can ensure the normal operation

166

and management of system by means of the emergency mechanism.

High-speed railway passenger query system uses railway LAN to realize network connectivity and data exchange between system devices.

3 SYSTEM SOFTWARE FUNCTION DESIGN

High-speed railway passenger query system realizes business management of railway passenger travel information query, the station maintenance and equipment supervision, etc. It covers passenger query subsystem and station maintenance subsystem. The former function modules consist of the station navigation, News bulletin, the train query, ticket query, remanent ticket query, train riding and meeting query, station service information query, knowledge of travel information, and the local tourist information [1]. The latter function modules consist of equipment management, equipment monitoring, file management, station management, system log management, user rights management and personal information management (see Fig. 4).

3.1 Passenger query subsystem

1. **The Station Navigation:** realizes the station base information display (i.e. the station introduction and layout plan of station).
2. **News Bulletin:** realizes station news and notice query, including temporary station notice, travel security bulletin, change information of timetable and stopstation, and etc.

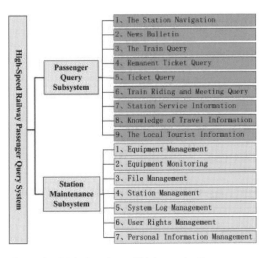

Figure 4. Main functions of high-speed railway passenger query system.

3. **Train Query:** provides appropriate route for passengers, including train timetable, train, and station.
   - Train timetable query: by inputting train number, it can query any train timetable information of station, including train number, the originating station, terminal station, the train types, departure time, arrival time, mileage, duration time, and etc.
   - Train number query: by inputting train number wanted, it can get the train timetable information queried.
   - Station site query: by inputting the destination station name using "the first letter of pinyin", it can display all train information between the station and the destination.
4. **Remanent Ticket Query:** by inputting the train number, it can get remanent ticket information within 5 days.
5. **Ticket Query:** can get the train price of first class, business class, and economy class according to train number and station site.
6. **Train Riding and Meeting Query:** can get the information of waiting area, the ticket area/port and platform.
7. **Station Service Information:** realizes the station service facilities information for passengers display, including counseling platform, special passenger services, entertainment facilities, medical service station, and station catering services, and etc.
8. **Knowledge of Travel Information:** provides common sense of train and knowledge of ticket to display.
9. **The Local Tourist Information:** provides station and surrounding areas traffic information, local tourist information, including bus lines, flight, hotel, commercial outlets, tourist attractions and tourist routes, and etc.

3.2 Station maintenance subsystem

1. **Equipment Management:** can realize centralized management of terminal equipment.
2. **Equipment Monitoring:** realizes the equipment condition monitoring, fault alarm and remote controlling. It also can carry on the statistics and analysis of the usage of the system and the equipment running status.
3. **File Management:** compiles, publishes and updates all kinds of "static" file.
4. **Station Management:** defines the station name on the railway bureau.
5. **System Log Management:** manages distributed software version log and data update log.
6. **User rights Management:** configures organization, personnel, roles and authorization in the system.

7. **Personal Information Management:** updates the user's personal information.

4 APPLICATION EFFECT OF SYSTEM

The section of Shijiazhuang-Wuhan passenger dedicated line in Henan and Hubei has ten railway stations, including Anyangdong, Hebidong, Xinxiangdong, Zhengzhoudong, Xuchangdong, Luohexi, Zhumadianxi, Xinyangdong, Minggangdong, and Xiaoganbei Railway Station.

Some of these stations belong to Zhengzhou Railway Bureau, and the others belong to Wuhan Railway Bureau. The line was put into service in December 26, 2012.

At present, high-speed railway passenger query system has been applied into these stations. There are 70 sets of touching screen query machines and some manual query terminals, and it obtains a good application effect. The system showed full of travel information about station, train and service, and passengers can conveniently get station service what they wanted.

The system established biographical account of query terminals, provided the support to centralized monitoring and management for query terminals. The system achieved real-time response to train timetable data, remanent ticket data, train riding data and train meeting data, by means of integration and sharing with Railway Passenger Service Integrated Management System, and it provided functions of query condition monitoring and remote control.

In addition, due to the different management method between Zhengzhou Railway Bureau and Wuhan Railway Bureau, the system needed to adapt to two kinds of application modes of centralized bureau management and station management. It was proved that the system showed a strong ability to adapt.

5 CONCLUSION

High-speed railway passenger query system based on Flex technology has solved some problems. It has strong ability of interactive interface, better the player interactive experience and high-speed query response. The system optimized the system structure and extended the system function. It has found successful application, and the key technologies are verified.

The next step of the research work are to applying appropriate data-mining algorithms and models based on collecting user data to provide more personalized service, and to improve the competitiveness of the railway transport enterprise.

ACKNOWLEDGEMENT

It is a project supported by the Innovation Fund of China Academy of Railway Sciences (1251DZ8403).

REFERENCES

Chen X, Zhu W.Q. Zhang Y et al. Optimization design and implementation of Railway Station Self-service Inquire System for high speed railway [J]. Railway Computer Application, 2011, (11):18–20.

Liu Y.X., Zhang Y et al. Design of railway passenger service integrated management system [J]. Railway Computer Application, 2011, (5):51–54.

Shi T.Y. A General Framework of Information System of High-Speed Passenger Railways [J]. Communication and Transportation Systems Engineering and Information, 2005, (1):92–106.

Zheng A.Q. Flex 4 Development Practices [M]. Beijing: Electronics Industry Press, 2011.

Zhu W.Q., Shi T.Y., Hu C.L. et al. Research and Application of maintaining Management Information System for large railroad maintenance machinery [J]. Chinese Railways, 2011, (5):51–54.

Computer, Intelligent Computing and Education Technology – Liu, Sung & Yao (Eds)
© *2014 Taylor & Francis Group, London, ISBN 978-1-138-02469-4*

Different rate double loop network control based on smith predictor

D.T. Liu, J.N. Li & H. Zhao
Guangxi Scientific Experiment Center of Mining, Metallurgy and Environment,
Guilin University of Technology, Guilin, China
College of Mechanical and Control Engineering, Guilin University of Technology, Guilin, China

ABSTRACT: The different sampling rate double loop network control system with random network delay is studied in the paper. The conventional Smith predictor and the modified Smith predictor are used to compensate for network delays. Some simulation of modified smith predictor and conventional smith predictor network control system is established. The simulation shows that the method is advantage of reducing network time-delay and improving performance, inhibiting for secondary disturbance in the system. Furthermore, the time-delay which is random and time-vary is difficult to estimate on the network. The control performance of modified Smith predictor is better than the conventional Smith predictor.

Keywords: different sampling rate; double loop network control system; smith predictor; network delay

1 INTRODUCTION

Because of network control play an increasingly important role in living and industrial, people begin to put forward higher requirements for the features of network control, such as fast, stability and accuracy, Network Control Systems[1] (NCSs) aroused the interest of many scholars. NCS can reduce the costs of cables and power, simplify the installation and maintenance of the whole system, and increase the flexibility. But time-delay caused by data transmission and packet drop will inevitably affect stability and accuracy of the NCSs.

Different sampling rate double loop network control system is composed of inner-loop and outer-loop which have different sampling periods. Gu Cheng-cheng[2] introduce that this system have many industrial applications, for example the velocity-position controlled for robot, current-displacement controlled for servo motor, velocity-attitude control in uniaxial for the aircraft. At present, the single NCS is more studied by scholars, but double-loop NCSs is little and different sampling rate double loop NCSs is a new issue in network control field. Double-loop NCSs consist of two sensor, two controllers, and an actuator, which are connected to the network. The inner and outer loop have different sampling rate, the speed and stability of the system is affected, so we requires compensate for this negative effect by means of optimization.

Smith predictor control method[3] is a compensation method in the time-delay system, which is pull in a feedback loop compensation device in the system, the time-delay of network will be offset,

thus the method will reduce the adverse effects of time-delay on the system.

Zhang Hai-Tao[4] make simulation based on smith predictor network control system; a class of Smith predictor based on neuron controller is presented. Chen Hui-Ying[5] introduce that the study of the long delay network, and design a fuzzy PI controller with Smith predictor for networked control systems with long time delay. Du Feng[6] proposes a new smith predictor, which is suitable that the delay of the network environment is difficult to accurately estimate. Kaya[7] introduce that a design method of modified Smith Predictor, which applied to cascade control system, to improve the performance of the system, but not in the network control.

2 DIFFERENT SAMPLING RATE DOUBLE LOOP NCSS

The structure of double loop NCSs is shown in Figure 1. $R(s)$ and $C(s)$ are input and output, $G_{c1}(s)$

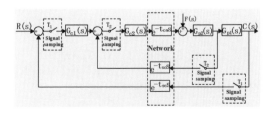

Figure 1. The structure of different rate bi-loop NCSs.

and $G_{c2}(s)$ are outer-loop and inner-loop controller. $G_{p1}(s)$ is controlled object, $G_{p2}(s)$ is controlled object, T_1 is outer-loop sampling period, T_2 is inner-loop sampling period, $F(s)$ is secondary circuit disturbance signal. Network often have a delay in the restricted communication protocols, bandwidth, signal conflicts and so on. $e^{-\tau_{ca}s}$ and $e^{-\tau_{sc}s}$ are controller-actuator network delay and sensor-controller network delay, which analog the network lag of simulation model.

The pulse transfer function of the system is

$$\frac{C(z)}{R(z)}$$

$$= \frac{G_{c1}(z)G_{c2}G_{p2}G_{p1}(z)z^{-\frac{\tau_{ca}}{T_2}}}{1+z^{-\frac{\tau_{ca}}{T_2}}G_{c2}G_{p2}(z)z^{-\frac{\tau_{sc}}{T_2}}+z^{-\frac{\tau_{ca}}{T_1}}G_{c1}(z)G_{c2}G_{p2}G_{p1}(z)z^{-\frac{\tau_{sc}}{T_1}}}$$

(1)

Different sampling rate double loop NCSs are some problems, owing to the system have two controllers and feedbacks, the equation (1) can be seen that the denominator of the output equation have many time delay, and double-loop sampling period are different, so the system need to an estimate model to optimal control.

3 DIFFERENT SAMPLING RATE DOUBLE LOOP NCSS BASE ON SMITH PREDICTOR

Assuming the estimate model of the controlled object $G_{p1}(s)$ and $G_{p2}(s)$ are $G_{m1}(s)$ and $G_{m2}(s)$. The delay $e^{-\tau_{ca}s}$ and $e^{-\tau_{sc}s}$ of the estimate model are $e^{-\tau_{cam}s}$ and $e^{-\tau_{cam}s}$. Based on the structure of double loop NCSs in Figure 1, the smith predictor is pulled in the primary circuit and the secondary circuit, shown in Figure 2.

The pulse transfer function of system is

$$\frac{C(z)}{R(z)} = \frac{G_{c1}(z)G_{c2}G_{p2}G_{p1}(z)z^{-\frac{\tau_{ca}}{T_2}}}{1+G_A+G_B}$$

$$G_A = z^{-\frac{\tau_{ca}}{T_2}}G_{c2}G_{p2}(z)z^{-\frac{\tau_{sc}}{T_2}}$$

$$- z^{-\frac{\tau_{cam}}{T_2}}G_{c2}G_{m2}(z)z^{-\frac{\tau_{scm}}{T_2}}+G_{c2}G_{m2}(z)$$

$$G_B = G_{c1}(z)[z^{-\frac{\tau_{ca}}{T_1}}G_{c2}G_{p2}G_{p1}(z)z^{-\frac{\tau_{sc}}{T_1}}$$

$$- z^{-\frac{\tau_{cam}}{T_1}}G_{c2}G_{m2}G_{m1}(z)z^{-\frac{\tau_{scm}}{T_1}}+G_{c2}G_{m2}G_{m1}(z)]$$

(2)

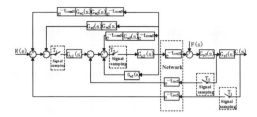

Figure 2. The different rate bi-loop NCSs based on smith predictor.

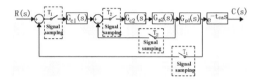

Figure 3. The structure of bi-loop NCSs based on smith predictor.

When the estimate model of the controlled object $G_{m1}(s)$, $G_{m2}(s)$ and of the delay object $e^{-\tau_{cam}s}$ and $e^{-\tau_{scm}s}$ are $G_{m1}(s)=G_{p1}(s)$, $G_{m2}(s)=G_{p2}(s)$, $\tau_{cam}=\tau_{ca}$, $\tau_{scm}=\tau_{sc}$, the prediction model and the real model are equal, the denominator is offset with time-delay, the pulse transfer function can be written as

$$\frac{C(z)}{R(z)} = \frac{G_{c1}(z)G_{c2}G_{p2}G_{p1}(z)z^{-\frac{\tau_{ca}}{T_2}}}{1+G_{c2}G_{m2}(z)+G_{c1}(z)G_{c2}G_{m2}G_{m1}(z)}$$

(3)

The formula (3) can see that the time lag of the denominator of the closed-loop transfer function is offset. The structure of NCSs can be equivalent to

It can be seen that double loop NCSs based on smith predictor reduced the impact of network delay on stability, the denominator delay of the transfer function is removed, it becomes a pure lag, which let the system lag and don't affect the stability of the system. However, the formula (2) can know that the accuracy requirement of the estimate model is relatively high, appropriate to the long time-delay on the network. Because of the network delay in NCSs is usually time-varying, it is difficult to estimate network delay $e^{-\tau_{ca}s}$ and $e^{-\tau_{sc}s}$.

4 DIFFERENT SAMPLING RATE DOUBLE LOOP NCSS BASE ON THE MODIFIED SMITH PREDICTOR

This paper proposed a design method of modified smith predictor on the different sampling rate

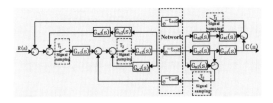

Figure 4. The structure of different rate bi-loop NCSs base on the modified smith predictor.

double loop NCSs, which can compensate the network delay. The modified smith predictor compensate method don't need to estimate the network time-delay, and can be used in the NCSs application situation, which have delay stochastic, time-varying, multi-sampling period, pack dropout. The smith predictor requires an estimate model in the controlled object, so the modified method is suitable to the remote network environments, which allow prediction model to join in the model. The double loop NCSs base on the modified smith predictor is showed as Figure 4.

The pulse transfer function can be written as

$$\frac{C(z)}{R(z)} = \frac{G_{c1}(z)G_{c2}G_{p2}G_{p1}(z)z^{-\frac{\tau_{ca}}{T_2}}}{1 + G_A + G_B}$$

$$G_A = G_{c2}G_{m2}(z) + z^{-\frac{\tau_{ca}}{T_2}}[G_{c2}G_{p2}(z) - G_{c2}G_{m2}(z)]z^{-\frac{\tau_{sc}}{T_2}}$$

$$G_B = G_{c1}(z)\begin{bmatrix} G_{c2}G_{m2}G_{m1}(z) + z^{-\frac{\tau_{ca}}{T_1}}(G_{c2}G_{p2}G_{p1}(z)) \\ -G_{c2}G_{m2}G_{m1}(z))z^{-\frac{\tau_{sc}}{T_1}} \end{bmatrix}$$

(4)

From (4), we can know that the system have the estimated model without $e^{-\tau_{ca}s}$ and $e^{-\tau_{sc}s}$. The denominator of the transfer function does not appear $e^{-\tau_{cam}s}$ and $e^{-\tau_{scm}s}$, so $G_{m1}(s) = G_{p1}(s)$, $G_{m2}(s) = G_{p2}(s)$, which can obtain (3), this means that the system has been improved which don't need to estimate the network time-delay. However, this method is only suitable that $G_{p1}(s)$ and $G_{p2}(s)$ can pull in $G_{m1}(s)$ and $G_{m2}(s)$.

5 SIMULATION

From Figure 1, the network delay A and B is fluctuation from 1 s to 5 s, the rate of data dropout is 0.1, the transfer function of $G_{p1}(s)$ and $G_{p2}(s)$ are $1/((10s+1)(s+1))^2$ and $1/(30s+1)$. $G_{c1}(s)$ Make PI control method, proportion coefficient is $K_P = 2.681$, integral coefficient is $T_i = 0.045$,

$G_{c2}(s)$ make P control method, proportion coefficient is $K_P = 0.05$. T_1 is outer sampling period, T_2 is inner sampling period. The simulation software will select Matlab/Simulink.

At first, when $T_2 = 1$ s, $T_1 = 15$ s, comparing different sampling rate double loop NCSs with smith predictor in Figure 2 and the different sampling rate double loop NCSs in Figure 1, calculating the control parameters, we can get the unit step response curve in Figure 5. The input of the system R is unit step signal. $Y1$ is the unit step signal of the different sampling rate double loop NCSs with smith predictor, $Y2$ is the unit step signal of the different sampling rate double loop NCSs. In order to compare the two systems anti-jamming capability, when keeping stability in the unit step response, the two systems were pulled in the secondary unit step disturbance $F(s)$ at t = 350 s, Figure 6 is shown.

From Figure 5, the dynamic performance control of the unit step signal of $Y1$ is better than $Y2$. From Figure 6, we know that the effect of the unit step disturbance of $Y1$ is less than $Y2$, so the

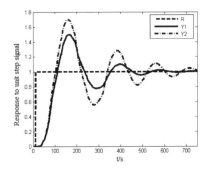

Figure 5. The unit step signal of different rate bi-loop NCSs with smith predictor and without predictor ($T_1 = 15$ s, $T_2 = 1$ s).

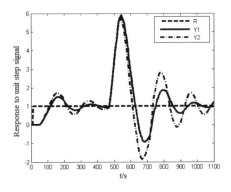

Figure 6. The unit step signal of NCSs with smith predictor and without predictor ($T_1 = 15$ s, $T_2 = 1$ s).

different sampling rate double loop NCSs with smith predictor are advantage of speed, stability, and anti-interference ability.

Comparing the different sampling rate double loop NCSs with smith predictor and with the modified smith predictor, the $G_{c1}(s)$ of the two system make PI control, proportion coefficient is $K_P = 2.681$, integral coefficient is $T_i = 0.045$, $G_{c2}(s)$ make P control, proportion coefficient is $K_P = 0.05$, the inner-loop sampling period is $T_2 = 1$ s, the outer-loop sampling period are respectively 2 s, 10 s, 15 s, 25 s, the network delay is fluctuation from 1 s to 5 s. The unit step signal of the two systems is shown at the Figures 7–10.

Analyzing the Figures 7–10, with inner and outer loop sampling rate increasing, $Y1$ curve remained stable change, $Y2$ curve change to unstable, and the rising time and settling time of $Y1$ curve become shorter, overshoot is smaller. Finally, the effect of modified smith control is better. When the rate of different sampling rate

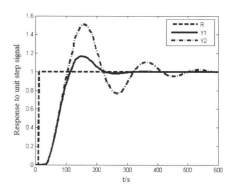

Figure 9. Comparing the modified smith control and smith control ($T_1 = 15$ s, $T_2 = 1$ s).

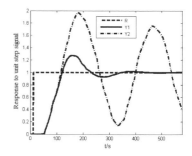

Figure 10. Comparing the modified smith control and smith control ($T_1 = 25$ s, $T_2 = 1$ s).

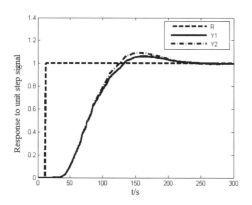

Figure 7. Comparing the modified smith control and smith control ($T_1 = 2$ s, $T_2 = 1$ s).

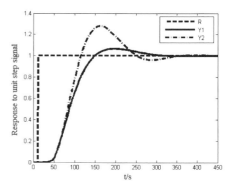

Figure 11. The different rate bi-loop NCSs with smith predictor in the fluctuation time-delay ($T_1 = 2$ s, $T_2 = 1$ s).

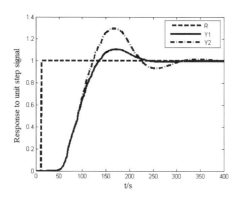

Figure 8. Comparing the modified smith control and smith control ($T_1 = 10$ s, $T_2 = 1$ s).

double loop NCSs are 25:1, different sampling rate double loop NCSs with smith predictor has been difficult to make a balance. As the time-delay fluctuation, the time-lag is difficult to accurately estimate, but the modified method doesn't need to estimate the network time-delay. Set the time-delay fluctuation of the simulation network A and

B are from 1 s to 9 s, inner-loop sampling period $T_2 = 1$ s, outer-loop sampling period $T_1 = 2$ s. The time-delay of the network with smith predictor is 5 s in Figure 11. From Figure 7, the different sampling rate double loop NCSs with smith predictor isn't impact by time-delay change, and the performance of the different sampling rate double loop NCSs with smith predictor is worse.

6 CONCLUSION

The different sampling rate double loop NCSs with smith predictor can overcome the influence of network and suppress external disturbance on the system. When the controlled object allow joining smith predictor model, due to the time-delay is random and the time-varying, the control method of the modified smith predictor is better than the smith predictor.

ACKNOWLEDGEMENT

This work has been supported by Guangxi Scientific Experiment Center of Mining, Metallurgy and Environment (Grant No. KH2011ZD003 and No. KH2012YB015), and Guangxi Key Laboratory of Auto parts and vehicle technology (Grant No. 2013KFMS03), and Doctoral Fund of Guilin University of Technology in 2012.

REFERENCES

[1] W. Zhang, M.S, Branieky, S.M. Phillips, 2001, Stability of networked control System, IEEE Control System Magazine, 21(l):84–99.
[2] Gu Cheng-Cheng, Liu Dian-Ting, Zhao Hong, Yang Lian, 2013, Research on modeling and stability of a class of different sampling rates of SISO network control system, Manufacturing Automation, 12:36–40.
[3] Smith O.J.M, 1959, Close Controller of Loops with Dead Time, Chemical Engineer Progress, 53(5).
[4] Zhang Hai-Tao, Li Zhen, 2012, Simulation of networked control system based on Smith prediction Compensation, Computer Engineering and Applications, 48(8):243–245.
[5] Chen Hui-Ying, Guan Qiu, Wang Wan-Liang, 2005, Design of a fuzzy PI controller with Smith predictor for networked control systems with long time-delay, Journal of Zhejiang University of Technology, 04:418–420+479.
[6] Du Feng, Qian Qing-Quan, Du Wen-Cai, 2010, Networked Control Systems Based on New Smith Predictor, Journal of Southwest Jiao-Tong University, 01:65–69+81.
[7] Ibrahim Kaya. 2002, Improving performance using cascade control and a Smith Predictor, ISA Transactions, 40(3):223–234.
[8] Li Jing, Zhou De-Jian, Liu Dian-Ting, Liu Liang, 2011, Design and simulation of fuzzy PID Smith controller based on MATLAB, Software Guide, 05:31–33.
[9] Huang Li-Lian, Chen Ji, 2012, PD control of networked control system based on Smith compensation and neural network, systems engineering and electronics, 09:1884–1888.

Computer, Intelligent Computing and Education Technology – Liu, Sung & Yao (Eds)
© 2014 Taylor & Francis Group, London, ISBN 978-1-138-02469-4

Feasibility assessment of large-scale photovoltaic power generation accessing Jilin Western Grid

Gan-Gui Yan, Ze-Hui Wang, Jun-Hui Li & Xin Tan
School of Electrical Engineering, Northeast Dianli University, Jilin, China

Wei-Hua Luo
Liaoning Electric Power Limited Company of State Grid, Shenyang, China

Li-Min Feng
Jilin Electric Power Limited Company of State Grid, Changchun, China

ABSTRACT: Photovoltaic (PV) power generation is an effective way to the large-scale development and utilization of solar energy resource. This paper aimed at Jilin western region which is rich in solar energy resource, introduced the distribution of solar energy resource in this region, analyzed the PV power generation planning, and assessed the feasibility of the PV power assessing Jilin Western Grid by using PSASP simulation software.

Keywords: photovoltaic power generation; Jilin Western Grid; feasibility assessment

1 INTRODUCTION

Energy shortage and environmental pollution are the worldwide problems which restrict the development of the human nowadays. To seek for the sustainable development, human increasingly pay attention to the utilization and research of renewable energy. As one of the most development potential of renewable energy, solar energy resource has shown the advantages in the economic production, development and utilization of solar energy resource is of great significance to the human society. PV power generation is an effective way to the large-scale development and utilization of solar energy resource, it is one of the fastest growing and the most active research field nowadays, and it has received the widespread attention all over the world [1].

The energy consumption of Jilin province mainly consists of fossil fuels, coal in primary energy consumption accounts for above 70% all the time, new energy and renewable energy account for a small proportion. Power source structure is unreasonable, the thermal power installed capacity accounts for a larger proportion, and most of the thermal power units are heat units. In order to achieve the energy conservation and emissions reduction during the "Twelfth Five-Year Plan", Jilin must optimize the existing energy consumption structure constantly, adjust the structure of power supply, reduce dependence of fossil fuels,

and develop renewable energy sources vigorously. Baicheng region which is in the west of Jilin is rich in solar energy resource, it is more suitable for large-scale centralized development of solar PV power generation.

This paper first summarized the solar energy resource in west Jilin, provided the PV power generation planning, and assessed the access planning feasibility of PV power generation based on the static security constraints of the power system.

2 SUMMARY OF SOLAR ENERGY RESOURCE IN WEST JILIN

The west Jilin province which has superior natural conditions is very suitable for development and utilization of renewable energy resource, especially Baicheng region is the most representative. Baicheng is located in the northwest of Jilin province, it is from east longitude 121 degrees 38 seconds to 124 degrees 22 minutes, north latitude 44 degrees 13 minutes 57 seconds to 46 degrees 18 minutes. The total area is 2.6 square kilometers, the annual average sunshine time is 2915 hours (1961–2000), the annual average temperature is 5.2 degrees centigrade, the average frost-free period is 144 days, and the annual average rainfall is 399.9 millimeters.

The total annual average radiation of Baicheng is 5570 MJ/m^2, according to the solar energy resource abundance grade evaluation criteria by

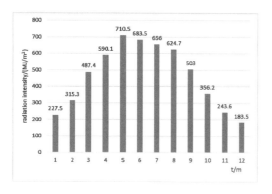

Figure 1. The monthly average radiation distribution of Baicheng region.

China Meteorological Administration, Baicheng region belongs to the area which solar radiation resource is quite abundant, and the solar energy resource is comparatively stable, it is quite suitable for the comprehensive development and utilization of solar energy resource. Figure 1 shows that the monthly average radiation distribution of Baicheng region [2].

3 PV POWER GENERATION PLANNING IN WEST JILIN

3.1 Summary of large-scale PV generation access point

In Baicheng region, Zhenlai County has a vast territory with a sparse population in which transportation is convenient, it is more suitable to the construction of solar PV power station. In this county, the sunshine is abundant and the sunshine time is long. The atmospheric transparency is good, sunshine time is close to 7.9 hours per day, annual average sunshine time is 2892.2 hours, annual average solar radiation is 5273.1 MJ/m². Zhenlai County is suitable for construction of large-scale PV power station. This paper regarded Zhenlai County as the access point of large-scale PV power station. Figure 2 shows the monthly average surface radiation intensity distribution of Zhenlai County from 1983 to 2005 in the database of National Aeronautics and Space Administration (NASA).

3.2 Calculation of large-scale PV power generated energy

This paper used the PVsyst software to calculate PV power generated energy. The main parameters include the latitude and longitude of PV power station location, the monthly average temperature

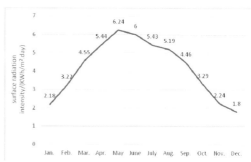

Figure 2. The monthly average surface radiation intensity distribution of Zhenlai County from 1983 to 2005.

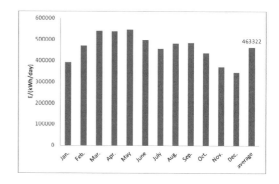

Figure 3. The monthly average distribution of output characteristic curve of 100 MW PV power station.

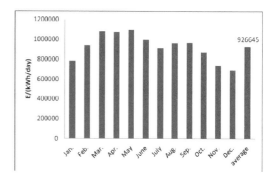

Figure 4. The monthly average distribution of output characteristic curve of 200 MW PV power station.

and total radiation for calculation. Before the calculation, it needed to set the related parameters, such as PV array angle of 30 degrees, azimuth angle of 0 degree and PV battery materials of polysilicon, according to different capacity of the selected PV power station, it can get the following output characteristic curves as shown in Figure 3 and Figure 4.

176

The result shows that, with the increasing capacity, the output character of PV power station increases in direct proportion to the increase in installed capacity. The maximum appeared in May and the minimum appeared in December, it is consistent with the radiation intensity distribution.

4 FEASIBILITY ASSESSMENT OF PV POWER GENERATION ACCESS BASED STATIC SECURITY CONSTRAINTS OF THE GRID

Due to the influence of the solar intensity, environmental temperature and weather conditions, the fluctuation and randomness of PV power generation are very obvious, and PV power station has no inertia link, it presents the characteristics of the active power step evolution change, grid integration of large-scale PV power generation puts forward the new challenges for the stability analysis and control of the grid. Therefore, determining the maximum access capacity of PV power generation is particularly important to the study on the influence of grid-connected large-scale PV power generation on the grid operation [3–5].

4.1 Summary of Jilin Western Grid

Zhenlai of the SongBai Grid is located in the northwest Jilin Grid, there are a number of wind power plants and thermal power plants. By the end of 2013, in the SongBai Grid, there will be two 500 kV substations and ten 220 kV substations, the main power plant installed capacity will reach 5673 MW, of which thermal power installed capacity is 2400 MW, wind power installed capacity is 3273 MW, load forecasting is between 650 MW to 1100 MW. Figure 5 shows 220 kV and above power system geographical diagram of SongBai Grid.

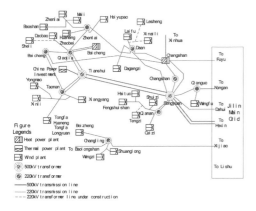

Figure 5. 220 kV and above power system geographical diagram of SongBai Grid.

4.2 PV generation maximum access capacity analysis based on static security constraints of the grid

To achieve the combination of PV power station with the existing grid, it is needed to determine the maximum access capacity of PV power station based on the grid requirements and combine with the characteristics of PV power generation to analyze the influence on the grid in order to guide the construction planning of large-scale grid-connected PV power station.

Because of the particularity of PV power station, solving the power flow calculation of the power system with PV power station must consider the characteristics of PV power generation. Typically, PV power inverter does not have the power regulating function, grid-connected inverter output power factor is controlled at unity power factor, PV power station can be set to the PQ node.

In the steady-state analysis, security constraints include:

1. Node voltage constraint: access node voltage runs in the range from 88% to 110% of the rated voltage;
2. Transmission line capacity constraint: in order to ensure the long-term running reliably of the transmission line, regard the relative smaller one of the allowed maximum load current of line current-carrying capacity as the constraint;
3. Transformer capacity constraint;
4. Active power and reactive power output constraints of PV power station.

Selecting Zhenlai 220 kV bus as the access point of the PV power station, PV power station operates at unity power factor. Assuming the PV power station access grid transformer capacity is not restricted, calculation only considers the transmission line capacity constraint and access point node voltage constraint. Increasing PV power output, the calculated P-V curve of PV power station access point is shown in Figure 6. The results show that, with the increase of the PV power output, the access point voltage increased first and then decreased.

This paper calculated the allowed maximum PV power station output of system steady-state running with the power flow simulation method, gradually increased the PV power output, and observed the system steady-state constraints whether are out of limit. In term of the system in Figure 5, when the PV power output set to 550 MW, Zhen Qiao line carrying capacity overloaded. Therefore, the allowed PV power station maximum output for the system steady-state security operation set to 540 MW. In addition to the line capacity constraint, other constraints with the PV power output of

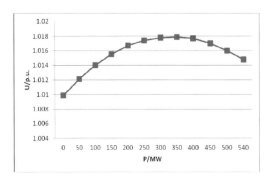

Figure 6. The calculated P-V curve of PV power station access point.

540 MW were within the limit. The result shows that transmission line overload is the main constraint to restrict the system steady-state running with the PV power station.

5 CONCLUSIONS

This paper regarded Jilin Western Grid as the research object, summarized the solar energy resource and the PV power generation planning in this area, and calculated the maximum access capacity of PV power generation based on the static security constraints. The results show that, with the increase of the PV power output, the access point voltage increased first and then decreased. The main factor which restricts the maximum access capacity of PV power station is the transmission line overload cased by PV power output. The results of the study on the local large-scale development of PV power generation have guiding significance.

ACKNOWLEDGMENTS

This work is supported by 2013 science and technology research project "Study on the Characteristics of Solar Power Output in Jilin Province" of State Grid Jilin Electric Power Co. Ltd, "National High Technology Research and Development Program of China" (No. 2011AA05A112) and Northeast Dianli University Doctoral Program Foundation (BSJXM-201205).

REFERENCES

[1] Xin AI, Xiaonan HAN, Yingyun SUN. The Development Status and Prospect of Grid-connected Photovoltaic Generation and Its Related Technologies [J]. Modern Electric Power. Vol. 30. No. 1 (2013), p. 1–4.
[2] Meteorological Industry Standard of the People's Republic of China. Assessment Method for Solar Energy Resources. (2013).
[3] Yi Lei, Zhengming Zhao. Overview of Large-scale PV Integration Key Technologies and Its Impact [J]. Power Electronics. Vol. 5 (2010), p. 16–23.
[4] Yuqiang Hou, Wei Li. Influence of Integration of Large-scale Photovoltaic on Grid and Key Factors Restricting Its Accepted Capacity [J]. Power System and Clean Energy. Vol. 29. NO. 4 (2013), p. 73–76.
[5] Weidong Yang, Feng Xue, Taishan Xu, Yongjie Fang, Bijun Li. Grid-connected Photovoltaic Influence on Power Systems and Some Related Issues [J]. Hydropower Automation and Dam Monitoring. Vol. 33. NO. 4 (2009), p. 35–39.

Mineral resources information manage system based on XML technology

Y. Gao
Capital Normal University, Beijing, China

M. Lv
General Hospital of Armed Police Forces, Beijing, China

ABSTRACT: Mineral resources is a kind of non-renewable territorial resources, is a important part of resources which is indispensable for human beings, it is a huge value to research the collection and management method for the data of mineral resources. The data of mineral resources has the following traits: huge amount of information, great variety and spatial information, a high requirement for validity and effectiveness, the traditional information manage system can not meet the requirement for the information management of mineral resources, especially difficult on the data collection and data management. This paragraph for using the XML technology, by visible development language C#, combine with GIS subunit, Arc Engine, visible tool extended development, this make the data of mineral resources with the function which is standard data collection and visible management and search statistics drafting, those make a great effect for raising work efficiency and also give a great push to faster collection and information management for mineral resource, in the practical application we have a better effect.

Keywords: XML; data collection; data management; GIS

1 INTRODUCTION

With the growing of development for mineral resources, how to rapid and timely collect the information of mineral resources and make the resources to be managed in systematization and ordering, are important matters we have. Based on researching the collection, arrangement and storage of mineral resources data information, make further efforts on permission controlling mechanism, database updating, maintenance mechanism and system updating etc., there is a major realistic meaning for the department which manage the mineral resources for supplying data sharing and distribution with information supervision and application.[1]

The source of mineral resources information is dispersed, varied, large quantities, the old management system can not meet those requirement for user, and however the XML technology use in management of mineral resources collection, will make a great efforts for data processing with fast and efficient.

2 DYNAMIC INTERFACE CREATING FOR XSD

XML Schema language means XML Schema Definition (XSD). For creating XSD documents, it needs raw data (image or table) for unified descripting the

feedback loading requirement of data exchange, therefore we create a one to one corresponding relation between the structure table and ordinary two-dimensional table shown by the Figure 1.

The main control table and the structure table (The definition of view), XSD documents, ordinary two-dimensional table (Specific view) have the following relation:

1. The main control table and structure table (The definition of view), XSD document, ordinary

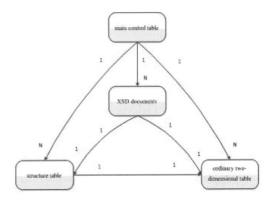

Figure 1. XML data conversion.

Figure 2.

2-dimensional table have the one to N corresponding relation.
2. Structure table, ordinary two-dimensional table have the one to one corresponding relation.

3 XML DATA EXCHANGE

XML stand for extensible markup language, Used in sign the electric documents and make them to be structural markup language, it can be used for signing data, define the type(s) of the data, it is a raw language which allow the user to define their own markup language. For storage, check and update XML data, it is necessary to realize the combination of XML and database, the types of database include relational database, object oriented database and object relational database have been used in mutual mapping with XML documents.[2–5]

4 THE PRIMARY FORM OF MANAGEMENT SYSTEM

The mineral resources information management system has two subsystems, the data collection subsystem and the data management system, the data collection subsystem makes the order of XSD documents, therefore it can realize the faster data collection, in the next step, analysis the XSD documents, load and store data into database, by using XML data exchange technology, based on the above step we can do the work for management and statistics.

4.1 *The data collection subsystem*

After the starting of collection system, it will make a judgment to the starting is whether the first time start or not for judgment whether is necessary to ask the register information, the completed information is stored in the system configuration documents, system will load the XSD documents (the different data information in different format, the user-defined format data is available for user) and user register information to create the main interface generation system. Editing, loading and storing the data which is necessary to be collected

in the main interface generation system, will realize the dynamic data information fast collection after the data has been checked by the system format examination and submitted the package of data information XML documents.

The specific process of data collection subsystem is shown by Figure 3.

4.2 *Data management subsystem*

Data management subsystem will analyze the loaded XML documents and extract the information files, and store the information into the corresponding database table, it also put the corresponding accessories into the name-ordered document path.

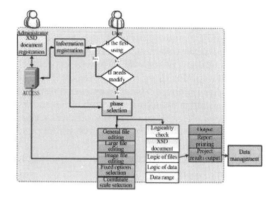

Figure 3. The specific process of data collection subsystem.

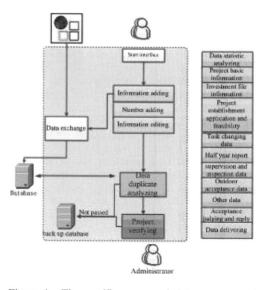

Figure 4. The specific process of data management subsystem.

We can realize the function of data reviewing and space duplicate analyzing by disassembling and processing the information of XML documents which will be storage in database.

4.3 System features function

4.3.1 Data format examination
After user complete the information loading, the data collection subsystem will give a data format examination which include format examination under the XSD define range and logic examination, the main intentions of the examination are Data format and logic checking.

4.3.2 Space query analyzing
In the GIS system, the space data and property data are organized whole, they will have meaning only after they are combined together. Data management subsystem manage the space data and property data though defining a GIS substance. Each geographical substance shown by the flowing four objects: substance ID (the only identification for substance), substance codename, space data ID, and property data chain table.

We can get the space information—space data about the geographical substance by the space data pel ID, and we can also get the information about the GIS substance object by checking the property data chain table, those realize the interflow and uniting for the space data and property data.[6]

Substance ID	Substance codename	Space data	Property data chain table

Space data query analyzing is the core function of this system function. We can seek overlapped area of different regional by checking the space database which show the result as highlight zone on map window, and give the information of overlapped area simultaneously shown with the map window, so that it help to avoid repetitions working.

5 CONCLUSION

This paragraph is about the problems of data collection in traditional management system.

By using the XSD dynamic interface technology and XML data exchange technology, with C# as the development language and GIS accessory for extended development, they design the mineral resources information management system which has the functions for data collecting, database creating and data managing. This system realizes the system management dynamic applying, map coordinates immediate updating, this system makes a directly vision display and make a great step for enhancing efficiency of the mineral resource management.

After the actual test, this system is multifunctional, stable in performance, highly operable, friendly interface. It makes a nice meeting for the requirements for the daily mineral resources information management and also give a great push for mineral resources management.

REFERENCES

[1] Yuan Jinjun, Guo Guihai, et al. Design and Realization on WebGIS Management system of Surveying and mapping information[J]. Science of Surveying and Mapping. 2010,35(6):200–202.

[2] Chung T.S, Park S., Han S.Y, Kim H.J. Extracting object-oriented database schemas from XML DT Ds using in heritance//Proceedings of the 2nd International Conference on Electronic Commerce and Web Technologies. Munich, Germany, 2001: 49–59.

[3] Johansson T, Heggbrenna R. Importing XML schema in to an object-oriented database mediator system [M.S. dissertation]. Computer Science, Uppsala University, Sweden, 2003.

[4] Fong J, Wong H.K, Cheng Z. Converting relational database into XML documents with DOM. Information & Software Technology, 2003,45(6): 335–355.

[5] Lee D.W, Mani M, Chiu F, Chu W.W. Nesting-based relational-to-XML schema translation // Proceedings of the 4th International Workshop on the Web and Databases. California, USA, 2001:61–66.

[6] Pan Junhui, Xiang Shengchang. Research on File Organization Structure of GIS Spatial Data[J]. Journal of Chongqing University of Science and Technology: Natural Science Edition, 2012,14(1): 128–130.

The application research on training the digital image information transmission ability of female university students

J. Wu & L.M. Sun
Shandong Women's University, Ji Nan, Shandong Province, China

ABSTRACT: Digital image information processing technology becomes the main form of Network culture. Accordingly, the career prospects are quite broad and the related characteristic specialties of the higher education spring up ceaselessly. In the nowadays society, the development about the talent of female university students is concerned by attention. We found that the female university students are more suitable for the image work of various creative design fields through continuous study. We resolve two problems mainly: 1, Comparing their own psychological and physiological characteristics with the distinctive features of the digital image information, we explore the late-model project-driven teaching cases method of digital image classes which is similar to the female university students. 2, According to the female university students' characteristic, We adopt new teaching patterns, such as "co-teaching", integration with the society, field practice method, provide them the social practice chances, let them take exercise getting to work, and it is also the best point connecting digital image education with society. Therefore, in order to promote the development of female university students, we must strengthen the exploration of science reasonable methods in the personnel training process of higher education, pay attention to the digital image information transmission ability of applications.

Keywords: digital image; female college students; transmission ability; network culture

With the popularity of the Internet and the rapid development of digital information era, focused on the spread of all kinds of modern information, people to see the information is no longer a pure obscure word, but add rich colors, shapes of pictures. People can imagine, abstract things intuitively use visual means.

Digital age, the image is an important media form to receive and convey information, and related computer software emerge in endlessly, make work can realize various powerful visual effect, application is very wide, web, advertising, three-dimensional, film and television animation and so on. These design is combined closely with the industry and commercial activities, employment range is very wide.

The rise of network culture, the digital image as a message of the more important content, effect is obvious, therefore, image processing is an important aspect of information dissemination study, the cultivation of the higher education policy target preferred also gradually, become the area of concern.

According to the actual situation, we think seriously about the advantages of the female university students in the process of study and work, and sum up the experiences of culture and combining with the characteristics of image information,

search for the success of female university students in today's society, the key opportunity and development direction.

1 THE APPLICATIONS AND CHARACTERISTICS OF DIGITAL IMAGE INFORMATION TRANSMISSION

Digital image has the advantage of intuition and concreteness, almost penetrated into every field in modern life, through the image dissemination of culture, communicating emotion, appreciating art, promoting products has become an important way in today's world, the culture of the people express more information for the image narrative, such as advertising, photography, film and television, network, etc. Through a lot of video media ways to intuitive understanding, understanding of all things in life, improving people's pursuit and yearning, to future human society this is important features of image information dissemination.

Graphic images is the most vigorous information expression of visual elements, occupied in the whole wide area can directly show its important degree, according to the need to reasonable use, in harmony on the basis of should be there is a contrast;

the main content is more outstanding. From an aesthetic perspective, text and image are distinctive supplement each other. The image is closely related to the text, the contents of pictures let us feast for the eyes at the same time, and have the ability to quickly receive information. Through the study of the research of digital image processing, application and practice, we summarize its features.

1.1 *Sentimental*

Image color is rich and exquisite detail. The unutterable contents can be described incisively and vividly, people will be in the form of image to express the deep sentimental meaning which makes people imaginative and understanding more deeply.

1.2 *Visualized*

In modern society, information is mainly based on the film and television, network, advertisement, cartoon and image representation which is transmitted to people, the real degree is higher. People can obtain relevant information easily by getting intuitive visual information and intuitive understanding of things quickly, so as to be infected and inspired.

1.3 *Interesting*

The content of the abstract is combined with intuitive penetrating image vividly, with interesting, people read from the text to image, then from image to the text, the reading comprehension into visual intuitive, which undoubtedly adds new interest and appreciate angle to reading and viewing.

1.4 *The large amount of information*

Plenty of enriched content of digital image information, people are easy to remember, understand and think imaginatively. Image and text gets complementary advantages, reason and sensibility brings out the best in each other, which improves the effect of the information transmission, and can inspire people to take the initiative to accept information of interest.

1.5 *Strong impact*

More and more beautiful pictures, network picture scroll, virtual space, are a great impact on people's vision. Generally speaking, the image is easy to form the visual focus on strong visual impact, commonly used to thrust in the word groups, appears neat and delicate, has the effect of the ornament and echo page theme, and gives people the feeling of the physical and mental pleasure.

From the print magazine ads to students' textbooks, from network game to the cartoon music, read from old photographs to the classics of the excellent illustrations, such as the CCTV Spring Festival Gala visual feast. Dazzling digital images, film and television culture and art form a network digital image transmission of the information environment, image centered perceptual form, become an integral part of contemporary daily life resources and information symbols.

2 FEMALE UNIVERSITY STUDENTS HAVE THEIR OWN ADVANTAGES OF THE PROCESSING IMAGE INFORMATION

Images make up intuitive and interesting pictures, can propagate direct and concise information content, give people fashion and joyful feeling, can convey information, broaden horizons, to improve the understanding of things, and develop the imagination. In relaxed atmosphere to accept information, more and more enterprises institutions use this way to promote aim, idea, and products.

University students especially like this way, especially female university students as an important group, physiological and psychological characteristics decide their own in the process of information communication. People pay attention to the concept of digital image information processing to express rich content, which makes the female university students in their own development goals and career direction to infiltrate into the field constantly. Success and development of the female university students, not only can realize their own value, but also is a very important social science research project, so the female university students in the field of digital image would be able to master relevant knowledge and skills, can be active thinking, which is the key to expand the development space.

In study of female university students psychology, treating them as vulnerable groups. There are weaknesses, such as: achievement consciousness weak, poor psychological quality, etc. This will cause some deficiencies of them in terms of the quality of the will, such as perseverance, decisiveness and self-control weaker, they have some advantages, however, which decide them can play in the field of digital image expertise, in career training pursuit in firm faith and dedication spirit, which make their own success.

2.1 *The visualization of thinking, imagination*

Digital images express information exquisitely and richly. In the process of handling needs the perfect state. Female university students in the image thinking ability and thinking of the comprehensive advantages are careful and meticulous, which is suitable for digital image processing, image design, art design, such as graphic design, film and television animation, web art, etc ... Their works often let a person feel harmonious, elegant and beautiful.

2.2 *Emotional is exquisite, has the aesthetic consciousness*

Designing integration of human material civilization and spiritual civilization, it requires that the designer have higher aesthetic level and solid image presentation skills, also to make thinking and research on the combination of technology and art, constantly inspire aesthetic awareness, which is associated with the level of development of social practice, and is conditioned by society, but also has the characteristics of one's personality. Female university students' aesthetic feeling, appeal and abundant experience, ideas and perfect them from the color of natural objects and image characteristics such as clear, beautiful, magnificent, elegant, beautiful feeling clean, which forms and develops a strong aesthetic consciousness.

2.3 *Solid resilient, having endurance*

Digital image processing is a hard work, need to bear hardships and stand hard work, and students must calm the mind to produce good works. We combine with related images found in professional course teaching. Female university students have a strong will, with the endurance and perseverance, they can solid learning technical operation and strengthen the practice ability art design, carry on the unremitting efforts, and continue to create a case.

2.4 *Active thinking, creative*

Digital image processing is the work needs to constantly having inspiration and new ideas. Active thinking ability is the source of creativity. Female university students' divergent thinking ability has such requirement, can create imagine image, which meets different needs, such as: network, advertising, knowledge dissemination, transmission, etc.

Female university students should be according to the actual conditions of the individual and the characteristics of the network era of digital images, play their own advantages, foster strengths and circumvent weaknesses. They must realize own value, grasp the opportunities, can have focus of the destination to develop the field of image processing, focus on improving their own ability and quality. They will be in accordance with the need to shape, to satisfy the requirement of unit. They can apply their school learning professional knowledge in society.

3 IMAGE INFORMATION TRANSMISSION ABILITY OF FEMALE UNIVERSITY STUDENTS CULTIVATE METHOD

Application areas of digital image, the rise of Internet media makes all kinds of image processing technology, which can be integrated together to performance. Teaching model method of digital image related majors in higher education is particularly rich, flexible. Now, we discuss about the characteristics of the female university students and the characteristics of digital image processing.

Network culture with broad scope, is rich in resources, and is a platform of personal showing individual character characteristic. In the process of learning, Teachers guide the female university students to reasonably use, upload to the network. The works of her training that conscious information dissemination expands the influence, whole, for future personal development.

3.1 *Being aimed at the individuality characteristic, cultivates their interests*

Contemporary university students' personality tends to stable, complete, personality, and so on. Every student has their own personality characteristics; especially the female university students need different students' personality for one-on-one instruction. Female university students themselves to what you see is what you get are very interested in digital images, and aesthetic ability is stronger. Therefore, training process does not demanding.

The so-called interest is the best teacher. The cultivation of students' interest in good quality is the important content. To maintain a strong interest in learning and seeking knowledge desire is the precondition of learning, and guarantee to active learning, actively explore. Teachers must guide them the purpose of rational utilization of network resources to create through the inquiry-based learning. Students can master the design method of digital image quickly. As the saying goes, "Teacher brought that take the door and success in the individual". Teacher is dominant in this process, stands in a certain height, outlines the main knowledge and creative design ideas clearly, and gives students more opportunities of practice, which makes up the disadvantages of their poor practical ability.

3.2 *Makes project case, the mission drives*

Only the interest not practical creation, design skills and creativity will dry up one day, "project driven" is a kind of teaching method based on constructivist teaching theory, conforms to the exploratory teaching patterns, which is applicable to cultivate students' innovation consciousness and ability. We stress how to give full play to its advantages, better than cultivate students' innovation consciousness and ability. So the teaching method is very suitable for digital image processing teaching practice.

Providing students with creative subject and the request, let the students give full play to the imagination of independent creation. Students under the guidance of the teacher, finish work that has distinguishing feature very much. In the process of each task to complete, the design work reflects the principle status of students, at the same time also gives students a creative space. The student creates the Flash animation, the theme is a personal resume, which is free in form, and rich flexibility closely unites with the employment, the effect is prominent.

3.3 Freedom group, emphasis on cooperation

Female university students have more psychological problems may be withdrawn, envy, vainglorious, paranoid, etc, so the team consciousness is poorer. Because digital image processing work is rich, creative, novel, and large. Individual work alone can't do perfectly; job needs students harmonious to cooperate with colleagues. Team spirit is very important and necessary. Therefore, in the process of cultivation, topic selection and grouping and flexible in form enhance the team cooperation ability, and develop female students' psychological health status.

The Flash animation works "Embarrassed balls day" are four female classmate's free combination into small team. They pay attention to team spirit, discuss changes unceasingly, and finalize the style. The work has the personality characteristics, and has unique, rich, interesting succinct creativity.

3.4 Strengthen practice, cultivating ability

The progress of computer technology promotes the rapid development of image technology. The proficient operation of the need for a variety of image processing software, a strong practical ability is the precondition of complete design creation work. But female university students in the side faces are relatively worse; the establishment of situation, methodology, let female university students in relaxed atmosphere processing, software operation, art, creative ability. For example, they create the campus school three-dimensional virtual roaming digital animation after growing image acquisition.

3.5 Participate in the competition, a firm confidence up

Stimulating students' interest in one of the major measures is to make them able to put this to use,

and obtain satisfaction. Urged female university students pay more attention to information, to participating in the animation design, plane figure of related aspects, such as graphic design, animation creation competition activities. For example, in 2008 and 2009, Shandong Qilu software series animation design competition has obtained the third prize of good grades respectively. And the honor enhances their learning interest and motivation, clears objectives, strengthens the faith that work in the graphic image processing.

21st century is the era of digital multimedia, is also a lot of use of graphics and image to convey information era. Although the fun of digital image processing is very strong, but you need to practice and endurance, after a long time in the learning process appears unavoidably fickleness, poor ability to resist setback. We must find solution in time, make it run smoothly, continuously explore and perfect the cultivation method, provide effective guidance, make the life of the university students' own development combining with social demand. We lay the foundation for employment and fostering female university student becomes a useful person.

"The study of network culture propagation on female university students themselves growth", 2008 year art science priority key topics Shandong Province, project number: 20080028.

This work was financially supported by "Research on the Application Of 3D Virtual Apparel Fitting of Interactive Platform in Electronic Commence", from youth key project in Shandong Women's University, Project number: ZD201101.

REFERENCES

Aimin Wang. The research of College Computer Basics teaching reform based on network education platform. [M]. E-Health Networking, Digital Ecosystems and Technologies (EDT), 2010 International Conference on, 2010.

Guangchun, Gao. Explorations on teaching reformation about mobile communications in application-oriented undergraduate education. [M]. Electrical and Control Engineering (ICECE), 2011 International Conference on, 2011.

Jian Mei, Wang. Bilingual teaching mode to course on Computer Software Technology. [M]. Computer Engineering and Technology (ICCET), 2010 2nd International Conference on, 2010.

Yong Gil Lee. The Teaching Method of Creative Education. Creative Education, 2013, Vol. 04 (06), pp. 25–30.

Yunwu, Wang, Chen Lin thinking [J] "modern education technology" about Chinese education technology discipline construction and special field construction, 2008 (8).

Computer, Intelligent Computing and Education Technology – Liu, Sung & Yao (Eds)
© 2014 Taylor & Francis Group, London, ISBN 978-1-138-02469-4

Application of virtual reality technology in the teaching of art design

Fang-Fei Wu
School of Information, Nanchang Institute of Science and Technology, Nanchang, P.R. China

ABSTRACT: The virtual reality technology is comprehensive information technology, rising at the end of 20th century, which has been used in fields of medicament industry, manufacturing industry, art design and many other application fields, and it has a great outlook in education application. For art design specialty, it has special relationship with the virtual reality technology, it has played an immeasurable role in teaching of art design specialty. This paper has analyzed firstly the characteristic of the virtual reality technology. Secondly, this paper has analyzed the innovation significance that the virtual reality technology has influenced the teaching of art design specialty. The teaching practice shows the virtual reality technology can change some deficiencies in traditional teaching of art design specialty, and has beneficial to innovation and reformation of art design teaching.

Keywords: virtual reality technology; art design; interaction; man-machine system; teaching modes

1   INTRODUCTION

With the rapid development of information technology and the advent of the knowledge economy, the creative ability training of art design have got enough attention and concern in society and education fields. Training of innovative art design need constant innovation, the education technology plays more and more important role in the teaching innovation, and the teaching innovation of art design based on virtual reality technology plays an important role.

2   THE CONCEPT AND FEATURE OF VIRTUAL REALITY TECHNOLOGY

Virtual reality technology is a developing technology that related with the advanced computer technology, Micro Electro Technology, simulation technology and, etc. It can produce the 3D real virtual environment by virtue of the 3D graphic technology, multi-sensor exchange technology and high-resolution display technology. The user cover some sensor equipment, such as special helmet and data glove sensor, or use the keyboard and mouse, and can enter virtual space, becomes a member of the virtual environment. The user can interactive in real time, apperceive and operate all kinds of object of the virtual world, and acquire systematic various information, acquire "you-are-there" experience. The virtual reality technology has three features.

2.1   The immersion

The immersion refers to the real degree of the user exists in the virtual environment as leading role. The user only enter the virtual environment as if be personally on the scene. The user who only feel as if he is part of the virtual environment, who can get a feeling of being surrounded by virtual environment. And the user can exercise freely under the virtual environment, interact with substance as if he was in real world.

2.2   The interaction

The interaction refers that the user gets feedback natural degree from environment and operable degree from the object of virtual environment. The virtual object is 3D interacting with users, and the user is interactive leading role. The user can interact with the virtual objects by different means of reality. Fox example, the user can grasp directly the objects of virtual environment, who can feel the sense of touch and the weight of object, and the object of scene will also move accompany with one's hands.

2.3   The imagination

The imagination refers that the user is indulged in hyperspace, acquires comprehensively knowledge by virtue of own cognitive and perceptual ability, and play the initiative to search the key and form a concept.

3 THE MEANING OF VIRTUAL REALITY TECHNOLOGY IN TEACHING INNOVATION OF ART DESIGN

The traditional teaching mode of knowledge transfer and acceptance is one-way and low efficiency, and the repeatability of transmission and acceptance is bad. The traditional teaching need invest massive capital in making the relative teaching model, students establishing the training room and laboratory. At present, in the circumstances of education funds insufficiency, the virtual reality technology is widely applied in the teaching innovation of art design because of its many advantages.

3.1 The verisimilar environment

The virtual reality technology can produce the lifelike virtual environment, bring students some organoleptic stimulus information of see, hear, taste and touch, and make them have an immersed sense by the hardware platform. The virtual reality technology stimulate students' brain cell in sensory, make them finish the memory of teaching content in accordance with excitement and activity, and it can attract students attention, also increase the memory content.

3.2 The teaching interaction

With development of the information society, communication skills play an very important role in teaching, and the virtual reality can provide the training method. Students can communicate with teachers by virtual gloves in real time, and teachers can also shortly collect students' information. Teachers can improve immediately the teaching modes, and construct a platform of stimulate students' study interest. On the platform, students can study independently, actively and purposefully, and it will change the traditional expository teaching.

3.3 The mutual cooperation

The system of virtual reality technology can create learning environment, so make students in the same virtual environment for learning, and communication each other. Students can finish together class design or practice work, take part in change processing of objects. In this virtual climate, students observe and learn intuitively all kinds of knowledge and skills, and point out some problems and defects. In system of virtual reality teachers can also enter the virtual environment as students to study, and cooperate with students, further to encourage and stimulate students' activity and initiative, in order to finish the study and teaching in virtual environment.

3.4 The stimulating creation

The imagination of the virtual reality technology can accomplish the virtual of various model, students can observe directly the result or effect of virtual environment by the virtual reality system. For example, In design of complex product, students can intuitively undertake design, which can avoid potential disturbances and unreasonable problem. The intuition is the most effective tool in inner design of fly and car, and the virtual reality technology plays a an irreplaceable important role in design. In teaching, teacher undertake the teaching of art design, which is better for encourage the creative thinking of students, culture the creativity of students.

3.5 The economy and practicability

Students can deal with various experiments by virtual reality system at doors, and acquire the experience just as in real experiment, At the same time the virtual reality system can enrich their perceptual knowledge, deepen the understanding of the teaching content.

3.6 The security guarantee

Students can make experiment and avoid danger of the real experiments with the virtual experiment. They can make various dangerous experiments and harmful experiments for human. For example, the virtual driving training can eliminate the serious accident of automobile collision because of students' inaccurate operation.

4 THE TEACHING INNOVATION METHOD OF ART DESIGN BASED ON VIRTUAL REALITY TECHNOLOGY

4.1 Constructing the teaching system of art design based on virtual reality technology

According to the characteristics of art and design disciplines integration, virtual teaching system should focus on the needs of future development, which should have the function of practical training, visit and investigation, user research, conceptual design, structure design, man-machine system, etc. At the same time, it also has a certain openness, and students can easily access it.

4.2 Constructing the virtual laboratory

We can establish various virtual laboratories, such as printing lab, model lab, metalworking lab, photo lab, etc. Students can make freely the various experiments. They can experience the pleasure of various professional laboratories by the virtual environment in the laboratory.

4.3 Constructing the virtual laboratory

By virtue of the Virtual reality immersion and interactivity, students can play a role in the virtual learning environment, who can devote themselves into the learning environment, so it is better for training students' technical skills. Students can make the various technical trainings, such as teaching skill, driving skills, appliance repair skills, equipment installation skills and other occupation skill training.

4.4 The virtual practice and investigation

For the traditional professional practice and investigation, students often have to go to out of school, and they spend too much time in going there and back. By the virtual technology, students can study by virtual investigation, and the time of study is very free. They can make investigation again and again, and improve the ability of find out problems and solve them. Students can accomplish a better combination of theory and practice.

4.5 The virtual conceptual design

The conceptual design implements the conception of products or components, which intent is to captive the basic shape of product. To introduce the virtual reality technology into computer aided design system is a good design method, which can make the virtual reality technology are combined with concept design, and enrich the interact methods. It can save them a lot of time for conceptual design in the virtual environment.

Students are engaged in conceptual design, whose intent is going on design innovation and comprehensive training. Because the constraint of the environment is relatively small, students' imaginative space is relative free. For the view of design, students' imagination and creativity can be developed rapidly, and the comprehensive quality can be improved as well as.

4.6 The virtual design

Students are engaged in virtual environment design, which includes curriculum design, design competition, project of enterprise consignment, virtual show and design assessment. Constructing the various platform by the virtual reality technology, and students can design the product according to own desires and imagination. For design of the structural product, students can intuitively make assembly, learn avoid some problems.

In the view of analysis of man-machine system, students can put the virtual design production into the virtual environment, and know momentarily the feedback information of man-machine, so that the mistake can be corrected in time. For design of

production, students show their the work of art by the "immersing" character of the virtual reality technology, and other students and teachers can appraise products. The students can correct or improve the product design on the basic of others suggestion, and it can make the product design much accord with scientific requirement, also meet the aesthetic need. For example, the automotive shape design becomes an important role in automation, which model was made with plastics ago.

The model will spend much time in modification and evaluation. If the models are modeled with the virtual reality technology, we can freely correct or improve the design, the model can be directly applied in simulation and machining when design is finished.

5 CONCLUSIONS

With the improvement of science, the virtual reality technology has penetrated into every aspect of arts education, promoted the teaching reform process. The virtual reality technology is taken as new excellent technology media, which plays an important role in constructing the training mode of art design. The fact prove that the application of virtual reality technology can not only enhance professional knowledge and demonstration effect, but also stimulate students interest and enhance the exploration of interactive skills training, and can well meet the teaching scene and the requirement of the natural alternation. We have reason to believe that the virtual reality technology will play more and more important role in the modern teaching by virtue of its advantages in the near future.

REFERENCES

Jing X.X. 2013. The Virtual Reality—The Better Connection between Technology and Art. *The design* 11:122–123.
Liu H.R. 2012. The Necessity of Introducing the Virtual Reality into Digital Art Design. *Big Stage* 12:202–203.
Tang X.H. 2008. Architechtural Artistic Design Teaching Widely Application Virtual Reality Technology. *The art and Design* 3:11–12.
Wang Z.F. 2011. Study on Virtual Reality Design Curriculum Teaching of Art Design Specialty in college. *Technology Information* 7:132–133.
Yuan Y. 2012. Application of the Virtual Reality Technology in Art Design. *Art Education Research* 11:112–113.
Zhen L.B. 2010. Application Field and Future Development of Digital Art Design. *Friend of Science Amateurs* 12:138–139.
Zhou Y.M. 2010. The Application of Virtual Digitalized Means in Exhibition Design. *Journal of Southwest Agricultural University (Social Science Edition)* 6(12):200–202.

Computer, Intelligent Computing and Education Technology – Liu, Sung & Yao (Eds)
© 2014 Taylor & Francis Group, London, ISBN 978-1-138-02469-4

Research and application of an improved data mining process model

Feng-Ying Nie

School of Information, Nanchang Institute of Science and Technology, Nanchang, P.R. China

ABSTRACT: The data mining has been taken as the research method of bank CRM, which the effectiveness of implement has played a key role in client analysis of whole banking business. This paper has improved and integrated the data mining process model based on the traditional the data mining process model, so that the data mining process model will become more detailed and scientific. In finally, this paper has applied the improved the data mining process model to the analysis of bank clients' fluctuation, which provide a new reference for Customer Relationship Management.

Keywords: data mining; customer relationship management; process model

1 INTRODUCTION

With the development of economy and society, the traditional management mode of account-based has been unable to meet the rapid need of promoting their own benefit in the market of the fierce competition and financial buyer. The competition clients-based has been thrust gradually the stage. In addition, some internal management system and the management flow of many banks face series of problems, and the business management mode has become developing the core of banking business. The building of customer relationship management system can make banking form the coordinated and bran-new relationship-entity each other in customer service and market competition, and bring sustainable advantage to the banking.

Along with the development and perfection of the customer relationship management system, a lot of customer datum of the system need be handled in real time. The data mining technology can extract potentially valuable information from data warehouse integrated with the computer science, statistics, database and other disciplines, and promote the effective running of the customer relationship management system. A good data mining process can collect all kinds of data, integrate with systematic information, so as to help the relative staff to obtain quickly decision-making plan, promote growth of bank business volume.

Based on the reading and the analyzing of domestic and foreign relative literatures, we can know that many researchers devoted to data mining algorithm and model improvement, and analysis the precise model of the solving method.

But they overlooked the study of the whole data mining flow. This paper has improved and integrated the data mining process model based on the traditional the data mining process model, so that the data mining process model will become more detailed and scientific. In finally, this paper has applied the improved the data mining process model to the analysis of bank clients' fluctuation, and obtain the improved customer flow analysis process model.

2 THE TRADITIONAL DATA MINING FLOW

There are two accepted data mining flows, such as SEMMA of SAS and GRISP-DM of SPSS. EMMA method analyzed the data processing procedure from the viewpoint of the algorithm, and the GRISP-DM model introduced synoptically the general direction of data mining from overall perspective. The SEMMA process model is shown in Figure 1. The the GRISP-DM process model is shown in Figure 2.

2.1 *SEMMA model process*

1. Sample—Data sampling. To analyze the data law based on representative data of massive datum can reduce the amount of data processing, save the system resource.
2. Explore—Analysis and pretreatment of the datum. To find out the relationship of data, analyze its law and tendency, classifying datum, which the process should be handle by visualized manipulation.

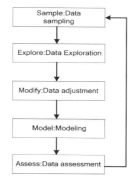

Figure 1. SEMMA model.

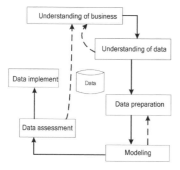

Figure 2. GRISP-DM model.

3. Modify—Data adjustment and technology selection. According to the specific inquiries of problems and law of data mining, the data will be adjusted properly. On the basic of it, we finish the process of data mining by selecting the suitable technology.

4. Model development and knowledge discovery: According the dataset features and achievable goals, choosing the suitable modeling method in accordance with several modeling methods. It is the core of data mining.

5. Model—Appraisement of model development and knowledge discovery: According the outcomes of above the process model, appraising synthetically the model, finding out the most suitable model, and appraising the model in accordance with some effects of the practical problem.

2.2 *GRISP–DM method process*

1. The understanding of business: Understanding the goals of data mining required from a business and commercial standpoint.

2. Understanding data: Collecting and analyzing the data, finding out the feature and

interconnected parts, the regularity and hidden information.

3. Data preparation: Before the modeling, the datum need be operated relatively, such as cleaning, checking, verification and protocol operation, so as to meet the need of modeling.

4. Modeling: Dealing with the datum by selecting different data models, adjusting the model of unsuitable data.

5. Appraisement: Appraising the outcomes of modeling according to real-life other influencing factor, so determine the best plan.

6. Deployment: According to the model generated results, summarizing the content knowledge value, making a reasonable implementation by combining with a series of conditions.

Some analysis can be seen from the above two kinds of data mining process model, the SEMMA method is the process of technology-based, whose analysis is mainly based on the data. While the GRISP-DM method is more inclined to the orientation of theory from analyzing problem to solving problem. They are two typical analysis models, but the two typical models have some defects, such as they analyze the datum without effective integrating the business and the whole system. This paper has modified and integrated with the two typical data mining process model, so as to obtain a more efficient and scientific model of the data mining process.

3 AN IMPROVED DATA MINING PROCESS MODEL

Because the purpose of the data mining is service the business target, we bring the data mining process into the business-making, and also bring various algorithms and technology into the business-making process. The improved model shows carefully and visually how to convert information from the business problem to data information, and the whole process of business making. The improved data is shown in Figure 3.

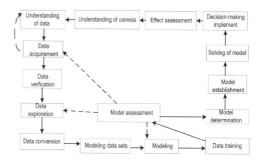

Figure 3. The improved model.

1. The understanding of business. To analyze the causes of banking business and abnormal situation, and find out the influence of large business links. For example, the banking business volume has not increased, whose reason may be high the turnover rate of big customer, and also may be irrational functional distribution.
2. The understanding of data. According to the analysis of banking business, after finding out the reasons, we need search the information of all customers from database. We need distinguish carefully the relative data, find out the internal relationship between data and implicit rules. During the process of data analysis, we may be find out the business understanding deviation of the upper stage, so as to review the business problem.
3. The data acquisition. On the basic of full understanding of data, we need extracted the relative datum, whose extraction procedure may be a variegated process. For example, we can extract a group of datum in accordance with certain relevance, analyze carefully the datum, and find out the feature and laws of data. In the process, we may be add or delete constantly data till the datum becomes the most reasonable. No matter what we use the extraction methods, the most basic rule are on certain laws and steps.
4. The verification, testing and cleaning of data. We need re-verify the complete data of extraction, so remove some datum, which does not come up to the requirements and defect. And we clean data in according in the abnormal data.
5. The exploration and pretreatment of data. We further analyze the reasonable data in accordance in the internal relations. The step whose intent is to find out potential and indiscoverable information, obtain the obvious laws. On the basic of it, We adjust properly the datum, and reassign the datum in accordance with features and laws.
6. The data conversion. The data mining algorithms are only more suitable for a certain level data. Some unassorted datum is unfit for dug. Generally, before implement the process of data mining, we need classify the data in accordance with data granularity, and class the data of equal granularity with the same classes. In the process, some other methods need be applied in the data mining.
7. The modeling of data set. By the above the process of data processing, the data can be collected completely. Next, we need provide for modeling, select the complete modeling data sets. In the process, we need classify the data sets in a proportion, which are classified as training data sets, testing data sets and evaluation data sets. Among them, the training data sets is used to implement data mining, so as to obtain the relative information; the testing data sets is used to deal with the evaluation of outcome, so as to validate the validity of modeling methods and algorithms; the evaluation data sets is used to evaluate the outcome of data mining, so as to obtain the most suitable the outcome of data mining.
8. The modeling. The modeling is the core process of data mining. We need choose suitable modeling methods to deal with data in accordance with feature and business goal of data feature. There are some the technical method in the process, such as mathematical statistics, correlation analysis method, analysis of classification & clustering, artificial neural network, and decision tree, etc. Under the condition of the current data processing software become gradually mature, we can modeling data through the use of several modeling methods.
9. Model Training. Because we often can not know which the algorithms and model is most effective and reasonable in advance, which need us verify the effect of model by unknown data in accordance with various models and algorithms. This is the spiritual message of choosing the training model in the early stage.
10. The evaluation and monitoring of model. This evaluation work of this phase is of vital importance. It can not only need the evaluation model, but also select suitable the evaluation model. In addition, It also need the evaluation model in accordance with the actual factors, and judge the merits of the model with the whole opinions. At this stage, there are always some declinational results, which need be revised by new variables and data assembly.
11. The determination of model. After finishing the above steps, a suitable and optimized model can be produced basically.
12. According to the data mining model results, we can get some direction and method of decision, then we integrate the relative business with the internal and external resource of bank, draw up the suitable model and plan of decision-making. Certainly, the plan of decision-making need to further be checked.
13. The solving of decision-making model. According to mathematical statistics methods, technical means, business operation rules and methods, finding out the most suitable outcome.
14. The implementation of the decision-making. Arousing the relative resources of bank and implementing the decision-making in accordance with decision-making model.

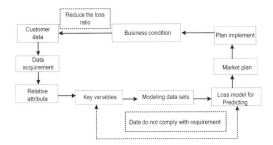

Figure 4. Analysis model of bank clients' loss.

15. The assessment of decision effect. After a period of the plan of decision–making is implemented, before and after the plan of decision-making is compared, which intent is to find out difference, analyze the implement effect. It need be wholly and scientifically evaluated in accordance with technicians, commercial personnel and experts. If there are still some unsuitable views at the stage, we need turn to the initial business problems, and analyze the relative information again and again.

4 THE APPLICATION EXAMPLE—AN IMPROVED ANALYSIS MODEL OF CUSTOMER LOSS OF BANKING

With the rapid development of the financial industry, the competition among banks is more and more intense, the customer has become the core resources of bank profit, how to attract and obtain the user become a top priority for banks. But they has apt to acquire new customers, while ignore the traditional customer. It not only wastes resources, but also brings a lot of advantages to risks of long-term development of bank. This paper has applied the improved the data mining process model to the analysis of bank clients' fluctuation, which provide a new reference for Customer Relationship Management. The model is shown in Figure 4.

5 CONCLUSIONS

This paper gives an introduction to the relationship management of bank customer, and puts forward the importance of data mining process in relationship management of bank customer. According to the idea of SEMMA and GRISP-DM model, improves and proposes the new data mining process model, which integrates data mining algorithm and technology with business goal and the whole banking system. we have applied the improved the data mining process model to the analysis of bank clients' fluctuation, and provide a new reference for customer relationship management.

REFERENCES

Han J.W, Micheline K. 2001. Data mining: concepts and techniques. *Beijing: China Machine Press.*

Liao Q. 2010. The Data Mining and Mathematical Modeling. *Beijing: Academic Press.*

Qi J.Y, Zhang L, Liu Y.P, et al. 2009. ADTreesLogit Model for Customer Churn Prediction. *Annals of operations research* 168(1):247–265.

Wang S, Zhang S, Ma H.B. 2005. The Theory and Practices of banking CRM. *Beijing: Electronic Industry Press.*

Zhang J, Chang G.R. 2003. Applying Data Mining Technology to Management. *Chinese journal of management science* 11(1):53–59.

Zhang J, Chang G.R, Huang X.Y. 2003. The application of Data Mining Technology in CRM System. *Journal of northeastern university (Natural science).* 11(11):1112–1115.

Computer, Intelligent Computing and Education Technology – Liu, Sung & Yao (Eds)
© 2014 Taylor & Francis Group, London, ISBN 978-1-138-02469-4

Analysis of key knowledge structure, core ability and basic quality of applied talents

X.Y. Lang & K. Zhang
School of Mechanical Engineering, Shenyang University of Technology, Shenyang, China

ABSTRACT: This paper expounds the elements, namely the knowledge, ability and quality at first, and then discusses the dialectical relationship among the key knowledge structure, core ability and basic quality that should be possessed with the applied talents. At last, the key knowledge structure, core ability and basic quality required for the growth of applied talents are concluded, and the growth model of applied talents is proposed on the basis of relative research. The results show that only the applied talents with all-round development can really become the useful talents popular with the enterprises.

Keywords: applied talent; key knowledge structure; core ability; basic quality

1   INTRODUCTION

Applied talents refers to a kind of professional and technical talents who can apply professional knowledge and skills to the engaged professional social practice, and are skilled in the basic knowledge and skills for social production and activity and mainly engaged in front line production. With the development of national economy, the society pays the increasing attention to the cultivation of applied talents, and the applied talents have become the one who are heavily short of in the society. Accordingly, the talent cultivation in university should adapt to the social demand. Through the theoretical knowledge impartment, practical skills training and comprehensive quality cultivation needed during college education, the knowledge impartment, ability cultivation, and quality improvement are combined to an integrity. Paying attention to the coordinated development of key knowledge structure, core ability and basic quality and cultivating the applied talents with high technology application ability, innovative spirit and innovative ability can meet the needs of the modern enterprise for talents.

2   CONCEPT OF KNOWLEDGE, ABILITY AND QUALITY

2.1   *Knowledge*

Knowledge is the fruit of human cognition, which can be generally classified into three categories, namely, natural science, social science and thinking science knowledge, including two aspects: book theory knowledge and practice experience knowledge. Along with the rapid development of science and technology, profound changes have taken place in knowledge itself, and human have a new recognition to the concept of knowledge. In the report "Knowledge-based Economy" issued by the international economic cooperation and development organization in 1996 [1], the forms of knowledge were made a clear definition. It was pointed out that not only can knowledge include encoding knowledge, such as the fact knowledge and principle knowledge, but also include tacit knowledge that can sense but not encode, such as skill knowledge, human knowledge, etc. For applied talents, it mainly includes the specialty foundation and professional knowledge and humanistic knowledge.

2.2   *Ability*

Ability is the personal mental characteristics of some activity performed smoothly by individual, which can be divided into the following aspects from different angles:

1. General ability and special ability: The former refers to intelligence, which is suitable for all kinds of activities, including observation, thinking ability, imagination and so on, also including the speed, flexibility and accuracy of the application of these factors.
2. Imitation ability and creation ability.
3. Recognition ability, operation ability and social ability.

Ability is formed through cultivation and practice based on the master certain knowledge. The abundant knowledge can promote ability enhancement, and the strong ability can facilitate knowledge acquisition. Specifically, the ability mainly includes the abilities to acquire knowledge, apply knowledge and innovate. For applied talents, it not only refers to the technique application ability, operation ability, and manual ability, but also includes the comprehensive vocational ability, such as knowledge, skills and attitudes.

2.3 Quality

Current understanding of quality can have two kinds [2]: Firstly, from the viewpoint of physiology and psychology, it can be seen as the personal inborn anatomy physiology characteristic, mainly including the traits of nervous system, sense organs, motor organs and brain; Secondly, from the meaning of pedagogy, it refers to the internal, relatively stable and long-term acting physical and mental characteristics and the basic quality structure of people gained by environmental influence and education training on the basis of congenital physiological quality. The research on quality in pedagogy belongs to the latter. It can be the level of development which has been reached by individuals at some stage, such as physical growth, health level, wisdom, will, emotion, attitude orientation toward people and things, etc. This quality is not born but derived, and is gradually formed in the process of human's development. Compared with the physical quality, this quality possesses more differentiation and plasticity. By the good environment and education, individuals tend to get better quality [3].

3 DIALECTICAL UNIFICATION OF KNOWLEDGE, ABILITY AND QUALITY

The relationship among knowledge, ability and quality is complementary to each other, and is the dialectical unification.

Knowledge is the foundation of formation and improvement of quality, and is the carrier of ability and quality. Knowledge has the indispensable basic status in the aspect of the formation of people's overall quality, no corresponding knowledge. Man cannot be internalized and sublimated for a higher psychological quality without relevant abundant knowledge.

Knowledge and ability are closely linked together, and possession of a lot of knowledge is the foundation of ability formation. On one hand, the speed and quality of grasping knowledge depend on the development of ability. On the other hand, knowledge provides the basis for the development of ability. A capable person is easier to get some knowledge, and the ability without the basis

of knowledge can be seen as a kind of low-level skill at the most, and even instinct. If there is no knowledge in some area, this area must be lack of capability. Due to the extensive migration of acquired knowledge, individuals form the systematic and generalized mental structure, thus forming some kind of ability. Based on the idea of quality education, in addition to professional knowledge, the knowledge imparted to students should pay more attention to the essential knowledge required for the growth of students, namely the related cultural, social, and natural science knowledge.

Ability is a kind of explicit form of quality. After the quality is practiced, it appears to be the ability. Without ability, the quality cannot exhibit, observe, confirm and grasp. As the externalization of quality, ability belongs to the category of practice activities. Compared with the quality, the ability is easier to operate and evaluate. Accordingly, which kind of ability of students should be cultivated is also very important. In the current society, more attention should be paid to cultivate the students' social intercourse, coexistence, co-work and cooperation with others, namely the cultivation of the ability of personhood.

Quality is closely related to the knowledge and ability. The basic elements of quality are knowledge and ability, and core is competence and values. According to the characteristics of the quality internality, people should convert acquired knowledge into one's own soul through option, absorption, integration and innovation, and internalize them into himself to form the quality. Consequently, the acquired education and guidance make the students voluntarily strengthen their own reform, which can form a good quality. However, quality is something deeper, whose improvement process is more complicated. Knowledge, ability and quality are not coordinate and parallel. From the perspective of talent training, imparting knowledge and cultivating ability tend to solve how to do things, but improving quality is inclined to solve how to behave. Only combining how to do things with how to behave organically, the ideal talents could be cultivated [4]. Therefore, the university education should focus on training students' skills, as well as quality and moral quality, which are the concerns of education quality enterprisers.

4 CULTIVATION OF APPLIED TALENTS WITH COORDINATED DEVELOPMENT OF KNOWLEDGE, ABILITY AND QUALITY

There are different types of talent structures in the society, and different types of talents have different demands on knowledge, ability and quality.

The applied talents mainly work in the grass-roots, who are the talents faced to the first-line production and employed in technology application, technology management and service. The university education should confirm the requirement of the key knowledge structure, core ability and basic quality, so as to better carry out the teaching reform about cultivation of applied talents.

4.1 Requirement for key knowledge structure

As the main workers who implement technology, applied talents must have the corresponding professional foundation knowledge, professional technical knowledge, which is the basis of exhibition of the professional technical ability. In order to better grasp the technology and technology management, they also need to have relevant professional auxiliary knowledge. At the same time, they should continuously learn and accumulate experience and knowledge in the practice.

In the learning of knowledge, attention should be paid to the basic knowledge. As a result of the rapid development of current technology, the changes of technical knowledge speed up. However, the basic knowledge is relatively stable, and possesses the higher absolute value. In addition, it can improve the occupation career adaptability of applied talents and lay a good foundation for the continuing education in the future growth.

The applied talents mainly work in the first line of production. They should give priority to study the application of mature technologies, and must strengthen the study on practical professional foundation knowledge and professional technique knowledge needed to form the technical application ability. Accordingly, they can have the required theoretical knowledge to solve technical problems on site, which makes them can do "not only know it, but also know how it comes" at work and improve their ability to analyze and solve problems. Meanwhile, they should pay attention to widen professional technique knowledge learning and emphasize professional composite knowledge learning. Besides, they should master certain new knowledge in related fields and form the relatively wide professional knowledge, so as to better guide their practical work.

With the growth of applied talent and the improvement of technology level, he not only has the technical ability, but also need to have other core competence, which includes participation in technical management, production management, cost accounting, guidance to low-level technology workers and so on. Consequently, in addition to technical knowledge, he also needs to master the management knowledge related to management and education and training.

French management expert Fayard proposed a vivid curtain-type knowledge structure [5]. He thought that for a business, the required knowledge mainly includes technique, management, finance, business, accounting and security. All the staff at different posts depends on these six types of knowledge in varying degrees. The post—knowledge weight diagram was drawn in Figure 1, which just likes the half-opened curtain, and should enlighten the cultivation of applied talents.

Emphasis on the experience knowledge learning is also very important for applied talents. In national occupation standard, the senior skilled talents require the ability to solve the unconventional technical problems. This ability is mainly depends on the accumulation and learning of experience in the working practice. With the growth of the grass-roots work experience, the accumulated experience knowledge is more and more rich, and the work tips are more and more plentiful. This is an important aspect of growth of the core ability of applied talents.

4.2 Requirement for core ability

Ability is the external manifestations or reflection of knowledge and quality, and knowledge and quality are exhibited by various abilities. Ability is a kind of quality structure formed by knowledge, skills and attitudes of workers, which is the foundation to complete the specific work. Ability of applied talents should comprise various aspects, including professional ability, such as technical operation skills, technical management ability, technical diagnosis ability and repair ability, and including general ability, such as cognitive ability, expression ability, social ability and production ability, also including dedication spirit, cooperation ability, willpower and health psychology. In fact, this idea is just the all-round quality education concept emphasized in our country, and is also the consensus in the training of professional technical talents by various countries in the world.

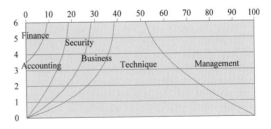

Figure 1. Curtain-type knowledge structure.
Digital representation: 0—workers; 1—class leader; 2—workshop director; 3—departments responsible person; 4—technical director; 5—manager; 6—general manager.

The applied talent has the stronger practical ability and operation skills, which are the main distinctive features from other talents. The applied talent is in the status of "middle talents". He should have the appropriate theoretical knowledge and the strong practical skills, and is the worker who mainly applies the intellectual skills.

4.3 *Requirement for basic quality*

Quality is the core of knowledge and ability. It represents the individual internalized and relatively stable quality. Some quality or character can be inherited, but more can be improved and changed through acquired practice. The quality education should focus on cultivating creative spirit and practical ability, and pay attention to train students' innovation spirit, practice ability and enterprising spirit, improve humanities literacy and scientific literacy, and promote proficient professional skills and the ability to adapt to change. This quality education has indicated the direction for technical education and cultivation of applied talents.

The applied talents work in the first line of production, construction, management and service. The required quality should include the following aspects from its form:

1. Ideology and morality: have good moral character; can correctly handle the relationships between individual and society, between individual and other people; establish a high sense of social responsibility; have good occupation moral; possess the ideology of working at the grassroots, serving the grassroots, and rooting in the grassroots.
2. Professional dedication and responsibility: possess the work attitude to work hard and bear the burden without complaint; can bear hardships and stand hard work; have the courage to undertake responsibility; have a strong sense of job responsibility; devote to the work; can actively study technique; have engaged in the occupation spirit.
3. Coexistence and cooperation: The applied talents work in the first line of production, and the grass-roots front-line work is often a collaborative working group. The applied talents are either the mumbers or the leaders of them. They should have the good organization and coordination abilities to deal with the various relation in production activities, which is very important for the applied talents to effectively apply their professional knowledge and skills into the production.
4. Physique and psychology: The healthy body and good psychological quality are the premise of all work. The good physical fitness is qualified to do the professional work. The good

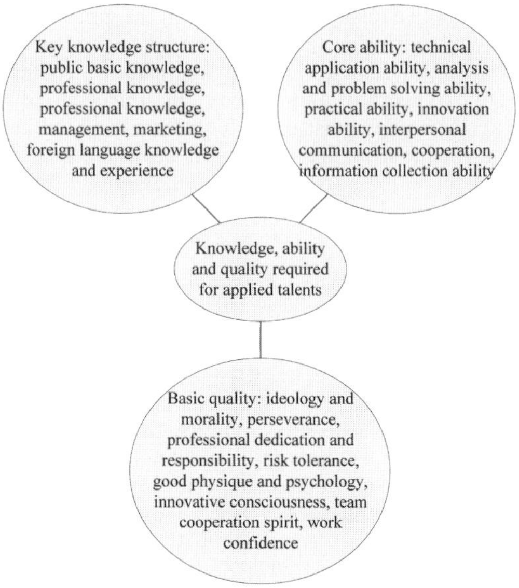

Figure 2. Knowledge, ability and quality required for applied talents.

psychological quality is critical to work in collaboration. They should have enough psychological enduring capacity to suffer the setbacks in the competition. Cultivating good personality and establishing effective psychological adjustment mechanism and defense mechanism can improve the whole quality of talents and give full play to their effectiveness.

Based on the above discussion and analysis, the key knowledge structure, the core ability and the basic quality required for applied talents can be summarized as shown in Figure 2.

5 GROWTH MODEL OF APPLIED TALENTS

The growth of modern applied talents needs the school education cultivation at first. It makes the applied talents possess basic professional skills and technical expertise, and talent quality qualified for the professional and technical requirements. Through the practice of social work, the knowledge of applied talents is enriched, and technical ability is enhanced. Their psychology is more stable, and the maturity of their knowledge, ability and quality increase. The innovative consciousness gradually transformed into innovation ability formation. The continuous education and training and job motivation promote their hard study and diligent work, and the further growth of knowledge and ability, which can form the innovative

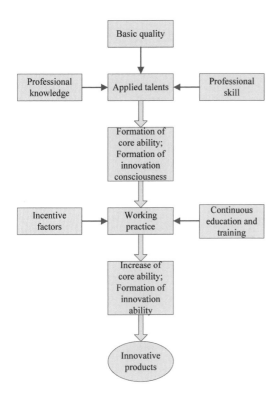

Figure 3.   Growth model of applied talents.

achievements in the work. This situation explains that the applied talents grow in the learning—practice—learning—practice repeated process. Figure 3 illustrates this growth process of applied talents. The requirements for every step of development process of applied talents can be clearly seen in this figure.

6   CONCLUSIONS

In a word, there are close relationship among knowledge, ability and quality. The university education should actively carry out the reform of education and teaching, and pay attention to cultivate the applied talents in accordance with the harmonious development of key knowledge structure, core ability and basic quality. Moreover, the applied talents should notice the continuous improvement of their working practice, promote the all-round development with key knowledge structure, core ability and basic quality, and really become the useful talents popular with the enterprises.

ACKNOWLEDGMENT

This research is supported by the General Program of Education and Science of Liaoning Province during the 12th Five-Year Plan Period, No. JG11DB207.

REFERENCES

[1] Y.K. Chen. "Teaching Evaluation", Beijing: People's Education Press, 1999.
[2] L. Yu. "Classroom Teaching Assessment", Beijing: People's Education Press, 2007.
[3] Z.R. Du, W.W. Liao. "Higher Education", Shanghai: Fudan University Press, 2003.
[4] Y. Lu. "A Study on Constructing a Quality Assurance System for Undergraduate Teaching at Regular Higher Institutions: Illustrated with the Case of E University", East China Normal University, 2007.
[5] J.H. Hong. "Strengthening Experimental Teaching Supervision, Improving Personnel Training Quality", Experiment Science & Technology, 2009(6).

Computer, Intelligent Computing and Education Technology – Liu, Sung & Yao (Eds)
© 2014 Taylor & Francis Group, London, ISBN 978-1-138-02469-4

Education for construction and security countermeasures of family wireless LAN

D.L. Hao & H.S. Zhang
*Sino-Dutch Demonstration Research and Training Center for Water Treatment (DETCWAT),
Environmental Management College of China (EMCC), Qinhuangdao, China*

ABSTRACT: Wireless local area network compared with the traditional twisted pair copper has advantages of relatively cheap, flexible movement, convenient installation, easy fault location and easy network adjustment and extended in the network. But for most non computer professional home, self-build are still a lot of difficulties. This paper aims to help people to make their own wireless local area network and enjoy the safe network life.

Keywords: wireless local area network; building; security countermeasures

Can be realized in the LAN computer file transfer between, shared disk, printer sharing and other functions, data transmission speed very fast and in the local area network, can greatly improve the transmission efficiency. But the old twisted pair copper wire network in some cases, unable to meet the needs of users. This deficiency is particularly prominent at home users.

Wireless local area network (Wireless Local Area Networks; WLAN) is the use of radio frequency (Radio Frequency; RF) technology, local area network instead of the traditional construction of twisted pair copper wire. Because the wireless LAN has a relatively cheap, flexible movement, convenient installation, fault location for fast and easy network adjustment and expansion and rapid development. And the traditional twisted pair network, If there is no advance pipe burying, Home will be filled with the spider web like pipeline, affect the beauty of a room, So the wireless LAN by the home network users and small and medium-sized office users.

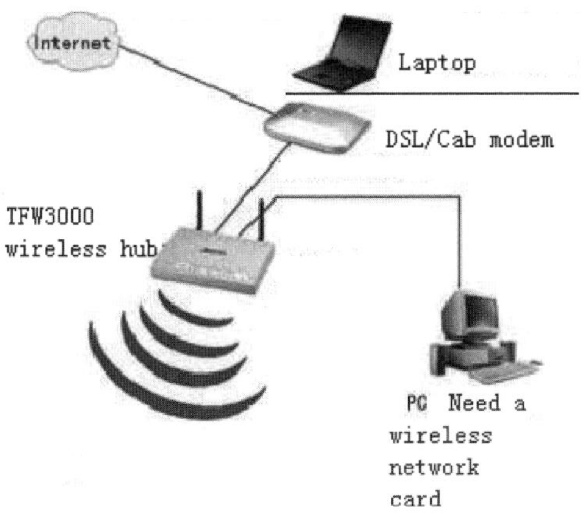

Typically wireless LAN include: Internet access, Computer terminal, The three part. Although less needed equipment, set up a simple and convenient. There are still a lot of difficulties but for most non computer professional homebuilding. Peer to peer network to achieve the most simple way of. Through the wireless router for a home wireless local area network intermediary. See for example (Fig. 1).

1 HARDWARE REQUIREMENTS

Wireless router, Broadband access. There are many mode of broadband access, Include: fiber-optic access, DSL access etc. Speed of Wireless local area network, finally depend on the speed of the Internet Network that your choice. Usually, laptop own wlan card, no need for extra equipment. But desktop computer, lacking of wireless network card, can not realize the wireless network access. Can by buying additional wireless network card to realize. See for example (Fig. 2), wireless network is not present.

Figure 1. The structure of wireless network.

Figure 2. Not connected to a wireless network.

2 THE ROUTER SETTINGS

2.1 The first step

The new router may not be able to use, because no setting wireless function. The function can be activated by web settings. By net wire, connecting up the router to the computer (Confirm the router has access to internet). Open internet Explorer, enter 192.168.1.1 in the internet Explorer address bar. Enter login account and password in the popup-style interface (Router's login and password). The default is admin. (Proposed modifications. If non-amended, the security of the system will greatly reduce). Getting into setting guide interface of wireless router. See for example (Fig. 3).

2.2 The second step

Choice "The next step" (Fig. 3) into the interface of work mode (Fig. 4).

2.3 The third step

Choice "The next step" (Fig. 4) into the interface of accessing the web, (Fig. 5). The SSID, is the name of the wireless LAN that you will be established, changes the name that you memory easily, of course, also can non—modified. But Wireless security options must be setted (Fig. 5). Your password, for security, should be composed of numbers and letters. If the password is over simple, your wireless network may be "shared". Your internet expirience will be reduced.

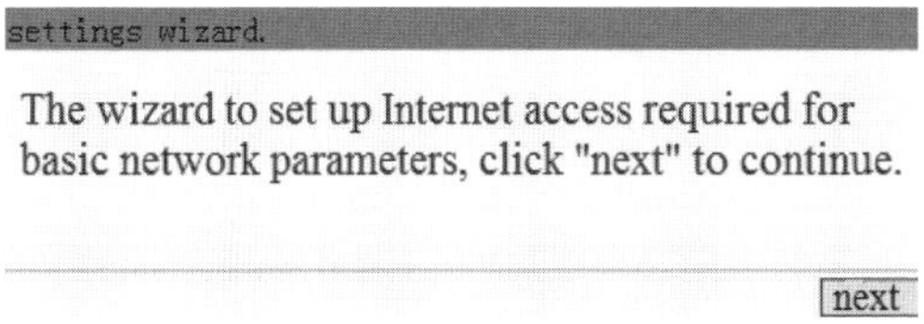

2.4 The fourth step

After wireless network name and password were setted, choice "The next step" (Fig. 5) into the operation interface of the way of accessing the web (Fig. 6). So far PPPoE mode can be selected.

2.5 The fifth step

Choice the ADSL virtual dialing of Figure 6, click the "next step". Then the interface of Account and password was activated (Fig. 7). Add your username and password that you got from internet providers to the Account and Password.

2.6 The sixth step

Account password after the export is complete, click "next", pop Settings Wizard to restart the interface, click on "reset" to complete setting up your wireless network. After the restart is complete, wireless network connection icon in Figure 2 will be turned into a Figure 8 shape, full set of work is over, users will be able to surf the Web using a wireless network.

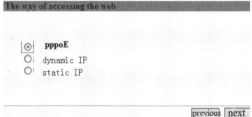

Figure 6. The way of accessing the web.

settings wizard.

The wizard to set up Internet access required for basic network parameters, click "next" to continue.

[next]

Figure 3. Not connected to a wireless network.

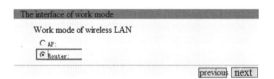

Figure 4. The interface of work mode.

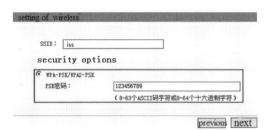

Figure 5. Setting of wireless.

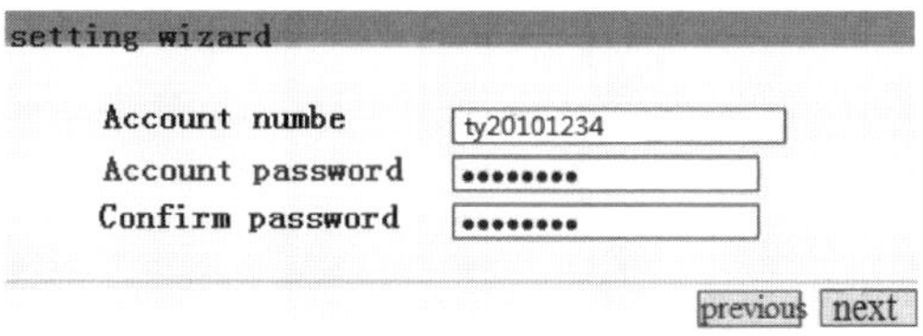

Figure 7. Account number and password.

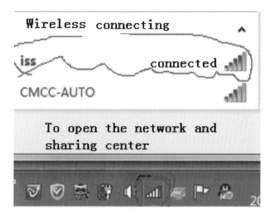

Figure 8. Wireless connecting.

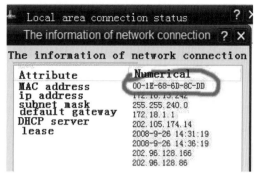

Figure 9. Local area connection status.

3 WIRELESS NETWORK SECURITY SOLUTIONS

Whether wired or wireless network, you need to have certain security measures. Although usually no specific confidential data, such as home networking, PC, but no one wants to see their networks being "edge network". Then we took some measures, ways to reduce unsafe hazard.

3.1 *Hardware is key*

First: select a competent, quality of hardware is the key. TP-link and D-link are a good brand and reputation at home and abroad, workmanship and value for money very good. Router manufacturers in most large brand design configuration increases security measures such as keys, no SSID broadcast, it was enough to provide effective security.

3.2 *Password are important*

Second: is the set of keys. Figure 5 setting the SSID and password settings must not be lazy, especially passwords must not be simplistic, it is best to use numbers with letters of the alphabet combine to form, or your home network will be more than "shared".

3.3 *Shut down function of SSID*

Third: turn off the broadcast feature. General router default is to allow broadcast SSID feature so people can search the wireless signal to your House and do some shuffling. If you turn off this feature, your wireless signal will not appear in the list of wireless search, this can significantly reduce the "edge network" risk.

4 CONCLUSION

Last may, through bonding capabilities to stop reaching for home LAN MAC address "rubs mesh hand". Each computer in the factory, is owned and only one MAC address, just like people's identity cards, are the only. Wireless LAN users in the wireless settings of the router and security settings set up MAC address filtering, so that your wireless network only those devices allow MAC (See for example Fig. 1) can enjoy.

Hope this article describes, capable of unlimited local area networks and networking among the families full play to help.

REFERENCE

Ma Xinluo. Wireless local area network construction and appli cation (2nd Edition) [m]. National defense industry press. August 2009.

Computer, Intelligent Computing and Education Technology – Liu, Sung & Yao (Eds)
© 2014 Taylor & Francis Group, London, ISBN 978-1-138-02469-4

The measurement of total nitrogen

D.L. Hao, L. Sun & Y.R. Dong
Sino-Dutch Demonstration Research and Training Center for Water Treatment (DETCWAT),
Environmental Management College of China (EMCC), Qinhuangdao, China

ABSTRACT: National standard method (HJ636-2012) in the determination of total nitrogen potassium persulfate oxidation-ultraviolet spectrophotometry, this method is simple, high sensitivity, sample volume of 10 mg/L the detection limit of 0.05 mg/L. Practice potassium sulfate found in itself a relatively big impact on the test blank absorbance, associated with the determination of several involving time link, such as storing alkaline potassium persulfate solution digestion time, reaction time, cooling time and what additional cooling cooling after digestion can cause abnormal experimental data. In view of this, we start from the above link-control analysis of the impact of these factors on determination of total nitrogen, and put forward appropriate recommendations for improvements.

Keywords: total nitrogen; digestion liquid storage time; digestion time; cooling time; cooling mode

National standard method (HJ636-2012) used in determination of total nitrogen potassium persulfate oxidation-ultraviolet Spectrophotometric method, this method is simple, high sensitivity.[1] But in practice potassium found itself outside the significant impact on test blank absorbance, alkaline potassium persulfate solution length of storage time, reaction time of digestion time controls, selection of cooling length after digestion, and what additional cooling cooling experimental data will cause an exception. Start with several links in this article from the comparative analysis of the impact of these factors on the determination of total nitrogen, and put forward appropriate recommendations for improvement.

1 EXPERIMENT

1.1 *Instruments and reagents*

Double-beam UV-Spectrophotometers, LDZX-30 KBS hand wheel type automatic-stainless steel vertical pressure steam sterilizer, 25 ml colorimetric tube with ground glass, 10 MM quartz cell. Potassium Nitrate (GR), Potassium Persulfate (GR), Sodium Hydroxide (AR).

1.2 *Experimental principle*

Under the 120~124 °C, alkaline potassium persulfate solution of nitrogen transformation to nitrate nitrogen compounds in a sample using ultraviolet spectrophotometry to wavelength and 220 nm, measurement of absorbance A220 and A275

respectively, according to the formula (1) calculate the corrected absorbance, and total nitrogen (n gauge) contents and correction is proportional to the absorbance.[1]

2 RESULT AND ANALYSIS

2.1 *Effect of storage time on the determination of aqueous solution of potassium sulfate*

International law (HJ636-2012) in preparation by alkaline potassium persulfate solution: 40.0 g persulfate 600 ml soluble in water; another 15.0 g sodium hydroxide dissolved in water 300 ml. Sodium hydroxide solution temperature after cooling to room temperature, mixing two solutions with constant volume to 1000 ml, deposited in polyethylene bottles, you can save a week.[1] Yi Tan[2] studies have shown that new storage with good alkaline potassium persulfate solution within 3 days, no impact on total nitrogen determination results almost; for more than 3 days, negative deviation of the measurement results will appear smaller; more than 7 d, there will be serious negative deviation. Table 1 according to the new store with good alkaline potassium persulfate solution blank absorbance within 3 days to meet the requirements HJ636-2012 blank absorbance values in, but when the storage time in the determination of relative error for 3 days 7.2% has already surpassed that total nitrogen content of the sample in the HJ636-2012 when >1.00 mg/L, determination of relative deviation of ≤5% quality control requirements. Yi Fang[3] believes that about 15 °C for more than

Table 1. Blank value of different storage time of alkaline potassium persulfate solution absorbance and 10 μg sample of measurements.

Storage time (day)	The absorbance of blank value	The absorbance of 4 standard sample	The value of 4 standard sample (μg)	Relative error
1	0.018	0.108	10.08	0.8%
2	0.020	0.106	9.88	1.2%
3	0.027	0.100	9.28	7.2%
4	0.032	0.096	8.88	–
5	0.048	0.092	8.48	–
6	0.116	0.090	8.28	–
7	0.237	0.089	8.18	–

6 days alkaline potassium persulfate solution cannot be used with best now and enjoy. Table 1 data indicate that storage of third day, data relative error began surpassing quality-control requirements, when storage time for 4 days and above, blank absorbance values than are available. In view of the above analysis, in order to guarantee data compliance, effective, with good alkaline potassium persulfate solution is best saved in a 4 °C environment, and best not store for more than 2 days, if conditions allow, with best now and enjoy.

2.2 Effect of digestion on the determination of the result

International law (HJ636-2012) requires the pressure sterilizer reaches 30 min [1 120~124 °C digestion]. Xianwei Zhang[4] research shows that digestion and lack of time, will not only make it difficult for nitrogen-containing substances samples is completely oxidized, but also have potassium persulfate is not fully decomposed, which will lead to the A_{220} serious high blank solution. Table 2 data shows that digestion time of 30 minutes under the national standard method, not only the blank absorbance 0.032 is greater than the value of the quality control requirements, but also standard relative deviation is greater than 5%, 4th, beyond allegations the requirements of GB, data is not valid. When digestion time is extended to 40 minutes, blank value of absorbance 0.027 comply with the quality control requirements, but also relative deviation of the sample, 4th is not in line with quality control requirements. Yuduan Xiao[5] recommends that the digestion time control at least over 40 min, to eliminate blank values and influence measurement results. Table 2 data shows that when the digestion time is extended to 50 or even 60 minutes, by measurement of absorbance data from blank values and measuring results will conform with the standard relative deviation of both laws (HJ636-2012) quality control requirements, data compliance and effective. Potassium persulfate itself

Table 2. Different digestion time blank absorbance and 10 μg sample test results.

Digestion time (min)	30	40	50	60
The absorbance of blank value	0.035	0.027	0.022	0.020
The value of 10.00 μg	–	9.28	9.58	9.88
Relative deviation	–	7.2%	4.2%	1.2%

has a strong absorption at wavelength 220 nm,[6] if incomplete decomposition of potassium, both the gap and the impact on the analysis results of samples is very large.[7] In view of the above, and data analysis, on the digestion time control, it is recommended that extends at least 50 minutes (conditional cases, 60 minutes digestion time better), blank absorbance value and determination of relative deviation in accordance with HJ636-2012 quality control requirements, data compliance and effective.

2.3 Effect of digestion on the determination of cooling time after

National standard method (HJ636-2012), the sterilizer in the clear after 30 min 120~124 °C, natural cooling, open the valve, remove the cover, remove the colorimetric tube cool down to room temperature.[1] After above does not explicitly remove the outer cover, colorimetric tube length of cooling. But in practice found that addition to cool down to room temperature, cooling time the choice of the length of the blank absorbance values and measuring results also have varying degrees of impact. Usually cooled at room temperature for half an hour, colorimetric tube temperature can be lowered to room temperature. Table 3 data shows cooling for half an hour or 1 hour, blank absorbance values greater than 0.030 HJ636-2012

Table 3. Different blank absorbance values and cooling time 10 μg sample of measurements.

The cooling time (h)	0.5	1	1.5	2	2.5
The absorbance of blank value	0.139	0.057	0.029	0.024	0.022
The value of 10.00 μg	–	–	9.08	9.51	9.58
Relative deviation	–	–	9.2%	4.9%	4.2%

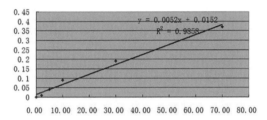

Figure 1. Cold water forced cooling 0.5 hour.

quality control requirements are not met, exceeded the data, invalid. When to extend the cooling time 1.5 hours, blank absorbance value absorbance reached 0.029 in HJ636-2012 a blank value quality control requirements, but the 4th sample measurements relative deviation of up to 9.2%, quality control requirements is greater than 5%, the data is not valid. When the cooling time to 2 hours or more, and both the blank absorbance and the determination of the relative deviation of the results are entirely consistent with the HJ636-2012 quality control requirements. Yi Fang[3] Yinan Cao[8] research also supports the cooling time is extended to 2 hours or more. Comprehensive analysis, in order to ensure the accuracy of data in accordance with the national standard for quality control requirements, compliance and effective, it is recommended that when taken out of the pressure cooker to extend the cooling time of 2 hours or more.

2.4 Effects of cooling after digestion method for the measurement of results

International law (HJ636-2012), although not taken in cooling mode cool down to room temperature with a clearly defined, after the Figure 1 is removed from the pressure cooker, forced cooling with cold water for half an hour of measurements. The data show that after cooling in the cooling process, excessive exception data. Recommended cooling without taking any mandatory cooling mode only in air cooled to room temperature.

3 SUMMARY

In order to ensure the use of national standard method (HJ636-2012) for the determination of total nitrogen data I can meet the quality control requirements, standard and effective. First, with alkaline potassium persulfate solution is best now and enjoy, if you need to save, it is best to store and keep it in a 4 °C conditions do not take longer than 2 days; second, in 120~124 °C conditions of digestion time extended to 50 minutes and above; third, emigration pressure sterilizer to cool for at least 2 hours and cannot take any compulsory cooling in the cooling process.

REFERENCES

Caiying Qiu. Alkaline potassium persulfate-ultraviolet Spectrophotometric method for the determination of total nitrogen in waste water [j]. Modern trade industries. 2012 (10): 182–184.

Chunfang Gan, Chaojuan Tan, Jianqiang Ma. Alkaline potassium persulfate oxidation-the ultraviolet Spectrophotometric method for determination of nitrogen content in starch phosphate ester [j]. Modern chemical, 2011, 40 (1): 106–109.

Xianwei Zhang. National standard method for determination of total nitrogen in the process of discussion on the common problems in China [j]. scientific observation. 2012 (3): 64–65.

Yi Fang. Analysis on the influencing factors of determination of total nitrogen in water [j]. Guangzhou chemical. 2012, 37 (3): 14–17.

Yi Tan, Xinan Liu, Biao Wei. UV-spectrophotometric method for determination of total nitrogen in water in sanxia reservoir area [j]. Journal of Chongqing University (Social Science Edition), 2006, 29 (6): 33–37.

Yinan Cao. UV-spectrophotometry of potassium persulfate digestion determination of total nitrogen in water by several points to note [j]. Shandong chemical. 2011,40: 40–41.

Yuduan Xiao. UV with alkaline potassium persulfate digestion determination of total nitrogen in water by Spectrophotometric methods [j]. Guangdong chemical, 2012, 39 (4): 165–166.

Computer, Intelligent Computing and Education Technology – Liu, Sung & Yao (Eds)
© 2014 Taylor & Francis Group, London, ISBN 978-1-138-02469-4

The design of rescue drills for coal mine explosion accident and the implementation research of virtual reality

B.W. Lei, B. Wu, Y. Peng & Z.Y. Jiang
Faculty of Resources and Safety Engineering, China University of Mining and Technology (Beijing), Beijing, China

ABSTRACT: The improvement of rescue level of coal mine rescuer is of great significance to reduce the loss of coal mine disaster accident. In order to improve underground disaster emergency capabilities of rescue crew, and to enhance the detecting and healing salvage skills of rescuers, the rescue drill training system of coal mine gas explosion, with the auxiliary means of 3DMax modeling software under the environment of Unity3D which is based on emergency rescue drill content of coal mine gas explosion, is designed and developed in this article. The practical application of virtual reality training systems in Datong Coal Mine Group shows that virtual reality technology can effectively simulate the coal mine gas explosion scene, the use of virtual reality technology in disaster relief training can improve the training effect for rescuer, and it also greatly reduces the training costs and avoids accidental injury in training.

Keywords: coal mine explosion; rescue training; virtual reality; accident simulation

1 INTRODUCTION

In recent years, with the improvement of technology and management of coal mine safety, coal mine accidents have greatly decreased. However, due to the high risk of coal industry, accidents like explosions, fires and other serious accidents still occur, which exerts great negative impacts on coal industry. After the accident, timely and effective emergency rescue can not only effectively reduce the accident losses and damages, but also can eliminate coal mine accidents and public's negative impacts.

Timely and correct emergency relief is the fundamental means to prevent accident enlarging and reduce casualties when coal mine disaster occurs. Mine rescue crew is the subject to undertake emergency rescue during disasters, in the daily training, a variety of equipments, drill roadway, etc, which simulated the underground disaster scene situation have been developed, but for safety, these facilities are difficult to reflect the situation of the coal mine disaster scene.

The rapid development of computer technology provides the possibility of solving the above problems. Applying the current advanced virtual reality technology and combining with the hardware and software to build the accident scene under different disaster conditions. It makes the rescuer understand and analyze various complex disaster relief environments better, so as to more accurately assess the risk characteristics and hazard level of various scenarios, therefore to greatly improve the

disaster relief capacity of the rescue crew (Zhang et al., 1999; Lin et al., 2012).

In this paper, virtual reality technology is used in coal mine rescue drill. The virtual reality rescue drill platform of coal mine explosion is developed by combining response process of emergency rescue. The platform can directly show the operation process of disaster relief and its precautions to the rescuer for making the relief training more vivid so as to improve the effectiveness of rescue training and reduce the training cost and hidden trouble.

2 DOMESTIC AND OVERSEAS ACTUALITY

Virtual reality technology combines computer technology, constructing the software systems of three-dimensional scenes and the display platform of multi-channel virtual scene, which will make users have immersive sense of realism. The technology has been widely used in operation training of human surgery (Zhang et al., 2011), evacuation drill of ground public disaster, reproduce scenarios of earthquake (Zhou et al., 2011), three-dimensional urban planning (Fang, 2007), etc.

Using virtual reality technology for training and education is an important direction of the application of virtual reality technology at home and abroad, foreign countries have carried out a series of virtual reality technology research on coal mine. Australia CSIRO Mine Engineering Group developed a virtual mine environment system to achieve an assessment of the mine safety production environment (Guy et al., 2000); the mines 3D virtual reality application system developed by Germany DSK mining companies not only can be used in design planning of the workplace (DSK, 2006), but also can on-site operate personnel's technical training; the room and pillar mining system of VR-MINE, FSV system of electric tramcar, job simulation system of strip mine single bucket truck etc. were developed by AIMS Research Center (Crawshaw et al., 1997) at the University of Nottingham can be used respectively for operating personnel training under corresponding environment. In mainland China, Qin Yixin (Qin et al., 1999) established virtual reality system of large space building fire, user can interact the system with mouse, data gloves and other operating equipment to control the process of roaming and simulation extinguishing of virtual human in the scene; Chen Xuexi (Chen et al., 2004) conducted a study on mine gas explosion simulation based on virtual reality, and achieved effects simulation of gas explosion, burning, smog; Yang Jichun (Yang et al., 2006) researched the overall design of virtual mine safety training system.

At present, the development of virtual reality training system specifically for coal mine rescuer in China is less, therefore, it plays an important role in improving the training effect of rescuer in coal mine by developing targeted coal mine rescue virtual drill system. Because rescuer can learn and experience the whole treatment process in simulated real scene through the ways of automatic roaming to auto-show the processing flow of the whole process after the explosion accident in coal mine.

3 THE DESIGN OF VIRTUAL DRILL SYSTEM OF EMERGENCY RESCUE

Depth analysis of the main point of gas explosion rescue techniques in coal mine and emergency rescue process is the basis for the development of virtual reality rescue drill systems. Since the training objects of the training system are the rescuers, the rescue skills and related relief theories mainly for rescuers have been designed. According to the *Coal Mine Safety Regulations*, *Mine rescue regulations* and related equipment operation regulation, the standard practices of the key link rescue process like accident report, phone answering, rescue crew on duty, rescue mission receiving, action plan layout, disaster area detection, disaster handling, disaster recovery etc. were designed, making the virtual reality drill system combine the accident simulation, rescue drill, rescue evaluation function into one.

3.1 *The design of accident simulation*

In order to improve the drill effect of rescue training, the simulate scene effect of coal mine gas explosion should enable trainees to have a good sense of immersion. Select a complete mine for the show, and then appropriately simplify the model by combining the region of coal mine gas explosion, the simulation shows the scene of inner roadway personnel evacuation, roadway and equipment damage in the process of gas explosion, the scene layout shown in Figure 1.

The explosion accident occurred in driving face 15 meters from the heading end had been designed, gas explosion of driving face caused by worker's irregularities, there were 10 people in driving face, five of them escaped, two people escaped into the refuge chamber (including one fractured), two people were killed (including one buried in the roof caving area near the explosion point), one person suffocated by CO poisoning. There were 32 people in adjacent working face, and 15 people in other regions. Among them, 44 people escaped, 3 people wore the self-rescuer and hided into intake airway of working face.

3.2 *The design of rescue drill*

Mine disaster relief drill subsystem is mainly for coal mine gas explosion rescue knowledge learning. Through the way of automatic roaming, the system automatically shows the processing flow of the whole process after the coal mine explosion, so that the people can learn and experience the whole process of coal mine explosion accident rescue in a simulated real-world scene.

This part shows the whole process of standardized emergency rescue action of coal mine explosion mainly based on Mine rescue regulations and the relevant technical requirements. It includes alarm dispatched, building underground disaster relief base, disaster detection and handling, disaster recovery, etc. The virtual drill design process of accident rescue of coal mine gas explosion is showed in Figure 2.

3.2.1 *Alarm dispatched*
After the watchman answers the alarm call, it is necessary to record the content of telephone calls and send a emergency dispatched alarm of gas explosion. Two squads of rescuers drive to the accident spot after checking the dress and carrying necessary rescue equipment. Rescue captain goes to the relief headquarters to report for getting a knowledge of the situation and accepting the task, and then explains the mine ventilation system overview (shown as Fig. 3) and disaster situation to the rescuer for tactical discussion and clearing

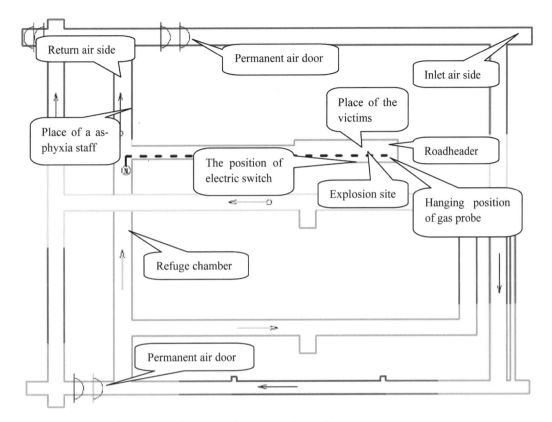

Figure 1. The scene layout schematic of coal mine gas explosion accident.

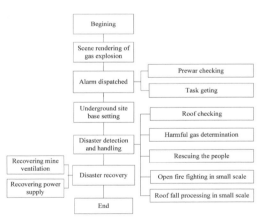

Figure 2. The virtual drilling design process diagram of accident rescue of coal mine gas explosion.

each other's responsibilities. The serial number in Figure 3 is the order for rescuer to check and travel, and the numbers also represent the checking location whether the disaster gas and roadway are normal.

3.2.2 Underground site base settings

Two teams enter the determined fresh air roadway with the minimum technical equipment for handling gas explosion, and regards the inlet A (shown as Fig. 3) as the underground rescue base. After the base is set up, the squadron leader serves as the base commander, and an rescuer will stay at the base to exclusively answer the call.

3.2.3 Disaster detection

Regarding the columns marked No. 1–13 in Figure 3 as the priority detective area of return air side, and No. 14–18 as the detective area of the intake airway, the content of detection are the situation of roadway, air door checking, water, site of the explosion, inspection records of roadway collapsed, impact scope of explosion, shot-point, concentration distribution of disaster gas, open fire checking, checking aid the victims in distress.

First, the return air side should be detected, mid-team leader send a team starting from the base to the disaster area for rescue work, and the wire telephone should be laid while walking to the disaster area. Every gas and roadway inspection results must be reported immediately to rescue

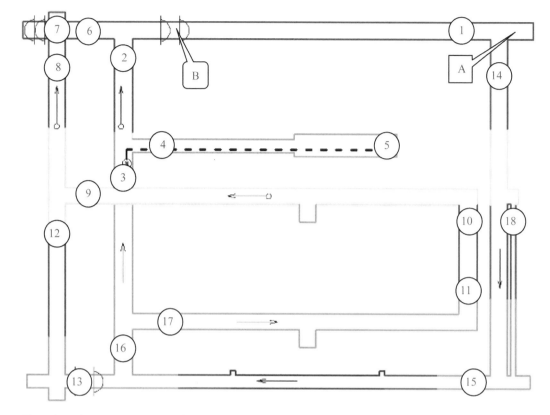

Figure 3.   The scene layout schematic of coal mine gas explosion accident.

base which need to mark the report information on the drawings after received the report. During the detection process, every inspection should be reported to the base, in addition, it also should be recorded on carried drawings by detection team. During the process of advancing and detection, the action of checking respirator pressure gauge should be showed at regular intervals (required 20 minutes). If you find respirator pressure drops too quickly, all the rescuers should immediately return, and then continue the detection along the original route after replacing the respirator. In the process of detection, immediately checking and related disposal should be done after finding people in distress, and then transport them to the mine rescue base. The further detection will be continued until the detection completed.

3.2.4   Disaster recovery

After the underground base receiving the command from headquarters, a team will sent to re-enter the mine to recover ventilation and power supply, remove the poisonous gas in disaster area, spray water for cooling and dust suppression.

First, recovering mine ventilation and power supply: in order to gradually exclude the methane inside the mine, first gradually closing the air door of B and checking the gas concentration of No. 6 in Figure 3. Mine power is recovered when air door of B is closed and the gas concentration of 6 reduces to 0.4%.

Second, recovering ventilation in driving face: after power is recovered, starting the auxiliary fan in driving face, discharging the methane. When the gas concentration of 4 reduces to 0.4%, entering the roadway to spray water for cooling and dust suppression, and then withdrawing the rescuer.

3.3   Mine rescue drill test subsystem

Mine rescue drill test subsystem is mainly used for the assessment of mine gas explosion rescue knowledge of rescuer. The system does the examination of disaster detection, rescuing victims, disaster recovery and other aspects based on *Coal Mine Safety Regulations*, *Mine rescue regulations*. Rescuers entirely operate themselves after entering the system, the whole rescue process is decided by themselves. The universal practice mode is used during operation, namely the next step can be operated only when the operation properly proceed. The operating system will automatically record. After the operation completed, the system will determine the operating points based on operating conditions, and automatically gives test scores and related assessment and recommendations, for making users know their own operational weaknesses, and thus does more targeted learning. The information of drill person and results automatically record to the information systems for management.

4 THE IMPLEMENTATION OF VIRTUAL REALITY SYSTEM

According to the functional design of virtual drill system of mine disaster relief, first, we should collect the relevant case data as well as rescue drill and rescue equipment operation videos of rescue crew in Datong Coal Mine Group, to obtain large amounts of base development data. Then using the CAD plan and collected mine roadway date to determine the layout of coal mine roadway, the

Figure 4.   The visual effect of rescue team responsing.

Figure 5.   The scene diagram of wounded person rescuing.

model such as shearers, hydraulic support, belt conveyor, heading machine and other structures of roadway have been built by using 3D modeling software of 3DMax, and then converting it to format. FBX for importing to Unity3D, then pasting pattern in Unity3D for adding lighting effects. After the completion of scene modeling, the interaction design of simulation system, and it including the interaction of roaming walking and interface menu. After the completion of the system, the performance testing and the executable files and network files are generated in last (shown as Figs. 4 and 5).

5 CONCLUSION

Aiming to develop the virtual reality rescue drill platform for coal mine explosion, this paper has applied the virtual reality technology to coal mine rescuer training, and has designed the rescue drill training system of coal mine gas explosion based on modeling software of 3DMax for auxiliary tool under the environment of Unity3D. The system provides three training modes including accident simulation, rescue drill and rescue evaluation with two human-computer interaction mode as interactive menus and interactive three-dimensional entities. The system accurately and intuitively presents the relief operation tools, operating procedures, safety precautions, important parameters indicators, and so on to the rescuer, so the disaster relief training can be more vivid, realistic and easy accepted, which can effectively improve the rescue training effect, and reduce training costs and hidden danger.

The system is mainly designed for emergency rescue operations to train the rescuers to conduct detection and rescue operations in disaster area. The next step will focus on the function development of disaster rescue command in coal mine, so as to improve the ability of emergency rescue command of officers.

REFERENCES

Chen Xuexi, Han Yuchun, Zou Hengyi, Chen Fu. 2004. Research on key issues of gas exploding simulation in coal mine based on virtual reality, *Journal of North China Institute of Science and Technology*, 1:1–6.

Crawshaw SAM, Denby B, McClarnon D. 1997. The use of virtual reality to simulate room and Pillaro Perations. *Coal international*, 1:20–22.

DSK, 2006. Virtual reality in the mining industry. http://www.parallelgraphics.com/products/sdk/success/dsk/.

Fang Xiaofeng, 2007. 3D Simulation Designing System for Urban Planning Based on Virtual Reality. *Computer Simulation*, 24:230–235.

Guy LeBlanc Smith, Con Caris, and Gil Carter. 2000. 4D visualsation of exploration and mine data. *Australia CSIRO Exploration and Mining Report*.

Lin Lin, Liu Xianmei. 2012. Design of Training System of Oil Field Simulation Based on Virtual Reality Technology. Computer technology and development, 22:205–208.

Qin Yixin, Xia Zhengyi, Wang Jian, Fan Weicheng. 1999. Application of Virtual Reality to Safety engineering, *China Safety Science Journal*, 9:49–53.

Yang Jichun, Zhong Xinxin. 2006. Genernal Design of Virtual Reality in Safety training system, *Mining Safety and Environmental Protection*, 33:80–83.

Zhang Dongqin, Adll Moming, Wang Ling, Qi Wenjun. 2011. Applications of virtual reality technology in medical surgery, *Machinery Design and Manufacture*, 11:62–64.

Zhang Ruixin, Ren Tingxiang D Schofield, B Denby, T Walsha. 1999. Research Progress in virtual reality technology for mine safety. *Journal of China Coal Society*, 24:70–73.

Zhou Baijia, Jia Qunlin. 2011. Application of virtual reality simulation technology to earthquake emergency drill. *Journal of Natural Disasters*, 20:59–64.

Computer, Intelligent Computing and Education Technology – Liu, Sung & Yao (Eds)
© 2014 Taylor & Francis Group, London, ISBN 978-1-138-02469-4

Improved ACO-K clustering routing algorithm for wireless sensor networks

Li Peng, Guo-Yong Dong & Fei-Fei Dai
School of IoT Engineering, Jiangnan University, Wuxi, Jiangsu, P.R. China

ABSTRACT: As the existing clustering routing algorithms commonly have the problems of uneven clustering and unbalanced overall network energy consumption, improved ACO-K clustering routing algorithm is proposed in this paper. K-medoids clustering algorithm can cluster random distributed sensor nodes, which is a good solution to the uneven clustering. Combined with improved ant colony algorithm, when replace the cluster head node and select the next hop for data transmission between the cluster head nodes, this algorithm can consider node residual energy and balance network energy consumption. Simulation results show ACO-K algorithm has better performance and longer network life cycle compared with other routing algorithms.

Keywords: wireless sensor network; ACO-K; routing algorithm; clustering algorithm

1 INTRODUCTION

The Wireless Sensor Network (WSN) is composed of many minute sensor nodes. Because of its flexibility and expandability, currently the WSN has been used extensively in numerous military and civilian areas. That probably plenty of sensor nodes may monitor the target zone in the same monitoring area leads to substantive redundancies of the information collected by adjacent nodes. If all the collected data were transmitted to the base station, it's likely to bring on massive wastes of energy and bandwidth. Moreover, sensor nodes for the most part are battery-powered and work in high-risk situations and it is not easy to replace batteries at any moment. Therefore, it is imperative to know how to save energy.

In recent years, many scholars at home and abroad have put forward new routing algorithms to solve the above-mentioned problems. Ant colony algorithm proves effective on solving the problem of network routing. Reference presents A Routing Algorithm (ARA) which is to find the shortest route from source node to target node, but this algorithm does not consider node residual energy, thereby leading to unbalanced overall network energy consumption. Reference presents itself from the perspective of energy, but has no regard for the WSN's characteristics.

On the basis of the above-mentioned algorithms, an improved clustering routing algorithm of ant colony optimization based on energy-efficient K-medoids clustering algorithm (ACO-K) is proposed in this paper. It first makes use of K-medoids clustering algorithm to cluster random distributed sensor nodes, which is a good solution to the uneven clustering. Combined with improved ant colony algorithm, when replacing the cluster head nodes and selecting the next hop for data transmission among the cluster head nodes, this algorithm can consider node residual energy and balance network energy consumption.

2 THE MODEL USED BY WSN

2.1 Network model

The following assumptions are made in this paper with regard to WSN Clustering Routing Algorithm model: The entire network is interconnected, and the transmit-receive is all-dimensional; The base station is far away from the monitored area; All nodes in the network have the same primary energy; All sensor nodes in the network constitute a set, $V = \{V_1, V_2, ..., V_n\}$ and are randomly distributed in a monitored area.

2.2 Energy consumption model

Communication energy consumption adopt the model of reference. When a source node needs to transmit k bit messages to the target node with its distance from the source node is d, the energy consumption of both the source node and the target node are as follows:

Emitted energy consumption:

$$E_{tx}(k,d)=\begin{cases}E_{tx-clec}\times k+\varepsilon_{fs}\times k\times d^2, d<d_0\\E_{tx-clec}\times k+\varepsilon_{amp}\times k\times d^4, d\geq d_0\end{cases}\quad(1)$$

Received energy consumption:

$$E_{rx}(k,d)=E_{rx-clec}\times k\quad(2)$$

$E_{tx-clec}$ stands for the emitted power consumption, $E_{rx-clec}$ the received power consumption. The model of Free Energy is used for the loss of power amplifier, if the transmission distance is not longer than the threshold value d_0, while the model of Multipath Attenuation is used if the distance is longer than d_0. ε_{fs} and ε_{amp} represent the energy needed when the unit power is amplified under both circumstances, and $d_0=\sqrt{\varepsilon_{fs}/\varepsilon_{amp}}$.

2.3 Data fusion model

Owing to less correlation among cluster, here only the data fusion inside clusters is discussed. Its model is assumed as follows: The cluster head node receives k *bits* data from each cluster member. No matter how many nodes exist within clusters, all those transmitted data are compressed into k *bits*. The energy consumption of data fusion is set as E_{DA}.

3 IMPROVED ACO-K CLUSTERING ROUTING ALGORITHM

3.1 Typical ant colony algorithm

Ant colony algorithm is a new type of simulation evolution algorithm, first systematically proposed in 1991 when M.Dorigo, a Italian scholar, published his doctoral dissertation through research on authentic ant colony behaviour. It was originally designed to solve various NP-complete problems such as Travelling Salesman Problem (TSP), Knapsack Problem and Assignment Problem, etc. Thanks to its good performance in the process of optimizing a variety of complex problems, Ant colony algorithm has been recognized by scholars home and abroad because of its broad prospects for development.

The original ant colony algorithm is applied to TSP. Here are concrete steps to make it work:

Step 1: For TSP of n cities, $N=\{1, 2, ..., n\}$, $A=\{(i,j)|i,j\in N\}$, the distance between cities is $D=(d_{ij})_{n\times n}$, and each arc (i, j) initial pheromones is

$\tau_{ij}(0)=1/|A|$. Suppose m ants were working and all ants started off from the same city i_0, $k:=1$. The current optimal solution is $W=\{1, 2, ..., n\}$.

Step 2: (Outside loop) If the algorithmic stopping rule is fulfilled, stop and output the computed optimal solution. Otherwise, the ant s would start off from i_0 and $L(s)$ would signify the set of cities traversed by the ant. The initial $L(s)$ equals 0. $1\leq s\leq m$.

Step 3: (Inner loop) According to $1\leq s\leq m$, suppose the ant was in the city i, $L(s)=N$ or $\{l\,|\,(i,l)\in A, l\notin L(s)\}\neq\varnothing$, then complete the computation of the sth ant. Otherwise, suppose $T=\{l\,|\,(i,l)\in A, l\notin L(s)\}-\{i_0\}\neq\varnothing$ and $L(s)\neq N$, then the probability is:

$$\begin{cases}\dfrac{\tau_{ij}(k-1)}{\sum\limits_{l\in T}\tau_{il}(k-1)}, & j\in T\\\\0 & , j\notin T\end{cases}\quad(3)$$

When the ant reaches j, $L(s)=L(s)\bigcup\{j\}, i:=j$; Suppose $T=\{l\,|\,(i,l)\in A, l\notin L(s)\}-\{i_0\}\neq\varnothing$ and $L(s)\neq N$, then we got $L(s)=L(s)\bigcup\{i_0\}, i:=i_0$ when the ant reaches i_0. Repeat step 3.

Step 4: $1\leq s\leq m$, compute the length of each path according to the order of cities regarding $L(s)$. If $L(s)\neq N$, the path length would be a sufficiently large number. Compare the path length among m ants. Suppose t stood for the ant who traversed the shortest path. $f(L(t))<f(W)$ brings $W:=L(t)$. The following formula strengthens the pheromone trace of the arcs in the path W and volatilizes the pheromone trace of other arcs.

$$\tau_{ij}(k)=\begin{cases}(1-\rho_{k-1})\tau_{ij}(k-1)+\dfrac{\rho_{k-1}}{|W|},(i,j)\text{ is an arc of }W\\\\(1-\rho\rho_{k-1})\tau_{ij}(k-1), \qquad\text{otherwise}\end{cases}$$
$$(4)$$

Then we get a new $\tau_{ij}(k)$, $k:=k+1$. Repeat step 2.

3.2 The improvement of ant colony optimization algorithm

The above-mentioned algorithm does not consider the current energy consumption of nodes. Therefore, improvements are made for ant colony algorithm in this paper and the residual energy of nodes is taken into consideration so as to select the next hop of cluster head nodes.

Firstly, the following formula optimizes the transition probability of the ant.

216

$$p^k_{v_i v_j}(t) = \begin{cases} \dfrac{\tau^\alpha_{v_i v_j}(t)\eta^\beta_{v_i v_j}(t)}{\displaystyle\sum_{\mu \in V_{allow}} \tau^\alpha_{v_i \mu}(t)\eta^\beta_{v_i \mu}(t)} & j \in V_{allow} \\[4ex] 0 & otherwise \end{cases} \quad (5)$$

α stands for the pheromone's weight and β represents the heuristic factors' weight. The pheromone is the reciprocal of the ant's energy distance from Node v_i to Node v_j:

$$\tau^\alpha_{v_i v_j}(t) = \frac{1}{E'_{d_{v_i v_j}}(t)} \quad (6)$$

Therein $E'_{d_{v_i v_j}}(t)$ represents the energy distance from v_i to v_j, and the energy distance can also be computed by the following formula:

$$E'_{d_{v_i v_j}}(t) = \frac{E_{d(v_i,v_j)}}{e_1(v_i) \times e_2(v_i,v_j)} \quad (7)$$

And in the formula:

$$e_1(v_i) = \frac{E_{cur}(v_i)}{E_{init}}$$

$$e_2(v_i,v_j) = \frac{E_{estimate}(v_i,v_j)}{E_{init}}$$

$$E_{d(v_i,v_j)} = E_{tx-elec} \times k + \varepsilon_{amp} \times k \times d^2_{v_i v_j}$$

And $E_{estimate}(v_i,v_j)$ is derived from the formula (8):

$$E_{estimate}(v_i,v_j) = E_{init} - \frac{E_{init} - E_{estimate}(v_i,v_j)}{time(v_i,v_j)}$$
$$\times [time(v_i,v_j)+1] \quad (8)$$

Therein E_{init} is the initial energy of the node and $E_{estimate}(v_i, v_j)$ is the estimated required energy of the node from v_i to v_j, while time(v_i, v_j) represents the time required from v_i to v_j.

When a node receives a data package, it will estimate the residual energy of its adjacent node, renew the routing chart and dynamically select the next hop.

After definite cycles, when the cycle number is multiples of the given fixed cycle index *roundtoupdate*, the volatilization of pheromones goes on as follows:

$$\eta(v_i,v_j) = (1-\rho) \times \eta(v_i,v_j) \quad (9)$$

Then each node strengthens the pheromone, and select the adjacent node which has the most

residual energy as the next cluster head (such as the Node v_j). The formula (10) represents the strengthening of the pheromone.

$$\eta(v_i,v_j) = \eta(v_i,v_j) + E_{d(v_i,v_j)} \quad (10)$$

Here ends the improvement of ant colony optimization algorithm.

3.3 *Data fusion algorithm on the basis of ACO-K*

K-medoids clustering algorithm initially selects k clustering objects and then continuously and circularly analyzes a central object and a noncentral object in order to select better clustering central objects. After grouping clustering objects, the clustering quality effects computed by cost function are analyzed. If the replacement of a clustering central object O_j leads to rapid decrease of the variance of cost function, the clustering center must be replaced immediately.

But traditional K-medoids algorithm is deficient in excessively fast constringency and low clustering quality. Therefore, K-medoids and improved ant colony algorithm are combined, thus introducing improved ACO-K clustering routing algorithm.

The description of ACO-K clustering routing algorithm:

Step 1: Initialize the ant colony and select the number of ants. *NC_max* serves as maximum iterations and the number m serves as the initial center. Suppose $(M_1, M_2, ..., M_m)$ as initial cluster head centers.

Step 2: Compute the distance between every two ants on the basis of euclidean distance formula. Follow formula (5) and consider the shortest path and the residual energy of nodes as a whole so as to determine the optimal path and clustering centre for the ant colony. Take the centre as the previous best position of the ant colony.

Step 3: On the basis of K-medoids, another cluster analysis is made for the previous best position of the ant colony in order to identify each ant's cluster and determine the center between clusters.

Step 4: For the newly formed ant colony, compute the optimal solution of each ant. Renew previous best position and globally optimal solution for the ant colony.

Step 5: Recompute the Euclidean distance between every two ants, establish the new cluster centre O_j and find the new optimal path.

Step 6: If terminal conditions are met (the ultimate optimal cluster centre or optimal path is produced), then end clustering. Otherwise, turn to step 3.

Step 7: According to the above-mentioned clustering, nodes in the same cluster begin transmitting data in a point to point manner. Data between clusters are considered uncorrelated. Select an optimal path between clusters according to the formula (5) and transmit the path to the base station.

Step 8: Each cluster gathers data respectively. When the number of transmissions is multiple of *roundtoupdate*, select a new cluster head according to the residual energy of nodes.

Step 9: The entire algorithm comes to an end when the energy of all nodes in the network gets totally exhausted.

Transmit data according to the result of clustering and referring to the cluster head replacement method of LEACH algorithm. Cluster head nodes are selected in each area before they make use of CSMA protocol to transmit broadcast data package, which contains nodes' information of becoming cluster head. Cluster nodes will join the cluster after receiving this data package. So far the stage of building clusters are completed. In the stage of stable operation, ordinary nodes use CSMA protocol to transmit data package, which tells they want to join, to their cluster heads. When cluster head nodes receive this data package, a TDMA timetable will be produced. Then cluster head nodes will distribute transmission time slot to all the cluster nodes and broadcast this timetable to all members. Thereafter, cluster head nodes begin to receive data gathered by each member, and transmit fused data to the base station.

4 ALGORITHM EMULATION AND PERFORMANCE COMPARISON

Emulation conditions in this paper: 500 sensor nodes are randomly laied out in a square area (500 * 500m). The base station is set up at the point (0, 0) in Figure 1. The above-mentioned numerical values are shown in Table 1.

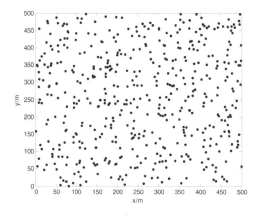

Figure 1. Network emulation scenario.

Table 1. The values of parameters.

Parameter	Value
NC_max	2000
m	1000
E_{init}	1 J
Data packet size	4000 bits
α, β	$\alpha = 2, \beta = 2$
ρ	0.2
roundtoupdate	20
$E_{tx-elec}$	50 nJ
ε_{fs}	10 pJ
ε_{mp}	0.0013 pJ
E_{DA}	5 nJ

4.1 The space complexity of the algorithm

The space complexity of the algorithm: Suppose the number of ants in the ant colony is m and the routing is in topology: Suppose the number of cluster heads as k and the number of nodes randomly distributed as n, then the space complexity of the algorithm is:

$$T = O(m * k * n) = O(1000 * 25 * 500).$$

4.2 Time complexity

In Step 1, the time complexity is:

$$T = O(m * NC\_max) = O(1000 * 2000)$$

In Step 2, the time complexity of Euclidean distance is:

$$T = \left(d^2 * m\right) = (d^2 * 1000)$$

In step 3, the time complexity of renewed reference point and cluster center is:

$$T = (n * k) = (500 * 25)$$

The overall time complexity is:

$$T = \left(d^2 * m + m * NC\_max + n * k\right)$$
$$= (d^2 * 1000 + 1000 * 2000 + 500 * 25)$$

4.3 The selection of cluster head number

Suppose the total energy of the network is E_{total} and the total energy consumption of each data transmission is E_{round}. Under ideal conditions

218

(namely all nodes have the same energy consumption), the total cycles (represented by R) of possible data transmission within the network's lifecycle equal:

$$R = E_{total}/E_{round} \tag{11}$$

If E_{total} is fixed, then the life cycle of the network depends on E_{round}. Assume that each cluster member node transmits k bit messages to the cluster head in each cycle of data transmission. After data fusion, each cluster head also transmits k bit messages to the observer. Then the energy consumption of each cycle of network data transmission is:

$$E_{round} = k(2NE_{elec} + NE_{DA} + n_{cus}\varepsilon_{amp}d_{tos}^4 + N\varepsilon_{fs}d_{tocus}^2) \tag{12}$$

Here is the meaning of each element. N means the total of sensor network nodes, n_{cus} the number of clusters. E_{DA} stands for the energy consumption of cluster head nodes when processing local data or practicing data fusion. d_{tos} represents the average distance between cluster heads and the observer, d_{tocus} the average distance between cluster members and cluster heads. If sensor nodes are randomly and evenly distributed inside a square whose length of side is M, then we get:

$$d_{tocus} = \frac{M}{\sqrt{2\pi n_{cus}}} \tag{13}$$

Put the value (13) into the formula (12). The first derivative equal to zero with respect to E_{round} leads to the optimal cluster head number:

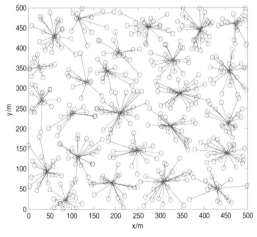

Figure 2. Clustering result.

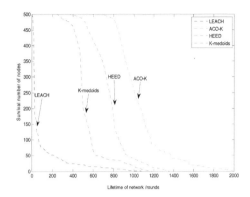

Figure 3. Performance comparison.

$$n_{cusopt} = \sqrt{\frac{N}{2\pi}}\sqrt{\frac{\varepsilon_{fs}}{\varepsilon_{amp}}}\frac{M}{d_{tos}^2} \tag{14}$$

Substitute specific numerical values into the Emulation Scenario, and the optimal cluster head number should be 25.

4.4 Speed comparison of nodes' energy consumption

Figure 3 presents speed comparison of classic LEACH protocol, HEED algorithm, K-medoids and ACO-K in regard to nodes' energy consumption. For nodes in classical LEACH algorithm, a cluster head selection is made every 20 cycles. Due to the uncertainty of cluster member number and node location, the energy consumption of cluster head nodes is sometimes extremely high and sometimes lower, leading to unbalanced energy consumption of the network. Likewise a node in the improved algorithm is selected as a cluster head about every 20 cycles, but each cluster has approximately equal number of member nodes and the energy consumption is stable. Therefore, to a great extent it helps balance network energy consumption and lengthen the network lifetime.

5 CONCLUSION

Improvements for ant colony algorithm are made in this paper. Meanwhile combining K-medoids clustering algorithm, a sort of new ACO-K clustering routing algorithm is proposed. The new algorithm considers the energy consumption of nodes as a whole and tries to balance the energy consumption of the entire network, thus collectively decreasing nodes' energy consumption and lengthening network lifetime.

REFERENCES

Akyildiz, I. & Kasimoglu, I. 2004. Wireless sensor and actor networks: Research challenges. Ad Hoc Networks 2(4):351–367.

Ji W.Y. & Shi, C.Q. & Zou, J. 2012. Routing algorithm of cluster heads selection in regions based on ant colony algorithm. Journal of Changsha University of Science & Technology (Natural Science) 9(2):75–80.

Liang, H.W. & Chen, W.W. 2007. ACO-based routing algorithm for wireless sensor networks. Chinese Journal of Sensors and Actuators 20(11):2450–2455.

Liao, W. & Kao, Y. 2008. Data aggregation in wireless sensor networks using ant colony algorithm. Netw. Comp. Appl 31(4):387–401.

Liu, B. & Towsley, D. 2004. A study of the coverage of large-scale sensor networks. Proc of IEEE Int'l Conf on Mobile Ad-hoc and Sensor Systems. Chicago.

Liu, C.T. 2010. Cluster-based routing protocol for multi-convergent points in WSN based on ant colony optimization. Computer Applications and Software 27(11):209–212.

Ma, Q. & Xie, J.Y. 2012. New K-medoids clustering algorithm based on granular computing. Journal of Computer Applications 32(7):1973–1977.

Marco, D. & Thomas, S. 2006. Ant colony optimization. Cambridge: The MIT Press.

Meng, Y. & Luo, K. 2012. K-medoids clustering algorithm method based on differential evolution. Application Research of Computers 29(5):1651–1653.

Shu, T. & Krunz, M. 2005. Joint power/rate optimization for CDMA-based wireless sensor networks. Proc of SenMetrics2005, the 3rd Int Work-Shop on Measurement, Modeling, and Performance Analysis of Wireless Sensor Networks. San Diego.

Wang, G.F. & Wang, Y. 2010. Clustering routing algorithm for wireless sensor network based on ant colony. Computer Engineering 36(18):73–75.

Wang, T.J & Yang, Z. 2007. An adaptive data fusion routing algorithm based on genetic algorithm for wireless sensor networks. Journal of Electronics & Information Technology 29(9):2244–2247.

Wang, X. & Wang, S. & Jiang, A.G. 2007. Cluster-based data fusion decision method in wireless sensor networks. Control and Decision 22(11):1208–1212, 1217.

Xia, N.X. & Su, Y.D. & Qin, X. 2010. Efficient K-medoids clustering algorithm. Application Research of Computers 27(12):4517–4519.

Zheng, W. & Liu, S. 2009. Energy efficient routing algorithm based on ant colony optimization for sensor network. Systems Engineering and Electronics 31(8): 1993–1996.

Computer, Intelligent Computing and Education Technology – Liu, Sung & Yao (Eds)
© 2014 Taylor & Francis Group, London, ISBN 978-1-138-02469-4

Based on vibration signal analysis of the Matlab to measure the motor speed

B.Q. Xu, X. Wang & Y.C. Dong
School of Electrical and Electronic Engineering, North China Electric Power University, Baoding, China

ABSTRACT: This article takes a large motor as typical study object, compares the advantages and disadvantages of the traditional motor speed measurement methods. Using Matlab as a software development platform, monitor vibration signal when the motor is running. The Matlab program will process the signal by Low-pass Filtering, Fourier Transform, Spectral Analysis, etc. Calculating the motor speed from vibration signal, realized the purposes that measuring the motor speed by vibration signal.

Keywords: vibration signal; Matlab; motor speed

1 INTRODUCTION

Motors are being used in a wide variety of industry applications. In many control system, the test of the motor speed is one of the most important parameters of the motor performance index and it is also important to discover the motor malfunction. In the study of motor vibration fault diagnosis, this paper presents a measurement theory of the motor speed which based on the vibration signal analysis in Matlab.

2 THE TRADITIONAL METHOD OF MOTOR SPEED MEASUREMENT

At present, there are many methods to test the motor speed such as photoelectric style, electromagnetic style, capacitive style, and measure the motor driving voltage directly [1]. What follows in the passage we will compared some of the motor speed measurement methods which are commonly used.

2.1 The method of photoelectric measurement

In the motor speed measurement system, the most widely used is photoelectric measurement method. Install a reflective paper and an open tooth disk on the motor shaft. When the gear disk and the motor circumgyrate with the same speed, photoelectric sensor detect the light signal which reflected by tooth disk (reflected style) or get across the tooth disk (transmitted style) [2,3]. Analysis of these signals, we will calculate the speed of the motor.

Photoelectric sensor can only measure the speed which is simple and convenient, and the reflective paper is easy to fall off and vulnerable to be polluted, if oil pollution and dust are severe, which will greatly reduce the reliability of the measurement. So this method is not appropriate for online monitoring, on the contrary it is generally used for offline monitoring.

2.2 The method of tachogenerator measurement

This method request output voltage and the speed is needed to keep linear relationship, moreover, time and temperature must keep stable. This method can obtain the motor speed accurately when the tachogenerator under proper functioning. But when the motor or tachogenerator have malfunction, it is a difficult problem to change rotor. The method of tachogenerator measurement is out of date.

2.3 The method of the eddy-current sensor measurement

The method of the eddy-current needs a special disc. The disk should be cut out and fixed with screw hole which is on the free end of the shaft. Unfortunately, the free end space is limited, so the scheme is not practical.

3 THE DESIGN OF MOTOR SPEED MEASUREMENT SYSTEM

In recent years, with the development of computer technology, motor performance test has changed from the traditional manual operation to computer operation, and is becoming network and intelligent gradually. Virtual instrument is the product that combines modern computer and instrument technology. It consists of the computer, the corresponding hardware and software, so it is a effective combination of computer hardware resources, instrument and control system hardware resources and virtual instrument software resources [4].

This design make use of the virtual instrument technology, which composing with the hardware and the Matlab development platform, aim at using Matlab and the related hardware to design a vibration signal analysis system, which can be used to calculate the motor speed. System structure is shown by the Figure 1.

3.1 The design and realization of the hardware system

Signal collection is the premise of the processing and the calculation. The accuracy of the collection system decided the validity of the following processes. The hardware is made of acceleration sensor, signal modulator circuits, and the data acquisition card. The main functions of the hardware are mainly completing signal collection and preliminary filter etc.

The first part is the sensor system, which include piezoelectric acceleration sensor and measurement part. Its effect is collecting vibration frequency when the motor under proper functioning.

This system uses Qinhuangdao Rand Corporation's production which is built-in IC piezoelectric acceleration sensor BZ1185. The sensor is based on piezoelectric transfer principle. It contains a tiny integrated circuit of the acceleration sensor. The standard output of the sensor is two wire 4~20 mA. Compared to the output of the charge output piezoelectric acceleration sensor, its output impedance reduced the millions of times, so the anti-interference ability has been increased greatly. Compared to the many wire voltage output type sensor, the environment factors such as cable resistance, wiring resistance temperature can't have any impact on the signal. The high and low frequency characteristics of the sensor and stability got breakthrough improvement.

The second part is the signal conditioning circuit. Because the signal data of the sampling card can only identify voltage signals, so the sensor signal should be converted to a certain range voltage signal. This will connected the regulated signal and virtual instrument. BZ1185 piezoelectric acceleration sensor's output is smaller 4~20 mA current signal, failed to reach collection scope of the data acquisition card, and the waveform control by Matlab shows a smaller amplitude which is not to the benefit of observation and analysis, so this will influence the calculation accuracy.

The system uses signal regulate module BZ2701 which support the piezoelectric acceleration sensor BZ1185, and its main missions are completing the function of signal filter and amplification. The anti-aliasing also has been manufactured. The signal regulate circuit can translate current signals into standard voltage signals.

The third part is the data acquisition card, which is the link of external signal and virtual instrument. Data acquisition card plugs in the expansion slot of computer standard buses, and the system uses the PCI standard bus which belongs to the computer itself. The data acquisition card is consists of MUX amplifier, the sample/hold circuits and ADC. The analog signals will be processed by sensor, and the signal disposal module will come across the data acquisition card and are converted into digital signals that can be recognized by computer.

In order to obtain a more accurate data, the system uses the PCI8210 PCI-based data acquisition card, which is the production of the Altai company in Beijing. It is equipped with a standard 64-pin parallel port data lines, used to put the input signal into acquisition cards. The biggest sampling rate of the card is 250 KS/s. It has many advantages such as high accuracy of measurement, high speed, simple programming, joins convenient, without external power supply and so on. Directly inserting the PCI8210 data acquisition card into IBM-PC/AT or compatible PCI slots can complete the data acquisition and processing.

3.2 The design and realization of the software system

Matlab programming language has the advantages of friendly man-machine interface, graphical programming languages and development

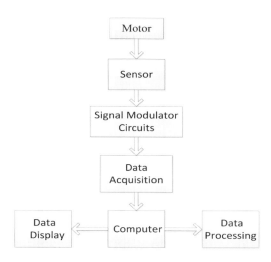

Figure 1. Structure of the motor speed measurement system.

environment, efficient programming, rich signal processing control, which make it works in a wide range of applications [5]. Based on those advantages, the software platform can reduce the cost and improve system flexibility, it can also greatly shorten the project development cycle and have a strong engineering practical value [6].

Matlab contained a large signal processing related function, these functions include time domain processing, frequency domain processing, filter design and window function selection. The human-machine interface was designed by QT-creator. The main completed work includes signal acquisition and preservation, signal processing, data shows, etc.

Firstly, data capture and display module are necessary, the main task of the module is collecting voltage signals generated by sensor and signal regulate circuit, and then the screen will show corresponding waveform figures. Then the program began from selecting a physical channel, set the sample rate and frequency and the voltage pulse signal on that channel. The high frequency eliminated by the low-pass filter also should be taken into account. Finally, one hand the results of the data passes the display control and then shows the value with the corresponding form, on the other hand, the data is processed by the data processing module.

4 CALCULATE THE MOTOR SPEED FROM THE VIBRATION SIGNALS

Through the piezoelectric acceleration sensor built in motor housings and reducer gear box monitor bearing and gear working condition. In order to get the motor speed by analysis motor vibration signal, the main mission is to collect motor running radial vibration displacement signal on site, and eliminating the high-frequency noise through the lowpass filtering. The purpose is to get time domain signals of vibration frequency (LPF). Using program to do Spectral analysis is that translating the time domain signal to frequency-region signal (FFT transform). And then we estimate the signal parameters via Multiple Signal Classification (MUSIC) algorithm. Get the greatest amplitude frequency from spectrum charts, which can work out the motor speed.

4.1 The implementation of the speed measuring software system's interface

The front panel interface of motor speed measurement system contained control area and display area. Control area mainly used for choosing physical channel, setting the sampling frequency,

selecting filter types, running or stopping control; Display space is mainly used for showing vibration signals, which include amplitude, variance, maximum or minimum value, mean square root, etc. After running the program the screen get the image of the signal, just as shown by Figure 2.

4.2 Vibration signal spectrum analysis

When domain sampling signals transform to frequency domain signals, many information included will become more obvious. As known as a common method is Fourier transform spectrum analysis, and the spectrum analysis program diagram is shown in Figure 3.

During spectrum analysis, the front panel as shown in Figure 4 shows the change rule, the radial vibration displacement signal strength of the motor unfold in order of the frequency, and then it become the function of frequency. It is not easy to analyze the superimposed signals and the amplitude from these signals. In order to get the main feature of the vibration frequency, we estimate the signal parameters via Multiple Signal Classification (MUSIC) algorithm [7].

Figure 4 shows the fundamental frequency is 37 Hz so the speed is about 37 rad/s. For the system, although the voltage and internal coil have many influences to the rotate speed during the motor is running, the motor rota speed can also deed the basic data to distinguish vibration signals. For example, according to the rotate speed, we can establish different warning value or dangerous value. When the vibration value exceeds the alarm time for certain time, the sound and light alarm will be sent out, and then the program will control

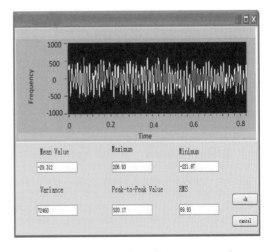

Figure 2. Software interface of the motor speed measurement system.

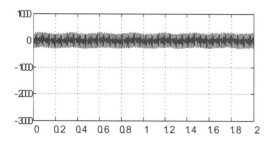

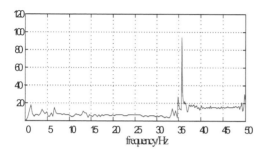

Figure 3. Block diagram of spectrum analysis.

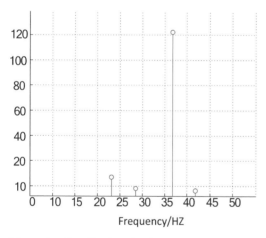

Figure 4. The vibration signal processed by MUSIC algorithm.

the motor accordingly. We can also judge every characteristic frequency on the basis of motor speed, which underline the fault diagnosis. Besides what we discussed above, frequency domain and time domain feature parameters can provide an overall indicator, which can help us processing model analysis to distinguish the working state of the motor.

5 LAST WORD

The Matlab and the data acquisition card based on Personal Computer construct virtual instruments to measure the motor speed. It is not only save time of program development, but the modular programming is also convenient for the expansion of the program and adding new functions module. This design uses the method of low-pass filter and spectrum analysis, which can calculate the motor speed from the vibration signal. This means needn't remake motor bearings or engine base, it also need not to measure the sensor and corresponding follow-up devices, it detecting the radial vibration signal through the piezoelectric acceleration sensor directly, and then we can get the motor speed value. This method widely used in motor on line monitoring and diagnosis system.

ACKNOWLEDGEMENTS

It is a project supported in part by the National Natural Science Foundation of China under Grant 51277077 and the Fundamental Research Funds for the Central Universities of China under Grant 11QG55. Paper no. TEC-00337-2012.

REFERENCES

[1] Ye Cheng-Xiang Photoelectric displacement precision measuring technology. [M]. Chengdu, publishing house of SI Chuan science and technology, 2003.
[2] Mao Yong-Yi, JiangGong. Monolithic frequency meter and application in the measurement of the motor speed. Micro-motor, 2002, 38(1):56–58.
[3] Jiang Hao, Kong Piao-Hong. The motor speed detection method and error analysis. China testing technology, 2003, 3(2):60.
[4] Zhang Jin-Mei. Based on virtual instrument of motor test system [D]. Jiangsu: Jiang Nan university, 2008.
[5] Yang Le-Ping, LiHaiTao, Yang lei. Matlab program design and application version. 2 [M]. Beijing: publishing house of electronics industry, 2005.
[6] Zhu Li-Hui, Zou Xuan, Xu Xin-Hua. Matlab based on the dc motor speed control system [J]. Instruments users, 2006, (1):14–15.
[7] Han Fang-ming, Zhang Shou-hong. Separation of coherent multipath signal with improved MUSIC algorithm [J]. Systems Engineering and Electronics, vol. 26, pp. 721–763, June 2004.
[8] J. Dmochowski, J. Bensenty. Direction of arrival estimation using the parameterized spatial correlation matrix. [J] IEEE Transaction on audio, speech and language processing, vol. 15, issue 4, May 2007, pp. 1327–1339.

Study on IGA-PID applied in optimizing cascade control

Xiao-Zhi Fang, Jin-Hua Wang & Shao-Li Wu
Fuzhou University, Fuzhou, Fujian, China

ABSTRACT: According to the shortage of conventional PID in thermal cascade control, this paper adopts off-line and online Immune Genetic Algorithm (IGA) to optimize PID controller, respectively. Experimental results show that off-line IGA-PID reduces overshoot effectively, and online IGA-PID not only eliminates overshoot, but also shortens settling time sharply. These experiments also prove that online immune genetic PID has a better application in optimizing thermal process control which has large inertia and nonlinear systems.

Keywords: PID; cascade control; online IGA; process control

1 INTRODUCTION

In the modern large-scale industrial manufacture, cascade control has been applied in many complicated systems to improve the control quality. Traditional cascade control often adopts conventional PID, which requires artificial experience to debug repeatedly. This method needs too much work and is difficult to attain good result. Some research use advanced algorithms, such as off-line Immune Genetic Algorithm (IGA), to optimize PID controller, but the PID parameters optimized by these methods are fixed and can't be adjusted automatically when system is changing or disturbed by external signal.

According to the shortage, this paper uses online immune genetic algorithm to auto-tune PID controller parameters, realizing the control optimization in cascade systems by taking advantages of flexibility and regulatory of online IGA.

2 CASCADE CONTROL

For the complex process, if object's capacity is large, it takes a long time to cause object change,
the system may be disturbed several times in this period. Ordinary single loop control would not act in time and often leads to bad result. In these systems, cascade control is a common strategy to improve control quality. For example, engineers generally adopt the cascade method to control main steam temperature, which uses the temperature of leading segment and inertia segment as the controlled parameters of deputy loop and main loop, respectively.

In a model of main steam temperature, the transfer functions of leading and inertia segments are

$$W_1(s) = \frac{8}{(15s+1)^2}, \quad W_2(s) = \frac{1.125}{(25s+1)^3} \tag{1}$$

W_1, W_2 represent transfer functions of leading segment and inertia segment, respectively.

Because the time constant of leading segment is much smaller than the inertial segment, deputy loop can eliminate input disturbances quickly, and make sure that disturbances would not enter into the main loop basically. In the cascade system, deputy loop plays the role of eliminating

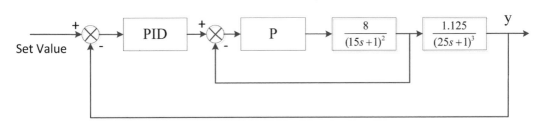

Figure 1. Cascade control model.

disturbance as son as possible and needs no exact requirement for performance, so P regulator is commonly used in deputy loop. While main loop usually adopts PI or PID regulator because inertia segment requires the output to be maintained at the set value. The cascade control system is shown in Figure 1.

In the traditional theory, parameters of P and PID regular are tuned base on Ziegler-Nichols method or 4:1 damped method (Xu 2004).

3 IMMUNE GENETIC ALGORITHM

Immune genetic algorithm is a newly developed artificial algorithm. It combines the genetic algorithm, which has the performance of heuristic global optimization, and the immune mechanism, which maintains antibodies diversity. IGA imitates the natural principle of "survival of the fittest", and could be well applied in PID parameters optimization for its advantages of opening structure and suiting to nonlinear and complex objects. It is a global parallel search algorithm which is different from normal random search algorithm. Under the guidance of performance indicators and immune action, population of each generation operate reproduction, crossover and mutation with a certain probability, and converge to the approximate optimal solution in the end (offline IGA) or auto-tune optimal parameters online (online IGA). The brief steps description of IGA in this paper is given below.

3.1 Encoding

Binary encoding and real number are two main encoding methods. In early time of genetic algorithm, almost all of the scholars use binary method for it is convenient to cross and mutate. But more and more people choose real number method now because it's more natural and accurate, and no need to transform solutions to other forms. This paper uses real PID number in immune genetic algorithm, and every code represents the actual PID parameter.

3.2 Initialization

The initial population of IGA is a set of solutions to the optimizing question. In this paper, initial population is produced randomly in the limited range. And the chosen population size is 30, which is decided comprehensively by search speed and premature phenomenon. Especially in online IGA, population size is influenced by sampling time, if population is too large, algorithm would not be calculated completely in a sampling time, while if population size is too small, PID will lead to bad online auto-tuning quality.

3.3 Fitness function

Fitness function is the only connection between IGA and the actual problems, and it also decides the optimization quality of IGA.

In off-line IGA, objective function is chosen in consideration of quickness, stability and accuracy of system response, it is be calculated by an equation as shown below:

$$J = \int_0^\infty (w_1|e(t)| + w_2 u^2(t) + w_4|e(t)|)dt + w_3 \cdot t_u \quad (2)$$

where $e(t)$, $u(t)$, t_u are input error, controller output and rise time, respectively. w_1, w_2, w_3 are weight constants, in this paper, $w_1 = 0.999$, $w_2 = 0.001$, $w_3 = 0.02$. w_4 is 0 when $e(t) > 0$, and will be large to 100 to depress the overshoot when $e(t) < 0$.

In online IGA, objective function equation is chosen to speed up the system's response at early time and to prevent the overshoot at later time. In this paper, each antibody's fitness in the population is calculated once at every sampling time, the equation is shown as

$$J(i) = \alpha|e(i)| + \beta|de(i)| \quad (3)$$

where $e(i)$ is input error of antibody i, $de(i)$ is error derivative of antibody i. α, β are weight constants. $\alpha = 0.95$, $\beta = 0$ when $e(i) > 0.75\,rin$, $\beta = 0.05$ when $e(i) < 0.75\,rin$, where rin is the input set value.

Fitness functions of off-line IGA and online IGA are the same and shown as:

$$f = \frac{1}{J + A} \quad (4)$$

where A is a very small value to prevent data from overflowing. J is the objective value of off-line IGA or online IGA (Liu 2001).

3.4 Probability calculation based on antibody concentration

This paper adopts the method of vector distance to calculate the antibody concentration and the selection probability. Firstly, calculate the vector distance of every antibody in the population as the equation (5) shown:

$$\rho(i) = \sum_{j=1}^N |f(i) - f(j)| \quad (5)$$

226

where i and j are antibody numbers. $\rho(i)$ is vector distance of antibody i, $f(i)$ is the fitness of antibody i. N is population size.

And the equation of selection probability based on antibody concentration is shown as:

$$P(i) = \frac{\rho(i)}{\sum_{k=1}^{N} \rho(i)} \qquad (6)$$

where $P(i)$ is the selection probability of antibody i.

From (5) and (6) we can see that the two equations don't need the priori parameters and are very efficient to calculate by computer (Sheng & Huang 2009).

3.5 Genetic operations

Generally, genetic operations contain selection, crossover and mutation. The three operations help population reproduce and evolve to reach the optimal solution (Teng et al. 2003).

Selection: This paper uses tournament method, which reproduce the antibody with bigger

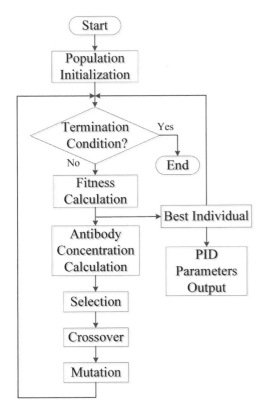

Figure 2.   Flow chart of online IGA-PID.

probability into next generation through comparing the probabilities of two randomly selected antibodies.

Crossover: The crossover's probability is 0.9. Two adjacent antibodies exchange parts of their values in the method of arithmetical crossover.

Mutation: The mutations probability is set to be 0.05. If some antibody's mutation signal happens, this antibody code will change into a random value in the limited range.

3.6 Flow charts of online IGA-PID

According to the principle of IGA from 3.1 to 3.5, the flow chart of online IGA-PID can be obtained as shown in Figure 2.

As the flow chart shown in Figure 2, online IGA auto-tunes PID parameters in every sampling time, and the PID parameters is changing during system responding.

4   EXPERIMENTS

The simulation experiments are conducted on MATLAB platform, controlled model is shown in Figure 1.

4.1 Conventional PID

The conventional PID parameters are tuned by traditional engineering setting method, and are further adjusted by experience. After a rough adjustment, the conventional PID parameters in main loop are $Kp = 2$ (proportional), $Ki = 0.021$ (integral) and $Kd = 7.5$ (derivative), and the proportional parameter in deputy loop is 1.5, while the system's sampling time is 1 s.

Set unit step signal as input, and the system's response under the control of conventional PID is shown in Figure 3.

In Figure 3, the overshoot is about 5.0%, settling time is about 164 s.

4.2 Off-line immune genetic PID

This paper uses off-line IGA to search the optimal PID parameters of main loop in some certain ranges. The ranges of Kp, Ki, Kd are [0, 10], [0, 0.1], [0, 10], respectively. Proportional parameter in deputy loop retains unchanged.

Under the function of off-line IGA, the optimal PID parameters are searched and tuned as $Kp = 2.1129$, $Ki = 0.0183$, $Kd = 9.6411$. Use unit step signal as input, and the system's response of off-line IGA-PID is shown in Figure 4.

As is shown in Figure 4, the overshoot is less than 0.04%, which is much better than conventional

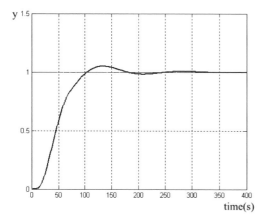

Figure 3.   Step response of conventional PID.

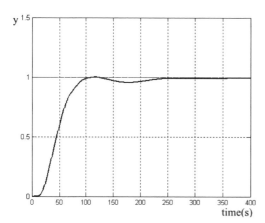

Figure 4.   Step response of off-line IGA-PID.

PID does. But the settling time is about 225 s, because PID tuned by off-line IGA is fixed, and off-line IGA emphasizes overshoot punishment which reduces the overshoot by "sacrificing" the settling time.

4.3   Online immune genetic PID

The sampling time (1 s) of thermal process control is large enough to operate and tune PID parameters by online IGA, so auto-tuning delay will not appear in this paper.

In this experiment, proportional and derivative parameters in main loop are auto-tuned online while other parameters retain unchanged. The proportional parameter in deputy loop and the integral parameter in main loop are the same to conventional PID.

The proportional parameter in main loop is auto-tuned in the range of [1.5, 2.5], and the derivative parameter is auto-tuned in the range of [5, 10]. Use unit step signal as input, and the system's response of online immune genetic PID is shown in Figure 5.

From Figure 5 we can see that there is no over-shoot in the response of online IGA-PID, and

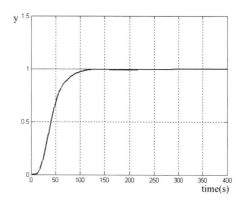

Figure 5.   Step response of online IGA-PID.

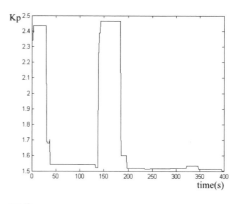

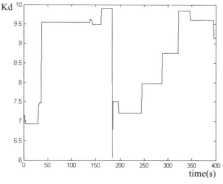

Figure 6.   Auto-tuning process of PD parameters.

228

settling time is about 107 s, which is much shorter than conventional PID and off-line IGA-PID.

The auto-tuning process of proportional and derivative parameters is shown in Figure 6, which clearly shows the adjustment of two parameters during system responding.

5 CONCLUSION

This paper mainly implements the simulation of online immune genetic PID in thermal cascade control, and proves that online IGA-PID has better dynamic performance than conventional PID and off-line IGA-PID. The study indicates that Online IGA-PID has a potential value of application in thermal process systems and other industrial control which has large inertia.

REFERENCES

Liu, J. 2011. *MATLAB Simulation of Advanced PID Control*. Beijing: Publishing House of Electronics Industry.

Sheng, M. & Huang, H. Artificial Immune Networks Algorithm Based on Vector Distance Used for Optimizing PID Controller Parameters. *Computer engineering and applications*. 2009, 45(12): 212–213.

Teng, T.K. & Shieh, J.S. & Chen. C.S. Genetic Algorithms Applied in Online Autotuning PID Parameters of a Liquid-level Control System. *The Institute of Measurement and Control*, 2003, 25(5): 433–450.

Xu, B. 2004. *Process Control*. Beijing: China Machine Press.

Computer, Intelligent Computing and Education Technology – Liu, Sung & Yao (Eds)
© 2014 Taylor & Francis Group, London, ISBN 978-1-138-02469-4

An improved ray tracing location algorithm based on the KNN

Xian-Qiang Peng
College of Computer Science and Technology, Chongqing University of Posts and Telecommunications, China

ABSTRACT: According to ray tracing online stage positioning of large amount of data, calculation of time-consuming and low efficiency, an improved algorithm has been proposed. Firstly, simplify the correlation degree of the characteristic properties of simple correlation, and then use the information entropy to weight for each property, next, utilize the KNN algorithm to match the corresponding data to arrive at the final positioning results. Experimental results show that the algorithm can effectively improve the positioning accuracy and response time.

Keywords: ray tracing; correlation degree; entropy; response time

1 INTRODUCTION

In recent years, with the development of mobile communication technology, the user's location information is becoming increasingly important. User location information and personal information combined play a significant meaning in the mobile network planning, storage of the user's information and other additional design features of radio resources. In addition, with the development of mobile computing devices and wireless communication technology, position estimation is more cause for concern, and the position estimation services has important applications in the ordinary business activities, scientific research, search and rescue and other industries until the emergency. Tracing system may use different time location information of tracked object, so that calculate its movement trend in the coming period. Meanwhile, location-based services have also been paid more and more attention in the field of public safety. It is very critical to estimate the exact location of mobile users for the military, police and fire radio network. Therefore, providing high accuracy and good position estimation service is now an urgent need for the community.

Location-based ray tracing can be overcome because of its mute-path propagation, NLOS (Non Line Of Sight) and other unfavorable factors affecting the traditional positioning technology, especially in densely populated urban micro-cell and interior, geometrically complex environments, poor radio propagation conditions, the positioning method can better play to their strengths, which is accepted by more and more scholars and applications. Ray tracing positioning calculation excessive, especially when high positioning accuracy requirements, the need for large amounts of data collection and matching calculation, so when users ask too much, in order to meet the real-time positioning, positioning must improve the efficiency of ray tracing algorithms. Ray tracing positioning includes the offline and online stage. Now a large number of scholars have studied the accelerated positioning of the offline phase, and have proposed a series of ray tracing acceleration algorithms, such as parallel ray tracing algorithm, dynamic partitioning method and mute-image method. However, online phase has less work study and the effect is not very effective. Currently, because of excessive data in the database, online matching is very slow and positioning accuracy is very low. In order to solve the above problems, the paper begins to analyze the correlation degree of positioning property and simplify the correlation, then weight for the rest of positioning property, reuse the KNN (K-Nearest Neighbor) algorithm to match, the final experiments show that the algorithm can effectively improve the positioning accuracy and response time.

2 BASIC KNOWLEDGE

2.1 *Ray tracing technology*

Ray tracing method is based on the GO (Geometrical Optics) theory to determine the reflection, refraction, and shadows by simulating radiation (light) propagation paths. Ray application conditions skipping technique is the high frequency wave propagation and scattering has localized at a given point in the field of observation field, without the initial field across the entire surface to obtain, but only limited to the surface of a section to strike.

This high-frequency field can make use of analytical methods of GO to deal with electromagnetic wave propagation and scattering problems. Location-based ray tracing is based on polyhedral surface model study area which was created to adapt to the mobile terminal location database, and then track the point of all rays from the source to the scene according to certain criteria. Ray tracing algorithm has a positive track and reflection tracking. Forward algorithm from the source point on ray tracing (beam), split or smooth surfaces encountered diffraction barrier they encountered building wall barrier will be reflected until the end of ray tracing. Reverse ray tracing algorithm is to determine the position of the field point to be calculated, the scene can find all the rays from a point source, then the field is calculated. Compared to these two algorithms, the forward algorithm to calculate quickly and effectively, the process is simple, easy programming strengths in these areas. Advantage of the reverse calculation algorithm is the higher accuracy of the results. Considering the characteristic of the attenuation and the positioning of the three or more reflective, more than twice the diffraction is negligible.

Found a scene from a point source (grid center) after all the rays, each ray can be calculated field strength in the presence of point, and the points of the rays with a first diameter and delay, and can be calculated for each of the arrival angle rays form field strength, delay and angle of arrival sequence, finally, all of which constitute an orientation vector. The calculated each ray vectors stored in the database, but also the use of tools such as GIS (Geographic Information Systems) geographic information database, thus completing the preliminary stage of work offline.

The main work in the online stage is to match and position. Get the mobile terminal to be positioned each ray field strength, the corresponding delay and angle of arrival and the total field strength data, or calculated from the information in the data, then form the corresponding sequence of formation. Because these sequences may not be identical to the data sequence to locate the data in the database, the corresponding algorithm will be used to match the most similar vector, thereby determining the positioning position. Now commonly used online matching algorithm is the nearest neighbor algorithm and some corresponding improved algorithms.

2.2 K-Nearest Neighbor algorithm (KNN)

K-nearest neighbor method was first proposed in 1968 in Cover and Hart, which is one of the most famous statistical pattern recognition methods, with a good robustness process, stability and simple method resistance in the classification,

which has become a hot topic of many scholars at home and abroad. The law currently commonly used to determine the similarity between the cases. N has a case, K-nearest neighbor algorithm will judge case by comparing x and Euclidean distance between each case, thereby find new stories x most similar cases, the reuse of its solutions. This method is simple and has wide range of applications. We can define the discriminate function as follows:

$$f_t(x) = \min_k (S_{case}(x, x_i)), i \in N \qquad (1)$$

Cases x and cases x_i of similarity $S_{case}(x, x_i)$ can be judged by its Euclidean distance to solve:

$$S_{case}(x, x_i) = \| x - x_i \| = \sum_{i=1}^{n} (x - x_i)^2 \qquad (2)$$

However, its biggest drawback is that lack of control strategy, so that it determines very blind and compares with each of the incidents, which will result in taking too much time to calculate some independent similar cases, leading to large amount of calculation. Thus this is an inefficient algorithm. When the database is not very, the speed and accuracy of positioning is less affected, but with the larger regional or precision positioning requirements are higher, the database will gradually become large, the efficiency of the algorithm greatly reduced.

2.3 The correlation characteristics of the property

In information theory, the entropy is a measure of the attribute corresponding to the event of uncertainty, the uncertainty of measurement information corresponding to the attribute of the event, both equal in absolute value but opposite in sign.

Presume S is a combination of data samples s. Assumed that attribute class label B has n different values, defining n different types of C_i ($i = 1, 2, 3, \ldots\ldots, n$). Let C_i the number of samples in the class s_i, then the definition of a given sample classification desired information is required:

$$I(s_1, s_2, \ldots \ldots, s_n) = -\mu \sum_{i=1}^{n} p_i \ln p_i \qquad (3)$$

where p_i is the probability of sample C_i, it is generally used to estimates s/s and $\mu = 1/\ln n$.

Suppose Characteristics of property A have v different values $\{a_1, a_2, \ldots\ldots, a_v\}$. S will be divided into v subsets by Characteristics of property A, denoted $(s_1, s_2, \ldots\ldots, s_v)$, where s_j contain some samples of S which have a value a_j on the A. Presume s_{ij} is samples of class C_i belonged to the subset of s_j, then entropy of characteristic property A is defined as:

$$E(A) = -k \sum_{j=1}^{v} \partial_j \, I\,(s_{1j}, s_{2j}, \ldots\ldots, s_{nj}) \qquad (4)$$

$$\partial_j = \left(s_{1j} + s_{2j} + \ldots\ldots + s_{nj}\right)\Big/s \qquad (5)$$

where ∂_j is right of the subset of j and $k = 1/\ln v$. According to the desired information calculation formulas given above. For a given subset s_j, its desired information has the following formula:

$$I(s_{1j}, s_{2j}, \ldots\ldots, s_{nj}) = -\mu \sum_{i=1}^{n} p_{ij} \ln p_{ij} \qquad (6)$$

$$p_{ij} = s_{ij}\Big/\sum_{i=1}^{n} s_{ij} \qquad (7)$$

where p_{ij} shows the probability of the sample of s_i belongs to the class C_j.

Then according to the formula (4) and (6), the correlation of characteristic property A can be drawn on t, the formula is as follows:

$$Corr(A) = I(s_1, s_2, \ldots\ldots, s_n) - E(A) \qquad (8)$$

After determining the relevant characteristics of the property, we have to set a threshold value based on experience, deleting those related to the characteristics of the property is less than the threshold value, meantime, keeping those related to greater than or equal to the threshold characteristic properties, and then weighted.

2.4 The weight calculation

After a correlation attribute reduction right after the characteristic attribute weight calculation formula is as follows:

$$w_A = \frac{[1 - E(A)]}{\bar{n} - \sum_{j=1}^{\bar{n}} E_j} \qquad (9)$$

where $\bar{n}$ is the number of characteristics property after the attribute reduction and E_j shows entropy value when characteristic property is j. It ranges $j = 1, 2, 3, \ldots\ldots, \bar{n}$.

3 MATCH PRETREATMENT

3.1 The purpose of the pretreatment

The purpose of the pretreatment is to reduce the workload and improve the matching

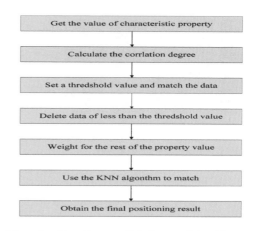

Figure 1. Flow diagram of the improved algorithm.

calculation speed. According to the basic principles of ray tracing, when the area of location becomes bigger and meets certain accuracy, signal parameters of the regional reference node number to locate the position of the offline stage to be collected will be more, namely the establishment of parameters-the location of the database is large, so that the calculation will result in a substantial increase in the amount of matching and the response time of the positioning will be longer. Therefore, this paper do a pretreatment before the match, narrowing the matching range, thereby improving the positioning speed, thereby improving the positioning speed.

3.2 The main idea and flow diagram

The core idea of the pretreatment begins to calculate the correlation degree of each characteristic property; then, there will be a threshold to match the correlation parameters and the corresponding data online, the procedure will be on and on until all the data are matched. We only use those data whose value is greater than the threshold, and those that are less than the threshold will be filtered. Thus, a data set with large correlation is drawn. Besides, process the final filter out data by entropy weighted method. Finally, match the weighted data and the data collected online by using the KNN algorithm. Extract the respective coordinate values until finding similar data.

Specific steps are shown in Figure 1.

4 SIMULATION DESIGN AND RESULTS

The following experiment is to verify whether the above theory applies to location based on ray tracing. For comparison, we select the experimental map in the Document 10 (wave frequency is 1.8 GHz) such as shown in Figure 2. First of all,

233

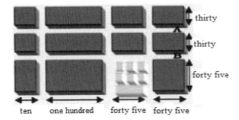

Figure 2. Simulation topographic plan.

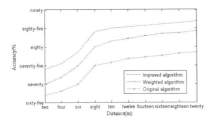

Figure 3. Comparison of difference algorithms.

create a database sequence of alignment parameters according to the terrain shown in Figure 2. The dark areas represent buildings of a height of 15 to 30 meters, the light areas represent bush of a height of 3 meters. This is a typical micro-cell structure. The transmitter has a height of 8.5 meters, which is located at the end of the street at the A zone. The receiver has a height of 1.5 meters, whose emission aperture is 0.2 degrees. The transmitter and the antenna to the radio antennas are omnidirectional and vertical polarization direction. Zone B is non-line of sight propagation area. Simulation platform is Intel i5 4430, 3.2 GHz, 4 GB RAM, VC++6.0, MATLAB7.1. Calculate the corresponding database by making use of the position of the transmitter and receiver and the ray-tracing program, and then complete offline phase.

Respectively, using the Document 10 algorithm, integrated weighted algorithm and our proposed algorithm in the literature, compare the results after calculated the position. The experiment is shown for comparison of various algorithms in Figure 3. As we can see from the figure, integrated weighted algorithm can improve the position accuracy to some degree, but our algorithm is more accurate, and has been greatly improved in the position accuracy of six to ten meters. Meantime, beyond ten meter, the position accuracy has also been improved.

Table 1 is the result of improved algorithms and pre-positioning results with the weighted combination algorithm after matching response time comparison table.

Table 1. Algorithm comparison table.

Compare items	Document 10 algorithm	Improved algorithm
Instances	Six thousand	Six thousand
Number of properties	Five	Five
Simplification	Three	Three
Matching rate/%	Eighty seven point six	Eighty nine point four
Matching time/s	Three point two	Two point four

As can be seen from Table 1, when matching the same number of instances and properties, the improved algorithm has improved the speed of the match. The reason is that after the pretreatment of the simplification correlation, positioning data has reduce a lot, which it is convenient to use the KNN algorithm for data matching and avoid a large number of blind match, so that positioning speed has been improved. Meantime, with the increase in the number of matches, the matching results will be better. This also shows the effectiveness of the algorithm, simultaneously, it shows this algorithm is more suitable for matching to relatively large number of data.

5 CONCLUSION

This paper studies the ray tracing positioning algorithm on online stage. Firstly, calculate the characteristic properties of simple correlation, and then use the information entropy weighting for each attribute, use the KNN algorithm to match the corresponding data to arrive at the final positioning results. Simulation results show that the algorithm improves the positioning speed of ray tracing and response times.

ACKNOWLEDGMENTS

This work was partly supported by the Natural Science Foundation of Chongqing (No. cstc2012jjA40064) and the National Natural Science Foundation of China (No. 61075019).

REFERENCES

[1] Yuan, Z.W. 2007. The Ray Tracing Positioning Theory and Method for Mobile Communication System Terminal [M]. Beijing Publishing House of Electronics Industry.
[2] Liu, H.T. & Li, B.H. 2004. Parallel ray tracing algorithm and its application in urban wave forecasts [J]. Radio Science Journal, 19(5):581–585.

[3] Yuan, Z.W, & Li, Y.C. 2010. Ray tracing Acceleration method based on dynamic partitioning [J]. Computer Engineering and Applications, 46(27):27–29.

[4] Son, H.W. & Myung N.H. 1999. A deterministic ray tube method for micro cellular wave propagation prediction model [J]. IEEE Transactions on Antennas and Propagation, 47(8):1344–1350.

[5] Jiang, Z.S. & Chen, L.P. 2007. Nearest neighbor examples retrieve similarity analysis [J]. Computer Integrated Manufacturing Systems, 13(6):1165–1168.

[6] Yang Y. 1999. An evaluation of statistical approaches to text categorization [J]. Information Retrieval, 1(1): 76–88.

[7] Wang, Z.M. & Wang, K.J. 2009. Entropy-based K nearest neighbor improved algorithm [J]. Computer Engineering and Applications, 45(30):129–131.

[8] Kohavi R. & John GH. 1997. Wrappers fort feature subset selection [J]. Artificial Intelligence, 97(12): 273–324.

[9] Cover TM. & Hart PE. 1968. The Nearest neighbor pattern classification [J]. IEEE Transactions on Information Theory, IT-13:21–27.

[10] Yuan, Z.W. & Jia, M.M. 2009. An improved ray tracing positioning algorithm [J]. Application Research of Computers, 26(8):2965–2967.

Computer, Intelligent Computing and Education Technology – Liu, Sung & Yao (Eds)
© 2014 Taylor & Francis Group, London, ISBN 978-1-138-02469-4

Research on LAN-based information security

Z.H. Wang & X.P. Li
Beijing Institute of Technology Continuing Education, Beijing, China

ABSTRACT: Due to its high efficient file transfer and resource sharing, local area network has been widely used in government agencies, enterprises and institutions, and significantly improved the working efficiency. But is because of the characters of open and Shared, LAN shows its weak side faced with today's complex interconnected network and intrusion technology. Because the phenomena of data loss, file tampering, network paralysis, system crash and so on often appear, information security has become a problem faced by LAN. By the analysis of the information security problems encountered in our unit' LAN and some potential problems, we have made an overall plan and put forward a corresponding solution, which has achieved good effect and guaranteed the network information security of the unit strongly.

Keywords: LAN; network; information security

1 INTRODUCTION

With the rapid development of network technology, the LAN possessing the rapid transmission of information and the sharing of resources has been more and more widely used, which brings massive information and great convenience to our work and significantly improves the efficiency and benefit of our work. In the normal life, LAN exists in many occasions including the government, schools, research institutions, banks, financial institutions, companies and enterprises, internet bars and so on, and we can realize many functions through it, such as the transmission of internal documents and data, the unified use of softwares and printers, the schedule of working group and the email. LAN provides its users a platform, on which can we share and exchange our information rapidly and conveniently, and through the connecting with external network, LAN opens a channel for exchanging information with the external.

However, the characteristics of open and sharing in LAN also bring security risks which can't ignore. For example, it is vulnerable to illegal attacks from the external and internal system, leading to the information resources within the host in high risk. At present, attacking technologies of the hacker are renovating, Trojan viruses are emerging in an endless way, leading to the increased possibility of the intrusion and destruction of information and data. LAN is faced with hitherto unknown challenge in information security. According to the 2012 Norton Internet Security Report, the network crime through computer virus has caused

a total economic loss of 289 billion yuan to individual users in our country. It is no doubt that the situation of network information security and virus prevention in our country is not optimistic. Therefore, the discussion of information security problems in LAN and seeking to the effective strategies are becoming more and more important.

In the practical application of LAN, our unit is also faced with the risk of network virus attack. Due to the lack of hardware and software protection strategy within the network and the consciousness of network security in some staffs, there appears many phenomena, such as network paralysis, data loss, virus attack, APR attack, etc., not only causing inconvenience to the work environment, but also influencing work efficiency. Therefore, establishing a multi-level security protection strategy from a holistic view is very necessary.

2 COMMON INFORMATION SECURITY PROBLEMS IN LAN

After the LAN installed, the computers can realize transfering information and sharing of resources within the unit's network. At present, the majority of Local Area Network (LAN) uses TCP/IP protocol as the ordinary Internet, as a result, lots of the hacker programs also can be used in LAN, and launch attacks on Local Area Network (LAN). Therefore, if the computers within the region did not do a good job in prevention of virus, with the help of information transfer, the virus will be spread to other computers in the LAN, which will cause greater damage. As lack of emphasis on the security setting of gateway router and independent protection of LAN server, our unit appeared the phenomena of loss of data, network congestion and so on, which almostly caused a paralysis to the website. Thus, Local Area Network (LAN) is a relatively fragile zone in the Internet information security management and should cause more attention. Analysing the source of the information security problems of Local Area Network (LAN) and finding out the crux, we can solve the problem better. In general, the source of information security problem of local area network mainly has the following categories.

2.1 *Use of mobile media*

Usually, through the collaboration between different departments, including the use, storage and copy of file data, file sharing and transfer, and mobile office, the internal local area network of the unit can improve its work efficiency. However, some staff do not have the awareness of information security who often ues some mobile media such as U disk, mobile hard disk, mobile phones and laptop computers to transfer copy and edit files. As a result, if them did not do a detailed safety inspection before those operations, the Trojans and viruses can easily get into computers, which not only greatly improve the probability of a single computer infected virus within local area network, but also make the hackers easily attack the internal of LAN, causing the consequences of leaking sensitive data and the spread of the virus.

2.2 *Disguised as a software or a website*

In order to seek illegitimate interests, on the Internet, some delinquents camouflage the virus as a normal application program to invade the system without the users' attention, which can steal LAN user's data, reveal information and affect the normal operation of local area network. Currently, phishing is the common mode for hackers stealing network account, password and obtain important information. In fact, hackers send deceptive spams, dangerous links, unknown data packets and other methods from the well-known Banks or other organizations (such as Tencent, Alipay, etc.) to induce the users to click on them, leading to the viruses and malicious codes be embedded into computers to steal users' login name, password, bank accounts and other sensitive information. In recent years, due to many large sites enhance the functions of real-time defense and fraud prevention, many fishermen begin to attention to some unknown small sites, especially some unhealthy websites visited by users, are easier to invade the system. In 2010, according to Internet security comprehensive report 2010, we capture a total of 9.398 million of malicious codes, compared with 2009, increased by about 30% [5]. As a result, the malicious code and procedure is an importance security threat to the current local area network. So units should strengthen their safety consciousness and handle the new information with more care. At the same time, when we meet someone who seems to be the phishing users, we should promptly notify the Local Area Network (LAN) management department, by the measures of rapid antivirus, changing passwords, data backup, etc. to protect and strengthen the ability of network security to avoid the important information and major property being damaged.

Moreover, not every user within the corporate LAN has a strong awareness of the information security, if they do not timely update the databases of anti-virus software and the patches of operating system and application program, some viruses are also easy to invade into the entire network through these gaps, especially the Trojan viruses and malicious softwares including backdoor, etc.

2.3 *Weak protection of sever*

Because there is no individual safety protection measures for server of unit's LAN, the server' ability of resistance to the virus is weak. With the fast and convenient data transfer, the spread of the virus becomes quickly and directly. If one computer in the network is attacked by virus, the server may also be infected through information transfer, to lead to all computers who use the server be infected by virus through information transfer. This has more harmfulness than one computer in the LAN being attacked by viruses. Although there are firewall and antivirus software in the gateway of the network to block foreign attack, it's hard to resist the threat from inside of Local Area Network (LAN) to lead to appear the phenomena of the web content illegally modified, losing data, and even the whole local area network paralysis. Therefore, it is necessary to set up independent LAN server protective measures. Usually, we can install independent network monitoring system and update virus database to make server operate safely and efficiently; or if we found other machines in the net being infected, we should immediately cut off the contact with the server and analyze the virus class and antivirus; or when the server is attacked by virus, we can use dual machine system and array system to protect the data.

3 STRATEGIES AND SOLUTIONS

3.1 *Security awareness training*

We should strengthen the information security education and training of unit's interior personnel, and improve their knowledge and safety awareness of network protection. Everyone should know that the network security is not the administrator's own business, but the responsibility of all users, once a user has problems, all the operations of the users' computers may be affected. In addition, we should also increase safety skills education and training besides the basic safety knowledge and be familiar with backuping and antivirus, etc. Strictly manage all kinds of mobile media in unit, decrease as far as possible the use of mobile storage devices and reduce pathways of virus invasion. Before the external mobile carrier access to unit interior network, we must carry out strict inspection and antivirus. And all internal computers must pass through safety equipment to connect to external computers, in another word, the way of internal ones directly connected to external ones is strictly forbidden. Man is not easy to control in network security, but is the most critical factor, therefore, strengthening the users' security awareness, making them be familiar with basic network security techniques and really mastering more knowledge of network, would make LAN become more secure.

3.2 Configure the firewall

Firewall technology is the most widely used network security technology. Through hiding the network internal structure, strengthening the access control between networks, limiting the information transmission between protected networks and other networks, preventing the external network users illegally access into the internal network to get the internal resources, we can protect the internal network operating environment. Its core thought is to establish a secure subnet inside the unstable network environment. The firewall for LAN is often installed on separate computers, and isolated from the rest of the Internet. It can separate the internal network and external network, limit their access to each other, and be able to record all the suspicious process and events, to avoid illegal invaders stealing network resources and data. Usually, the configuration techniques for firewall include deep packet processing, access to the network process tracking, TCP/IP termination, etc.

3.3 Vulnerability scanning and intrusion detection

Through putting the network attack methods mastered into the whole scan process and search TCP/IP ports of various servers, the vulnerability scanner can detect the local host system and remote information system. In network simulation attack, it can record the response of the target host, collect useful information about certain items in a short period of time to find security vulnerabilities in the network

system and help the network security administrator accurately master the security situation of the network. By defining network vulnerability, pertinently using the various security defense measures, such as the optimized system configuration, patching and so on, to make up for the latest security vulnerabilities and eliminate the hidden safety troubles. As a beneficial supplement for firewall, Intrusion Detection System (IDS) can help network system rapidly detect network attack. By monitoring the network behavior, security logs, audit data or network packets, it can detect and recognize the behavior of violation of security policies in the local area network, so as to provide real-time protection against the internal attack, exterior attack and misoperation and guarantee the information resources of system from attack, and also expand the ability of the safety management of network administrators.

3.4 Install antivirus software

To install antivirus software for each computer in the LAN, regularly upgrade the software database and kill virus and assess the system safety, we can timely find loopholes and defects, and guarantee the safety of network system to make the possibility of hacker attack for the server reduced to a minimum. In addition, we should monitor running all computers in the local area network and use the ways of reminding or blocking to force the computers which isn't installing antivirus software to install one.

3.5 Backup and restore

Based on the considerations of content, configuration, log and so on, we can establish a complete disaster recovery and backup system. The project construction of system and data disaster backup uses the program of application level. In the process of system construction, we should not only consider the for data center, but also consider the different locations fault-tolerance for critical business system for disaster tolerance and make timing and real-time backup for important data. Habitual backup for network system can not only protect itself when a mistake came up in the network system hardware or human behavior, but also protect the data integrity when met the invaders illegal access or network attack. In this way, can we ensure that high security and the key business data of end users not lost.

4 CONCLUSION

The information security in Local Area Network (LAN) brings together many factors, such as software, hardware, network and personnel. In addition to strengthen the safety awareness and safety knowledge, we can also take strong technology methods of network security and build a perfect multi-level protection system avaid phishing, network virus and network attack, to ensure that the information system of local area network operate safely and reliably. Through closing together security technology and management mechanism, the network information security of my units has got a big step. I also know that, as a Local Area Network (LAN) Management, Professional Skill Have a direct impact on information security management and the effectiveness of the virus prevention of local area network. Therefore, it is necessary to improve our vocational skills. By constantly learning new technology and new trend of network information security, and deepening the understanding of relevant knowledge and application, we can improve the scientific nature and effectiveness of the network information safety management, and create a healthy, safe and orderly local area network environment for the enterprises and institutions' efficient production and management in the end.

REFERENCES

[1] Practical Technology of Computer and Network Security, Yunjiang Yang. Beijing, Tsinghua University Press, 2007.

[2] Introduction to Information Security of Unit Local Area Network, Ruifeng He. Sci-Tech Information Development & Economy, 2011(21).

[3] Introduction to Information Security and prevention measures of LAN, Shuxian Wei. Information technology application research, 2013(1).

[4] Effective Strategies for Information Security in LAN. Yangjie, Public Communication of Science & Technology, 2010(12).

[5] Information Security and Virus Prevention of Local Area Network (LAN), Zhihuan Gao, Li Fang. Computer Knowledge and Technology, 2011(7).

Computer, Intelligent Computing and Education Technology – Liu, Sung & Yao (Eds)
© 2014 Taylor & Francis Group, London, ISBN 978-1-138-02469-4

The intelligent evaluation model for mathematics learning ability based on BP neural network and the application in the interactive learning system

Qian-Kai Ma
School of Mathematical, Beijing Normal University, Beijing, China

Zhong-Hai Li
School of Automation, Shenyang Aerospace University, Shenyang, China

ABSTRACT: The existing network interactive learning system lacks of intelligence and feedback information. This paper designs the learning ability evaluation model by use of the ability to process information of BP neural network, and establishes test questions and knowledge base based on the network interactive mathematics learning system, determines the corresponding level according to the time of solving question and correct rate, Then designs the two neural networks for used time analysis and error feedback, and reasons out student's learning situation. Finally, proves the accuracy of the determination by experiment.

Keywords: interactive learning system; BP neural network; intelligent learning; mathematics learning ability

1 INTRODUCTION

With the rapid development of multimedia technology and network technology, network interactive learning system has made great progress. Also, intelligent learning system got development. The contents of traditional design is stored in a computer through Intelligent learning system, such as personalized counseling by designing learning knowledge, learning process, learning materials, adding the learner's experience, using information technology provides an effective auxiliary means to improve the learning efficiency. Network interactive learning abroad began to development since the 1980s, ten years later, the domestic network interactive learning system began to gradually rise. In 2001, Melis raised a question-solve support technology, providing an intelligent aid and found solutions [1]. In 2003, Intelligent solution provides incomplete information or wrong solutions to give students a feedback information, helping students to learn from their mistakes [2]. In 2007, northeast normal university education technology professional learning has conducted the thorough research to the network interactive learning environment process, constructing a learning system based on case teaching [3]. 2011, Klasnja–Milicevic put forward a demand on designing course in order to adapt to the requirement of the students'

learning style in the interactive learning [4]. But these existing network learning system studies through the design question, but the lack of intelligence and feedback during the learning process, it can not pointed out the problems existing in the students in time, analyzing students' learning situation and providing the corresponding Suggestions. Therefore, this article introduces the BP neural network and designs the learning ability evaluation model, establishing test questions and knowledge can reflect the students' learning situation on the basis of network interactive mathematics learning system, and according to the accuracy and time-consuming of students to do test established two neural networks, reasoning out the students' learning situation, and provides the corresponding Suggestions. Relevant experiments have proved that the determination results of the model error comparing with the teacher's judgement results is less than 5%, it can be achieved to effectively determine the situation of students' learning.

2 MATHEMATICAL INTELLIGENT LEARNING SYSTEM DESIGN

In the mathematics intelligent interactive learning system, not only including the learning of basic knowledge, but also a special design of the test questions. In order to reduce the difficulty of mathematical information interaction, all of the exercises design using objective way of expression function, each topic has both evaluation and training value. As the training problems, it should be clear the problem involved knowledge, thinking the difficulty coefficient, analysis table error value may appear. As a test problem to design different value or the information carrier options. To include the test level, learning ability and learning skills of students knowledge on each item. In the design of choice, there should be the function of each option, for example.

In database design, attention to the distribution of contact and interaction between the title. Require bidirectional detail design subject table according to the curriculum standards, to ensure the full coverage of course topic labeling requirements of content. In the difficulty coefficient design, pay attention to the relationship between topics, it will establish a variety of interactive relations between topics. Including the scope of knowledge, coefficient of difficulty, error type and capacity disadvantages. The scope of knowledge is to make the title according to the knowledge scope which is establish interrelated topics. The formation of a single knowledge problem, double knowledge problem, three issues of knowledge problem, four issues of knowledge problem and comprehensive knowledge of problem. To establish contacts with the same knowledge point. When three knowledge points errors occur to the students, it will automatically provide her three double knowledge problems associated with the three knowledge points. For the analysis to the result of what knowledge point error, then according to the double knowledge mistakes to her the knowledge points. If no errors, it will provide the same knowledge points higher difficulty problem. Until analysis of the main knowledge problems of the student. For each question in the test list will have the corresponding settings. And corresponding to the value of experience, for example you get a correct value of how many experience, and recorded the wrong records.

3 THE DESIGN OF MATHEMATICS OF KNOWLEDGE BASE IN INTELLIGENT LEARNING SYSTEM

Intelligent mathematics learning systems, for example, mathematics learning process based on receiving from low to high level of knowledge, be divided into six parts: conceptual understanding, knowledge application, operations, reasoned argument, spatial, abstract summary. When you design a knowledge base, there are concepts, formulas,

Table 1. Students' students answer the error message table.

Name	Type	Description
User ID	Varchar	User ID
Login time	Time	Login time
Gainianlijieerro	Int	Understand the concept of error number
Zhishiyingyongerro	Int	A number of knowledge application error
Jisuanerror	Int	The calculation error number
Tiyilijieerror	Int	Comprehension error number
Siweidingshierror	Int	A number of thinking errors
Total	Int	The total number of jobs

Table 2. Student learning record storage table.

Name	Type	Description
User ID	Varchar	User ID
Login time	Time	Login time
Use time	Float	Use time
Gainian lijie	Int	The understanding of the concept of experience
Gnljtime	Float	In the understanding of the concept of time
Gnljge shu	Int	A number of questions
Zhishi ying yong	Int	Knowledge application experience gain value
Zsyytime	Float	In the application of knowledge in
Zsyygeshu	Int	A number of questions
Yunsuanqiujie	Int	Access to computing solving experience value
Ysqjtime	Float	In the computation of time
Ysqjgeshu	Int	A number of questions
Tuililunzheng	Int	Gain experience value reasoning
Tllz time	Float	In reasoning argument of time
Tllz geshu	Int	A number of questions
Kong jian xiang xiang	Int	Obtaining spatial imaginative experience value
Kjxx time	Float	In the space of imagination in
Kjxx geshu	Int	A number of questions
Chou xiang gai kuo	Int	Abstract summary of experience acquired
Cxgktime	Float	In the abstraction in
Cxgkgeshu	Int	A number of questions
Total	Int	The general experience
Zonggeshu	Int	A number of questions

Table 3. Student learning the action code rule table.

Name	Type	Description
RuleID	Varchar	Encoding rules
Studentgrade	Varchar	Students' grade
KnowledgestuID	Varchar	Knowledge coding
KnowledgeSkillID	Varchar	Knowledge and skills of application code
Action	Varchar	Action code

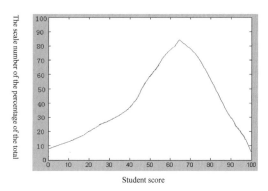

Figure 1. Score distribution statistics.

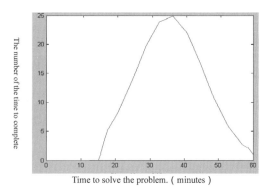

Figure 2. Time statistics to solve the problem.

topics, sample questions, and other basics, and for students to practice exercise, test, experiment, and thugs and so on. Students' Students answer the error message table is shown in Table 1 and Students learning record storage table is shown in Table 2, Student learning the action code rule table is shown in Table 3.

4 STUDENTS LEARNING EVALUATION MODEL DESIGN

Finish on students in each class, the understanding of the concept of degree, the application level of knowledge, mathematics ability level these aspects are not the same, if not timely remedy, accumulate over a long period, will form the so-called "bad students" and "good students". We randomly selected 100 students in a middle school as the analysis object, from two aspects of time and the score distribution were analyzed to solve the problem. Each band number accounts for the percentage of the total number of results shown in Figure 1. The number of time to solve the problem TAB as shown in Figure 2.

Can be seen from the statistics, student achievement distribution and time distribution are normally distributed, to solve the problem that the test more scientific. This data can be used to establish the university students' learning quality evaluation model.

According to the time and error rate to solve the problem of statistical results will students into class A and class B, C, D, E five grades. Each level of the students' intelligence level, the absorption of knowledge, to master and application degree is different. A-class said good, better class B said, class C said general, D said is poorer, E said is very poor. The specific classification rules as shown in Table 4.

Divide students into different levels, to the student model, using the neural network with the master degree of knowledge and the application of knowledge skills, compares students situation—action code rule table to find out the corresponding code. As shown in Figure 3.

Table 4. Students rank analysis table.

Use the time (min)	Error rate				
	Grade				
	<5%	5%–20%	20%–40%	40%–70%	>70%
<20	A	A	B	C	D
20–30	A	B	B	D	D
30–45	A	B	C	D	E
45–55	B	C	D	D	E
55–60	B	C	D	E	E

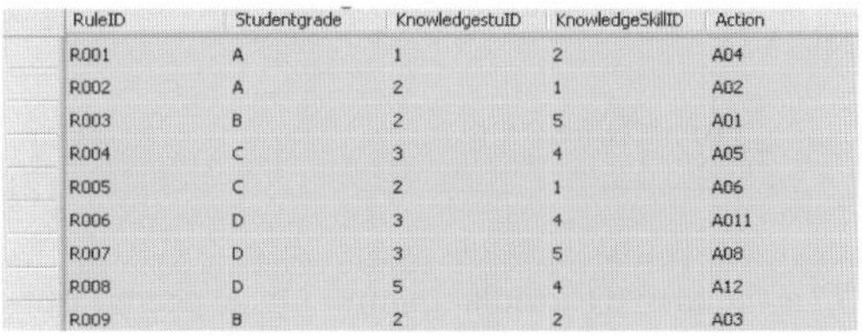

RuleID	Studentgrade	KnowledgestuID	KnowledgeSkillID	Action
R.001	A	1	2	A04
R.002	A	2	1	A02
R.003	B	2	5	A01
R.004	C	3	4	A05
R.005	C	2	1	A06
R.006	D	3	4	A011
R.007	D	3	5	A08
R.008	D	5	4	A12
R.009	B	2	2	A03

Figure 3. Student's action code rule table (Part of the data).

243

5 THE REASONING DESIGN BASED ON THE BP NEURAL NETWORK

By BP neural network to realize fuzzy logic based learning condition analysis process, in order to realize accurate student knowledge condition diagnosis and intelligent interactive learning environment in learning. By recording the exercise behavior of students, analysis of the practice time, experience worth points and make the title number, imitate the teacher to the student status through neural network diagnosis of reasoning, analysis learning error, to find the next study suggest. According to part 3 the establishment of knowledge base and part 4 student model, to design the BP neural network model.

1. The basic principle of BP neural network
The BP neural network is composed of input layer, hidden layer and output layer, it is a kind of multi-layer network of reverse transmission error. There is no connection between nodes of the same layer. When the input signal is propagated to the hidden layer, through the function, input signal of hidden layer is propagated to output layer. The Sigmoid function is selected as the node function model as following:

$$f(x) = \frac{1}{1+e^{-x}} \tag{1}$$

When forward propagation, the incoming sample is passed input from the input layer, and bamboozled by hidden layer to output layer. If the actual output and the expected output layer of output is not same, then it turns error back propagation phase. Error back propagation is that the output error in some form through the hidden layer to the input layer back propagation step by step, to get the error to all elements of each layer. The error signal is used as the basis for correct weights of each unit. The signal of the layers of positive communication and error back propagation weight adjustment process is carried out repeatedly. The process of Weights are constantly adjusted, that is, the training process of the network. This process has been to the network output error reduced to an acceptable level, or to the pre-set number of learning. For the sample M calculation, the error function is:

$$Ep = \frac{\sum_i (tp_i - Op_i)}{2} \tag{2}$$

In the above formula, tp_i and Op_i expected output and network computing output respectively. Neural network model is shown in the figure below.

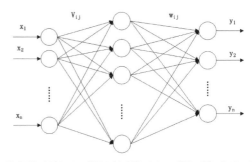

Nodes of the input layer   Nodes of the hidden layer   Nodes of the output layer

Figure 4. Neural network model.

2. BP Neural network modeling process
According to the design of knowledge in section 3 and intelligent interactive math learning system in the practical application, doing questions in accordance with the situation when error conditions and the use to establish two BP neural network models, that is the analysis and the use of neural networks. Through these two get two kinds of neural networks according to diagnostic conclusions on student learning situation analysis, finally get a comprehensive proposal.

5.1 Error feedback neural network

Established BP neural network model, we must first determine the input layer nodes. The principle to select the input node is a greater impact on the results to be no correlation between each other, for error feedback neural networks, to understand the concept of the learning process in the number of error, knowledge application error number, calculate the number of error, the number of errors to understand the meaning of problems, the number of errors mindset to do problems accounted for a percentage of the total number of these five characteristics as input node. Determining the output layer node, output layer node is equivalent to the first student learning neural network model and is a knowledge levels of determination, including a mastery of knowledge, knowledge mastery of two, three mastery of knowledge, knowledge mastery of four, The degree of mastering the knowledge five level five state, each state corresponds to a different range of values.

To determine the error feedback neural network hidden layer node number. Determination of hidden layer nodes is crucial for the neural network. Through the experiment get the following rules: Count is too little training on the students knowledge of the law, As well as the problems in learning, Fault tolerance is poor; The hidden layer nodes too much, The training time becomes longer, Will display some non regular things out, But also reduce the generalization ability. This paper through trial and error method combined with the experience of the past, reduced BP neural network learning cycle, The number of hidden layer node structure of formula (3).

$$k \geq \sqrt{n+l} + a \text{ or } k \geq \sqrt{n \cdot l} \qquad (3)$$

Among them, K is the number of nodes in hidden layer, n is the number of input nodes, L is the number of output nodes, A is a constant between 1–10.

The error feedback neural network to select three layer network structure, The input layer node number 5 and the output layer nodes number 5, Application of the Matlab toolbox in BP network design function newff () function, The grammar is:

net = newff(PR,[S1,S2, ..., SN],
    {TF1,TF2, ..., TFN},BTF,BLF,PF)

Among them: PR is expressed by each input vector of the maximum and minimum values of R*2 matrix; Si said the number of neurons in layer I network; TF said the transfer function layer I network, the default is tansig, The optional transfer function with Tansig, logsig or purelin; BTF said string variables, for the training of the function name network, can choose in the following functions: traingd, traingdm, traingdx, trainbfg, trainlm etc., The default is trainlm; BLF represents a string variable, function name for learning network, the default is learngdm; BF represents a string variable, as the performance function of the network, the default is mean variance 'mse'.

Application of MATLAB neural network simulation function of SIM to carry out simulation test, call format is:

[Y,Pf,Af,E,perf] = sim(net,P,Pi,Ai,T)

Among them, Y: function return value, the network output; Pf: function return value, the final output delay; Af: function return value, the final layer delay; E: function return value, the network error; perf: function return value, network performance; net: neural network for simulation; P: Pi network input;: initial input delay, default is 0; Ai: initial layer delay, default is 0; T: network object, the default is 0. Design the same way analysis neural network. The desired output of two neural network is shown in Tables 5 and 6.

5.2 When using neural network analysis

When using neural network analysis is to be used when, in understanding the concept of the reasoning in, when using, in space imagination in abstraction in knowledge application, in use, in the

Table 5. The expected output error feedback neural networor network.

| | The degree of mastering | | | | |
| | The knowledge level | | | | |
Output	One level	Two level	Three level	Four level	Five level
Y_1	1	0	0	0	0
Y_2	0	2	0	0	0
Y_3	0	0	3	0	0
Y_4	0	0	0	4	0
Y_5	0	0	0	0	5

Table 6.

| | Application of knowledge skill level | | | | |
Output	One level	Two level	Three level	Four level	Five level
Y_1'	1	0	0	0	0
Y_2'	0	2	0	0	0
Y_3'	0	0	3	0	0
Y_4'	0	0	0	4	0
Y_5'	0	0	0	0	5

computation in percentage of total time of these 6 features as the input layer nodes. The output node is mainly to determine the knowledge application ability, which includes knowledge application skill level, knowledge application, knowledge application skill level two skill level three, knowledge application, knowledge application skill level Four skill level five of five states. Similar error feedback neural network to identify other relevant content, get the following output in Table 6.

6 EXPERIMENTAL VERIFICATION

Use in a school of 100 students drawn to do problems as training samples of records, some of the data shown in Figure 5, 6, for different levels of students through the neural network training a neural network model.

Now for twenty students in learning and training, record student learning in the database. One of the students according to their status and error rate with time, determine that the student is in class B level, For error feedback neural network for the error percentage of its inputs (1,5,2,0,1). In matlab designed as follows:

UserID	Logintime	Ganhanjieerro	Zhishiyingyongerro	Jisuanerror	tiyijieerror	siweidingshierror	Total
001	2012-12-01	1	5	7	3	1	30
002	2012-12-01	0	1	4	0	2	30
003	2012-12-01	1	3	1	1	5	28
004	2012-12-01	2	2	0	0	4	27
005	2012-12-01	4	4	4	5	5	22
006	2012-12-01	7	5	1	7	1	30
007	2012-12-01	0	4	5	7	1	30
008	2012-12-01	4	1	6	8	4	30
009	2012-12-01	3	0	2	5	0	30
010	2012-12-01	0	7	8	2	0	27

Figure 5. Student's answers error condition information table (Part of the data).

UserID	Logintime	Ganhanlijeerro	Zhishiyingyongerro	Jisuanerror	tiyijieerror	siweidingshierror	Total
001	2012-12-01	1	5	7	3	1	30
002	2012-12-01	0	1	4	0	2	30
003	2012-12-01	1	3	1	1	5	28
004	2012-12-01	2	2	0	0	4	27
005	2012-12-01	4	4	4	5	5	22
006	2012-12-01	7	5	1	7	1	30
007	2012-12-01	0	4	5	7	1	30
008	2012-12-01	4	1	6	8	4	30
009	2012-12-01	3	0	2	5	0	30
010	2012-12-01	0	7	8	2	0	27

Figure 6. Student's learning record storage table (Part
of the data).

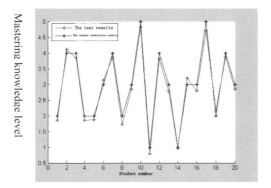

Figure 7. The comparison chart between knowledge
forecast and teacher evaluation.

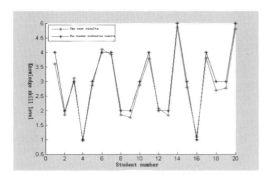

Figure 8. The comparison chart between knowledge
application forecast and teacher evaluation.

n1 is the answer error condition information table data, then prepared the database records into matrix. Each column represents the various parts of each student answer error conditions. 100 students have 100 rows as the training samples, x1 = sin(n1*0.1) as the training objectives.

n2 is the desired output shown in Table 5, test target: x2 = sin(n2*0.1);
Hidden layer nodes: NodeNum = 20;
Output dimension: TypeNum = 1;
Training input: p1 = xn_train;
Training Output: t1 = dn_train;
Training times: Epochs = 1000;
Test input: P = xn_test, namely [1,5,2,0,1];
Test output: T = dn_test;
Network parameters: TF1 = 'logsig'; TF2 = 'purelin';

The function of BP neural network in design net = newff(minmax(p1), [NodeNum TypeNum],{TF1 TF2}, 'trainlm'); After the training net = train(net,p1,t1); Output is that Y = sim (net,P) = [0.017,1.973,0.131,0.024,0.157], So the student's can get the second grade of the knowledge level. The same method is realized in Matlab input [5,16,2,5,3,2] to analysis the neural network, the output is [0.017,1.973,0.131,0.154,0.015,0.144], the student's knowledge application skills similar to belong to Now for twenty students in learning and training, record student learning in the database. One of the students according to their status and error rate with time, determine that the student is in class B level, For error feedback neural network for the error percentage of its inputs (1,5,2,0,1). In matlab designed as follows:
n1 is the answer error condition information table data, then prepared the database records into matrix. Each column represents the various parts of each student answer error conditions. 100 students have 100 rows as the training samples, x1 = sin(n1*0.1) as the training objectives.

n2 is the desired output shown in Table 5, test target: x2 = sin(n2*0.1);
Hidden layer nodes: NodeNum = 20;
Output dimension: TypeNum = 1;
Training input: p1 = xn_train;
Training Output: t1 = dn_train;
Training times: Epochs = 1000;
Test input: P = xn_test, namely [1,5,2,0,1];
Test output: T = dn_test;
Network parameters: TF1 = 'logsig'; TF2 = 'purelin';

The function of BP neural network in design net = newff(minmax(p1), [NodeNum TypeNum], {TF1 TF2}, 'trainlm'); After the training net = train(net,p1,t1); Output is that Y = sim(net,P) = [0.017,1.973,0.131,0.024,0.157], So the student's can get the second grade of the knowledge level. The same method is realized in Matlab input [5,16,2,5,3,2] to analysis the neural network, the output is [0.017,1.973,0.131,0.154,0.015,0.144], the student's knowledge application skills similar to belong to.

7 CONCLUSION

On the network interactive learning system, The establishment of mathematical learning knowledge base, According to the correct rate of students do test and time-consuming evaluation, using BP neural network learning model, reasoning that student learning, and gives relevant suggestions. The experiments also confirmed judgment result obtained by this model and the teacher's error is less than 5%, can effectively determine the learning of students.

REFERENCES

[1] Regina Stathacopoulou, George D. Magoulas, Maria Grigoriadou, Maria Samarakou. Neuro-fuzzy knowledge rocessing in intelligent learning environments for improved student diagnosis [J]. Information Sciences 2005,170:273–307.

[2] Jan Moons, Carlos De Backer. The design and pilot evaluation of an interactive learning environment for introductory programming influenced by cognitive load theory and constructivism [J]. Computers & Education, 2012,60:368–384.

[3] Yan Zhao. Based on the case study teaching network interactive learning environment [D]. The northeast normal university, 2007.

[4] Maria C. Busstra, Paul J.M. Hulshof, Jan Houwen, Lucy Elburg, Peter C.H. Hollman. Nutrient analysis explained for non-chemists by using interactive e-learning material [J]. Journal of Food Composition and Analysis 2012,25:88–95.

[5] Mei Li. "Interactive learning method" in the mathematics teaching implementation strategy [J]. Science and education wenhui. 2006,03:105.

[6] Xiaoyan Jin. Mathematics interactive learning practice and research [J]. China's education technology and equipment, 2010,22:56.

[7] Maning Wang, Yong Guan. The application of artificial intelligence technology in computer assisted instruction [J]. Micro computer information, 2006, 5:257–260.

Computer, Intelligent Computing and Education Technology – Liu, Sung & Yao (Eds)
© 2014 Taylor & Francis Group, London, ISBN 978-1-138-02469-4

New enhancements to part-based hand gesture recognition system with a Kinect camera

F.Z. He
Department of Electronics and Information Engineering, Huazhong University of Science and Technology, Wuhan, China

Z.Y. Lai
Department of Electronics and Information Engineering, Huazhong University of Science and Technology, Wuhan, China
Institute for Interdisciplinary Research, Jianghan University, Wuhan Economic and Technological Development Zone, Wuhan, China

B. Feng & W.Y. Liu
Department of Electronics and Information Engineering, Huazhong University of Science and Technology, Wuhan, China

ABSTRACT: The recently developed Kinect-based hand gesture recognition systems have provided new tools for human-computer interaction. These systems segment hand shape using depth information, detect fingers using shape decomposition method, and match finger parts with templates using Finger-Earth Mover's Distance (FEMD). Because of FEMD's sensitivity to the finger part variations, we propose two enhancements to these systems. Firstly, we present an improved FEMD to resist the influence of finger part variations and noise. Secondly, we present the Hand Shape Decomposition (HSD) method to segment finger parts from palm accurately and efficiently. When these two enhancements are embedded, both qualitative and quantitative results confirm that the overall part-based hand gesture recognition system can achieve state-of-the-art performance.

Keywords: human-computer interaction; hand gesture recognition; Kinect camera

1 INTRODUCTION

Hand gesture recognition based on computer vision becomes a popular topic in Human-Computer Interaction (HCI) in recent years. The Kinect camera provides new opportunities for contactless hand gesture recognition. The earliest part-based hand gesture recognition system with a Kinect camera mainly consists of hand segmentation, finger detection and template matching.

The Finger-Earth Mover's Distance (FEMD) was presented for template matching. Considering that this method is very sensitive to the variations and noise of finger parts, we improve FEMD by taking the finger number into account.

As for finger detection, Near-Convex Decomposition (NCD) and Perceptual Shape Decomposition (PSD) have their own shortcomings.

To further improve the accuracy of finger detection, we present the Hand Shape Decomposition (HSD) method based on the Discrete Curve Evolution (DCE).

Our hand gesture recognition system framework is shown in Figure 1. With the use of improved FEMD and HSD, the overall system can achieve the state-of-the-art recognition accuracy and efficiency.

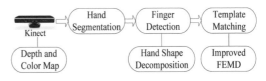

Figure 1. Our new enhancements to the part-based hand gesture recognition system with a Kinect camera.

2 RELATED WORK

We will review on template matching and finger detection of part-based hand gesture recognition systems with a Kinect camera.

2.1 Template matching

Although hand segmentation can obtain hand shapes from environment, the low resolution of the depth map will bring noise into the obtained hand. To handle the noise of hand shapes, a part-based method called FEMD is proposed for template matching.

Considering the distortion in finger segmentation, the finger size and position as penalty may not reflect the invariance of gestures sufficiently. The invariance of finger number does well in compensating this shortcoming, so we add it to the objective function of FEMD.

2.2 Finger detection

Table 1 presents a comparison among shape decomposition methods for finger detection. The NCD method formulates shape decomposition as a combinatorial optimization problem. The PSD method used DCE and skeleton pruning to construct the negative minimum set and its symmetry set. However, they have their own disadvantages for finger detection. Therefore, our HSD is proposed to further improve the robustness and efficiency of finger detection.

3 IMPROVED FINGER-EARTH MOVER'S DISTANCE (I_FEMD)

Ren et al. proposed Finger-Earth Mover's Distance (FEMD) for dissimilarity measure, which is based on Earth Mover's Distance (EMD). Supposing that $R = \{(r_1, \omega_{r_1}), \ldots, (r_{\bar{m}}, \omega_{r_{\bar{m}}})\}$ is the first hand signature with $\bar{m}$ clusters, where r_i is the cluster

Table 1. The comparison among the state-of-the-art shape decomposition methods for finger detection.

	NCD	PSD
Advantages	Detect the finger parts accurately	Better tradeoff the efficiency and accuracy
Disadvantages	Easy to be affected by shape variations, time consuming	Not always robust against shape variation, can't be solved in real time

representative and ω_{r_i} is the weight of the cluster; $T = \{(t_1, \omega_{t_1}), \ldots, (t_{\bar{n}}, \omega_{t_{\bar{n}}})\}$ is the second hand signature with $\bar{n}$ clusters. The FEMD between R and T is defined as the least work needed to move the fingers plus the penalty on empty fingers:

$$FEMD(R,T)$$
$$= \beta E_{move} + (1-\beta)E_{empty}$$
$$= \beta \frac{\sum_{i=1}^{\bar{m}} \sum_{j=1}^{\bar{n}} d_{ij} f_{ij}}{\sum_{i=1}^{\bar{m}} \sum_{j=1}^{\bar{n}} f_{ij}} + (1-\beta) | \sum_{i=1}^{\bar{m}} \omega_{r_i} - \sum_{j=1}^{\bar{n}} \omega_{t_j} | \tag{1}$$

where d_{ij} is the ground distance from cluster r_i to t_j, and f_{ij} is the flow from cluster r_i to t_j. The importance between the first and second terms is regulated by parameter β.

The FEMD only shows the differences of fingers' position and area, which cannot be well preserved during finger segmentation. Considering that the invariance can be well preserved by finger number, we add it into the objective function of FEMD and thereby obtain the improved FEMD (I_FEMD):

$$I\_FEMD(R,T)$$
$$= \beta E_{move} + \alpha E_{empty\_1} + (1-\beta-\alpha)E_{empty\_2}$$
$$= \beta \frac{\sum_{i=1}^{\bar{m}} \sum_{j=1}^{\bar{n}} d_{ij} f_{ij}}{\sum_{i=1}^{\bar{m}} \sum_{j=1}^{\bar{n}} f_{ij}} + \alpha | \sum_{i=1}^{\bar{m}} \omega_{r_i} - \sum_{j=1}^{\bar{n}} \omega_{t_j} |$$
$$+ (1-\beta-\alpha) | \bar{m} - \bar{n} | \tag{2}$$

where parameters β and α are the adjustable parameters to better reduce the influence of finger part variations.

4 HAND SHAPE DECOMPOSITION (HSD)

In order to get more efficient finger parts for template matching, we propose the Hand Shape Decomposition method. There are two key observations: 1) One finger part has only one fingertip located at the convex corner of the hand shape boundary; 2) At least one end point of the finger part cut is located at the concave corner of the hand shape boundary. These two observations motivate us to decompose the finger parts by firstly finding the convex corners corresponding to fingertips and then peaking up the concave corners associated with these convex corners for finger part cuts. The main procedures for our HSD are shown as follows:

1. Corner detection: evolve the hand shape boundary by Discrete Curve Evolution (DCE) method

until that the minimal weight among the rest vertices is no less than a predefined threshold *D_max*. This threshold is proportional to the size of the palm which can be measured by the radius of the maximal inscribed disk of the hand shape. Then the corners are located at vertices of the evolved polygon, as shown in Figure 2(a).

2. Corner convexity checking: find the two directed vectors of the evolved polygon associated with each corner and calculate the dot product between the first vector's vertical vector and the second vector. Then determine the corner convexity according to the sign of this dot product, as shown in Figure 2(b).

3. Fingertips detection: remove the unnecessary convex corners that have the distance less than a threshold *b* from the center of the maximal inscribed disk of the hand shape. Merge the adjacent convex corners such that one convex corner can represent one fingertip, as shown in Figure 2(c).

4. Cut construction: If there are two concave corners at the two sides of a convex corner, connect these two concave corners for cuts. If there is only one concave corner at one side of a convex corner, construct a cut connecting this concave corner and the nearest boundary pixel located at the other side of this convex corner, as shown in Figure 2(d).

As for the analysis of computational complexity, we consider all the procedures inside our HSD. On one side, the computational complexity of the corner detection using DCE method is $O(N \log N)$, where N is the number of boundary points.

One the other side, the corner convexity checking, the fingertips detection and the cut construction take $O(n)$, $O(m)$ and $O(l)$ respectively, where *n, m* and *l* are the number of the original corners, the original convex corners, and the retained convex corners. Usually, *n, m* and *l* differ from N by an order of magnitude, thus the total computational complexity is $O(N \log N)$. In order to reflect the efficiency of HSD, we compare the computational complexity of HSD with NCD. NCD is made up of the concavity calculation between any two boundary points and the solution of Binary Integer Linear Programming problem, whose computational complexities are respectively $O(N^2)$ and $O(2^{N^2})$. Thus, compared with NCD, our HSD achieves a great improvement in the computational efficiency.

5 EXPERIMENTS

We conduct a series of experiments to substantiate the superior of our Kinect-based hand gesture recognition system with the HSD and I_FEMD embedded on the NTU-Microsoft Kinect Hand Gesture dataset. Some of gestures are shown in Figure 3.

5.1 Hand Shape Decomposition (HSD)

Firstly, we evaluate the robustness of our HSD by comparing it with existing decomposition methods. In Figure 4, three rows show the hand shape decomposition results from NCD, PSD and HSD, and the parts marked in ellipses are redundant or undetected. The first row has incorrect decomposition in multiple hand shapes and the second row has a redundant part in the first gesture, while the last row has correct decomposition in all hand shapes, showing that our HSD is more robust against orientation, scale and articulation changes.

Figure 3.   Examples of ten pre-segmented gestures.

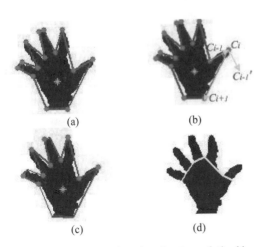

Figure 2.   (a) Corner detection (vertices of the blue polygon), (b) Corner convexity checking (the convex corners with pink), (c) Fingertips detection (fingertips with pink), (d) Cut construction (cut lines with yellow).

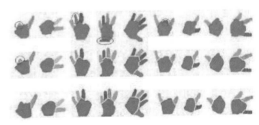

Figure 4.   The decomposition of hand shapes.

Secondly, we evaluate the efficiency of our HSD as listed in Table 2. The decomposition time for original NCD is 45.6132 s, which is of great computational complexity. Although the improved NCD reduce the decomposition time to 3.9705 s by using fast optimization tools, it is still time-consuming. As for PSD, the decomposition time is reduced to 1.875 s because of smaller searching space. Our decomposition method HSD can further reduce the implementation time to 0.265 s due to the implementation simplicity.

Thirdly, we evaluate two important thresholds of HSD—the DCE threshold D_max in the simplification of hand shapes and the distance threshold b in the fingertips detection. Empirically, the settings of D_max and b to be 30% and 1.85 can achieve very robust and accurate decomposition results.

5.2 Improved Finger-Earth Mover's Distance (I_FEMD)

In this subsection, we evaluate the influence of two significant parameters β and α on the recognition accuracy of I_FEMD. As shown in Figure 5, we can see that the values of β and α for the best recognition accuracy are 0.4 and 0.1 respectively.

5.3 Overall system performance

In this subsection, we confirm that the HSD and I_FEMD embedded Kinect-based hand gesture recognition system achieves performance improvements. Here we fixed the HSD thresholds $D\_max = 30\%$, $b = 1.85$ and I_FEMD parameters $\beta = 0.4$, $\alpha = 0.1$. The confusion matrix of our system is shown in Figure 6. There are no seriously confused categories.

The mean recognition accuracy and mean execution time of various shape recognition systems is shown in Table 3. The mean recognition accuracy of our HSD and I_FEMD embedded recognition system (95.5%) is higher than that of NCD-based FEMD (93.9%), because of the more robust finger part detection and matching. In addition, the speed of NCD-based FEMD (4.0012 s) is slower than that of our system (0.428 s) owing to the

Table 2. The mean decomposition time on the NTU-Microsoft Kinect Hand Gesture Dataset.

	Original NCD	Improved NCD	PSD	HSD
Decomposition time	45.6132 s	3.9705 s	1.875 s	0.265 s

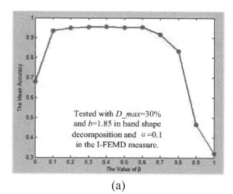

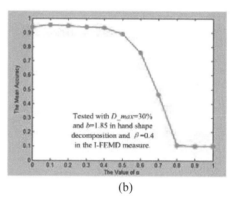

(a)

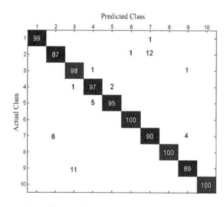

(b)

Figure 5. The influences of parameters β and α on the recognition accuracy.

Figure 6. The confusion matrix of the part-based hand gesture recognition system using our HSD and I_FEMD.

more complex decomposition process for finger detection. In a word, Table 3 demonstrates that the HSD and I_FEMD embedded recognition system achieves the highest mean accuracy at the lowest mean execution time cost.

Table 3. The mean accuracy and the mean execution time for various hand gesture recognition systems.

	Mean accuracy	Mean execution time
Shape context	83.2%	12.346 s
Skeleton matching	78.6%	2.4449 s
NCD + FEMD	93.9%	4.0012 s
PSD + FEMD	94.1%	1.967 s
HSD + I_FEMD	95.5%	0.428 s

6 CONCLUSIONS

The pursuit of more robustness, accuracy and efficiency requires better design and optimization on the hand gesture recognition systems. In this paper, we embed two enhancements into the existing part-based hand gesture recognition system to improve its performance. The Finger-Earth Mover's (I_FEMD) is improved to weaken the impacts of finger part variations, and the HSD is proposed to improve the robustness and efficiency of finger detection. Considering the promotion of performance by I_FEMD and HSD synthetically, our part-based hand gesture recognition system embedded these two enhancements achieves 95.5% mean recognition accuracy and 0.428 s mean execution time, which goes beyond all the current hand gesture recognition systems.

ACKNOWLEDGMENTS

Corresponding author of this work is B. Feng. This work was supported by the National Natural Science Foundation of China (No. 61173120).

REFERENCES

Bai X and L.J. Latecki, "Path similarity skeleton graph matching," *IEEE Transactions on Pattern Analysis and Machine Intelligence*, vol. 30, no. 7, pp. 1–11, Jul. 2008.

Bai X., L.J. Latecki, and W. Liu, "Skeleton pruning by contour partitioning with discrete curve evolution," *IEEE Transactions on Pattern Analysis and Machine Intelligence*, vol. 29, no. 3, pp. 449–462, Mar. 2007.

Belongie S., J. Malik, and J. Puzicha, "Shape matching and object recognition using shape contexts," *IEEE Transactions on Pattern Analysis and Machine Intelligence*, vol. 24, no. 24, pp. 509–522, Apr. 2002.

Datta R., D. Joshi, J. Li, and J.Z. Wang, "Image retrieval: Ideas, influences, and trends of the new age," *ACM Computing Surveys*, vol. 40, no. 5, pp. 1–60, Apr. 2008.

Lai Z., W. Liu, F. Zhang, and G. Cheng, "Perceptual Distortion Measure for Polygon-Based Shape Coding," *IEICE Transactions on Information and System*, vol. E96-D, no. 3, pp. 750–753, Mar. 2013.

Longin Jan Latecki and Rolf Lakämper, "Convexity Rule for Shape Decomposition Based on Discrete Contour Evolution," *Computer Vision and Image Understanding*, vol. 73, no. 3, pp. 441–454, Mar. 1999.

Microsoft Corporation. Kinect for XBOX 360. Redmond WA.

Murthy G.R.S. and R.S. Jadon, "A review of vision based hand gesture recognition," *International Journal of Information Technology and Knowledge Management*, vol. 2, no. 2, pp. 405–410, Jul.-Dec. 2009.

Ren Z., J. Yuan, J. Meng, and Z. Zhang, "Robust part-based hand gesture recognition based on finger-earth mover's distance," *IEEE Transactions on Multimedia*, vol. 15, no. 5, pp. 1110–1120, Aug. 2013.

Ren Z., J. Yuan, and W. Liu, "Minimum near-convex shape decomposition," *IEEE Transactions on Pattern Analysis and Machine Intelligence*, vol. 35, no. 10, pp. 2546–2552, Oct. 2013.

Wang C., W. Liu, Z. Lai, and H. Wang, "Perceptually friendly shape decomposition by resolving segmentation points with minimum cost," *Journal of Visual Communication and Image Representation*, vol. 24, no. 3, pp. 270–282, Apr. 2013.

Computer, Intelligent Computing and Education Technology – Liu, Sung & Yao (Eds)
© 2014 Taylor & Francis Group, London, ISBN 978-1-138-02469-4

The rural land dividends simulation based on SD: A case of Xiaoshan, Hangzhou

W.P. Xu, S.F. Yuan, Y. Chen, Y. Zhang, L. Sun & S.C. Zhu
Department of Land Resources Management, Zhejiang Gongshang University, Hangzhou, China

ABSTRACT: In recent years, with the rapid development of industrialization and urbanization in our country, a large number of agricultural land transform into non-agricultural land, and because of the changes in supply and demand, and external investment, the land eventually achieve a substantial value-added. Based on land value increment principle, analysis of the factors affecting land shares dividends, in this paper the system dynamics model of Xiaoshan area of land shares dividends is established and simulated. The result shows that benefit-sharing compensation makes the distribution between these three subjects reasonable, and narrows their gap. System simulation serves a good method for land value increment distribution study.

Keywords: land shares; SD simulation; peasant rights and interests; Xiaoshan

1 INTRODUCTION

The rural land shareholding system uses the land use rights or land contract authorities as investment under the premise of insisting on keeping the land property rights, to make the operating system of intensive management and gaining material profits come true. The rural land shareholding system was created in the1980s, the Pearl River Delta of China; then followed by the other coastal areas like somewhere in Changjiang Delta. Land shareholding system managed and operated by the village collective, and investors combined to set up joint-stock companies to jointly develop, land shares, and farmers account for a rights issue standard, stock dividends, farmers in the form of stock certificates have their right to the land as part of its acquisition of farmland by levy the value-added benefits of compensation[1,2]. With the development of society and economy, the values of land income distribution problems become to be the focus[3]. As in land ownership reform model, functions and interest distribution pattern of joint-stock system has made remarkable progress in areas such as[4–7]. On the basis of current research, summarizing and developing the theories of land income distribution, exploring farmers relative satisfaction with the absolute life guarantee of compensation, is where the main purpose of this study.

2 THE METHOD OF SYSTEM DYNAMICS

2.1 *Overview of system dynamics*

System Dynamics appeared in 1956, used by professor Forrester in 1958, for the analysis of production management and inventory management, and which is a simulation method for enterprise's system. SD is a discipline of information feedback system, and is a cross-disciplinary of understanding system problems and solving system problems[8]. Compared to the mathematical model, the dynamics model for application of system can be more fully reflect the dynamics change trend and the systems of nonlinear structure, because the model looks at the overall objectives of the system, rather than pursuits the best goals of subsystems, which contributes to the coordination of population, resources, environment and socio-economic.

2.2 *The principles of SD structure modeling*

SD stream map is defined by special symbols to represent the relationships of each variable in a causal loop. It can express more information of system structure and system behavior, which is an essential part of establishing the SD model, and it plays an important role in establish SD model. In the system dynamics, level, flow rate, flow, and information are the four basic elements, which form a whole, playing a role in the feedback loop, and described the changes of real system process vividly, which is the key to the system dynamics.

2.3 *The basic feedback loop simulation and analysis of DYNAMO*

DYNAMO is an acronym for Dynamic Model, and it is the most common SD model, which takes the practical problems into dynamic models with feedback structuring, and through computer simulation by dynamic behavior of the system varies with time. This model consists of two statements: (1) the formula statement (either directly for simulation calculations), and (2) the command statement (used to control the simulation of processes, inputs and outputs). It is important to note two points: first, the DYNAMO in the variable name is no more than 6 characters, but the first character must be a letter; second, with the exception of "*" and "RUN" beyond the statement and other statements can be arbitrary sequence. There is a strict order for simulation when DYNAMO language runtime.

3 THE KINETIC MODEL SIMNULATE ANALYSIS THE MODEL OF LAND SHARES IN XIAOSHAN DISTRICT

3.1 Study area

Xiaoshan affiliated with Hangzhou, Zhejiang Province, located in northern Zhejiang Province, South coast of Hangzhou Bay, is the strongest comprehensive County (city, district) in mainland China, has been awarded as "top ten counties of China(cities, districts)". The total land area is 1412.05 square kilometers of land in Xiaoshan District, there is 51,810 hectares of cultivated land and a population of 1.23 million, only 0.042 hectares of cultivated land per capita, seriously below the national average per capita arable land ownership. Xiaoshan has large population and fewer lands, combined with the rapid development of economy and society and the rapid advance of urban construction, the protection of arable land and land conflicts have been becoming increasingly prominent.

3.2 Parameter settings

The research data 70 km² (of which 15% left to the village collective economic organizations, that is, 10.5 hm²), which was taken over land area. Reference to the relevant land shares converted standard [9,10], and combined with the actual situation of Xiaoshan, Put an acre of land to a shares, a shares convertible into 5,000 yuan, land shares implement guaranteed dividends, annual dividend per share minimum guarantee of 500 yuan and then 80% summary of annual operating income dividends on shares, 20% of revenue as the company's development cooperation funds. And year guaranteed dividend per share at the end of a certain period be adjusted based on the ratio of rising food prices. Refer to recent years

of national food (rice) minimum purchasing prices average growth rate and combine the actual local conditions, determine 8.9% guaranteed dividend increase speed[1]; while Basis in recent years, the average growth rate of per capita net income of rural residents and performance target of 2012 in Xiaoshan District to determine net operating earnings growth of 12%[2].

3.3 Build SD flowchart

According to the general law of the appreciation of land, based on the analysis of influencing factors on land shares dividends, build the SD stream map about farmer of sharing land value increment revenue as shown in Figure 1. Build model equation:

$$M = \sum_{i=0}^{n} K_i + L_i(1 + 0.8) \tag{1}$$

$$K_{i+1} = K_i(1 + r)$$

$$L_{i+1} = L_i(1 + a)$$

In the equation, M for farmers' income of dividends on shares, K_i for the i year of dividends on shares guaranteed, r for the increase speed of

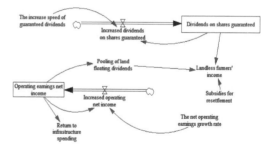

Figure 1. The SD stream map about farmer of sharing land value increment revenue.

[1]Consult 'Notice about increasing the minimum purchase price in 2009' (National Development and Reform Commission [2009]NO.19,); 'Notice about increasing the minimum purchase price in 2010' (National Development and Reform Commission [2010]NO.115,); 'Notice about increasing the minimum purchase price in 2011' (National Development and Reform Commission [2011] NO.60,); 'Notice about increasing the minimum purchase price in 2012' (National Development and Reform Commission [2012]NO.17,).
[2]Consult 'The Statistics Yearbook of Zhejiang Province in 2013'; 'The work summary of 2011 from agricultural and rural work office in 2012' (Agricultural Office[2012] NO.1).

guaranteed dividends, L_i for the i year of operating earnings net income and a is the net operating earnings growth rate, n is the year.

4 THE VALUE OF LAND FARMERS' SHARE OF THE INCOME DISTRIBUTION AND SD SIMULATION

4.1 SD model operations

Application of vensim simulation on a computer, the simulation time is 0–25 years, running the models, shareholder dividend income for farmers over the next 25 years was shown, as Table 1.

Based on SD simulation experiments, we can find that, after farmers participate in the rural land shareholding system, their dividend income has steadily increased. Over the long term, it also contributes to improving the farmer's satisfaction. At the meantime, according to calculations, farmers, government and land units of collective representation about 24:34:42, the ratio of allocation between these three tend to be reasonable, narrow the gap between the main distribution, optimize the agricultural value-added income distribution mechanism, it will also be conducive to safeguarding farmers' rights [11–13].

4.2 Model optimization

From the results, dividends on shares have balanced distribution between the main shareholder dividends the share of proceeds, and land shares can mobilize the landless farmers' production and living initiative, improving the income level of farmers, so as to speed up economic development. Therefore, we optimize the mode of land shares and case, it will be reasonable to enable farmers to share the most reasonable value added income.

Table 1. Farmers' income of dividends on shares.

Time (Year)	Landless farmers' income	Time (Year)	Landless farmers' income
0	1250.00	13	3382.04
1	1337.70	14	3680.72
2	1434.03	15	4009.10
3	1539.83	16	4370.15
4	1656.07	17	4767.16
5	1783.76	18	5203.73
6	1924.06	19	5683.86
7	2078.21	20	6211.91
8	2247.60	21	6792.73
9	2433.75	22	7431.62
10	2638.34	23	8134.44
11	2863.19	24	8907.65
12	3110.35	25	9758.36

Dividends on shares amount mainly relates to the accumulation of "dividends on shares guaranteed" and "operating earnings net income", both of them are having an great impact on farmers' income, and that they were affected by "the increase speed of guaranteed dividends" and "the net operating earnings growth rate" two speed variable, so if we want to improve the income of farmers, must raise both rates.

4.2.1 The optimization to the increase speed of guaranteed dividends

We assume that other conditions are the same, only change the speed of the increase of guaranteed dividend. As shown in Figure 2, curve 1 represents the increasing speed of guaranteed dividends is 12%; curve 2 represents the increasing speed of guaranteed dividends is 9.5%; curve 3 represents increasing speed of guaranteed dividends is 8.9%.

4.2.2 The optimization to the net operating earnings growth rate

In Figure 3, curve changes only vary according to changes in the net operating earnings growth rate.

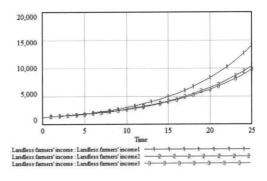

Figure 2. Simulation results of changing the increasing speed of guaranteed dividends.

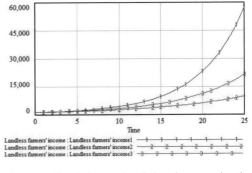

Figure 3. Simulation results of changing operating the net operating earnings growth rate.

Curve 1 represents the net operating earnings growth rate is 24%; the curve 2 represents the net operating earnings growth rate is 18%; curve 3 represents the net operating earnings growth rate is 12%.

On the basis of the curve in Figures 2 and 3, changing the increase speed of guaranteed dividends or the net operating earnings growth rate, will make the final values of the curve 3 points larger. This means that the much more the farmers' incomes increase, the much more value of land they would share, which is conducive to better protect the crows' loss before interest in the process.

5 SUMMARIES

1. Using System Dynamics to simulate land income distribution model of Xiaoshan Zhejiang dynamically, taking Xiaoshan as an example, to roughly determine farmers, government and land units of collective representation about 24:34:42. It is conducive to build the dynamic distribution mechanism of land value-added income in the process of farmland conversion, and effectively protect the interests of expropriated farmers' right, ensure farmers can share land value-added income with reasonable equity. It will have some practical import when get promoted throughout Xiaoshan even the whole Zhejiang province.

2. In recent years, the implementation of cash + shares land allocation pattern in Xiaoshan District gets farmers' recognition. The rural land shareholding system improve the distribution ratio of the land-requisitioned peasants in a certain extent. But it still need to constantly optimize the distribution mechanism and innovate operation mechanism to improve agricultural productivity, and increase farmers' income.

ACKNOWLEDGEMENTS

Our deepest gratitude goes first and foremost to Professor Yuan, our supervisor, for his constant encouragement and guidance. He has guided us through all the stages of the writing of this thesis. Without his consistent and illuminating instruction, this thesis could not have reached its present form. Second, we would like to express our heartfelt gratitude to National Natural Science Foundation of China (41171151) and (41371188), Human Social Science Foundation of the Chinese Ministry of Education (10YJA630197) and (11YJC630254), The 2013th Young and middle-aged leading academic project in universities of zhejiang province (pd2013173) and Zhejiang Xinmiao TalentPlan (2013R408043), which give us great support.

REFERENCES

[1] Han Shucheng, Pu Lijie, Yan Xiang, et al. 2009. Coupling of regional land use and socio-economic changes in spatial distribution—a case in Jiangsu Province. *Journal of Ningxia University (natural science Edition)*, 30 (2): 183–188.
[2] Fang Bin, Chen Jian, Jiang Boliang. 2012. The development pattern and path of the rural land shareholding system. *Land resources in Shanghai*, 33 (4): 7–11.
[3] Zhao Yan. 2010. On the perfection of China's rural land shareholding system. *Agricultural economics*, (6): 73–74.
[4] Xu Jianchun, Li Cuizhen. 2013. Rural land shareholding system reform practice and exploration in Zhejiang Province. *China land science*, 27 (5): 4–13.
[5] Zhang Xiaohan, Zhang Ying. 2009. The rural land shareholding system performance analysis by the Perspective of efficiency and fairness. *The rural economy*, (1): 20–23.
[6] Zhang Liping, Zhong Zhangbao. 2007. Land shares: the effective way of protection of the interests of the peasants. *The statistics and decision making*, (10): 53–55.
[7] Yuan Shaofeng, Yang Lixia, Sun Le, et al. 2012. Summary of agricultural land transfer land value increment allocation process research. *Land resources in Shanghai*, 33 (1): 35–40.
[8] Jia Renan, Ding Ronghua. 2002. *System dynamics—dynamics of complex analyzes feedback*. Beijing: higher education press.
[9] Shen Nianqiao. 2009. Innovative stake mechanisms, dig resource potential, motivate factors. *http://www.cnny.org/html/main/xwdtView/200903176209.html*.
[10] Lv Dong. 2009.The rural land shareholding system, farmers have the harvest do not Shimoda. *The mass daily*.
[11] Zhang Yuyang. 2012. Compensation standard of land requisition in China under the background of urbanization – a case study of Chongqing as an example. *Guangdong agriculture science*, (4): 229–232.
[12] Zhu Peixin, Tang Peng.2013. Agricultural land and supply of land value-added tax revenue allocation mechanism innovation—based on empirical analysis of Jiangsu Province. *Journal of Nanjing Agricultural University (natural science)*, 13 (1): 66–72.
[13] Liang Shuang.2009. Distribution of income in the process of non-agricultural land and reasonable evaluation—a case study of Zhuozhou City, Hebei Province. *China land science*, 23 (1):4–8.

Computer, Intelligent Computing and Education Technology – Liu, Sung & Yao (Eds)
© 2014 Taylor & Francis Group, London, ISBN 978-1-138-02469-4

Project teaching exploration and practice of web design and production courses of higher vocational education

C.Y. Yu & Y.Y. Zhu

College of Information Engineering, Binzhou Vocational College, Binzhou Huanghe, Shandong, China

ABSTRACT: Based on the characteristics of web design and production courses of higher vocational colleges, this paper combines with the students' actual cognitive level, and elaborates the concrete application of the project teaching in practice. This method allows students to transit from "learn to answer" to "learn to question", and "learn to master" to "learn to learn", so that colleges can cultivate students' web design and production skills.

Keywords: higher vocational; project; web design and production; practice teaching

Higher vocational education is an important composite part of higher education. Different from ordinary higher education, higher vocational education is a system to teach skills. With the rapid development of the Internet in recent years, the social demand for web design and production talents is on the increase on a yearly basis. Web design and production skills have become one of the basic skills for modern people. This paper focuses on the practicability and strong technical feature of web design and production courses, project-based teaching methods are adopted in this paper, which can effectively improve students' ability to apply technology and adapt to jobs.

1 SUMMARY OF PROJECT TEACHING

In terms of the features of project teaching, it is based on the teaching objectives of the course, and uses one or more large projects through the entire course. Every big project is also divided into several sub-projects. Each subproject is mutually independent and interrelated. In addition, each subproject is a relatively complete learning unit, with clear teaching objectives. When every student has learnt a subproject, they can master an essential skill, and when completing all subprojects, they can acquire the knowledge and ability to learn the whole course.

Web design and production courses emphasizes on training students' practical skills and sense of teamwork. Project teaching is more conducive to realizing the teaching goals of courses, and improving the quality of teaching.

2 THE APPLICATION OF PROJECT TEACHING IN WEB DESIGN AND PRODUCTION COURSES

2.1 *Course orientation*

Defining course orientation is a prerequisite for the implementation of project teaching. Web design and production course can cultivate vocational ability, which is the required course of multiple majors in our school, such as computer application technology, and network technology. It mainly trains high-quality skilled professionals engaging in website construction and management in the fields of production, construction, management, and service. The employment post cluster includes web designers, web art designer, website planners, among which web designer is the core position.

2.2 *Project selection*

Selecting the appropriate project can guarantee the success of project teaching. Through the market research analysis, the course can determine employment post cluster that the course faces so as to summarize the professional competence and professional quality that the post requires. After analysis and arrangement, the typical tasks are placed in order, and the course objectives can be further clear. Ultimately, the curriculum system can be determined, which constitutes by the teaching program represented by "Tesco network" construction and the training program represented by "department website", as shown in Figure 1. In addition, the teaching project can be refined into six modules in accordance with the theoretical knowledge from

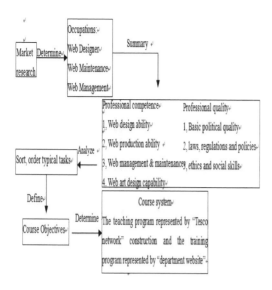

Figure 1.　Selection process of project teaching content.

shallow to deep, and the operational skills from simple to complex. The modules contain website appreciation, website planning, website design, web programming, website landscaping, project integration and release. Each module project is set with a number of tasks and subtasks.

2.3　Implementation of organization projects

The implementation of a project is the core phase of the project teaching process. Project teaching implementation of web design and production courses involves six links: project proposal, analysis, design, implementation, acceptance and summary. The specific process is as follows:

2.3.1　Situation setting, project introduction
In order to quickly draw students' attention to the classroom, teachers should first introduce the specific situation setting into the project, and then inform students the requirements and difficult points so that they can have a clear understanding of the mission and teaching goals. Afterwards, the teacher can show the previous works. On the one hand, this allows students to preview the program in advance, and stimulate their creation desires; on the other hand, it can help students to avoid repetitive errors in producing works by analyzing the advantages and disadvantages.

2.3.2　Project information, disseminating information
To enable students to successfully complete the project, teachers guide students to make a brief

review of the knowledge and skills required in the project. In addition, they can distribute the learning materials in the forms of PPT, Flash animation and videos to students. Students can seek help from the learning materials when encountering problems in the production process.

2.3.3　Role-playing, forming program
Students are divided into different working groups. Each group has double identities: a client and a web design company. As a client, they would propose their requirements to the next group, and fill out the customer demand tables in detail. There are clear divisions from the planning ideas of web pages, art design and color matching to design production. Moreover, the same task of different projects will be took charge of by different students so that each student can experience different tasks throughout the process; website design company is responsible for designing website for the previous group according to customers' demands. The group leader and his team members are respectively the project manager and web designers. The team leader is in charge of elaborating the needs of customers to the team members. They work together to develop a preliminary plan in order to complete the project. Teachers actively participate in student discussions, and give a timely guidance.

2.3.4　Program displace and defining target
The project manager displays the program, and the team members make a supplement. Teachers simulate various types of clients to guide and assess the program from multiple perspectives. In order to encourage students to learn from each other in mutual emulation, teachers should also guide other students to review the programs; after each group has determined and revised their program, the final scheme can be determined.

2.3.5　Task decomposition, combat drills
Teachers combine teaching objectives to divide the project into multiple tasks. Each member of the group should carry out web design as per customers' demands step by step; teachers visit the classroom so that they can deal with difficult problems in time. They can focus on the demo for common problems, and separately answer individual questions.

2.3.6　Results exchange, process evaluation
Each group elects its best work to participate in the outcome exhibition. Designers make a presentation by means of multimedia. They should in detail introduce design ideas, the technology applied and its uniqueness, the difficulties encountered and the treatment methods. Other group members express their views about the work and the designers

make an explanation; teachers and students work together to make an analysis, affirming the strengths while proposing a revise scheme for the weaknesses. Each group carries out a self-evaluation and a group evaluation according to the project evaluation criteria, and finally "the Best Graphic Design", "the Best Web Production", "the Best Employee" can be selected.

2.3.7 Summary and improvement

First, teachers let the students review the experience and acquisition in producing the project, and then teachers summarize and emphasize on the key points, difficult points and actual meaning of the project again, so that students can deeply know how to use what have learnt, and experience a sense of accomplishment through the completion of the project.

2.3.8 Job layout, learning by analogy

Homework is divided into two different levels: basic homework faces all the students, which is an important part for review and consolidation; improving homework faces students who can manager more profound learning, so that they can improve on the existing basis.

2.4 Project teaching harvest and experience

2.4.1 The theoretical level and operation ability of teachers need to be higher

Project teaching request that the teaching content corresponding to the real projects (product) of the enterprise, which requires all teachers should not only in-depth grasp and understanding of the theoretical knowledge, but also be able to utilize this knowledge. Relative to the traditional teaching methods, project teaching request that the teachers must have a higher skill levels. For this reason teachers use their spare time to study into the enterprise, participate in training exercises, gain practical work experience. All this has played an important role in improving their level of teaching practice. At the same time, the college hired technical backbone employees from the forefront of production as practice guidance teachers, which improved specially appointed teachers' professional skill.

2.4.2 Students' job professionalism and professional capabilities further enhance

After the implementation of the project teaching, the course constructs a curriculum system in a real online shopping site. It refines the teaching content to sub-projects, and students are divided into groups to complete the project tasks. Allowing students to obtain knowledge and improve skills in the implementation process

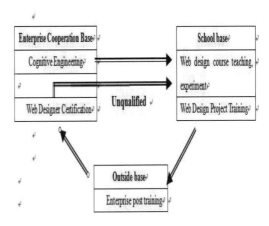

Figure 2. Work and study, school-enterprise cooperation process.

of specific objectives and tasks, which can fully play the students' collective intelligence, train the methods and the concept of independent learning, and improve students' jobs professionalism and professional competence (practical application ability, the ability to self-exploration, teamwork, etc.).

2.4.3 Work and study, school-enterprise cooperation further strengthens

Prior to the implementation of project teaching, students receive school education alone. What they can learn is discrete and isolated knowledge. In addition, they lack practicality and targeted awareness on the knowledge. But after applying the project teaching to the curriculum, schools and businesses jointly run the school, and there is a close cooperation between schools and enterprises. Gradually, the students can study in the enterprise business norms first, and get familiar with the site design process, etc. After coming back to schools, they continue to complete the theory and practice teaching courses. Finally they return to business post training until they have passed a new teaching system after assessing and accrediting, as shown in Figure 2.

3 THE REFLECTION OF PROJECT TEACHING APPLICATION

Project teaching can link the curriculum teaching with business needs, which can achieve "classroom enterprise" and "student and employees integration". Students can convert roles in advance. This has achieved remarkable teaching effects, but reflection and improvement is still needed.

3.1 The teacher guidance should be comprehensive and timely

In the whole process of teaching, teachers should pay close attention to all the students involved in the situation, pay attention to all aspects of the full participation. To guide and direct when it is necessary, put an end to the students in a timely manner in "sitting, waiting, relying on" phenomenon.

3.2 Classroom management needs to be strengthened

The initiative of teaching in project teaching is no longer held by teachers, but the students. However, this is by no means allowing the students to be unchecked and take a liberal attitude. Otherwise the classroom order is out of control, and teaching objectives cannot be completed properly. Teachers should have a good control of classroom, and know how to handle the situation better. To do this, teachers must be lowered stance, and interact with students in an equal status so that students can learn in a harmonious atmosphere.

3.3 Hierarchical teaching needs to be solved

The basis of higher vocational students differs greatly. Even in the face of the same project tasks, some students can easily complete them while some students will be at a loss what to do. Although the number of latter is a few, teachers should strive to find a balance. How to divide the teaching level and how to better teach students in accordance of their aptitude need to be thought about in the future of teaching.

4 CONCLUSION

Practice has proved that when the project teaching is applied in the curriculum reform of web design and production in higher vocational education, the quality of teaching will be greatly improved. Students' web design capability and the ability to integrate theory with practice have also been significantly enhanced. Three consecutive graduates have reached a rate of over 90% in passing web designers qualifying examination, among which more than half of the students are now engaging in web design and production-related work. Therefore, the project teaching is an effective teaching method that can improve the overall students' comprehensive quality and ability in higher vocational colleges.

REFERENCES

[1] Dai Shihong. Vocational education classroom teaching reform [M] Beijing: Tsinghua University Press, 2007.
[2] Wan Leung, Huang Jinzhu. Reform exploration of web production technology courses [J]. Chinese Vocational and Technical Education, 2007 (7).
[3] Ouyang Weihao, Wu Zhenfeng, Luo Zhuojun. Course teaching reform of "web design and production" based on the working process [J]. Computer Education, 2010 (4).
[4] Zhang Jianguo. Evolution of Vocational Education Curriculum Development Model and Its Implications [J]. Education Forum, 2007 (4).
[5] Jiang Dayuan. New Theory of Vocational Education Research [M] Beijing: Education Science Press, 2007.

Computer, Intelligent Computing and Education Technology – Liu, Sung & Yao (Eds)
© 2014 Taylor & Francis Group, London, ISBN 978-1-138-02469-4

The case method in the information security management major

F.X. Sun & K. Wang
*School of Information and Safety Engineering, Zhongnan University of Economics and Law,
Wuhan, Hubei, China*

ABSTRACT: The Information Security Management is a newly starting major, about which the instruction and practice is still at the exploratory stage, and no mature experience can be used for reference, especially in financial colleges. How to play the advantages of the finance and economic institutions, to combine with the applications of information security in economy, law, management field., and to foster inter-disciplinary talents are all worth studying. This paper proposes a method which introduces the computer crime cases into information security theory teaching class, to foster the students' abilities of theory application and practice.

Keywords: information security major; instructional improvement; computer crime; case teaching-method

1 GENERAL INTRODUCTION

With the extensive application of computers in the public finance, economy and other fields, its management and operation approach have had a change from the traditional counter services to the network and information service. However, the fragility of computer itself, normalization of management system and perfecting information security management are causing potential unsafe factors in information system, making traditional security mechanism face new threats. Therefore information security management talents who not only grasp information theory and technology but also master the business knowledge of economy, judicature, management are badly needed.

2 INFORMATION SECURITY MANAGEMENT

At present, the needs for information security talents have different levels and different direction. So universities should formulate relevant training goals, classes, course arrangement and exert the advantages according to their own situation. The information security major can cultivate talents who do research in different direction. In engineering universities, the information security management is closer to the information and communication engineering major, computer science and technology major and the cryptography. Information security personnel in those colleges also focus on the technical level more.

As judicial institutions, the colleges should grasp the advantages in judicial research and combine the demand of information security major. So they introduce the computer crime case-method. First of all, among information security problems, the most extreme should be the computer crime. Therefore it's good for students to understand the nature and the importance of information security from this point of view. At the same time, law courses as compulsory courses in the judicial institutions have lay a good foundation of computer crime knowledge for students. Last but not least, the law laboratory, moot court and legal aid students team in colleges have provided a good platform for the computer crime case teaching.

3 THE CASE METHOD

3.1 *The case method*

The Case Method is a case-based teaching [1]. The Case is essentially putting forward a dilemma situation of education which has no specific solution. Teachers act as the designers and motivators who encourage students to take part in the discuss actively. This method is not the same as the traditional teaching methods. It transforms the actual real situation into cases which can be used by students to think, analyze and judge, promoting analyzing and solving ability of students. It puts theory into practice and adopts a way of inter-active questioning, promoting students' autonomous learning, cooperative learning and inquiry learning [2].

3.2 The case method of computer science

The emphasis of this paper lies in integrating the computer crime judicial analysis into the teaching of information security.

One of the important measures to study computer crime is the extraction of computer evidence which is also known as electronic evidences. Since electronic evidences involves all aspects of the computer system and Internet, the workers of recognizing and getting electronic evidences need to have a solid grounding in fundamental knowledge of computer technique and judicial theory. Thus the paper use evidences' generation, analysis, acquisition and storage as case to guide students to learn the related knowledge of information security and judiciary.

The case method introduces electronic evidences in the perspective of computer system, including many aspects, like tampering, exception or hidden files and data, malware, unauthorized access, remote control, information theft, E-mail and so on. Student utilizes software tool to compare changes in system to obtain evidence in the level of judiciary. By using tools, they can learn the operation mechanism of system in a more direct and clear way and learn the related principles from the bottom of computer. In the meantime, analyzing problems in the perspective of judiciary rather than technology can make students acquire complex knowledge and become inter-disciplinary talents.

4 THE DESIGN OF CASE METHOD

Taking the model of PDCA in management science as lessons to design the flow of the case method of computer science, it consists of six procedures: case selection, case implementation, evidence collection, evidence analysis, results commitment and discussion, effect evaluation. They are in order [3], move in cycles, go round and round and improve itself continuously. It is shown in the Figure 1.

4.1 The choice of teaching cases

Whether the cases are well chosen influences the final result of teaching directly. Therefore the cases that are close to real situations should be chosen so that students can consider and solve problems from a practical perspective. In the case of the computer crime, typical virus, Trojan horse virus and other rogue software should be chosen to simulate the real computer crime.

4.2 Case implementation

In the first phase, the teacher teaches the knowledge structure and key content. In the second phase, the

Figure 1. The frame of case method.

teacher sums up the cases after the case discussion and systematically teaches related knowledge according to the cases summed before; this case analysis and discussion-teaching pattern can avoide the limitation in traditional teaching methodology.

The scheme divides the simulation into five parts, which are attack precaution, attack implementation, protection, evidence obtaining of the crime spot, evidence analysis and result submitting. The students are grouped. Each group of students start gaining evidence in different scenarios or segments. At first students independently operate, get to know the usage, and then record the environment of the system, especially synchronous vulnerable data which are easy to lose, facilitating the comparison of evidence obtained after being attacked, recovery of the system and the conduction of different attacks to the main frame.

4.3 Evidence collection

Tools used for gaining evidence are tcpdump, Argus, NFRS, EnCase, tcpwrapper, sniffers, honeypot, Tripwires, Network monitor and so on. At this stage, crime spot should be protected and evidence should be gained. Students can collect evidence from the scene, protect physical evidence and other evidences such as seal of present computers, network facilities, codes on papers, CD-ROOM, USB flash disk and mobile devices [5].

4.4 Analysis of evidence

At this stage, students confirm attacks of virus and Trojan horse virus by comparing the data before and after. Analysis starts from the following two aspects: on one hand, system of the main frame needs to be analyzed, including operating system types, hidden partitions, and suspicious partitions. Through comparison, students can see if there is any traces of tampering. On the other hand, system data and network data also need to be analyzed. Use tools to analyze network connecting, data packets sending, firewall log data, and then the registry information and system starting items, and finally sums up all the evidence, utilizing the scientific method to examine and test the conclusion.

4.5 Results submission and discussion

Record the whole process in details. Work with group members to submit an electronic experiment report and attach own learning experience. Computer evidence gaining is also involved in judicial cognizance. It requires a complete set of standardized procedures and processes. Case-method cultivates students' rigorous research attitude and habit through assessing and supervising the evidence gained, broadens students' horizon and enlarges students' knowledge by providing them the chance to communicate with professionals in judicial apartment and public security organs.

4.6 Evaluation of effect

Examine students' proficiency in relevant knowledge to evaluate and sum up the result of the case method. And then improvement schemes and new goals would be set for getting into the next cycle.

5 EVALUATION OF CASE-METHOD

In order to understand promotion effect of case method on students' learning,the paper introduce the grey relational analysis to model analysis.

5.1 Grey relational analysis

The grey systemic analysis has several different methods according to different problems, grey relational analysis is one of them. Use grey correlation analysis to each subsystem, to seek numerical relationship among each subsystem or factors in the system [4]. In the process of system development, if the degree of synchronous changes between two factors is higher, the change trend is consistent, then you can think it has a bigger correlation degree. Concrete steps of gray correlation analysis:

1. To make the various factors comparable, and compare all factors in different dimension and different order of magnitude, it needs to process the raw data with non-dimensional and non-magnitude, to standardize it into data which are from 0 to 1.

2. In the computing of comparative sequence, it defines

$$x_i = \{x_i(1), x_i(2), ... x_i(l)\}, \quad i = 1, 2, ..., n \quad (1)$$

as the connection coefficients (the subsequence), and x_0 sequence as the mother sequence.

3. Correlation coefficient between the reference sequence and the connection coefficients at k time is:

$$\xi_i(k) = \frac{\Delta(\min) + \xi\Delta(\max)}{\Delta_{0i}(k) + \xi\Delta(\max)} \quad (2)$$

To weaken the influence of the maximum absolute differences due to excessive distortion, and improve the difference significance of comparative sequence at the same time, paper define ξ as the resolution factor, it values from 0 to 1, and 0.5 generally.

4. The number of the correlation coefficient is so many that make the information too scattered, so it is difficult to compare correlation. Therefore, paper set the correlation coefficient as one value, and then use its average as the reflection of relational degree.

So correlation coefficient between the reference sequence and the connection coefficients is:

$$r_{0i} = \frac{1}{l}\sum_{k=1}^{l} \xi_{0i}(k) \quad (3)$$

And it is also the comprehensive measures value of the i participating object.

Table 1. Statistical data about class teaching quality.

Setting	Class 1	Class 2	Class 3	Class 4	Class 5
x_0	8	9	7	3	5
x_1	7	8	6	5	5
x_2	9	9	8	4	4
x_3	8	9	7	2	5
x_4	8	9	5	2	4
x_5	6	7	5	4	4

Table 2. Standardization.

Setting	Class 1	Class 2	Class 3	Class 4	Class 5
x_0	0.889	1	0.778	0.333	0.556
x_1	0.875	1	0.75	0.625	0.625
x_2	1.	1	0.889	0.444	0.444
x_3	0.889	1	0.778	0.222	0.556
x_4	0.889	1	0.556	0.222	0.444
x_5	0.857	1	0.714	0.571	0.571

Table 3. Corresponding difference sequence.

Setting	Class 1	Class 2	Class 3	Class 4	Class 5	Min	Max
$\|x_0(k) - x_1(k)\|$	0.014	0	0.028	0.292	0.126	0	0.292
$\|x_0(k) - x_2(k)\|$	0.111	0	0.111	0.111	0.112	0	0.112
$\|x_0(k) - x_3(k)\|$	0.	0	0.	0.111	0.	0	0.111
$\|x_0(k) - x_4(k)\|$	0.	0	0.222	0.111	0.112	0	0.222
$\|x_0(k) - x_5(k)\|$	0.014	0	0.064	0.238	0.015	0	0.238

5.2 The effect assessment

According to the main contents which include teaching quality assessment, six indicators is chosen, x_0: the degree that case method is imported into courses, x_1: broadening horizon, x_2: refined and full content, appropriate depth and breadth, x_3: the desire to acquire knowledge, active class atmosphere, x_4: inspiring to think, x_5: developing quality, training ability.

The mother sequence is:

x_0 = {0.889, 1, 0.778, 0.333, 0.556}, each son sequence is shown in the graphs above.

Firstly, count the corresponding difference sequence graph.

Use the formula (2) with $\zeta = 0.5$, Max difference 0.292, Min difference 0.

Calculate the related coefficient $\xi_1(k)$ between compared sequence x_1 and referenced sequence x_0.

$\xi_1(k) = (0 + 0.292*0.5)/(0.014 + 0.292*0.5) = 0.9125$

$\xi_2(k) = 1$ $\xi_3(k) = 0.839$ $\xi_4(k) = 0.333$ $\xi_5(k) = 0.530$

With the same algorithm to calculate the related coefficient $\xi_1(k)$ between compared sequence x_2 and referenced sequence x_0

$\xi_1(k) = 0.568$, $\xi_2(k) = 1$, $\xi_3(k) = 0.568$, $\xi_4(k) = 0.568$, $\xi_5(k) = 0.567$

Then x_3 is: 1, 1, 1, 0.568, 1

x_4 is: 1, 1, 0.397, 0.568, 0.567

x_5 is: 0.9125, 1, 0.695, 0.380, 0.907

Calculate the association degree. Use the formula (3) to calculate the average of association degree of all numbers in the compared sequences.

$r_1 = (0.915 + 1 + 0.839 + 0.333 + 0.530)/5 = 0.7234$

$r_2 = 0.654$ $r_3 = 0.9136$ $r_4 = 0.7064$ $r_5 = 0.779$

From the data above: $r_3 > r_5 > r_1 > r_4 > r_2$. The related coefficient of r_3 is largest. Based on the survey result, the case method is most closed to the third indicator, namely the desire to acquire knowledge and active class atmosphere, it conforms to the previous expectations which can enhance the learning enthusiasm of students. The second closed indicator x_5: developing quality and training ability, which can be achieved by case-method combined with practice, developing students' practical ability.

6 CONCLUSION

Combining the characteristic of information security management in arts background. This passage applys the computer crime case teaching method to class, which improves teaching quality and is good for the cultivation of creative thinking and practical ability.

ACKNOWLEDGMENT

This research is supported by the research project of ministry of education (31540911205–2009093). and the education research of Zhongnan University of Economics and law (21433511304).

REFERENCES

[1] P.J. Mcwilliam.The Case Method of Instruction Teaching Application and Problem-Soloing Skills to Early Interventionists. Journal of Early Intervention 1992.

[2] Jennifer L. Goeke. A Preliminary Investigation of Prospective Teachers' Reasoning About Case Studies with Expert Commentary. Teacher Education and Special Education, 2008.

[3] Chris Argyris. Some Limitations of the Case Method: Experiences in a Management Development Program. Acad Manage Rev April 1, 1980 vol. 5 no. 2 291–298.

[4] C.L. Lin, J.L. Lin, T.C. Ko. Optimisation of the EDM Process Based on the Orthogonal Array with Fuzzy Logic and Grey Relational Analysis Method. The International Journal of Advanced Manufacturing Technology February 2002, Volume 19, Issue 4, pp 271–277.

[5] Richard. Computer Crime Investigation & Computer Forensics. Information Systems Security, Summer 97, Vol. 6 Issue 2, p56, 25p.

Computer, Intelligent Computing and Education Technology – Liu, Sung & Yao (Eds)
© 2014 Taylor & Francis Group, London, ISBN 978-1-138-02469-4

The target-oriented inquiry-discovery teaching model in course design assisted by computer

J.B. Zhang, J.W. Wang & X.Q. Xu
College of Mechanical Engineering, Tongling University, Tongling, P.R. China

ABSTRACT: For application-oriented talents, the mastery of Professional knowledge and skills and the application of computer-aided techniques are equally important. An inquiry-discovery teaching method is applied in the design curriculum which occupies an important position and plays a key role for training applicative talent the professional quality and computer application ability; its operation model is built based on target teaching method by classifying the learners and grating the teaching aims. The model is performed by designing planar-table at the thought of Bloom's objective theory, setting up studying groups including a specific number of students with different learning abilities, forming teaching team containing a quantity of teachers with various knowledge backgrounds, devising realistic meaning projects. The inquiry-discovery individualized teaching is carried out in specific situation, emphasizes the guiding function of studying group's leader, the subject position of group numbers and the guide of teachers, and significantly stimulate students' creative ideas and exploring consciousness, promotes the students to learn and discovery self for their abilities of cooperation innovation via computer technology. It is demonstrated that the inquiry-discovery teaching method is an exemplification of innovation for the training mechanism and teaching model in application-oriented college and university.

Keywords: computer-aided techniques; course design; inquiry-discovery teaching method; target teaching

1 GENERAL INTRODUCTION

The application of Computer-Aided Technology (CAT) markedly develops the techniques of manufacturing, greatly reduces the cycles of product design and production and realizes the requirements of large-scale products, high-speed and high-precision. CAT has become a core technology of modern manufacturing for transformation and development. In the process of the development of advanced manufacturing, the highly skilled personnel are an important constraint factors.[1–3] Therefore, in application-oriented colleges and universities, the students should be trained as applied talents, not only do who have solid expertise, superb professional competence, but also who comprehensively, profoundly understand CAT, roughly comprehend its basic principles, development model and actual application situation, to become usability engineers and technicians. Consequently, we always devote ourselves to the intergrading CAT with course design in daily teaching.

For engineering or technique professions, the practice teaching, e.g. course design, is an important part of the training project for applicative talents; its role is more important for the students in accumulating engineering experience and innovating than that of the theory teaching. However, there are still a lot of imperfections in the practice teaching in our country at present: teaching method is single, organizing form is very mechanical; course content is outmoded; performance appraisal relies excessively on exam score, etc. In brief, the existed practice teaching is out of step with the times, less practical applications and creativity against the students' practical abilities and innovative capabilities.[4,5]

It has been an important issue of the teaching reform how to strengthen the students' innovative trainings and exercises; improve their engineering accomplishment and practical abilities. In this paper, based on the target teaching theory, an Inquiry-Discovery Teaching Method (IDTM) is established to bring the relative individualized education into effect by classifying course targets and grading teaching objects. IDTM has successfully been carried out in the teaching practices of course design, plays positive roles in reaching the teaching goals. IDTM provides a innovative reference of educational mechanism for the applied talents in the application-oriented universities.

2 DESIGN TEACHING GOALS

Target teaching is a teacher-led, goal-oriented, student-centered teaching method, it can the

Table 1. The multi-parameter two-dimensional chart of target taxonomy for *Processing design aided by computer for asynchronous hot rolling steel plate.*

| Cognitive process | Knowledge and technology system | | | |
| | A. of the course | B. of related courses | C. of the discipline | D. of related discipline |
	Theories and techniques of synchronous rolling, numerical simulation and hot rolling	Theory of plastic deformation, roll forming, and plastic mechanics	CAT of the Office AUTOCAD, UG or Proe, Deform and Matlab	Theories and techniques of experimental design and data analysis, numerical calculation, and optimized design
1. Memory	A1, I, a	B1, I, a	C1, I, a	D1, II, b
2. Compredend	A2, I, a	B2, II, a	C2, I, a	D2, II, b
3. Apply	A3, I, a	B3, II, b	C3, I, a	D3, II, b
4. Analyze	A4, I, a	B4, II, b	C4, II, a	D4, III, c
5. Estimate	A5, II, b	B5, II, b	C5, II, a	D5, III, c
6. Innovate	A6, II, b	B6, III, c	C6, II, b	D6, III, c

*The element "C6, II, b" in the table means that teaching goals C6 is class II, should be achieve by object of grade b or higher, and so on.

farthest mobilize students' enthusiasm and initiative, and promote effectively teaching objectives.[6] We delve into target teaching theory; propose an Individual Target Teaching Method (ITTM) by decomposing course knowledge, classifying teaching target and grading teaching object. Its teaching theories, teaching strategies and implementing model have all been illustrated in another article, not repeated here. The curriculum design is a crucial course for the students to independently investigate the questions and learn new knowledge by using their professional knowledge, abundant application and rich experience of CAT. The students with different levels of learning ability can fully train and exercise, and severally receive appropriate harvest in this process. On the basis of the relative theory and technology, a multi-parameter two-dimensional chart of target taxonomy should be filled for ITTM. For example, Table 1 is a well exemplification of target taxonomy chart of the course design named *Processing design aided by computer for asynchronous hot rolling steel plate.* As the base of the chart, ITTM will be carried out to better facilitate IDTM.

IDTM are whether students can gain new knowledge, establish their ways of thinking and exercise their creation in the process of solving problems or not.[7] The conventional inquiry teaching or discovery teaching emphasizes the student-centered, teacher-led policy, focusing on the interaction of both teachers and students.

To fit in with the characteristics of design course assisted by computer, we perfect that policy as mentioned above; creatively present a strategy of "triad" consisting of "member-centered, leader-led and teacher-guided". That is to say, relying on the purpose of course, the students are divided into a few of design groups at the same quantity as the research topic in the design course. A leader is responsible for the organization of the inquiry study in one group; its members work in common, initiatively carry out inner exchange and cooperation to solve the design problems; the teachers from the teaching team help the students relieve their confusion not to comprehend themselves. So, the students and teachers interactively accomplish the teaching activities in IDTM.

3 THE MODE OF INQUIRY DISCOVERY TEACHING

The ideas of Inquiry teaching and discovery teaching are strongly advocated, developed by Dewey and Bruner, have gradually become modern teaching models, widely used in the world education. Discovery is a kind of creation of active learning, and is a kind of creative self-study; inquiry is to research problem for solutions. The concerns of

3.1 *Designing situational research topics*

Interest is regarded as the best teacher and the strongest spiritual motivation for the active learning and self-exploration. The interest of research topics is a crucial factor, which determines if the students achieved innovation and form creative consciousness or not. Taking the actual situation as a starting point to the course design, we simulate the class teaching as an actual production; design some problems of the course as virtual engineering technical problems or actual production needs. Then, the teaching problems convert into engineering requirements or technical objectives, the students transform into engineers, the teachers change into technical directors or enterprise customers. For example, in the design course of *processing design aided by computer for asynchronous hot rolling steel plate*, combined with the engineering situation and the principle of relationship of theory to practice, a series of engineering practice situational topics is devised as showing below:

1. *How does the ratio of roll velocity affect the force of asynchronous hot-rolling plate?*
2. *How does the ratio of roll velocity affect the shape of asynchronous hot-rolling plate?*
3. *How does the coefficient of friction affect the force of asynchronous hot-rolling plate?*
4. *How does the coefficient of friction affect the shape of asynchronous hot-rolling plate?*
5. *How does the reduction in thickness affect the force of asynchronous hot-rolling plate?*
6. *How does the reduction in thickness affect the shape of asynchronous hot-rolling plate?*

And so on.

A practical complicated processing problem of asynchronous hot rolling plate is decomposed into several interrelated design issues, each of which contains a wealth of expertise, production technology, field experience and professional disciplines associated with the theory and technology. The broad space and gigantic dynamic force will provide every one of the students with a desire of "becoming a good engineer".

3.2 *Establishing design groups*

In recent years, there is a new teaching pattern named "design thinking education and practice" in international higher education, which stresses that the student groups are the innovation main bodies. The "student team" is taken as the form of innovative talent cultivation, the students and teachers together study. This model again called "the syndicate law" is a companion learning method already proven feasible and practical.[8] In view of the ideas of "production is the production team, business efficiency is the team effectiveness, innovation is the team innovation", one class is divided into some design groups been in proportion to the rate of student at different levels, to cultivate the students concept of cooperative learning and cooperation innovation. The quantity of design groups is equal to that of design topics for ITTM. The leader of one study group is responsible for organizing the crew to carry out the course design via CAT.

3.3 *Constructing integrated instructor team*

IDTM requires the students to carry around the study topics, neatly use their theory and technology to explore issues, gain knowledge and develop skills. Therefore, their needs are diverse and mutative, not well served by one teacher or two. It is a good way to establish an interdisciplinary instructor team, which is composed of a few of teachers with different learning experiences and knowledge backgrounds. The team must have a certain academic level, understanding academic frontiers, and have an innovative spirit and dedication to the instructors of the design group. All members of the instructor team take collectively part in lesson preparation and communicate with group members face to face in classroom, or through various interactive tools as E-mail, BBS, Chartroom, Blog, Wiki, WeChat, and so on, outside classroom.

3.4 *Conducting inquiry discovery teaching*

3.4.1 *Teachers creating production situations and designing engineering problems*

By use of simulation scenarios method, the teachers should creates a virtual scenario of hot rolling plate, and design a group of gradient level engineering problems, from the primary purpose of course design and the actual situations of students. The interest of the stimulated problems must induce the students to explore the design issues.[9] During the teaching of the course design as mentioned above, the digital virtual design room of school models a engineer studio of rolling mill, the design work simulates a process development study, the students play the engineers and the teacher act as chief engineer. The "chief engineer" first proposes the following technical problems:

1. *Now, what is the techno-economic indicator of some product in our mill, does it need improvement?*
2. *What are the advantages of asynchronous rolling technology, what constraints to its application?*
3. *Do we have the possibility, capability to improvement of asynchronous rolling?*
4. *How will you get the optimal parameters of asynchronous hot rolling processing for a product?*
5. *What will your result be, will it be practicable?*

At this time, the adventurous psychologies of the "engineers" are inspired by nature so that they are eager to want to do. Next, leaves enough time for the "engineers" to think about: What should I do? What can I do? How to do? The students are impatient to begin. In the last, the "chief engineer" shows them the research topics of design course timely; clear the research contents and objectives, and organizes the design groups to claim their design topics.

In the good learning environment set up particularly, the students must participate in the teaching process in a relaxed and happy mood, actively learn and creatively complete their "missions".

3.4.2 Students exploring issues and discovery learning

The research and exploration of design groups is a key link of inquiry discovery teaching. After claiming the design topics, the head of design group organizes the other members to analyze the design and collect information, and formulate this group research tasks and goals. Division as well as cooperation is an important prerequisite for success in teamwork innovations. The specific items of course design are stipulated for the groups and assigned individually to each member from his or her capability. Every one of the members shoulders responsibility for the completion of the matter assigned with other members collaboration. As a result, one design group completes its research work, achieves "1 + 1 > 2" team effect.

3.4.3 Teachers guiding students in accordance with their aptitudes

During the design groups plan their matters of design course, the teachers opportunely grasp the group division of labor, require that each member should take on the right amount of design jobs with adaptive difficulty adapting to her or his level of learning capacity. In this case, everyone must work hard to achieve their own group project; everyone must take some revolutionary exercise for the purpose of innovation.

On the other hand, in the discovery processes of student, the instructors utilize different types of strategy to guide different levels of object expressed by the multi-parameter two-dimensional chart of target taxonomy. The distinguishing demands on the relative knowledge and technology of discipline and specialty should be made to the personal study. The higher the learning level of one student is, the higher her or his demands on difficulty of designing are, and the more she or he is widely and deeply instructed. So, the policy of personalized guidance in ITTM is adequately practiced in the course design.

3.4.4 Teachers and students exchanging and mutually assessing

After the members have completed their tasks or the groups have finished their research topics, some discusses and appraisements within the internal members of design group are carried out under the organizations of their head; next, some communions and assessments within the external heads of design group are conducted under the leadership of teacher. In terms of their design research outcomes, every one of the groups and its leader are fully estimated on their performances; meanwhile, according to their study results, every one of the members are impartially evaluated on her or his study achievements. Based on that, every member accomplishes a study report on her or his own work, and every head presents a synthesis report on her or his group work. The teaching links described above will systematically exercise the metacognitive abilities and upgrade their discovery capabilities of student.

3.4.5 Instructor team scientifically evaluating and fairly assessing

In the following design oral defense organized by instructor team, the respondent of group briefly introduces the group work and replies the questioners. At this time, the others will be permit to consummate their group view. Each instructor independently assesses the students based on the work of work organization, communication expression, knowledge level and learning innovation, and form tutor evaluation report. Finally, the instructor team objectively and impartially examines and scores each student on her or his comprehensive characters of study report, synthesis report and tutor evaluation report.

4 SUMMARIES

The course design via CAT is an important leaning step for the students to directly train engineering practice skills and explore innovation, as well as a vital component of applied talent training scheme. We introduce the improved inquiry teaching method and discovery teaching method into practice teaching. An IDTM is successfully built up as the primary teaching way of course based on target teaching theory. It carries out the policy of classifying course targets, grading teaching objects and implying ITTM. The many years' practices show that the IDTM presented in this paper is able to efficiently improve the quality of course design, to evidently boost the personal abilities. It also indicates an alternative path to the reform and innovation of training model of applicative talent in application-oriented colleges and university.

ACKNOWLEDGMENTS

This work is sponsored by Education Department of Anhui Province ender grant No. 20101015 and Tongling University under grant No. JY10003.

Their advice and financial support are gratefully acknowledged.

REFERENCES

[1] Y.B. Son, Y.Y. Wang. A computer aided instruction (CAI) system CFFP [J]. Journal of Harbin Institute of Technology, 1995, 27(4): 39–44.
[2] H.Y. Xue, Y. Hong, C.X. Yang. The practice of the organic chemistry network aided instruction [J]. Journal of Science of Teachers' College and University, 2012, 32(5): 105–107.
[3] H.B. Zhao, J.Y. Wang, M. Zhang. A novel CAPP system based on SML for variant design of process planning [J]. Journal of Wuhan University of Technology, 2006(3): 820–823.
[4] Y. Zhang. Key issues exploration of personnel training of computer assistant design and manufacturing specialty in higher vocational colleges [J]. Journal of Guang Dong Communications Polytechnuc, 2012, 12(2): 90–94.
[5] W.z. Yang, D.L. Zhou, P. Zhang, etc. Engineering practice teaching innovative in research universities [J]. Journal of Higher Education, 2012, 29(4): 39–41.
[6] K.D. Zhong. Explore on teaching mode of university basic computer courses based on "objective teaching" theory [J]. China University Teaching, 2008(8): 38–39.
[7] T.J. Zhi. From Discovery Teaching to Project-Learning [J]. Theory and Practice of Education, 2002, 22(1): 43–46.
[8] X.Z. Liao, H. Jiang. Design thinking: students' interdisciplinary teamwork innovation [J]. Modern Communication (Journal of Communication University of China), 2011(5): 127–130.
[9] Z.X. Huan, X.L. Yi. The Application of the Scenario-based Teaching in Economic Law Course [J]. Journal of Central South University of Forestry & Technology (Social Sciences), 2011, 5(6): 185–187.

Computer, Intelligent Computing and Education Technology – Liu, Sung & Yao (Eds)
© 2014 Taylor & Francis Group, London, ISBN 978-1-138-02469-4

Cloud sharing technology based on android platform

Zheng-Rong Lei, Ya-Wu Xu & Yang Shi
Laboratory Center and Network and Modern Educational Technology Center, Guangzhou University,
Guangzhou, Guangdong, China

ABSTRACT: This paper describes the realization of the principle of cloud-sharing technology based on Android platform, detailing its implementation process through an example. Android client transfer contacts and files on phone with Java server which establishing the communication mechanism of Socket, in order to achieve cloud sharing of human and file resources between the Android client.

Keywords: cloud sharing; android client; Java server; contacts; files

1 GOALS

With the popularity of smart phones and wireless networks, more and more people use smart phone applications (APPs) such as QQ, Weibo, and so on to chat or read news. Although those APPs has been far exceeded the current PC, laptops, or other computer equipment programs in mobility and user experience, are not as convenient as computer in the information exchange and resource sharing. Therefore, this paper introduces an Android platform based on cloud sharing technology to achieve information exchange and resource sharing between Android phones.

2 IMPLEMENTATION PRINCIPLES

Through this cloud sharing technology platform, users will be able to share mobile phone stored contacts resources with other Android users whenever and wherever possible. As a C/S architecture based platform, the Android APP, client, achieves interactive function to share mobile phone contacts and exchange document resources as UI; while Java server accepts user requests, to process input and output data, and saves user's file resources. The back-end MySQL Database stores Cloud sharing user information.

The realization principle to achieve contacts and documents sharing is: establishing a Socket connection between Android client and Java server,

Figure 1.

Android client program encapsulates receivers' user name. contacts, and files into objects and sends to server via socket output stream Then Android receiver program receives from the Android sending end to share contacts and file resources from the server through the socket input stream.

3 TECHNOLOGY ROUTE

3.1 *Defining several serialized JavaBean objects in Java server and Android client, respectively, to descript transmission content, transmission object types and shared users*

3.1.1 *Mes.java: Defining the transmission content*
private ArrayList<String> exname = new ArrayList<String>();//Names of contacts
private ArrayList<String> exnum = new ArrayList<String>();//Phone numbers of contacts
private ArrayList<String> filename = new ArrayList<String>();//Document name

3.1.2 *TranObjectType: Defining the transport object types*
public enum TranObjectType
{

    EXCON, //contacts
    EXFILE, // received files
    WANTEXFILE, // send Files

}

3.1.3 *TranObject.java: Shared object types and users*
private TranObjectType type;// shared object types
private int fromUser;// from which user
private int toUser;// sending which user

3.2 Defining multi-thread Java server-side mechanism to handle multiple concurrent requests such as connection and input & output data streams

Multi-threaded multi-user concurrent logon is not a very simple question because when it relevant to critical resources, thread synchronization is the key. So lock mechanism are applied in ObejcetOutput-Stream classes and critical resources related code. The specific implementation process explained as following: server instantiates input and output Thread objects for each logged-on user and outputs Thread objects into a Map. When a message is required to a particular user, the server gets corresponding output Thread from Map and sends messages to the client.

```
private Socket socket = null;
private InputThread in;
private OutputThread out;
private OutputThreadMap map;
public SocketTask(Socket socket) {
        this.socket = socket;
        map = OutputThreadMap.getInstance();
}
public void run(){
// From which the user then instantiate write the
message thread, the writing thread of correspond-
ing user is stored in the map buffer
out=new OutputThread(socket,map);
        in=new InputThread(socket,out, map);//
        Then instantiate reading message thread
        out.setStart(true);
        in.setStart(true);
        in.start();
        out.start();
}
```

3.3 Defining methods of sending and receiving shared contacts and files in Android client classes

3.3.1 Through the Socket data output stream, the Android client send shared contact information to the Java server

```
final String name[] = (String[]) mContactsName.
toArray (new String[mContactsName.size()]);
ArayList<String>exname=newArrayList<String>
();
ArrayList<String>exnum=new ArayList<String>();
Client client = application.getClient();
ClientOutputThread    out    =    clent.getClient
OuputThread();
Mes m=new Mes("excon");
m.setexname(exname);
m.setexnum(exnum);
TranObject<Mes>  o  =  new  TranObject<Mes>
(TranObjectType.EXCON);
o.setFromUser(myaccount);
```

```
o.setToUser(dfaccount);
o.setObject(m);
out.setMsg(o);
```

3.3.2 Through the Socket data output stream, the Android client send shared files to the Java server

```
final String name[] = (String[])filename.toArray(new
String[filename.size()]);
ArrayList<String>  chosefile  =  new  ArayList
<String>();
Client client=application.getClient();
ClientOutputThread    out=client.getClientOutput
Thread();
Mes m=new Mes("excon");
m.setfilelist(chosefile);
TranObject<Mes>  o  =  new  TranObject<Mes>
(TranObjectType.WANTEXFILE);
o.setFromUser(myaccount);
o.setToUser(dfuser);
o.setObject(m);
out.setMsg(o);
```

3.3.3 Through the Socket data input stream, the Android client receive shared contacts from the Java server

```
final String name[] = (String[])exname.toArray(new
String[exname.size()]);
ArrayList<String>        chosenname        =        new
ArayList<String>();
ArrayList<String> chosennum = new ArayList<
String>();
Client client = application.getClient();
ClientOutputThread out = clent.getClientOutput
Thread();
Mes m = new Mes("msgback");
m.settype("someconok");
m.setexname(chosenname);
TranObject<Mes>  o  =  new  TranObject<Mes>
(TranObjectType.MSGBACK);
o.setFromUser(sender);
o.setObject(m);
out.setMsg(o);
```

3.3.4 Through the Socket data input stream, the Android client receive shared files from the Java server

```
final String name[] = (String[])exfile.toArray(new
String[exfile.size()]);
Client client = application.getClient();
ClientOutputThread out = clent.getClientOutput
Thread();
Mes m = new Mes("excon");
m.settype("somefileok");
m.setfilelist(chosenfile);
TranObject<Mes>o=newTranObject<Mes>(Tran-
ObjectType.EXFILE);
o.setFromUser(sender);
```

```
o.setToUser(receiver);
o.setObject(m);
out.setMsg(o);
```

4 PROSPECTS

In the current era of information explosion, how-ever, each of us only has very limited resources. If everyone is willing to share their useful resources with others, our life will be more convenient unquestionable Through cloud sharing platform introduced by this paper, we can use an Android phone as network disk storage to backup user Contacts and documentation resources. Through the cloud sharing technology to its network of resources and file share resources with other users, so between users can quickly and easily sharing resources, which is PC and notebook unmatched advantages. In the near future, this technology and promotion of information exchange will change the way we present the Internet, and has broad application prospects.

REFERENCES

[1] Huang Yong-mei, Wu Chun-yu and Wang Ai. "The Co-construction and Sharing of Information Resources under the 'Cloud Sharing' Pattern." Sci-Tech Information Development & Economy 4 (2013): 111–112.
[2] Li Chunlan, Deng Zhonghua. "Research on Interactive Sharing Patterns about Cloud Computing Resources." Journal of Information Resources Management 1 (2012): 12–18.
[3] Zhao Guang-ming, Zhu Yong and Jia Hua-wei. "Application and promotion of "campus cloud share" services platform." Internet of things technologies 3.7 (2013): 87–89.
[4] Wu, Xiaoxin, et al. "Composable io: A novel resource sharing platform in personal clouds." Cloud Computing. Springer Berlin Heidelberg, 2009. 232–242.
[5] Sundareswaran, Smitha, Anna Squicciarini, and Dan Lin. "Ensuring distributed accountability for data sharing in the cloud." Dependable and Secure Computing, IEEE Transactions on 9.4 (2012): 556–568.
[6] Sundareswaran, Smitha, Anna Squicciarini, and Dan Lin. "Ensuring distributed accountability for data sharing in the cloud." Dependable and Secure Computing, IEEE Transactions on 9.4 (2012): 556–568.

Computer, Intelligent Computing and Education Technology – Liu, Sung & Yao (Eds)
© 2014 Taylor & Francis Group, London, ISBN 978-1-138-02469-4

Design and implementation of a SOA-based health management system

H. Wang, Y.L. Wu & F. Wu
Department of Information, The 309th Hospital of PLA, Beijing, China

ABSTRACT: To improve health condition of surrounding residents, based on service-oriented architecture, the 309th Hospital uses a unified protocol, standardized data conversion, application of modern information network technology and the latest health management theory, designs and implements health management information system based on the health records. Data center is built based on the hospital's existing information network infrastructure to form individual-centered health records by integrating data from various sources, which improves resident' health and quality of life and reduces the incidence of chronic disease.

Keywords: health management; service oriented architecture; health record; data center

1 INTRODUCTION

Health management is a personalized health affairs management on the basis of personal health records, and it is built with modern medicine and information management technology. Using existing resources and guiding clients change the irrational style of life, bad behavior and habits, health management can provide comprehensive health care services to clients to give effective intervention to chronic disease risk factors, and to change health care treatment from passive to active preventive in order to achieve the restoration of health.

With the continuous development of health management, health management information system has become an essential foundation. There are currently more than 60 international medical expert systems based on personal health records[1] (Personal Health Record, PHR), Google Health platform[2] and Microsoft HealthVault network platform[3] are both online PHRs. Google health platform provides third-party applications from the electronic health records and give user free management; Microsoft's HealthVault network platform has two types of users for doctors and patients, provides five services which are keep fit, lose weight, manage blood pressure, family health and emergency management, allows users to monitor and manage health information of his family members, and provides online tools to connect third-party alternative services.

To improve health condition of surrounding residents, based on service-oriented architecture, the 309th Hospital uses a unified protocol, standardized Web Service is a software system designed to support interoperable machine-to-machine interaction over a network. It has an interface described in a machine-processable format (specifically WSDL). Other systems interact with the Web service in a manner prescribed by its description using SOAP messages, typically conveyed using HTTP with an XMLserialization in conjunction with other Web-related standards. This paper uses web service technology to define a set of health-related business logic services which can be remotely invoked to make data from hospital and affiliated medical institutions can be accessed openly to the remote user in a unified way.data conversion, application of modern information network technology and the latest health management theory, designs and implements health management information system based on the health records. Data center is built based on the hospital's existing information network infrastructure to form individual-centered health records by integrating data from various sources, which improves resident' health and quality of life and reduces the incidence of chronic disease.

2 RELATED TECHNOLOGY

This section briefly describes related technologies involved in this paper, including personal main index technology, Web Service technology, and SOA (Service Oriented Architecture) technology.

2.1 Enterprise master patient index

EMPI (Enterprise Master Patient Index) is standards following IHE specification used across multiple medical institutions or health care systems to associate the same patient information. In the regional medical information sharing process, various medical institutions don't use unified application system, so the same patient in different medical institutions may have different identification information which resulting in unnecessary waste of resources and cost. EMPI's role is to associate different medical institutions with different information that identifies the same patient to build the foundation for regional health information sharing.

2.2 Web service

Web Service is a software system designed to support interoperable machine-to-machine interaction over a network. It has an interface described in a machine-processable format (specifically WSDL). Other systems interact with the Web service in a manner prescribed by its description using SOAP messages, typically conveyed using HTTP with an XMLserialization in conjunction with other Web-related standards. This paper uses web service technology to define a set of health-related business logic services which can be remotely invoked to make data from hospital and affiliated medical institutions can be accessed openly to the remote user in a unified way.

2.3 SOA

Service-Oriented Architecture (SOA) is a software design and software architecture design pattern based on discrete pieces of software providing application functionality as services to other applications. This is known as Service-orientation. It is independent of any vendor, product or technology. The health management information system in this paper is designed and developed using SOA principles to achieve cross-platform, loosely coupled, and scalable features.

3 DESIGN

3.1 Design principles

Supplemented by personal health self-management, doctors' health portal and management decision support and following the principle which is sustainable development of health management information, the health management information system in this paper uses technologies and concepts such as personal main index, service-oriented architecture and Web Service throughout the user's main health management to provide users with comprehensive health management services and efficient health management platform. In the design and implementation process the system should follow these principles:

– Security. Use strict authentication and auditing, encrypt data to achieve the security of the Internet data transmission (such as VPN, SSL), and unify management of user and permission.
– Service-Oriented Architecture (SOA). Service-oriented architecture is used among the various modules design which can effectively respond to future changes in health management information system back-end database. Through non-invasive integration technology and the use of open architecture, we can extend the promotion easily.
– Normative standards. Follow national standards and health industry standards, learn foreign mature standard in data exchange and integration, and comply with HL7, IHE, CDA and other standards.
– Efficiency. The amount of data for each health care system is enormous, high-speed hardware and networks are configured and data processing is optimized to make health profile data processing flow effectively.

3.2 Network topology

The network topology of health management information system is shown in Figure 1. A unified health management gateway server takes interfaces of HIS database and physical examination system as a data source, and extracts health information to health management database center. Doctors and health ordinary users can access administration portal via the network, and system administrators can perform system administration and configuration through the management workstation.

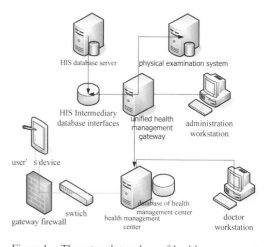

Figure 1. The network topology of health management information system.

278

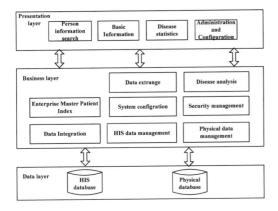

Figure 2. Software architecture.

Figure 3. Shared health management platform.

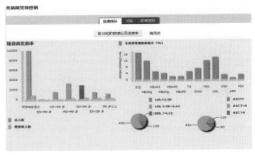

Figure 4. Health analysis and statistics module.

3.3 *Software architecture*

The software architecture shown in Figure 2.

The software architecture is defined as client server architecture that makes the user interface, data storage, data access, and functional process logic maintained and developed as independent modules.

The data layer contains database management functions. Its purpose is to optimize data from HIS database and physical database without having to result to the usage of proprietary database management system languages. This layer makes sure that the data is consistent throughout the environment with features like data locking, replication, and consistency.

The business logic tier provides ability for providing health management functions among heterogeneous applications via web services. The business logic of the system is packaged as web services, which provides a common way to operate data and business logic functions, and finally provides mobile and cross-platform ability.

The presentation layer presents data to the users and is a unified portal where users will get access the data within the system. All health management system follows a unified system of standards and information security technology. This layer calls the web services, and then presents the results to the user with the standard SOAP protocol.

3.4 *Implementation*

The health manage system in this paper is developed based on J2EE (Java 2 Platform, Enterprise Edition). J2EE is a Java platform designed for the mainframe-scale computing typical of large enterprises. Sun Microsystems (together with industry partners such as IBM) designed J2EE to simplify application development in a thin clienttiered environment. J2EE simplifies application development and decreases the need for programming and programmer training by creating standardized, reusable modular components and by enabling the tier to handle many aspects of programming automatically.

Figure 3 shows the interface of shared health management platform that integrates patient medical record, exam information and laboratory information to provide the overall show of the health information. Figure 4 is the interface of statistical analysis of the health management system, which makes health analysis and statistics based on the data center providing a bar chart and pie chart styles to show the abnormal visual indicators, ranking and other factors.

4 SUMMARIES

By implementing the above functions, our hospital has built a health management system based on hospital's existing information systems, and has changed the status quo "heavy medical treatment, light prevention". The system will extend health management services from the hospital to surrounding residents and reduce their health risk factors to improve the health of our hospital management level and reduce incidence of chronic diseases.

The system can also make contribute to the control of chronic disease development which indirectly enhance the quality of life of the surrounding residents and reduce medical expenses.

REFERENCES

[1]. AHIMA e—HIM Personal Health Record Work Group. The Role of the Personal Health Record in the HER f J 1. Journal of AHIMA, 2005, 7: 64A.

[2]. Google Inc. Google Health Team[S/OL]. 2008-05-20. https://www.google.com/healtlr/.

[3]. Microsoft.Microsoft Healthcare Solution Team [S/OL]. 2009-04-01. http://www.heahhvauh.com/personal/index.htm1.

[4]. Newcomer Eric, Lomow Greg. Understanding SOA with Web Services. Addison Wesley, 2005.

Computer, Intelligent Computing and Education Technology – Liu, Sung & Yao (Eds)
© *2014 Taylor & Francis Group, London, ISBN 978-1-138-02469-4*

Study on Web-based learning of SNS platform based on six degree of separation

Z.M. Zhang

Yangtze Normal College of Education and Science, Chongqing, China

ABSTRACT: In the wake of the rapid internet development and on the advent of network era, Web 2.0 is widely applied to internet and network is developing an increasingly close relationship with study and life. As one of the important means in Web 2.0 era, SNS has played a vital role in the community activities from simple social interaction and game to interest-themed learning since 2003. This dissertation is aimed at analyzing the role of SNS platform in the learning process based on the unit of circle and the interest-driven learning in the hope of exploiting the advantage of circle and teaching optimization.

Keywords: web-based learning; model; circle; SNS

1 SOCIAL NETWORKING SERVICE

SNS, the abbreviation for social networking service, refers to social network community, namely, the networking of social relationship. It moves social circles in real life to internet and establishes self-owned social circles.

As another important means of Web 2.0 after Blog, Rss, Tag and Wiki, SNS alters people's modes of working, learning and life, as it penetrates every aspect of social life. SNS, the abbreviation for social networking service, refers to social network community, namely, the networking of social relationship. It moves social circles in real life to internet and establishes self-owned social circles. SNS is the network constructed according to the theoretical model of Six Degrees of Separation, and the websites offering the services such as SNS friend-making to students in campus are campus SNS websites. Since March 2003, SNS website has emerged in the United States and witnessed a rapid spread across the North of the United States in five months. In China, SNS was specially designed for the internal communication of special industries or groups, with large SNS website focusing on college students. Since the end of 2005, a variety of campus social networking websites imitating Facebook have sprung up, such as www.renren.com, www.kaixin001.com, and www.douban.com.

2 SIX DEGREES OF SEPARATION

Six Degrees of Separation was established in 1967 by Stanley Milgram (1934–1984), professor of Psychology from Harvard University. [1] Six degrees of separation means that everyone and everything is six or fewer steps away, by way of introduction, from any other person in the world. [2] According to six degrees of separation, everyone's social circle keeps expanding into a large network, which proves to be the early understanding of social networking. Afterwards, in accordance with this theory, someone established internet service for social networking so as to expand social networking through a friend of a friend. This is the so-called SNS. [3]

SNS is the network constructed according to the theoretical models of Six Degrees of Separation, and the websites offering the services such as SNS friend-making to students in campus are campus SNS websites. Since March 2003, SNS website has emerged in the United States and witnessed a rapid spread across the North of the United States in five months. In China, SNS was specially designed for the internal communication of special industries or groups, with large SNS websites focusing on college students. [4]

3 PLATFORM APPLICATION STRATEGY

Competitive learning turns out to be an obstacle of collaborative learning. SNS environment can eliminate the negative factors such as pressure, anxiety and nervousness, contributing to the relaxing and happy mood during the collaborative learning between teachers and students as well as students. The learning in SNS environment can increase user stickiness and improve teaching interaction.

3.1 Revolve around teaching objective and clear topic to establish collaborative learning team

Teachers will determine the teaching objectives and learning contents and work out the learning topic according to the degree of learning, and then establish collaborative learning team in light of the knowledge and student's characteristic information that may be involved in this topic. Having determined the learning topic, teachers should raise questions on the basis of students' interests as well as provide leaning resources and the guidance of learning methods for students with greatest efforts. This is aimed at making sure that the members of collaborative team are capable of describing personal experience, event, impression and feeling according to requirements, writing an essay in light of ordinary topic or outline, as well as thinking and doing exercise in a positive manner based on the immersion in varieties of real scenarios. Only by doing this, will students be able to improve their understanding in the process of emotional integration, viewpoint collision, and wisdom integration, and then to master the basic knowledge, methods and skills of writing. Therefore, SNS can be applied to making up for the deficiencies of traditional writing teaching, arousing student's subject consciousness and sense of participation, and expanding the channel and platform for student's information exchange to enrich their thoughts and improve their writing skills and expression abilities.

3.2 Teacher's monitoring, inter-group exchange and learning optimization

Groups should address the problems in SNS by dint of leaning resources and the rich network resources, and meanwhile, teachers need to monitor, organize and guide the process so as to ensure the successful fulfillment of tasks. This will contribute to fostering strengths and circumventing weaknesses as well as to achieving the complementation of advantages. Considering that SNS integrates text, image, audio and video, group members are supposed to use appropriate media for learning. In study, exchange always plays an important role, with inter-group exchange being accompanied by problem-solving process. Due to the openness of SNS, students can use other group's solutions for references at will to inspire themselves and then achieve optimization effect.

3.3 Learning conclusion and reflection, and teacher's evaluation

SNS will record the learning process of all groups, and teachers will not only evaluate the learning process of each group to present some opinions and suggestions, but also summarize and assess problem-solving process. Meanwhile, teachers will organize all groups to reflect on the collaborative learning process, asking students to write their learning insights in SNS. Then, teachers will judge whether the teaching objective is attained according to the performance, achievement report, final solution and learning insights of all groups. If it is attained, the learning will stop and the experience will be summarized. Otherwise, learning should be restarted, and meanwhile, efforts should be spent in reflecting on the failure to achieve teaching objective to provide references for the restart of learning.

4 PLATFORM DESIGN

4.1 Model structure [5]

Model structure consists of three modules, namely, teacher, student, and group community. Teacher space is intended for teaching resources, such as teaching calendar and software. Student space is designed for learning journal and related leaning management, and group community is

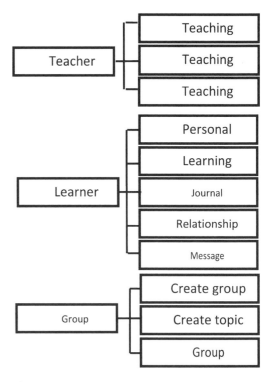

Figure 1.

aimed at exchanging and creating new topic for the discussion and research between teachers and students as well as between students.

4.2 Platform analysis

The fact shows that SNS is more striking in the form of Web 2.0, and campus SNS becomes overwhelmingly prevalent. College students establish a nearly real relationship in virtual space by dint of this platform, where they build not only a circle for the exchange between teachers and students as well as between students, but also a photographic platform for teaching exchange based on the teaching objective. The members in the circle often establish interest-centred resources after having determined a topic. In the circle, teachers should serve not only as a guide and a resource builder to upload relevant teaching resources according to platform characteristics but also as a communicator equaling other members so as to achieve the objective of teaching optimization.

Facing rich internet resources and mass information, students will be prone to cyberspace phenomenon especially in web-based learning process. The course circle established by SNS platform can engage students in pre-class learning, in-class learning, after-class learning, and update resources constantly to keep up with the times by dint of self-owned advantages in accordance with the policies of educational management department and educational research development as well as student's characteristics. This not only consists with actual teaching but also contributes to an easy update. At present, nearly every student has an internet-connected computer that is conducive to flexible and convenient learning. Thus, in study, the students will be sure to love the circle that is applicable to the present time facing the rapid update of computer software and hardware, textbooks, and teaching concept and a variety of different teaching methods, as well as based on the starting point of interest, the prerequisite of real identity, the objective of resource sharing and teaching, and the joy of friends making.

5 CONCLUSIONS

At present, SNS's application focuses primarily on game and friends making in China and only stays at preliminary development stage in learning, whereas SNS will show more advantages in future teaching and learning due to its outstanding characteristics. SNS learning mode is favorable for the fulfillment of learning tasks and able to yield twice the result with half of the effort by moving traditional collaborative learning to internet.

REFERENCES

[1] Yang Xiangtian, Wu Bin, Zhang Jun, Yin Jiao, Jin Chang. Study on the Development Strategies of SNS Model based on Six Degrees of Separation [J]. Economic Forum, 2013(8):42.
[2] Cao Yuyue, Dong Juan. Analysis on the Development of SNS Website [J]. Journalism Lover, 2008(11).
[3] Li You. Analysis on Features and Value of Communication [J]. Contemporary Communication 2009(3).
[4] Malan, Sheng Qunli. Overview on Dimensions of Learning [J]. New Teaching Theory: 35–18.
[5] Hong Xinhua. Design of Informing Learning Community based on SNS Campus [J]. 2113(3):108–110.

New challenge of CAM technology

M.L. Bao

Shandong Transport Vocational College, Shandong Weifang, China

ABSTRACT: The CAM technology has produced far-reaching influence to manufacturing industry. It's development in recent almost several tens years has been prompt domestic and overseas. But in our country, although the CAM technology is in application all round, there are masses of problems of CAM technology application. The super-speed production puts forward new demand for CAM technology. The CAM technology is faced with new challenge. It's update and development is extremely urgent.

Keywords: CAM technology; application; current situation; new challenge

1 INTRODUCTION

Now, in mechanical manufacturing industry, NC machining occupies the absolute leadership position with the advantages of high precision, high quality and high efficiency. Traditional NC machining relies on manual programming, only for simple processing object, inefficient, fallible, that limits the application of CNC machine tools. With the development of manufacturing industry, more and more complex parts emergence. Manual program can't complete complicated outline curve's processing and must make use of automatic program to carry out. At present, CAD/CAM interactive graphic automatic programming has been applied widespreadly. Complex parts as Figure 1.

The CAM technology, computer aided manufacturing technology, processes the parts route and the process content by computers, In order to obtain the processing tool trajectories and NC program. The core is the computer digital control,

is the technology of application of computer in production manufacturing.

2 PRACTICAL CURRENT SITUATION OF CAM TECHNOLOGY

The research of CAM technology started in the last stage of 60s' in our country, so to speak primarily cogradient with industry developed countries, but the application of CAM technology isn't very universal so far. Many large-scale and middle-scale enterprises don't have fine benefit, so don't have economic strength to purchase advanced NC equipments and softwares. Most enterprises in villages and towns are short of technology troops, that limits the application of CAM technology. Currently, CAM technology is most applied still in aerospace industry, shipbuilding industry, large civil enterprise and scientific research institutions supported by country.

Our country is big manufacturing country already and overall manufacturing scale is fourth rank only second to the United States, Japan and Germany in the world but isn't strong manufacturing country. The development tendency of manufacturing in the future is flexibility, intelligentialaize and networking. Mechanical manufacturing industry will become brand new mechanical manufacturing industry as leading by information and will adopt advanced production model, advanced manufacturing technology and advanced management pattern. CAM technology is new leap that computer technology is putted into use in the production of parts. But to see at present, in our country, CAM technology exists prodigious disparity not only at the lavel of the research of software but also at the degree of commoditization and marketization.

Figure 1. Complex part of automatic programming.

3 THE MAIN ISSUE OF CAM APPLICATION

3.1 Limit of NC equipment

3.1.1 Lack of advanced NC equipment

Now, the most advanced NC equipments exist in Westerm country, then Japan, then Taiwang. The NC equipments fall behind enormously. In Eerope, especially Germany, versatile milling machinings are very general, but multi-axes milling machinings concentrate in coastal advanced cities, etc. Shanghai, Shenzheng. Such as Weifang, relatively advanced NC machine tools rare as before.

This year, the NC profession's students of our college entrance certain enterprise to practice the operation of NC machine tool. The NC machine tools that the enterprise use are common, equipped intermediate rail or underdrive NC systems. The parts that can be manufactured are very simple, low precision. Manual programming can solve all questions. So as advanced programming means, CAM technology has no any chance. The parts can be manufactured in anywhere and the enterprise hasn't the parts possessing technology, so the enterprise has little competitive power.

3.1.2 Advanced NC machines don't advanced

some enterprises pay high price to buy preferable NC machine tools, but most don't bring into play those function. Even some tools are used as specified tool, the program have been edited already from foreign and don't be modified and renewed never. The machine tools lose flexibility completely.

3.2 Limit of software

3.2.1 Limit of the computer's level

The development of modern computer's technology make the period of product update more and more shorten. But our country, this response ability isn't very good, with the addition of lack of macroscopical control and short-term action in trade interior, which impact the development of computer's technology greatly. So the property, quality, variety and spread etc. all lag behind the world level.

3.2.2 Limit of the software's level

In our country, the self-research softmares are less and behindhand. And prirate softwares prevail. Many enterprises absence commendable technology trin, which make CAM work in a circle.

3.3 The issue of Import foreign CAM

3.3.1 High price

Many enterprises, especial middle and minitype enterprises, aspire to use new technology to enhance the efficiency and benefit. But responsing

widespreadly, the price of CAM softwares is very high in market and too complex, difficult to use. There is no simplified CAM softwares for middle and minitype enterprises to use.

3.3.2 Inconvenient to use

Due to display in English, difficult to use. Even if university graduated students, also must be trained to use. So this case limits the use and popularization of foreign CAM software in our country. Although there are some softwares that are translated, certain degree to use advantageous, but the software can't be bringed into play best.

4 THE PROBLEM OF CAM RESEARCH

4.1 Limit of research mode

Inland, utility software is all closed from establishing the item, investment, research to use, which results the software difficult to popularization at large area. Meanwhile, because of absence mutual communication, the phenomenon of repetitive research of software is comparative serious. This aggravates shortage of researcher and fund.

4.2 Limit of researcher

In our country, softeware researchers are quite dispersive. In enterprises, the researcher mainly work to fulfil the production and management demand of their own side. Because of the different use circumstance, these softwares are difficult to entrance marketplace as merchandises. The researchers in institution of higher learning, only research as demands or cheaper labourers that are employed by computer company, so their capability is restricted to put to good use.

4.3 Without data sharing with CAD

Some enterprises that CAD is good have realized two dimension drawing and three-dimensional modelling by computers, also can generate craft automatically. But all works use different softwares and are implemented by different departments. The data can't be shared and integrated as a whole.

5 THE NEW CHALLENGE OF CAM TECHNOLOGY

5.1 New demand of manufacturing industry

In recent years, supreme hotspot of new manufacturing technology is super-speed production technology. This technology has been approved and used extensively which can enhance product quality and shorten production period by simplifying production craft, reducing the later working, enhancing production efficiency and surface quality. Super-speed production puts forward new demand for CAM technology. Super-speed processing as Figure 2.

5.1.1 The demand of higher security

Super-speed process uses little cut speed, little cut
Output, high feed speed. General feed speed of feature production is more ten times for traditional processing. Under the condition of high feed speed, once occurring overcut, geometric interference, consequence will be very serious. So security requirement is the first.

5.1.2 Higher efficiency

High efficiency is embodied in two aspects:

1. High efficiency of programming: Manufacturability requirements of high speed production are much higher than traditional NC machining. The lenghth of tool path is more hundred times for traditional processing. General time of programming is more long than time of processing, so efficiency of programming has become one of the key factors to impact overall efficiency.
2. Optimization of tool path: Effective avoid air travel and feeding optimization etc. can improve the cutting efficiency of 30%.

5.1.3 Better production craft

Super-speed processing requires smooth tool path, to avoid trajectory angle of tool path (suddenly to turn) and air cutting, overcut and less cut, etc. So CAM systems must have higher analysis and processing capacity.

5.2 The developmental tendency of CAM technology

The CAM technology is one comprehensiveness technology, development in recent almost several tens years has been prompt, has produced far-reaching influence to manufacturing industry. The CAM technology is in application of our country all round, but fall behind advanced country. So it's update is urgent.

5.2.1 Facing object, facing craft

CAM system will can distinguish and extract all craft features and regions that possess specific craft features automatically according to the demand of production craft, which make integration, unifition, automation, intelligentize of CAD/CAPP/CAM become possible.

5.2.2 Intelligentize of CAM technology

CAM system should not only inherit and estimate intelligently craft features but also have the capability that can contrast models and analysis and estimate surplus models, making the tools routes more optimized, higher efficiency. Meanwhile, the form of facing whole also have function of avoiding to cut too much and collide, enhance security of production and fit the demand of super-speed production.

5.2.3 Networking of CAM

CAM as the core of manufacture need to establish network, provides various manufacture supporting service, such as productablity of product design, simulation of production process and test of parts. Integration enterprises can link and share with the information quickly.

Of course, the development of CAM technology must be supported by powerful hardware and software of computer. Future, terrace of CAM software will be WindowsNT or Windows 2000 and terrace of CAM hardware will be slap-up PC or NT work station. With the development of NC control system and specialization and intelligentize of CAM, programming on machine tools also can develop vastly.

The development of CAM will be high integration of CAD/CAPP/CAM. Among CAD/CAPP/CAM system, CAM is the link that can bring into play efficiency mostly, which palys very important role to enhance the producation quantity and precision, shorten time of research and achieve production automation. The update and development of CAM technology is extremely urgent.

Figure 2.   CNC super-speed machining.

REFERENCES

[1] Guo Qian. Status and Development Direction of Automatic NC Programming [J]. Value Engineering. 2011, 28: 41–42.
[2] Zhao Guozeng. Machinery CAD/CAM [M]. Beijing: China Machine Press. 2005.
[3] Ma Jinying. The Application and Development of Digital CAD/CAM [J]. Machine Tool & Hydraulics. 2009, 37(4): 159–160,175.

Computer, Intelligent Computing and Education Technology – Liu, Sung & Yao (Eds)
© 2014 Taylor & Francis Group, London, ISBN 978-1-138-02469-4

The Generalized Kalman Filter and application

Ming-Zhan Zhao, Jie Yue & Qing-Lin Wang
Hebei University of Architecture, Zhangjiakou, Hebei, China

ABSTRACT: The classical kalman filter can be used to estimate real-time state, it depends on the given system model. But, it is difficult to get the system mathematic model beforehand.

The Generalized Kalman Filter (GKF) is a method which is based on a generalized linear model. The coefficients of the linear model are fixed, and are not needed to be distinguished on-line or predefined. The GKF can be used to estimate the real-time estate of the continuous system, especially; the GKF can be used to estimate the estate of the mobile objective. The GKF is based on the minimum mean-square error. The recursive formula of the generalized kalman filter was also presented. Different from the EKF published on the magazines, the GKF doesn't need to build the system model, so its ability of calculate and accuracy is improved.

Lastly, conclusion was given: In the application to non-linear system, the GKF can be used widely, and the method of GKF can realize the real-time estate estimate of the mobile objective.

Keywords: Generalized Kalman Filter; recursive formula; step response

1 GENERAL INTRODUCTION

The kalman filter is based on the given system model (see Modern control theoretical Basis), but it is difficult to find the assured system model in many field. There are two methods to build the model of unknown system now. The one is to create an acceleration model, because the acceleration is vector, in other word, it is varying at any moment; obviously, the application of the acceleration model is weaken. Further more, the real-time operation is limited. And the other way is to build the approximate power series inside the field δ around the point $t = t_0$, and the power series need to be rebuilt beyond the field $t_0 \pm \delta$. Obviously, the method is also confined.

2 THE GENERALIZED LINEAR MODEL

In practical project, the measured track curve is usually substituted by its approach curve (see Generalized kalman filter signal modeling for airborne targets and Fig. 1), where x_{k-i} is measured value; $z(t)$ is the best approach curve for $x(t)$; z_{k-i} is the value of $z(t)$ cross the time point $k-I$; w_{k-i} is the difference between x_{k-i} and z_{k-i}, $i = 0, 1, ..., \mu$. So $z_{k-i} = x_{k-i} + w_{k-i}$.

According to the difference function:

$$\frac{d^\mu z(t)}{dt^\mu} = \frac{d^\mu x(t) + d^\mu w(t)}{dt^\mu} = 0$$

A formula is gotten (see Formula 1).

$$x_k + w_k = \sum_{i=1}^{\mu} (-1)^{i-1} C_\mu^i \left(x_{k-i} + w_{k-i} \right) \qquad (1)$$

The right of formula 1 is the linear expression of the left of formula 1, where $z(t) \approx x(t)$ or $z(t) = x(t) + w(t)$. Since $z(t)$ is best approach of $x(t)$, w_k can be designed small enough (see Parameter varying generalized kalman filter based on generalized linear model).

The expression of x_k can be obtained (see Formula 2).

$$x_k = \sum_{i=1}^{\mu} (-1)^{i-1} C_\mu^i \left(x_{k-i} + w_{k-i} \right)$$
$$= \sum_{i=1}^{\mu} (-1)^{i-1} C_\mu^i x_{k-i} + \sum_{i=1}^{\mu} (-1)^{i-1} C_\mu^i w_{k-i} \qquad (2)$$

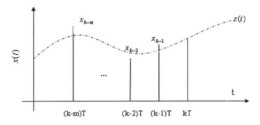

Figure 1. Continuative process.

And it can also be expressed as a concise form (see Formula 3).

$$x_k = \Phi_{k/k-1:k-\mu} x_{k-1:k-\mu} + \Phi_{k/k-1:k-\mu} w_{k-1:k-\mu} \quad (3)$$

Formula 3 is the generalized linear model inside the field $[t_1, t_2]$, where:

$$\Phi_{k/k-1:k-\mu} = \left[C_\mu^1 - C_\mu^2 \cdots (-1)^{\mu-1} C_\mu^\mu \right] \quad (4)$$

is named for transfer matrix of the generalized linear model. And:

$$\begin{aligned} x_{k-1:k-\mu} &= \left[x_{k-1} \; x_{k-2} \cdots x_{k-\mu} \right]^T \\ w_{k-1:k-\mu} &= \left[w_{k-1} \; w_{k-2} \cdots w_{k-\mu} \right]^T \end{aligned} \quad (5)$$

is the generalized state and generalized error.

3   THE ESTIMATE MODEL OF THE GKF

The symbol of y_k is the output that can be measured, and v_k is the noise. Hence:

$$\underset{m \times n}{y_k} = H_k \, x_k + v_k \quad (6)$$

where the symbol y_k and v_k are all m dimension vectors, H_k is a $m \times n$ dimension matrix.

Since v_k is white gauss noise, its expectation and variance is:

$$\begin{aligned} E v_k &= \bar{v}_k \\ E[(v_k - \bar{v}_k)(v_l - \bar{v}_l)^T] &= R_k \delta_{kl} \end{aligned} \quad (7)$$

where δ_{kl} is:

$$\delta_{kl} = \begin{cases} 1, & k = l \\ 0, & k \neq l \end{cases} \quad (8)$$

4   THE FILTER MODEL OF THE GKF

The linchpin of building the filter model is to find the estimated vector for x_k. And the estimate of x_k is linear, it is:

$$\hat{x}_k = \sum_{l=0}^{k} F_{kl} y_l + d_k \quad (9)$$

where d_k is a constant vector and F_{kl} is a $n \times m$ dimension constant matrix. The error from estimate is ε_k (see Formula 10).

$$\varepsilon_k = \hat{x}_k - x_k \quad (10)$$

Now the emphases are finding the best d_k and $F_{k0}, F_{k1}, \ldots, F_{kk}$. The mean square error is:

$$\begin{aligned} E[\delta_k \delta_k^T] &= E[(\hat{x}_k - x_k)(\hat{x}_k - x_k)^T] \\ &= E\left[(x_k - \bar{x}_k)(x_k - \bar{x}_k)^T\right] \\ &+ E\left[\left(\sum_{l=0}^{k} F_{kl} H_l(x_l - \bar{x}_l)\right)\left(\sum_{l=0}^{k} F_{kl} H_l(x_l - \bar{x}_l)\right)^T\right] \\ &+ E\left[\left(\sum_{l=0}^{k} F_{kl}(v_l - \bar{v}_l)\right)\left(\sum_{l=0}^{k} F_{kl}(v_l - \bar{v}_l)\right)^T\right] \\ &- E\left[\left(\sum_{l=0}^{k} F_{kl} H_l(x_l - \bar{x}_l)\right)(x_k - \bar{x}_k)^T\right] \\ &- E\left[(x_k - \bar{x}_k)\left(\sum_{l=0}^{k} F_{kl} H_l(x_l - \bar{x}_l)\right)^T\right] \end{aligned}$$

$$(11)$$

A group of important recursion formula can be deduced based on principle of minimum mean square error (see The research of the minimum mean square error of the generalized Kalman filter). While the process is too prolix, it is difficult to expatiate. The full deduction can be seen in author's another paper (see Deductive proof of generalized kalman filter recursive formula). Author's dissertation is also a good choice, and it is easily to be found through Google.

The group of recursion formula is named for the recursion formulas of GKF (see Formula 12 to 19).

$$\hat{x}_k = \hat{x}_{k/k-1:k-\mu} + K_k \{ y_k - (H_k \hat{x}_{k/k-1:k-\mu} + \bar{v}_k) \} \quad (12)$$

$$\underset{n\mu \times 1}{\hat{x}_{k/k-1:k-\mu}} = \Phi_{k/k-1:k-\mu} \hat{x}_{k-1,k-\mu} + \underset{n\mu \times 1}{\Phi_{k/k-1:k-\mu} \bar{w}_{k-1:k-\mu}}$$

$$(13)$$

$$K_k = P_{k/k-1:k-\mu} H_k^T \times (H_k P_{k/k-1:k-\mu} H_k^T + R_k)^{-1} \quad (14)$$

$$\begin{aligned} P_{k/k-1:k-\mu} &= \Phi_{k/k-1:k-\mu} P_{k-1:k-\mu} \Phi_{k/k-1:k-\mu}^T \\ &+ \Phi_{k/k-1:k-\mu} Q_{k-1:k-\mu} \Phi_{k/k-1:k-\mu}^T \end{aligned} \quad (15)$$

$$\underset{n \times n}{P_k} = (P_{k/k-1:k-\mu}^{-1} + H_k^T R_k^{-1} H_k)^{-1} \quad (16)$$

$$\begin{aligned} Q_{k-1:k-\mu} &= E\left[(w_{k-1:k-\mu} - \bar{w}_{k-1:k-\mu}) \right. \\ &\left. \times (w_{k-1:k-\mu} - \bar{w}_{k-1:k-\mu})^T\right] \end{aligned} \quad (17)$$

$$R_k = E[(v_k - \bar{v}_k)(v_k - \bar{v}_k)^T] \quad (18)$$

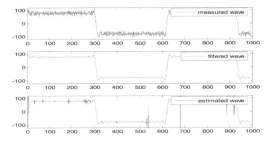

Figure 2. The measured wave, flitted wave and estimated wave.

$$P_{k:k-\mu+1} = L \begin{bmatrix} P_k & 0 & \cdots & & 0 \\ 0 & \ddots & & & 0 \\ \vdots & & P_{k-\mu+2} & & 0 \\ 0 & 0 & 0 & & P_{k-\mu+1} \end{bmatrix} L^T \quad (19)$$

5 EXAMPLE

The self-adaptive calculation can be gotten through the group of recursion formulas. The future value can be estimated by the former 6 value, and the transfer matrix is.

$$\Phi_{k/k-1:k-\mu} = \begin{bmatrix} 6 & -15 & 20 & -15 & 6 & -1 & 0 & 0 & 0 \\ 0 & 6 & -15 & 20 & -15 & 6 & -1 & 0 & 0 \\ 0 & 0 & 6 & -15 & 20 & -15 & 6 & -1 & 0 \\ 0 & 0 & 0 & 6 & -15 & 20 & -15 & 6 & -1 \end{bmatrix}$$

The example present the measured wave, the filtered wave and estimated wave of a step signal (see Fig. 2). The most noise of the measured wave is filtered out.

6 CONCLUSION

The GKF is more widely applied in many field such as navigation and so on, moreover the better result can be obtained based on GKF.

REFERENCES

Xie, X.K. 1981. *Modern control theoretical Basis.* Shenyang: Liaoning People Publisher.
Zhao, M.Z. 2006. Deductive proof of generalized kalman filter recursive formula. *Journal of Shenyang Institute of Aeronautical Engineering.* 23: 82–84.
Zhao, M.Z. 2005. The research of the minimum mean square error of the generalized Kalman filter. *Journal of Shenyang Institute of Aeronautical Engineering.* 22: 47–49.
Zhao, M.Z. 2005. Generalized kalman filter signal modeling for airborne targets. *Aircraft Design.* 4: 77–80.
Zhao, W.C. 2007. Parameter varying generalized kalman filter based on generalized linear model. *Control Engineering of China.* 14: 21–23.

Computer, Intelligent Computing and Education Technology – Liu, Sung & Yao (Eds)
© 2014 Taylor & Francis Group, London, ISBN 978-1-138-02469-4

Design and development of calibration data processing system for the structure strength test data acquisition equipment

J. Zuo & J.F. Zhang
Full Scale Aircraft Static/Fatigue Structure Aviation Science and Technology Key Laboratory, Aircraft Strength Research Institute of China, Xi'an, China

J.L. Liu
Department of Aeronautical Structure Engineering, School of Aeronautics Northwestern Polytechnical University, Xi'an, China

ABSTRACT: With the scale of static structure test increasing, the calibration workload of data acquisition device channel will rising, and artificial processing data has lot of problems about low efficiency, high error rate, and the long processing cycle. In order to deal with these problems, based on Delphi program development environment, the mass calibration data processing system was designed and developed. The system through the template of Excel realized interaction between Delphi and data. Batches of calibration data are processed automatically including data extraction, analysis, discrimination for standards compliance, and automatically generate data according to demands for the calibration table. This system greatly simplified the calibration data processing work, and improved the degree of automation for the structure strength test acquisition system calibrating.

Keywords: data acquisition system; calibration; data selection; delphi

1 INTRODUCTION

The Data acquisition system is indispensable to structural static test measurement equipment. It can measure input signals from sensors, transmitter and other signal source, and in some way to data storage, processing, display, print, or record for the measured value [1]. In order to ensure the accuracy of test requirements, each channel of acquisition equipment needed to be calibration on a regular basis. Calibration is refers to under prescribed conditions, in order to determine the value indicated by the measuring instrument or measuring system, or represented by a material measure or standard material quantity, with the corresponding surface by the standard of value between a set of operations. It is a widely attention in the field of measuring method. Measuring instrument is confirmed to be working within the instrument technical indicators, it is necessary to guarantee the accuracy of the instrument [2–3].

At present, according to the national metrology calibration specification "JJF1048 data acquisition system calibration specification requirements", the method of calibration for data acquisition instruments of Aircraft Strength Research Institute of China was established. The calibration flow is illustrated as follows. Standard strain or standard voltage signals are inputted in the system signal input terminal, and then the system collects and outputs data. The collected data are selected firstly, and then the measurement error, linearity, zero drift error was analyzed. Based on these analysis results, the data acquisition system is calibrated. But in the actual calibration process, only for one channel, 12 groups of collected data need to be picking out and find four data from each group, which could satisfy the requirement of discrimination. For an acquisition instrument with hundreds of channel, the amount of calibration data need to be processed is very huge. At the same time, there is no special calibration data processing software at present. The selection of data and importation and exportation of selected data were accomplished by manual operation. The process is very onerous, low efficiency, high error rate and long processing cycle. With the continuous expansion for the scale of structure strength static test measurement in recent years, the largest measurement scale has been developed from previous hundreds of channels to tens of thousands of channel now. For the tens of thousands of channels of data acquisition system, the existing calibration data processing method is unable to meet the requirements. Therefore, a program was need to be developed to process the calibration test data automatically, involving data selecting, data analyzing and calibration data discriminate for standards compliance, and other functions. For the purpose of solving above problems, a calibration data processing system was developed for the structure strength test data acquisition equipment in Delphi7.0 program development environment. This system successfully realized the mass calibration measurement data automatic processing and the function of data switching between Delphi program and Excel spreadsheets. Batches of output for multi-channel calibration data was accomplished, and operating efficiency was improved significantly.

2 THE METHOD OF CALIBRATION TO DATA ACQUISITION SYSTEM

Data acquisition system for our enterprise, it mainly used for measuring physical quantity of strain, temperature, voltage. It used the data acquisition system of the measured physical quantity into digital signal through the computer to recording, display, printing and processing. Acquisition system commonly was used with series of SDAC, ST, and HBM. The user can accord needs flexible configuration of the acquisition system scale, it can generally be configuration consisting of mini data acquisition system, and also can form a large data acquisition system of thousands of channels.

2.1 The selection of signal points

In the measurement range from EL to EH, and chooses signal not less than 11 calibration signal: Ei (I = 1, 2 ...... 11), Ei uniform distribution in the range of domestic demand, and as far as possible to choose integer, as shown in Figure 1:

E_L—Channel measurement lower limit
E_H—Channel measurement upper limit
E_r—Channel measurement range
$E_r = E_H - E_L$
$E_{11} \geq E_L + E_r \times 95\%$
$E_1 \leq E_L + E_r \times 5\%$.

2.2 Measurement error, the linearity of calibration

1. Select a measurement channel as the standard source.
2. Load signal, launch measurement, start to recording data.
   a. Calibration of strain and voltage channel, will be the school standard access channel, in the positive and negative to the calibration range choose not less than 12 calibration

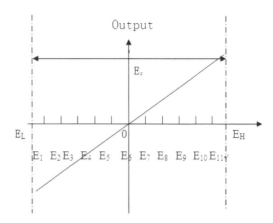

Figure 1. The system input and output characteristics.

point (E1~E11, namely, the E6 is positive and negative value), start the acquisition system, record each output value Xi, respectively.
   b. To simulate the calibration temperature calibration method (only applicable to ST series and DH3815 series temperature data acquisition system), which simulate thermocouple output voltage of the DC standard signal source, change of DC potentiometer reading, measured by the system, and record the measurement result.
3. If the error of measurement and linearity are within the error range, the calibration results completely meet the requirements of the model system measurement features.
4. Change the channel, and repeat the above operation until the completion of all of the channel calibration.

2.3 Data acquisition system calibration data selection method

In the calibration process, the most tedious work is selected from a large number of data meets the requirements of the data. From of the table was shown in Table 1, and form of the required data in Table 2.

Table 1 as the prototype of the measurement data, and the first row is channel names. According to the different collection system, channel name is different. Each corresponding channel as the collected data, and data is divided into 12 range value (E1~E11, which the E6 is positive and negative value), specific standard column in the scope as shown in Table 2, each range value, there are at least 10 measuring values, but we must choose the four meet the need of the calibration value (see Table 2 measurements of Xi1~Xi4).

Table 1. Samples of collection data.

Channel_07_01_001	Channel_07_02_001	Channel_07_03_001	
−0.354166677	−2.979166755	−0.270833341	……
−0.062500002	−2.541666742	−0.125000004	……
−0.541666683	−1.812500054	−0.145833338	……
−0.187500006	−0.89583336	−0.166666672	……
1.729166718	−0.854166692	−0.145833338	……
−0.229166673	0	−1.354166707	……
0	0.020833334	2547.229243	……
0.145833338	1998.895893	1995.500059	……
1997.229226	1996.250059	1996.166726	……
1997.895893	1998.604226	1996.166726	……
1997.229226	1998.791726	1996.104226	……
1997.104226	1998.56256	1996.062559	……
1998.00006	1998.00006	4982.645982	……
−0.604166685	4975.041815	4982.625148	……
……	……	……	……

Table 2. Need to select the calibration data.

Standard values (με)	Measured value X_i (με)			
	X_{i1}	X_{i2}	X_{i3}	X_{i4}
−20000	−20433.9	−20433.9	−20434.1	−20433.4
−15000	−15246.4	−15247.4	−15247.5	−15247.5
−10000	−10112	−10112.2	−10112.2	−10112.3
−5000	−5031.75	−5031.98	−5032.02	−5032.54
−2000	−2007.4	−2007.04	−2007.38	−2007.08
0	−1.08333	−1.29167	−1.33333	−0.45833
0	1.729167	−0.22917	0	0.145833
2000	1997.896	1997.229	1997.104	1998
5000	4983.875	4983.542	4983.354	4983.563
10000	9911.375	9911.396	9910.938	9914.5
15000	14793.13	14792.46	14792.48	14792.71
20000	19629.96	19629.52	19630.19	19629.46

3 THE SYSTEM ARCHITECTURE DESIGN

This system mainly includes the extraction of data collection and data import, extraction, calibration, data analysis, discrimination, and calibration data automatic export function modules. The processing of this system as shown in Figure 2.

4 DESIGN AND IMPLEMENTATION OF KEY TECHNOLOGY

This system mainly involves problems include:

1. The realization of the Delphi calling Microsoft Excel technology;

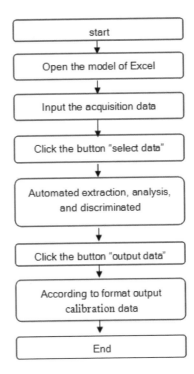

Figure 2. System flow chart.

2. Automatic generation of Excel document;
3. Choose the import of data files;
4. According to the needs, select the test data;
5. Calibration data is derived.

4.1 The realization technology of the Delphi calls Microsoft Excel

Three methods can be used call Excel in Delphi [4]:

1. Using Delphi provide Severs control calls to Excel.
2. The automation technology, which used CreateOleObject active the Excel, and then to control the Excel by Ole manners.
3. Through the Delphi controls TOleContainer, embedding the Excel.

This system mainly adopts the former two methods to generate, calling Excel documents.

4.2 Template of Excel on the data information to import

By means of Delphi this module used Create OLE-Object controls called Excel [5], in fact, it is OLE. But this method can actually control the Excel, using Excel various attributes, and write your own code is essentially the same in the VBA. But it can do not need to use the default code. This way to start the Excel and Delphi program score two forms, the disadvantage is that not when using Delphi code hinting, exception handling, are all need to write your own. Specific code is as follows:

uses ComObj; //Use ComObj statement, ComObj is a function sets of operating the OLE object
var
    ExcelApp,Workbook:Olevariant; // Define the OLE object
    Begin
    ......
    ExcelApp: = CreateOLEObject('Excel.Application');// Create Excel object
    Workbook: =   ExcelApp.Workbooks.Open (OpenDialog1.FileName); // Open the dialog box by the Excel template file

Choose in Delphi TstringGrid components to interact with Excel document. TstringGrid component is a form component, and it is used to display the data in the table. The results of each record will add to the TstringGrid component. In order to achieve the bulk data entry, table control must be as a carrier of information input. [6]

Specific code is as follows:

```
......
for i: = 1 to ExcelRowCount+1 do
    for j: = 1 to ExcelColCount+1 do
        begin
            StringGrid1.Cells[j-1,i-1]:  =  Workbook.
WorkSheets[1].Cells.Item[i,j];
            ......
        end;
......
```

Calibration data import completely interfaces as shown in Figure 3: main interface.

4.3 The calibration data

According to the calibration data selection principle, the establishment of the data selection function

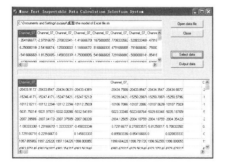

Figure 3.   Data calibration main interface.

Select (a, b, c, d, e, f: string), using TstringGrid component characteristics, controlling String-Grid1. Cells control cell to calculate, then needed calibration data results are obtained. The calculation results as shown in Figure 3.

4.4 The calculation results of the export

The calculation results of export and import Excel template information similar. First, it will establish the connection with Excel controls, and to build Excel document, then open the Excel document. All information derived specific code is as follows:

```
......
for i: = 1 to StringGrid1.RowCount do
    for j: = 1 to StringGrid1.ColCount do
        begin

ExcelWorksheet1.Cells.Item[i,j]:=olevariant(String
Grid1.Cells[j-1,i-1]);
        ......
    end;
......
```

5   CONCLUSION

This system realized by standard template of Excel spreadsheet as the carrier of the mass calibration data import. According to the acquisition system calibration specification to deal with calibration data automatically such as selection, calculation and criterion, then in the form of Excel spreadsheet output the function of the selection of calibration data items. To Excel data calibration template as numerous experimental data processing in the process of circulating medium, the system was used to test calibration data processing, improved the efficiency of data transmission, simplified the procedure of dealing with test data, improved the efficiency of the experimental data processing, greatly reduced the errors caused by human factors. The application of this system can simplify the process of equipment calibration, and the automation and standardization of measurement equipment calibration to programming is step closer.

AUTHOR BIOGRAPHY

J. Zuo was born in Xi'an, Shaanxi, in 1979. She received MS from Xi'an University of Science and Technology in 2007. Now she is an engineer in Aircraft Strength Research Institute of China, Shaanxi. Her research interests in full scale aircraft static/fatigue structure test data measurement and analysis.

J.F. Zhang, full scale aircraft static/fatigue structure test senior engineer.

J.L. Liu, Ph.D student, Department of aeronautical structure engineering.

REFERENCES

[1] Fan Xiaolian. "Aircraft Strength Research Institute of China metrology calibration specification". 2012.

[2] Zhang Yu, Chen Yan. "To research of data acquisition system calibrating". Electronic Measurement Technology. Vol. 35, No. 8, 2012, pp. 98–100.

[3] Yu Haiyan, Song Qi. "Design of Data Acquisition System of Ship Measurement and Control Device Check Equipment". Industrial Applications and Communication. Vol. 31, No. 7, 2012, pp. 60–62.

[4] Feng Fan. "Delphi and Excel communication method based on OLE technology". Journal of software space-time. No. 10, 2007.

[5] Zhao Sheng. "based on delphi7.0 excel linked data integration design and application". Computer software and application. No. 11, 2011.

[6] Zhang ling, Song kun. "Delphi application development paradigm" [M]. 2006.

Computer, Intelligent Computing and Education Technology – Liu, Sung & Yao (Eds)
© 2014 Taylor & Francis Group, London, ISBN 978-1-138-02469-4

Influence of electromagnetic interference on reliability of high-voltage switchgear

Sheng Chen
Hitachi Yonge Electric Equipment Co., Ltd., Xi'an, Shaanxi, China

Yuan Yuan & Wen-Zhu Ren
Xi'an High Voltage Apparatus Research Institute, Xi'an, Shaanxi, China

ABSTRACT: The reliability of high-voltage switchgear is very important to ensure the safety of power system. This paper analyzed the electromagnetic disturbance sorts that the effect of switchgear reliability, and according to the reliability evaluation principle, the main of characteristic parameters were proposed, which combined with the correlation national standards and switchgear application stages, each test type was executed, and the test data were recording, analyzing. The next, it was using analytic hierarchy process, On the basis of judgment matrix construction, the weight of each immunity sort for reliability evaluation has been founded, The experimental results indicate that the surge immunity test has destructivity, EFT and oscillatory waves immunity test are easier to bringing about switchgear failure, but it's not causing devastation. The analytical methods can offer reference to reliability evaluation on high-voltage switchgear.

Keywords: reliability evaluation; electromagnetic interference; test statistics; analytic hierarchy process (AHP)

1 INTRODUCTION

High-voltage switchgear is the basis for the normal operation of the power system. With the rapid development of science and technology, more and more electronic technology was applied into the high-voltage switching equipment. So the electromagnetic compatibility gets attention in the fields of high-voltage switchgear. The electromagnetic compatibility includes electromagnetic interference and immunity to a disturbance. Now the high-voltage switchgear immunity tests become a hot topic. That is the high-voltage switchgear and control device extensive use of electronic components, and the electromagnetic disturbance on the impact of these electronic equipments directly related to the reliability of high-voltage switchgear works.[1–5]

This paper based on the working principle and composition, the high-voltage switchgear can be divided into the high voltage switch cabinet, Circuit Breakers (CB) and intelligent Gas Insulated Switchgear (GIS). The author in accordance with relevant standards and these types of equipment condition, focus described the Electrical Fast Transient/burst (EFT) immunity test, oscillatory waves immunity test, surge immunity test. Then combined with the large number of experimental data calculated the

proportion of different immunity test factors and made a statistical analysis, the influence weighing of different disturbances on the different high-voltage switchgear were obtained. According to the data conclusions analysis, it provides technical guidance for high-voltage switchgear equipment manufacturers, at the same time benefits of the whole life-cycle management of high-voltage switchgear.

2 THE RELIABILITY EVALUATION INDEX OF THE HIGH-VOLTAGE SWITCHGEAR AND THE SELECTION OF ELECTROMAGNETIC INTERFERENCE SOURCES

2.1 *The reliability evaluation index*

According to the switchgear operating conditions, combining with the concept of reliability for establish a scientific evaluation system. We selected the characteristic parameter follow three principles as follows: scientific principle practical principle and scalability principle.[6]

According to selection principles of the evaluation index, failure items characteristics of auxiliary and control equipment of high-voltage switchgear. This paper chooses non-reparable characteristic parameters as follows to evaluate the reliability of the high-voltage switchgear.

1. Reliability: Refers to the probability of the equipment complete the required functions under the required conditions and time (or the number of operations). So reliability (R) is the function of time t, which could be labeled as $R_{(t)}$, called as the function of reliability. For example, Select n sets of equipment complete any one item of electromagnetic immunity test, under required time t (t > 0) applied the electromagnetic interference source to required number of equipment, if $m_{(t)}$ sets of equipment can't complete expected functions. Therefore the reliability of product approximate recorded as:

$$R_{(t)} \approx \frac{n - m_{(t)}}{n}(m_{(t)} \leq n) \qquad (1)$$

2. Instantaneous failure rate: Equipment is in available state at time t, the rate between conditional probability of appear failure at time (t, t + Δt) and interval length Δt, defined as failure Probability, that is to say, the failure probability of unit time after time t, expressed as λ(t). Assume n sets of equipment is applied once the source of interference from the beginning of time t = 0 successively, when time t arrivals, there are certain amount of equipments applied, the number of failure equipments are $m_{(t)}$, at time t + Δt, the number of applied equipments increased, the number of failure equipments are $m_{(t+\Delta t)}$, Then the failure rate λ(t) can be approximated as the following formula.

$$\lambda_{(t)} \approx \frac{m_{(t+\Delta t)} - m_{(t)}}{[n - m_{(t)}]\Delta t} \qquad (2)$$

3. Mean life: Use the equipments with similar wok principle or structural design. Due to differences in raw material performance, manufacturing process instability, differences between the assembly and technical of testers and so on. That will lead to the use life of these equipments are different. Since the destructive of life test, we selected n sets of equipment of randomly and the each equipment must complete any one item of electromagnetic immunity test repeat until this product lose efficacy. Recorded the use life of n sets equipment as t_1, t_2 until to t_n, non-respectively. This constitutes a sub-sample of use life. The mean life (t) of this sub-sample can be represented as:

$$\bar{t} = \frac{1}{n}\sum_{i=1}^{n} t_i \qquad (3)$$

From the above index of characteristic parameters, it is can be seen that these three parameters are all the function of time. In the test, Time t is related to the number of test. Namely, they are the function of the number of test.[7–10]

2.2 Selection of the main source of electromagnetic interference

The auxiliary switch equipment and control equipment are highly intelligent. In the practical application, the primary side of switching equipment is not easy to be disturbed, the main effect of electromagnetic disturbance is which the secondary system of the electroweak element. Refer to standards, only the secondary systems need to be tested, the main packs including electronic equipment need to proceed with the packing disturbance test, in this paper, combined with switching equipment running condition, expounding at the following aspects of susceptible to electromagnetic disturbance, and also the user and manufacturer concerned aspects.

1. The Electrical Fast Transient burst (EFT) immunity test

The Electrical Fast Transient burst (EFT) is generated by the switching of inductive loads. This switching transient is commonly referred to as fast transient. When the switch equipments are being tested, EFT is mainly used to simulate the switching situation of the secondary loop. Figure 1 is electrical fast transient/burst waveform.

2. Oscillatory waves immunity test

Oscillatory waves immunity test represents the switching of the insulator of the high-voltage, mid-voltage substation outdoor. The switch brake and open operations will cause the steep waves, its time will be tens of nanoseconds. In the test of switch equipment, oscillatory waves immunity test is mainly used to simulate the situation caused by opening and closing of the main circuit. Figure 2 is oscillatory waves immunity test waveform.

3. Surge immunity test

Surge voltage is mainly used to simulate the effects of high energy pulse. Figure 3 is surge voltage waveform.

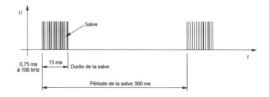

Figure 1.   Electrical fast transient/burst waveform.

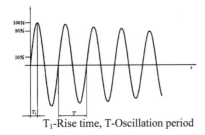

T₁-Rise time, T-Oscillation period

Figure 2.   Damped oscillation waveform.

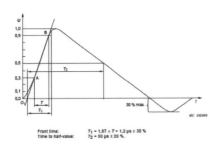

Front time: $T_1 = 1.67 \times T = 1.2\ \mu s \pm 30\ \%$
Time to half-value: $T_2 = 50\ \mu s \pm 20\ \%.$

Figure 3.   Impulse voltage waveform.

3   TEST DATA STATISTICS OF ELECTROMAGNETIC INTERFERENCE

According to the working condition and the working principle of high voltage switchgear, divided into high voltage switch cabinet, circuit breaker and GIS. The statistics according to their test condition of electromagnetic disturbance in recent years, and also keeps an account of fault record of test results.

3.1   The test statistic data of switch cabinet

A total of 25 sets of equipment test of switchgears are completed, including 12 kV switch cabinet, 126 kV metal enclosed switch, etc. and test conditions are shown in Table 1.

You can get from Table 1 that the monitor of switchgear is susceptible to interference from electrical transient bursts. The interface board of secondary system is easy to be damaged under impulse voltage.

3.2   Test statistics of circuit breaker

A total of 25 sets of equipment test of breakers are completed, including 12 kV outdoor vacuum circuit breaker, 10 kV intelligent vacuum circuit breaker, etc., test conditions are shown in Table 2.

You can get from Table 2 that due to the structure of breaker is relatively simple. The number of

secondary system is less. The interference resistance ability is stronger.

3.3   Test statistics of GIS

Intelligent GIS get great development in recent years, including external test (The overall field test), packaging test of the main intelligence units, etc, due to the EMC test project of the intelligent GIS is too much. In this paper, there will be only three trials, does not make instructions for other test, and failure caused by other test was not in the table, test cases are shown in Table 3.

Table 3 shows that GIS applies sufficiently the modern intelligent electronic technology. When disturbed by the EFT in test, the display may be blackout.

4   ANALYSIS OF THE TEST DATA

With the reliability evaluation indicators and test results, the evaluation of data can be obtained of the each category equipment. The evaluation indicators research from the—following two aspects. On the basis of in-depth study on evaluation indicators system, the methods can be analogy, the influence of electromagnetic interference on reliability of switchgear to expand to more fields.

4.1   Reliability of the characteristic quantities calculation

1. Reliability. According to the formula 1, the Table 4 shows the calculated data.
   Through the analysis of the Table 4, these three immunity tests with the minimum effects on the CB. Due to the smaller sample selection, the reliability data are estimates of 1.0. If increase the number of tests, the actual reliability must less than 1.0.
2. Instantaneous failure rate. According to the formula 2 and statistical data, the Table 5 shows the calculated data.
   Through the analysis of the Table 5, the instantaneous failure rate that the 0%/times does not exists. If increase the number of tests and will certainly increase the actual instantaneous failure rate.
3. Mean life. Considering the destructive of life test, we only theoretical analysis. Individual products under different conditions of the interference, the life has relatively large differences. However, the mean life expectancy of data has the certain regularity and obeys a certain distribution function. Here we will not go into details of them. Photographs should be with good contrast and on glossy paper. Photographic reproductions cut

Table 1. High voltage switch cabinet test statistics.

	Test item		
Test results	EFT	Oscillation waves	Surge
Pass (number)	23	25	22
No pass			
Number	2	0	3
Failure recording	Two displays are black screen	/	A device control function is lost. Two devices interface boards are breakdown.

Table 2. Circuit breaker test statistics.

	Test item		
Test results	EFT	Oscillation waves	Surge
Pass (number)	13	13	12
No pass			
Number	0	0	1
Failure recording	/	/	A device break-brake instruction is invalid

Table 3. GIS test statistics.

	Test item		
Test results	EFT	Oscillation waves	Surge
Pass (number)	5	6	6
No pass			
Number	1	0	0
Failure recording	One device display is black screen	/	/

Table 4. Reliability data analysis.

	Name		
Reliability	Immunity test name		
Equipment category (test number)	EFT immunity test	Oscillatory waves immunity test	Surge immunity test
High voltage switch cabinet (75)	0.920	1.0	0.880
CB (39)	1.0	1.0	0.923
GIS (18)	0.833	1.0	1.0

from books or journals, photocopies of photographs and screened photographs are unacceptable. The proceedings will be printed in black only. For this reason avoid the use of colour in figures and photographs. Colour is also nearly always unnecessary for scientific work.

4.2 The weight of each interference factor analysis

In this paper, only the weights of the analysis carried out for the three immunity test. Assume that the three immunity test in the sum of the influence factor of reliability of high-voltage switchgear is

Table 5. Instantaneous failure rate data analysis.

Instantaneous failure rate	Name		
	Immunity test name		
Equipment category (test number)	EFT immunity test	Oscillatory waves immunity test	Surge immunity test
High voltage switch cabinet (75)	6.9%/10 times	0%/times	7.2%/10 times
CB (39)	0%/times	0%/times	2.56%/times
GIS (18)	8.3%/times	0%/times	0%/times

Table 6. Judgment matrix construction.

Equipment category	Immunity test name ratio scale	Factor and factor ratio	Quantized values
High voltage switch cabinet	EFT: Oscillatory waves	More important	5
	Surge: Oscillatory waves	Strong important	7
	Surge: EFT	Slightly important	3
CB	EFT: Oscillatory waves	Equally important	1
	Surge: Oscillatory waves	More important	5
	Surge: EFT	More important	5
GIS	EFT: Oscillatory waves	More important	5
	Surge: Oscillatory waves	Slightly important	3
	Surge: EFT	Slightly important	3

Table 7. The weight of each immunity for reliability evaluation.

Equipment category	Immunity test name	Comprehensive weight
High voltage switch cabinet	EFT	0.3675
	Oscillatory waves	0.0883
	Surge	0.5442
CB	EFT	0.1512
	Oscillatory waves	0.1512
	Surge	0.6976
GIS	EFT	0.5101
	Oscillatory waves	0.1225
	Surge	0.3674

In view of the reliability evaluation system, we are constructing judgment matrix, according to the statistical data for determine the proportion of influencing factors. Table 6 shows the judgment matrix construction.

Using the judgment matrix in Table 6 and combining with evaluation data of the characteristic parameter. Through with the normalization method in AHP and matlab simulation, the weight of the reliability evaluation index was obtained. Table 7 shows the weight.

Each immunity test in the aspects of the impact of different types of switchgear reliability weight is also different. So, the switchgear reliability has significant differences in the different way of working.

1. Combining the above statistics and data analysis results, the influence of electromagnetic interference on Reliability of high-voltage switchgear weights are obtained.

We used the Analytic Hierarchy Process (AHP) to judge, the AHP is an effective method for people to make an objective description of subjective judgment. According to different immunity test items, the determined by comparing two different test items for switchgear reliability affects the relative important degree, it's a combination of qualitative and quantitative, at the same time, it's the basis of the establishment of a scientific, fair index weight evaluation.

5 CONCLUSION

1. Influence of Electromagnetic interference on reliability of high-voltage switchgear, the oscillatory waves less than others. Now displays more applications, if they are exposed to high-energy EFT, there is no protective measures or take appropriate measures, the display usually black screen. But restart the switchgear that is can return to work again. Surge immunity test have higher severities, the manufacturers usually take protective measures, such as adding

surge suppressor, the pass rate is higher. But if breakdown, the secondary-side interface board will damage, and can't recover for their-self, only replace the interface board.

2. For the high voltage switch cabinet, surge impulse interference have the biggest impact on the reliability, the weights almost more than six times the oscillatory waves, and the EFT impact on its reliability can be accounted for 30% of its overall weight. For the CB, surge impulse interference impact on its reliability occupies the absolute weight, it is weight almost as five times as others. For the GIS, EFT impact on its reliability can be accounted for 51% of the overall weight, the surge impulse interference nearly 37% of the weight. The oscillatory waves has the weight is about 12%.

3. The high-voltage switchgear withstands the electromagnetic interference frequency each year in field. Combining with the experimental data and table, the high-voltage switchgear reliability trend are obtained and improve the expected service life prediction. For the manufacturers, improve to switchgear performance by the test data analysis, the anti-interference ability of the electromagnetic compatibility and work reliability of will enhance.

REFERENCES

[1] Zhao Zhen-dong, Lou Yun-yong, Zhang Ya-dong, Wang Yan-jun. Structure of Reliability Evaluation Model for Electric Power Communication Network [J]. Electric Power Technology, 2010,19(9):74–77.
[2] Min Ding-fu. Reliability Appraisal of Insulators for Extra-high Voltage Transmission Line [J]. Power System Technology, 1999,23(5):40–41.
[3] Ma Shi-xiao, Lin Xin, Wang Yu, Shi Fei. Jugement method of reliability of life span of high voltage circuit breaker[J]. Journal of Liaoning Technical University, 2006,25 (11):170–172.
[4] Richard Redl. Electromagnetic Environ mental Impact of Power Electronics Equipment [J]. Proceedings of the IEEE, 2001,89(6):926–938.
[5] Zhu Pu-da. Analysis on Reliability of Machine Tool Electrical Apparatus Under Plateau Environment Conditions [J]. Electrical and Electronics, 2009 (8):9–11.
[6] GB/T3187-94, Reliability and maintainability terms [S].
[7] GJB 813-90, Reliability Model and Prediction [S].
[8] Lu Jian-guo, Zhang Nai-kuan, Li Kui. Low-voltage electrical testing and detection [M]. BeiJing: China Electric Power Press., 2007.
[9] Lu Jian-guo. Overview on Reliability of Low-Voltage Electrical Apparatus and Their Development Prospects [J]. Journal of Hebei university of technology, 2009,38(1):1–5.
[10] Li Xiao-jian, Kang Rui, Dai Fei, Jiao Shu-yuan. A Method of EMC Analysis Based on Reliability Math [J]. Telemtry, Tracking and Command, 2010(1):65–70.
[11] GB/T11022-1999, Common Specifications for high-voltage Switchgear and controlgear standards [S].
[12] GB/T14598-2006, Electrical relays [S].
[13] IEC61000-4-1:2000. Electromagnetic compatibility-Testing and measurement techniques-Overview of immunity tests [S].
[14] IEC61000-4-4:2004, Electromagnetic compatibility-Testing and measurement techniques-Electrical fast transient/burst immunity test [S].
[15] IEC61000-4-12:1995, Electromagnetic compatibility-Testing and measurement techniques-Oscillatory waves immunity test [S].
[16] IEC61000-4-5:2008, Electromagnetic compatibility-Testing and measurement techniques-Surge immunity test [S].
[17] Nie Jun-lan. Wang Jing-qin. Establish of Low Voltage Switchgear Reliability Index Based on Analytic Hierarchy Process [J]. Low Voltage Apparatus, 2005 (5):3–6.

Computer, Intelligent Computing and Education Technology – Liu, Sung & Yao (Eds)
© 2014 Taylor & Francis Group, London, ISBN 978-1-138-02469-4

Study of overvoltage monitoring method based on compound integration Rogowski coil

Fang-Cheng Lv, Xiao-Zhou Fan, Hong-Yu Liu, Yong-Xia Wang & Ming-Hai Ma
North China Electric Power University, Baoding, China

ABSTRACT: On the basis of the leakage current of capacitive equipment, to optimize the online monitoring of overvoltage, this paper presented a method to measure the leakage current of the tap of bushing based on Rogowski coil. According to the deficiency of common integral circuit of the Rogowski coil, a novel compound integration circuit is designed. The measurement band was broadened through mutual cooperation between the spectral characteristics of each component. The Parameters of compound integration circuit were calculated based on the existing coil of the lab, which extend the measuring-band and make the low limit cut off frequency 0.27 Hz and upper cut off frequency 3.5 MHz, and keep the Sensitivity of the coil 98 mV/A, to meet the requirement of the leakage current measurement.

Keywords: compound integration; Rogowski coil; overvoltage; monitoring

1 INTRODUCTION

As indicated by previous operating experience and research result, overvoltage is the main cause for grid failures and insulation defects[1]. So it becomes very important to apply real-time monitoring for grid overvoltage.

Rogowski coil is one of the most commonly used methods to monitor real-time voltage and electric current. In our paper, we designed a compound integral Rogowski coil combined with self-integrator and out-integrator. It satisfied the requirement of measuring the leakage signal of electric current from the tap of casing's end screen in common overvoltage situations. Through simulation and analysis, we proved that the new design of Rogowski coil can measure overvoltage signals under common situations.

2 PRINCIPLE OF OVERVOLTAGE MEASUREMENT AND CHARACTERISTICS OF THE CURRENT SIGNAL OF BUSHING TAP

2.1 Principle of overvoltage measurement

The fundamental principle of overvoltage signals restored from leakage current of capacitive devices is as followed. Typically, capacitive bushing can be approximately represented by an equivalent capacitance C. When the grid is invaded by overvoltage u, there will be current i flowing through the bushing tap. The following formula shows the rationale:

$$u = \frac{1}{T}\int i(t)d_t \tag{1}$$

where T is the integration constant.

2.2 Characteristics of current signal of bushing tap

As showed in formula (1), the determining success factor is to accurately measure the leakage current, which requires selection of the reasonable current sensor. Furthermore, it will facilitate the selection of the most suitable current sensor, if we clearly understand the characteristics of the differential current to be measured.

As we have known that:

1. Under common grid voltage, the current of bushing tap is at mA level;
2. Under operating overvoltage, the current is approximately 2-3A; under standard lighting overvoltage, the current of bushing tap can reach hundreds of A;
3. Under impulsive overvoltage, the current of bushing tap also shows impulsive waveform. The wave front and half peak time are less compared to original overvoltage waveform, and the waveform is steeper;
4. Under different voltages, frequency of the current flowed through bushing tap is mainly in between of 1 Hz~3 MHz.

Our research chose Rogowski coil as the current sensor to capture current signal of the bushing tap.

3 COMPOUND INTEGRATOR DESIGN

Traditional Rogowski coil can be separated by its working status; self-integral working and out-integral working. The output voltage from the sensing head of self-integral Rogowski coil is proportional to measured current. The output voltage from the sensing head of out-integral Rogowski coil is the differential of measured current. The signal has to be restored by an external integration circuit. In our study, we designed a compound integrator combined with self-integrator and out-integrator. The compound integrator can keep the sensitivity, at the same time expand the working bandwidth, and realize required functionalities of the sensor.

As showed in Figure 1, the compound integrator is composed of Rogowski coil high frequency self-integrator, passive RC intermediate frequency out-integrator, active R_1C_1 low frequency integrator and high frequency filtering part. The resistor R_L in active integrator is feedback resistor.

It can effectively reduce the direct current gain, reduce output offset, effectively inhibit the integration drift, and prevent the integrator output saturation.

The transfer function for the compound integral part can be indicated as:

$$H(s) = \frac{sM}{1+T_a S} \cdot \frac{T_L(1+T_1s)}{T_1(1+T_Ls)} \cdot \frac{1+T_2s}{1+T_0s} \cdot \frac{T_hs}{1+T_hs} \quad (2)$$

where $T_0 = (R_0 + C_0)C_0$, $T_2 = R_2C_0$, $T_L = R_LC_1$, $T_h = R_hC_h$.

If $T_L = T_h, T_0 = T_1, T_2 = T_a$, formula (2) can be further simplified as:

$$H(s) = \frac{M}{T_0} \left(\frac{T_Ls}{1+T_Ls} \right)^2 \quad (3)$$

We made a rectangular Rogowski coil skeleton with 200 turns. The sensitivity of the sensor designed in our research is 98 mV/A. In our study, we used MATLAB to do simulations. We got the

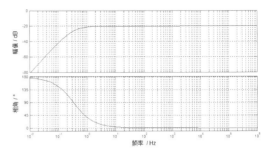

Figure 2. Compound integration transducer Bode-diagram.

frequency of sensor under the condition of $\omega < \omega_c$, as Figure 2 showed.

Further considering the limitation of characteristic angle, and the upper limit frequency of the sensor is set as 3.5 MHz. Within the range of working frequency bandwidth, the amplifier frequency and phase-frequency characteristic are not influenced by the measured signal. The output signal and measured signal do not have phase changes. The output signal can effectively reflect the current being measured.

4 SIMULATION ANALYSIS AND VERIFICATION

Based on the above discussion, we build up the theoretical model for the feasibility analysis of our simulation. We combined the use of EMTP and MATLAB in our simulation. We build up the capacitive bushing tap model through the use of EMTP, and we can get the current of the bushing tap from the simulation. Based on the model of compound integral circuit, the theory of restoring signal of overvoltage through current signal, and the current sensor simulation model and integral circuit using MATLAB, we finally capture the gird overvoltage signal.

In order to test the measurement performance of lighting overvoltage, our paper adopted the standard lighting overvoltage which is 1.2/50 μs, amplifier frequency is 450 kV. The simulation result is showed in Figure 3.

To further verify the measurement performance of impulsive overvoltage, our study adopted the standard operating impulsive overvoltage which is 250/2500 μs, the amplifier frequency is 450 kV. The simulation result is showed in Figure 3.

According to the above simulation results showed in Figures 3 and 4, whether for operating overvoltage or lighting overvoltage, both the wave front time and wave tail time can be measured relatively accurate. Both rising and falling edges can

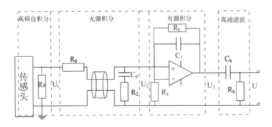

Figure 1. Compound integration transducer circuit diagram.

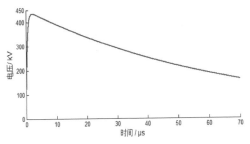

(a) Waveform of standard lighting overvoltage

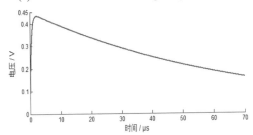

(b) Simulation result for voltage measurement

Figure 3. Standard lighting overvoltage simulations.

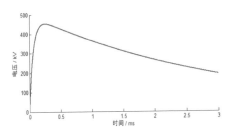

(a) Waveform for standard operating impulse overvoltage

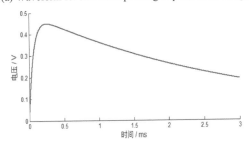

(b) Simulation result for operating voltage

Figure 4. Standard impulsive overvoltage simulations.

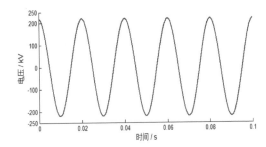

(a) Waveform of grid overvoltage

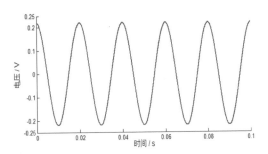

(b) Simulation result for voltage measurement

Figure 5. Power frequency overvoltage simulations.

power frequency overvoltage with twice of the voltage under normal working status, which is 220kV, to simulate and test the accuracy of the method proposed by our research.

As indicated by Figure 5, the method proposed by our study can accurately restore and measure power frequency overvoltage. The simulation results further indicate that the method proposed in this research can meet the requirements of phase frequency and amplifier frequency.

5 CONCLUSIONS

In our research, we proposed a new method to measure grid overvoltage by restoring the current signal of bushing tap using Rogowski coil. By making use of characteristics of different parts of the compound integral circuit, we achieved the goal of expanding frequency bandwidth, and met the requirements of measuring current signal. Our findings are identified as below:

1. The voltage of the circuit is restored from the bushing tap current signal, which does not require changes to the electrical equipment wiring. The safety performance is also satisfactory.

be better restored. The above findings indicate that the design in our research can efficiently and effectively restore the grid impulsive overvoltage.

Power frequency overvoltage is the common phenomenon in power systems. Our paper used

2. The level of current signal of the bushing tap ranged from mA to A. The frequency bandwidth also ranged from Hz to MHz level. Using Rogowski coil as current sensor can satisfy all the requirements.

3. The compound integral Rogowski coil is used as current sensor in our study. The working bandwidth of the sensor is ranging from 0.27 Hz to 3.5 MHz. The sensitivity of the sensor also increased to 98 mV/A. The above working bandwidth and sensitivity meet the requirements of measuring leakage current.

4. As indicated by simulation results, by applying the method designed in our study, we can effectively measure the common grid overvoltage. The measurement performance is accurate and reliable.

REFERENCES

Hewson C.R, Ray W.F, Davis R.M. Verification of Rogowski current transducer's ability to measure fast switching transients[C]. Applied Power Electronics Conference and Exposition, APEC'06, 2006, 573–579.

Jayaram S, Xu X.Y, Cross J.D. Highdivider ratio fast response capacitive dividers for high voltage pulse measurements[J]. IEEE Trans. on Industry Applications, 2000,36(3): 920–922.

Michael A. Brubaker, Christopher P. Yakymys hyn. An Electro-Optic Voltage Sensor for Electrion Beam Position and Current Monitoring[J]. IEEE transaction on plasma science. 2000,28(5):1440–1444.

Patrick P. Chavez, Farnoosh Rahmatian, Nicolas A.F. Jaeger. Accurate Voltage Measurement with Electric Field Sampling Using Permittivity Shielding[J]. IEEE trans on power delivery. 2002,17(2):362–368.

Ray W.F., C.R. Hewson. High Performance Rogowski Current Transducers. Industry Applications Conference, 2000, 3083–3090.

Computer, Intelligent Computing and Education Technology – Liu, Sung & Yao (Eds)
© 2014 Taylor & Francis Group, London, ISBN 978-1-138-02469-4

Constructions of space-resource curriculums of higher mathematics based on network platform in the world university city

Hai-Yan Zhen

Shandong Institute of Commerce and Technology, Jinan, China

ABSTRACT: The world university city uses the mutual teaching and learning as the core concept, and can quickly establish a interactive learning platform of resources cooperative building and sharing for each agency and a powerful lifelong learning space for everyone. The paper takes the higher mathematics course as an example, introduces the function of the cloud space in the world university city on curriculum construction, and discusses concept of curriculum construction, procedure and the application effect of teaching platform of the cloud space in the world university city.

Keywords: the world university city; higher mathematics; construction of network course

1 INTRODUCTION OF THE WORLD UNIVERSITY CITY

The world university city is a network—virtual city. It uses Web2.0, Sns, Blog, Tag, Rss, Wiki and so on as the core, bases on the six degrees of separation, XML, Ajax and other theories and technical design, takes interactive network distance-education as the core, and integrates remote teaching, network office, timely communication, business management, social media, digital library and other functions. So, it is both a virtual and real university community platform and is a social lifelong learning campus. The world university city's aim is to create the mutual educational platform which is also global and remote. The web site of the world university city is: http://www.worlduc.com/. Its Chinese domain name is world university city.

As the world's largest open-course platform abroad and home, the world university city arouses more and more widespread concern in the community. The world university city uses the mutual teaching and learning as the core concept. It can quickly establish an interactive learning platform of resource cooperative building and sharing f or each agency and build a powerful lifelong learning space for everyone, whose functions of institutional platform and personal space are stronger than traditional network. With those powerful characteristics of Web2.0 and remote software service, remote platform service, remote basic logic architecture service, remote online data storage service and mobile application service based on cloud computing, the world university city has become the largest public cloud-computing service

platform at home. Moreover, it combines the advantages of the SNS, KNS, WNS architecture in the most advanced field of Internet. Furthermore, it aggregates video sharing, live video, community friends, interactive electronic classrooms, online learning, online examinations, instant messaging, blogs, podcasts, micro-blog, electronic commerce and other powerful functional modules. It only takes a few seconds to register to open a new era of social network with a powerful interactive website not only for individual, but also for unit. There are digital libraries, famous—teacher classrooms, masters of photography forums, famous university—teacher forums, famous-teacher forums in primary and middle schools and other columns on the platform. Now there are social activities, learning, teaching, management and other activities which come from thousands of high schools and middle schools home and abroad in the world on the platform of the world university city. The number of teaching plans and articles increases by more than 1 million and thousands of videos increases every day on the platform. Now there has been millions of tutorials and video courseware of all kinds.

So far, there have been more than 500,000 personal spaces of teachers and students and more than 200 platforms built on the platform of world university city. On the one hand, the world university city lets the student-centered autonomous learning concept gradually form and become a reality. On the other hand, the world university city makes the real implementation of the learning, teaching, management of 24 hours possible. And, on this account, the world university city brings about a revolution in education information which is relied on its openness.

2 CONSTRUCTIONS OF THE SPACE PROGRAM OF HIGHER MATHEMATICS

2.1 Concept of curriculum construction

First, serving the students better and improving the comprehensive quality of students are the main line. Second, serving the professional course better is the purpose of service. Third, providing a good mathematical foundation for the lifelong development of students is the higher goal. Fourth, the demand of higher mathematics teaching syllabus of higher vocational colleges is the basis. Based on that, we design teaching content and teaching ideas of higher mathematics. At the same time, we establish curriculum resources of the cloud space of higher mathematics in the world university city.

2.2 Ideas of curriculum construction

Firstly we should do in-depth research on every second-level institute so that we can know the demand for higher mathematics of every major. Then we can define proper content settings and focus plate settings of higher mathematics according to different students. All that we do is to build the dominant idea of curriculum construction meeting the professional service. Secondly, we do some researches to investigate the need for the further study of students. For example, some students have needs for self-examination, and some students have the need for rising only this and postgraduate entrance exams. In the light of the surveys, according to the different needs of students to recombine the learning content, the higher mathematics curriculum is divided into the professional basic-need space, the improving plate and the second—classroom plate. All above makes full use of the cloud space of network platform of the world university city to realize the open and interactive teaching.

2.3 Establishment of columns and navigations of constructions of space curriculums according to the course characteristics of higher mathematics

The curriculum program of the cloud space is the overall framework of space-curriculum resources. According to the inherent characteristics of functions of the world university city and curriculum characteristics of higher mathematics, the construction of curriculum resources of higher mathematics establishes the construction of key-space curriculums the second—classroom, teaching management and other one—level columns. And, each one—level column has also established a number of two-level columns. For one example, the teaching column sets up probability theory and mathematical statistics, mathematical modeling, linear algebra and other two-level columns. For another, the column of second-classroom sets up rural counseling, counseling for rising only this, counseling for the postgraduate entrance examination and other two-level columns. Likewise, the teaching management sets up classroom attendance, teaching log, teaching schedule, midterm and final examination and other two-level columns. And, some two-level columns set up three-level columns. For instance, probability theory and mathematical statistics which is two-level column also establishes syllabuses, teaching plans, electronic lesson plans, teaching courseware, exercises and other three-level columns. what's more, all settings of columns are relatively flexible and there is no strict definition, so, in order to serve the teaching and learning better, teachers can set columns according to their own habits or needs.

Since that teaching hours of the higher mathematics is limit, not only in order to obtain good results of teaching and learning, but also to avoid wasting time of students to find resources in the learning process, we also set up a striking navigation bar, showing syllabuses, teaching plans, electronic lesson plans, teaching courseware, teaching schedules and other sides of higher mathematics clearly, which provides a clear path for students learning.

2.4 Establishment of other plates related to teaching of space curriculums

In order to make better use of the cloud space of the university city to teach and learn, the world university city also sets some important interactive plates. There are close relationships in "my teaching and research section", "online self-testing" etc. "My teaching and research section" is the group that is composed of students who are taught by the teacher. "My teaching and research section" is called my group in the old version of the cloud space of the world university city, but now it is changed to "my teaching and research section". The name now can reflect the significance of its existence more clearly. In "my teaching and research section", teachers and students can express various topics and activities about learning, such as discussing problems during learning, reformation of teaching methods and assessment methods and so on. In the "online self-testing", teachers can give examinations to students. The test paper is generally formed by the name, the time when finished it, type of paper (extracting the random test paper from question bank or self—forming test paper from teachers). After forming the paper, the teacher can arrange the test and after the test the computer automatically gives results list, bringing great convenience to the teacher who tallies the scores.

In addition to make students communicate better to promote their learning, the cloud space of the university city also sets up a message broad and a private-letter column.

3 COMPARISON OF APPLICATION AND EFFECT IN TEACHING OF THE NETWORK CURRICULUM OF "HIGHER MATHEMATICS"

The characteristics of students in higher vocational college are the poor mathematical basis, being late to school and absenteeism easily, and not finishing the homework on time. According to these, the use of the cloud space in mathematics teaching in the university city plays a very good effect on learning management of students. Firstly, each lesson uses the classroom attendance column of the cloud space to check on-site attendance and to record the students being late or absent on the spot, which has a deterrent effect for other students. Then, for the problems of homework, the work can be put into online self-testing, and the timeliness of online self-testing allows students to complete and submit, eliminating the phenomenon of not handing or leaking homework.

Because curriculum resources of the cloud space are very rich, according to the needs of different specialties and different levels of students, teachers can link the teaching courseware to different plates when teaching higher mathematics. For instance, when teaching higher mathematics to the students who are major in accounting, teachers can link the relevant chapters to the cases about economy in curriculum of mathematical modeling. When teaching the good-degree students for higher requirements, we can link the relevant knowledge to the examples of undergraduate textbooks. The type being Single and flat teaching in tradition becomes into three-dimensional and diverse.

Because the class hours of higher mathematics in higher vocational colleges is less, the abundant teaching resources of higher mathematics on the platform in the cloud space provide great convenience for the students' autonomous learning. As a result, teachers can guide students to learn so that they can use the cloud space to learn after class according to the needs of students who are with different majors and different degrees. For example, the students who need self-examination are able to use class courseware, self-taught Zhenti of the self-taught column to learn after class.

In addition, the exchange of teachers and students through the cloud space platform of the world university city is more diverse. The teacher can set homework, comment on the homework, show excellent reviews through the space. Besides, the teacher can counsel students one-on-on through the message plate and the private-letter column. As well as, the teacher can guide good-degree students to do development of learning through the plate of the second—classroom. The cloud space of the world university city considers the network platform as the carrier, and as long as the network terminal exists, you can learn and exchange higher mathematics whenever and wherever possible, breaking the limitation of classroom, time and space. Of course, teaching and learning has also been broken 45 minutes of the traditional classroom, no doubt that students can learn through browsing the teachers' class videos or courseware whenever and wherever possible. Equally, students who are after graduating from school to work can also enter into the classroom space and call space resources for independent and self-service learning. Thus, in a word, the cloud space of the world university city provides a platform for students' lifelong learning.

4 INVESTIGATION AND ANALYSIS OF THE TEACHING EFFECT OF THE CLOUD SPACE

We give different teaching methods to two administrative classes, information 1 and 2 of level 2012, respectively. The teaching method of class 1 is space curriculum, including space for classes, giving homework, online tests and so on. Besides, other students who have problems can communicate with teachers through "my teaching and research section", message boards, or private letters in the space, and teachers guide students to study by themselves through the space. The teaching method of class 2 is traditional. After a semester of teaching, under investigation of learning situation, we find that compared with the traditional teaching method, using space-curriculum resources to teach can stimulate more interests of students in learning, at the same time, students' learning enthusiasm is higher and their autonomous learning ability is stronger. Through the final exam results, we find the scores of class 1 with cloud space teaching are significantly higher than that of class 2 with the traditional teaching method.

With higher mathematics teaching by the cloud space of the world university city, students can come into the classroom space at any time through the network, are easy to find the knowledge they need through the eye-catching column navigation, and watch the teachers' teaching videos, improving the fun of learning and learning efficiency. In addition "my teaching and research section", message boards and private—letter columns provide teachers and students a good platform for the exchange. Also, the real-name system and eye-catching portrait shorten the distance between teachers and students, making the communication more smooth and learning more interested. Teaching of the cloud space makes the concept of student-centered education come true, achieves the independent learning and open learning, and provides the material foundation for their lifelong learning.

REFERENCES

[1] Wang Jian. The computer application of exploring new mechanisms and creating new ways of constructions of education information—practice and prospect of education information of HuNan [J]. *Chinese Information Education: Higher And Vocational Education*, 2011,(9):12–13.

[2] Wang Fucheng. Self-regulated learning system of college students based on cloud computing [J]. *Science and Technology Innovation Herald*, 2011,(7):16–17.

[3] Jiang Dayuan. The basic trend and enlightenment of curriculum reform of vocational education in the world [J]. *Vocational Technology,* 2008,(11):11–12.

[4] Luo Zhian. Construction and application of space-resource course based on the network platform of the world university city—take "community rehabilitation" course as an example [J]. *Chinese Rehabilitation Theory and Practice*, 2013,(19).

[5] Xie Quanfeng. Construction of space group on Shinkansen platform and interactive mode of classroom teaching of vocational education of the world university city. *Journal of Changsha District Vocational Technical College,* 2011,(2).

[6] Chen Hongjun. Discussion on six function of teachers' personal space of the world university city. *Chinese Information Education,* 2012,(5).

Computer, Intelligent Computing and Education Technology – Liu, Sung & Yao (Eds)
© *2014 Taylor & Francis Group, London, ISBN 978-1-138-02469-4*

The research of radio and television programme-oriented intelligence analysis system

M. Zhao, T.Z. Zhang & J.P. Chai
Information Engineering School, Communication University of China, China

ABSTRACT: Aiming at the communicator-centered situation in radio and television market, we put forward an oriented intelligent analysis system for broadcasting and TV programs. In order to build such a system, we use the technological means of data mining and data collection, and make use of the audience rating system, data base, model base and method base to realize the analysis function of providing distinctive recommendation service for different service objects.

Keywords: radio and television; programme orient; data mining; audience rating system; database

1 INTRODUCTION

Under the trend of the integration of three networks which combines telecommunication network, computer network and cable network, broadcasting and television industry faces thousands of opportunities, and faces huge challenges at the same time. The integration of the three networks takes brilliant changes to broadcasting and television industry. Facing the drastic competition, except continually improving the hardware facilities, it still needs to know what the audiences need indeed.[1]

Let *Gantry escort* as an example. Its click is very high on the Internet, but its ratings are unsatisfied on TV. Why does this phenomenon happen? *Gantry escort*'s major audiences are young people, who seldom watch TV and often click the program on the Internet. Even most of young people who would watch TV on time dislike these sets of teleplays such as *Gantry Escort*.

In response to this phenomenon, we should do something. Based on the accurate user data, we analyze audiences' need to win chances for the broadcasting and television industry in the fierce competitions. This paper proposes the models of data acquisition and data mining to solve the above problems.

2 MODEL OF INTELLIGENT ORIENTED ANALYSIS SYSTEM IN THE BROADCASTING AND TELEVISION INDUSTRIES (MOIOASITBATI)

The traditional broadcasting and television industry chain provides communication from programme producer to user only. The other four components have no idea about the consumer's requirements.

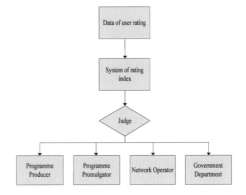

Figure 1. *MOIOASITBATI*.

To solve the above problem, this paper proposes *MOIOASITBATI*. Through analyzing the consumer's internal data and external data, it may find out the consumer's requirements. Data acquisition accomplishes data preprocessing, data mining and ratings system offer corresponding service for the government department, programme promulgator, programme producer and network operator, as shown in Figure 1.

3 SERVICE OBJECTS

3.1 *Programme producer*

The major product in broadcasting and television industry is the programme that is made by programme producer. The aim that consumer watches TV is to get the contents of the programme. When judging the programme is successful or not, the most important thing is consumer's attitude.

Via *MOIOASITBATI*, programme producer can know which type of programme is popular in audience, and know why the programme success, or fail. At the same time, they produce different types of programme to appeal to audiences by analyzing the audience's characters. They also can know which communication platform they could choose by the system.

3.2 *Programme promulgator*

Choosing programmes, arranging programmes time and showing programmes are the programme promulgator's duties. They need know the audience's different requirements in different time. Analyzing the consumer's demand accurately will help them to push programmes.

Via *MOIOASITBATI*, programme promulgator could judge which type of programme would be imported and arrange programmes properly. It can help the programme promulgator to establish popular platform and form a big number of loyal consumers.

3.3 *Network operator*

Network operator is the indispensable part in the broadcasting and television industry. The most important thing for the network operator is to know the performance and the success of the programme producer and programme promulgator.

Via *MOIOASITBATI*, the network operator could judge what programme producer and programme promulgator could operate with. Choosing correct cooperative partner is beneficial to improve the value of the brand and management.

3.4 *Government department*

Broadcasting and television is an important place where government department can propagandize the sound of the Party. As a public media, it undertakes the tasks of transmitting information, entertainment and serving for society. These functions enrich people's life and promote society's improvement. As the public culture's supervisor, government department need to know the evolution and the trend.

Via *MOIOASITBATI*, government department could judge the evolution and direction. So they could form corresponding policy to make the industry improve orderly and transmit positive culture.[5]

4 DATA PROCESSING AND DATA ANALYZING

4.1 *Data processing*

The original data in the paper is entire network data which comes from some province. Using entire network data is to be more typical and more accurate. Accurate data subserves the conclusion.

In this paper, the data is divided into 2 sectors: programme warehouse and user rating warehouse. Programme warehouse records programme information and user rating warehouse records user's viewing behavior. As show in Table 1.

As the jargon is "garbage in, garbage out". In order to get the accurate conclusion, the data needs preprocess. The pretreatment process is data selection, data cleaning, data conversion and data statute.[2],[6]

4.2 *Data analyzing*

In the era of big data, data stand for authority. This paper analyzes *broadcasting proportion*, *rating proportion*, *rating*, *Reach(%)*, *Rtg(%)*, *Shr(%)* and *Audience loyalty*, and compares these indicators synthetically.

$$Broadcasting\ proportion = \frac{a}{b} \qquad (1)$$

where a = a type of programme's broadcast time, b = all programmes' total broadcast time.

$$Rating\ proportion = \frac{v}{u} \qquad (2)$$

where v = a type of programme's viewing time, u = all programmes' total viewing time.

The *broadcasting proportion* and *rating proportion* show the supply and the demand of all kinds of programme.

$$Rtg(\%) = \frac{\sum_{i=1}^{n} S_i(\min) * w_i}{t * m} * 100\% \qquad (3)$$

Table 1. Data situation.

Underlying data	✧ Programme start time
	✧ Programme end time
	✧ Numbers of programme
	✧ User start watching the programme time
	✧ User end watching the programme time
	✧ Channel
	✧ User top box ID
Middle data	❖ *Reach(%)*
	❖ *Rtg(%)*
	❖ *Shr(%)*
	❖ Audience loyalty
	❖ Broadcasting proportion
	❖ Rating proportion
Resulting data	➢ Forecast the popular programme
	➢ Forecast audience's concerns

where S_i = the viewing time thar the user i watches some programme, w_i = the weight of the user i, n = all users who watch the programme, t = some programme's total time, m = total users.

$Rtg(\%)$ observes the percent of the numbers of the watching the programme's or the channel's users among the all users.[3]

$$Reach(\%) = \frac{\sum_{i=1}^{n} S_i^t * w_i}{m} * 100\% \qquad (4)$$

where S_i^t = the all users who meet the requirements in some specific period of time, w_i = the weight of the user i, m = total users.

$Reach(\%)$ observes the percent of the numbers of the watching the programme's or the channel's nonredundant users among the all users in the specific time. The value reflects reflects the scale of the audiences and dissemination universality.[3]

$$Shr(\%) = \frac{r}{ra} * 100\% \qquad (5)$$

where r = the rating of some channel or programme, ra = the rating of all channels or programmes.

$Shr(\%)$ observes the percent of the numbers of the watching the programme's or channel's users among the all users who are watching programme or the channel in the specific time. The value reflects the competitiveness of the programme or the channel in the specific time.[3]

$$Audience\ loyalty = \frac{r}{re} * 100 \qquad (6)$$

where r = the rating(%) of some channel or programme, re = the reach(%) of some channel or programme.

Audience loyalty observes the degree of the users' loyalty. The value is bigger, the number of the programme's of channel's loyal audiences is bigger.[3]

4.3 Service object

In section 3, it tells us what the every department cares about.

By analyzing these indicators, it can tell the programme producer and programme promulgator about the supply and demand of all kinds of programmes and which type of programme is popular, which programme has a big number of audiences, which programme is downturn. And it can help the network operator judge which platform is worth cooperation. It also can tell the government department what type of event that the people care about.

By observing the change of the indicators for some time, and analyzing the reason why the indicators change. Give the report to relevant departments, helping them to make decisions.

5 CONCLUSION

In the background of integration of three networks, this paper proposes the Model Of Intelligent Oriented Analysis System In The Broadcasting And Television Industry (*MOIOASITBATI*). This paper analyzes their requirements of programme producer, programme promulgator, network operator, government department, builds the Model of intelligent oriented analysis system in the broadcasting and television industry, introduces data and analyzes the indicators or factors which are relevant to each department in the broadcasting and television industry. The intelligent oriented analysis system in the broadcasting and television industry can give different service to different object, it can enhance the competitiveness of this industry.

ACKNOWLEDGEMENT

This paper is supported by the national sci-tech support plan project Key Technology Research and Application of Stereo Vision Content Services which numbered 2012BAH37F03. Thanks for the work of the refereeing.

REFERENCES

[1] Yin F, Chai J. Research of Data Acquisition and Data Mining for Broadcasting and Television Systems[C]// Management and Service Science (MASS), 2011 International Conference on. IEEE, 2011: 1–4.
[2] Pyle D. Data Preparation for Data Mining[M]. Morgan Kaufmann, 1999.
[3] Liu Y N. Television Ratings Analytic: Investigation, Analysis and Application[M]//The Publisher of Communication University of China, 2006.
[4] Song J B, Chai J P, Kan K. The Research on Broadcasting and Television Public Opinion Analysis[J]// Journal of Communication University of China Science and Technology, 2009, 16(2).
[5] Li G Z. The Guiding Role of Television Entertainment programs Should Be Valued[J]//News Spread, 2013 (008): 309–309.
[6] Jian Z G, Jin X. Research on Data Preprocess in Data Mining and Its Application[J]//Application Research Of Computers, 2004, 21(7): 117–118.
[7] Wang H W. Introduction to television ratings index analysis[J]. Science & Technology Information (25).
[8] Wan B B, Zhang T Z, Chai J P, et al. Research of User Experience and Data Mining for Stereo Vision[J]. Applied Mechanics and Materials, 2014, 457: 984–987.

Computer, Intelligent Computing and Education Technology – Liu, Sung & Yao (Eds)
© 2014 Taylor & Francis Group, London, ISBN 978-1-138-02469-4

A hand gesture recognition method based on inertial sensor

Hui-Xia Wang, Ping Yang, Qian Xiao & Jian-Bao Wang
School of Mechatronics Engineering, University of Electronic Science and Technology of China, Chengdu, China

ABSTRACT: Gesture interaction technology has become a hotspot. We mainly study gesture recognition methods based on the inertial sensor. Following easily recognizable principle, we propose a simple and practical approach. Firstly, 14 kinds of gesture are defined and are classified as 3 categories. Secondly, according to the kinematic characteristic of different gestures, acceleration and angular velocity signal characteristic are extracted. Thirdly, for recognizing specific gesture, we adopt the decision tree classification algorithm to classify. Finally, the recognition rate reached 96% in our experiment, meanwhile, the gesture recognition time is less than 0.01 s.

Keywords: gesture recognition; decision tree classification; human-interactive; inertial sensor

1 INTRODUCTION

People is becoming increasingly focus on user experience[1]. For the real-time recognition of gestures by an arbitrary person, a simple and accurate recognition method is indispensable[2].

Currently, there have some researches about gesture recognition methods based on MEMS IMU[3]. Because of the variations of users' operation, the response signal for the same gesture is not same. So it is not easy to build accurate hand gesture template, such as (HMM)[4]. Based on the analysis above, a new gesture recognition method based on MEMS inertial sensor is proposed by us. It is by extracting the kinematics feature of gesture to recognize hand gesture. The algorithm we apply is not only satisfying the real-time, accuracy and continuity requirements for human-interactive of embedded system, but also improving the applicability of users.

2 GESTURE DEFINITION

In my study, the principle we uphold is that the movement is easily to learn and to operate, meanwhile, the movement need to have distinctive feature which is easily to recognize. Therefore, given the requirements above, we define 14 kinds of hand gestures which are classified as 3 categories, under the premise that movements don't need to any basis movements. The defined gesture is shown as Table 1.

3 RECOGNITION ALGORITHM

The overall goal in gesture recognition module is to build a robust classifier to classify hands gestures. Gesture recognition model is shown as Figure 1.

3.1 Signal preprocessing

The six position calibration method is adopted to calibrate Scale Factor (SF) and bias[5]. Firstly, the device is fixed on the flat, then the device is put upward and downward placement respectively along the XYZ axis.

Under every state, the output of each sensitive axis of accelerometer only contains the gravitational acceleration. The computing methods about SF_{acc}, B_{acc} and acceleration calibration formula are shown as following.

$$SF_{acc} = \frac{V_{+g} - V_{-g}}{2g} \tag{1}$$

Table 1. Gesture definition.

Gesture category	Movement	Instruction
Rotation		Holding device rotates 90 degree once or twice, clockwise or counterclockwise
Swing		Holding device swings once or twice, up or down
		Holding device swings once or twice, left or right
Shaking		Shaking device up and down, or, left and right

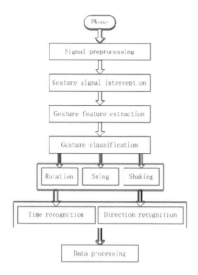

Figure 1. Gesture recognition model.

$$B_{acc} = \frac{V_{+g} + V_{-g}}{2} \qquad (2)$$

$$a = \frac{9.8(V_{acc} - B_{acc})}{SF_{acc}} \qquad (3)$$

where, V_{+g} and V_{-g} are the voltage output in each axis of the accelerometer when it's aligned and opposite to the direction of the gravity. V_{acc} is the output signal of accelerometer, a is the real acceleration value.

As to the gyroscope calibration, the bias of each axis is measured by averaging T_{bais}. T_{bais} depends on the quality of gyroscope, and can be estimated by Allan Variance analysis[6]. SF_{gyro} can be obtained by formula 4.

$$SF_{gyro} = \frac{V_{gyro} - B_{gyro}}{\omega_{rate}} \qquad (4)$$

where, V_{gyro} (v) is gyroscope output with a standard input ω_{rate} (rad/s), B_{gyro}(v) is the gyroscope bias[7,8]. The gyroscope calibration equation is shown as following.

$$\omega = \frac{V_{gyro} - B_{gyro}}{SF_{gyro}} \qquad (5)$$

Continuous length of a gesture signal is between 0.3 S–1 S, so the frequency of hands gesture is between 1 Hz–4 Hz. From that, we can see that the signal sampling frequency is 100 Hz. Given the sampling frequency[9], we adopt a 3rd order Butterworth low-pass filter.

3.2 Segmentation of gesture signal

The first step is to detect the start and the end of the gestures. The acceleration and angular velocity signals are shown as Figure 2.

When movement of the gesture is stopped, acceleration signals and angular velocity signals are stable. When gesture movements begin, acceleration and angular velocity signals change dramatically. The difference of signals expresses the intensity of the signal change. Therefore, we choose the acceleration signals and angular velocity signals to detect the start and the end of gestures.

The calculation methods are shown as following.

$$\Delta a_k = \left| a_{x_k} - a_{x_{k-1}} \right| + \left| a_{y_k} - a_{y_{k-1}} \right| + \left| a_{z_k} - a_{z_{k-1}} \right| \qquad (6)$$

$$M_{a_k} = \frac{1}{N} \sum_{k=1}^{N} \Delta a_k \qquad (7)$$

$$\Delta \omega_k = \left| \omega_{x_k} - \omega_{x_{k-1}} \right| + \left| \omega_{y_k} - \omega_{y_{k-1}} \right| + \left| \omega_{z_k} - \omega_{z_{k-1}} \right| \qquad (8)$$

$$M_{\omega_k} = \frac{1}{N} \sum_{k=1}^{N} \Delta \omega_k \qquad (9)$$

Δa_k and $\Delta \omega_k$ are relatively acceleration difference and angular velocity difference in the kth point. M_{a_k} and M_{ω_k} are regarded as the kth point's acceleration difference and angular velocity difference.

If $M_{a_k} \geq a_{th}$, the kth point is the start point of gesture acceleration signal, otherwise, is the end point. If $M_{\omega_k} \geq \omega_{th}$, the kth point is the start point of gesture angular velocity signal, otherwise, is the end point. a_{th} and ω_{th} are relatively the start and the end point detection threshold of acceleration and angular velocity. The condition that the kth

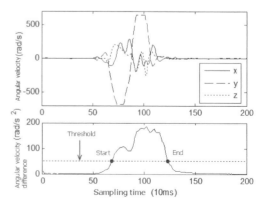

Figure 2. Gesture start point detection.

point is the start or the finish point is only when the start point and the end point are detected at the same time or the time interval is less than 0.1 s.

3.3 Extraction of gestures feature

The time length of gesture T_L:

$$T_L = t_{end} - t_{start} \tag{10}$$

The average energy of gesture segmentation E_a and E_ω

$$E_a = \frac{1}{T_L}\sum_{i=1}^{T_L}(a_{x_i}^2 + a_{y_i}^2 + a_{z_i}^2) \tag{11}$$

$$E_\omega = \frac{1}{T_L}\sum_{i=1}^{T_L}(\omega_{x_i}^2 + \omega_{y_i}^2 + \omega_{z_i}^2) \tag{12}$$

where, a_{x_i} is X axis's acceleration value, a_{y_i} is Y axis's acceleration value, a_{z_i} is Z axis's acceleration value. ω_{x_i} is X axis's angular velocity value, ω_{y_i} is Y axis's angular velocity value, ω_{z_i} is Z axis's angular velocity value.

3.3.1 Peaks

To eliminate the disturbance of unconscious trembles, the adopted method as following: we first traverse the gesture signals' data to find those points which intersects with the abscissa axis, such as C1–C6 (as shown in Fig. 3). Then we find the maximum or minimum acceleration between every two adjacent intersections. And compared with the threshold we set before. If the maximum or minimum acceleration is greater or lesser than the threshold, we add one in the amount of peaks.

3.3.2 The order of the peaks and troughs

When calculating the wave-trough order, 200 ms gesture signals are intercepted after the start of the gesture, so that assure that there only appear one

peak or one trough in every interception. Every two adjacent peaks are compared because there will appear one peaks and one trough between every three adjacent intersections. Like between C1 and C3, there have one peak P1 and one trough P2, then we will compare the value of P1 and the value of P2. If P1 > P2, then P1 is peak and P2 is trough, and vice versa.

3.4 Gesture classification algorithm

After extracting the feature vectors of gestures, a valid classification algorithm[10] is needed to classify different gestures. The decision tree algorithm can convert complex multi-classification problems to many simple classification problems. Accordingly, to reduce the complexity of classification, the decision tree is chosen to classify different gestures.

The first layer of classification: kinematic characteristics of shaking gesture mainly concentrate on acceleration signal. The lasting movement of shaking gesture is longer and the energy of shaking gesture is greater than other gestures, at the same time, the peaks of shaking gesture is greater than or equal to 3. Yet we use the gesture energy and peaks to identify the shaking gesture.

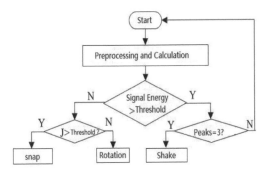

Figure 4. Gesture classification decision tree.

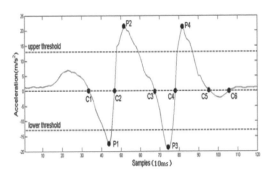

Figure 3. The way to calculate peaks.

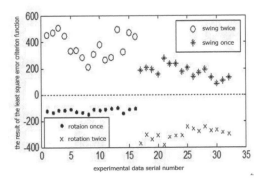

Figure 5. The result of least square criterion function.

319

Table 2. Experiment results.

	G_1	G_2	G_3	G_4	G_5	G_6	G_7	G_8	G_9	G_{10}	G_{11}	G_{12}	G_{13}	G_{14}
R_1	93		7											
R_2	2	91		7										
R_3	5		95											
R_4		4	1	95										
R_5					98		2							
R_6					2	96		2						
R_7					6		94							
R_8						5	3	92						
R_9									99		1			
R_{10}									1	98		1		
R_{11}									2		98			
R_{12}										2	3	95		
R_{13}													100	
R_{14}														100

Table 3. Gesture explanation.

G1–G2	Clockwise rotation once or twice
G3–G4	Counterclockwise rotation once or twice
G5–G6	Upward swing once or twice
G7–G8	Downward swing once or twice
G9–G10	Leftward swing once or twice
G11–G12	Rightward swing once or twice
G13	Up and down shaking
G14	Right and left shaking
R1–R14	The experiment results of G1–G14

The second layer of classification: this layer mainly identifies the swing gesture and the rotation gesture. Since kinematic characteristics of swing gesture mainly concentrate on acceleration signal and kinematic characteristics of rotation gesture mainly concentrate on angular velocity signal, only using the feature of acceleration or only using the feature of angular velocity cannot reach a high accuracy. Therefore, least square error criterion function is adopted to identify swing gesture and rotation gesture.

In the experiment phase, we collect 16 times rotation gesture (including clockwise and counterclockwise), 32 times swing gestures and 16 times shaking gesture from 10 users. We obtain the weight vector which is [5, –9, 13]. Discriminating function is: $J = 5N_{a_{max}} - 9N_{\omega_{max}} + 13$. If J > 0, the gesture is swing gesture, otherwise, is rotation gesture. Where, $N_{a_{max}}$ is the number of points, whose point's the maximum signal axial acceleration energy of is greater than the upper threshold. Meanwhile, $N_{\omega_{max}}$ is the number of points, whose point's the maximum signal axial angular velocity energy of is greater than the upper threshold.

Another ten people help us test the effect of decision tree classification. The outcome of final is shown as Figure 5.

3 EXPERIMENT RESULTS

To verify the accuracy and adaptability of decision tree algorithm for different users, we pick out 20 experimenters.

From Tables 2 and 3, we can obtain that the recognition rate for most of gestures is high. However, some gestures' recognition is low, the reason causing some low recognition rate have two. One is that experimenters are easy to jitter due to their own operation habits. The other is that when using the data, we don't eliminate the gravity. In the nutshell, the average recognition rate for the decision tree algorithm exceeds 96%.

4 CONCLUSIONS

Combined with gyroscope's output data, this method not only eliminates the limit of only using accelerometer for device gesture, but also realizes high recognition rate for any device gestures. However, for the algorithm we used which is not involved with the device gesture, we don't eliminate the gravity when the acceleration data is used, so the recognition rate is affected. What's more, in our experiment, the output data of gyroscope is not fully used. Therefore, in the further study, combining acceleration data with gyroscope data will be considerate to recognize the device gesture better.

ACKNOWLEDGEMENTS

This paper is supported by "the Fundamental Research Funds for the Central Universities".

REFERENCES

[1] Jun-Ki Min, Bongwhan Choe, Sung-Bae Cho. "A Selective Template Matching Algorithm for Short and Intuitive Gesture UI for Accelerometer-Builtin Mobile Phones," IEEE Second World Congress on Nature and Biologically Inspired Computing, Fukuoka, 2010, pp. 660–665.

[2] Toshiyuki Kirishima, Kosuke Sato. Real-time Gesture Recognition by Learning and Selective Control of Visual Interest Points. IEEE Transactions on Pattern Analysis and Machine Intelligence. 2005, 3(27):351–353.

[3] Huang Qiyou, Dai Yong. Gesture Recognition Based On Gyroscope 2011, 11(37)22:153–155.

[4] Liu Rong, Liu Ming. Gesture Recognition Base on Acceleration Sensor[J]. Computer Science, 2011,12(37):141–143.

[5] Song Lijun, Qin Yongyuan. Six Position Testing of MEMS Accelerometer[J]. Measurement & Control Technology, Vol. 28, pp. 11–14, July, 2009.

[6] Zhao Si Hao, Lu Mingquan. Allan Variance analysis method of error coefficient based on MEMS inertial device[J]. CHINA SCIENCE, 2010, 42(5): 672–675.

[7] IEEE Standards (2006), IEEE Standard Specification Format Guide and Test Procedure for Single-Axis Laser Gyros.

[8] Johann Boren, Lauro Ojeda and Surat Kwamuang, "Heuristic Reduction of Gyro Drift For Personnel Tracking System," Journal of Navigation, Vol. 62, pp. 41–58, Jan. 2009.

[9] Wang Wanliang, Yang Jingwei.Motion Sensor based Gesture Recognition[J]. Chinese Journal of Sensors and Actuators, 2011, 12(24):1723–1726.

[10] Yang Dong-sheng, Peng Xiao-hong. Orangization collaboration net and decision-making tree[J]. Aerospace Electronics Information Engineering and Control, 2006, 1(28):63–67.

Computer, Intelligent Computing and Education Technology – Liu, Sung & Yao (Eds)
© 2014 Taylor & Francis Group, London, ISBN 978-1-138-02469-4

Research and practice of how to cultivate computational thinking in the college computer foundation course

Tao Zhan & Lei Deng
School of Computer Science and Engineering, Northwestern Polytechnical University, Xi'an, Shaanxi, P.R. China

Z.L. Liao
IBM China Development Laboraty, Xi'an, Shaanxi, P.R. China

ABSTRACT: "College Computer Foundation" is an entry course of university computer science courses. With the urgent requirement of quality education that requires to cultivate students innovative spirits and practical abilities, it is essential for modern college students to master the computer knowledge and thinking. Based on the long-time experience of teaching university computer course, teaching reform of "College Computer Foundation" is introduced in this paper. The goal of the reform is to teach computational thinking as well as professional knowledge and skills. The investigation shows that the final result is positive and there is still a long way to go.

Keywords: computational thinking; computer foundation course; education reform

1 COMPUTATIONAL THINKING IS THE CORE TO CHANGE THE CURRENT STATUS OF "COMPUTER FOUNDATION" COURSE

Computational thinking is introduced by Prof. Zhou of Carnegie-Mellon University [Zhou 2007]. It is defined as "the capability to use basic concept of computer science to resolve problem, design system and understand human behavior". It reflects the essential features and the core methods to resolve problem of computer technology. It could lift the information capability for non-computer science students. Moreover, it could cultivate the thinking pattern of computer concept, hence affects the students in life scale. In 2010, Professor Chen Guoliang, academician of the Chinese Academy of Sciences, promoted that the Computational Thinking capability should become the entry point of reform of "Computer Foundation" [Chen 2011]. In July 2012, State Education Commission and Xi'an Jiaotong University hosted the 1st conference of "Computational Thinking and Innovation of College Basic Computer". In July 2013, the 2nd conference was hold in Cheng Du, China. All these show that the Computational Thinking is an important direction for computer course reform.

In the process of course "College Computer Foundation" teaching, some phenomena appear gradually. On one hand, the content is a mini version of the whole bunch of computer science, which is too much and with many branches. On the other hand, some universities, especially some average universities, focus too much on computer operation. As many students have mastered some computer operation skills in their high school period, they show little interest in this course.

The root cause is that the content and orientation cannot meet the command of current age. Targeted Teaching shortens the gap a little bit, but still help little to cultivate the computational thinking. The key to improve the quality and effectiveness of the course is cultivating the computational thinking.

The authors think that it is the "College Computer Foundation" in which is more appropriate to train the Computing Thinking. There are several reasons. Firstly, "College Computer Foundation", as the first computer course for an undergraduate, is more suitable to teach foundational knowledge and thinking about computer science. Secondly, the computer courses for non-computer science students has too many threads, which making many students confused and poor quality in learning. Therefore, if students could construct a global view of computer science in their first computer course, it would be helpful in their future learning of other computer courses. Exploration and practice to embody computational thinking in "Computer Foundation" is a hot spot in the course reform.

2 COMPUTATIONAL THINKING CULTIVATION IN "COMPUTER FOUNDATION" TEACHING

2.1 Burning issues

There are 2 goals for innovation of "Computer Foundation". Firstly, the quality of teaching should be improved to cultivate the creative talents. Secondly, computational thinking must be the cornerstone of whole process of computer teaching. Therefore the students could master the effective computational thinking based on computer operations, and use it actively and systematically. Based on these goals, the content of the course needs to be redesigned with the core of computational thinking; and the teaching method should be adjusted to make sure the students mastering the concept. We proposed following issues to be addressed:

Issue 1: What computational thinking should be cultivated in limited classes?

Computer science is comprehensive and progressing dramatically. It is important to identify what is more essential to cultivate the computational thinking and should be taken into the course.

Issue 2: How to practice the concept learned in class under the condition of no programming language mastered?

The target students are freshmen, typically with little programming skills. It is a key problem to cultivate the computational thinking with minimal programming practice.

Issue 3: How to cultivate the computational thinking for students with different background and different majors?

The course reform must address these problems.

2.2 Design target teaching, professional integration of teaching content

NorthWestern Polytechnical University (NWPU) is multidisciplinary and comprehensive science university, emphasizing on the education and research in aeronautical, astronautical and marine engineering. Different major has different computer skill requirement, and most students just have a little computer operation experience. Hence, in the reform of "Computer Foundation" course, the targeted learning is introduced which good results have been achieved [Deng 2013]. Considering the different requirement of liberal arts and science students, as well as advanced requirement of some special major or special groups of students, the teaching contents have 3 different types:

• Type I: For science and engineering majors

• Type II: For liberal arts and management majors
• Type III: For Experimental College Education and Excellence Class Students.

In NWPU, a key university of science and engineering, type I students are in majority. As the data of 2013 shows, the proportions of 3 types are about 62%, 17%, 21% respectively. The main principle for designing content is "2 Integrations": The first integration is of teaching college computer foundation and cultivating computing thinking, mainly focused on computational thinking capability. Another integration is of college computer foundation and students' major profession.

The first integration, focused on computational thinking cultivation, is to teach the essential and long-lasting concepts of computer science to students. It emphasizes to make non-computer science student understand the core theories of computer science, learn how to transform the problem into the form of computer science, root the thinking pattern to analyze a problem from essential and global view. Therefore, students could make a solid base to learn their major profession and apply computer knowledge in future study.

The second integration, based on students' profession, allows teacher to choose the teaching content dynamically according to profession features and requirements. It is a customized teaching system, exploring category and level teaching.

The "2 integrations" concept has distinctive characteristics in teaching computer science to non-computer science students. It forms a hierarchy of vertical classification, horizontal stratification of teaching content, shown in Figure 1. Each direction consists 4 modules: basic computer concepts, basic Computing Thinking, problem solving and profession integration. The content of module differs according to student category. Take direction I, which is for science and engineering majors, as an example. The teaching plan consists

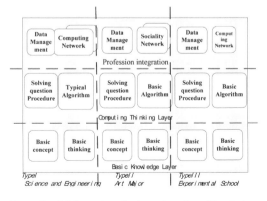

Figure 1.   Major and profession oriented teaching design.

of 32 class hours. The contents of direction I can be classified by 3 layers:

1. Basic Knowledge layer. This part focuses on basic computer concepts, the history of software/hardware development and future trends. It includes the development of computation concept and computing tools, the progress of software, the network evolving, emerging computing model, etc. The layer also includes basic thinking part, which covers binary, von Neumann computer, Turing machines, computational complexity and other important basic concepts of computer. In this part, students begin to study in depth the underlying computing systems thinking and operating mechanism. Though this part is similar to basic knowledge part of previous "Computer Foundation" course, it is reconstructed in this innovation. The important concept of the "abstraction" is emphasized as the main line. It should be useful for students to understand the underlying Computing Thinking.
2. Computing Thinking layer. In the Solving question procedure part, students learn how to use computer to solve problems, including solving framework, typical calculation algorithms, including solving thinking, processes and methods. Another part, Typical algorithms, includes sorting and searching algorithms, typical recursive algorithms and some typical heuristic algorithms such as genetic algorithms. This is a trend in computer science education.
3. Profession integration layer. From the perspective of data processing and network computing, this part makes students know the application models in current computer science, so as to apply them in their own domain. This part is of big changes, still needing expanded from a large number of cases and application model closely related with students' domain.

From the horizontal perspective of Figure 1, All categories share the same content of the basic knowledge layer, which provides the minimal computer science knowledge base and fundamental computation knowledge. The second layer is computational thinking layer. Students will learn core concepts and thinking of computer science from typical algorithms and solving procedures. The highest layer is profession integration layer. Students will learn to promote their computational thinking in learning profession knowledge.

From the vertical perspective of Figure 1, the content of each category in base layer is the same. In second layer, students in experimental education school will learn algorithms with more complexity. It embodies the spirit of target learning. In the highest layer, science and engineering students learn different contents with the liberal arts and management students. Science and engineering students will learn data processing and network knowledge, while liberal arts and management students emphasize on data process and social network study with computer skills.

2.3 Typical computational thinking experiments with visualization

The course includes 24 hours' experiment classes. The experiments include 2 phases:

First phase is: Practice on fundamental computer knowledge, including usage of Windows, usage of common computer tools and common network applications. In this phase, the goal is to mastering basic computer operation skills and common computer tools.

Second phase is: Experiment on Computing Thinking. In this phase, students need to use programming knowledge to implement typical computer algorithms.

Computer science is a practical science in nature. In theory teaching process, students can could understand the theory in depth by practicing. But as mentioned in 2.1, students at this stage have little experiences and skills to program. The adoption of visual programming tool is an effective way to solve the problem. User could construct the user interface like playing blocks with the controls provided by visual programming tools. Nowadays, visual programming is very popular in programming domain.

In the reform of "College Computer Foundation" course, Raptor (the Rapid Algorithmic Prototyping Tool for Ordered Reasoning), a flowchart-based programming environment, is introduced to solve the problem that students have little programming skills. RAPTOR programs are created visually and executed visually by tracing the execution through the flowchart. It also supports to convert the flowchart to C++, Ada or Java codes. Giving these merits, it is widely used by universities, including Carnegie-Mellon University, in more than 22 countries. Moreover, the beginners could focus on algorithm itself instead of the implementation method, hence avoiding the grammar frustration in programming language. This is especially meaningful for non-computer science students.

In our experiment teaching, 6 hours are used to learn Raptor and each student is required to use Raptor to implement at least 8 rudimental algorithm designs. Students are also required to use Raptor to finish their homework of algorithm. The feedback of using Raptor is quite positive, which can be seen from both class atmosphere and investigation.

3 PRACTICES AND SUMMARY OF INNOVATION

3.1 Results of teaching

In academic year 2012–2013, we reformed the teaching content and conducted a pilot teaching in some classes, relevant majors including materials science, automation engineering and electronics engineering. The result and feedback were positive. Some investigations were conducted to both students and instructors. Table 1 shows the survey about how instructors feel like the reform.

On one hand, instructors felt the course harder than before and took longer time on class preparation. On the other hand, the atmosphere in class was more active, and the content was more attractive. Especially in experiment class, students showed great interest on flow chart programming with Raptor. They actively took part in the class discussion and understood the knowledge more quickly.

The investigation results of students are abbreviated for convenience, shown in Figures 2 and 3.

Figure 2 shows that the majority of students (>50%) understood the concept of Computing Thinking.

Table 1. Survey from teachers.

Test item	Result
Preparation teaching	Difficult
Atmosphere in class	Better
Concentration in class	Higher
Comprehension	Good
Participation	Better

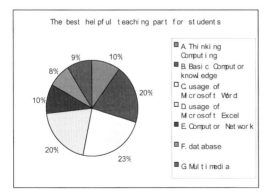

Figure 2. Surveys about how students understand the "Computing Thinking".

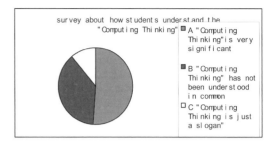

Figure 3. Surveys about which teaching part is best helpful for students.

From Figure 2 students are showed that they realized the importance of both computer fundamental knowledge and Computing Thinking. They understood it not just a tool to use, but with great power in studying professional knowledge in future. They began to foster their computational thinking seriously. Figure 3 shows which part was more useful for students investigated. More than 10% students advocated for Computing Thinking, in runner-up place. It indicated the students realized the importance of Computing Thinking, and showed great interest in study. Nevertheless, many students still thought it hard to understand, as it consists of many concepts, scales to large extent and lacks of learning materials.

3.2 Summary

Based on the investigation results of instructor and students, following summaries could be made. Firstly, the computational thinking is important to foster the creativity. It plays an important role in building a comprehensive developed, high quality student. The class feedback and investigation show that the innovation is along the correct direction and is advocated by most students as well as instructors. Secondly, it is shown that the innovation still needs refined gradually. The instructors also need to understand the computational thinking in depth. With the limited class hours, how to organize the teaching content effectively needs to pay more attention. Last but not the least, the textbook of computational thinking oriented computer foundation still needs to be improved, and the teaching method on computational thinking is still immature.

ACKNOWLEDGMENT

Our work is supported by The Nature Science Basis Research Plan of Shaanxi Province of China under Grant No. 2013 JQ8028, the Basic and Rearch

Foundation Project of Northwestern Polytechnic University under Grant No. 2011GBKY1011, the Education mode Innovation Project of NWPU in 2013.

REFERENCES

Chen Guoliang & Dong R. 2011, Computing Thinking and College Computer Fundation Education. China Education of College. (1):7–11.

Deng Lei & Jiang X. 2013. Implement integration with majors and improve the ability of students of science and egineering. Industry and Information Technology Education. 6(6):37–41.

Zhou Y. 2007. Computing Thinking. Communications of the CCF [J].

Computer, Intelligent Computing and Education Technology – Liu, Sung & Yao (Eds)
© *2014 Taylor & Francis Group, London, ISBN 978-1-138-02469-4*

Research and optimization of duplicate records detection algorithm based on clustering tree

M.W. Wu, H.L. Dong, R.G. Wang & Z.N. Zhang
Software School, Xiamen University, Xiamen, China

ABSTRACT: With the wide application of the Data Warehouse, the data quality issue related to the Data Warehouse construction and effective application of data become more and more important. Therefore, data cleaning is necessary before importing the data into the data center, especially the cleaning of duplicate records. This paper begins with a brief introduction to data cleaning and study of the existing basic duplicate records detection algorithm. Then we propose an incremental detection algorithm based on clustering tree. Furthermore, we analyze the shortcomings of this algorithm and propose some improvement ideas, which optimize the efficiency of algorithm to some extent.

Keywords: incremental data cleaning; duplicate records detection; clustering tree

1 INTRODUCTION

More and more departments integrate their data to build the data warehouse in order to help managers make decisions. However, due to large numbers of heterogeneous data, the data quality in data warehouse is difficult to guarantee, which affects the data query and results in decision reliability (Monge 2000). What's more, the multi-channel sources of data increases the duplicate records, which impacts on the utilization of the data and quality of decision making.

Therefore, data cleaning, especially the detection and elimination duplicate record is very important in constructing a data warehouse. Next, the paper will focus on the issue of duplicate records cleaning. Mainly discuss the research and optimization on incremental detection algorithm based on clustering tree.

2 RESEARCH ON DUPLICATE RECORDS DETECTION

2.1 *Definition of duplicate records*

Duplicate records represent the same entity in the real world, but due to the different expression or spelling problems make the database management system can't recognize it as a duplicate record. Duplicate records could do harm to the consistency of information, resulting in a waste of resources, inefficient OLAP queries and the wrong data mining models (Qujiang & Ming 2008). Therefore, the detection of duplicate records is the key link in a data cleaning.

2.2 *Principles of data cleaning*

Data cleaning mainly use backtracking thinking (Hasimah et al. 2011). It begins with analyzing data form the dirty data source. Then it inspects each process of data collecting to extract data cleaning rules and policies. Finally, these data sets rules and policies are applied to clean dirty data and find dirty data. Figure 1 shows the principle of data cleaning.

2.3 *Current researches on duplicate records detection algorithms*

Traditional duplicate records detecting mainly uses the distance function model (Bilenko & Mooney 2003), method based on q-gram

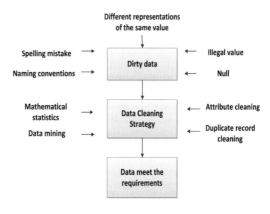

Figure 1. Principles of data cleaning.

algorithm and the standard string metric (Minton et al. 2005).Currently the basic idea for detecting duplicate records in large data center is "sort–merge". First, sort the records in the database, and then detect by comparing adjacent records similarity. Currently detect duplicate records methods are mostly based on this ideology (Leitao et al. 2013).

Lots of the detection algorithms such as the Sorted Neighborhood Method (SNM), Multi-Pass Sorted Neighborhood (MPN) algorithms are based on the static data set. If the system receives a new data set, it must merge with the processed data set, and then handle the entire data set. The majority of time is wasted in the repeat calculation of data set which has been processed. If the data model and rule for matching keep the same, we only need to observe the recently arrived increment data, which is the core of incremental algorithm for detecting duplicate records.

The following of this paper will mainly discuss the research and optimization on incremental detection algorithm based on clustering tree.

3 INCREMENTAL DETECTION ALGORITHM BASED ON CLUSTERING TREE

3.1 *Clustering tree algorithm flow*

On the basis of many incremental duplicate record identification ideas, we can consider a detection algorithm, regarding the duplicate records set as a class. Using the concept of a clustering tree, partition records by building the clustering tree, and identify the duplicate records on the basis of partition. There are following two treatments for each new record into the data set: join an existing class or create a new class (Fang & Fei 2005).

Incremental data cleaning algorithm based on clustering tree has the following related concepts:

1. Attribute Reduction: Extract part of attributes which have major impact on the target output from the large amounts of data attributes, retaining part of as the partition attributes, the other as the determine attributes.
2. Internal node of clustering tree represents a partition divided by classification attributes, and leaf nodes are duplicate records collection.
   1. Leaf node: a one-dimensional array of length q (q is the number of determine attributes) which is used to store determine attributes.
   2. Internal node: a triple (data, m, LS), in which data is the representative value of the priority queue, m is the length of the priority queue and LS is a priority queue used to store the similar partition attributes.

3. Each element: a tuple (value, point), in which value is the value of the partition attribute and point points to the next child node.

Algorithm's strategy is as follows: Given the dataset D containing n records, with A_1, A_2 ... A_r attributes. Firstly, carry out the attribute reduction, picking out P attributes, namely A_{i1}, A_{i2} ... A_{ip} (wherein A_{i1}, A_{i2} ... A_{ik} represent No.I record's partition attributes and $A_{i(k+1)}$, $A_{i(k+2)}$ ... A_{ip} are No.I record's determine attributes). Then, construct a cluster tree on the set D for cleaning.

Suppose that T_{mq} is the No.q node on the No.m layer of the tree. Clustering tree is constructed as follows:

1. Put the first record's partition attribute A_{11} into the first layer node T_{11}. Construct T_{11} as formula (1):

$$T_{11}.data = A_{11}$$
$$T_{11}.m = 1$$
$$T_{11}.LS[0].value = A_{11} \tag{1}$$

2. Then put the second partition attribute A_{12} into T_{21}. Construct T_{21} as formula (2):

$$T_{21}.data = A_{12}$$
$$T_{21}.m = 1$$
$$T_{21}.LS[0].value = A_{12} \tag{2}$$

Make T_{21} as T_{11}'s children node shown in formula (3):

$$T_{11}.LS[0].po\,int = T_{21} \tag{3}$$

3. The remaining partition attributes (A_{13}, A_{14} ...) are put into the previous attribute node's children respectively and determine attributes into leaves node array.
4. Read in the next record and compare its first attribute value A_{21} with A_{11}, calculating their similarity.
5. If the similarity is greater than the threshold, put the value of A_{21} into the T_{11}'s priority queue, and use A_{21}'s value to represent the queue.

$$T_{11}.data = A_{21}$$
$$T_{11}.m++$$
$$T_{11}.LS[1].value = A_{21} \tag{4}$$

6. Otherwise, generate a new node T_{12} as shown in formula (5):

$$T_{12}.data = A_{21}$$
$$T_{12}.m=1$$
$$T_{12}.LS[0].value = A_{21} \tag{5}$$

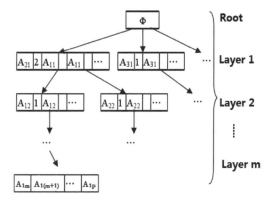

Figure 2.   Clustering tree structure.

In this way, continue to compare A_{22}, A_{23} ... A_{2k} attribute. By comparing partition attributes, the record data can be partitioned. The more selected partition attributes are, the more partition.

Then compare determine attributes in the same partition. Pair the determine attributes with each other, namely A_{2i} compares with $A_{1i}(k + 1 \leq i \leq p)$, using the majority decision principle. When more than $(P - K)/2$ determine attribute value's similarity greater than threshold, the records are regarded as approximate duplicate. In this way, sequentially read in other record, and identify each data record. Clustering tree constructed by the above method to complete the data cleaning. The Clustering tree structure is shown in Figure 2.

4   ANALYSIS AND DISCUSSION

4.1   *Improvement of clustering tree detection algorithm*

Compare with the MPN method, the clustering tree algorithm overhead time is half of MPN. Clustering tree algorithm has the following advantages:

1. Support incremental duplicate records identification without scanning the sorted data set.
2. Data input is independent of the sequence, avoiding the problem that SNM, MPN algorithm can't identify some duplicate recorded approximation since they can't be sorted in the adjacent position.

Although the algorithm can solve the duplicate records detecting issue in the incremental database, but its accuracy and efficiency is not high, which is needed to be further improved. The main reason resulting algorithm accuracy and efficiency is not high mainly due to the use of the attribute reduction and the process of constructing clustering tree.

These problems can be improved from the following aspects:

1. Use the rank method to set weight for each attribute (i.e., the attribute weight means the degree of influence on the final result). Reduce the attribute has little effect on the result and the remaining attributes rearrange by descending order according to the weight. In this way, in the process of structuring clustering tree, the attributes of the heavy weight partition before the attributes of the small weight, reducing the above-mentioned error and improving the accuracy of the algorithm.
2. Add a record similarity (i.e., the attribute similarity) threshold H: Before determining whether the attribute is similar to the prior record, judge whether the record similarity threshold is more than H. If similarity is more than H, the rest of the attribute will not have to compare, which improving the efficiency of the algorithm.
3. Add the pruning step: after record partition, add a backward step, using the backtracking algorithm to detect whether attribute value for each partition is correct. Then using pruning function cut the node which attribute values are different with the original data and reconstruct the node.
4. Calculate the dataset complexity: Set a threshold value. When the dataset complexity exceeds threshold, select other detection methods. Select the suitable data to construct clustering tree, avoiding lowefficency of the algorithm due to the large size of the tree.

5   CONCLUSIONS

Currently some researchers still think that data detection and cleaning process requires a lot of labor. In fact, there are still a lot of things need to study on finding more flexible framework detection algorithm and improving the efficiency of record identification (Jian-zhong et al. 2010). In the multilingual environment, the research on how to accurately identify duplicate records from multilingual texts is necessary. In future work, we will keep on doing researches and improvements on the following areas:

1. Carry on further study to solve the problems on incremental duplicate records detection.
2. Keep on research on heterogeneous data or database similar records cleaning. Today many exiting incremental duplicate records cleaning methods are specific to the isomorphism data or database. The heterogeneous data and database cleaning needs further researches.

331

ACKNOWLEDGEMENTS

Supported by the Key Technology R&D Program of Xiamen, Fujian under Grant No. 3502Z20103001, 3502Z20101002; the Key Technology R&D Program of Quanzhou, Fujian under Grant No. 2009G29; the Leading Academic Discipline Program, "Project 211 (the 3rd phase)" of Xiamen University; the Fundamental Research Funds for the Central Universities, Xiamen University under Grant No. 2010121071, 2011121023, CXB2012012, CXB2012013, 201212G007, CXB2013016; Shenzhen Key Laboratory for High Performance Data Mining with Shenzhen New Industry Development Fund under grant No. CXB201005250021 A.

Thanks to Zhongnan Zhang who is corresponding author, Huailin Dong and Ruguang Wang all kindness and help.

REFERENCES

Bilenko M & Mooney R. 2003. Adaptive name matching in information integration. *IEEE Intelligent Systems* 18(5): 16–23.

Cao Qu-jiang & Dong Ming. 2008. A new clustering methods for detecting duplicate records in high-dimensional space test. *Computer Engineering and Applications* 44(29).

Hasimah Hj Mohamed & Tee Leong Kheng & Chee Collin & Ong Siong Lee. 2011. E-Clean: A Data Cleaning Framework for Patient Data. *IEEE computer society* 32(11):63–68.

Leitao, L. & Calado, P. & Herschel, M. 2013. Efficient and Effective Duplicate Detection in Hierarchical Data. *IEEE Transactions on Knowledge and Data Engineering* 25(5): 1028–1041.

Liu Fang &He Fei. 2005. An incremental algorithms of data cleansing based on clustering tree. *J. Huazhong Univ. of Sci.&Tech. (Nature Science Edit ion)* 33(3).

Monge, AE. 2000. Matching Algorithms within a Duplicate Detection System. *IEEE Data Engineering Bullet* 23(4): 14–20.

Minton, S & Nanjo, C & Knoblock C et al. 2005. A heterogeneous field matching method for record linkage. Proceedings of the 5th International Conference on Data Mining (ICDM2005). Washington:*IEEE Computer Society*: 314–321.

Zhang Jian-zhong & Fang Zheng & Xiong Yong-jun & Yuan Xiao-yi. 2010. Optimization algorithm for cleaning data based on SNM. *Journal of Central South University (Science and Technology)* 41(6).

Computer, Intelligent Computing and Education Technology – Liu, Sung & Yao (Eds)
© 2014 Taylor & Francis Group, London, ISBN 978-1-138-02469-4

The analysis model of students' achievements based on Weighted Naive Bayes Classification

X.L. Wang
Yunnan Economic and Management College, Yunnan, China

Y. Jie
Yunnan Metallurgy College, Yunnan, China

ABSTRACT: Now many universities have begun to use data mining technology to conduct study of educational data, then some valuable rules and information are extracted to improve and adjust teaching strategies. This paper uses the Weighted Naive Bayes Classification to predict and analyze students' test scores, the weight of each attribute is given by a method based on mutual information. And the experiments show that the prediction for the result is encouraging and better in accuracy.

Keywords: Weighted Naïve Bayes model; mutual information

1 INTRODUCTION

Nowadays there has been a dramatic increase in the number of students in many universities, then large amounts of resources about student learning achievements are accumulated in the process of teaching. However, it's difficult to find valuable information in such mass data by using traditional method. The teaching managers and policymakers urgently need to uncover the rules in teaching by using a higher level of data analysis[1], so as to carry out a better work in education. Thus many scholars began to use data mining technology to study the knowledge and information hidden in these data of education, then it can provide more scientific and effective support for the university teaching improvement and reform. In this paper, we suggest that the Weighted Naïve Bayes models can be used to forecast and analyze student achievements, so we can find some potential influence factors from the students' information data sets, then it's useful for educational to improve and adjust teaching strategies.

2 WEIGHTED NAÏVE BAYES CLASSIFICATION

2.1 *Naïve Bayes classification*

Naïve Bayes has been widely used for classification and becoming an important aspect of data mining[2]. The classifier is easy to constructed: given an instance X that is represented by a vector $(x_1, x_2, ..., x_n)$, where $x_1, x_2, ..., x_n$ denote n attributes for X, and the class variable Y can be represented by $(y_1, y_2, ..., y_m)$. In Naïve Bayes, it is assumed that the attributes of instance X are independent of each other given the class. Each attribute x_i has only one class variable as its parent[3]. Then the $P(X \mid y_m)$ is computed according to:

$$P(X \mid y_m) = \prod_{i=1}^{n} P(x_i \mid y_m) \tag{1}$$

where the $P(x_k \mid y_m)$ can be obtained by the training dataset we gathered.

According to the Bayes rule, the posterior probability for instance X and class variable Y is:

$$P(y_m \mid X) = \frac{P(X \mid y_m) P(y_m)}{P(X)} \tag{2}$$

The Naïve Bayes classification consider that X should belong to the class that has the maximum posterior probability, since for each instance X, the value of $P(X)$ is a constant, then the instance X is classified to class y_i if and only if:

$$P(y_i \mid X) > P(y_j \mid X), 1 < j < m, i \neq j \tag{3}$$

2.2 *Weighted Naïve Bayes classification*

The Naïve Bayes classification has the minimum error rate compared with other algorithms, but its limitation is obvious for the dependency assumption, the dependence among attributes may have significant influence on the accuracy of classification. And in the application of our study, it's difficult to satisfy this condition between several attributes of students' performance. For example, the teacher qualification may have a certain correlation to teachers' evaluation from students, and the major can also affect the computer proficiency, and so on. Thus Weighted Naïve Bayes Classification (WNBC)[3][4] is proposed in this paper to reduce the constraints of the conditional independence assumption, it relax the assumption by assigning weights for each attributes in the training data. The WNBC can be defined as:

$$V_{wnd}(X) = \arg\max_{y} P(y) \prod_{i=1}^{n} p(x_i \mid y)^{w_i} \tag{4}$$

where w_i is the weight of attribute x_i. Obviously the larger the weight w_i, the more important the attribute x_i. Therefore, the key to WNBC is to determine the weights for all the attributes.

3 WEIGHTS BASED ON INFORMATION THEORY

This paper proposed a WNBC model based on information theory[5], the weights for each attributes are analyzed according to the mutual information, which is a measure of the amount of information that one random variable contains about another[6][7]. For an instance $X = \{x_1, x_2, ..., x_n\}$ and class variable $Y = \{y_1, y_2, ..., y_m\}$, the mutual information for x_i and y_j is:

$$I(x_i; y_j) = \log \frac{p(x_i \mid y_j)}{p(x_i)} = \log \frac{p(x_i y_j)}{p(x_i)p(y_j)} \tag{5}$$

If $p(x_i) = p(x_i \mid y_j)$, the mutual information $I(x_i; y_i) = 0$, then x_i and y_j are statistically independent. If $p(x_i \mid y_j) > p(x_i)$, then y_j and x_i has much information communicated, and if $p(x_i \mid y_j) < p(x_i)$, it means that x_i and y_j share less information. Then we can use the mutual information as the correlation index for the attribute variable x_i and class variable y_j.

Then we can get the weights for each attributes x_i:

$$w_i = I(x_i; Y) = \sum_{j=1}^{m} p(x_i y_j) \log \frac{p(x_i \mid y_j)}{p(x_i)} \tag{6}$$

When designing the analysis model of students' performance, we obtain the weights for each attributes, then we can know the importance of each attribute to the classification. The attribute with higher weight w_i contributes more than others to the probability estimation in the classification.

4 CONSTRUCTING THE ANALYSIS MODEL OF STUDENTS' ACHIEVEMENTS

In this study, data gathered from university fresh students who are required to have the computer course. The data was gathered in 2013, and included records of 3780 students. We sorted out the factors that may affect the computer examination, including: arts/science, origin of students, major, proficiency, teacher evaluation, teacher title, and interest. The data was collected in a table, and some fields for the attributes are transformed as necessary, then we can get students' information table for our experiment. The attributes and their fields are shown in Table 1.

The database management we chose is Microsoft SQL Server 2008, and the programming environment for the application is Matlab. We extracted 70 percents records from the database as the training dataset to construct the analysis model, then the left records is used as the test dataset to check out the accuracy of the classification model.

The WNBC algorithm discussed above is used in the experiment, each student is considered as an instance X, and then the weights for all the attributes can be obtained by formula (6), as given in Table 2.

After calculating the weight for each attribute, we can use formula (4) to estimate an instance X belongs to which class. In other words, it's useful to determine whether a student can pass the computer examination or not.

In order to verify the accuracy of the method in this paper, we compared the WNBC with the

Table 1. The students' information.

Student ID	The student ID is used only as an index, it's not
Arts/science	Arts (A), Science (S)
Fundamental skills	High (H), Middle (M), Low (L)
Major	Accounting (AC), Advertisement (AD), Financial Management (FM), Marketing Management (MM)
Proficiency	High (H), Middle (M), Low (L)
Teacher evaluation	Excellent (E), General (G), Terrible (T)
Teachers title	Professor (P), Lecturer (L), Assistant (A)
Interest	High (H), Middle (M), Low (L)

Table 2. The weights for the attributes.

Arts/science	Fundamental skills	Major	Proficiency
0.3541	0.8511	0.8023	0.8549
Teacher evaluation	Teachers title	Interest	
0.7543	0.8109	0.8072	

Table 3. Accuracy comparison.

Records number	500	1000	1500	2000	2500	3000
WNBC	60.63	64.18	71.25	85.62	90.56	92.14
NBC	61.45	65.47	70.48	83.06	86.15	89.62

traditional NBC, different numbers of dataset were tried, and the result was given in Table 3.

The experiment above shows the WNBC out-performed NBC, and the advantage is more obvious with larger training dataset. Therefore, the WNBC based on mutual information is effective in the application of educational environment.

5 CONCLUSIONS

The study in this paper utilities weighted Naïve Bayes Classification to analysis university students' achievements, and the weights for each attribute are obtained through mutual information based on Information Theory. The experiment shows the method in this paper is more accurate than traditional NBC in the application of education, and it can be considered as an effective way to analyse students' achievements.

ACKNOWLEDGEMENTS

This work was supported by the College Project Foundation and the Cultivation Scheme for Young Teachers of Yunnan Economic & Management College.

REFERENCES

[1] Liying Kong, The Application of Data Mining in Computer Grade Examination[J], Computer Education, 2010,1,38–41.
[2] Pang-Ning Tan, Michael Steinbach, Introduction to Data Mining[M], Posts&Telecom Press, 2011,1,141–145.
[3] Harry Z, Sheng S. Learning Weighted Naïve Bayes with Accurate Ranking[J]. The Fourth IEEE International Conference on Data Mining, 2004, 341–356.
[4] Mark Hall. A decision tree-based attribute weighting filter for naive bayes. Knowledge-Based Systems[J], 2007,20(2).
[5] Li-Ping Li, Ming-You Zhang, Introduction to Information Theory[M], The Electronic Science and Technology University Press, 2005,32–70.
[6] Long-Fei Zhang, The Research of Improved Mutual Information-based Naïve Bayesian Classification[D], JiLin University, 2010,27–38.
[7] Zhen-Zhang, Xue-Gang Hu, Classification model based on mutual information[J], Journal of Computer Application, 2011,6.

Computer, Intelligent Computing and Education Technology – Liu, Sung & Yao (Eds)
© 2014 Taylor & Francis Group, London, ISBN 978-1-138-02469-4

Reactive power optimization compensation research of medium and lower voltage distribution network in modernization function district

Y. Mao, S. Liang, X.L. Liu & X. Fan
College of Electrical and Information Engineering, Hunan University, Changsha, China

ABSTRACT: Reasonable reactive power optimization compensation is a prerequisite for power system's safe and reliable operation. This paper will investigate the reactive power optimization compensation of the Southern Base of China Mobile comprehensively. The result of the research show the effect of reactive power compensation in terms of reducing loss.

Keywords: power system; reactive power compensation; economic operation area; security and reliability

Electricity industry is an important pillar of the national economic development and stable power supply is an important guarantee for people's normal and orderly lives and for stable economic development. Since the 1970s, grid collapse accidents happened one after another in some countries around the world, their common characteristic is the voltage collapse which caused a large-scale of power outage so that the reactive power becomes the focus of the electric power researchers (Cheng & Wu 2004).

1 THE INFLUENCE OF THE REACTIVE POWER FOR POWER SYSTEM

The transmission of active power needs the support of reactive power in the power system. Reactive power is necessary for completing energy transmission for power system. A shortfall of reactive power in the power system will cause the electrical device unable to maintain the rated operating state and the electrical device's terminal voltage drops, therefore, in order to ensure the normal operation of electrical equipment, reactive power compensation device with appropriate capacity will be needed to configurate to compensate the reactive power shortfall in the power system.

2 THE MODEL FOR REACTIVE POWER OPTIMIZATION COMPENSATION METHOD

2.1 Reactive compensation

Reactive power compensation is the practical application part of reactive power optimization, it enables the system to minimize the network loss while meeting all kinds of constraint conditions through determining the installation location and capacity of the capacitor reasonably (Fu 2012). Proper use of reactive power compensation can effectively improve the system voltage stability, the voltage quality, the utilization rate of equipment, the security and reliability and also reduce line loss.

2.1.1 The method of reactive power compensation

The method of reactive power compensation for distribution network has four kinds:

Substation centralized compensation mainly aims at the reactive power balance in transmission grid, which is aimed to improve the power factor of the grid, the terminal voltage of transmission line and compensate the reactive power losses of the main transformer however, the existing problem is that it has no substantial effect on reducing the wastage in the 10 kV distribution network.

Pole reactive power compensation sets capacitor on line tower and compensates reactive power for utility transformers along 10 kV feeder line, which is suitable for the low power factor and long distribution lines with heavy load. Compensation capacity should not be too much, or overcompensation will cause the line voltage too high thus affecting the normal use of electrical equipment and harming the insulation of electrical equipment while the load is light (Liu 2011, Jiang et al. 2010).

Low-voltage centralized compensation conducts concentrated compensation at the 380 V side of low-voltage distribution transformer, and its compensating devices usually use low-voltage shunt capacitor cabinets controlled by microcomputer and put into different number of capacitors to tracking compensation when the user load changes. Its main purpose is to improve the power factor and voltage quality of the user's dedicated transformers to achieve a balance of reactive power on the spot. This paper focuses on low-voltage centralized compensation combined with actual example.

User terminal compensation directly compensates reactive power at the user terminal, this method can sharply reduce the line loss, improve voltage quality and the ability to supporting loads. Its disadvantage is that compensation capacity usually determined by the biggest reactive power demand of distribution transformers low-voltage side which easy causing the utilization rate of equipment is not high (Jiang et al. 2010, Zhu 2011).

2.1.2 The method to determine reactive power compensation capacity of low-voltage distribution transformer

Reactive compensation capacity can be determined by the following methods: with the purpose to reduce the loss, with the purpose to improve the power factor, with the purpose to improve the operating voltage levels and with the purpose to compensating reactive power loss of transformer itself (Yang 2009). Among them, determine the compensation capacity by improving power factor is currently one of the more common methods (Jiang et al. 2010):

$$Q_c = P\left(\tan\varphi_1 - \tan\varphi_2\right) kvar \qquad (1)$$

where P is load power with kW as unit; φ_1 is impedance angle before compensation; φ_2 is impedance angle after compensation.

2.1.3 Economic operation area of transformers

We consider using the active power which transformer load rate β changes in the region of the best economic operation area of the transformer. Its load rate is $\beta = P_2/(S_e\,cos\varphi_2)$, where P_2 is active power of low voltage side, S_e is rated capacity of transformer, $cos\varphi_2$ is power factor of low voltage side.

Active power loss $\Delta P\%$ have minimum value while the load rate equals β_0. For a two-winding transformer, the value range $1.33\ \beta_0^2 \le \beta \le 0.75$ is called as best economic operation area of the transformer in which the active power loss rate of transformer is closely to the minimum power loss rate $\Delta P_d\%$.

2.1.4 Reactive power compensation of cable line

Because most of the lines adopt cable line in modernization function district, thus we should analyze whether the voltage of the end of the cable line beyond the allowed scope of voltage fluctuation or not to determine whether the cable lines reactive compensation is demanded.

Forward and backward substitution method will be used in this paper to analysis the actual voltage of the high side of low-voltage distribution transformer. Because the load is not connected to the feeder trunk directly in the actual network, solving the voltage and the power distribution after obtaining the transformer's high side load power S_{LD}' which equals the sum of the low side load power S_{LD}, winding loss ΔS_T and excitation loss ΔS_0 of the transformer (He & Wen 2002).

Its winding loss and excitation loss are

$$\Delta S_T = \left(P_{LD}^2 + Q_{LD}^2\right)\left(R_T + jX_T\right)/V_N^2 \qquad (2)$$

$$\Delta S_0 = \Delta P_0 + jI_0\%S_N/100 \qquad (3)$$

where no-load loss ΔP_0 and no-load current $I_0\%$ can be obtaining by accessing to relevant technical parameters manuals of electrical equipment (Fang & Fang 2011). The computation formula of R_T and X_T are

$$R_T = \Delta P_S V_N^2 \times 10^3 / S_N^2 \qquad (4)$$

$$X_T = V_S\% \times V_N^2 \times 10^3 / 100S_N \qquad (5)$$

where ΔP_S and $V_S\%$ also can be obtaining by accessing to relevant technical parameters manuals of electrical equipment (Fang & Fang 2011).

The computer program of forward and backward substitution method is written by using MATLAB. Its program flowchart shown in Figure 1.

3 REACTIVE POWER OPTIMIZATION COMPENSATION RESEARCH FOR SOUTHERN BASE OF CHINA MOBILE

Southern base of China Mobile is a center integrates the internet innovation and promotion center,

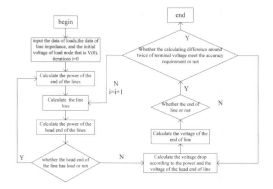

Figure 1. Flowchart of the forward and backward substitution method.

the centralized operation center, international cooperation center and industrial cluster promotion center with "based in Guangdong, serving the entire country, radiation to global" as its orientation. Its function orientation determines the high requirements to the power supply's reliability and security, moreover, reasonable reactive power optimization compensation is a prerequisite for power system's safe and reliable operation.

3.1 The reactive power compensation of low-voltage distribution transformer

3.1.1 Economic operation area of specified transformers

Low-voltage distribution transformers configured in pairs in building2 and building3 in the first-stage project of the southern base. Because there're no ordinary load before generator switch cabinet, so that transformer's load rate should be not high thus considering while a transformer fails, the other one can take the all load, at this moment the load rate of the transformer should not be greater than 100%. Then the best economic operation area of the transformers of building2 and building3 is $45\% \leq \beta \leq 55\%$. Consider other storied buildings in the same way, we can get the best economical operation area of each building.

3.1.2 The configuration of reactive power compensation equipment capacity of distribution transformer

In order to improve the security and reliability, we conduct the reactive power compensation for each dedicated transformer of the southern base and determine the compensation capacity with the purpose to improve the power factor. The power factor before compensation unified use 0.9 which used to programming the southern base to calculate. Since the load of southern base requires voltage with high quality, we consider increasing the power factor to 0.95 after compensating.

We can get reactive power compensation equipment capacity that need to configure of each building according to the above-mentioned method and list them in Table 1.

3.2 Reactive power compensation of cable line

Here only analyze each building of the first-stage project by using the method above. While doing calculation, we consider load rate of each building reach the ceiling of the best economic operation area of the transformers and transformer's resistance use the value at 120 degrees Celsius. We can number each line from a to i.

While calculating, we suppose power point voltage is 10.5 kV, the initial value of the load point

Table 1. Reactive power compensation capacity of each ban.

Building	Capacity kvar
1	$2 \times 4 \times 50$
2	$10 \times 2 \times 100 + 2 \times 2 \times 50$
3	$10 \times 2 \times 100 + 4 \times 4 \times 50 + 8 \times 1 \times 100$
4	$2 \times 3 \times 50$
5	$5 \times 3 \times 50$
6	$10 \times 1 \times 100 + 14 \times 4 \times 50$
7	$3 \times 6 \times 50 + 4 \times 3 \times 50$
8	$4 \times 3 \times 50$
9	$2 \times 3 \times 50$
10	$1 \times 4 \times 50$
11	$1 \times 1 \times 100$
12	$14 \times 4 \times 50 + 10 \times 1 \times 100$
13	$10 \times 5 \times 50$
14	$5 \times 5 \times 50$

voltage $V(0)$ is 10 kV, and ended the iteration while the calculating difference around twice of terminal voltage is less than 0.00001 kV. Compute program is written by using MATLAB. The iteration meet the requirement after iterating 3 times. The point with the lowest load voltage in the calculating results is point c which is 10.415523 kV and its voltage deviation is 0.8045% which is still in the allowed range and as a result, we don't have to consider the reactive power compensation of cable line.

3.3 Active loss and voltage loss analysis after compensation

3.3.1 Active loss of transformer

We suppose active load is P and reactive load is Q. Ignore the transformer's branch to the ground, R_T represents the resistance of transformer, X_T represents the reactance of transformer, the capacity of compensation equipment that input is Q_c, so that we can deduce the reduce percentage of loss of power in the light of the transformer power loss formula before and after the compensation as follows:

$$\Delta(\Delta P)\% = \left(2QQ_c - Q_c^2\right)\Big/\left(P^2 + Q^2\right) \times 100\% \quad (6)$$

In the computed result, the lowest is 9.85% and the highest is 14.65%. That is to say, investing reactive power compensation equipment reduce the reactive power flow through the transformer so as to reduce the active power loss of transformer obviously.

3.3.2 *Voltage loss of transformer*

On account of the length of the cable lines between the specified transformers for southern base and each building are short, we suppose the first and the terminal voltage phase angle of cable line are equal thus we ignore the horizontal component of the voltage drop. We can deduce the reduce percentage of voltage loss in the light of the voltage loss formula before and after the compensation as follows:

$$\Delta(\Delta V)\% = Q_C X_T / (PR_T + QX_T) \times 100\% \qquad (7)$$

The smallest reduce percentage of voltage loss is 24.52% and the biggest is 41.60% among the computed result. That is to say, investing reactive power compensation equipment reduce the reactive power flow through the transformer so as to reduce the voltage loss of transformer and better the voltage quality of electrical equipment.

4 CONCLUSION

In this paper, we analyze reactive power optimization compensation of specified transformer and the cable line for southern base of China Mobile. Analysis result shows that timely input and quit of capacitor group can not only compensate the reactive power gap but also prevent voltage's outside the specified range caused by overcompensation, thereby making sure the safety of power supply.

REFERENCES

Cheng, Z.H. & Wu, H. 2004. *Reactive power and voltage stability of power system.* Beijing: China Electric Power Press.

Fang, D.Q. & Fang, Y.M. 2011. *Practical electrical and electronic manual for check and calculate.* Beijing: Chemical Industry Press.

Fu, S.X. 2012. Reactive power optimization and reactive power compensation of Power system. *Technology Innovation and Application* 14:125.

He, Y.Z. & Wen, Z.Y. 2002. *Electric power system analysis.* Wuhan: Huazhong University of Science and Technology Press.

Jiang, N., Zhao, J.F., Wang, C.N., & Xu, C.S. 2010. *Technology on voltage reactive power control and optimization.* Beijing: China Electric Power Press.

Liu, J. 2011. Reactive power optimization compensation of 10 kilovolt transmission line in distribution network. *China Power Enterprise Management* 14:125–127.

Yang, X.Y. 2009. Reasonably determining reactive power compensation capacity. *China New Technologies and Products* 23:126–127.

Zhu, Y.L. 2011. Research and analysis of distribution network reactive power optimization compensation. *Mechanical and Electrical Information* 36:57–58.

Computer, Intelligent Computing and Education Technology – Liu, Sung & Yao (Eds)
© 2014 Taylor & Francis Group, London, ISBN 978-1-138-02469-4

Existence of a minimal positive solutions for some singularity elliptic equation

Zhi-Yang Liu

Guangdong University of Science and Technology, Guangdong, P.R. China

ABSTRACT: In this paper, using implicit function theorem and upper and lower solution methods, we discussed the existence of a minimal positive solutions for some singularity elliptic equation with crtical Sobolev-Hardy exponent.

Keywords: critical Sobolev-Hardy exponent; sigularity elliptic equation; minimal positive solutions

1 INTRODUCTION AND MAIN RESULTS

This article will study the existence of the minimal positive solutions for the following elliptic equation:

$$\begin{cases} -\Delta u - \mu \dfrac{u}{|x|^2} = \dfrac{u^{2*(s)-1}}{|x|^s} + \lambda u + \sigma f(x), \ x \in \Omega \\ u > 0, \ x \in \Omega \\ u = 0, \ x \in \Omega \end{cases} \quad (1)$$

where $0 \le \mu < \overset{-}{\mu} = ((N-2)/2)^2$, $\Omega \subset R^N (N \ge 3)$ is a bounded smooth domain, $0 \in \Omega$, $0 \le s < 2$, $2*(s) = 2(N-s)/N-2$ is the critical Sobolev-Hardy exponent, $\lambda \in (-\infty, \lambda_1)$, λ_1 is the first eigenvalue of the operator $-\Delta - \mu I/|x|^2$, and $\sigma \ge 0$ is a real parameter, $f(x) \in L^\infty(\Omega)$ satisfies $f(x) \ge 0$ and not identically equal to zero.

The reason that we are interested in the problem is because the problem has a boundary singularities and contains the critical Sobolev-Hardy exponent resulting in the corresponding energy function loss compactness, and then which cause a series of interesting existence and nonexistence of phenomena. Since the pairs of elliptic problems with critical indicators are discussed

$$\begin{cases} -\Delta u = u^{2*-1}, \ x \in \Omega \\ u > 0, \ x \in \Omega \\ u = 0, \ x \in \partial\Omega \end{cases} \quad (2)$$

In recent years, the research of the Sobolev embedding loss compactness has made a huge development. Where $2* = 2*(0) = 2N/(N-2)$ is the critical Soblev exponent? In [1] Brezis studied the following well-known elliptic equations

$$\begin{cases} -\Delta u = u^{2*-1} + \lambda u, \ x \in \Omega \\ u > 0, \ x \in \Omega \\ u = 0, \ x \in \partial\Omega \end{cases} \quad (3)$$

For λ different range, we get a very fine results for the existence and nonexistence of the solution, finally, Deng in [2] studied the existence of multiple positive solutions for the following problem,

$$\begin{cases} -\Delta u = u^{2*-1} + \lambda u + \gamma f(x), \ x \in \Omega \\ u > 0, \ x \in \Omega \\ u = 0, \ x \in \partial\Omega \end{cases} \quad (4)$$

in [3], as $s = 0$ the authors studied the existence of the minimal positive solution for the problem (1). This article will further study as $0 \le s < 2$ the existence of the minimal positive solutions for the equation (1) and generalize the results of the literature [3]. The following theorem is the main result of this article:

Theorem 1 For $\lambda \in (-\infty, \lambda_1)$, as $0 \le s < 2$, $0 \le \mu < \overline{\mu}$, there exists a positive number $\sigma^* < +\infty$ such that for any $\sigma \in (0, \sigma^*]$, the problem (1) exists a minimal positive solution, however as $\sigma > \sigma^*$, the problem (1) has no solution.

2 THE PROOF OF THEOREM

In the following, C, C_i will be used to represent the normal number, we will give the proof of theorem 1 through a series of lemmas and by using the theorem of the implicit function and the solutions of the upper and lower

Lemma 2.1 Let $\Omega \subset R^N$ be a bounded domain containing the origin, and $g: \Omega \times R \to R$ a

Caratheodory function, that is for $x \in \Omega$, $g(x,u)$ can be measured, for $u \in R$, $g(x,u)$ is continuous, and simultaneously satisfies the growth conditions

$$|g(x,u)| \le C(1+|u|^{p-1})a.e.\Omega,$$

where $2 \le p < 2^*$. If $u \in H_0^1(\Omega)$ is a weak solution of $-\Delta u - \mu\, u/|x|^2 = g(x,u)$, then for any $r > 0$ satisfied $B_r(0) \subset \Omega$ such that $u \in L^\infty(\Omega \setminus B_r(0))$, further $u \in C_{loc}^{1,\alpha}(\Omega \setminus B_r(0))$.

Proof please refer to Appendix B in [4] or Lemma 1 in [3].

Lemma 2.2[5] Let $\Omega \subset R^N$ be a smooth bounded domain, and $u \in C^1(\Omega), \Delta_p u \in L_{loc}^2(\Omega), u \ge 0 \quad a.e.\Omega$ and $\Delta_p u \le \beta(u)a.e.\Omega$, where $\beta:[0,+\infty] \to R$ is consecutive diminished function, $\beta(0) = 0$ and satisfies one of the following two conditions: There exists a positive number $t > 0$, such that $\beta(t) = 0$; or for all the positive $t > 0$, $\beta(t) > 0$ holds, however $\int_0^1 (j(t))^{-1/p} dt = \infty$, where, if u isn't identically equal to zero in Ω, then u is greater than zero everywhere in Ω.

Lemma 2.3[3] Suppose that λ_1 is the first eigenvalue of the operator $-\Delta - \mu\, I/|x|^2$, $\varphi(x)$ is the first characteristic function, then $\lambda_1 > 0$, $\varphi(x) > 0 a.e.\Omega$.

Lemma 2.4 For any $\lambda \in (-\infty, \lambda_1)$, as σ small enough, the problem (1) exists a minimal positive solution.

Proof Let $F(\sigma,u) = -\Delta u - \mu\, u/|x|^2 - u^{2^*(s)-1}/|x|^s - \lambda u - \sigma f(x)$,

Then the mapping $F: R^+ \times H_0^1(\Omega) \to H^{-1}(\Omega)$ is Frechet differentiable, continuous, and $F'_u(0,0)\varphi = -\Delta\varphi - \mu\,\varphi/|x|^2 - \lambda\varphi$, furthermore, for all $(\sigma,u) \in U$ (U is an open neighborhood of $(0,0)$), it is not difficult to prove that $F'_u(\sigma,u)$ is existent and continuous, from the theorem of the inverse operator, we get $F'_u(0,0)^{-1} \in L(H^{-1}(\Omega), H_0^1(\Omega))$. Also $F(0,0) = 0$, from the theorem of the implicit function, there exists a sufficiently small positive number σ, such that $u = u(\sigma)$, $F(\sigma,u(\sigma)) = 0$, as $\sigma \in (0,\sigma)$. By Lemma 2.1 and Lemma 2.3, we get $u(\sigma) > 0 \quad a.e.\Omega$. Therefore, for $\sigma \in (0,\sigma)$, $u(\sigma)$ is the solution of the problem (1), and is the lower solution. The method of the upper and lower solutions shows that the problem (1) exists a minimal positive solution $v(\sigma)$ to satisfy $0 < v(\sigma) < u(\sigma)$. The proof is completed.

Lemma 2.5 For $\lambda \in (-\infty, \lambda_1)$, as $0 \le s < 2$, $0 \le \mu < \mu$, there exists a constant $C > 0$, such that for any $\sigma > C$, the problems (1) has no solution.

Proof Since Ω is a bounded domain and $2^*(s) - 1 > 1$, so there exists a positive number C_1, $C_2 > 0$, such that for any $u > 0$ satisfies

$$\frac{u^{2^*(s)-1}}{|x|^s} \ge \frac{u^{2^*(s)-1}}{C_1^s} \ge (\lambda_1 - \lambda)\mu - C_2$$

Let u be the solution of problem (1), Then

$$-\Delta u - \mu \frac{u}{|x|^2} = \frac{u^{2^*(s)-1}}{|x|^s} + \lambda u + \sigma f(x).$$

Thus

$$\int_\Omega \left[(-\Delta u)\varphi - \mu\frac{u\varphi}{|x|^2}\right] dx = \int_\Omega \left(\frac{u^{2^*(s)-1}\varphi}{|x|^s} + \lambda u\varphi + \sigma f\varphi\right) dx$$

where $\varphi(x)$ is the first characteristic function of the operator $-\Delta - \mu\, I/|x|^2$, by integration we get

$$\int_\Omega u\left(-\Delta\varphi - \mu\frac{\varphi}{|x|^2}\right) dx = \int_\Omega \left(\frac{u^{2^*(s)-1}\varphi}{|x|^s} + \lambda u\varphi + \sigma f\varphi\right) dx$$

So

$$\lambda_1\int_\Omega u\varphi dx \ge (\lambda_1 - \lambda)\int_\Omega u\varphi dx - C_2\int_\Omega \varphi dx + \int_\Omega(\lambda u\varphi + \sigma f\varphi)dx$$

That is $\sigma\int_\Omega f\varphi dx \le C_2\int_\Omega \varphi dx$, further $\sigma \le C \stackrel{\Delta}{=} C_2\int_\Omega \varphi dx / \int_\Omega f\varphi dx$. The proof is completed.

Lemma 2.6 For $\lambda \in (-\infty, \lambda_1)$, as $0 \le s < 2$, $0 \le \mu < \mu$, there exists a positive number $\sigma^* < +\infty$, such that for any $\sigma \in (0, \sigma^*)$, the problem (1) exists a minimal positive solution, However as $\sigma > \sigma^*$, the problem (1) has no solution.

Proof For $\lambda \in (-\infty, \lambda_1)$, let $\sigma^* = \sup\{\sigma \in R^+ |$ the problem (1) exists a minimal solution$\}$

By Lemma 2.4 and Lemma 2.5 we can see $0 < \sigma^* < +\infty$. From the definition of σ^*, for any $\sigma \in (0, \sigma^*)$ there exists $\bar{\sigma} \in (\sigma, \sigma^*)$, such that the problem (1) has a minimal positive solution $u_{\bar{\sigma}}$. It is not difficult to prove that $u_{\bar{\sigma}}$ and 0 are respectively upper and lower solutions of the problem (1). Using the monotone iterative method and the strongly maximum principle we can prove that the problem (1) exists a minimal positive solution u_σ to satisfy $0 < u_\sigma < u_{\bar{\sigma}}$, $x \in \Omega \setminus \{0\}$, $\sigma < \bar{\sigma}$. The proof is completed.

Remark 1 If $\lambda \ge \lambda_1$, hen the problem (1) has no solution. In fact, if u is the solution of problem (1), then

$$\lambda_1\int_\Omega u\varphi dx = \int_\Omega\left[(-\Delta u)\varphi - \mu\frac{u\varphi}{|x|^2}\right]dx$$

$$= \int_\Omega\left(\frac{u^{2^*(s)-1}\varphi}{|x|^s} + \lambda u\varphi + \sigma f\varphi\right)dx > \lambda\int_\Omega u\varphi dx$$

Therefore $\lambda < \lambda_1$. Note $B = \{u_\sigma | \sigma \in (0, \sigma^*)$, u_σ is the minimal positive solution of the problem (1)$\}$.

By Lemma 2.6 we get B is not empty. In order to prove Theorem 1 was established, just to demonstrate the problem (1) exists a minimal positive solution as $\sigma = \sigma^*$. Therefore, we first give two lemmas.

Lemma 2.7 If u_σ is the minimal positive solution of the problem (1), then for given $\lambda \in (-\infty, \lambda_1)$, $\sigma \in (0, \sigma^*)$, the corresponding eigenvalue problem

$$-\Delta\varphi - \mu\frac{\varphi}{|x|^2} - \lambda\varphi - (2*(s)-1)\frac{u^{2*(s)-2}\varphi}{|x|^s}$$

$$= \delta\varphi, \varphi \in H_0^1(\Omega) \tag{5}$$

has the first eigenvalue $\delta_1 > 0$ and the corresponding characteristic function $\varphi_1(x) > 0\, a.e.\Omega$.

Proof
Note $I(u) = \int_\Omega \left(|\nabla u|^2 - \mu\frac{u^2}{|x|^2} - \lambda u^2 - p\frac{u_\sigma^{p-1}u^2}{|x|^s}\right)dx$

$\delta_1 = \inf\left\{\int_\Omega\left(|\nabla u|^2 - \mu\frac{u^2}{|x|^2} - \lambda u^2\right.\right.$

$\left.\left. - p\frac{u_\sigma^{p-1}u^2}{|x|^s}\right)dx\Big| u \in H_0^1(\Omega), \int_\Omega u^2 dx = 1\right\}$

where $p = (2*(s)-1)$. Suppose that $\{v_j\} \subset H_0^1(\Omega)$ is a minimizing sequence of the above minimization problem. From Hardy inequalities and Hardy-Sobolev inequality, it is not difficult to prove that there exists a constant $C > 0$, such that $\int_\Omega|\nabla v_j|^2 dx \leq C$, so there exists a subsequence (still denoted by $\{v_j\}$), as $j \to \infty$, to satisfy
  $v_j \to v$ converges weakly to $H_0^1(\Omega)$
  $v_j \to v$ converges strongly to $L^\alpha(\Omega)$, $2 \leq \alpha < 2*$,
  $v_j \to v\, a.e$ in Ω
  by Vitali's Theorem, we get $\int_\Omega v^2 dx = 1$, so $\delta_1 \leq I(v)$.
  Next we will prove

$$I(v) \leq \delta_1 = \lim_{j\to\infty} v_j \tag{6}$$

For $\forall \varepsilon > 0$ let $K_\varepsilon = \{u \in H_0^1(\Omega)|I(u) \leq \delta_1 + \varepsilon\}$, using the Brezis-Lieb lemma in [1] we can prove I is a continuous convex functional, According to Mazur's theorem in [6], we can prove K_ε be weakly closed, so for any $\varepsilon > 0$, $I(v) \leq \delta_1 + \varepsilon$, the equality (6) holds. Let $\varphi_1(x) = |v(x)|$, by the strong maximum principle. We get $\varphi_1(x) > 0\, a.e.\Omega$.
For $\sigma \in (\sigma, \sigma^*)$, let $u_\sigma, u_{\bar\sigma}$ is all the minimal positive solution of the problem (1), then $u_\sigma \leq u_{\bar\sigma}$ and satisfies

$$-\Delta u_\sigma - \mu\frac{u_\sigma}{|x|^2} = \frac{u_\sigma^p}{|x|^s} + \lambda u_\sigma + \sigma f(x),$$

$$-\Delta u_{\bar\sigma} - \mu\frac{u_{\bar\sigma}}{|x|^2} = \frac{u_{\bar\sigma}^p}{|x|^s} + \lambda u_{\bar\sigma} + \bar\sigma f(x).$$

The above two type of subtraction

$$-\Delta(u_{\bar\sigma} - u_\sigma) - \mu\frac{u_{\bar\sigma} - u_\sigma}{|x|^2}$$

$$= \frac{u_{\bar\sigma}^p - u_\sigma^p}{|x|^s} + \lambda(u_{\bar\sigma} - u_\sigma) + (\bar\sigma - \sigma)f(x).$$

The above equality is multiplied by the re-integration on the both sides, using the Taylor expansion

$$\int_\Omega\left(-\Delta(u_{\bar\sigma} - u_\sigma) - \mu\frac{u_{\bar\sigma} - u_\sigma}{|x|^2}\right)\varphi_1(x)dx$$

$$\geq \int_\Omega\frac{pu_\sigma^{p-1}(u_{\bar\sigma} - u_\sigma)}{|x|^s}\varphi_1(x)dx + \int_\Omega\lambda(u_{\bar\sigma} - u_\sigma)\varphi_1(x)dx$$

From [5] and $u_\sigma \leq u_{\bar\sigma}$, we get $\int_\Omega\delta_1\varphi_1(x)(u_{\bar\sigma} - u_\sigma)dx > 0$, therefore $\delta_1 > 0$. The proof is completed.

Lemma 2.8 There exists a normal number C unrelated to σ, such that for any given $u_\sigma \in B$, satisfies $\|u_\sigma\|_{H_0^1(\Omega)} \leq C$.
Proof for any $u_\sigma \in B$, by Lemma 2.3 and Lemma 2.7, we obtain

$$\int_\Omega\left(|\nabla u_\sigma|^2 - \mu\frac{u_\sigma^2}{|x|^2}\right)dx = \int_\Omega\left(\frac{u_\sigma^{2*(s)}}{|x|^s} + \lambda u_\sigma^2 + \sigma f u_\sigma\right)dx \tag{7}$$

$$\int_\Omega\left(|\nabla u_\sigma|^2 - \mu\frac{u_\sigma^2}{|x|^2}\right)dx - \int_\Omega\left(p\frac{u_\sigma^{2*(s)}}{|x|^s} + \lambda u_\sigma^2\right)dx$$

$$\geq \delta_1\int_\Omega u_\sigma^2 dx \tag{8}$$

$$\int_\Omega\left(|\nabla u_\sigma|^2 - \mu\frac{u_\sigma^2}{|x|^2}\right)dx \geq \lambda_1\int_\Omega u_\sigma^2 dx \tag{9}$$

where $p = (2*(s)-1)$. From (7) to (9), after simple calculation we show that

$$(p-1)(\lambda_1 - \lambda)\int_\Omega u_\sigma^2 dx \leq p\sigma\int_\Omega f u_\sigma dx$$

For any $\sigma \in (0, \sigma^*)$, by the Holder inequality and Young inequality, for any $\varepsilon > 0$, there exists a constant $C_3 > 0$ such that

$$(p-1)(\lambda_1 - \lambda)\int_\Omega u_\sigma^2 dx \leq p\sigma$$

$$*C_3\left(\frac{\varepsilon}{2}\int_\Omega u_\sigma^2 dx + \frac{1}{2\varepsilon}\int_\Omega f^2 dx\right)$$

Taking ε sufficiently small, such that

343

$$(p-1)(\lambda_1 - \lambda) - \frac{p\varepsilon\sigma^* C_3}{2} > 0$$

Then there exists the constant $C_4 > 0$ independent of σ to satisfy

$$\int_\Omega u_\sigma^2 dx \le C_4$$

According to the Sobolev embedding theorem, the Hardy inequality and the Poincar inequality license, there exists a constant $C > 0$ independent of σ such that $\|u_\sigma\|_{H_0^1(\Omega)} = \int_\Omega |\nabla u_\sigma|^2 dx \le C$. The proof is completed.

The proof of Theorem 1

Assume that $\{\sigma_j\} \subset (0, \sigma^*)$ is increasing sequence and $\lim\limits_{j\to\infty} \sigma_j = \sigma^*$, the sequence of solutions corresponding to the above sequence is denoted by $\{u_j\} \subset B$. By Lemma 2.8, we firstly take the subsequence, still denoted by $\{u_j\}$, such that $u_j \to u$ converges weakly in $H_0^1(\Omega)$, where $u \in H_0^1(\Omega)$ is a non-negative function. Be similar to the proof of Lemma 2.7, it is not difficult to get u is a solution of the problem (1) as $\sigma = \sigma^*$, since for all $\sigma > 0, 0$

are all the solutions of the problem (1) as $\sigma = \sigma^*$, by monotone iterative method, we can find a minimal positive solution of the problem (1) as $\sigma = \sigma^*$. The proof is completed.

REFERENCES

[1] Brezis H, Lieb E. A relation between pointwise convergence lf functions and convergence lf functionals [J]. *Proc. Amer. Math. Soc.*, 1986, 88(3):486–490.

[2] Deng Y B. Existence of multiple positive solutions for $-\Delta u = u^{N+2/N-2} + \lambda u + \mu f(x)$ [J]. *Acta Math Sinica*, 1993, 9(3):311–320.

[3] Zhang Yuling. Existence of a minimal positive solution for $-\Delta u - \mu u / |x|^2 = u^{2^*-1} + \lambda u + \sigma f(x)$ [J]. *Journal of Lanzhou University(Natural Sciences)*, 2007, 43 (4):118–126.

[4] Struwe M. Variational Methods [M]. 2nd ed. Berlin:Springer-Verlag, 2000.

[5] Vazquez J L. A strong maximum principle for some quasilinear elliptic equations [J]. *App Math Option*, 1984, 12:191–202.

[6] Yosida K. Functional Analysis [M]. 6th ed. Berlin:Springer-Verlag, 1999.

A study on the adjustment strategies of Dongguan's vocational education major structures under the background of industry transformation

Shui-Ping Huang & Mei-Ling Guo
Guangdong University of Science and Technology, Guangdong, P.R. China

ABSTRACT: With the upgrading and transformation of Dongguan's economic industrial structure, the talent demand structure has taken fundamental changes. To fit the background of industry transformation, Dongguan's vocational education should strengthen the combination between major and local economy, build a major layout corresponding to local main industries, improve the major connotation and strengthen major characteristics. So that the major structure can be well adjusted and enhance the sustainable development of vocational education and local economy as well as society.

Keywords: Dongguan city; industry transformation; vocational education; major structure adjustment; strategies

According to *The Medium and Long Term Educational Reform and Development Plan* issued in February 2010, developing vocational education is emphasized to meet the economy and society demand for laborers with high quality and skilled talents.[1] Dongguan which is among the critical period of industry upgrading and transformation, is deadly in need of laborers with high quality and skilled talents. So it's a top priority as well as a developing strategy to put the vocational education on the strategic position of pressing ahead the transformation of both economy and society, and to accelerate the connection of vocational education structure and industry transformation.

1 CURRENT DEVELOPMENT OF DONGGUAN'S VOCATIONAL EDUCATION MAJORS

As an internationally prestigious manufacturing city, Dongguan's local booming industries calls for a great amount of medium as well as senior technical talents. In accordance with the need of era, Dongguan's vocational education has achieved a lot. Until the end of 2011, Dongguan has established "26 secondary vocational schools (including 1 technical school), with 48.2 thousand students at school",[2] "6 common higher education schools including 3 undergraduate universities and 3 junior colleges, with 45.1 thousand students. The annual number of undergraduate and junior college students has reached 16.8 thousand, and the graduates reached 9463. In the year 2011, the number of students taking part in the college entrance examination is 22.3 thousand, 21.4 thousand enrolled in colleges, and 3357 in higher vocational schools".[2] In the past years, secondary vocational schools alone "have cultivated 250 thousand junior and medium technical talents",[3] which has effectively promoted the upgrading of Dongguan's industrial structures and made great contributions to Dongguan's economic and social development.

So far, 26 secondary vocational schools have established over 30 majors, including electronics, computer, accounting, finance, garment, molds, digital control technology, vehicle maintenance, touring service and management, etc, among which 9 majors are titled as provincial key majors by the ministry of education; 3 higher vocational schools have established nearly 40 majors, including computer application technology, mold design and manufacturing, vehicle inspection and maintenance, accounting computerization, financial management, hospitality management, marketing, industrial and commercial management, logistics management, and apparel design, etc.

With the upgrading and transformation of economical and industrial structure, the present major structure of Dongguan's vocational education cannot meet the need of industry development for the diversified and complicated talents, which can be reflected from the following aspects:

1.1 The disharmony between major structure and industry layout

It mainly reflects in that the major setting is not closely connected with Dongguan's economy development. Majors like computer, English, secretary, management, etc, are set up widely, making high major homoplasy, major excess, and employment insufficiency. However, the most needed majors of Dongguan's key industries, like advanced manufacturing, electric apparatus, textile and garment, shoes and toys manufacturing, biology and medicine, new energy and resources, new materials, etc, are lagged behind, some are even not set up yet. The blindly expanding mode of major construction has become a big choke point hampering the quality of Dongguan's vocational education. So it's high time to break the choke point, gradually realize the great-leap-forward development of Dongguan's vocational education, provide skilled talents for Dongguan's industry transformation and upgrading, and accelerate changing the vocational education structure from blindly amount increasing to backbone majors developing.

1.2 The major setting is disjointed with actual employment needs

Presently, for lack of sufficient market research and scientific management, Dongguan's vocational education majors are disjointed with market demands. This problem directly influences the structure and standard of Dongguan's future talents, lowers the ability of vocational education serving economy development, and then hampers the self-development of vocational education. So the adjustment of vocational education major structure is extremely urgent to realize the coordinated development of vocational education and regional industry.

1.3 The disharmony between cultivation quality and professional requirements

The development of regional economy calls for a great amount of talents who are adequate to enterprise technology development and professional requirement. But presently, many talents from secondary and higher vocational education schools can not meet the enterprises' actual needs on quality and ability structures. The main reason lies in that the cultivation standard and goal are not combined with the professional position's requirements for knowledge, ability and quality; the teaching content and course system didn't absorb new knowledge, new technology and new techniques adopted by enterprises, so that the professional talent cultivation process is seriously disjointed with enterprise's needs. Improving talent cultivation quality and realizing effective connection between major development and enterprises' need is an inevitable choice for vocational education development.

2 FEASIBLE ADJUSTMENT STRATEGIES OF DONGGUAN'S VOCATIONAL EDUCATION MAJOR STRUCTURES

To accomodate Dongguan's transformation from resource-based economy to innovation driven economy, and realize "Dongguan innovating" from "Dongguan manufacturing", the adjustment of Dongguan's vocational education major structures has became the era trend, not only the key measures of realizing transformation and upgrading of Dongguan's economy and society, but also a grand reform for the realization of the sustainable development of Dongguan's vocational education.

2.1 Actively boosting traditional major reform and avoiding major homoplasy

Major is the carrier of vocational schools for talent cultivation, the joint point of vocational schools and social need. Whether the vocational education meet the social need and to what extent it meet, always need to be reflected from the majors and the talents. The prominent problem of the adjustment of Dongguan's vocational education major structures is to reorganize and reform of the exiting traditional majors. However, quite a lot of secondary and higher vocational schools generally are unwilling to close the majors with bad enrolling and employment situations. Then it needs the further investigation for talent demand by Dongguan's government, who can master the talents demand of related majors and development situation of industry transformation. As for the majors with relative saturated market and less demand, the government should adopt elimination, merger, transformation and optimization to adjust these majors compulsorily according to features of each regional industry, so as to avoid the blind competition between higher and secondary schools, and try to construct the good state of major mispalce development. Moreover, the education authorities should consider the economic development requirments and actual situation of each vocational schools, guide the vocational schools to establish major structures that are suitable for Dongguan's industry development, distribute new majors and strictly control the stationing of majors in view of industry situations. With regard to the majors with too much stationing, few demand and insufficient operating conditions, the education authorities need to assess them, take the measures of closing, stopping, merger and transformation, decrease the present major numbers, and develop characteristic majors combined with Dongguan's industry development so as to avoid the phenomenon of repeat major setting and the disconnection of talent cultivation with talent demand.

2.2 Based on the development characteristics of Dongguan's economy, establishing major layout corresponding to local dominating industries

The existence and development of vocational education cannot live without the development of regional economy. Dongguan's vocational schools should actively integrate with regional economy construction, interact with Dongguan's economy, closely follow Dongguan's dominating industries, advantage industries and characteristic industries and construct proper major layout. From the perspective of the actual development of Dongguan's economy, manufacturing industry will still occupy a great portion in the future development, but its industry chain will gradually develop to the two ends of the smiling curve. In the future, the talent need will concentrate on such high and new technology industries as LED electronic lighting, communication technology, information technology, machine manufacturing, mold processing, materials, etc. In addition, with the development of Dongguan's modern service industries, and the seperation of a batch of serving positions from traditional manufacturing industries, the demand for service industries talents will greatly increase, like marketing, electronic commerce, exhibition, financial service, planning, industry design, inquiry, intermediary agent, agency, logistics, service outsourcing, park management, etc. When setting up new majors or major directions, Dongguan's secondary and higher vocational schools should focus on the industries with great potential demands prospectively, scientifically, and flexibly, and constantly adjust and optimize major structures for better connection with market demand and industry structures. Additionally, Dongguan's secondary and higher vocational schools should attempt to widen the breadth and depth of the connection between the major structures and regional industry development, strengthen the deep cooperation with pillar industries and leading enterprises, and expand the present school-enterprise cooperation from enterprises supporting schools to schools supporting enterprises, so as to realize the win-win situation of schools and enterprises.

2.3 Based on industry reality, building competitive brand majors and characteristic majors

No characteristics means no advantages and hence no competitiveness, either. Major characteristics is formed according to its inner development rules in the long—term education practice. It is the essence of major characteristics projects, and the base on which characteristic majors, advantage majors and brand majors (or key majors) are formed. The cultivation goal of major characteristics is to closely follow education orientation, and reflect history advantages, regional features and industry characteristics. Dongguan's secondary and higher vocational schools should closely combine major development, education conditions, and major features with development features of regional industry development and the need for skilled talents. Focusing on reforming the talent cultivation mode, vocational schools should strengthen its cooperation with enterprises, follow the working process of enterprises, reform the course system and teaching content, and strengthen the construction of training conditions. Vocational schools should also cultivate double-certificate teaching groups with high qualities, centralize superior resources to develop brand majors that are acknowledged by society and meet the need of the regional economic and social development with competitive advantages, so as to form the advantage of "people has, I better" and improve core competitiveness. Meanwhile, relying on the exsiting teaching staffs and traning conditions, vocational schools should continuously detail the major directions and form the advantage of "people has, I best". In view of the sunrise industries with great potentials, Dongguan's vocational schools should set up some majors out of the directory on the basis of adequate investigation, form the advantage of "people without, I have" and make every effort to develop major characteristics.

2.4 Breaking barriers between schools and jointly building regional sharing type of professional teaching repository

Dongguan's secondary and higher vocational schools should give full play to the advantage of characteristic majors and key majors. Based on brand majors, vocational schools should seek for enterprises's support, adopt commonly built and shared cooperation modes, integrate resources like excellent teaching resources, classic cases, key technology, enterprises' technology standard, and core knowledge of a certain major, etc. Meanwhile, vocational schools should incorporate technology standard, training resources, production design projects, and training materials of enterprises, etc, build a highly shared major teaching repository. By building such a repository, vocational schools can guide their students to self-learning, which can offer technology service for soical industries, carry out various forms of advanced skill and new technology training, provide diversified further education for enterprise staffs and society members, and ultimately increase the social service abilities of Dongguan's secondary and higher vocational schools.

2.5 Deepening coordination between schools and enterprises, and exploring new mechanism of schools and enterprises jointly building majors

Vocational education should be guided by employment, carry out cooperation with enterprises, combine learning with practice. To meet this, Dongguan's secondary and higher vocational schools need ceaselessly strengthen cooperation and communication with enterprises, invite enterprise experts and technical personnels to the teaching processes, so that they can master the position demand and professional requirements, establish corresponding course systems, integrate teaching content, innovate teaching methods and reform assessment ways. By cooperating with enterprises on course construction, teaching materials development, training bases construction and faculty training, vocational schools can learn the experiences as well as requirements of enterprises directly and realize the seamless joint between major development and professional positions so that students can be qualified for jobs as soon as graduate, which can cultivate fresh troops for enterprises' reform and development and realize the mutual beneficial and win-win situation between schools and enterpises.

REFERENCES

[1] The Medium and Long Term Educational Reform and Development Plan (2010–2020) [EB/OL]. *http://www1.ahedu.gov.cn/jyfz/*. 2010-2-23.
[2] Dongguan Statistics Bureau, National Economy and Society Developed Statistical Bulletin 2001 of Dongguan [EB/OL]. *http://www.dgs.gov.cn/website/web2/art_view.jsp?articleId=5139*. 2012-5-8.
[3] Dongguan Municipal Education Bureau, Vocational Education Attracts People's Attention in 2010, *Dongguan Vocational Education*, 10(1):19.
[4] Zhang, H. 2010. Several Problems on Major Structures Adjusting of Colleges and Universities in Tianjin, *Journal of Tianjin Academy of Educational Science*, 10(2):31–33.
[5] Li, L. & Gu, C.L. 2009. Strategies for Major Structures Adjusting of Vocational Education, *Journal of Guangxi University*, 09(6):144–148.
[6] Wu, J.J. 2009. Major Structures Adjusting of Vocational Education Under the Background of Regional Industrial Transformation, *Jiangsu Education*, 09(5):31–33.

Computer, Intelligent Computing and Education Technology – Liu, Sung & Yao (Eds)
© *2014 Taylor & Francis Group, London, ISBN 978-1-138-02469-4*

A layout algorithm for social network visualization based on community information

Z.N. Zhong, Y. Wu, N. Jing & X. Li
College of Electronic Science and Engineering, National University of Defense Technology, ChangSha, China

ABSTRACT: In order to show the clustering feature in visualization of social network, a novel layout algorithm based on community information for social network visualization was proposed. The community information and the relationships between communities are introduced into the visualization layout, and the visualization layout of the whole social network is realized through three processes. The first process is to do layout of all communities based on community contact degree. The second process is to do layout of nodes in very community based on relationships between nodes. The final process is to adjust the positions of community link nodes. Results of experiments demonstrate that Layout Algorithm based on Community Information (LACI) is better than current visualization layout algorithms not only in showing the clustering structure of a social network, but also in performance. Furthermore, the algorithm can be used to evaluate the community detection and social network data.

Keywords: social network; community; visualization layout; force-directed algorithm

1 INTRODUCTION

Since visualization can help improve the efficiency and quality of data mining, the combination of data mining and visualization has become a research focus. As a subfield of data mining, community detection technology has been brought significant advances in social network analysis in recent years (Fortunato 2010). The main aim of community detection is to analyze the clustering feature of social network, which is the most important characteristic of social network, and divide the social network into different communities. However, current community detection research works are rarely related to the visualization of social network, and current layout algorithms of network (or graph) visualization cannot well show the clustering feature of social network, so users cannot intuitively perceive the clustering structure of social network.

The aim of showing the clustering feature of a social network is to automatically draw the communities of the social network on computer screen in aesthetic standard, i.e. communities of the social network and nodes of every community can be distributed on reasonable positions, the relationships among communities and relationships among nodes can be expressed distinctly, and the layout try to avoid edge crossing, node overlapping and community overlapping.

Current research works related to showing the clustering feature of a social network include com-munity detection algorithms and layout algorithms of network (or graph) visualization. Community detection is to discover the node set with clustering feature from a complicated social network. Since the most popular community detection algorithm was proposed by Girvan & Newman (2002) (GN algorithm), many other algorithms have been appeared. These community detection algorithms can be assorted to the following five categories (Fortunato 2010): the graph algorithms, the hierarchical clustering algorithms, the greedy optimal algorithms, the random walk algorithms and the data field algorithms. These algorithms focus on discovering communities from complex social networks in different methods, but that how to divide community boundary nodes and noise nodes to correct community is a common problem faced by these algorithms. Moreover, that these community detection algorithms are used to discover communities from a same social network may have different results, and a community detection algorithm is not suitable for processing all types of social network. Therefore, people should take part in detecting communities from social network and determine the final results. However, it embarrasses people's judgment in detecting community that current community detection methods do not take into account the visualization of mining procedures and cannot visually express the community detection results.

The core of data visualization is layout algorithm. Shneiderman et al. (2006) divided all visual layout algorithms of network into nine categories: force-directed layout, map layout, circular layout, the relative spatial layout, clustering layout, time layout, layer layout, manual layout and random layout. Known as mainstream information layout algorithms of network data visualization, the force-directed layout algorithms are different from other layout algorithms that the force-directed layout algorithms calculate the layout of network only using information contained within the structure of the network itself, rather than relying on domain-specific knowledge. Graphs drawn by force-directed layout algorithms are simple and tend to be aesthetically pleasing. Force-directed layout algorithm was originally proposed in 1984 by Eades (1984). The basic idea of the algorithm is to consider the network as a physical system, which replaces the nodes by steel rings and replaces each edge with a spring. The system is placed in an initial state and let go so that the spring forces on the rings move the system to a minimum energy state. After been developed for nearly 30 years, the force-directed layout has formed an algorithm family, and many well-known variant algorithms have been proposed, for example the KK algorithm proposed by Kamada & Kawai (1989), the DH algorithm proposed by Davidson & Harel (1996), the FR algorithm proposed by Fruchterman & Reingold (1991), the multi-level force-directed algorithms proposed by Hadany & Harel (2001), David & Yehuda (2002), Walshaw (2003), Chan et al. (2003), Hu (2005) and so on. These variant algorithms inherits the characteristic of the force-directed layout, i.e. calculating layout of a network meets the most aesthetic standards, and these algorithms gradually reduce the complexity of the original force-directed algorithm proposed by Eades (1984) from $o(n^3)$ to $o(nlogn)$ (n present the number of nodes in the network). But all current force-directed algorithms can't express the clustering feature of network. Wu (2011) proposed a Subgroup Analysis Layout (SAL) algorithm, which integrates visualization and social network analysis techniques. But the SAL algorithm only uses the relationship information among different communities and different nodes to calculate the layout of social network, and does not consider the clustering information of communities. In addition, the algorithm need to calculate the shortest path of all nodes in the network, so the whole calculation is complex, and complexity of the algorithm is high. Zhu (2011) proposed a network topology visualization layout algorithm based on community division of social network. The algorithm attempts to visualize the clustering features of a social network, but graph layout calculated by the algorithm is difficult to identify the different communities of a social network.

The goal of this work is to study an efficient layout algorithm for showing the clustering feature of social network. Assumed that the community information could already be included in the social network data, or can be calculated by community detection algorithms, we propose a Layout Algorithm based on Community Information (LACI). The community information and the relationships between communities of social network are introduced into the visualization layout algorithm, and social network is drawn through three processes. Experiments demonstrate that the LACI algorithm can not only efficiently express the clustering feature of social network, but also evaluate the community detection.

2 COMMUNITY CONTACT DEGREE

Communities divide nodes of a social network into different clusters. The community information of a social network includes the number of communities in the social network, as well as the number of nodes in each community (i.e. the size of the community). Since nodes of the same community are joined by many edges, and nodes of the different communities are joined by comparatively few edges, the relationships between nodes in a community are more compact than the relationships between nodes in different communities.

In order to draw the clustering feature of a social network, the core of display layout is to calculate the suitable positions of communities and nodes. An intuitive idea for visualization is to draw the nodes of the same community closely, and lengthen the distance between different communities. The layout of nodes in a community can be easily calculated by traditional force-directed algorithms, but it is difficult to calculate the layout of communities because a community is a node set and relationships between different communities are different. On the other hand, if the layout of social network only focuses on the clustering features of the social network, and ignores its connectivity features including the connection of nodes and the connection of communities, the layout will not show the real structure of the social network, and will reduce the aesthetic appearance due to low utilization of space. Therefore, the relationship between communities should be an important factor for visualization layout of social network. In order to describe the relationship, Community Contact Degree is defined as following:

Definition: A social network can be abstracted into a graph $G = (V, E)$, V is a node set, in which the nodes represent the objects of the social network. E is an edge set, in which the edges represent the relationship between objects. Community V_i is a subset of the node set V, and, $V_i \subseteq V, V_i \underset{i \neq j}{\cap} V_j = \varnothing, \overset{n}{\underset{i=1}{\cup}} V_i = V$, in which n indicates the number of communities. The *Community Contact Degree* of two communities V_i and V_j can be defined as

$$SL(V_i, V_j) = \frac{\underset{\substack{(a,b) \in B \\ a \in V_i, b \in V_j, i \neq j}}{\sum} (a,b)}{\min \left(\underset{\substack{(c,d) \in B \\ c,d \in V_i}}{\sum} (c,d), \underset{\substack{(e,f) \in B \\ e,f \in V_j}}{\sum} (e,f) \right)} \quad (1)$$

By calculating the ratio of the edges between the communities and within the community, *Community Contact Degree* reflects the degree of contact between two communities, the larger the value, the more close the relationship between two communities. Furthermore, appointing the community contact degree between a community and itself to 0, i.e. $SL(V_i, V_i) = 0$, the relationships between any two communities in the entire social network constitute a community contact degree matrix:

$$MSL = (SL_{ij})_{n \times n} = (SL(V_i, V_j))_{n \times n} \quad (2)$$

Compared to the node contact matrix (i.e. edge matrix), the community contact matrix reflects connection relationships between clusters of a social network, and it is very important for the layout of the social network.

For two communities, the value of community contact degree: $0 \leq SL < 1$. If the value is equal to 1 or even more than 1, then it shows that at least a community division is inappropriate.

3 LAYOUT ALGORITHM BASED ON COMMUNITY INFORMATION

3.1 Layout processes

The visualization layout of a social network involves the layouts of communities, nodes and the relationships between communities and nodes. In accordance with the visualization layout idea of dong layout from whole to parts, we propose LACI algorithm. The layout processes of LACI include three steps shown in Figure 1.

The first step is overall layout. The main aim of the process is to locate all communities of a social network. The second step is to do layout of the nodes in each community. The final step is the fine-tuning of the above two step processes.

3.2 Overall layout based on the community contact degree

The overall layout of a social network should have such feature: the distribution of two communi-

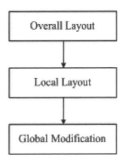

Figure 1. Layout processes of LACI.

ties with higher community contact degree should be closer, while the two communities with lower community contact degree should be distributed farther. The feature is similar to the KK algorithm (Kamada & Kawai 1989). KK algorithm is the first improved algorithm of the Eades's basic force-directed algorithm (Eades 1984) in the family of force-directed layout algorithms. In KK algorithm, the layout distance of two nodes on the graph is proportional to their shortest path. Since KK algorithm has to calculate the shortest path of each pair of nodes, the complexity is relatively high.

In LACI, we refer to KK algorithm and define the elasticity energy between community V_i and V_j as following:

$$E_{ij} = \frac{1}{2} k \left(x_{ij} - L_{\max} \cdot \frac{Sl_{ij}}{Sl_{\max}} \right)^2 \quad (3)$$

x_{ij} indicates the current distance of the two communities V_i and V_j. In order to limit the distance between two communities, $L_{\max}$ represents the maximum distance. $sl_{ij} = \ln(1/SL_{ij})$ is the coefficient to determine the distance based on the community contact degree. $sl_{\max} = \ln(1/SL_{\min})$ is the greatest impact coefficient, in which $SL_{\min}$ is the smallest community contact degree of a social network, and $SL_{\min}$ is not equal to 0. Using logarithm is to limit the distribution range of coefficient. When the community contact degree is 0, there is $E_{ij} = 1/2\, k(x_{ij} - L_{\max})^2$. Therefore, the final elasticity energy could be expressed as:

$$E_{ij} = \begin{cases} \dfrac{1}{2} k \left(x_{ij} - L_{\max} \cdot \dfrac{\ln SL_{ij}}{\ln SL_{\min}} \right)^2 & SL_{ij} \neq 0 \\ \dfrac{1}{2} k (x_{ij} - L_{\max})^2 & SL_{ij} = 0 \end{cases} \quad (4)$$

In the Equation 4, the absolute value of bracket item represents the size of the elastic force, and

351

the sign of bracket item represents the direction of elastic force. '+' represents gravitation, and '−' represents repulsion. Based on Equation 4, the elasticity energy of the whole social network can be expressed as following:

$$E = \sum_{i=1}^{n-1} \sum_{j=i+1}^{n} E_{ij} \qquad (5)$$

When drawing a social network, the communities of the social network can firstly be distributed randomly. After the elasticity between communities have operated for a period of time based on Equation 4, the distribution of the communities will gradually meet the overall layout feature: the distance between closely linked communities is closer, and the distance between less linked communities is longer. Since the number of communities of a social network is far less than the number of nodes, and the computational complexity of community contact degree is also far lower than the shortest path calculation, the overall layout process of a social network is very fast.

3.3 Local community layout

The local community layout is mainly to process the layout of nodes within a community. The requirements of the local community layout should be: drawing the nodes within communities in aesthetic appearance, and avoiding community distribution overlap as much as possible.

FR algorithm (Fruchterman & Reingold 1991) is another variant of the basic force-directed algorithm. Its characteristics of layout are that connected nodes are close to each other, and ensuring that unconnected nodes are not too close to each other. In LACI algorithm, FR algorithm is introduced as local community layout algorithm. In order to control the distribution of each local community, some factors of FR algorithm, including canvas range, initial random distribution of nodes and the initial temperature are adjusted based on the size of each community.

Assuming that the position coordinate of community V_i is $Center_i(cenx_i, ceny_i)$ after overall layout, then the initial positions of nodes in the community V_i will be randomly distributed around $Center_i$. The layout range of the community will be limited to a rectangular area: the horizontal range is $[cenx_i − length_i, cenx_i + length_i]$, and the vertical range is $[ceny_i − length_i, ceny_i + length_i]$, in which $length_i = |V_i| \times l_0$, $|V_i|$ is the node number of the community V_i, l_0 is a constant. As the control factor of node movement, the temperature t_i is initially set to $length_i$ and its iterative Equation is $t_i = t_i \times 0.95$.

After the local layout of each community has been completed, the layout results can be directly placed on the overall layout. In the procedure of local community layout, the nodes of each community are far less than the nodes of the entire social network, so speed of the layout is very quickly. Furthermore, the layouts of various communities are mutually independent, parallel process can be introduced as an optimization strategy to improve the efficiency.

3.4 Global modification

The overall layout can place communities on appropriate positions, and local community layout can distribute nodes of each community in aesthetic appearance. However, these two processes do not consider the distribution of the community link nodes, which belong to a community and have edges to link other communities. A "good" social network layout should be able to reasonably show these nodes, i.e. Community link nodes should be located at the edge of the community, which they belong to, point and close to the communities, which they connect to.

Global modification is to achieve above target through global adjust based on FR algorithm. In the process of global modification, some changes are introduced to FR algorithm: ①the initial position of each node is set to the location, which is calculated by overall layout and local community layout; ②the layout range is not limited; ③adjust the initial temperature and accelerate the rate of decline of the temperature; ④elasticity equation in the FR algorithm is changed to meet our goals.

In FR algorithm, the repulsive force between any two points is defined as follows:

$$f_r(d) = -k^2 / d \qquad (6)$$

d represents the distance between two points, k is the spring coefficient. The attraction force between two points with edge connected is defined as following:

$$f_a(d) = d^2 / k \qquad (7)$$

d represents the distance between the two points with edge connected, k is the spring coefficient.

The layout of the FR algorithm make nodes with edge connected close to each other, it reflect the initial relationship between nodes in social networks, but it does not reflect the characteristics of the community, that is the nodes of a community should be gathered together. We introduce community information to the calculation of attraction force in FR algorithm, and redefine the attraction force as following:

$$f_a(d) = (1+Q)d^2/k \qquad (8)$$

In which, d represents the distance between the two nodes with the edge connected, and k is the spring coefficient.

$$Q = \begin{cases} de, & nodes\ belong\ to\ same\ community \\ 0, & nodes\ belong\ to\ different\ community \end{cases} \qquad (9)$$

The constant de can be determined according to experiment results. Our experiments show that de can be taken a number between 10 and 60. By modified the attraction force, the nodes in the same community will be close together, and the nodes in different communities will be away from each other. Meanwhile, due to the existence of the initial attraction force, the community link nodes will be located on the community periphery.

In the procedure of global modification, it is not expected that nodes move a large range, and modification time is too long. So the initial value of the temperature t in global modification is set to $max(length_i)_{i=1...n}$, and its iterative equation is $t = t \times 0.8$.

4 EXPERIMENTS AND ANALYSIS

In this section, our LACI algorithm is first compared with KK algorithm and FR algorithm on three classic social networks, and then it is demonstrated that LACI can be applied to evaluate the social network data and community mining results. Finally, the time efficiency among LACI algorithm, KK algorithm and FR algorithm are compared.

4.1 Layout comparison

Karate network (Zachary 1977), Dolphin network (Yang et al. 2007) and Football network (Wu & Huberman 2004) are three classic social networks used by social network community detection algorithms. Many community detection algorithms use these network data to verify correctness of community detection. When the results of these community detection algorithms are visualized, generally, these social networks are firstly drawn by typical force-directed layout algorithm, and then different colors are used to depict different communities. In this section, we have done some experiments to compare the layout results of typical force-directed layout algorithms and our LACI algorithm based on the three classic social networks.

Karate network was constructed by the sociologists Zachary, and depicted the relationships between members of a non-official karate club in an America university. As the issue of fees, the club was split into two small groups, which one supported coach and another supported manager. Many algorithms can divide the two groups correctly, such as the classic GN algorithm (Girvan & Newman 2002), the FEC algorithm (Yang et al. 2007) and the WH algorithm (Wu & Huberman 2004), Figure 2 shows the layout result of the Karate network of the LACI algorithm, the KK algorithm and the FR algorithm. We can see that the layout results of KK algorithm and the FR algorithm cannot intuitively separate the two communities, and LACI algorithm can clearly represent the clustering feature of the social network and the relationships between communities.

Dolphin network was a social network established by the zoologist Lussean who studied the situation of dolphins living in the Antarctica New Zealand Doubtful Sound. Due to the death of one of the members, these dolphins gradually divided into two small groups. As the same as the Karate network, it is a standard social network data which is used to test the correctness of community detection algorithms, and there are also a lot of algorithms which can distinguish the two groups. Figure 3 shows the layout results of the Dolphin network drawn by the LACI algorithm, the KK algorithm and the FR algorithms. Being similar to Figure 2, our LACI algorithm is better than KK algorithm and FR algorithm in exhibiting clustering feature of the social network.

The Football network depicted the 2000 season of the United States colleges and universities rugby League. All 115 teams in the league were

Figure 2. The layout results of the Karate social network by the three algorithms: KK (left), FR (middle), LACI (right).

Figure 3. The layout results of the Dolphin social network by the three algorithms: KK (left), FR (middle), LACI (right).

divided into different 12 unions due to their geographic positions. According to the schedule, the number of games between teams in the same union was more than the games between different union teams. However, there were some teams whose number of games with the different union teams was more than the number of games with the same union teams. These teams brought difficulties to the community detection. So far, there are not community detection algorithms which can correctly divide the 12 unions, including the most classic GN algorithm and newly emerging TJ algorithm (Traag & Jeroen 2009). Figure 4 is the layout results of the Football network by the LACI algorithm, the KK algorithm and the FR algorithms. To KK and FR algorithms, the layouts are very confused even with colors to express communities. The layout result of the LACI algorithm cannot completely show the correct 12 community, but its ability to express the clustering information of the social network is much stronger than the traditional force-directed layout algorithms.

4.2 Further analysis

Another characteristic of the LACI algorithm is that its layout procedure can be used to analyze the social network data, and the algorithm can also be used to judge results of the community detection. By LACI algorithm, the nodes of 'good' communities in a social network should be drawn closely, and the space between communities should be clear. In our experiment using Football data, the actual community information of the Football social network is known. But in fact, there are three unreasonable communities in the 12 communities of the Football network according to the classical community theory. Figure 5 shows the local lay-out of the three unreasonable communities and the overall layout of the Football Network by the LACI algorithm. Shown in Figure 5, the A community and B community both have an isolated team, which doesn't have games with the teams in the same community. Therefore, the actual division of the community is not in line with the classical community theory. In the C community, only two teams have the inner game, while the other three team's games are not in the community, so the C community should not be considered as a reasonable community of social network. It is impossible that community detection algorithms can properly detect the 12 communities because of the existence of these nodes and these communities. If an algorithm is claimed that it can correctly divide the 12 communities, we can assure that the algorithm is false. In other words, our LACI algorithm can be used to judge the community detection results and analyze the social network data. Firstly, the overall layout results of a good community detection algorithm can show the clustering distribution of communities. Secondly, the local layout of communities should not appear isolated nodes.

4.3 Comparison of time efficiency

KK algorithm and FR algorithm are typical force-directed algorithms, and are widely used in the layout of network data visualization. The KK algorithm's time complexity is $o(n^3)$, and the FR algorithm's time complexity is $o(n^2)$, Which n represents the number of the nodes in the network. LACI algorithm extends KK algorithm and FR algorithm by being introduced community information and the relationships between communities to draw social network, and realizes the layout by three steps, i.e. overall layout, local layout and global modification. In these steps of layout, overall layout is to locate the communities, this step is very fast due to the community number of a social network is far less than the nodes of the social network. The procedure of global modification is also fast because this step only does some adjustments and the number of iterative calculations is few. So the layout time of LACI algorithm is mainly spent on local layout.

The local layout of LACI algorithm is based on FR algorithm. Assumed that the number of communities in the social network is represented as M, the time complexity of the FR algorithm can be expressed as $o((\sum_{i=1}^{M} N_i)^2)$, in which N_i represents the number of nodes in i community, the time complexity of local layout in LACI algorithm can be expressed as $o(\sum_{i=1}^{M} N_i^2)$, and then the time complexity of LACI algorithm is slightly larger than $o(\sum_{i=1}^{M} N_i^2)$. Therefore, the time complexity of LACI algorithm community is less than FR algorithm

Figure 4. The layout results of the Football social network by the three algorithms: KK (left), FR (middle), LACI (right).

Figure 5. The Football network and its three unreasonable communities (A, B, C).

Table 1. The time efficiency comparison of the three algorithms.

	$|V|$	$|E|$	KK	FR	LACI
Karate	34	78	1.521 s	1.141 s	0.351 s
Dolphin	62	159	8.358 s	3.991 s	1.015 s
Football	115	613	34.233 s	13.163 s	1.999 s

and KK algorithm. Based on above three classical social network data, the experiment of time efficiency comparison among KK, FR and LACI algorithms has been done. The experiment was developed in Matlab, and was carried out on a PC with an Intel Core i3 2100 3.1G CPU and 4G memory. The result is shown in Table 1. We can see that the layout speed of LACI algorithm is much faster than the other two algorithms.

5 CONCLUSIONS

It has become a research hot spot that using visualization techniques to improve the quality of data mining and analysis. Since current visualization layout algorithms of social network cannot express the clustering feature of social network, these algorithms are not suitable for supporting social network analysis, especially community detection. In this paper, a layout algorithm based on community information is proposed. The algorithm can show the clustering feature of social network in aesthetic standards and less time. Furthermore, the algorithm can be used to analyze the characteristics of social network data, judge quality of divided communities in a social network, and evaluate community detection algorithms.

The visualization of large-scale network data is a challenge for visual layout algorithms. In our future work, we will research parallel computing technology to further improve the time efficiency of our LACI algorithm, and make it be suitable for large social network analysis.

REFERENCES

Chan, D.S.M. & Chua, K.S. & Leckie, C.A. & Parhar, A. 2003. Visualization of Power-Law Network Topologies. *Proceedings of the Eleventh IEEE International Conference on Networks, Sydney, Australia*: 69~74.

Davidson, R. & Harel, D. 1996. Drawing graphs nicely using simulated annealing. *ACM Transactions on Graphics (TOG)* 15(4): 301–331.

David, H. & Yehuda, K. 2002. A fast multi-scale method for drawing large graphs. *Journal of Graph Algorithms and Applications* 6(3): 179–2002.

Eades, P. 1984. A heuristic for graph drawing. *Congressus numerantium* 42: 149–160.

Fortunato, S. 2010. Community detection in graphs. *Physics Reports* 486(3–5): 75–174.

Fruchterman, T. & Reingold, E.M. 1991. Graph drawing by force-directed placement. *Software—Practice and Experience* 21(11): 1129–1164.

Girvan, M. & Newman, M.E.J. 2002. Community structure in social and biological networks. *Proc of the National Academy of Science* 9(12): 7821–7826.

Hadany, R. & Harel, D. 2001. A multi-scale algorithm for drawing graphs nicely. *Discrete Applied Mathematics* 113(1):3–21.

Hu, Y.F. 2005. Efficient and high quality force-directed graph drawing. *The Mathematica Journal* 10: 37–71.

Kamada, T. & Kawai, S. 1989. An algorithm for drawing general undirected graphs. *Information processing letters* 31(1): 7–15.

Shneiderman, B. & Aris, A. 2006. Network visualization by semantic substrates. *IEEE Transactions on Visualization and Computer Graphics* 12(5): 733–740.

Traag, V.A. & Jeroen, B. 2009. Community detection in networks with positive and negative links. *Physical Review E* 80(3): 036115–036121.

Walshaw, C. 2003. A multilevel algorithm for force-directed graph drawing. *Journal of Graph Algorithms and Applications* 7(3): 253–285.

Wu, F. & Huberman, B.A. 2004. Finding communities in linear time. A Physics approach. *European Physical Journal B* 38(2): 331–338.

Wu, P. & Li, S.K. 2011. Layout algorithm suitable for structural analysis and visualization of social networks, *Journal of Software*, 22(10): 2467–2475.

Yang, B. & Cheng, W.K. & Liu, J. 2007. Community mining from signed social networks. *IEEE Transactions on Knowledge and Data Engineering,* 19(10): 1333–1345.

Zachary, W.W. 1977. An information flow model for conflict and fission in small groups. *Journal of Anthropological Research,* 33(4): 452–473.

Zhu, Z.L. & Lin, S. & Cui, K. & Yu, H. 2011. Network Topology Layout Algorithm Based on Community Detection of Complex Networks. *Journal of Computer-Aided Design & Computer Graphics,* 23 (11): 1808–1815.

Computer, Intelligent Computing and Education Technology – Liu, Sung & Yao (Eds)
© 2014 Taylor & Francis Group, London, ISBN 978-1-138-02469-4

Study on wind farms tourism development in China based on the triple helix theory

S.Y. Wang
Department of Economics and Management, North China Electric Power University, Baoding, Hebei Province, China

ABSTRACT: At present, the lack of systematic planning for the wind farms tourism. Besides, public awareness is relatively low. In view of the present situation of wind farms tourism development in China, this paper analyzes government, tourism and wind power enterprises division of roles, and puts forward the corresponding countermeasures and suggestions based on the triple helix theory.

Keywords: wind farms tourism; triple helix theory; countermeasures and suggestions

At present, the domestic wind farms tourism in general is still in the "goes it alone" stage, the lack of systematic planning for the whole industry, public awareness is relatively low. This situation is not conducive to the development of the new type of wind farms tourism industry. Based on the triple helix theory, we explore the China's development way of wind farms tourism in the following text.

1 THE TRIPLE HELIX

In the triple helix, the reason that each helix can make movement and interaction is that each helix is a rational organization which can make decisions independently, which the theory premises is contained. Different helix pursuit of different interests, three parties play their own respective strength and work together.[1]

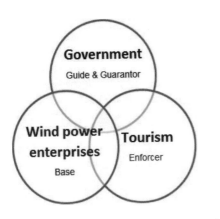

Figure 1. The Triple Helix of wind power enterprise-tourism-government.

At the same time, the trinity of three dimensions will form a three-way interaction of hybrid innovation network (Fig. 1).

Introduction of triple helix model will be able to be more clearly in systematic analysis of interactions among government, tourism and wind power enterprise. It is conducive to build suitable wind farms tourism development patterns for China.[2]

2 THE APPLIED PRINCIPLE OF TRIPLE HELIX THEORY

As the three main bodies, government, tourism and the wind power enterprises, they work independently and collaborate. In the development process, the government is guide and guarantor, wind power enterprise is fundamental, and tourism is the implementer of specific measures.

3 PRACTICAL APPLICATION OF THE TRIPLE HELIX THEORY

3.1 Government

Implement the tourism brand driven strategy. Uphold the principles: government-sponsoring, scientific planning, enterprise accomplishing, marketing operation, society participating, to establish and improve the tourism brand to develop mechanism. Government assumes a dominant position in brand building, makes brand position according to wind power resource advantage, demand of tourism market, current status of tourist industry and development trend.

1. Planning for tourism development

The government plays a leading role in the development of wind farms tourism. The cognition, positioning and planning of wind farms tourism of government, will be the foundation of wind farms tourism development sustainable. According to the goals and strategies of wind farms tourism, government draws up the overall planning from the distribution of social resources, tourism resources development and environmental benefits of compiling wind tourism development from the aspects.

2. Creating a favorable development environment

The current tourism legal system in China is not perfect. There are many problems in tourism industry. The development of the market environment is not conducive for tourism. On the one hand, the government should strengthen the legal laws and regulations construction of tourism to perfect legal system. On the other hand, it should formulate relevant policies conducive to the development of the wind farms tourism. On the other hand, government should prepare to promote investment and capital introduction. So as to creating a favorable environment for the development of the wind farms tourism.

3. Establishing a perfect tourism coordination system

In order to realize the development of the tourism cluster effectively, it is indispensable for each scenic spot to coordinate with each other. All the wind farms locations are remote and rather dispersed. To develop wind farms tourism smoothly, the government should coordinate in aspects such as perfecting tourism transportation, information system, to ensure smooth communication among different subjects, strengthen the mutual cooperation among different tourism.

4. Supporting popular science education base construction

Wind power industry is a high and new technology industry. The government can support wind power enterprise to develop wind power science and technology museum or science education base, organize academic seminars on the development of new energy, build communication platform to spread scientific knowledge about wind power.

3.2 Tourism

1. The design of tourism souvenir

In the primary period, both ecological tourism and academic visit will spread wind farms tourism well. Nevertheless, it should give full play to the advantages of industrial clusters, thus the value of the tourism products can be maximized. At the beginning, tourism should catch the customers of home mature tourism projects; build one-stop high-quality

good line. Developing tourism with other tourist scenic spot to achieve maximum value.

2. Training of the relevant professional talent

Guide interpretation system should be established. Attention should be given to the important role of tour guides in the wind farms tourism, as well, strengthen the professional training of wind power enterprise employees, explain the work of wind power industry, etc. Making them becomes wind knowledge disseminator, to conduct activities smoothly, improve the quality of tourism.

3.3 Wind power enterprise

1. Strengthen the consciousness of independent development

In combination with the practical situation of wind farm area, building wind power culture exhibition hall in the surroundings. The exhibition contents include wind turbines and related production equipment models to represent the wind farm daily work life scenes. In order to improve wind tourism culture connotation, wind power culture art also can be carried out etc.

2. Strengthen landscape management and maintenance

Wind farms are responsible for the reception of visitors for sightseeing. They also should deal with wind landscape in daily management and maintenance. On the basis of the protection of the normal operation of wind power generators, they ought to keep the equipment clean and working well. Meanwhile, strengthen propaganda of environmental protection and importance of protecting the environment and facilities in the process of tourists visiting.

3.4 Triple cooperation

It is a complicated, systematic project to push wind farms tourism development forward, for the mutual coordination requires a lot of effort within the process. The government, tourism and wind power enterprise play different roles and assume their respective responsibilities. Meanwhile, each of them cannot work without the other two parties. The completion of each task need all three parties work jointly.

The government makes tourism development strategies with policy guidance; wind power enterprise and the tourism is responsible for the specific implementing of policy. It can adopt joint office wait for means to promote the development of wind farms tourism.

1. The service facilities

Wind farms tourism development is still in initial stage, the infrastructure construction needs to rely on government funding support. On the one hand, government can establish tourism development funds; on the other hand, draw a certain proportion from the tourist comprehensive development funds to support the wind farms tourism.

Tourism can use policy and financial support provided by the government. Giving full play of the advantages of its own resources to strengthen the construction of information system based on the existing tourism website adding function about wind power project information to spread service information. In addition, the government should take to strengthen the construction of traffic planning as support wind tourism major initiatives. The government could allocate special funds key rehabilitation arena wind farms, roads, giving priority to the road network traffic capacity expansion to strengthen transport links between the wind farm; Under the guidance of the government policies, tourism could strengthen the dining facilities, tourist service center, tourist resting area, suitable for tourist service facilities giving new construction, reconstruction and equipped with professional personnel to provide consulting services for tourists. Besides, sending tourist map, travel brochures etc., to the tourist. At the same time, they should properly arrange wind power bus equipped with to enhance the capacity of scenic spot tourism services.

2. The development of tourism products

Tourism souvenir is a very important part of the wind farms tourism development. When it properly exploited, it will bring lots of benefits. It requires product exploitation, production and promotion vigorously synergy. A fine wind souvenir can not only bring satisfaction to tourists, but also to give wind tourism a second propaganda and to expand its influence. Product exploitation can be divided into three steps:

A. Wind souvenirs development is guided by the government, participated by the tourism, and wind power enterprise, by hiring professional design personnel participating in the development to expand product series and improve the level of products. Souvenirs can include windmills fight inserted toys, pendant, and other articles for daily products with wind industry elements, etc.

B. Combine commodity sales with sightseeing. On the premise of commodity authorization, the sales agencies of licensed products with the characteristic of the wind can be established at wind farms, museum and other areas;

C. Exanimated and approved by the government, conducted by the tourism enterprises, through reasonable layout of tourist shopping networks, in order to establish a kind of theme store.

3. Travel security

Travel security issues need to be concerned by all the participants. Through cooperation to create a kind of safe environment. Related organizers in tourism activities have a duty to guarantee the life property safety of the tourist. On the one hand, professional staff from the wind power enterprise to take safety education for the tourists, in order to raise the awareness of self-protection; On the other hand, to take security measures, such as forcing visitors to wear safety helmet protective devices, ban visitors near the danger zone, etc., to keep safety of the tourist.

First, wind farms ought to ensure the safety production in order to provide guaranteed support for sightseeing; identify and differentiate to visit tour area to avoid the tourist activities affect the normal production and operation of the wind farm. As a place for tourism activities provider, it also provides security safety protection facilities, equipment, training, and security personnel, in order to achieve all-round guarantee the personal safety of tourists and staff. At the same time, together with government and tourism, wind power enterprise establishes risk prevention and treatment system, to ensure opportune measures could take when danger occurs. Finally, the management and maintenance of wind tourism infrastructure should be taken periodically to assure the carrying out of the sustainable development of wind farms tourism.

It is noteworthy that the whole tourism chain will be affected when facing crisis. Thus, the coping mechanisms and post-disaster reconstruction measures should be formulated in advance before unknown hazards happen. Establishing long-term monitoring, forecasting, and early-warning mechanism, to ensure a quick reaction when disasters occur.

The government, the tourism and wind power enterprise are the three entities to promote the development of wind farms tourism that is inseparable in wind farms tourism development. Only coordinate with the interests of the relationship among the three can the common goal of the wind farms tourism development be achieved.

4 SUMMARY

China wind farms tourism development mainly exist these problems: lack of cognitive, propaganda is insufficient, resource is scanted, insufficient practice, the research does not reach the designated position, as well as individually work, such problems origin matter is the lack of co-ordination. Although the whole society hold a positive attitude on the wind farms tourism development, the government is noncommittal to the wind farms tourism project development, the rejection of tourism for the wind power enterprise and wind power enterprise is not positive to tourism performance. All the factors make the collaboration stagnation and the wind farms tourism development is difficult to use existing resources effectively. Only the government, tourism and wind power enterprise get tripartite mutual coupling, interaction and interdependence can make the development of wind farms tourism better florescent.

REFERENCES

[1] Leydesdorff L. The Triple Helix—University-industry-government relations: A laboratory for knowledge based economic development [J]. East Review, 1995,14(1):14–9.
[2] Min Wu, The research of the triple helix on the regional creation system [J]. China Technology Forum, 2006,(1):36–4.

The design and implementation of mobile learning platform based on WLAN

G.X. Wang & Y.L. Gao
Information Technology Center of Jiujiang University, Jiujiang, Jiangxi, China

ABSTRACT: The development of mobile learning provides the possibility for people's lifelong learning, the rapid development of communication technology and network technology will whenever and wherever possible the concept of lifelong learning has gradually become a reality. The paper starts with the mobile learning, expounds the emerging WLAN technology application in the field of mobile learning. We had built a platform of mobile learning to achieve whenever and wherever mobile learning that using the embedded system technology and the wireless network technology.

Keywords: WLAN; mobile learning platform; android; streaming media technology

1 GENERAL INTRODUCTION

1.1 *Foreword*

With the continuous development of communication technology, the development and application of mobile Internet technology is changing the way people work and study habits. As a new way of distance learning, more and more people is fond of mobile learning that learners can achieve self-learning anytime and anywhere. December 4, 2013, the Ministry of Information and Internet Technology of China granted the three state-owned operators—China Mobile, China Unicom and China Telecom—4G licences based on the country's home-grown TD-LTE standard. This indicates that mobile learning ushered in a new era.

Mobile learning platform based on WLAN technology is a multimedia learning system that based embedded systems and pervasive computing. It combines a wireless network, smart phones, PDA, iPad, PC, etc. It reached a more perfect balance between mobility and processing capabilities, both showing a more complex multimedia content, and can be comparable in mobility and mobile phones. It made more diverse forms of mobile learning content richer. Paper constructs a multimedia mobile learning platform to facilitate the movement of people needs to learn.

1.2 *Mobile learning overview*

Mobile learning is also known as M-Learning, is a typical application of digital learning. Mobile learning in a broad sense refers to the aid of digital mobile communication device distance learning such as WAP phones, PAD, handheld computers and laptops and other tools. Paul Harris scholars believe that mobile learning should enable learners to access to education anytime, anywhere via mobile phone or PDA, to use his own words is "enjoy and educational moment". Mobile learning is developed on the basis of the digital learning together, and is an extension of digital learning. It is different from the general learning, the learning environment of mobile learning is mobile and based on the scenario of. Learners can make use of mobile intelligent terminal learn anywhere, any time for self-study, the impact is not limited to the traditional learning environment.

2 MOBILE LEARNING PLATFORM DEVELOPMENT TECHNOLOGY

2.1 *Preparing the new file with the correct template*

Development of mobile learning platform need related to communications, embedded systems development, wireless network technology. At present, mobile communication technology include GSM, GPRS, CDMA2000, W-CDMA, TD-SCDMA, etc. With the development of 3G technology and mature, and the rise of 4G technology, the concept of mobile learning based on mobile communication technology more easily accepted by people.

Wireless LAN (WLAN) is a computer network which created in a certain local area using wireless communications technology. A computer network and wireless communication technology product of the combination, which is based on wireless multiple access channel as a transmission medium, offers traditional LAN functionality is limited, users can make true broadband network access anytime, anywhere. WLAN is a computer network and wireless communication technology product of the combination. It is based on wireless multiple access channel as a transmission medium, offers traditional LAN functionality, the user can make a real broadband network access anywhere, anytime, and is a complement of 3G networks and wired networks. Currently, medium and large enterprises and university campuses establish WLAN to improve working and learning efficiency. WLAN technology based mobile learning platform has a rapid deployment to achieve convenient, can be effective anywhere, anytime learning, teachers and students to achieve real-time interaction, thus improving the efficiency of learning.

3 DESIGN AND IMPLEMENTATION OF MOBILE LEARNING PLATFORM

3.1 The overall design of mobile learning platform

Mobile Learning relying more mature Wireless LAN (WLAN), mobile Internet and multimedia technologies, the use of mobile devices, wireless Internet access on campus WLAN, etc., system access through mobile learning system Learning Resources (Web servers, streaming media on-demand server, database servers, etc.), easy and flexible way to implement interactive mobile teaching activities. WLAN-based mobile learning platform framework map as shown in Figure 1.

The mobile learning platform mainly consists of three parts: background server-side, ford-end mobile learning application and wireless LAN part.

3.1.1 Background server-side
The background server-side include the necessary Web server, database server and mobile learning

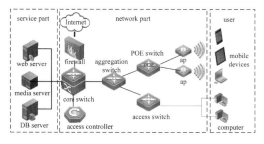

Figure 1. Framework map of mobile learning platform WLAN-based.

resources on-demand streaming media server. Web server is primarily responsible for curriculum management, interactive communication, resources, downloads and other services; mobile learning resource database servers mainly provide data services, including querying, storage services, data backup services; demand streaming media servers mainly provide real-time multimedia and non-real-time multimedia Demand for complete real-time voice and video interaction and video-on-demand courseware and teaching non-classroom services.

3.1.2 Fore-end mobile learning application
It is native mobile learning applications and APP application based on smartphone operating system, or mobile learning system based on Web browsers manner, or mobile learning software which push short message SMS-based. These applications are all made out of the way through the programming software system, through which learners could carry out mobile learning activities. Realization of front-end applications employ Web programming based on Android framework.

3.1.3 Wireless LAN (WLAN) part
From Figure 1 we can see that WLAN as the key part of the mobile learning platform is also a mobile learning platform supporting environment, play important effect which connecting front-end mobile learning applications and back-end server. There are many ways to build a wireless LAN, currently more popular wireless networking is the core of the cable network core switch access layer switches, and then communicate with the remote POE switch (Power Over Ethernet switch), POE switches wireless access points AP Client support and provide electricity to transmit signals. AP that is client wireless access point controlled by wireless controller called AC. Currently, AP can transmit signals and transmit 2.4G and 5G, wireless network access to meet the needs of the current multi-user intelligent terminal.

3.2 The design of mobile learning platform function

WLAN-based mobile learning platform software system includes course management, resources, downloads, online test, interaction modules. Course Management module includes compulsory and elective courses, online learning. Download module includes the required course curriculum and associated curriculum resources, such as PPT, video and audio. Online test modules for learners' progress and needs based on course of study, learning on their own knowledge testing and inspection. When learners complete the online test, the system will give the distribution of test scores and knowledge, so that learners grasp their own learning, to make up for deficiencies. Interactive communication module for the exchange of teachers and students, and between students discuss provided for convenience. Mobile learning platform function structure shown in Figure 2, and software structure shown in Figure 3.

3.3 Implement mobile learning platform

3.3.1 Android-based development environment to build

Android is a complete development platform, Android allows developers to freely develop excellent variety of performance, the perfect support for mobile Internet applications. Various applications that developed by programmer can be use of rapidly developing ARM processor and GPU to realize 3D acceleration, and realize location services using GPS technology (LPS), and provide the perfect user experience. The platform uses the

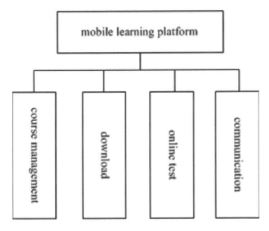

Figure 2. The structure of mobile learning platform function.

web browser	AV player
jQM	eclipse
libraries	android runtime
linux core	

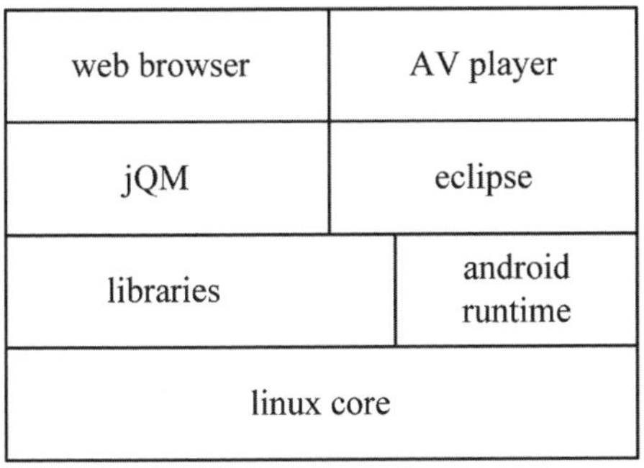

Figure 3. The software architecture of mobile learning platform.

Eclipse integrated development environment for client development based on Android SDK, the server uses Servlet container was apache-tomcat-6.0.35. Install Android Development on Eclipse Tools for Android development.

Java JDK and JRE require a full installation and set up the Java environment variable% JAVA_HOME%. Java and Eclipse downloaded directly from Oracle.com and Eclipse.org official website and install; Android SDK by executing the program from the Android SDK Manager to download the official website after the completion of the batter installation. ADT is installed via the Eclipse Software Updates function, after the Software Updates screen reproduction of the input URL ADT installed automatically. By building Android system development environment, we can develop applications for Android mobile learning system.

3.3.2 Build a browser-based mobile learning environment

Embedded browser is an indispensable part of the mobile learning system. Learners can through Wireless LAN (WLAN) using a Web browser way to experience mobile learning. The mobile learning platform intends to adopt the one most of commonly used mobile Web development framework—jQuery Mobile (jQM) framework. The framework is based on mature and stable Javascript framework jQuery, is a lightweight open source framework. It combines with the popular HTML5/CSS tightly, to enhance the appearance and behavior of the HTML element, such that the program interact with the style and the native platform close control can greatly enhance Web pages on a mobile device availability. The appearance and behavior of jQM application easy to customize, with jQuery and HTML/CSS-based developers can quickly get started. jQM support for common mobile browsers, such as UC and so on.

Access through the browser B/S architecture mobile learning server, database server, mobile learning resource server, students can access mobile learning course management systems, resources, downloads, online testing and interactive communication module, and can query courses and score, and be learning activities in real time interaction.

3.3.3 User Interface (UI) development

User interface consist of the screen view, touch screen events and keyboard events. In order to make the user interface fit a variety of different Android devices, the system provides a framework for defining the user interface, including the user interface layout and user interface events. The layout of the user interface include user resource directory, view components and view of the container, the layout of the components (Layout) and layout parameters (LayoutaParams). User resource directory for storing user interface resource classification data, views, components and containers component contains a lot of subclasses View and ViewGroup. View is the basic building blocks of a graphical interface, essentially all of the high-level UI components are integrated and implemented the View class. By setting the parameters of the layout module Layout and Layout LayoutParams interface design; method by writing trigger interface layout components, trigger and monitor interaction events between the user and the application. For example, in the interface when a button is clicked, the system framework will call onTouchEvent () method of the button object. In order to make more effective listener calls and more meaningful, we must override these methods are usually provided through the view class nested interfaces completed.

3.3.4 *Resource server program development*
The system to distribute curriculum resources using JAVA WEB MVC pattern way to achieve in web server. Text and images resources stored in the database, to obtain the data directly from the database When a user makes a request (Direct access to text, HTML and other content; video, audio resource then get their URL), and finally displays all dynamic web content via JSP. Part of the code is as follows:

```
Try
{
//Database access object of curriculum resources
instantiation
ResDAO resdao=new ResDAO();
// Get the resource list
ArrayList<Resource>reslst=resdao.getResource
List();
// The resource list is set to the scope
Request.setAttribute("RES_LIST", reslst);
RequestDispatcher
dispatcher=reques.getRequestDispatcher("/res.
jsp");
// Forwarded to the Resource Display page
patcher.forward(request,response);
}
Catch(Excepton e)
{
// Exception Handling...
}
```

3.4 *Multimedia technology implementations of mobile learning platform*

Multimedia applications in WLAN-based mobile learning platform include live classroom learning and multimedia courseware on demand. Through the WLAN access mobile learning and teaching

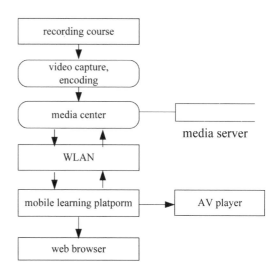

Figure 4. Data flow diagram for streaming media VOD.

resource server and internet resources, learners can check courses, online learning, interactive communication, resources, downloads and other mobile learning activities anytime, anywhere, but also be able to publish through mobile learning system receives curriculum centers associated with the course of study the instant messaging, easy to move learners to grasp lessons and learning to meet the information flow, reasonable arrangements for study time.

Design class live and on-demand multimedia courseware modules required to achieve the acquisition, encoding, network transmission of audio and video streaming, receiving, decoding and playback. Figure 4 shows the real-time streaming media on-demand data flow model. Streaming audio and video capture, coding, transmission is completed by the mobile network teaching server; front-end mobile learning system is responsible for receiving RTP media stream, after decoding, caching and other treatment, to play in front of a mobile learning system embedded player.

4 CONCLUSION

This paper presents a design model and implementation programs on mobile learning platform based on WLAN. Combined with the entire mobile learning platform gives the realization of the principle functions of the platform structure and multimedia applications such as video-on-demand, providing a reference for the development of WLAN technology based mobile learning platform.

With the promotion and implementation of mobile learning projects, mobile learning platform has a broad market prospect, the emergence of a variety of mobile learning platform will further enrich and facilitate the movement of people to learn life. Of course, the current mobile learning platform is imperfect, there are situations such as simulation, emulation interactive, online teaching evaluation function to be studied. Provide better mobile learning experience and mobile learning services, and this is the next step to continue the study of the subject.

REFERENCES

[1] Paul Harris. Goin Mobile Learning Circuits ASTD Magazine All about eLearning. http://www.astd.org/LC/2001/0701_harris.htm, 2001.

[2] Ye Chenglin, Xu Fuyin, Xu Jun. Review of Mobile Learning Research[J]. E-education Research, 2004.3:18.

[3] Ye Chenglin. Research on Modelling and Design of Mobile Learning System Based on Grid[D]. School of Information Technology in Education of South China Normal University, PhD thesis, 2006.4.

[4] Li Yushun, Ma Ding. Status and trends of mobile learning[J]. Information Technology Education, 2008,(3):9–11.

[5] Wikipedia. Multiple phone web-based application framework[EB/OL]. http://en.wikipedia.org/wiki/Multiple_phone_web_based_application_framework, 2013-05-16.

[6] The jQuery Foundation. jQuery Mobile Introduction[EB/OL]. http://view.jquerymobile.com/1.3.1/dist/demos/intro/, 2013-05-15.

Computer, Intelligent Computing and Education Technology – Liu, Sung & Yao (Eds)
© 2014 Taylor & Francis Group, London, ISBN 978-1-138-02469-4

Solving stochastic expected value models with stochastic particle swarm optimization algorithm

N. Xiao

Computer Science Department, Shaanxi Vocational and Technical College, Xi'an, China

ABSTRACT: Aiming at being hard to solve the stochastic expected value models in uncertainty programming field, a new hybrid intelligent algorithm which used the stochastic simulation and stochastic particle swarm optimization is proposed, and detail steps is designed, it overcomes the defaults such as needing a long time, complex calculation, falling into local optimum in the hybrid intelligence algorithm based on Genetic Algorithm, the result of experiment shows effectiveness of the algorithm.

Keywords: stochastic expected value models; stochastic particle swarm optimization; random simulation

1 INTRODUCTION

"Particle Swarm Optimization" (PSO) algorithm that is a new intelligent technology was first pioneered by Eberhart and Kennedy in 1995[1]. Be similar to Genetic Algorithm (GA), it also employs global search strategy based on population. However, it hasn't genetic operation and only use simple V-S model to finish searching optimum in entire solution space. The algorithm only need adjust a few parameters. It owns many merits such as simplicity, easier realization, more rapid convergence, better precision and so on, its dominance has been exhibited in solving or application of all kinds of problems [2–4].

As far as stochastic variable in stochastic programming problem is concerned, because of different manage goal and technology demand, method of adoption is also different, however, the most natural method is that average value of stochastic variable corresponding function is used. In expected value constraint, model which makes expected value of goal function acquire optimum is named Stochastic Expected Value Models (SEVM). The main method of solving SEVM is that stochastic simulation (Monte-Carlo simulation) is combined with intelligent algorithm [5–8], in which GA is excellent so far. However, genetic operation process such as selection, crossover, mutation are not only complex but also slower convergence and worse precision. At present researcher of various countries are going on researching new, more effective algorithm for solving this problem [5–8].

The advantage of PSO algorithm lies in simple concept, easy programming, the object function doesn't be continuous, differentiable conditions, so, it's worth that the PSO algorithm is applied in SEVM problem, however, in view of earlier convergence of original PSO, for more precise solving SEVM problem, in this paper, SEVM problem is solved by hybrid intelligence algorithm based on stochastic simulation and Stochastic Particle Swarm Optimizer (SPSO) which substitutes for GA [9] in section6. The simulation results illustrate the effectiveness of the algorithm. Thus the hybrid intelligent algorithm based on PSO succeeds in resolving continuous space SEVM problems in quality of solution.

2 ORIGINAL PSO ALGORITHM

In original PSO algorithm, each particle of particle swarm which is defined in D-dimensional space (called solution space) are flying with velocity V_i ($V_{i1}, V_{i2} \ldots V_{id}$) through the search space. Begin with, the algorithm initializes a group of random solution ($x_1, x_2 \ldots x_N$, N is number of particle), and then, particles dynamically adjust their position and velocity according to their own volatile experience and volatile experience of entire swarm, at the same time, the fitness is used to evaluate the "goodness" of a potential solution (indivial). "Pbest" (personal best position) and "Gbest" (the best position found by the entire swarm so far) are picked out, and then, record their position, according to equation (1), (2), (3) updates position, velocity of next iteration once again, that is, PSO algorithm is iterative process. The mathematical equation of the algorithm is as follows:

$$V_{id}(t+1) = \omega * V_{id}(t) + C_1 * rand() * (P_{id} - X_{id}(t))$$
$$+ C_2 * rand() * (P_{gd} - X_{id}(t)) \qquad (1)$$

$$\begin{cases} V_{id} = V_{max} & \text{if} \quad V_{id} > V_{max} \\ V_{id} = -V_{max} & \text{if} \quad V_{id} < -V_{max} \end{cases} \tag{2}$$

$$X_{id}(t+1) = X_{id}(t) + V_{id}(t+1) \tag{3}$$

where ω is an inertial weight and c_1, c_2 are two positive acceleration constants, $rand()$ is a uniformly distributed in the range $(0,1)$, P_{id}, P_{gd} are the personal best position found by ith particle and the best position found by the entire swarm so far, respectively, in (2), the most velocity of particles are restricted: if the velocity of some dimension V_{id} exceeds the prefixed limit V_{max}, then the velocity of this dimension (namely V_{max}) is restricted.

3 SPSO ALGORITHM

In original PSO algorithm, if $\omega = 0$, the flight velocity of particle depends on $x_{id}(t)$, p_{id} and p_{gd}, moreover, velocity itself is no memory. So, the particle near the global optimum will remain stationary, other particles will tend to the weighted center of their individual best position and global best position. Namely, particle swarm will contract the current global best position, it is more like a local algorithm; if $\omega \neq 0$, particles have a trend of expanding searching field, namely it has some global searching ability. ω is bigger, global search ability is stronger. According to the above analysis, when $\omega = 0$, equation (3) is given as follows:

$$X_{id}(t+1) = X_{id}(t) + C_1 * rand() * (P_{id} - X_{id}(t))$$
$$+ C_2 * rand() * (P_{gd} - X_{id}(t)) \tag{4}$$

compared with the original PSO, equation (4) makes global searching ability weak and local searching ability strong. When $X_j(t) = P_j = P_g$, particle j in the history best position will not evolve by equation(4), the particle are generated randomly in the search space to replace the particle j, it and the other particles of updating P_i, P_g will together evolve by equation (4), if $P_g \neq P_j$ and P_g is not updated, all particles will evolve by equation (4), if $P_g \neq P_j$ and P_g has been updated, there is $f \neq j$, it makes $X_f(t+1) = P_f = P_g$, particle j stops to evolve and generates from searching space again, and other particles which have been updated P_i, P_g will evolute by equation (4). In some generation of evolution, at least one particle j meets $X_j(t) = P_k = P_g$, that is at least one particle which is randomly generated in searching space, so the ability of global searching can be enhanced.

4 THE DESCRIPTION OF SEVM

In expected value constraint, model which makes expected value of goal function acquire optimum is named stochastic expected value model, it can be described as follows:

$$\begin{cases} \max E[f(x, \xi)] \\ \text{s.t} \\ E[g_j(x, \xi)] \leq 0, \quad j = 1, 2 \dots, p \end{cases}$$

where x and ξ are decision vector and stochastic vector respectively. $f(x, \xi)$ is goal function, $g_j(x, \xi)$ is constraint function, E is expected value operator.

According to the priority structure and target levels set by the decision-maker, we can also formulate a stochastic decision system as an expected value goal programming:

$$\begin{cases} \min \sum_{j=1}^{l} P_j \sum_{i=1}^{m} (u_{ij} d_i^+ + v_{ij} d_i^-) \\ \text{s.t} \\ E[f_i(x, \xi)] + d_i^- - d_i^+ = b_i \cdot i = 1, 2 \dots, m \\ E[g_i(x, \xi)] \leq 0, \quad j = 1, 2 \dots, p \\ d_i^+ - d_i^- \geq 0, i = 1, 2 \dots, m, \end{cases}$$

where P_j is the preemptive priority factor which expresses the relative importance of various goals, $P_j \gg P_{j+1}$, for all j, u_{ij} is the weighting factor corresponding to positive deviation for goal i with priority j assigned, v_{ij} is the weighting factor corresponding to negative deviation for goal i with priority j assigned, d_i^+ is the positive deviation from the target of goal i, d_i^- is the negative deviation from the target of goal i, f_i is a function in goal constraints, g_i is a function in real constraints, b_i is the target value according to goal i, l is the number of priorities, m is the number of goal constraints, and p is the number of real constraints.

5 STOCHASTIC SIMULATION

Stochastic simulation is based on the theory background of probability and statistics, it is numerical calculation method of using random number and computerization. Although it only gives the statistical estimation and spends a large amount of computation time, but it is an effective tool for solving of complex problem which can not be resolved by analytic method, this technology has been applied to a typical mathematical problems and statistical physics etc. It is particularly suitable for large, new product project on computer and other risk analysis of containing lots of uncertain decision factors.

6 A HYBRID INTELLIGENT ALGORITHM BASED ON STOCHASTIC AND SPSO FOR SOLVING SEVM

When SEVM problems are solved by the PSO algorithm, it is critical that stochastic function is computed, obviously, it can be computed by stochastic simulation which is embodied in checking feasible solution and evaluating fitness value. Expected value evaluation algorithm of stochastic simulation is given as follows:

Assume that ξ is a n-dimension random vector in probability space (Ω, A, Pr) f: $R^n \rightarrow R$ is a measurable function, then $f(\xi)$ is stochastic variable. Compute $E[f(\xi)]$ by stochastic simulation. In view of the need this paper, expected value evaluation algorithm of stochastic simulation can be described according to the following steps:

step 1: Let $L = 0$.
step 2: Generate sample ω from Ω according to probability measure Pr.
step 3: $L \leftarrow L + f(\xi(\omega))$.
step 4: Repeat the second to third steps for N times.
step 5: $E[f(\xi)] = L/N$.

Integrate stochastic simulation, SPSO algorithm, we can get a hybrid intelligent algorithm for solving SEVM problem, we describe it as follows:

step 1: Initialize particle swarm in D-dimensional space: let *popsize* be the particle number of the swarm, generate a random number from feasible area of decision vector x, calculate value of $E[g_j(x,\xi)]$ by expected value evaluation algorithm of stochastic simulation, check feasibility of this random number (that is, judge x whether or not it satisfies $E[g_j(x,\xi)] \leq 0$) repeat this process until *popsize* times. So, the *popsize* feasible particles $(x_i = (x_{i1},x_{i2} \ldots x_{id}, i = 1,2 \ldots popsize)$ are generated, and then initialize velocity, fitness $(E[f(x, \xi)])$ of particles etc.
step 2: if $x_j(t) = p_j = p_g$, the position of particle j is randomly generated and calculates its fitness, personal best value, other particles will evolve by equation (4) and calculate their fitness and personal best value.
step 3: if $P_g \neq P_j$ and P_g is not updated, all particles will evolve by equation (4).
step 4: if $P_g \neq P_j$ and P_g has been updated, there is $f \neq j$, it makes $X_f(t+1) = P_f = P_g$, particle f stops to evolve and generates from searching space and calculate its fitness and personal best value, other particles will evolve by equation (4).
step 5: Check feasibility of the updated particles: if they are feasible, then they are accepted, and calculate their fitness and personal best value else their position are kept.
step 6: search the global best particle p_g.
step 7: Repeat the second to the sixth steps until a sufficiently good fitness or a maximum number of iterations.
step 8: Report the best particle and corresponding fitness as the optimal solution and the corresponding optimal value.

7 NUMERICAL EXAMPLES

For illustrating the effectiveness of the algorithm and more easy comparison, we give numerical examples that from [7]: Example one: let's consider the following SEVM in which there are three decision variables and three stochastic variable:

$$\begin{cases} \min E\left[\sqrt{(x_1 - \xi_1)^2 + (x_2 - \xi_2)^2 + (x_3 - \xi_3)^2}\right]. \\ \text{s.t} \\ x_1^2 + x_2^2 + x_3^2 \leq 10, \end{cases}$$

where ξ_1, ξ_2 and are uniform distributed variables U(1.2), normally distributed variables N(3,1), exponentially distributed variable EXP(4), respectively.

Example two: let's consider the following SEVM in which there are four decision variables and four stochastic parameters:

$$\begin{cases} \text{lex} \min\{d_1^-, d_2^-, d_3^- + d_3^+\} \\ \text{s.t.} \\ E[\cos(x_1 + \xi_3 x_3^2 + \xi_4 x_4^2) + \sin(x_2 + \xi_2)] + d_1^- - d_1^+ = 0 \\ \quad \text{the first priority level} \\ E[\sin(x_3 + \xi_3) + \cos(x_4 + \xi_4)] + d_2^- - d_2^+ = 0 \\ \quad \text{the second priority level} \\ E[(\xi_1 x_1^2 + \xi_2 x_2^2)/(1 + \xi_3 x_3^2 + \xi_4 x_4^2)] + d_3^- - d_3^+ = 1 \\ \quad \text{the third priority level} \\ 0 \leq x_i \leq 2, \quad i = 1,2,3,4 \\ d_j^+, d_j^- \geq 0, \quad j = 1,2,3, \end{cases}$$

where ξ_1, ξ_2, ξ_3 and ξ_4 are normally distributed variable U[1,1], normally distributed variable N(2,1), normally distributed variable N(3,1) and normally distributed variable N(4,1) respectively.

In example one: parameter values are same with [7]: simulation times: 3000, generations in the PSO algorithm: 300, *popsize*: 30, run time: 1.

In example two: parameter values are same with [7]: simulation times: 5000, generations in the PSO algorithm: 2000, *popsize*: 30, run time: 1.

Our programs (written by VC++6.0) are performed on a personal computer: For example one: so far as solution's quality is concerned: the results are shown in Table 1. It is obviously that they are superior to [7]; in order to exhibit iteration process more clearly, the process is sampled 15 times, which is shown in Figure 1: our algorithm is not only more rapid convergence but also more high precision, the optimal value of the 20th generation has overtaken the one that [7] acquire at the 300th generation. At the same time, in order to avoid being this result by chance, the program is run 50 times, average are shown in Table 1, it is evident that average optimal value are all better than [7] and results of each time are all better than [7]. For example two: so far as solution's quality is concerned: the results of 10 times and average are shown in Tables 2 and 3, it is self-explanatory.

As mentioned above, as far as quality of solution is concerned, our algorithm goes beyond [7], Why is it? For one thing, the PSO algorithm hasn't complex genetic operator like GA, it only change the individual position by individual stochastic velocity in solution space, it exhibits more strong randomicity and makes compute complexity extremely decrease. However, chromosome in GA shares information with each other, thus the whole population moves like one group towards an optimal area; in the PSO algorithm, only the 'best' particle gives out the information to others, the entire population's movement only follow the current optimal solution; furthermore, particles have the property of "memory", they study from "ego" and "companion", therefore, the next generation may inherit more useful information from the previous generation, thus may get the best solution in a short time. Moreover, in solution, GA has poor local searching ability, this is for the probability transferring characteristics of GA which determines it's easy to fall into local optimization.

Table 1. Results comparison of example one.

	x_1	x_2	x_3	Optimal value
GA([7])	1.1035	2.1693	2.0191	3.56
SPSO	1.4615	2.0972	1.7522	3.17
Average (50)	1.1471	2.1865	1.8663	3.17

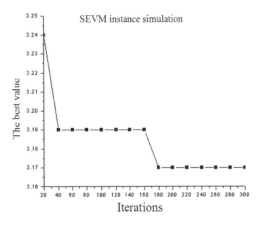

Figure 1. Figure of sampled data of example one.

Table 2. Results comparison of example two.

Algorithm	x_1	x_2	x_3	x_4	d_1^-	d_2^-	$d_3^- + d_3^+$
GA([7])	0.000	1.689	0.000	0.565	0.00	0.00	0.45
SPSO	0.000	1.711	0.000	0.573	0.00	0.00	0.38

Table 3. Example two statistical results of run 10 times.

Run time	x_1	x_2	x_3	x_4	d_1^-	d_2^-	$d_3^- + d_3^+$
1	0.0091	1.7147	0.0016	0.5203	0.00	0.00	0.24
2	0.0120	1.7258	0.0005	0.5181	0.00	0.00	0.24
3	0.0033	1.7264	0.0011	0.5127	0.00	0.00	0.23
4	0.0006	1.7828	0.0002	0.5480	0.00	0.00	0.22
5	0.0081	1.7100	0.0009	0.5333	0.00	0.00	0.25
6	0.0018	1.7339	0.0040	0.5278	0.00	0.00	0.25
7	0.0055	1.7361	0.0001	0.5299	0.00	0.00	0.24
8	0.0047	1.7380	0.0009	0.5325	0.00	0.00	0.23
9	0.0014	1.7543	0.0020	0.5160	0.00	0.00	0.22
10	0.0037	1.7612	0.0007	0.5417	0.00	0.00	0.24
Average	0.0050	1.7383	0.0012	0.5280	0.00	0.00	0.24

8 CONCLUSION AND FUTURE WORK

SEVM which has widely practical application backgrounds belongs to a class of stochastic programming, in this article we proposed a hybrid intelligent algorithm based on SPSO algorithm for SEVM, its quality surpasses the hybrid intelligent algorithm which is based on the GA by simulation experiments; At the same time, it also extends application area of PSO algorithm study and further exhibits superiority of PSO algorithm.

Remarkably, the hybrid intelligent algorithm of stochastic simulation and SPSO algorithm has also succeeded in resolving continuous space's stochastic chance-constrained programming and stochastic dependent-chance programming in our experiments by comparing with the hybrid intelligent algorithm based on the GA, it isn't discussed here for lack of space.

Moreover, our algorithm only considers the quality of solution, in practice, computing time should not be ignored, so, in future work, the algorithm based SPSO of solving SEVEM will be further developed in order to improve the comprehensive performance of the algorithm.

ACKNOWLEDGEMENTS

This research is supported by college-based project of Shaanxi Vocational & Technical College (NO: Y1311).

REFERENCES

[1] Kennedy, J, Eberhart, R. Particle swarm optimization. in proc. International conference on Neural Networks. Perth, WA, Australia, 1995:1942–1948.

[2] Zeng, J.C., Cui, Z.H., Jie, D., Particle Swarm Optimization, *Science publishing company, BeiJing,* 2004.

[3] GE, X.S., Sun, K. Optimal control of a spacecraft with deployable solar arrays using particle swarm optimization algorithm. *Science China Technological Sciences,* 2011.54(5):1107–1112.

[4] Zhang, Z.X., Cui H.Q. Localization in 3D Sensor Netwourks Using Stochastic particle Swarm Optimization. *Wuhan University Journal of Natural Science,* 2012,17(6):544–548.

[5] Zhou, J. Uncapacitated facility layout problem with stochastic demands. Operations Research Society of China Academic Exchange Conference Proceedings. 2000 Global-Link publishing company (HongKong): 904–911.

[6] Wang, Y.X., Tao, G.L, Zhou, S.H., Wang, Y.F. Pipe Friction Factor Inversion Based on Expected Value Model. *Journal of DaQing Petrolem Institute,* 2012, 36(1):92–94.

[7] Liu, B.J., Zhao, R.Q., Wang, G. Theory and Practice of Uncertain Programming, *Tsinghua University publishing company, Beiing,* 2003.

[8] Peng, J., Liu, B.J., Uncertain Programming: Current Status and Future Prospects, *Operations Research And Management Science,* 2002,11(2):1–10.

[9] Zeng, J.C., Cui, Z.H. A Guaranteed Global Convergence Particle Swarm Optimizer. *Journal Of Computer Research And Development,*2004,41(8):1333–1338.

Computer, Intelligent Computing and Education Technology – Liu, Sung & Yao (Eds)
© *2014 Taylor & Francis Group, London, ISBN 978-1-138-02469-4*

Research of improving C++ programming experimental course teaching effect combined competition and teaching

N. Xiao
Computer Science Department, Shaanxi Vocational and Technical College, Xi'an, China

ABSTRACT: For more effective improving experimental teaching effect of C++ Programming course which is difficult for the beginners of computer specialty, selection of experimental topic, type of experimental content, design of the experimental content and program debugging and so on are researched by combining software competition and teaching work in this paper. The teaching practice shows that it is effective on improving experimental teaching quality and effect.

Keywords: C++ programming; software competition; teaching effect

1 INTRODUCTION

At present, in the higher vocational education, competition especially engineering class competitions, such as the national mathematical modeling contest, "LanQiao Cup" national professional software design and entrepreneurship competition (shorter form: software competition) and so on has been an auxiliary and promotion of education development and reform, it effectively improves students' ability of applying knowledge to solve practical problems and training innovative ideation, and it checks and promotes goal of the quality of teaching and talent training.

C++ programming is a specialized basic course of computer application specialty, its theory is closely related with practice, it is a introductory courses of our freshman entering the world of programming, and it is syntactically rich, flexible algorithm, supports oriented-process and object-oriented mechanism, implementation of high efficiency, easy development etc, it has been difficult to learn for students and to teach for teachers, especially in experimental class, students generally reflect that theory course can understand, but programming by themselves is very difficult, how to improve students' practical programming ability and the effect of experimental teaching has been the C++ teachers' goal. Therefore, in this paper, I combined with pre competition counseling of the software competition (group C++) to students, methods that improve teaching effect of experimental courses is explored, which firstly ensures normal teaching goals, at the same time, it can improve students' comprehensive abilities, creative consciousness, social competence and school's competitiveness.

2 THE MAIN PROBLEMS IN EXPERIMENTAL TEACHING

(1) Most vocational students have many faults, such as low grades, poor foundation, low learning enthusiasm, almost no preview, review habit, learning ability is not strong; moreover, rich and colorful activities in the college attract students, they take part in community activities course and it only takes them a short time to see evident results, however, the professional courses study is opposite: It is difficult to see the obvious learning effect in a short time, and they are lack of persistence, perseverance of overcoming learning difficulties, in learning, they easily have a psychological fear and give up study of courses. (2) Confirmative experiments are too much in class, there is no independent play space for students. Therefore, it is very difficult to stimulate students' interest in learning. (3) In experimental class, the management of experimental process is not strict enough, furthermore students' themselves have many arbitrary, to students' management, teachers' work is not enough obviously, it affects effect of experimental teaching. (4) In debugging programming, encountering problems or errors, they rely too much on teacher, and lack of self-confidence, self-learning ability is not enough. (5) In limited experimental class, to teacher', the tutorial time is limited, teachers are hard to guarantee to answer all students' questions or real-time one on one counseling, timely assessment of learning effect. (6) Students' cultivation of

non intelligence factors and comprehensive ability are lack in experimental teaching process, it is not beneficial to students' sustainable development. (7) Students' individual need hasn't getting enough attention in experimental class, it causes to be no interested in learning C++.

3 EXPLORING C++ EXPERIMENTAL COURSE TEACHING

3.1 Pay attention to selection of experimental topic

A boring experimental topic of being described is very difficult to arouse students' interest, motivation of learning. But the software competition topic and living in close contact with the strong interest, we can learn from its style and make experimental topic Interesting and life, so that students can see its use, for example, a topic of "LanQiao Cup" software competition in 2012: Great mathematician Euler met two peasants who are both his village in the marketplace with an empty basket respectively. They say hello to him and told him they just sold out all eggs. Euler casually asked: "how many eggs do you sell ?", however, one of them said: "we sell own eggs respectively, we both sell 150 eggs in all, although we sell eggs either many or little, but we just get the same amount's money, please guess?" but Euler didn't given answer at once. And the other added again: "if I sell them according to her price, I can get 32 Yuan, and if she sells them according to my price, she can get 24.5 Yuan." Euler thought it about and told them correct answer. We are not mathematician, and we are also lazy to list the formula to analyze it. But computer can "brute force attack", it can test all possible answers, until hit it! Please write the number of each person's eggs (didn't limit order), and separated by commas. We let students themselves choose algorithm, data structure to solve, interesting experiment subjects greatly enhance students design desire and creative power, it makes learning from passive to active, and better achieve teaching objective. Furthermore, introducing competition-related subjects, they can make students not only advance understanding difficulty of competition subjects but also lay the foundation for students participating in competition.

3.2 Pay attention to type of experimental content

In order to strengthen students' theory knowledge, experimental content should be diversified in form, such as filling program code, filling program results, updating program code, writing function, programming etc, they are beneficial to multi-directionally strengthen knowledge. Moreover, sometimes, students do not understand how to give data to test their written programming, the principle of software competition can be used, namely, they contains description of the problem, sample input, sample output, thus it can verify correctness of the program.

3.3 Pay attention to design of experimental content

In order to meet the needs of different levels students development and development of the same student at different study stages, learning content which is from the shallower to the deeper and step by step may be divided optional question and compulsory question, which makes every student have things to do and complete their learning task: The first level is basic knowledge practice, generally, it is a single algorithm, we require all students to master it, for example: after completing the teaching of control statements, we let students judge any integer whether is a prime or not by three cycles. The second level is extension exercises or practical problems, for example: requiring students to realize output 1~100 primes with three cycles; the third level may choose topics of competition or deriving from competition, for example, a topic of "LanQiao Cup" software competition in 2012: prime which is an integer is no longer separated. Such as 3, 7, 11. But 9 is not a prime, because it can be divided into 3 equal parts. Generally, the smallest prime is 2, then 3, 5, ... please tell me: What is the 100002nd prime? The teacher may arrange students to choose method according to their own situation, in addition, we inspire students to multi-angle think about problem and complete one question with multiple solutions as much as possible, which can make students contact, classify, compare knowledge and form a relatively complete system of knowledge. Moreover, it is beneficial to cultivating the quality of the students' independent creation and the students' innovation ability.

3.4 Pay attention to program debugging, cultivating students' ability of independent analysis and solving problem

For students, programming error is a very trouble thing, however, an important factor of measuring the programming ability is ability of debugging programming. Debugging programming namely is error exclusion. Usually, it may be divided into the compiler errors and logic errors. To compile errors, computer can give error message to students, many students don't translate error message, or don't patiently read error, or ignore error message, which often make a simple mistake is difficult to be found and corrected, and discourage passion of learning; to logic errors, because system doesn't give prompting, finding and correcting mistakes is more impossible, so, program debugging is very important. Just as "Give a man a fish and you feed him for a day. Teach a man to fish and you feed him for a lifetime". For the former, we can adopt measures as follows: through ways of inspiration and guide, teacher together with students reads and translates error messages by teaching and practice, and then, finish checking errors and modifying errors; moreover, we may hand out material such as translation of common mistakes, classification of errors, summary of errors and so on to students, when they meet similar problems, they can solve them by themselves, if they don't solve them, teacher give them help by the way of inspiration again; For the latter, teacher may inspire students check errors based on examples using setting breakpoints, single step execution method, adding note and using Watch, Variables and Memory windows to observe variable value by the way of teaching and practice. It makes students obtain theory knowledge as well as practice, in this way they can be more faster and realer understanding the importance of debugging method and consciously accumulate methods, skills of program debugging, good hands-on skills, analytical ability and comprehensive ability of solving problem.

3.5 Pay attention to timely evaluation of students' practical learning effect

For evaluation exercise content of practical class, according to the number of students completion and program according to correctness of results, perfection of function, efficiency of algorithm, readability of algorithm, normalization of algorithm, comprehensive consideration question or a hidden errors in the program and so on, score is given in time and as the practice course grades. At the same time, we should praise the students who finish them with good effect, are good at thinking and questioning in time, this is great benefit to set a good example and encourage each other in learning progress.

3.6 Strengthen course coaching, timely solving problems of students

In class, students' problems or questions must be explained or analyzed by teacher in time; after class, we should make full use of network platform through Interactive way such as blog, QQ and email etc to coach students timely, for students, this can avoid problems accumulation generating quantitative to qualitative consequences, it is beneficial to improve enthusiasm of learning.

3.7 Strengthen management of experimental course

In order to help students to overcome playing games, chatting, listening to music and other randomness in experimental class, their experimental task should be arranged by teachers in advance, we may let students think independently or discuss and then finish first draft of program, so that in the practice class they bring the problems to purposefully program in front of computer, rather than not knowing how to do, for teachers, finishing situation of students' experimental topics should firstly be checked before class every time, and then, students mainly finish editing, debugging program, finally writing and submitting standardized training report in experimental course, in this way, it also helps to save valuable practice time.

3.8 Make full use of network platform

Now, network platform has been well known to everyone, making full use of network method can effectively extend our experimental course teaching, it is better for experimental course teaching. Specifically speaking, teachers' teaching courseware, experiment guide book, some teaching case, some typical algorithm, some typical error analysis, simulation test, past years' software competition topics and so on may be posted to blog or QQ space to make students share and exchange them. On the one hand, they are good for helping students to preview before class, class once more, after-class review, pre-competition training, self test, on the other hand, it is very good for promoting teachers to rethink about their daily teaching and better carry on own teaching work.

4 CONCLUSIONS

The normal teaching goal is firstly ensured, at the same time, we combine with software design competition, ideas and questions of competition, own teaching experience of recent years are drawn into the conventional experimental course teaching, improving C++ experimental course teaching effect is discussed from eight aspects in this paper, it has played a positive role in promoting teaching, improving students' learning interest, learning enthusiasm, learning ability, comprehensive quality and employment competitiveness.

REFERENCES

[1] Wang, H., Wu, W.H. New Ideas of Tsinghua Practice Based on Competition and Teaching. *Computer Education*, 2006(7):10–12.

[2] Cui, Y.H. Object-oriented C++ Programming Design. *Beijing University Press,* 2008.

[3] Zhao, Y.L., Chou, G.W., Xia, Q. C++ Programming Design. *Tsinghua University Press.* 2013.

[4] Chen, Z.B. C++ Programming Design. *Posts & Telecom Press. 2008.*

[5] Liu, Y.C. A Phenomenographic Approach to the Debugging Ability of Programming Novice. *Modern Computer.* 2010.8:28–31.

[6] Lu, R.H., Zhang, W.F. The Building of Practice Teaching System for Object-oriented C++ Programming. *Journal of Xiangnan University.* 2012,33(2):83–86.

[7] Zheng, T. Chen, Q.H., Zhou, Y. Study and practice of the teaching Approaches of Programming. *Journal of Higher Education in Science and Technology.* 2010,29(1):122–125.

[8] Sun, R., Zhang, Q., Shi, Q.T. C++ language of the Experimental Teaching of Inquiry. *Computer Knowledge and Technology*. 2012,33(8):7986–7987.

[9] Wang, Y.C. Improving Programming Practice of C++ Teaching with Students Study Group. *Journal of Guangdong Polytechnic Normal University.* 2005,6:6–8.

Computer, Intelligent Computing and Education Technology – Liu, Sung & Yao (Eds)
© *2014 Taylor & Francis Group, London, ISBN 978-1-138-02469-4*

Research on color image retrieval based on spatial distance

S.L. Zhang & J.T. Dong
College of Physics and Electronic Information, Yan'an University, Yanan, Shaanxi Province, P.R. China

Z.Y. Feng
Yangquan College, Taiyuan University of Technology, Yangquan, Shanxi Province, P.R. China

ABSTRACT: The number of certain pixel is counted in color retrieval. On the base, we introduce the characteristic vector of spatial distance, and amend Euclidean distance as the similarity measure to retrieve color images, and realize the anticipated retrieval performance as predicted.

Keywords: index technology; spatial distance; similarity measure

1 INTRODUCTION

Image retrieval refers to the process of finding out the image with specified characteristic or containing specified content in the set of target image according to the description of image content.[1] Spatial relationship expresses the relationship between each part within the image, which is a very obscure definition. More often than not, they cannot be clearly described with a definite expression; instead, they are often defined by a group of mutually related but contradictory conditions, with each condition being met to varying degrees under specific circumstances.[2] Generally speaking, the frequently-used spatial relationship covers orientation relationship (also referred to as projection relationship) and topological relationship. Both the former and the latter can also be described in natural language. A kind of characteristic which has certain particular connection with spatial relationship can be called structural characteristic.[3] The expression of spatial relationship can be divided into two types: the expression based on target and that based on relationship.[4] Starting from the non-linear characteristic of images, such scholars as Zhang Jianpei and Yangjing[5] study the location of correlation (information) of color space in images and then put forward a approach of image retrieval integrated color-space informations. Mei Chengli and others[6] proposed a mode to substitute the representation to image contents by image joint feature for single image feature and then introduced the indexing method of spatial data structure after defining the similarity of images in the Euclidean space. Considering the estimated high dimension characteristic of the image joint feature, presented the method of indexing image joint feature based on X-tree spatial data structure for retrieving image contents. Jia Kebin and Fangsheng[7] put forward a new method to acquire similarity, which not only considers the characteristic of color content, but also includes the spatial relationship characteristic of images. The number of certain pixel is counted in the process of retrieving color images, the paper introduces the characteristic vector of spatial distance and then amends Euclidean distance as similarity measure to retrieve color images, thus realizing the anticipated retrieval performance as expected.

2 EXPERIMENTS AND METHODS

2.1 *Extraction of color feature*

Although histogram retrieval is not affected by rotation and translation changes, it has its own limitations, whose major defect is that it fails to express the spatial distribution information of color. As a result, the action for adding the statistics of pixel spatial distribution can make the combination of space and color characteristics possible.

For a color image, we introduce a one-dimensional characteristic vector $C(k)$, which expresses the number of all the pixels with color k. It can be assumed that the distance between two pixel points, p_i and p_j, is $d(p_i, p_j)$. Then the distance is defined as Euclidean distance, as is shown in formula (1):

$$d(p_i, p_j) = \sqrt{(x_i - x_j)^2 + (y_i - y_j)^2} \qquad (1)$$

where, (x_i, y_i) and (x_j, y_j) are respectively the coordinates of Pixel p_i and p_j.

The average distance from pixel with color k to all the pixels with color k is defined as follows:

$$m(k,i) = \frac{1}{C(k)-1} \sum_{\substack{j=1 \\ j \neq i}}^{C(k)} d(p_i, p_j) \qquad (2)$$

This average distance can be regarded as a characteristic of Pixel p_i, which expresses the degree of distance from Pixel p_i to other pixels with color k.

For the true-color image, the pixel value of each color component ranges from 0 to 255. Therefore, for each color component in the selected query image and database image, the results of 256 average distances can be obtained after Formula (2), Which is used to calculate the average distance between pixel points. After that, this group of average distance is expressed in the form of one-dimensional vector:

$$V = (m_0, m_1, m_2, \dots m_k, \dots, m_{255}) \qquad (3)$$

Here, m_k is the average distance of all the pixel values with color k.

In this way, three one-dimensional vector of color characteristic can be obtained from three color components of the true-color image, which are separately expressed as V_R, V_G and V_B. Then, these three one-dimensional vectors are retrieved as the color feature of color images.

2.2 Similarity measure

After the characteristic vector of one-dimensional spatial relationship is introduced in this paper, Euclidean distance is employed as the standard of similarity measure, as is shown in Formula (4):

$$P(Q,D) = \sqrt{\sum_{i=0}^{255} (m_{Qi} - m_{Di})^2} \qquad (4)$$

where, m_{Qi} and m_{Di} respectively stand for the average distances of pixels with color value being i in the query image and database image. From this, three average distances of R, G and B can be obtained, namely-P_R, P_G and P_B. If these three color components make the same contribution in the process of retrieval, then Formula (5) will be regarded as the final formula for similarity measure:

$$P(Q,D) = \left(\frac{1}{3} P_R^2 + \frac{1}{3} P_G^2 \frac{1}{3} P_B^2 \right)^{1/2} \qquad (5)$$

2.3 Method improvement

If the query image makes very obvious requirements about certain color, then Formula (5) will be amended, as is shown in Formula (6):

$$P(Q,D) = (W_r P_R^2 + W_g P_G^2 + W_b P_B^2)^{1/2} \qquad (6)$$

where, W_r, W_g and W_b respectively represent the weight (weighting coefficient) of red, green and blue component, with the following condition of Formula (7):

$$W_r + W_g + W_b = 1 \qquad (7)$$

3 RESULTS AND ANALYSIS

3.1 Retrieval results

According to the above analysis, the specific steps are:

1. To find the image similar to the query image in image library through manual work; in other words, to judge whether each image in image library is similar to the query image or not. This judgment completely depends on the subjective visual psychology of the experimenter; moreover, the color of images is often employed as the main basis for making judgment.
2. Then, to respectively employ Formula (5) and Formula (6) to make experiment.
3. Finally, drawing PVR Curves of different experiments in the same system, this is helpful for vivid comparison with retrieval performance at different values.

Here, we make the retrieval experiment on the image library including a bag of 50 national flags and the query image is the national flag of Morocco with priority given to red. Therefore, in the retrieval process, the experimenter consciously increases the value of W_r on purpose, the values of W_b and W_g are the same. According to the similarity, the first eight images are listed in descending order from left to right and from top to down.

3.2 Performance analysis

It is reasonable and objective to retrieve the same image database, and use the same evaluation criteria to evaluate the retrieval performance.

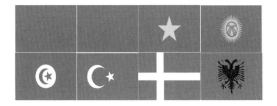

Figure 1. The retrieval result of formula (5).

378

Figure 2. The retrieval result of $W_r = 0.6$.

Figure 3. The retrieval result of $W_r = 0.8$.

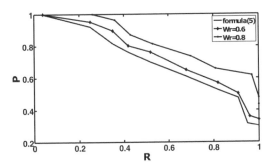

Figure 4. The performance curve of retrieval performance.

Using different weight coefficients to retrieve, we draw the PVR curves in the same coordinate system, as is shown in Figure 4.

PVR curve shows directly that when the proportion of certain required color coefficient increases, the retrieval performance should be improved.

However, in the process of retrieval, we can find out that as the statistics of pixels with each color component in images and the calculation of average distance are added in this algorithm, the time for retrieval increases. Therefore, the method proposed in this paper is very effective when high precision in retrieval is required without high requirement in retrieval time.

REFERENCES

[1] Shi, J. & Chang, Y.L. Overview of image retrieval. Journal of Xidian University (Natural Science Edition), 2003, 30(4): 486~491.
[2] Bimbo, A. 1999. Visual Information Retrieval. Morgan Kaufmann Publishers, San Francisco.
[3] Zhou, X.S. & Huang T.S. Edge-based Structural Features for Content-based Image Retrieval. Pattern Recognition Letters, 2001, 22(5):457~468.
[4] Zhang, Y.J. 2003. Visual information retrieval based on content. Science Press, Beijing.
[5] Zhang, J.P.; Yang J.; Yu Z.S. An Image Retrieval Approach of Integrated Color-spatial Informations. Journal of Harbin University of Civil Engineering and Architecture, 1998, 31(4): 120~124.
[6] Mei, C.L.; Yang J.T.; Zhou, Y.H. Image Retrieval Based on Spatial Data Structure. Journal of Shanghai Jiaotong University, 2002, 36(6): 796~799.
[7] Jia, K.B.; Fang, S.; Shen L.S. Color Image Retrieval Based on the Color and Spatial Features. Acta Electronica Sinica, 2003, 31(6): 895~898.

Development and application of Fault Tree Analysis system based on computer technology

Huan-Ming Zhou, Lang Huang, Dong-Tao Hu & Ying Sun
Sinosteel Corporation Wuhan Safety and Environmental Protection Research Institute, Wuhan, China

ABSTRACT: Fault Tree Analysis (FTA) is one of the most important analysis method of safety system engineering, the FTA can finish the qualitative analysis and the quantitative analysis, the consequences of accidents described with FTA are intuitional, intelligible, clear and logical, is now the recognized practical methods to the security and reliability analysis of complex system. In this paper, based on advanced computer theory and technology, combined with fault tree analysis method, determine the system functions, completes the design of system structure, furthermore, the integrated analysis environment that combines the Fault Tree graph creation and Fault Tree dynamic analysis is constructed based on computer. The FTA analysis system supplies high efficiency and correct technology and measures for accidents analysis and safely assessment.

Keywords: computer technology; fault tree analysis; system

1 INTRODUCTION

1.1 *Fault tree analysis method*

Fault Tree Analysis (FTA) is one of the most important analysis method of safety system engineering, it starts with the analysis of the accident or failure (top event), analyzing the reasons layer upon layer, until find out the main causes of the accident, namely the fault tree bottom event (basic events). It describes the dynamic developmental process of the accident, with FTA, the fatalness of the various kinds of system can be distinguished and evaluated, not only the direct causes of the accidents but also the potential causes can be deeply opened out[1]. The consequences of accidents described with FTA are intuitional, intelligible, clearly and logical, the FTA can finish the qualitative analysis and the quantitative analysis. On the whole, the FTA analysis system supplies high efficiency and correct technology and measures for accidents analysis and safely assessment[2].

1.2 *The problem of traditional calculation method*

Applied to practical engineering accident tree structure is complex and large, the structure design, generate and analysis of traditional fault tree analysis method are based on artificial method, When solving the accident probability of top event, in addition to the establishment of fault tree, also use Semanderes method or Fussell method to work out the cut set and the least cut set and the minimization algorithm and so on, until calculate the occurrence probability of top event. In these basic steps, when the fault tree that analysis is very complex, the amount of calculation is huge, Namely produce so-called "combinatorial explosion" problems, the calculation process is time-consuming, laborious and not reflect the dynamic process of the accident probability, so it is necessary to develop the accident tree analysis software based on modern advanced computer technology[3].

2 FUNCTION OF FAULT TREE ANALYSIS SYSTEM

In order to achieve the target of fault tree analysis and rating, fault tree analysis system should have

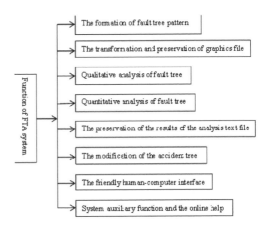

Figure 1. Function of FTA system.

more perfect function, must realize the integration of the graphics generation and accident dynamic analysis, this is the fundamental aim of the system development, the main functions of the system is shown in Figure 1.

3 THE DESIGN AND IMPLEMENTATION OF COMPUTER AIDED FAULT TREE ANALYSIS

Fault tree computer-aided analysis and calculation program based on the computer-aided fault tree drawing, with the advantages of the fast computer operation speed and the powerful function, improve the efficiency of fault tree analysis process, reduce the impact of human factors on the results of the analysis. The development uses VC++.

3.1 *The design of overall system*

The system core can be divided into two parts:

Qualitative analysis:

1. Calculation of minimum cut sets.
The fault tree cut set, is a collection of basic events that leading to the top event. That is to say, a set of basic event of the fault tree that can cause the top event, this set of event is called cut set. The so-called minimum cut sets, is the minimal set of basic events that cause the top event, so the minimum cut set is the sufficient conditions of the top event happens. After find out the minimum cut sets, can know all the possible ways that lead to system accidents[4].

This program uses Fussell algorithm to work out the minimum cut sets of fault tree. Its theoretical basis is "and" make the cut set capacity increased, but not increase the number of cut set; "Or" increase the number of cut set, without increasing the capacity of the cut set. This approach starts from the top event, the next layer of events instead of the above layer, the events that connected by "and" arranged in line according to the horizontal; the event that connected by "or" arranged in vertical columns. In this way, step by step down, until each basic event, list several lines, and simplify, at last reached the minimum cut sets[5]. Flow chart of Fussell algrithm is shown in Figure 2. Applicate the dynamic data structure of VC ++, according to this algorithm, can easily find out all the minimal cut set of fault tree.

2. Calculate the minimum path sets.
The calculation of minimum path sets is similar to the calculation of minimum cut sets.
Quantitative analysis:
Include computing structure important degree, probability importance, critical importance,

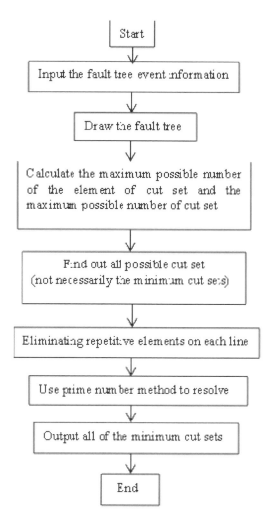

Figure 2. Flow chart of Fussell algorithm.

calculate the probability of top event by first approximation method, calculate the probability of top event by average approximation method.

3.2 *The storage structure of fault tree*

Using VC ++ document/view structure, choose the array class in collection classes, the fault tree information is stored in an array class object. Input initial data of the fault tree, the order of the door can be random, in order to make the algorithm simpler, after the data input, join a program to make the door information deposited in the array class object according to the fault tree door from top to bottom, from left to right, which make the system design more convenient[6].

This procedure using the two dimensional array method code, namely use a two-

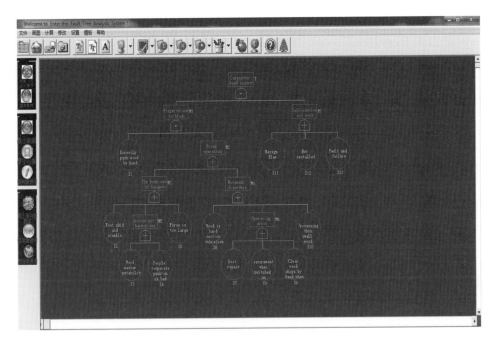

Figure 3. The fault tree of carpentry processing hand injury.

dimensional array Si [m, n] to deposit the results of m logical events Si, get the complex logic operations into integer array operations. The key to implement also is all participate in the operation of arrays, are all made of the dynamic array[7]. After one dynamic array complete the operation function, immediate release the memory that this dynamic array take up immediately, save space, so as to realize large logic calculation[8].

4   THE PRACTICAL APPLICATION

For example, carpentry processing hand injury, using the software drawing fault tree as Figure 3 shows.

5   CONCLUSION

1) From the system's operation and application and analysis results, the system can realize the function of the design objectives, to analysis and evaluate safety of the accident, have convenient, practical, efficient, and high accuracy characteristics, have popularization and application value.

2) The system has stronger practicability. Besides the function of fault tree qualitative and quantitative analysis required by traditional method,

the most important thing is to realize the fault tree generation, modify and improve process, realize the integration of the graphics generation and system analysis function, improve the accuracy of the analysis of the accident, greatly strengthened the accident process control, provide advanced analysis techniques and means for safety management and supervision departments and enterprises.

3. The system developed under the Windows environment, with the mouse can complete most of the function, easy operation, even don't understand computer users can also according to the prompt to complete the operation. System also provides perfect online help function, the user can at any time using system help during the process of.

REFERENCES

[1] Wang Yuanhui. Safety System Engineering [M]. Tian Jin: Tianjin University Press, 2010, 22–23.
[2] Wang Y, Teague T, West H, etc. New algorithm for computer-aided fault tree synthesis [J]. Journal of Loss Preventionin the Process Industries, 2002, 15(4): 256–277.
[3] Wei Lian-jiang, Zhou Fu-bao, Shen Long, etc. Research on open type framework of mineventilation simulation system [J]. Coal Science and Technology, 2008, 36(4):77–80.

[4] Fan Ying. The construction of security of the database server based on the SQL Server 2008 [J]. Journal of Gansu Lianhe University (Natural Science Edition). 2009(S2):33–34.

[5] Xiao Guiping, Nie Lei, Li Xin. Method for Inputting the Image of Computer Aided Fault Tree Analysis [J]. China safety science journal. 2001, 11(4):54–57.

[6] XU Zhisheng, Wu Chao. Safety System Engineering [M]. Bei Jin: China Machine Press, 2007, 93–97.

[7] Wen Shao Peng, Bao Hong. Visualization In Scientifc Com puting' Application And Research In Phase Diagram [J]. Software of time and space. 2006, 22(11):227–229.

[8] Tang Zesheng, Sun Yankui, Deng Junhui. Advances in the study of visualization in scientific computing[J]. Tsinghua University Journal. 2001, 41(5):201–203.

Computer, Intelligent Computing and Education Technology – Liu, Sung & Yao (Eds)
© 2014 Taylor & Francis Group, London, ISBN 978-1-138-02469-4

The importance and feasibility of leisure-aesthetical education in sports colleges in China

Hong-Qiang Qu & Jun-Biao Tu
Institute of Physical Education, Luoyang Normal University, Luoyang, China

Ning Li
Institute of Preschool Education, Luoyang Normal University, Luoyang, China

ABSTRACT: As the social development, leisure has become more important in people's life and made effects on education. What's the connection between leisure and aesthetics, should the sports colleges emphasize leisure-aesthetical education. This article adopts documentary data method and logic analysis method, making comments on the importance and feasibility of leisure-aesthetical education in sports colleges in China, making analysis on the relationship of leisure and aethetics, how the leisure-aesthetical education is important to the social needs and the sports college students., and comes to the conclusion that leisure and eathetics are inherently related, aesthetics should be the pursuit of leisure, leisure should be guided by aesthetics, leisure-aesthetical education is the need of the times and important to the sports college students, the feasibility of the leisure-aesthetic education into the sports colleges should be considered in 3 aspects: 1 sound atmosphere in colleges, 2 carry out the aesthetical education through certain curriculum and teaching process, 3 blend the leisure-aesthetical education into the campus culture of the sports colleges.

Keywords: leisure-aesthetical education; importance; feasibility; sports colleges in China

1   INTRODUCTION

Recently, as the change of the economy and the society, the sports academia has paid attention to the leisure sports domain, but as to the relationship between leisure and aesthetics, the relationship between leisure-aesthetical education and physical education, and weteher the leisure-easthetical education is important to sports colleges students, how to carry it out, in order to make clear the problems above, this article makes comments on the issues and finally comes to relevant conclusions.

2   LEISURE-AESTHETICAL EDUCATION

2.1   *Leisure and aesthetics*

The word "leisure" has frequently shown up in people's daily lives nowadays, it seems to be about "relax, recovery and amusement", people have focused on leisure for quite a long time. Ever since the ancient Greek philosopher aristotle, who claimed "people's welfare lies in their leisure", he thought leisure should be the center of life, philosophy and science arise from leisure.

About the concept of leisure, scholars in different culture think differently. It is defined as "free activity in leisure time, out of free spirit" in China.

Deep inside, leisure deeds come from people's inner needs. The results is more important than the process, therefore "leisure could be either active and healthy or negative and harmful",[1] like over-drinking, drunk-behaviours which would be harmful to the people.

As to the "uncontrolledness" of the leisure behaviours, we should confine them from the aesthetical perspective. Aesthetics is key to the problem, leisure should be aesthetically carried out.

A researcher in China claimed that: leisure belongs to people, and the emphasis of it is how the people feel during leisure, and leisure is aesthetical.[2] In short, aesthetics is the pursuit of leisure.

Another sport scholar in China points out: "in the forthcoming leisure time, aesthetics will help us find the meaning of leisure and spend the leisure in better ways, it will cultivate better citizens"[3]. In a word, aesthetics guides the leisure.

Leisure needs the guide in aesthetics, the same way, with the improvement of the people's aesthetical taste, leisure will be better. So leisure and aesthetics are inherently related.

2.2   *About the leisure-aesthetical education*

Leisure study contains a few relative subjects, such as: leisure education, leisure ethics, leisure sports and leisure aesthetics. Leisure-aesthetical education is a mixed conception of leisure education and leisure aesthetics, it is the aesthetical education in leisure domain.

"aesthetical education itself is mental, is important in human being development", but due to the cultural background and the traditional cause "aesthetical education is neglected in different times in China".[3]

Aesthetical education is vivid and pleasant. Its aim is to improve people's taste and creativity. Its trait is same with the essences of leisure, chasing free spirit and beauty.

3 THE IMPORTANCE OF LEISURE-AESTHETICAL EDUCATION

3.1 *Leisure-aesthetical education is the need of the time*

Nowadays as the development of the economy and society, people's lives are getting improved, new technology made changes in people's lifestyle and mind, and brought about more leisure.

Labour's day, national day and traditional spring festival became legal vacation since 1999 in China, teachers and students have more leisure time. The people are getting more leisure and they value it, which means the society is changing into the "leisure time" in China.

In leisure time, sports are getting popular with the people. "as the improvement of the people's financial status and their consciousness, with the economy rising and people's mind updated, people are pay more attention to how the spend the leisure. Leisure sports is spontaneous, it is out of the care about life, it aims to purse healthy amusement and perfection of life".[4]

In the "times of leisure", it is necessary to adopt the leisure-aesthetical education to the students in sports colleges, for they are likely to be the guide for the social sports, they should fit the need of the times. Besides the speciality in sports, they also need to know about leisure culture, and have the aesthetical ability, so that they can guide the social sports better.

It is the need of the times, the need of social sports that calls for leisure aesthetical education in sports colleges.

3.2 *Leisure-aesthetical education helps the students develop in many aspects*

The importance of leisure-aesthetical education not only lies in the need of the society but also in the need of the development for the students.

The mentality of the students can be divided into 3 parts: recognition, feeling and mind.

Speciality belongs to recognition, while the other two parts are comparatively neglected.

Leisure aesthetical education is just for the feeling and mind. The college students are mostly teenagers, it is a crucial time to form the view of life, by leisure aesthetical education the students will be able to get better taste, be more creative, finally they can form a sound personality, get developed for the future.

In the west, leisure education is a compulsory lesson, it begins at school and will last for lifetime, it shows how leisure education is emphasized in the west.[5] Due to the culture and tradition, leisure education just begun these years, while aesthetical education is still neglected. In the future, we must put enough emphasis on leisure-aesthetical education.

4 THE FEASIBILITY OF LEISURE-AESTHETICAL EDUCATION IN SPORTS COLLEGES

4.1 *The principals and the teachers' support is the premise*

Whether the leisure-aesthetical education could be carried out in sports colleges firstly depends on the principals' attitude. Under the authorization of the educational ministry, there are 5 sports colleges in China which has set up the major "leisure sports", leisure-aesthetical education should be valued. On the other hand, the teachers should play their guiding part well, during the teaching process, the beauty of their remarks, behaviour and spirit will affect the students unconsciously. So the atmosphere comes from the principals and the teachers.

4.2 *The ways how the leisure-aesthetical education be carried out in sports colleges' curriculum*

Leisure-aesthetical education is not only mental but also rational, it requires the guidance of the relative subjects. Only by the teaching of the leisure studies and the aesthetics, will the students have a grasp of the systematic theory, and have a rational judgement of the beauty.

4.3 *How the leisure-aesthetical education be carried out during the teaching process in sports colleges*

First, all the teaching elements should be considered, the teachers, the students, and the teaching contents. The Chinese scholars Chen Junqin and Wang Shen did the research on the students, according to the results, they put forward the methods of how to carry out aesthetical education during the sports teaching process, the argued that the students should be the "the role to undertake the experience", the teachers should be "the role to clarify the sports culture", the teaching contents should be "the symbols to release the beauty".[6]

4.4 Blend the leisure-aesthetical education into the campus culture of the sports colleges

The campus culture is a important part of the schooling, it is made by the teachers and the students' ideas and behaviours, it is the surroundings for teaching, and has a effect on the students' development.

The campus culture in sports colleges is more about sports culture. The campus culture and sports culture can inspire the students to work out actively and enjoy the sports, and improve their abilities to feel and create the beauties, and help them form a sound personality. Therefore, the sports campus culture has its trait, it is educational.[7]

The sports campus is educational, blending the leisure-easthetical education into the campus culture, through different kinds of activities, will help the students feel and experience the beauty, so that they will naturally develop. In the long term, the leisure-easthetical education should be blend into the campus culture.

5 CONCLUSION

As the the development of the economy and society, the people's lives are changing. Leisure has taken up more portion. Leisure education is necessary, leisure education and physical education are related, leisure pursues aesthetics, aesthetics guides the leisure. It is important to implement the leisure-aesthetical education to the sports colleges students. It is the need of the society and the need for the students' growth. Leisure-aesthetical education in sports colleges, we can plan in 3 aspects: 1 sound atmosphere in colleges, 2 carry out the aesthetical education through certain curriculum and teaching process, 3 blend the leisure-aesthetical education into the campus culture of the sports colleges.

REFERENCES

[1] Zhong-Guang Li, Chang-Chong Lu. Basic leisure study; Social science press, 2004: 21. (in Chinese).
[2] Hui-Di Ma. Sports in leisure times-the speech abstract in the international leisure seminar; the institute journal of Guangzhou P.E institute, 2008 (28)2: 1~3. (in Chinese).
[3] Xiao-Ming Hu. Sports aesthetics; higher education press. 2009:231. (in Chinese).
[4] Xu Ji. Leisure sports and its background in China; the institute journal of Guangzhou P.E institute, 2005(25)5:115~117. (in Chinese).
[5] Li Bin. The meaning of "play" to the children in growth. Sports culture journal, 2009(11):19~22. (in Chinese).
[6] Jun-Qi Chen N, Wang Shen. The aesthetical traits and methods of the teenagers in China; the Chinese sports science journal; 2009,45,(3):94~100. (in Chinese).
[7] Xue-Jin Yao, Ai-Min Zhu. Comments on campus sports culture in colleges; journal of the Jilin P.E institute. 2006,22,(3):19~20. (in Chinese).

Computer, Intelligent Computing and Education Technology – Liu, Sung & Yao (Eds)
© *2014 Taylor & Francis Group, London, ISBN 978-1-138-02469-4*

Mode selection algorithm in H.264 based on macroblock merging

Xiao-Yan Zhao & Gong-Li Li

College of Computer and Information Engineering, Henan Normal University, China

ABSTRACT: H.264 adopts brand-new technologies to achieves higher compression efficiency, but the computational complexity restricts it's real-time application in a way. In order to reduce the computation redundancy, a kind of encoding option selection scheme and H.264 low-complexity mode selection algorithm, which is suitable for real-time interactive application is proposed. The proposed algorithm is based on motion vector merging, divides 16 × 16 macroblocks into 4 8 × 8 block. The small blocks will be merged when they match the merging conditions. Meanwhile 1/4 pixel precision detailed motion estimation is adopt to reduce the code rate, average bitrate and average D-value of macroblock edge are used to perform pre-judgment in intra-frame encoding mode to narrow the mode selection range. The test results show that compared with the existing fast mode decision algorithm, the proposed algorithm significantly decreases the encoding time about 48.98% averagely and without increasing of code rate on the basis of ensuring image quality.

Keywords: intra-frame prediction; mode selection; motion estimation; H.264

1 INTRODUCTION

H.264/AVC is digital video encoding standard made by JVT, which is described in [1]. H.264 adopts many new technologies, including 4 × 4 integer transformation, multiple macroblock partitioning modes, multiple reference frames and 1/4 pixel precision motion compensation, etc. Compared with previous standards, H.264 can save about 50% bit resources under the same visual quality which is validated as [2]. However, the compression efficiency will be improved at the cost of codec computational complexity, so it is difficult to apply H.264 to real-time application.

In order to reduce the effect of encoding complexity, many optimized encoding mode selection methods were proposed. For example, an improved fast intra prediction mode decision algorithm is proposed in [3], which presents a fast and computationally efficient mode prediction and selection approach[4]. proposes a kind of improved algorithm in accordance with proportion situation of different encoding mode of interframe for standard test sequence [5–6]. predicts RD cost threshold and dynamic parameter update model to terminate the complex mode decision process [7–8]. proposes a fast algorithm to different interframe prediction modes by improved rate-distortion optimization function, but simplified function makes the estimation of price inaccurate. Although these algorithms reduce the predicted computation time in a certain extent, they will improve code rate and

seriously affect peak signal-to-noise when the code rate control is not started. Based on the existing mode selection algorithm in H.264, this paper analyses the encoding options and propose a kind of H.264 prediction mode optimization algorithm, which can effectively reduce H.264 encoder's computational complexity on the basis of without increasing PSNR and code rate, to meet the requirements of real-time video communication.

2 H.264 ENCODING OPTIONS

2.1 *Multiple reference frame selection*

Recently, H.264 introduces many encoding tools and encoding options with high computational complexity to interactive real-time application, e.g. video conferencing system, due to there are no special media processors, so need to analyse these encoding tools and options, to propose a kind of interactive application encoding algorithm, which is suitable for low-complexity and low-latency.

The main idea of multiple reference frame selection is to increase a sequence component to motion vector and select a most matched macroblock from multiple reference frames. Document [9] shows that: multiple reference frames causes higher video encoding efficiency only to periodic motion video sequences, however, the results of different sequences are different, so, they are not all-purpose. The encoding performance of 1 reference frame is declined than what of 5 reference frames, but the decreasing amplitude is small. Especially for the video conferencing with high real-time demand, predict the additional multiple reference frames, if there are X reference frames, the computation of motion estimation will be X times of a reference frame, this is a challenge for real-time terminal with limited computing power, so the algorithm of this paper selected 1 reference frame.

2.2 Macroblock encoding mode selection

H.264 adopts many kinds of partitioning prediction mode to interframe macroblock, in order to facilitate compare various performance of various block mode, this paper simulated six kinds of possible merging of block mode, of which including mode 1: 16×16; mode 2: 16×16, 8×8; mode 3: 16×16, 16×8, 8×16; mode 4: 16×16, 16×8, 8×16, 8×8; mode 5: 16×16, 16×8, 8×16, 8×8, 8×4, 4×8 and mode 6: 16×16, 16×8, 8×16, 8×8, 8×4, 4×8, 4×4. It can be found that only under the unsmooth image or relative large code rate, the smaller block will enhance the performance of encoding. Under the condition of relative small code rate, the smaller block will not enhance the performance of encoding. On the contrary, the computational complexity of motion estimation will be further improved. For low-code rate and low-latency interactive real-time multimedia application, the terminal's process capacity has a certain limit, should adopt less block mode as far as possible under the premise of not reducing encoding performance. The only selection of four modes of 16×16, 16×8, 8×16 and 8×8 will achieve a better systm-gain, at the same time minimize the computational complexity of algorithm.

3 OPTIMIZATION ALGORITHM OF MACROBLOCK ENCODING MODE SELECTION

3.1 Merge algorithm

Regardless of its size, each prediction block needs to a motion vector to describe motion estimation displacement of block, and each motion vector and prediction block mode selection must be coded in data rate, the data rate will be increased and computation will be increased manyfold, the optimization of H264 motion extimation will eliminate the computation redundancy.

In case of the motion vector of 16×16 macroblock in motion estimation is MV, if divide this 16×16 macroblock into $16 \ 4 \times 4$ or 8×8 small blocks, the motion vector of all blocks can be approximately estimated by MV, though MV may be not the best motion vector of these small blocks, generally MV is the better motion vector.

Perform motion estimation to several small blocks, if the obtained motion vectors are same and meet the combination conditions, then can combine these small blocks into a big block, to make the number of motion vector to be as one.

Merge algorithm mainly includes the following four steps:

Step 1: First part a 16×16 macroblock into four 8×8 blocks with code of 0, 1, 2 and 3.
Step 2: Carry out motion estimation to all 8×8 blocks with integer precision, for each 8×8 block, not only keep an best motion vector, but also can keep a plurality of better candidate motion vector, to facilitate subsequent merging steps of algorithm.
Step 3: Each 16×16 macroblock contains $4 \ 8 \times 8$ blocks, we can inspect these 8×8 sub-macroblocks to determine whether they have the same candidate motion vector among themself. If have same motion vector, it can be merged to 16×8, 8×16 and 16×16 blocks respectively.

The specific merging rules are: if block 0 and 1 have same motion vector, while block 2 and 3 have same motion vector, they can be merged to two 16×8 blocks. If block 0 and 2 have same motion vector, while block 1 and 3 have the same motion vector, they can be merged into two 8×16 blocks.

Step 4: Inspect macroblock to determine whether the two merged 8×16 blocks or 16×8 blocks are existed, if yes, compare them to determine whether they have same motion vectors, if have, they can further be merged into 16×16 block. Conversely, they will not be merged. Merging steps and examples of algorithm are shown in Figure 1. The D, H,

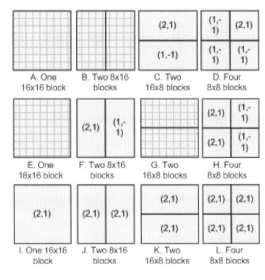

Figure 1. Merging steps and examples of algorithm.

L is different macroblock 8 × 8 motion estimation results. According to the merging rules, the macroblock D can be merged into two 16 × 8 blocks, shown in Figure C. The macroblock H can be merged into two 8 × 16 blocks, shown in Figure F. The macroblock L can be merged to two 8 × 16 blocks, shown in Figure J, also it can be merged into two 16 × 8 block, shown in Figure K. Because macroblock J and K have two same motion vector, it will eventually be merged into one 16 × 16 block, shown in Figure 1.

3.2 Mode selection algorithm

The mode selection algorithm is to get the best mode through comparison with other candidate mode pricing after getting several better modes on the basis of merging, the algorithm mainly includes two steps:

Step 1: Obtain 1/4 pixel precision refining motion estimation through four kinds of better mode integer motion estimation vector.

Shown in Figure 2, for integer pixel precision motion vector (x, y), first perform motion estimation (marked as circle in the figure) to 8 1/2 pixel precision points around (x, y), to obtain a best 1/2 pixel precision motion vector, then with the obtained motion vector as the center, and 8 1/4 pixel precision points around it, you will obtain a best 1/4 pixel precision motion vector.

Step 2: Perform pre-judgment to whether adopts intra-frame mode.

Intra-prediction is important feature in H.264 encoder to improve compression efficiency. It predicts the current block with surrounding pixels to reduce the special redundancies but at the cost of high computational complexity. The searching algorithm used to select the best mode is computationally expensive. The computation of macroblock RDcost under multi intra-prediction modes makes the macroblock RDcost increasing several times over.

This paper performs pre-judgment to decide whether the termination condition is satisfied by tow parameters: AR (average bitrate) and ABE (average D-value of macroblock edge), which are required by coding current macroblock residual data and obtained by interframe prediction. If meet the condition, coding of the intra-prediction will be skipped to improve the coding speed and the mode selection range will be narrowed. If AR is small enough or AR < K*ABE, will not need to test intra-frame mode again.

Step 3: Select current smallest RDcost as best encoding mode aiming at several candidate modes of macroblock while comparing with SKIP pricing.

4 TEST RESULTS

This paper selects JM10.2 in the test to achieve improved algorithm which is proposed and then it will be compared with the mode, which doesn't adopt optimization algorithm. During testing, selected two parameters: total motion estimation time (including integer pixel motion estimation time and 1/4 pixel motion estimation time) and total encoding time. We can find from Table 1 that, the algorithm of this paper has a certain improvement on performance, besides, the total motion estimation time is reduced of 35.19% and encoding time is reduced of 48.98%.

Table 1. Test results of algorithm in this paper.

Sequence name	Improved PSNR (algorithm in this paper)	PSNR (no algorithm)
Foreman	0.54	35.01
Container	0.68	35.80
News	0.56	36.57
Foreman	0.42	35.72
Container	0.35	35.89
News	0.87	37.59
Average value	0.57	35.01
Average motion estimation time (second)	29.657	45.763
Average encoding time (second)	17.141	33.596

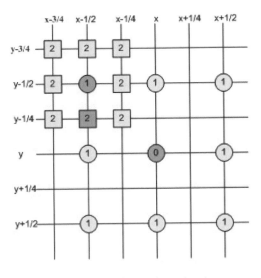

Figure 2.   1/4 pixel precision motion estimation.

ACKNOWLEDGMENTS

This work is supported by National Natural Science Foundation of China (No. U1204609) and Education Department of Henan Province Science and Technology Key Project (No. 14A510011) and Youth Science Foundation of Henan Normal University (2012QK21).

REFERENCES

[1] ITU-T Rec. "H.264/ISO/IEC14496-10 AVC", Draft ITU-T recommendation and final draft international standard of joint video specifications, 2003.

[2] Chen Xiaolei, Zhang Aihua and Lin Dong, etc, "Adaptive H.264 Computing Resources Allocation Algorithm", *Computer Engineering*, vol. 38, no. 17, pp.211–213, 2012.

[3] Ren Jianfeng, Kehtarnavaz N, Budagavi M, "Computationally efficient mode selection in H.264/AVC video coding", *IEEE Transactions on Consumer Electronics*, vol. 54, no. 2, pp. 877–886, 2008.

[4] Zoran Milicevic, Zoran Bojkovic, "H.264/AVC standard: A proposal for selective intra- and optimized inter-prediction", *Journal of Network and Computer Applications,* vol. 33, no. 2, pp. 686–691, 2011.

[5] Wang H.M, Lin J.K, Yang J.F, "A successive termination and elimination method for fast H.264/AVC SATD-based inter mode decision", *IET Signal Process*, vol. 3, no. 3, pp.165–176, 2009.

[6] Jin Xiaocong, Sun Jun, Huang Yiqing, "Fast H.264/AVC DIRECT mode decision based on mode selection and predicted rate-distortion cost", *IEICE Transactions on Information and Systems*, Vol. E94. No. 8, pp.1653–1662, 2011.

[7] Jin Young Lee, Samsung Adv. Inst. of Technol., Samsung Electron. Co., Ltd., Suwon, South Korea, "A fast mode decision method based on motion cost and intra prediction cost for h.264/avc", *Circuits and Systems for Video Technology, IEEE Transactions on*, vol. 22, no. 3, pp. 393–402, 2012.

[8] Wang Hanli, Kwong S, Kok C—W, "An efficient mode decision algorithm for H.264/AVC encoding optimization", *IEEE Transactions on Multimedia*, vol. 9, no. 4, pp. 882–888, 2007.

Computer, Intelligent Computing and Education Technology – Liu, Sung & Yao (Eds)
© 2014 Taylor & Francis Group, London, ISBN 978-1-138-02469-4

Analysis the form beauty of glass material

Z.D. Zhang & L.Q. Xiang
Hunan University of Technology, Zhuzhou, China

ABSTRACT: According to the application forms characteristics of glass material in daily life, this article is to explore the form beauty of glass material. Through the study of the relations of "virtual" and "real", to interpret the form beauty of virtual and real; Through the study of the relationship of light and shadow, to interpreted the form beauty light and shadow; Through exploring the inner meaning of glass material products, to interpret the forms beauty of imaginative; Through exploring the relationship "time" and "space", to interpret the forms beauty of "time" and "space"; Through the study of the external attraction of glass material products, to read interesting beauty.

Keywords: glass; form; virtual and real; images; interesting

1   GENERAL INTRODUCTION

Form is the basic factor to associate with visual aesthetic, and on the human perception it has the performances such as strength, speed, and rhythm, moreover, it gives a person emotional associations and aesthetic pleasure. In the design, form is the direct cause of emotional arousal and aesthetic feeling. It is precisely because materials exist in a variety of forms, we are able to enjoy the form beauty of materials in various design. Glass item, with its glittering, translucent bright and clean surface, and its smooth transition of light and shadow, gives a person the mysterious and romantic feeling. It emits a sense of tranquility and purity. These are the expressions of form beauty in the design. From the perspective of the uniqueness of glass material, the form beauty of glass material, in the design, is mainly reflected in "virtual" and "real" beauty, light and shadow beauty, image beauty, space and time beauty, and interesting beauty.

2   GETTING STARTED

2.1   *The "virtual" and "real" beauty of glass*

"Virtual" is internal, deep, indirect, abstract, and spiritual. "Real" is external, superficial, direct, concrete, and physical. Abstract controls concrete and invisible masters tangible. In the design of glass products, "virtual" and "real" alternate each other, depend on each other, and foil each other, and then, they constitute an integral whole.

One of the Taoist ideas is to divide the world into tangible and intangible. "Intangible" and "subtle" feeling is perceived by "tangible" and "strong" feeling. Tangible thing is just superficial and existing, and it will never be as wide as invisible thing, because the intangible surrounds tangible, and to some extent, beyond the tangible. In terms of glass material, it is the design form to make intangible "emotion" flow and melt in the still and tangible glass material. But the intangible "emotion" is not what we usually understand; it comes not only from the feeling of life, but also from a purely aesthetic emotion.

Ancient Greek philosopher Heraclites once said, "invisible harmony is more beautiful than visible one". "Nothing" is not just a negative concept, but full of positive meaning. It represents the form that is beyond formality, out of substance, and without limitation, and then, it enters into an infinite state. The "virtual" and "real" beauty interpreted by glass material is a special kind of aesthetic effect, and it is an ultimate vision of aesthetic state and content conception. When glass material is applied in the design, it should be separated from everything which deviates from formal target, and turn tangible to intangible, and then a kind of pure aesthetic pleasure can be brought, and an extreme purity can be reached as well.

Properties of glass, such as gloss and transparency, are "virtual" which contrast clearly with "real". And different combination of dot, line and plane varies the modeling art of design, and riches modeling language of design. As shown in Figure 1, "Smile Bowl" is the work designed by Claus•Jensen and Henrik•Holbaek. Hollow glass ware, opened a "smiling mouth", this small design detail wins the fashion and practicability of this industrial products at the same time, The "virtual"

Figure 1.　Smile bowl.

Figure 2.　National theatre.

and "real" is proper, and the position and size of openings hit the spot.

2.2　The light and shadow beauty of glass

Light and shadow are interactive forms of special properties, light generates shadow, and shadow reflects light. Glass material creates a hazy intermediary state space through the movement of light and shadow, and shape is created together. Light and shadow is the soul of glass.

Only set off by shadow, can light reflect its value. Shadow is the missing of light. Although shadow is illusory, it is just expressive. Shadow is dark, and light is bright, but light and shadow actually reveal a kind of interdependent relationship. Just as Hegel said, "in the relationship with the object, light displays no longer a pure light, but it becomes light and dark, and light and shadow which itself has embodied specially". Figure 2 is the "egg-shell" form of national grand theatre designed by renowned French architect Paul•Andreu. Shell surface, skillfully joined together by 18398 pieces of titanium plate and 1226 pieces of ultra white glass, creates a visual effect that stage curtain opens slowly. This design is novel, avant-garde, and unique, and it is the combination of tradition and modernity, romance and reality. In this design, light and shadow created the abstract form of a special visual effect, and broke the normal vision, so the perceptual reaction is developed, and then, a strong property is formed, making the viewer's eyes or head produce optical illusion and illusion. Light and shade pursuit the pure feeling of form and color, and exclude all natural reproduction. It is an art of approximate visual psychological test which combines with the scientific knowledge. Light and shade lead people to look into visual perception

and texture and reflect the peculiar shape beauty of the glass material at the same time, which builds a wonderland of light and shadow.

2.3　Image beauty of glass

Image is also called mental imagery. It refers to the knowledge representation of objects or events which do not exist at present. Image represents a certain object or event transmitting the information of them, and it has distinct perceptual characteristics. The image beauty of glass material is mainly manifested by its basic characteristic—transparency.

Glass is a frost and hard material having pure and transparent visual imagery, and it passes to people not only the clean, delicate, glittering and translucent aesthetic feeling, also conveys a kind of personality combined with pure, magnanimous, selfless quality. Transparent texture feature of glass material invites meditation. People can make any analogy and imagination, and its feature also constitutes the emotional appeal and feeling which can't be imitated by other materials.

Glass possesses both the mechanical neat character of industrial society and a natural and simple, and warm and lovely style. The charm of glass is given priority to its transparent material, and it provides the glass a great performance space. The transparency of glass is an extremely distinct characteristic, and what it emphasizes is a completely different space concept compared with traditional visual perception. Glass provides the unlimited space which does not possessed by other material carrier. It is also a special viewpoint that the glass designer provides to the user consciously. The transparency of material motivates all sorts of metaphor and imagination and creates a form floating in the uncertain, air-like, and void, and it acts as a hidden way for plane.

As shown in Figure 3, it is the world's thinnest, and glittering and translucent glass keyboard designed by Kong Fanwen from South Korean. Both the appearance and the use of the product, it can create a form floating in the uncertain, air-like, and void, also it acts as a hidden way for plane.

"Transparency is not only a physical state, but also a kind of new visual properties, and it implies a broader space order. Transparency means perceive different spatial locations at the same time. Space in a continuous movement is not back, but changing." For glass products, the significance of transparency lies not only in the dimension increase but also the simplification and digestion of the structure system. In the practice of modern glass material design, designers gradually try to apply glass to flatten and body the structural system as a hidden way for plane, and then, a dynamic structural system is formed, rather than a fixed, rigid one. This is a major advancement of modern glass material applications.

The image aesthetic effect of the glass comes from its transparency, and also from its refractive effect. For a designer who focuses on using materials according to their nature and is good at taking advantage of their particularities, when transparency and refraction combining into form a special image is produced.

2.4 *Time and space beauty of glass*

In philosophy, "time" and "space" constitute two basic existing forms together for moving. Time refers to the continuity and succession of substances in moving process. Space refers to the existing extension of substances.

The time and space beauty of glass can be found in the modern glass artistic works. In the illusory space of modern glass art, the flowing time consciousness is immersed, highlighting the "diachronic" concept in the concern state, which requires turning "static" to "dynamic". The flowing sight, the rhythmization of activity, and the melting external space rhythm into time rhythm of heart make the modern glass works become a "time tasting way".

Glass works is a volume viewed from the internal, it created a time images measured by forms of substance movement. This substance is entirely composed of various concrete objects and air volume with determined shape, but it is not fleeting. It is fixed in the interior space of glass art, and it is visible and sensible. As shown in Figure 4, Blue Horizon—the glass artistic work designed by glass maestro Tom Patti, which is made of lead glass, using fusion, casting, grinding, polishing and other processes. We can review the formation and flow of time from this work, time becomes the pure form of inner feeling and the important composition part of glass art. It is no longer a simple chronological time, but a kind of spiral time, and a strengthen to all the moments. Glass art strengthens every moment and provides the possibility of permanence. This permanence is the instantaneous explosion of time, the generation and vanishing of each fractured moments, and aimless self consumption of time. We affirm this generation and vanishing by initiative way, and Contribute time to the pure flow in the internal space of glass art.

The relationship between time and space is not motivative and successive, but symbiotic. As "intrinsic form" the image of time and illusory of space exist in the form of glass works, becoming an important concept of glass works, and leading the design and creation of glass form.

2.5 *The interesting beauty of the glass*

There are two explanations for interest in "Ci Hai": one is meaning, and the other is an aesthetic noun,

Figure 3.   Glass keyboard.

Figure 4.   Blue horizon.

Figure 5.   Glassware.

the ability of analyzing and appreciating beauty, especially the ability of identifying and criticizing after appreciating artistic work. The interest of the glass form discussed in this paper refers to the meaning of the glass product has shown.

The interest of the glass product form means the product's form and the story related to the form which can attract consumers, have a certain resonance with consumers, and create happy pleasant aesthetic experience of the product. The interest of the form is not means unconventional, unorthodox, or pursuit the unordinary of modeling, but the natural and elegant shape. It arouses the new aesthetic feeling in flat and provides possibilities in modeling design. As Figure 5 shows, the glassware won the Red Dot Design. Its shape is full and round giving a visual aesthetic comfort. This ware is not unique from its shape, but under the background of blue glass material, its round shape shows distinctive visual beauty.

Any kind of product form possesses ambience of age and culture. Because of its characteristics of material, glass products often appear accidental effect which breaks common in the melting process. The products are able to show their rich uniqueness, personalized qualities. Glass products with interest have the characteristics of relaxed, humorous and cheerful, reflecting kind, lovely, funny and energetic psychological feelings. They are harmonious links between people and tools.

3   CONCLUSION

It's simple and insufficient by using boring terminology or poetic fiction to narrating the special beauty of glass materials. All the imaginative description and explanatory instruction of the glass material is beyond reach. The only way to seize glass material is through perceiving and understanding the product itself, and appreciating it through itself. The form beauty is just one of the characteristics of this material, and its dreamy color beauty is also very important to every designer.

ACKNOWLEDGMENT

This article is a Humanities and Social Science funded project of Ministry of Education in China, project label: 13YJC760116.

Computer, Intelligent Computing and Education Technology – Liu, Sung & Yao (Eds)
© *2014 Taylor & Francis Group, London, ISBN 978-1-138-02469-4*

Inter-disciplinary IT service outsourcing talent cultivation mode in China: A school-enterprise integration cooperation perspective

J. Mao, Z.H. Dang & Y.Y. Fang
Jiaxing Vovational and Technical College, Jiaxing, Zhejing, P.R. China

ABSTRACT: With the rapid development of service outsourcing industry, universities and corporations need to explore the innovation way of outsourcing service talent cultivation. Based on multi-level school-enterprise cooperation mechanism, this paper presents an innovative mode of inter-disciplinary IT service outsourcing talent cultivation, which mainly consists of school-enterprise integration mode, innovative three-stage teaching mode based linkup of formal education and occupational training in high vocational college. Over 5 years experience has proved that it has obvious effects on improving student comprehensive quality and occupational skills.

Keywords: inter-disciplinary talents; school-enterprise integration; IT outsourcing service; project teaching

1 INTRODUCTION

For the current stage of rapid development of China's service outsourcing industry, the inter-disciplinary service outsourcing talent shortages become the bottleneck of industrial development.

In addition to necessary professional skills, the inter-disciplinary service outsourcing talents must have international characteristics of ability to communicate, and occupational features of personal qualities.

From the perspective of talent training industry, service outsourcing talents need to have more comprehensive quality, strong professional skills, certain expertise, industry knowledge, and social knowledge, in addition, need have good professional attitude and strong learning ability [Tian Y.J, 2012].

In the face the talent demand increasingly, universities have carried out a series of reform exploration on service outsourcing talent cultivation mode [Wang Fen-mao, 2010; Feng Jin-yan, 2009; Chen Wei, 2008], then talent cultivation philosophy focused on from school-enterprise cooperation to the progressive development of school-enterprise integration [Qin Fugao, 2011; Pu Xing, 2010; Li Luo, 2010]. Although the talent cultivation mode reform has achieved some results, but there are some drawbacks. Research and practice has proved that the government, universities, businesses, training institutions, and talent service agencies should build sustainable development system of service outsourcing talent cultivation or training mode together for innovative talent cultivation mode or training mode.

2 INTER-DISCIPLINARY IT OUTSOURCING TALENT CULTIVATION MODE

2.1 School-enterprise integration cooperation mode

School-enterprise integration cooperation mode is developed based on "school-enterprise cooperation mechanisms of multi-level service outsourcing talent cultivation" [Dang Zhong-hua, 2011], it includes three macro-level, intermediate-level and micro-level. The macro-level is formed by government departments, supplying macro guidance for talent cultivation, to build industry platform. The intermediate-level is formed by industrial park, industry associations, vocational education group and so on, being responsible for implementation of macro policy of government, to build a school-enterprise cooperation platform. The micro-level is formed by the cooperative enterprise, specialty teaching guidance committee, talent training institutions, talent service agencies, specialty (group), college, etc., is responsible for the planning and implementation of school-enterprise cooperation talent cultivative projects, see Figure 1.

According to the requirements of the implementation of school-enterprise cooperation, an implementation level is embedded into the micro-level of school-enterprise integration cooperation mode, the implementation level is consisting of the platform-based enterprise and the team of school-enterprise integration cooperative project, be responsible for the implementation of cooperative project.

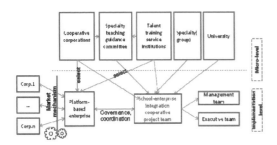

Figure 1. The structure of school-enterprise integration cooperation mode (part).

Platform-based enterprise and formation, operation and management of school-enterprise integration cooperative project team is the key to the success of school-enterprise cooperation. The so-called platform-based enterprise means strength, big impact on the industry, large-scale, with professional training and management agencies (or branches). These companies generally use local policy information of service outsourcing industry development, understand the industry development and human resource needs and other information, can cooperate with universities running.

Within the framework of school-enterprise, platform-based enterprise and university shared governance and coordination of school-enterprise integration cooperative project, the enterprise fully participated in the development of talent cultivation programs and (part of) implementation, and enterprise was responsible the talent dispatch. School-enterprise carried out integration cooperative projects jointly with a third party. Platform-based enterprises contact with their affiliated corporations or cooperative companies relying on market mechanisms.

In implementation level of school-enterprise integration cooperation mode, school-enterprise integration cooperation project team consists of cooperative corporations (including platform-based enterprises), specialty teaching guidance committee, talent training institutions, talent service agencies, specialty (group) and the university, the team is divided into management team and executive team. The management team composed of representatives of platform-based enterprise and representatives of university, they act as co-leader of the team. The executive team mainly consists of platform-based enterprise project managers, technical experts and administrative staff, teachers of the specialty (group), they accept direction of the management team.

2.2 Semester project teaching courses

Outsourcing curriculum and teaching mode innovation is the key to achieve inter-disciplinary

service outsourcing talent cultivation objectives. To this end, we reform both the curriculum development and teaching mode to strengthen the cultivation of students' core occupational competencies and comprehensive qualities. On the basis of approach refer to [Cao Ji-qing, 2010], [Qin Fugao, 2011], in terms with the actual teaching and students situation, we implement "semester project teaching course" to develop students' core occupational competencies.

The so-called "semester project teaching course" refers to aiming specialty talent cultivation objectives and requirements, each semester arrange 1 to 2 specialty key (or core) courses to fully project teaching for each specialty. In order to enhance students' practical skills, we must follow the principle of gradual improvement, decompose enterprise project into specialty key (core) courses, to ensure that every semester 1 to 2 integrated projects for practice teaching.

The characters of semester project teaching is that specialty develops projects, the project set course, projects will be divided into multi-levels, courses include corresponding projects. Specialty develops projects means that semester projects are developed by the platform-based enterprise and specialty teaching office. Project set course, that is according to the nature of the enterprise projects, the difficulty and the progress of teaching, curriculum standards, decided the project should be included in the specific course content. Courses include corresponding projects, that is all the key (core) course must be implemented project teaching mode.

For example, specialty arranged "Object-oriented programming (C#)" as the project course in semester 2, "Web programming (.net)" and "Database programming (SQL Server)" as projects course in semester 3, ".Net Framework programming with C#" as the project course in semester 4, arranged a comprehensive course "Software development for enterprise application (J2EE)" as project course for J2EE specialty direction in semester 5, as well as "Engineering enhancement practice (.Net)" as project course for .Net specialty direction in semester 5. In semester 5, all the projects for corresponding course are enterprise project (either provided by corporations or decomposed by corporations). All the project course must construct accordance with the requirements for university key (excellent) courses, and university provides appropriate funding to support the course construction of school-enterprise cooperation, teacher team building, student competitions, to ensure quality of course construction.

In the implementation process of semester project course, we also formed characteristics different from the literature [Cao Ji-qing, 2010], [Qin Fugao, 2011], we absorb the practice session in the teaching process of the project teaching course, there are order corporations involved in the teaching process or inspected teaching results from to the late 4th and 5th semester. Within a limited period of time, to ensure smooth joint between the teaching content and vacant posts, improving the focalization of teaching. As students have clarity of learning purpose, their enthusiasm for learning improved, the teaching effects are highlighted.

3 TALENT CULTIVATION MODE UNDER SCHOOL-ENTERPRISE INTEGRATION COOPERATION

3.1 "Order Class" mode

In accordance with the service outsourcing talent demand for different vacant posts specifications in the future, platform-based enterprise signed the agreement with the university. Then university and cooperative corporation or training institutions developed jointly talent cultivation programs under the service outsourcing enterprises posts requirements, the number of talents. University and cooperative corporations shared teachers and practice base, teaching in schools and businesses respectively through alternation of working and learning manner. With this talent cultivation mode, the qualified graduates will be directly employed by service outsourcing enterprises.

3.2 "Skill + Education" mode

University and platform-based enterprise cooperative education, open service outsourcing specialty, undergraduate education (adult education). Graduate students can get on adult education, undergraduate diploma and "Software Outsourcing engineer" vocational qualification certificates awarded by provincial service outsourcing talent training base/training institutions. The purpose is to cultivate international software service outsourcing talent, to recruit students for the customized training for the service outsourcing corporations. Training institutions are responsible for the daily management of the school running, the university is responsible for the main teaching tasks, to ensure the quality of teaching. The university provides students with teaching, experiment/practice venues and accommodation conditions. When student enrolled, talent training institutions signed employment recommendation agreement with students.

3.3 "Corporate Training" mode

"Corporate Training" mode is a special case of "Order Class" service outsourcing talent cultivation mode, which in addition to meet the "Order Class" cultivation mode required conditions, its most prominent feature is that the enterprise entrusted new employees to training institutions/schools for training in the form of "order", the training program is developed by the corporation in general, and the quality of training is assessed by corporation. This form will evolve into that training institutions is commissioned by the company in accordance with the corporation's employment criteria for recruitment of new staff and customized training, training institutions collaborate with schools to provide "Recruitment + Training" one-stop service.

3.4 "School in the factory"/"Factory in the school" mode

At the insistence of the principles of teaching and producing parallel, university introduced platform-based enterprise or other high-quality resources of enterprise into provincial demonstration training base, to build "school in factory", to establish training environment consistent with corporation real production processes. Now we have been built a BPO talent training base in service outsourcing enterprises in Jiaxing City China, as the "School in factory". These "Schools in the factory/Factory in school" collectively referred to as "compact practice base."

3.5 "Teacher studio + Student team" mode

Professional teachers and platform-based enterprises established studios or "Gallery in school", to undertake part of the enterprise business enterprise, professional teachers lead some outstanding students to form technical services team, so as to cultivate the students' innovative ability and practical ability.

4 THE EFFECTS OF INNOVATIVE TALENT CULTIVATION MODE IMPLEMENTATION

After more than five years of practice of IT talent cultivation mode reform, information technology department of Jiaxing Vocational and Technical College have achieved remarkable results in talent cultivation. The past three years, more than 400 undergraduates have participated in school-enterprise cooperation outsourcing talent training, and more than 400 graduates were train by school-enterprise cooperation. Information technology department of Jiaxing Vocational and Technical College has become an important service outsourcing talent training base in Jiaxing City China.

Table 1. Talent training mode implementation effect comparison.

Evaluation item	Before implementation	After implementation
Enrollment	Average 35	100
Undergraduates training	0	About 400
Graduates training	0	>=400
Top 10 Chinese service outsourcing corporation employment	Average 4	About 1/3 qualified graduates
Word fortune 500 corporation employment	0	>10
Cooperative corporations	Average 3	>=8
Professional counterparts rates of graduates	About 38%	>78%
Social satisfaction of graduates	About 45%	>80%

The service outsourcing talent cultivation mode based on school-enterprise integration cooperation effectively promoted the specialty development and reform. With software technology specialty (direction) as an example, the annual enrollment becomes from 35 to 100 people, students employed by Chinese service outsourcing companies becomes from only four graduates to nearly 1/3 of graduates in 2013 (see Table 1), students employed by the top 10 Chinese outsourcing corporations and World Fortune 500 corporations have been more than 10 people in nearly two years, the quality of employment has improved significantly. Table 1 gives a synopsis of implementation results of the talent cultivation mode, it shows the talent cultivation quality comparative data of software technology for three years.

5 CONCLUSION

School-enterprise integration talent cultivation mode has the following features, based on multi-level school-enterprise cooperation mechanism, occupational ability development oriented (to implement semester project teaching courses), employment-oriented ("Order Class" talent cultivation, etc.), comprehensive quality cultivation (occupational quality cultivation, foreign language skills training, etc.), academic education and vocational training cohesion. Practice has proved that the model adaptable, schools and enterprises to achieve win-win situation in terms of inter-disciplinary service outsourcing talent cultivation. The main problem of school-enterprise integration talent cultivation mode is difficult to form a long-term mechanism and construct a teacher-team. The ideal mode of school-enterprise integration cooperation is "school-enterprise community", but it is still in the exploration.

ACKNOWLEDGEMENT

This work is supported by Highly Skilled Talent Research Project of Science and Technology Department of Zhejiang Province (2012R30038), Demonstration Training Base in Higher Vocational Colleges of Zhejiang Province—Software Research and Development Training Base, Zhejiang International Service Outsourcing Talent Training Base—Information Technology Department of Jiaxing Vocational and Technical College.

REFERENCES

Cao Ji-qing. Practice and Exploration on Higher Vocational Education Semester Project of Software Outsourcing Talents. Journal of Hubei Polytechnic Institute (China), 2010, (2):42–46.

Chen Wei, Li Hua. Study of talent cultivation mode of service outsourcing. Modern Management Science, 2008, (1):96–98.

Dang Zhonghua, Mao jie, Cai Xiang-dong. Exploration on multi-level school-enterprise cooperation mechanism in service outsourcing talent training. Foreign Investment in China, 2011,(10):210–212.

Feng Jin-yan. Study of Talent Supply-Demand Chain for Software and Information Service Outsourcing Companies. Master Dissertation of Beijing University of Posts and Telecommunications, 2009, P10–11.

Li Luo, Gu Ling-lan, Wang Qing-ming. Practice of the "Three Phases Skills Advanced" Talent Cultivation Mode of Software Technology Specialty of Higher Vocational Education. Vocational and Technical Education (China), 2010, (32):12–15.

Pu Xing, Yu Guo-hong. Study on the talent cultivation Mode of higer vocational college software service outsourcing. China Electric Power Education, 2010, (36):34–35.

Qin Fugao, Zhuang Yanbin, Wang Wenqin. Software Outsourcing Talents Training Mode on School-enterprise Integration. Computer Education (China), 2011, (20):32–35.

Song Zhuan-mao. Research on employment orientation, school-enterprise cooperation and higher vocational education talent cultivation mode. Vocational Education Research (China), 2009, (12): 30–31.

Tian Y.J, China Outsourcing website. The qualities and skills demand on service outsourcing talents [EB/OL]. http://www.chnsourcing.com.cn/outsourcing-news/article/39796.html, 2012-06-15.

Wang Fen-mao, Zheng Yong-guo. Exploration on the school-enterprise cooperation talent cultivation mode of higher vocational college software service outsourcing. Education and Vocation (China), 2010, (27):96–97.

Yang Dong. Exploration on the service outsourcing talent cultivation mode of higher vocational education. Chinese Vocational and Technical Education, 2011, (20):30–32.

YE Jian-ming. Practice of school-enterprise community—taking Fair Friend institute of electronmechanics as an example. China Higher Education Research, 2009, (12):62–64.

Computer, Intelligent Computing and Education Technology – Liu, Sung & Yao (Eds)
© 2014 Taylor & Francis Group, London, ISBN 978-1-138-02469-4

Research the association of dangerous driving behavior and traffic congestion based on C4.5 algorithm

Zheng-Wu Yuan & Yue Dong
College of Computer Science and Technology, Chongqing University of Posts and Telecommunications, China

ABSTRACT: The traffic jams which are caused by dangerous driving behavior will have very great harm to transportation. To get the association between the two can effectively alleviate the traffic situation. C4.5 algorithm is used to classify and conclude the factors of traffic congestion which caused by dangerous driving behavior in this paper, combined with the K-means clustering method for the prediction and classification of continuous data, more important factors can be used in the experimental analysis, and to get the knowledge and the representation automatically of the model. Simulation results show that the algorithm has higher reasoning efficiency and accuracy rate.

Keywords: traffic congestion; dangerous driving behavior; C4.5 algorithm; clustering

1 INTRODUCTION

Traffic congestion[1] is a situation which often encountered in the day life. It is one of the focuses of the traffic manager to calculate the traffic congestion and relief it timely. At present there are many reasons to cause traffic jams, and the dangerous driving behavior will be very difficult to deal with when it happens. Analyzing the driving behavior[2] caused by traffic accident by scientific and effective method, is a very important and far-reaching social significance of improving the city road traffic safety level. This kind of behavior[3] is mainly consists of six kinds of behavior drunk driving, speeding, running red lights, forcible over-taking, overcrowding and fatigue driving.[4] In the actual operation process, the driving behavior are often influenced by multi-source information, no matter what happens on the road will have some impacts more or less.

At present, many researchers mainly use the rough set, association rule mining network and some other methods based on artificial intelligence to get and express knowledge. Among them the rough set[5] method can effectively analyze and deal with the information such as imprecise, inconsistent, incomplete, and finding the connotative knowledge in it. But generally it can't obtain knowledge automatically, and it has poor real-time. Association rule mining method can produce clear and useful results by processing large data, and we can get the consumption of calculation for testing. And it has its problem when the data volume is increasing, it is difficult to determine which attribute is available and identify the rare

but useful data. The C4.5[6] decision tree method is used in this paper to solve the problem caused by dangerous driving behavior. One of the reasons is that the method is simple and the knowledge acquired by it has a good representation and intuitionistic.[7] Besides there are many large amounts of continuous data set related to this paper. Experiments show that using the K-means clustering algorithm to replace the two discretization methods of the C4.5 algorithm can greatly improve the quality and efficiency of the decision tree with the problem.

2 BASIC KNOWLEDGE

2.1 The principle of decision tree

Decision tree is a kind of tree which is used to represent the decision and the corresponding relationship between the results. And each node which has no leaf represents a decision in a tree, the values of the decision is directly lead to different decision result or effect.

2.2 Information entropy

Information entropy[8] is mainly used to solve the problem of the information measurement in the system. When the systems' data is very pure, its measurement should be 0. And if a systems' data is more orderly, the information entropy will be lower. On the contrary, more chaotic the system it is, the higher information entropy it will gets. The information entropy can also be regarded as a measure to identify the system whether it is order of sequence. The formula for the calculation is as follows.

$$I(S) = -\sum_{i=1}^{C} p_i \log_2(p_i) \tag{1}$$

Among them, S is a collection as s amounts data samples, assume that there are c kinds of classes like $(i = 1,2, ..., c)$, p_i represents the probability of sample if it belongs to the i class, which accounted for the proportion of i samples.

2.3 Information gain

Information gain[9] is the reduce amount of desired information or information entropy which if effective. It can be interpreted as the difference of the information. As it is used with the classification problem by the decision tree, the meaning is the information difference between the division of attributes and after partition.

And set the attribute F with V different values as $\{a_1, a_2, ..., a_v\}$, using the F to divide the S attribute set into v subset like $\{s_1, s_2, ..., s_v\}$. If the F attribute is the best splitting attribute, and these subset which from the partitioning process will connect to the branches from the S. $E(F)$ is the entropy of the subset after the partition of attribute F. The calculation equations are as follows.

$$E(F) = \sum_{j=1}^{v} \frac{s_1 + s_2 + \cdots + s_{cj}}{s} \left(-\sum_{i=1}^{c} p_{ij} \log_2(p_{ij}) \right) \tag{2}$$

From the above equation, giving the idea that if the calculation of entropy are smaller, the higher purity of subset after partition. The $I(s_1, s_2, ..., s_{cj})$ is stand for the desired information of every subset s_j. The information gain among attributes, as follows.

$$Gain(F) = I(S) - E(F) \tag{3}$$

2.4 Information gain ratio

Information gain has a characteristic is partial to choose the attribute have more values.[10] The information gain's normalization which using the data set relative to the attribute value distribution entropy is called the information gain rate. The information gain ratio which the C4.5 algorithm uses can be simply understood as the amount of information that branch of need. The calculation formula is as follows.

$$Split\ I(F) = -\sum_{j=1}^{v} p_j \log_2(p_j) \tag{4}$$

Information gain ratio is calculated as follows.

$$Gain\ ratio(F) = \frac{Gain(F)}{Split\ I(F)} \tag{5}$$

2.5 Combined with the K-means clustering algorithm

In the study of continuous attributes we use the clustering algorithm to classify the data with decision tree algorithm. A plurality of clustering will get the continuous attributes into discrete attributes. Then according to the C4.5's basic process of splitting attribute selects the largest information gain rate to generate decision trees. By this way, algorithm can effectively reduce the calculation process overhead, and get the segmentation point of decision tree more accurate. This paper is applying the K-means instead of the two powder method from C4.5 to set the sample data into k numbers clusters. The specific process is described as follows.

1. Preparing the input data, the data set has n numbers of row to be clustered $C = \{c1, c2, c3 ... cn\text{-}2, cn\text{-}1, cn\}$.
2. To keep the attribute in the discrete data set conform from table C, processing the vacant value and the error one in an attribute table.
3. To select k numbers data as the initial cluster center in C data set. Among the continuous attributes, the way to calculate each data object is as follows:

$$c^{(i)} = \sum_{i=1}^{n} \sum_{j=1, x_i \in K_j}^{k} |(x_i - k_j)^2| \tag{6}$$

Among them, k_j is the jth numbers class of the data set j. k_j is the average value of the k_j. x_i is the data object in k_j. n represents the numbers of elements in one cluster. k is the numbers of classes to clustering. $c^{(i)}$ is the sum of square error of each data object.

4. Calculating the Euclidean distance of the data object to each cluster center of data set C and divide the data object into its minimum distance clustering. Calculating the Euclidean distance formula is as follows.

$$d = \sqrt{\sum_{n=1}^{q} (x_{in} - y_{jn})^2} \tag{7}$$

d is the Euclidean distance between two data objects. q represents the data object has q numbers data attribute. i and j are stand for two kind of different data objects.

5. Calculating all the data objects' average value of in the *k* class, and the value is the new clustering center. And repeat the above procedure until the data convergence, the algorithm terminates.

3 ANALYSIS OF THE ACCIDENT BASED ON DANGEROUS DRIVING BEHAVIOR

3.1 Data acquisition

This study uses the traffic incident data of a section from Chongqing traffic management departments as the analysis of the data source. Because of the data set is not completely, data representation is not standardized and has noise exits. So after the data pretreatment, this experiment selects 1016 traffic incident data for analysis. The data samples are divided into two parts, one part is used to build a decision tree as 80% of the total number. The other part is used to validate the generated decision tree.

3.2 The environmental factors of traffic congestion caused by dangerous driving behavior

Many factors could affect the duration of traffic incident and not all factors are collected in fact. Table 1 gives 7 kinds of main influence factors which contain 5 discrete attributes and 2 continuous attributes. Namely the event type, whether it involves crash, weather factor, number of casualties, the accident time, whether the day is holiday and the vehicle type. According to the factors of these effects to count information gain could construct decision tree and form knowledge system.

3.3 Determine the congestion state

The index CI is used in this paper and based on the daily traffic incidents the congestion state is divided into smooth, mild congestion, congestion

Table 1. The basic attributes of dangerous driving behaviour.

Attribute name	Value
Event	Drunk_driving, speeding, run_red, overtake, overman, fatigue_driving
Weather	Sunny, rainy, foggy, snow
Cartype	Large, middle, small
Holiday	Yes, no
Hurts	Count>=0
Time	0<time<=24)
Crash	Yes, no

Table 2. The value list of information gain ratio value.

Information gain ratio value	
g (E) = 0.5595629568	g (H) = 0.8285514663
g (W) = 0.1100688498	g (T) = 0.7806749057
g (C) = 0.2278862115	g (S) = 0.7024142036
g (D) = 0.5310641504	

and serious congestion four states. The data set consists of (*s*, *l*, *c*, *h*). Under normal circumstances, the standard to evaluate the traffic of different road is not the same. In this paper the standard is determined by counting ratio between the time of vehicles through two different signal detectors and the situation with no traffic. The location of the detector is near the traffic light. The way of calculating the CI value is as follows.

3.4 The training data set

According to Table 1 make sure the data in the database are sorted out and standardizing. And afterwards fill in the missing data.

Table 2 lists gives part of the training sample. In it, gain ratio is shorted as *g*. The maximum of information gain ratio is number of injured. In this paper the attributes of the dataset are represented with the standard value of characters.

4 DEVELOPMENT AND TESTING THE MODEL OF DECISION TREE

4.1 Developing a decision tree

In order to check the validity of the algorithm, the research group uses the simulation to deal with the data. The running environment of experiment is Windows XP operating system, the hardware configuration of PC is Intel(R) Core (TM)2 Duo@1.99 GHz CPU and memory has 2048M. The programming language uses the Java, chooses the eclipse as the programming environment and Oracle10 g as the backstage database. Due to the use of the training data as a classification success rate may be cause the result over fitting and relatively optimistic. So the information after processing will be divided into 2 parts before the start of each experiment. In it 80% of the data as a training set and the remaining 20% for test data.

4.2 Decision tree of knowledge representation

According to the decision tree by classification algorithm, there are 162 nodes and corresponding 104 rules in it. And using the IF—THEN format can get all kinds of classification rules, four examples is as follows.

1. IF hurts < = 4 AND time > 16 AND event type = drunk_driving AND crash or not = yes AND weather = "rainy", THEN the type of congestion is h.
2. IF hurts > 4 AND crash or not = no AND hurts >5 AND event type = run_red, THEN the type of congestion is l.
3. IF hurts > 4 AND crash or not = no AND hurts > 5 AND event type = fatigue_driving AND weather = sunny, THEN the type of congestion is h.

4.3 *Model validation*

During this experiment the model uses the method of model 10 times cross validation. And the degree of association's accuracy rate is as shown in Figure 1. The average index of comparison about the decision tree based on C4.5 algorithm is 70.25%. And the accuracy of clustering algorithm

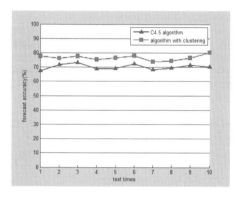

Figure 1. The accuracy rate of classification and prediction diagram.

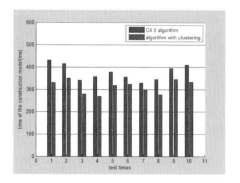

Figure 2. Relational graph between time and experiment times.

by k-means algorithm can reach 77.50%. The average false positive rate is 22.50%. Comparing with those without clustering algorithm has a great improvement. Considering k-means algorithm need to repeat the calculation of distance between the different objects and each calculation cluster center will have to spend a lot of time, the choice of a good initial cluster centers will have great improvement in calculating the efficiency of the algorithm. Figure 2 shows the time consumption of the two algorithms in traffic data processing. The average consumption of 10 experiments is respectively 375.4 and 312.5 ms showing the superiority about the efficiency of clustering C4.5 algorithm.

5 CONCLUSION

Dangerous driving behavior will cause a lot of damage in transit in the normal operation, which directly or indirectly lead to different degree of traffic congestion. Mainly addresses the following issues in this paper: (1) the dangerous driving behavior and traffic congestion levels associated with automatic knowledge acquisition and representation. (2) Traffic blocking relational model has caused by dangerous driving behavior is represented by decision tree with high reasoning efficiency. It is in favor of traffic control department to analysis the current level of traffic congestion with a high real-time. (3) The use of k-means clustering algorithm for continuous attribute of data sets can improve the efficiency of data processing of the C4.5algorithm.

ACKNOWLEDGEMENTS

This work was partly supported by the Natural Science Foundation of Chongqing (No. cstc2012 jjA40064) and the National Natural Science Foundation of China (No. 61075019).

REFERENCES

[1] Ture M, Tokatli F, Kurt I. Using Kaplan–Meier analysis together with decision tree methods (C&RT, CHAID, QUEST, C4. 5 and ID3) in determining recurrence-free survival of breast cancer patients[J]. Expert Systems with Applications, 2009, 36(2): 2017–2026.
[2] Wu F, Deng X, Jiang Q, et al. Analysis of lake vulnerability in the middle-lower Yangtze River catchment using C4.5 decision tree algorithms[J]. Journal of Food, Agriculture & Environment, 2012, 10(2): 1245–1247.
[3] Zeng Dan. Study on the problem of Dangerous driving behavior[J]. Jintian, 2013, 05:258–259.

[4] Xiong Hou-kun. Analysis of Dangerous driving behavior[D]. Jilin University, 2012.

[5] Franco-Arcega A, Carrasco-Ochoa JA, Sanchez-Diaz G, et al. Building fast decision trees from large training sets[J]. Intelligent Data Analysis, 2012, 16(4): 649–664.

[6] Lira F, Perez PS, Baranauskas JA, et al. Prediction of antimicrobial activity of synthetic peptides by a decision tree model[J]. Applied and Environmental Microbiology, 2013, 79(10):3156–3159.

[7] Venkatesan P, Yamuna NR. Treatment Response Classification in Randomized Clinical Trials: A Decision Tree Approach[J]. Indian Journal of Science and Technology, 2013, 6(1):3912–3917.

[8] Sivatha Sindhu SS, Geetha S, Kannan A. Decision tree based light weight intrusion detection using a wrapper approach[J]. Expert Systems with Applications, 2012, 39(1):129–141.

[9] Wang Xiao-yuan, Yang Xin-yue. Study on Decision Mechanism of Driving Behavior Based on Decision Tree[J]. Journal of System Simulation, 2008, 20(2):415–419.

[10] Fang Li-xia, Wei Lian-yu, Yan Wei-yang. Prediction of Traffic Congestion Based on Decesion Tree[J]. Journal of Hebei University of Technology, 2010, 39(002):105–110.

Computer, Intelligent Computing and Education Technology – Liu, Sung & Yao (Eds)
© 2014 Taylor & Francis Group, London, ISBN 978-1-138-02469-4

Research on the mold process design system with case-based reasoning

Jian-Bo Zhao

Shandong Transport Vocational College, Shandong Weifang, China

ABSTRACT: Mold design process mainly depends on the experience in personnel preparation work. In order to improve efficiency and reduce the design cycle, should mold process research and development of computer-aided design system to adapt to the rapid development of mold manufacturing. This article will explore the use of Case-Based Reasoning techniques (CBR) to classify the type of mold, mold process designed to establish a database and computer-aided design system for mold problems.

Keywords: mold process design; case-based reasoning; object-oriented; relational database

1 INTRODUCTION

Mold design process mainly depends on the experience in personnel preparation work. In order to improve efficiency and reduce the design cycle, should mold process research and development of computer-aided design system to adapt to the rapid development of mold manufacturing. This article will explore the use of Case-Based Reasoning techniques (CBR) to classify the type of mold, mold process designed to establish a database and computer-aided design system for mold problems.

Case-based reasoning (Case-based Reasoning) is a relatively new field of artificial intelligence in the rise of an important knowledge-based problem solving methods. It is a simulation methodology of human reasoning and thinking process, but also the construction of intelligent computing systems methodology, the core idea is the direct use of past successful experience during problem solving. The basic process is: when you enter a new case, the system according to a given search strategy retrieved in the case library, find a case with the most similar to the input examples, with similar examples of solutions or adapt their solutions after modifications and applied to new instances. Thus, the description of the new cases and solutions and saved as a new case in the case library. With increasing instances of library systems have the ability to solve problems increases, the system's ability to learn. Thus, retrieval, modification, storage, and constitute the entire learning process of CBR.

Application of CBR technology is based on similarity mold process design, the use of case-based reasoning approach to identifying the reference case, referring to the process of the case to assist the process design.

CBR technology to the development of the CAPP system, to facilitate the collection in the accumulation of expertise, so that CAPP system is more practical.

2 MOLD PROCESS DESIGN CASE STUDY OF REPRESENTATION

Since the basic research questions include the CBR case representation, retrieval, modification and learning, in order to complete the design process, you first need to understand is the case of representation. A collection of stories that could lead to the results of a series of specific characteristics of the property. Association on the most complex form, examples of problem solving is the formation of a sub-structure of a collection of stories, CBR system, the main task is to determine the appropriate case characteristics, including field definitions and terminology experts in order to solve the problem of representation cases collection.

The case include the following questions: choose the information, how to organize the information. Common methods of expression: expression method of IF-THEN rules-based framework for expressing method based on feature-based expression, the expression of neural network-based, object-oriented representation methods. Based on the advantages and disadvantages of various methods and conditions, we use the object-oriented approach to the mold design case.

3 THE OBJECT-ORIENTED REPRESENTATION OF CASE

In this paper we use the object-oriented representation of mold design case.

Classification of the mold design process can be divided into the following categories: stamping die design, die design punching, bending mold design, mold design drawing, bulging mold design, special stamping die design.

Based on the characteristics of the mold process design examples, considering the characteristic properties of instances, the use of object-oriented approach to represent the case, the object model to build extensions to enable them to express and process design knowledge topological relationships between features part shape.

Object Model (extended objectmodel, EOM). Defined as:

ExtObj = (id, A, M, R, C) where: id to uniquely identify an instance of an object model; A is a set of attributes; M is a method (ie, a function of the operating properties) collection; R for the expression of each characteristic shape between topological relationship (including adjacency relationships and attachment) and parts of a relation between the shape characteristics, C storage for process design knowledge.

The use of a relational database MS Access database software to store cases, the establishment of case libraries. Mold process case library, each case contains basic information, feature information, process planning information.

4 THE SCREENING METHODS BASED ON FUZZY COMPREHENSIVE EVALUATION OF CASE

For the reference case mold design process with greater reference value, made examples of screening methods based on fuzzy comprehensive evaluation to establish mold process design case retrieval model. Fuzzy evaluation method based on fuzzy mathematics is fuzzy numerical information for the quantitative evaluation of utilization. Fuzzy Evaluation of expression is not used to measure the size and value, but with the program for the evaluation of certain concepts (such as excellent, good, poor) level of membership, membership, or by statistical methods can be used to select the appropriate membership functions obtained. Also in practice, evaluation (or assessment) of a thing, often involving multiple factors or multiple targets, then it would require a number of factors based on comprehensive evaluation of things to make, not only from a certain factor to evaluate the situation of things, which requires comprehensive evaluation.

The use of fuzzy comprehensive evaluation method to create a set of factors that affect the choice of the reference case, weight set and evaluation set, the fuzzy mold process examples of screening methods;

On the basis of case screening on the use of the nearest neighbor method to establish similarity model case of mold process design, process design to achieve die case retrieval matching algorithm;

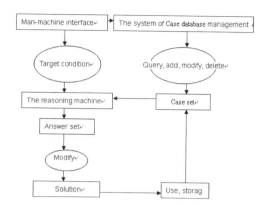

Figure 1.   The structure of the system flow chart.

The use of MS VC ++, the case library case to achieve input, delete, query, etc. displayed on the UG platform management functions. The flow chart of the system is shown in Figure 1.

5 CONCLUSION

Mold design process is to build creative thinking in the design of a wealth of experience and knowledge of experts on the basis of, but also a succession of knowledge, integration, innovation and management process. Requires a lot of knowledge and expertise in the field in the design process, skill, but also requires a lot of scientific computing and analysis. Therefore mold design process is a difficult and lengthy process, in order to shorten the design cycle, meet market demand, the paper case-based reasoning research and development mold design system is presented. CBR technology will be applied to the secondary process design mold design system based on the use CBR technology can be more effectively used in the design process the accumulated experience and knowledge. The use of object-oriented approach, which means that the mold design process design examples, build a relational database instance. Examples of screening methods proposed based on fuzzy comprehensive evaluation. Through the above studies, case-based reasoning approach is applied to the mold design system, both to promote the application field of CBR, but also the design of the mold design process presents a faster updates. Case-based reasoning technology will play an increasingly important role in this field.

REFERENCES

[1] Agnar Aamodt and Enric Plaza. Case-based reasoning: Foundational issues, methodological variations, and system approaches. Artificial Intelligence Communications, 1994.

[2] Qijun Xia 1, Ming Rao. Dynamic case-based reasoning for process operation support system. Engineering Applications of Artificial Intelligence 12 (1999) 343–361.

[3] C.M. Vonga, T.P. Leungb, P.K. Wong. Case-based reasoning and adaptation in hydraulic production machine design. Engineering Applications of Artificial Intelligence 15 (2002) 567–585.

[4] Pei-Chann Chang a, b, Chen-Hao Liu B, Robert K. Lai C. A fuzzy case-based reasoning model for sales forecasting in print circuit board industries. Expert Systems with Applications 34 (2008) 2049–2058.

[5] Dongkon Lee, Kyung-Ho Lee. An approach to case-based system for conceptual ship design assistant. Expert Systems with Applications,1999,16.

[6] Ma Zhenlin, at Yingjie. Study of fault diagnosis expert system [J]. RBR and CBR micro computer information, based on 2010, 26 (2): 111-.

[7] The [17] field inspring. Knowledge discovery based on case reasoning [D]. of Wuhan University of Technology in 2004.

[8] GuoYanhong, DengGuishi. CaseBased Reasoning (CBR) phase 21 study of [J]. computer engineering and application of 4–8 in 2004.

[9] Bao Sheng, Bin Bin, Wang Fengying. Research on case retrieval inference system design examples of [J]. China manufacturing information based on 78–81;2004 02.

[10] Wang Lingzhi, Ou Zongying, Yang Xin hua, Hao Guoxiang. Application of [J]. computer aided engineering CBR technology in stamping die design; 2003 01; 44–50.

[11] Xie Jijian, Liu Chengping. Fuzzy mathematics method and its application. Huazhong University of Science and Technology press, 2005.

[12] Min Shanhua, he Zhongxiong. A fuzzy mathematics. Chinese Youth Press, 1985.

[13] Jin Lu. The utility of fuzzy mathematics. Science and Technology Literature Press, 1989.

Computer aided design system based on 3D GIS for park design

S. Lu
Landscape Department, Beijing University of Agriculture, Beijing, P.R. China

F. Wang
Beijing Landscape Architecture School, Beijing, P.R. China

ABSTRACT: Use the 3D GIS characteristics of three-dimensional to descript and analyze regional space objects, computer aided Design System based on 3D GIS for park design construct with 3D visualization GIS system. The spatial information of the element in park can be known and analyzed clearly by 3D GIS query, browsing and statistical analysis, contour generation, viewshed analysis, path analysis, and so on. Then designer adjust park design according to feedback scheme with scientific and intuitive method. The framework of this design system and the implementation method are presented.

Keywords: 3D GIS; aided design system; park; ArcEngine

3D visualization GIS system of park can realize the spatial information of geographic elements for better analysis and management rely on interactive, dynamic and omnidirectional display of park scenes. And it is an effective means to improve and perfect the design, to evaluate design and participate actively management for public (Drummond WJ, SP. 2008). ArcEngine is an ArcGIS platform tools to create a GIS desktop application. It can achieve two-dimensional GIS function, but also it has the advanced function of 3D display, three-dimensional analysis. The combined application of SketchUp, 3DSMax modeling and ArcEngine can be achieved in 2D and 3D GIS query and analysis function so as to combine better site modification design and scheme.

1 THE MAIN METHOD OF 3D MODELING AND TECHNOLOGY FOR PARK SITE

There are many methods to establish model. It is the most important how to most quickly and meet the requirements of the construction especially for aided design. Faster model building means higher design efficiency. Generally, model should be established by building software, such as 3DSmax, SketchUp, Rhino, MAYA and other 3D software. But SketchUp may be a better soft to establish model than other 3D software.

1.1 Construct plant model

Plant model is the most difficult to establish because of its complexity. In general, park design

not need to identify the specific plant species, and only it can identify the classification trees, shrubs, grass, flowers. So the model can make full use of the plant model database that download from internet and the library of SketchUp software. The component library model can meet the demand of common 3D GIS. Accurate model can also be combined with the free hand drawing tool which implemented in SketchUp, but such models are often large system data, it is not preferred.

1.2 Construct architecture and structure model

The architecture and structure model can make up by SketchUp which can be directly modelling, SketchUp play the advantages of modeling include given material and texture to buildings. And the map of model texture can be derived from the scene photographs of the site.

1.3 Construct road and path model

The road and path in the park have characteristics such as area, perimeter, so they can be considered the space body with certain area and thickness. For example, the road can be seen as surface with a certain width. If the river and road is located in the rugged terrain, they can be extruded, suspension, paste printing process by using SandBox which a plugin soft tools in SketchUP. By this way, the sense of reality of the model in the park. We can use the plug-in makes modeling more realistic, such as Road Instant Road, Instant site Grader Pro.

1.4 Construct the others model in scenes

In the park, the other model in scenes can model directly by SkethUp with relatively regular geometry, such as landscape sketch modeling, landscape lamp, sketch, the trash.

1.5 Terrain model

The terrain is the base of the park design. Therefore the terrain model in the park must need accurate data to directly generate modeling. The accurate date of terrain come from the data file. The date can generrater terrain file through professional software, like as ArcMap, XianYuan Control Detailed Planning of CAD System, CityMaker, GARLAND. And then the *TIN* model can generate as the terrain or save as DWG file format.

2 MODEL TRANSFORMATION BETWEEN SKETCHUP AND 3D GIS SOFTWARE

It is one of the main reasons for using SketchUp modeling as a modeling tools that the model which format "skp" of SketchUp can transform into relevant GIS software format each other. The Plug-in that named SketchUp ESRI implements 3D scene model with interchange format. By this way, The ArcMap and ArcScene data can be used by SketchUp, and as the basic map or the reference layer to aided modeling. After install SketchUp ESRI, All the element include TIN model in the ArcMap can export to SketchUp. So it realizes the process of the GIS model into SketchUp model.

SketchUp can easily construct various 3D model in the park and simulate on regional terrain quickly. It is enough to the park design that SketchUp made all kinds model (L.J. Song & J. Wang. 2010). At the same time, the SketchUp ESRI plugin can also convert the SketchUp model (.skp) to Multipatch model ESRI Multipatch (.mdb) with all attribute information for each Multipatch model. All kinds of model elements stored in the GeoDatabase, as the three-dimensional data source, and then they loaded into ArcScene software for the further analysis.

3 AIDED DESIGN SYSTEM

3.1 System development technology based on 3D GIS

Basic idea of system development is pixel map and terrain data of park design theme as basic data. Through ArcMap processing, software export 3D modeling of design theme to SketchUp, and All the rest of the model of designed theme were

create by SkethUp. Then all model data were loading to ArcScene. As a program developing tools for 3D GIS, ArcEngine derive 3D virtual scene for the park theme.

The common management of spatial data combined with attribute data in the park improve the design. Based on the 3D scene visualization software program developing tools, the system function are integrate to construction of 3D GIS application of the system, so that the park design is based on the digital basis, and it will be more scientific and intuitive than groovy design.

3.2 The design of database system

GeoDatabase uses the object-oriented method. According to the model and the rules, geographical sets of features was combined in GeoDatabase. And GeoDatabase provide good support for feature class which include its topological relation, composite grid, the relationship between factors and support other object-oriented elements, so it is fit to management and operation for spatial data (Y. Cheng & C.L. Wang, 2005). Spatial data placed in the binary file with index and attribute data in the DBMS table are linked with the identification public code. Our system is unified manage spatial data and attribute data by GeoDataBase, including plants, waters, roads, squares, buildings, structures and other data elements in the park. The layer's data stored in the GeoDataBase in *feature Class* form. According to different landscape objects in the park, such as sprinkler system, tour

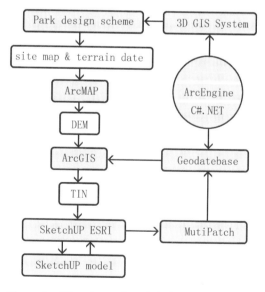

Figure 1. The chart of technical route for aided system.

road, plants, water, road, square, buildings, structures, the layer be divide to different type in the system. The attributes information of landscape objects in the park is the basic information in the design scheme. Those basic information include the site area, plant species, furniture information, site information, touring route.

3.3 *The functional design of computer-aided design system*

Function design mainly take advantage of outstanding function of 3D GIS in the analysis, forecasting, decision-making, survey, query and other field, so the information and data obtained from 3D GIS can aid the park design (Fig. 2).

1. Attribute query. System can required information in 3D scene model including the original object and designed object. By this means, designer can obtain information freely including plant distribution, square, water, buildings and so on. A quick check of terrain parameters, such as the terrain slope, coordinate, elevation information can be read quickly by designer.
2. Spatial analysis. System can aid spatial 2D or 3D analysis. 2D provides automatic measurement on area, distance, profiles and so on. 3D provide analysis support including the following contents:

   Slope and aspect analysis: Based on DEM digital elevation model, system can generate park slope, analysis chart, and provides direct reference for the road or path line selection, recreation activity location.

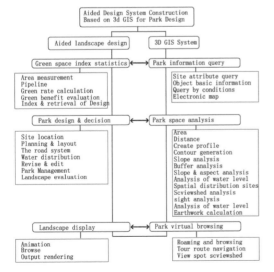

Figure 2. Framework design of the aided system.

Scenic visual analysis: On viewing point designed can be see the sight prior to putting into practice. In turn, designer can layout important scenic spots or spots of the place in the park through the analysis of visibility of a point which have highly sensitive areas.

Spatial scale analysis: The objective is to have a good grasp of the landscape scale. Through the GIS spatial scale analysis easily accurately control the space sight, the most suitable for viewing distance relate landscape presents to the people.

Line of sight permeability analysis: For people enjoy the scenery as much as possible on the route in park, the line of sight is very important. By the technology of GIS accurate permeability analysis function can achieve the desired effect of the landscape.

Buffer zone defined: The buffer area is relative to the protection of the region that can control impact on scope of people's behavior, the activities scope. It considers the influence on the natural landscape, resources and the environment, the population and safety. It is very important to design in scheme stage that designer have measure to adjust drawing prior to implementation.

3. All-round browsing: Because model is generated using modal superpose method with the superposition of model that accurate terrain data based remote sensing images. The model is nearly perfect. Relayed on generated 3D model and the help of the tree mapping technology, 3D visualization park virtual reconstruction. System can realistically simulate the design route of landscape change when it is in the real environment status and position, and it can show visual navigation and animation also. Designer observe carefully the three-dimensional scenes from any angle with 3D landscape pitch, zoom, pan and so on. So it is help for designer to modify and improve the design content, to avoid the omission.

4   REALIZATION METHOD OF COMPUTER AIDED DESIGN SYSTEM

4.1 *The information query module*

The 3D attribute query function is run with attribute query tool. User obtain the feature of selected objects through attribute by the query tool. The mouse click on the screen coordinates will change to geographical coordinates; elements identify in the *Campuse class* through the coordinates of the points to get the click, returns the object value; System can acquires attribute information from the object and displays various objects in 3D scene layer, name and three-dimensional coordinate information.

4.2 Statistical analysis module

3D terrain statistical analysis module is the focus of application development, system based on TIN model or the digital elevation model, the analysis algorithm obtain some information related to the study area and spatial characteristics. User can get the result closer to practical analysis, and more direct access to obtain all kinds of information related to spatial features. The module have some functions including achieve the level measurement, vertical measurement, area measurement, angle measurement, linear calculation and other functions.

1. Draw the three-dimensional cross-section. Drawing section line mainly use the *GetProfile* attribute on the *ISurface* interface, it can realizes the connection between two arbitrary section display and output.
2. Extract contour lines: User can click point directly on TIN graphics, then module can be generated contour lines base the point on. The module obtain contour lines by *Get Contour* method on *ISurface* interface.
3. Slope & aspect analysis: Loading TIN surface data and setting the gradient map parameters and the output path, this modules generate gradient map of slope and aspect. TIN model provides the slope and triangular surface information. So modules can make thematic map by using SLOPE and ASPECT field, which include slope map and aspect map.
4. Analysis water elevation. Add height datum defined as surface layer in the *Ax Scene Control*, then set the height specified reference value, it can be calculated between the TIN surface and the horizontal plane of the specified designed height on 3d space. And number of water body surface area and volume is calculated.
5. Analysis of 3D visibility: It is the important to borrow scenery whether two points on the 3D model is visible. Use the mouse draw a line between two points which need to analyze, system will display 3D coordinate line between two endpoints and results whether is visible in the query output window. The distance between any two points and three dimensional is display also.
6. Analysis of three-dimensional visual field: For a given observation point based on some relative height, it range within a given observation point search for visibility coverage of the area, the results of the analysis is a data set, namely, it is visibility range.
7. Surface area and fill and excavation earthwork calculation: In the setting of a certain height, the system will calculate the filling volume and digging volume of earth excavation.

4.3 All-round browsing module

Browsing relies mainly on *Toolbar tools* in the control, such as translation, zoom, roaming and other functions. Dynamic roaming is the main method to browsing 3D terrain, all-round browsing have manual flight and automatic flight. Manual flight is operate mouse or keyboard to achieve. Automatic flight can set the characteristics of tour routes to create animation frame. The *Ptracks AddTrack* will add track to *trackSet*. Key frame create in the *SceneControl* control. Output AVI video animation mainly used *ISceneExporter3D* and *IAVIExporter* interface.

5 CONCLUSION

Computer Aided Design System based on 3d GIS for park design provide scientific reference for the selection of park attractions location and overall layout in the park. Designers can arrive at a particular location and view scene quickly. From a predefined angle, system simulate all-round browsing. According to accurate data form analysis based on terrain model and other models date, designer have scientific reference to modify and adjust the design scheme.

As an embedded software, ArcEngine development based on AO structure, and simplifies the difficulty of development program. With the help of SketchUp 3D rapid modeling and its large number of models available, ArcEngine can construct GIS system by itself powerful function. System can meet the park project better management and the 3D visualization analysis based on spatial data form 3D GIS. *Computer Aided Design System based on 3d GIS* is very powerful, it is important to note that it also has its limitations, such as system operation requires professionals with rich experience.

REFERENCES

Cheng Y. & C.L. Wang, 2005. The Analysis of Land Exploitation Landscape Pattern of Fuyuan County Based on Geodatabase geometrics. Spatial Information Technology 35,(5) 1–7.

Drummond W.J, SP. 2008. The Future of GIS in Planning: Converging Technologies and Diverging Interests. Journal of the American Planning Association 74(2):161–174.

Mach, R. Workflow for Interactive High-end 3D Visualization in Site Planning.-In: Buhmann, E., M. Pietsch & M. Heeins (Eds.):Digital Design in Landscape Architecture. Proceeding at Anhalt University of Applied Sciences.-Wichmann, Heidelberg, 2008:174–179.

Song L.J. & J. Wang. 2010. Construction of GIS System Based on ArcEngine and SketchUp. Mine Measurement (4):44–46.

Wang F.X. & S.J. Ma, 2011, Design and implementation of 3D Terrain Visualization System Based on ArcEngine. Geospatial Information 09(3):38–40,43.

Computer, Intelligent Computing and Education Technology – Liu, Sung & Yao (Eds)
© 2014 Taylor & Francis Group, London, ISBN 978-1-138-02469-4

Large-scale image denoising using incremental learning method

Chao Chen
Naval Academy of Armament, Beijing, China

Xue-Wen Wu, Bo Sun & Jun He
School of Information Science and Technology, Beijing Normal University, Beijing, China

ABSTRACT: We address the image denoising problem with Gaussian white noise. The approach taken is based on sparse and redundant representations over a learned overcomplete dictionary. It has been proved that the K-SVD algorithm is a highly effective method of training the overcomplete dictionaries for sparse signal representation. However, when the training datasets become extremely large in scale, this algorithm will be no longer effective as it is batch processing algorithm which deals with all the training samples at each iteration. In this paper we present an efficient incremental learning alternative implementation of this algorithm, which both improves performance and adapts to large datasets with millions of training samples. The denoising experiments conducted with both large-scale image and training dataset demonstrate that our proposed method is much effective to large-scale image denoising task.

Keywords: image denoising; sparse representation; incremental learning; overcomplete dictionary

1   INTRODUCTION

Images are one of the significantly important ways to obtain information for us. However, in the practical application, images are often suffering from a variety of noise, so that solving the image denoising problem becomes much important which has been extensively studied in the past several decades. It is the simplest problem among the family known as Inverse Problems, aiming to recover a high quality signal from a degraded version. In this paper, we address the classic image denoising problem: An ideal image is measured in the presence of an additive zero-mean white Gaussian noise, with standard deviation. The image denoising problem is important, not only because of the extensive applications it serves. Being the simplest inverse problem, it provides a convenient platform over which image processing algorithms and techniques can be assessed. Indeed, many contributions have addressed this problem from many and different points of view in the past several years. Statistical estimators, spatial filters, transform-domain methods, and other approximation methods are some of the many methods explored in this research area. In this paper, we have no intention to provide a survey of these methods. Instead, we intend to focus on the method that utilizes sparse and redundant representations on overcomplete dictionaries for image or image sequence denoising, extending the work reported by Elad & Aharon (2006). Several

algorithms have been proposed for learning such overcomplete dictionaries based on sparse representation recently. For example, MOD (Engan et al. 1999), K-SVD (Aharon et al. 2006) and etc. are such algorithm which learns an overcomplete dictionary from the training data. Researchers have shown that these algorithms can achieve outstanding performances in image compression (Bryt et al. 2008) and denoising (Elad et al. 2006) tasks.

However, most recent methods for dictionary learning are iterative batch processing algorithms, which deal with all the training samples at each iteration to minimize the objective function under sparse constraints. Therefore, another problem we may encounter is that when the training set becomes very large, these batch methods are no longer efficient. To overcome this bottleneck, an online algorithm for dictionary learning which applies stochastic approximation method has been proposed in the literature (Aharon et al. 2008, Mairal et al. 2010). To address these issues, we propose an incremental learning approach that processes one sample (or a small subset) of the training set at a time. This is particularly important in the context of image and video processing tasks, where it is common to learn dictionaries adapted to small image patches. The training samples set may include several millions of these patches. Our proposed approach is expected to efficiently handle large training set and effectively perform image denoising task.

The outline of this paper is organized as follows. In section II, we briefly introduce the principles of sparse and redundant representations and their deployment to image denoising. Then we discuss the batch dictionary learning algorithm and propose the incremental dictionary learning method for large-scale training samples in section III. In section IV, the experimental results are given compared to several competitive denoising algorithms with different kinds of dataset. Conclusions and future works are presented in the final section.

2 DENOISING BY SPARSE REPRESENTATION

Consider the problem of estimation of x from the observed signal y with additional noise n, thus

$$y = x + n, \text{ where } n \sim N\{0, \sigma^2 I\} \quad (1)$$

where, n denotes the zero-mean white and homogeneous Gaussian noise. We desire to design an algorithm that can remove the noise from y, getting as close as possible to the original image x. Image denoising method based on sparse representation assume that x has a sparse representation over an over-complete dictionary Φ, i.e. $x = \Phi\alpha$ with a small $\|\alpha\|_0$ (the number of nonzero elements of a vector) and also assume that the estimation of the present noise $\|n\|_2 \leq \varepsilon$ is provided.

The sparsest representation we are looking for, is formulated as,

$$\hat{\alpha} = \arg\min_{\alpha} \|\alpha\|_0, \, s.t. \, \|y - \Phi\alpha\|_2 \leq \varepsilon \quad (2)$$

Some pursuit algorithm such as Orthogonal Matching Pursuit (OMP) (Tropp et al. 2004) and Basis Pursuit (BP) (Chen et al. 2001) algorithms can be used to resolve this minimization problem. Once the sparsest solution of Eq. 2 has been found, we can recover the approximate image by $\hat{x} = \Phi\hat{\alpha}$. Sparse representation of noised image is conducted on the predefined dictionary or trained dictionary. Briefly, image denoising based on sparse representation includes three steps:

1. Training samples: Divide noised image into small blocks. The training data is constructed as a set of block patches of size 8×8 or 16×16 pixels, taken from the noised image or a database of natural images. Each block is rearranged into a column vector y and getting the matrix $Y = [y_1, y_2 \ldots y_n]$.
2. Dictionary training: We exploit the MOD, K-SVD algorithms or our proposed incremental learning algorithm to train an adaptive over-complete dictionary with L elements. The

coefficients are computed using OMP algorithm with a fixed sparsity K. Note that better performance can be obtained by switching to Lasso. We use OMP because of its simplicity and fast execution.
3. Image denoising: We conduct adaptive sparse representation on noised image and get denoised x′, rearrange each column of x′ into an image block, combine all the blocks and average the overlapped pixel, get the denoised image $\hat{x}$.

3 DICTIONARY LEARNING

3.1 Batch dictionary learning

The MOD and K-SVD algorithms are both batch dictionary learning algorithms often used to find the optimal dictionary D that leads to the lowest reconstruction error given a fixed sparsity factor K. In practice, it has been observed that K-SVD converges with less number of iterations than MOD. It motivates us to select the K-SVD algorithm to be compared with our proposed incremental method. We now briefly describe the K-SVD algorithm.

The K-SVD algorithm accepts an initial overcomplete dictionary D_0, a number of iterations k, target sparsity K and a set of training signals arranged as the columns of the matrix Y. The algorithm aims to iteratively improve the dictionary to achieve sparser representations of the signals in Y, by solving the optimization problem.

$$\min_{D, X} \left\{ \|Y - DA\|_F^2 \right\} \quad s.t. \, \forall i, \|\alpha_i\|_0 \leq K \quad (3)$$

The K-SVD algorithm summarized in Algorithm 1 uses two basic steps, which together constitute the algorithm iteration and each iteration involves the all training samples: (i) the signals in Y are sparse coded given the current dictionary D, producing the sparse representations matrix A, and (ii) the dictionary elements are updated given the current sparse representation coefficients. The

---

Algorithm 1. K-SVD.

1: Input: Signal set Y, initial dictionary D_0, target sparsity K, number of iterations k.
2: Output: Dictionary D and sparse matrix A such that $Y \approx DA$
3: Init: Set D: = D_0
4: for n = 1 ... k do
5: $\forall i: \quad \alpha_i := \text{Arg}\min_{\alpha} \left\{ \|y_i - D\alpha\|_2^2 \right\} \quad s.t. \|\alpha\|_0 \leq K$
6: for j = 1 ... L do
7: Apply SVD decomposition to update D_j
8: end for
9: end for

418

sparse coding part is commonly implemented using OMP or Lasso algorithms. The dictionary update is performed with one element at a time, optimizing the target function for each element individually while keeping the rest fixed. The problem can be solved directly via SVD decomposition.

3.2 Incremental dictionary learning

Large-scale training set is a reasonable extension in learning tasks such as large-scale image denoising or inpainting. However the aforementioned dictionary learning schemes fail to handle large-scale dataset problem. For this reason, we explored the incremental dictionary learning method for large-scale training set. Inspired by Bottou & O. Bousquet (2007), Mairal et al. (2010) use the expected objective function to replace the original empirical objective function, obtaining a novel dictionary learning scheme:

$$\min_{D} \frac{1}{2} E_y \left[\|y - D\hat{\alpha}\|_2^2 \right] \qquad (4)$$

where $\hat{\alpha}$ denotes the sparse representation coefficients computed in the sparse coding stage. To solve the above problem, they propose a stochastic gradient descent learning algorithm for dictionary updating.

The approach we propose in this paper is a block-coordinate descent algorithm, and the overall algorithm is summarized in Algorithm 2. In this algorithm, the i.i.d. samples y_t are drawn from an unknown probability distribution $p(y)$ sequentially. However, since the distribution $p(y)$ is unknown, obtaining such i.i.d. samples may be very difficult. The common trick in online algorithms to obtain such i.i.d. samples is to cycle over a randomly permuted training set. The sparse coding steps are same as K-SVD algorithm. The dictionary update steps are different from K-SVD algorithm. The

---

Algorithm 2.   Incremental dictionary learning.

1: Input: $y \in R^m \sim p(y)$ (random variable and an algorithm to draw i.i.d samples of p), $\lambda \in R$ (regularization parameter), T (number of iterations).
2: Output: Dictionary D
3: Init: Set D: = $D_0 \in R^{m \times k}$ (initial dictionary)
4: $A_0 \leftarrow 0$, $B_0 \leftarrow 0$ (reset the "past" information)
5: for t = 1 to T do
6:   Draw y_t from p(y)
7:   Sparse coding: compute a_t using OMP
8:   $A_t \leftarrow A_{t-1} + a_t a_t^T$
9:   $B_t \leftarrow B_{t-1} + y_t a_t^T$
10: Compute D_t according to Eq. 5, with D_{t-1} as warm restart
11: end for

---

new dictionary D_t is computed by minimizing the following cost function.

$$f_t(D) \triangleq \frac{1}{t} \sum_{i=1}^{t} \frac{1}{2} \|y_i - D\alpha_i\|_2^2 + \lambda \|\alpha_i\|_1 \qquad (5)$$

where, the vectors α_i are computed during the previous spare coding steps of the algorithm.

4   EXPERIMENTAL VALIDATION

In this section, we present experiments on natural images to demonstrate the efficiency of incremental dictionary learning and verify our method to the application of large-scale image denoising. Firstly, incremental dictionary training experiments are conducted on a standard image dataset. Secondly, we apply the proposed method to denoise a large-scale natural image with zero-mean white Gaussian noise.

4.1 Incremental training on the image patches

For our experiments, we randomly select 1×10^6 patches with size 8×8 from the standard image dataset showed as Figure 1 to construct the training dataset. These patches are equally divided into two subsets A and B. We use the two subsets to incrementally train a 64×256 dictionary and assess the representation performance.

In the following dictionary training process, we normalize the patches to have unit $\ell_2 - norm$ and $\lambda = 1.2$ in all of our experiments. We use the first part of the training set to train a dictionary. Then we use subsets B to continually train the dictionary. The learned dictionaries are showed as Figure 2. In the first training stage, the time of computation for dictionary learning is 18.467 seconds and the value of loss function of Eq. 5 is 0.2745. In the second training stage, the time of computation for dictionary learning is 19.11 seconds and the value of loss function is 0.2735.

4.2 Denoising on large-scale image

Our last experiment demonstrates that our algorithm can be used for a large-scale image denoising task from the corrupted 4-Megapixel image (2560×1600) of Figure 3. We learn an overcomplete

Figure 1.   The images used for training the dictionary.

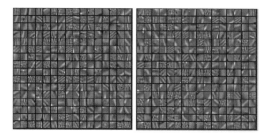

Figure 2. (Left) Learned dictionary for 8×8 image patches, trained using the first half of the training set. (Right) Learned dictionary for 8×8 image patches, continually trained using the second half of the training set.

Figure 3. Denoising task on a 4-Megapixel image. Top: Original image (left) and noisy image (right). Bottom: Wiener filter denoised image (left) and our proposed method denoised image (right).

dictionary with 1024 elements using the roughly 1×10^6 blocks with size 16×16 from the noisy image. Once the dictionary has been learned, we denoise the image using this dictionary, averaging the denoised blocks when they overlap in the result using the sparse coding technique described in section II. Here we will not widely evaluate our learning algorithm in denoising tasks, which would require a thorough comparison with other techniques on standard datasets. Instead, we just wish to demonstrate that the proposed method can indeed be applied to handle a realistic denoising task on a large-scale image. In the experiment the PSNRs of the noisy image, wiener filter denoised image and our proposed method denoised image are 22.11 db, 29.47 db and 33.67 db, respectively.

5 CONCLUSION

In this paper we introduce a novel image denoising framework based on sparse representation using incremental learning algorithm to obtain an over-complete dictionary which is adapted to large-scale training data. The experiments demonstrate that it is effective on large image denoising tasks that may involve millions of training samples. In the future work, we plan to use the proposed learning framework for image and video restoration tasks such as deblurring and inpainting, etc.

ACKNOWLEDGMENTS

This work is supported by the Fundamental Research funds for the Central Universities (Grant No. 2012YBXS10). Corresponding author is Xue-Wen Wu (Email addresses: xuewenwu@hotmail.com).

REFERENCES

Aharon, M., Elad, M. & Bruckstein, A. 2006. K-SVD: An Algorithm for Designing Overcomplete Dictionaries for Sparse Representation, IEEE Trans. on Signal Processing, 54(11), 4311–4322.

Aharon, M. & Elad, M. 2008. Sparse and redundant modeling of image content using an image-signature-dictionary, SIAM Imaging Sciences, 1, 228–247.

Bottou L. 1998. Online algorithms and stochastic approximations. In D. Saad, editor, Online Learning and Neural Networks. Cambridge University Press, Cambridge, UK.

Bottou, L. and Bousquet, O. 2007. The tradeoffs of large scale learning. In NIPS.

Bryt, O. & Elad, M. 2008. Compression of facial images using the k-svd algorithm. J. Vis. Comun. Image Represent., 19:270–282.

Chen, S.S., Donoho, D.L., & Saunders, M.A. 2001. Atomic decomposition by basis pursuit, SIAM Review, vol. 43, no. 1, pp. 129–159.

Elad, M. & Aharon, M. 2006. Image denoising via learned dictionaries and sparse representation, presented at the Int. Conf. Computer Vision and Pattern Recognition, New York, Jun. 17–22.

Engan, K., Aase, S.O. & Husøy, J.H. 1999. Frame based signal compression using method of optimal directions (MOD), IEEE Intern. Symp. Circ. Syst.

Mairal, J., Bach, F., Ponce, J. & Sapiro, G. 2010. Online learning for matrix factorization and sparse coding, Journal of Machine Learning Research, 11:19–60.

Tropp, J.A. 2004. Greed is good: Algorithmic results for sparse approximation, IEEE Trans. Inform. Theory, vol. 50, no. 10 pp. 2231–2242.

Computer, Intelligent Computing and Education Technology – Liu, Sung & Yao (Eds)
© *2014 Taylor & Francis Group, London, ISBN 978-1-138-02469-4*

Microcomputer principle and assembly language teaching

Chang-Ming Dai & Chun-Mei Du & Ting-Yu Yan
Hebei University of Architecture, Zhangjiakou, Hebei, China

ABSTRACT: This article is the author in the teaching of microcomputer principle and assembly language experience, from the status of the assembly language, the discipline of teaching content, teaching emphasis and difficulties, and other disciplines cross between knowledge points and program design and so on has carried on the detailed summary and conclusion.

Keywords: teaching; computer; assembly language; program design

1   INTRODUCTION

"Microcomputer principle and assembly language" is one of core curriculum of college computer, automatic control, microcomputer principle, single-chip computer, operating system, such as the necessary core curriculum courses. Because assembly language instructions is boring, and program requirements have been familiar with hardware, so there are some difficult, here is the microcomputer principle and the assembly language teaching in the actual situation for the purpose of this course to do the brief analysis of how to improve the teaching quality. This article mainly from the following four parts to explain microcomputer principle and the teaching method of the assembly language.

2   MASTER DISCIPLINE FOUNDATION, CLEAR THE TEACHING CONTENT

Microcomputer principle and assembly language curriculum development up to now, the research field of development and change constantly, at the same time with many courses related to discuss problems exist. To improve the quality of teaching, must first clear the primary teaching content of courses. Assembly language and high-level language does not have different portability, Z80 to 6502, and then to 8086/8088 and now Pentium how are and their supporting assembly language. Due to 8086/8088 of the typicality, so most of microcomputer principle and assembly language teaching are given priority to with 8086/8088, at the same time in the process of teaching by introducing some new high-grade machine the expansion of CPU instructions and programming methods, such as the proportion of base indexed addressing mode, and 32-bit programming, etc.

Microcomputer principle and the composition of the assembly language teaching should begin from the CPU, internal memory storage principle, and addressing mode, this paper tells several basic programming method. Focus on practice and DEBUG applications, and introduces some knowledge of the DOS operating system and operation order, causes the student to the internal information of programming and computer closely together, so as to understand the meaning of the design for the machine language. For several hexadecimal number and its transformation, the original, and the definition of complement is the totem of course content (introduction to digital logic and computer). Along with the computer hardware and peripheral equipment system program constantly update, and a computer control system, instrument and meter, and household appliances such as application development, to speed, strong function and assembly language to make thorough analysis. The practical course, to tell a large number of examples and do more practice and use the computer.

3   PAY ATTENTION TO THE EMPHASIS AND DIFFICULTY OF CLASSIFIED AND TEACHING

Assembly language teaching in the way to the way of addressing, familiar with and master all kinds of addressing mode is the foundation of all programming. Addressing mode as the name suggests is looking for ways to address of the operand, it will be divided into two classes, namely the addressing mode and related to the data related to the transfer address addressing mode. In 8086 system, for example, it is related to data addressing mode can be divided into seven kinds, namely the number immediately addressing, register addressing, direct addressing, register indirect addressing, register relative addressing, base indexed addressing, relative base indexed addressing.

3.1 By way of the 7 kinds of addressing the source operands analysis can be divided into the following three categories

1. Directly given by several immediately (immediately addressing), and other ways of addressing the difference is the operand exist with the code;
2. The operands given by register (register addressing);
3. Operands exists in memory (the rest of 5 kinds of addressing mode), its salient features are existed in the statement "[ ]".

3.2 Some kind of addressing in memory addressing is formed by the junction of two other ways of addressing

Base indexed addressing MOV AX, BX + SI] and direct addressing MOV AX, h [1000] of the combination of two addressing modes constitute a relatively indexed addressing MOV AX, [BX + SI + 1000 h], similar to this and direct addressing and indirect addressing constitute registers relative addressing.

3.3 Two pairs of similar appearance comparison and distinguish between addressing mode

The number of addressing immediately and directly address, one of the main difference is the source location is different, the former deposited in the code segment, which is stored in the data segment, the second is different appearance, with "[ ]" for the direct addressing, "[ ]" here refers to the memory.

Register addressing and register indirect addressing, the difference is similar to 1 is the location of the operands are different, register indirect addressing because there are a "[ ]" in the statement that the content of the register are as valid address appears in the memory.

Induction and summary for the above three ways of addressing learning are of great help.

4 MICROCOMPUTER PRINCIPLE AND CROSS KNOWLEDGE OF ASSEMBLY LANGUAGE AND OTHER COURSES

Microcomputer principle and many of the assembly language knowledge and other knowledge is achieve mastery through a comprehensive study of the course, many knowledge in this course are seen in other courses. As a result of these knowledge, we cannot treat as the same, should be kept separate.

The following is my summary of the main cross knowledge.

a. System and code system
   This is the first chapter of the assembly language knowledge points, the main teaching of transformation between numerical system, coding method and internal computer data format. Through the study of the syllabus found in digital logic, composition principle, single-chip computer courses such as the content, and a prior course is taught as the key in the digital logic, therefore in the process of teaching should not be as a key, as long as do the review.

b. The segment of the memory management
   The knowledge is the basis of the content behind. In the aftermath of the assembly language in the course "microcomputer principle and interface technology" will learn, therefore in the process of telling must be clear, let the students grasp the physical address, offset (effective address), segment address, the relationship between the logical address, and the calculation method of physical address.

c. Stack
   The concept has also appeared in the data structure, but in the heart of the data structure as linear table, and stack is in assembly language as part of the storage unit. Besides with linear characteristics, its storage unit, address coding principle and the method of data storage are similar to the storage unit must be "the principle of high and low", for example, the smallest unit of storage for words and so on.

d. Subroutine
   Any kind of programming language, including advanced language will be the subroutine and low-level language, subprogram is to simplify the code. With high-level language called directly, in assembly language subroutine design, need to remind the students pay attention to the protection and restoration of breakpoints and register, the parameters of the transmission.

e. The interrupt
   Strictly speaking the interrupt is one of the subprogram, is called the interrupt subroutine, interrupt is the speaker's content in the microcomputer principle and interface technology, here only teach the BIOS and DOS interrupt call methods, clear inlet parameters and export the application of the can.

5 ASSEMBLY LANGUAGE PROGRAMMING METHOD

Using assembly language program to program design is the purpose of this course of study, said in front of the assembly language is a language operate directly on the hardware, so the writing program, want to consider a lot of problems such as: (1) the distribution of memory space. (2) the procedures used in the data representation (precision), and the types of I/O devices. (3) the structure of the program to keep it simple, clear hierarchy, time, space, high efficiency to do. (4) source code readability and maintainability. Must have a lot of practice at the same time, students are required to master the DEBUG of the various commands such as: R, G, D, L, T and program debugging and operation method, otherwise will cause between theoretical knowledge and practical operation.

6 CONCLUSION

This course teaching from the view of computer hardware, emphatically taught 16-bit machine hardware programming concept. At the same time should pay attention to integrate theory with practice, pay attention to the vivid and interesting, lecture to help students understand the course, cultivate their interest in learning, improve teaching efficiency.

ACKNOWLEDGEMENT

This project won the 2013 Hebei Institute of Architecture and Civil Engineering research fund support.

Heart left thanks.

REFERENCES

Xie, X.K. 1981. *Modern control theoretical Basis.* Shenyang: Liaoning People Publisher. 53–55.

Zhao, Mingzhan. 2005. Generalized kalman filter signal modeling for airborne targets. *Aircraft Design.* 4: 77–80.

Zhao, Mingzhan. 2006. Deductive proof of generalized kalman filter recursive formula. *Journal of Shenyang Institute of Aeronautical Engineering.* 23: 82–84.

Zhao, Mmingzhan. 2005. The research of the minimum mean square error of the generalized Kalman filter. *Journal of Shenyang Institute of Aeronautical Engineering.* 22: 47–49.

Zhao, W.C. 2007. Parameter varying generalized kalman filter based on generalized linear model. *Control Engineering of China.* 14: 21–23.

Computer, Intelligent Computing and Education Technology – Liu, Sung & Yao (Eds)
© 2014 Taylor & Francis Group, London, ISBN 978-1-138-02469-4

Wind energy conversion system modeling and control study

Ting-Yu Yan, Chang-Ming Dai & Chun-Mei Du
Hebei University of Architecture, Zhangjiakou, Hebei, China

ABSTRACT: Wind power is the most development potential and current technology of clean and renewable energy. This paper is a study on modeling in various parts of wind energy conversion system foundation, through to the wind energy conversion system four parts to mathematical modeling and dynamic modeling research, consider as much as possible to meet the actual situation of the fan running, and the control and operation of wind turbines and strategy are studied.

Keywords: wind energy; conversion system; modeling; the operation and control

1 INTRODUCTION

Wind power is an involved in electrical, mechanical, computer science, meteorology and other interdisciplinary. With the rapid development of economic society, the growing demand for energy, represented by wind and renewable energy into the line of sight of people. Existing will to power is given priority to with coal power structure type diversity, energy "clean", "green". "Control" plays a very important role in modern wind farms. Wind power has a serious instability, in order to maximize reduce wind turbines power grid to the adverse impact of the power grid, reduce wind turbine aerodynamic load and mechanical load, which requires high performance, high reliability of wind power conversion and control device. And that for in order to enhance the service life of wind turbines, raise the efficiency of the wind farm has a positive role.

2 THE WIND ENERGY CONVERSION SYSTEM AND SYSTEM MODELING

The main component of wind energy conversion system for wind wheel, transmission system and power generation system. In the process of modeling, the wind energy conversion system is divided into "pneumatic subsystem", "mechanical subsystem", "electrical subsystem", "pitch servo system" four system module, as shown in Figure 1.

Figure 1. Wind energy conversion systerm.

For a wind turbine, the relationship between the wind wheel conversion system components as shown in Figure 2. For wind power generation, mechanical subsystem should be composed of a transmission part and a supporting part. While the electrical subsystem is mainly used to describe the mechanical energy into electrical energy to the core process of wind power generation.

3 WIND ENERGY CONVERSION SYSTEM MODELING

Wind energy conversion system model is actually connected, function and composition of the organic combination of mutually relying on several subsystems of the model.

3.1 Modeling the pneumatic subsystem

Pneumatic main function subsystem is the wind energy transformation acting on blades to drive the rotor rotational energy. In the real environment, there are often quick disturbance and turbulent wind speed, wind direction and the irregular change of the vertical component of recurrent and lead, it is the weather fan in the natural environment is likely to encounter. It means that we should be in when the gas dynamic system modeling need

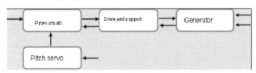

Figure 2. Speed and plasma subsystem is a wind energy conversion system.

to consider more factors, but the superposition of many conditions more complex dynamic models often do not give a relatively reliable pneumatic subsystem state description.

Among them, the pneumatic system input is the rotor speed Omega r wind V, pitch angle, rotational and axial. The output is a pneumatic torque and thrust.

$$\begin{bmatrix} F_T \\ T_R \end{bmatrix} = \begin{bmatrix} \dfrac{\rho \pi R^2}{2} C_T & \left(\dfrac{\Omega_r R}{V_e}, \beta \right) V_e^2 \\ \dfrac{\rho \pi R^3}{2} C_Q & \left(\dfrac{\Omega_r R}{V_e}, \beta \right) V_e^2 \end{bmatrix}$$

3.2 *Modeling the mechanical subsystem*

Wind turbine is a complicated mechanical structure, the main equipment of wind power generation is the wind power generator. Wind power generator consists of head, body, tail, leaves and other parts.

The mode shape of horizontal axis wind turbine, "generally include torsion shimmy, tower body bending, blade, the force disturbance" from the three-dimensional wind field. This leads to the complexity of the mechanical system model in a certain extent, also indirectly led to the relevance and complexity of mathematical model. However, we can also from the simple mathematical model, find some characteristics of wind energy conversion system dynamic mode.

4 WIND POWER SYSTEM CONTROL OBJECT AND STRATEGY

4.1 *Control object*

For wind power generation, the control is mainly in order to ensure the safe operation of the unit in the extreme weather conditions and as much as possible to achieve maximum energy conversion and utilization efficiency and ensuring the quality of electric energy to meet the requirements of the access grid. This is the local control object control of the blower to refine some interrelated, these control objects and in some cases even need according to the actual needs of the optimization of the two cases. Local control object includes the following three parts:

Energy conversion: to ensure the safe and stable operation of wind turbine case, as far as efficiency conversion increase wind amount possible, reduce energy loss.

The mechanical load: including mechanical driving part of the safety control strategy and the prevention of the whole system cannot withstand

the mechanical load and the instantaneous load, prolong the service life of the mechanical equipment of fan and reduce the failure rate.

Power control: a power control in power grid can range safety acceptance of wind power, improve power quality and stability.

4.2 *Control strategies*

The control of the wind turbine is to try to make the wind turbine power curve is close to ideal and let the wind turbines as far as possible in a variety of conditions to ensure the stability of wind turbine safety. Wind environment in general construction is in adverse natural conditions, which leads to poor environmental conditions of wind turbines, and wind, and often need to run automatically, unattended, this leads to the requirement of wind farm currently running on the relatively strict control. For the grid connected wind turbine, especially the total installed capacity of large wind farm area, due to natural conditions and similar, which leads to the universality and large-scale wind turbine emergency, so that the wind turbine can be safe and reasonable into and off the grid, is the key to wind turbine operation control.

Has great difference for the grid connected wind turbine and conventional energy power generation unit. First of all, wind speed changes with the changes in the atmosphere, and the more obvious changes. And the temperature, pressure, humidity this kind of weather condition is more random and uncontrollable, which leads to the wind in the wind turbine blade is stochastic, uncertain, not controllable. According to the theory of Bates, one of the largest wind power wind wheel with coefficient of 0.593. In order to effectively convert wind energy, and the tip speed ratio to achieve great in not, rotor wind turbine rotating speed is not very high, and the generator rotational speed difference is quite big, between the generator and wind turbine can not be directly connected, l-speed gear box must pass a certain ratio of transmission. So between the generator and the wind machine rigidity is greatly reduced. In other words, between the wind turbine and generator two system is flexible connection.

5 CONTROL THEORY IN THE APPLICATION OF WIND ENERGY CONVERSION AND CONTROL SYSTEM

Because of the difference of wind turbines and particularity, different wind energy conversion system with the design objectives and expected effect is different, which led directly to the control system in different wind energy conversion system and uniqueness. Study on control system has been the important part of wind energy conversion system. From the actual application, a wind power generation system of electric energy, if not through control and correction of wind power conversion and control system of wind power, then the initial state does not have the grid conditions, it will affect the power grid. Affect the stability of regional power network and good operation, garbage power also is often said that the Mentioned above, the highest goal of wind power conversion and control system is implemented to improve the conversion efficiency, energy and security problems and improve the power quality and enhance the wind turbine. Wind energy conversion system has very strong nonlinearities, for the different regions of the face of every field parameters are uncertain, this has intensified the difficulty of dynamic modeling of wind power. With the rapid development of information technology, power electronics technology, the Internet of things technology, how to apply advanced control method is the most appropriate, the appropriate application to the wind turbine operation, maintenance and conversion of electrical energy in the system, is the most problem.

Parameters of wind energy conversion system very much and unknowable. In this case, design a control system is simple and practical and relatively reliable is an important issue. Sliding mode variable structure control is essentially a switch type of discontinuous control, it requires control state is frequent, fast switching system. Sliding mode control structure compared to other control structures with real-time response and partial parameters on the system is insensitive, which are for the wind energy conversion system provides an effective control method.

6 CONCLUSION

This paper starts from the research on control of wind turbines, each part of the wind power system is analyzed in the paper. Research on Modeling and control strategy. Using some modern control theory to the practical application of wind energy conversion and control system are analyzed, and achieved good results.

REFERENCES

Du Chunmei, fan blade monitoring research, 2013.1 Journal of Hebei Institute of Architecture and Civil Engineering, 117–118.

Xie, X.K. 1981. *Modern control theoretical Basis.* Shenyang: Liaoning People Publisher.

Yang Junhua, modern control technology in wind energy conversion system application, 2012.4 *the solar journal,* 100–102.

Zhao, Mingzhan. 2005. Generalized kalman filter signal modeling for airborne targets. *Aircraft Design.* 4: 77–80.

Computer, Intelligent Computing and Education Technology – Liu, Sung & Yao (Eds)
© 2014 Taylor & Francis Group, London, ISBN 978-1-138-02469-4

Research on virtualization technology of IO device

Hui-Min Zhang, Hai-Rong Hu & Yang-Xia Xiang
Department of Information Engineering, Academy of Armored Force Engineering, Beijing, China

Lu-Lu Fang
Academy of Computer, Beijing University of Posts and Telecommunications, Beijing, China

ABSTRACT: The virtualization technology is continually developing; the functions of the memory virtualization and CPU virtualization also become consummate. However, the device virtualization is still the bottleneck that restricts the overall performance. In the paper, the author introduced the related technology of virtualization and analyzed the defects in the current device virtualization technology. Then the author presents an improved model of VMM. Finally, the author designs a method of device virtualization by using this model. The experimental results show that the scheme has the better performance.

Keywords: virtualization; virtualization machine; virtualization machine monitor; device virtualization

1 INTRODUCTION

Virtualization[1] is the abstraction of physical resources, i.e., the physical components run in a virtual environment. For example, it produces a plurality of logical CPU by the abstracted CPU; it generates the virtual memory by memory abstraction;[2] it provides multiple logical devices to different customers by abstracting a single device to more than one, etc. Emergence of virtualization technology greatly improves the efficiency and utilization of computer resources. But with the development of virtualization technology, the maturing in function of memory and CPU virtualization, the device virtualization is still a bottleneck in the system virtualization.[3] Therefore, to improve the efficiency and performance of device virtualization is a key issue to be solved at present. This paper proposed a method of an improved VMM-based device virtualization technology after describing the key technologies of system virtualization, and the experiments show that the schema has a high performance.

2 DEVICE VIRTUALIZATION TECHNOLOGY

Device Virtualization[4] is what simulates a limited number of physical devices into multiple logical devices for clients to use. It can be seen from the Figure 1: When a plurality of client OS running on the VMM request to access to the physical device. Due to the limited physical devices, VMM will need to use the device virtualization technology to simulate them into many logical devices. Device virtualization uses the way of Software Simulation[5] to achieve the transparent access, that is to say, user can use the devices without knowing the actual position of them and the underlying implementation technology. Device virtualization technology is mainly divided into two categories: VMware represented with direct drive and Xen represented with separate drive.

2.1 Direct Drive[6]

In this way the driver is placed in the VMM. The model of Direct Drive contains the virtual device

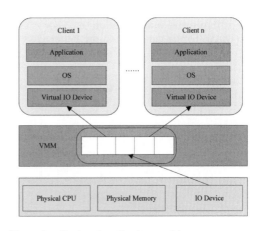

Figure 1. Device virtualization model.

layer, the client driver program, the VMM device drivers, the IO stack and the physical equipment.[7] Virtual Device simulates the physical device, the client can identify them. The IO data stack is used to deal with the data communication in the VMM layer and maps the IO devices access-address of the client OS in the VMM. Whenever a client OS requests to access to the device, it will operate the physical device via the VMM layer. Because multiple client OS need to share a physical device, only the VMM can ensure that every client can correctly access to the device. So every time the client needs to access the VMM before the physical device.

Because every time the client computer accessing to physical devices needs to use the VMM layer to achieve, if the multiple client OS simultaneously initiated the request, the efficiency will be greatly reduced, which makes the VMM become the bottleneck of System Virtualization.

2.2 Separate Driver[8]

The Separate Driver divides the traditional structure into two parts: the Front-end Driver and the Back-end Driver. The Back-end Driver is that if we properly change parts of driver in the traditional OS that we can access the device. The Front-end Driver can not directly access the device, but receives access request from the client OS. Then it will pass the request to the Back-end Driver to handle. Xen provides a different interface from the traditional ways to the client OS, the client OS needs to install the special driver program in every virtual device. The driver program will pass the IO operations of the client OS to the OS in Domain0 which is in the privileged domain. The client computer will call the appropriate physical device to complete the request after accepting the access request.

Direct Driver and Separate Driver have their own advantages and disadvantages in performance,[9] compatibility and fault isolation, etc. For example, Direct Driver can provide the better QoS in

performance; Separate Driver is easy to reuse the driver program and has the better compatibility; Separate Driver has the stronger isolation with the driver program into the Domain0.

3 AN IMPROVED MODEL OF DEVICE VIRTUALIZATION

Currently, the device virtualization solutions have one thing in common, that is, the device processing components independently exist, such as the Domain0 in Xen runs in the form of virtual machines; the Qemu in KVM[10] runs in the form of monitor process, which is Separate Driver mentioned in the previous section. Although this method enhances the stability of the system and reduces the complexity, its negative impact is obvious: VMM still need to manage some management units, which causes the loss of performance; the processing components need to be dispatched with other virtual machines at the same time, which causes the time delay; the frequent switch between VMM and the device processor also increases the losses. After descripting and analyzing the method of device virtualization, we find that any kind of models are inadequate. So in order to solve this problem, this paper proposes an improved VMM model.

3.1 The design of improved VMM model

The core idea of this solution is to transfer the processing unit in the IO device from VMM to a privileged processor which is called IO Processor Machine (IOPM). The status of the privilege processor is equal with the VMM. It can be seen from the Figure 2.

In terms of structure, this model belongs to the mode of Separate Driver. It is a new VMM structure after optimizing the Separate Driver model of Xen.[11] The improved VMM on multiprocessor platforms uses the way of hardware division to create multiple processor systems. There is some

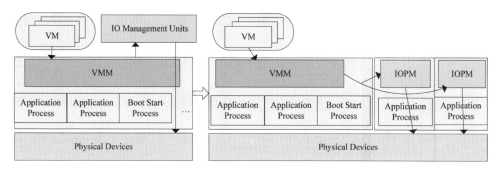

Figure 2. The improved VMM model.

relative independence between the processor systems. The device processing modules stored in the processor machine to control some parts of the hardware. Device processing module is moved from the VM to IO processor which has the privilege. Thus, it forms the coordinate and cooperative structure between the IOPM and VMM. As can be seen from Figure 3, the main control system has become the combination of VMM and IOPM from the VMM. The main function of VMM is to implement the virtualization of memory, processor, and some other device. IOPM is directly used to control the external devices and provides virtual device model to the client. Considering the stability of the system and the optimization of resources, we can add a plurality of IOPMs when it realizes and assign corresponding application processor to each IOPM. The rest of guide processor and application processor are managed by VMM.

Placing the module device processor in a separate privileged system will improve the processing efficiency of the system IO. Because the IOPM works independently, the requests of access from VMM to the device processing module in the IOPM are no longer using the traditional transfer mode of soft interrupt, but directly adopt the way of physical disruption. Even the IOPM is processing the device's request; it can always occupy the processor, which solves the problem of time delay caused by the device dispatch. Moreover, IOPM and VMM have the same privilege level, it can directly access to physical devices. So the clients do not need to switch privilege level frequently when they access to physical devices. Through the above analysis we can see that the improved VMM can effectively improve the efficiency of the physical device virtualization.

3.2 The model of device virtualization based on the improved VMM

This paper designed the model of device virtualization based on the improved VMM, shown in Figure 3.

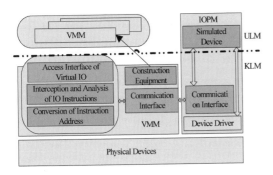

Figure 3. The model of device virtualization.

3.2.1 The functional subsystems of device virtualization

As the Figure 3, in order to complete the device virtualization and to handle the requests which the clients access better, the model of device virtualization based on the improved VMM is divided into four major functional subsystems:

Based On the Improved VMM.

1. Construction Equipment: in VMM it uses the reasonable way to make sure that client OS can "discover" the virtual IO devices. Only in this way that when the client OS starts, it can load the related device driver program according to the appropriate information, which is the prerequisite of device virtualization.

2. The Interception and Analysis of IO Instructions: this function is used to intercept the client OS's request of access to the virtual device, and analyses the request, then transfers it to the IOPM to manage. It includes intercepting the instructions of MMIO and IO port.

3. The Conversion of Instruction Address: during the procedure of dealing with the IO device's access request, the VMM address space, the client computer address space and the data sharing area of IO device are required to transfer the data and transform the address.

4. The Simulated Devices: its main role is to deal with the request passed from VMM and return the results. The process is described as follows: firstly, accepting the access request from VMM; secondly, sorting the priority of the requests according to the dispatch strategy and hand it over to the device driver to process; finally, returning the results and notifying the client.

3.2.2 The device access process

Completing the device virtualization requires the above-described four functional subsystems to cooperate with each other; the process is as the following:

1. Process Initialization: when you start the client, one of the functional subsystems—Construction Equipment constructs a virtual device to the client OS and provides the interface of device access request to the client to accept the access request coming from the client OS.

2. Intercept the IO instruction: it uses the way of limiting the IO access instructions in VMCS and the specific area of memory to intercept the instructions of IO devices access request from clients.

3. Instructions parsing: it determines the source address and destination address by parsing the instructions intercepted and converts them to access the real IO devices.

4. Send Instructions: it packages the instructions which have been parsed and sends them to the IOPM by VMM and the communication module of IOPM.
5. Complete the Access Request: after accepting the instructions of IO devices access, IOPM will access to the real device according to its operation mode and address. Finally, it will return the results.

4 PERFORMANCE TEST

Using the schema proposed in this paper to simulate the DMA can theoretically achieve higher rate of data transfer. Since a large number of disk read and write operation completed by DMA, so we can use the way of reading and writing IDE disk to test DMA.

Experiments use the standard of IOZone in the Linux OS to test the disk's IO property. In order to verify the efficiency of the proposed model, we respectively test three cases: non-virtualized environment, VMware9.0 virtualized environment and the proposed schema environment. We compare the different performance by recording the speed of data block's reading and writing in different environments. Under the three environments, IOZone gets the disk IO rate through reading and writing different size file block. The Data block size was 1 MB, 2 MB, 4 MB, 8 MB, 16 MB and 32 MB. The results shown in Figures 4 and 5: the vertical axis is

the disk transfer rate (KB/S), the horizontal axis is the data block size (MB).

Through these tests can be seen that the loss of reading and writing speed is from 15% to 20% by using the schema proposed in this paper comparing to the traditional non-virtualized environment, but its performance is better than the VMware environment. Thus it turns out that, to some extent, the schema presented in this paper can improve the efficiency of the DMA operation.

5 CONCLUSION

With the rapid development of memory and CPU virtualization, IO device virtualization becomes the bottleneck of the system virtualization. So how to improve the performance of device virtualization becomes an urgent need problem to be solved. This paper proposed an improved VMM model by describing the deficiency existed in current device virtualization technology, and finally demonstrates the superiority of this model through experiments. It builds a strong foundation for the future research of devices virtualization.

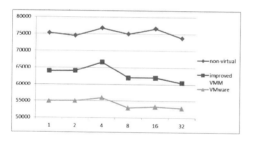

Figure 4. Performance comparison of reading.

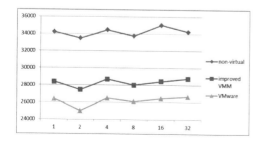

Figure 5. Performance comparison of writing.

REFERENCES

[1] Zhen Tan. 2012.1. Research on Cloud Computing Virtualization Technology. IT and Information: 54–57.
[2] Creasy, R. 2011.9. The Origin of the VM/370 Time-Sharing System. IBM Journal of Research and Development: 483–490.
[3] Jingbo Liu. 2011.4. Research on Key Technology of Device virtualization. PLA Information Engineering University for the Degree of Master of Engineering.
[4] Ole, A. & Alex, G. 2012.12. The evolution of an x86 virtual machine monitor. ACM SIGOPS Operating Systems Review 44(4):3–18.
[5] Abramson, D. & Jackson, J. 2010. Intel Virtualization Technology for Directed I/O. Intel Technology Journal 10(3).
[6] Xiaoming Guang & Jie Hu. 2012.10. The Principle and Implementation of Virtualization Technology. China: Electronic Industry Press.
[7] Qinge Ge. 2011.10. Virtualization: Technology, Applications and Challenges. Communication Technology: 91–94.
[8] Barham, P. & Dragovic, B. Xen and the Art of Virtualization. In Proceedings of the nineteenth ACM Symposium on Operating Systems Principles (SOSP19). New York: ACM: 164–177.
[9] Gangjian Li. 2011.2. Research on the Architecture of Cloud Computing Platform based on Virtualization Technology. Journal of Jilin Institute of Architectural Engineering: 79–81.
[10] Xinmei Huang. 2008.5. Research on Device Virtualization Technology on X86 platform—design, improvement and application. University of Electronic Science and Technology for the Degree of Master of Engineering.

Computer, Intelligent Computing and Education Technology – Liu, Sung & Yao (Eds)
© *2014 Taylor & Francis Group, London, ISBN 978-1-138-02469-4*

Heuristic virtual experimental teaching for computational thinking

Y.F. Chen, H.J. Chang & F.X. Li
School of Computer Science, Beijing Institute of Technology, Haidian, Beijing, China

ABSTRACT: The purpose of heuristic virtual experimental teaching for computational thinking is to visualize the computer world, make abstract theories concrete, inspire students to summarize regulations or propose methods in the exploration, and then use computational thinking to solve problems. This research choose the computer network teaching as an example to conduct explorations of virtual experiment in the portion of virtual teaching experiment platform network, and have obtained good results in actual college computer basic teaching.

Keywords: computational thinking; heuristic; experimental teaching

1 INTRODUCTION

In recent years, with the proposing and rising of computational thinking [1], many universities are beginning to re-examine and study new opportunities and challenges of computer teaching [2], Chinese academician Guoliang Chen et al advocate a teaching reform which focus on the cultivation of the computational thinking. Some scholars, including Peizeng Gong etc., overall design the reform from many perspectives, like the set of course content, the analysis of teaching status, the reform of program and so on, and have published some relevant books that have been used in teaching practice. Another part of this exploration is cultivating students' computational thinking through changing the teaching forms, strengthening the combination of theory with practice in the existing education.

It is a question worth exploring that how to better conduct the cultivation of computational thinking. Computational thinking is neither a form of teaching, nor a knowledge of the contents, but an ability and quality, so it can be obtained by students though active thinking and learning. It's easy for us to teach students how to use computer and demand students to remember and understand some basic knowledge, but we cannot teach the ability of computational thinking, so the more important function of college computer education is to provide students such an environment, which can guide students to thinking and obtain the ability of computational thinking actively.

2 CURRENT STATUS ANALYSIS

The core of computational thinking is structure, however, we usually just tell students the results of structure and rarely consider how to enable students to learn to construct by themselves as important. Here we choose web-based teaching as an example to analyze the traditional process of web-based teaching and discuss the existing typical problems.

2.1 *Modularity of content classification*

According the tradition of teaching, computer basic textbook usually divide the knowledge that network technology is involved into a number of basic modules according to the correlation, includes communication foundation, network architecture, network protocols, network security and so on, and then subdivided into some submodules, includes transmission media, network devices, and other traditional services and so on. This teaching method also have advantages, it is systematic and can introduce the knowledge of network foundation to students in an organized way completely and comprehensively.

However it is difficult to let the students agree with this teaching process, and it is also contrary to human cognitive processes. For students, they would prefer to be able to understand the basic principles of operation of the network and guide their own exploration in the network through this understanding, and lay the foundation for future work and life, but not just to remember a list of exhaustive and organized knowledge, this makes them either take scripted operations or do not know how to start to solve when they face real problems.

From the effects of practice teaching, some students reflect that they have some understanding in most knowledge they have learnt already and cannot learn any useful new knowledge. The others stress that even if there is some new knowledge, we also cannot come into contact with that in future, so they have no interest in learning that separately, on the other hand, the basic problems about network applications that they real care have not been resolved, such as: Why my computer network speed is slow, and how can I ensure the security of my important files.

2.2 *Passivity of knowledge transfer*

The development of computer basic knowledge has experienced a very long period, from the computer point to point communications at the beginning to now the ubiquitous network, it has experienced a sixty years history. At the same time, relevant knowledge is constantly expanding and improving, the improvement of each knowledge point have experienced large amounts of researches and practices of many Researchers and engineers in order to be finalized, and knowledge points are still constantly evolving.

In the traditional teaching process, the complex network evolution is presented to students in the form of static "snapshot" of the latest technologies without any thinking of the evolution history, after been formalized, these static "snapshot" have been taught to students, what student need to do is just receive the knowledge passively without any independent thinking and understanding. On the one hand these knowledge may have been or will soon be obsolete, that makes the knowledge transfer process meaningless; the other hand, that hinder the cultivation of students' ability of independent learning and exploration capabilities, so that student don't have the ability to automatically update and expansion for the knowledge that they have learnt, because of the rapid development speed of the computer field, knowledge we have learnt just now may be out date already before we graduate, so it's not surprised that many students' evaluation of computer basic courses always tend to "useless".

2.3 *Applications have become apparent*

In fact, learning computer basic knowledge from the perspective of application has been one of the issues considered by the computer basic teaching, from the earliest basic ability to use computer to the Learn and use of Office software, both of them have reflected the request. But the request of development tendency of computer applications cannot be satisfied if we just position college computer basic teaching on these applications. Therefore, another discuss about teaching of applying their knowledge is also be synchronized, but this application is still stay on the level of solving common problems, such as how to configure the computer

network parameters, how to configure the firewall machine, and then gives step-by-step instructions, and ultimately achieve the purpose of successful applications.

But this exploration still stay in this stage that just make a simple application of basic knowledge, those applications are programmed to a series of basic operating procedures, that makes students become a machine completing this process operation, but not the master of programs that possess computational thinking. Although students showed a positive attitude for such applications teaching method, and obtain some good teaching results, achievements that this applications teaching method can make are very limited, which can be used to solve numerous problems that the computer world is facing now and the professional problems that students will face in the future.

3 HEURISTIC VIRTUAL EXPERIMENTAL TEACHING

In view of the present problems of computer basic education, we take the basic knowledge of computer network as an example and design the heuristic teaching method based on computational thinking, we carry out the reform in the following aspects.

3.1 *The continuity of the content*

The essence of computer network is to realize the inter connection of computers, so the core of this part is to tell students how communicate between computers. One of the most common communication methods between computers is e-mail, so we design the analysis of network communication process based on e-mail delivery process, in the process of the analysis, the knowledge of all aspects of the wide area network communication is involved basically, in order to inspire students' thinking, we are equipped with a virtual experiment for this part, the experiment is designed as follows.

The experiment simulate the process of sending e-mail from the computer to the mail server, which involves two parts, the first is to obtain corresponding IP address of the mail server domain form DNS server, and then send the e-mail to the server through the method using IP routing. The coverage of knowledge includes: domain name, IP address and subnet mask, e-mail service system, point-to-point communication, network adapter and data link layer, end-to-end communication, router and network layer and so on. Experiment is designed not to emphasize a certain knowledge point, but from a system perspective, to let the students understand how the network works and know the roles each part plays.

In this way, we can cascade the main knowledge of computer network foundation in the typical background of applications, not only can students understand the relevant knowledge points in the study process, but can know the function and significance of the giving knowledge point in the network, and promote students' application ability of this knowledge.

3.2 *The heuristic of knowledge learning*

On the basis of sorting out the learning content effectively, it is the crucial problem of computer basic teaching that how to guide students to learn autonomously and inspire students to promote their abilities of computational thinking. The acquisition of basic knowledge of computer is a continuously evolving process rather than being accomplished overnight. Therefore, from this perspective, what basic knowledge of computer should introduce is not the latest achievements, but the critical evolution process, and reappear the process through guiding students to think actively. This plays an important role in having thorough understanding of the problem and cultivating the ability of computational thinking of the problem.

In order to inspire the students' thinking, we designed a small virtual experiment of local area network system, which simulate the process of communication between two computers (see Fig. 1). And we try to guide students to think through the following questions:

- How to ensure the independence between different communications.
- How to know who is who is the sender, who is he receiver.
- How to know the e-mail is sent to a local computer or a remote computer.

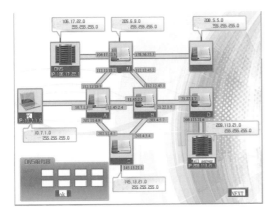

Figure 1. Virtual experiment of e-mail sending and network transmission.

Then we organize students to discuss these questions, at the same time, introduce following relevant knowledge points and make them understand the basic principles of them through the way of guidance:

- The principle of Ethernet communication using carrier sense multiple access/collision detect (CSMA/CD) protocol.
- The encapsulation format of information based on message.
- IP address and subnet mask

Students can think about or even summarize the basic characteristics of LAN communications by their own understanding by means of the virtual simulation of experiment described above.

3.3 *Expansion of applications based on understanding*

Through the cultivation of computational thinking in the virtual experiment, students further deepen the comprehension and memory of the knowledge, what's more, we have developed students' ability of computational thinking by means of this heuristic experiment method. We obtain the expected effect that not just giving a fish, but teaching to fish, and equip students with the abilities of flexible development in the fast developing information world in the future.

We carry out some in-depth expansion discussion of applications in the questions of virtual experiment class. For example, still with computer network speed, such common problem as the background, we simulate the scene of network worm attacks using virtual experiment to help students to understand the shared resources of the network, students could have a further understanding of network worm virus and key points of the guard, or even they can get to the bottom of this and obtain the answers of a series of questions: how to find the machine with a virus? How to improve the efficiency of network and reduce the influence of bottleneck of resource sharing?

4 THE ANALYSIS OF THE EXPERIMENT EFFECT

This semester we introduced the virtual experiment as an auxiliary teaching way in college computer foundation course, and launch an anonymous questionnaire investigation in eight natural classes of two majors, more than 200 students took part in the investigation and took back 162 effective questionnaires.

According to the survey results, we found that now students think the proportion of them who use computer is very high (see Fig. 2), but the degree of mastery of computer basic knowledge is relatively low (see Fig. 3), so it is necessary to learn computer basic knowledge.

However, when we analyzed the teaching content we found that, students do not like these knowledge teaching methods of pure theory, and are more willing to use applied or experimental way to learn (see Fig. 4). After completing the virtual experiment teaching most students think that heuristic virtual experiment teaching has played a good role (see Fig. 5).

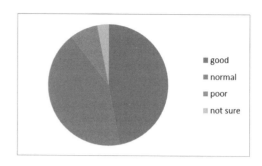

Figure 5.   Survey results of virtual experiment effect.

5   SUMMARY

After the analysis and practice above we found that the heuristic virtual experimental teaching method based on understanding is favored by students, the guidance based on applications not only solve the problems of computer basic knowledge teaching and the cultivation of abilities of computer application, more important is through cultivating students' abilities of computational thinking make them can think independently and offers a solid foundation for solving the more complex problems that they meet in work and life.

This work is supported by Doctoral Program of Higher Specialized Research Fund of China. (Grant No. 20101101120024).

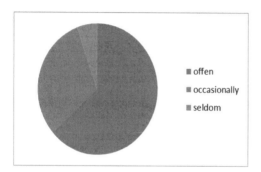

Figure 2.   Survey results of computer using frequency.

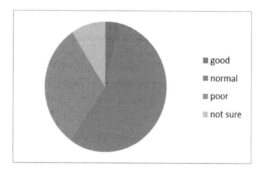

Figure 3.   Survey results of computer science basis.

REFERENCES

[1] Jeannette M. Wing. 2007. Computational Thinking. *Communications of the CCF* 3(11): 83–85.
[2] Qinming He, Hanquan Lu & Boqin Feng. 2010. The core task of computer basic teaching is to calculate the ability of cultivation of thinking—<A joint statement of computer basis teaching development strategy of C9 League > unscramble [J]. *China University Teaching* 65(1): 13–16.
[3] Guoliang Chen & Rongsheng Dong. 2011. Computational thinking and university computer basic education [J]. *China University Teaching* (1): 7–11.
[4] Minghua Zhu, Mingwei Zhao, Jing Zhao & Hongfei Lin. 2012. The discussion of cultivation of computational thinking in computer basic teaching. *China University Teaching* (3): 33–35.
[5] Peizeng Gong & Zhiqiang Yang. 2012. The cultivation of computational thinking in computer basic teaching [J]. *China University Teaching* (5): 51–54.
[6] Xiaohong Yuan, Percy Vega, Yaseen Qadah, Ricky Archer, Huiming Yu & Jinsheng Xu 2010. Visualization Tools for Teaching Computer Security [J]. *ACM Transactions on Computing Education* 9(4): 1–28.

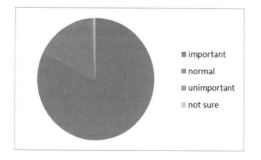

Figure 4.   Survey results of virtual experiment importance.

Computer, Intelligent Computing and Education Technology – Liu, Sung & Yao (Eds)
© 2014 Taylor & Francis Group, London, ISBN 978-1-138-02469-4

The design and implementation of cloud data computing and storage platform

Shi-Qing Tang, Yun-Long Li & Hai-Rong Hu
Academy of Armored Forces Engineering, Beijing, China

ABSTRACT: The cost of the traditional calculation and storage is very high, and the parallel programming is very difficult to be programmed. To solve the question, after telling about the core technologies of Hadoop, this paper uses the distributed technology and virtual technology to build a computing and storage platform of cloud data. Finally, the experimental result shows that, the platform has the high performance, meanwhile, the coefficient of physical resource utilization has been improved comparing to the traditional computing way of single computer and multi-node physical computers.

Keywords: Hadoop; cloud computing; cloud storage; virtual technology

1 INTRODUCTION

With the development of Internet technology, Digital information is exponentially increasing. According to the report of Digital Universe issued by Internet Data Center, the amount of data will reach 40 ZB during the next eight years equivalent to 5200 G data by each produced[9]. How to efficiently calculate and store the vast amount of data is becoming a challenge that the Internet enterprise will face. Most of the traditional mass data processing use parallel computing, grid computing, distributed high performance computing, etc. It will consume expensive storage and computing resources. And the effective allocation and reasonable segmentation for large-scale data computing tasks need complex programming to realize[2]. The emergence of the distributed cloud platform based on Hadoop becomes the good ways to solve these problems. After telling about the core technologies of Hadoop: HDFS and MapReduce, this paper uses the VMware to build an efficient, extend easily cloud computing and storage platform based on the Hadoop distributed technology, and through the experiment verifies the advantage of distributed computation and storage.

2 HADOOP AND RELATED TECHNOLOGY TYPE AREA

Hadoop[5] is the product of the development of parallel technology, distributed technology and grid computing technology. It is a kind of developed model framework in order to adapt to mass data computing and storage. Being a framework platform of distributed computing and storage under Apache company, Hadoop can efficiently store mass data and write distributed applications to analyze mass data. Hadoop can run in a lot of cheap hardware devices clusters and provide reliable and stable interface to build high scalability and high reliable distributed systems to the applications. Hadoop has some advantages of low cost, high reliability, high fault tolerance, strong expansibility, high efficiency, strong portability, free and open source[6].

Hadoop cluster is typical Master/Slaves structure. Cloud computing and storage framework model based on Hadoop is shown in Figure 1.

2.1 *Distributed file system—HDFS*

HDFS[7] is a distributed file system, which runs on a large number of cheap hardware. It is the underlying file storage system of Hadoop platform, mainly responsible for data management

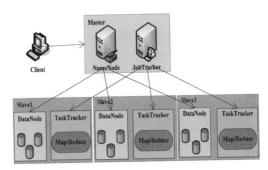

Figure 1. Cloud computing and storage framework model based on Hadoop.

and storage and with good performance for the data access of large files. HDFS is similar to the traditional distributed file system, but there are also some differences. It has the characteristics of hardware failure, large data sets, simple consistency, data streaming access, convenience of mobile computing, etc[4]. The work process and structure of HDFS was shown in Figure 2.

A HDFS cluster has a NameNode and multiple DataNode. As it is shown in the above, the NameNode is a central server, which is used to manage metadata information in the file system and client read and write access to a file. It maintains file system tree and all files and directories under its child nodes. The information is stored on disk in the shape of Editlog and FsImage. The NameNode also temporarily record the DataNode information where each Block is located. Its main functions are: management of metadata and file, simplify the metadata update operation, monitor and handle the request[8].

A node usually has one DataNode in the cluster. The DataNode is used to store and retrieve data blocks, respond the command of NameNode to create, copy, delete the data block, and regularly send "heartbeat" to NameNode. It reports its own load to NameNode through the heartbeat information. At the same time through the heartbeat information, it accepts the instructions of NameNode; The NameNode determines whether the DataNode fails through "heartbeat" information. It regularly pings each DataNode, if within the prescribed time did not receive feedback of DataNode that this node fails, then load adjustment to the whole system. In HDFS, each file is divided into one or more blocks that stored separately in different DataNode, and among DataNode copy each other data blocks to form a multiple backups.

2.2 Map/Reduce programming framework

Map/Reduce[3] is used as a simple and easy programming framework by Hadoop which handle

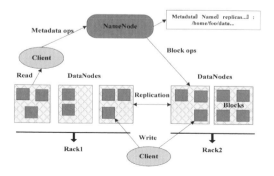

Figure 2. The work process and structure of HDFS.

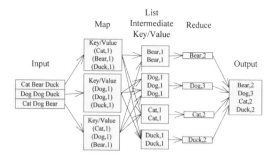

Figure 3. Calculation process diagram of MapReduce.

mass data in the cloud computing. Programmers can write program to handle mass data without the need to understand the underlying implementation details. Using Map/Reduce technology can carry out tasks in the thousands of servers at the same time in advertising business and network search, and can easily deal with data at different levels, such as TB, PB, and even EB levels.

Map/Reduce framework is composed of the JobTracker and TaskTracker. JobTracker has only one, which is the master node, responsible for task allocation and scheduling, manages a few TaskTracker. TaskTracker has one in every node, which is used to accept and handle tasks from JobTracker.

MapReduce conducted distributed computing for a cluster of large data sets, its entire framework composed of Map and Reduce functions. Map first, then perform the Reduce when dealing with data. The concrete implementation process is shown in Figure 3. It divides input data before performing the map function. Then different fragment is assigned to different map. The map function output in the form of <key, value> after processed. Before entering the reduce phase, the map function first divides original <key, value> into intermediate key/value pairs, and then sent to a reducer for processing; Finally reduce function merge the same key value, and output the results to the disk.

3 CLOUD COMPUTING AND STORAGE PLATFORM DESIGN BASED ON HADOOP

At present, extensive use of multi-core computer in the building Hadoop cluster system, multiple tasks to each DataNode node will have competition for resources. For example, memory, CPU, input and output bandwidth, etc. This will lead to resources that not used at one time idle, resulting in some waste of resources and the extension of response time. Increases in resource costs will eventually

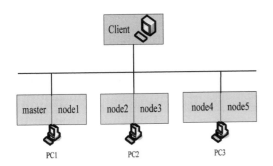

Figure 4. A model based on combining VMware virtual machine and Hadoop.

Table 1. The hardware and software configuration information.

Hardware	Processor: Intel Core i5 CPU: 2.4 GHz Memory: 4 G
Software	OS: Red Hat Linux OS5.0 JDK version: jdk_1.6 Hadoop version: hadoop-1.0.3

Table 2. Hadoop cluster configuration information.

Host name	IP	Function	Memory	Disk
Master	192.168.1.100	NameNode, JobTracker	1G	20 G
Node1	192.168.1.101	DataNode, TaskTracker	1G	20 G
Node2	192.168.1.102	DataNode, TaskTracker	1G	20 G
Node3	192.168.1.103	DataNode, TaskTracker	1G	20 G
Node4	192.168.1.104	DataNode, TaskTracker	1G	20 G
Node5	192.168.1.105	DataNode, TaskTracker	1G	20 G

lead to a drop in performance of the system. To solve this problem, we put forward a kind of cluster environment model based on combining VMware virtual machine and Hadoop, as shown in Figure 4, Namely in a computer set up more than one virtual operating system[1]. This approach has the advantage that can increase the DataNode and TaskTracker node, and can make full use of physical resources, improve the efficiency of computation and storage.

4 THE EXPERIMENT PLATFORM BUILDING

4.1 Hardware environment configuration

Prepare three dual-core computers and install two VMware virtual machine softwares, in a virtual machine install the Linux OS, which will be three computers expanded into six computers, three computers with the same configuration, specific configuration as shown in Table 1.

Hadoop cluster include one NameNode server and five DataNode servers, configuration information as shown in Table 2.

4.2 Build of Hadoop environment

Hadoop environment to build process: configuration of the cluster hosts list, install the JAVA JDK system software, configure the environment variables, generating landing key, to create the user accounts and Hadoop deployment directory and data directory, configuration of the hadoop-env.sh environment variable, core-site.xml, hdfs-site.xml, mapred-site.xml.

Format files after configured, command as follows: /opt/modules/hadoop/hadoop-1.0.3/bin/ hadoop namenode—format. And then start all nodes, input command: start—all. Sh. Whether the cluster deployment is successful or not can be seen through the interface. First check if the NameNode

and DataNode node is normal, open the browser input URL: http://master:50070. If the number of Live Nodes is six, then all nodes start successfully. Then check the JobTracker and TaskTracker node, input the URL: http://master:50030. If there are six Nodes, then nodes start successfully.

5 THE EXPERIMENT CONTENT AND THE ANALYSIS OF THE RESULTS

In the deployed cloud computing and data storage platforms based on Hadoop, advantages of the method based on distributed data computing and storage in data computing and storage is proved through the experiment.

1. Experiment 1: running Monte Carlo's program base on Hadoop to compute PI, validate distributed cloud computing efficiency. Computing task is set to 10. Calculated amount is 3, 4, 5, and 6 of 10 square.

   Environment 1: single-machine running;
   Environment 2: running in the cluster system build by three physical machines;
   Environment 3: running in the cluster system build by six virtual machines. Cluster environment running log as shown in Figure 5.

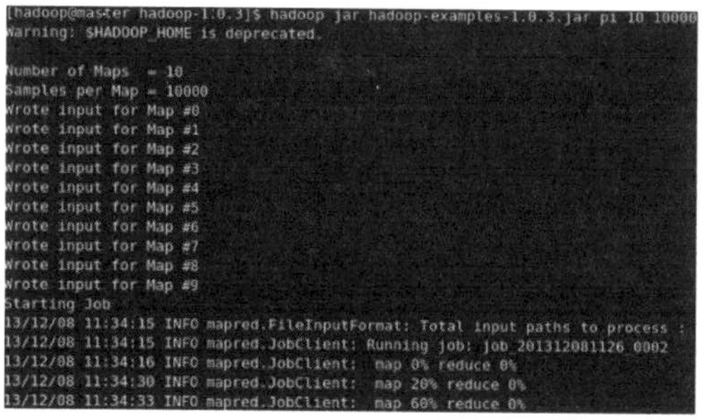

[hadoop@master hadoop-1.0.3]$ hadoop jar hadoop-examples-1.0.3.jar pi 10 10000
Warning: $HADOOP_HOME is deprecated.

Number of Maps = 10
Samples per Map = 10000
Wrote input for Map #0
Wrote input for Map #1
Wrote input for Map #2
Wrote input for Map #3
Wrote input for Map #4
Wrote input for Map #5
Wrote input for Map #6
Wrote input for Map #7
Wrote input for Map #8
Wrote input for Map #9
Starting Job
13/12/08 11:34:15 INFO mapred.FileInputFormat: Total input paths to process :
13/12/08 11:34:15 INFO mapred.JobClient: Running job: job_201312081126_0002
13/12/08 11:34:16 INFO mapred.JobClient: map 0% reduce 0%
13/12/08 11:34:30 INFO mapred.JobClient: map 20% reduce 0%
13/12/08 11:34:33 INFO mapred.JobClient: map 60% reduce 0%

Figure 5. Running log of Monte Carlo's program to compute PI.

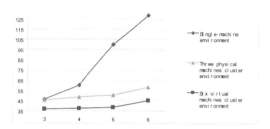

Figure 6. Performance comparison of Monte Carlo's program running in three kinds of environments.

[hadoop@master hadoop-1.0.3]$ hadoop jar wordcounter.jar com.hadoop.mapredu
anyword.txt /user/hadoop/output20131208
Warning: $HADOOP_HOME is deprecated.

13/12/08 19:11:55 INFO input.FileInputFormat: Total input paths to process :
13/12/08 19:11:55 INFO mapred.JobClient: Running job: job_201312081908_0005
13/12/08 19:11:56 INFO mapred.JobClient: map 0% reduce 0%
13/12/08 19:19:09 INFO mapred.JobClient: map 100% reduce 0%
13/12/08 19:28:21 INFO mapred.JobClient: map 100% reduce 100%
13/12/08 19:28:26 INFO mapred.JobClient: Job complete: job_201312081908_0005

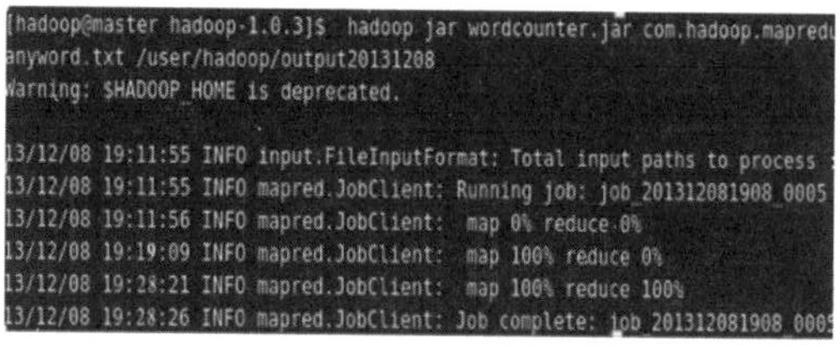

Figure 7. Running log of the characters statistical program.

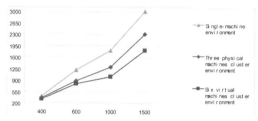

Figure 8. Performance comparison of the characters statistical program in three kinds of environments.

Each group of experiment is run for 5 times to compute the average needed time. The computing results of execution time are shown in Figure 6. Longitudinal axis is time/s. Horizontal axis is calculation/power. We can see from the figure that the operation time in the single-machine environment is far greater than that in the distributed system. And the more nodes in cluster, the faster of computing speed.

2. Experiment 2: by running the characters statistical program (wordcounter.jar), test reading and writing efficiency based on Hadoop distributed cloud to verify the storage performance of data. There are 4 sets of data, whose capacity are respectively 400 MB, 600 MB, 1 GB and 1.5 GB.

The Hadoop block size set up in this experiment is 16 M (default is 64 M). Redundancy backup parameter is set to 3 (the default). Experimental environment is the same as experiment 1. The program runs 5 times. Record the time, and calculate the average. Running log is shown in Figure 7.

Results are shown in Figure 8. Longitudinal axis is the execution time/s. Horizontal axis is the amount of data/MB. We can see from the figure that data reading and writing speed in the single-machine environment is obviously lower than in the distributed environment. And reading and writing speed faster the more nodes.

As you can see, compared with the traditional data calculation and read/write mode, in this paper, cloud computing and storage platform, built in a virtualized environment based on the Hadoop distributed technology, can effectively improve the speed and efficiency of mass data analysis and read/write. Compared with the physical machine cluster, the cluster which is built taking advantage of virtualization technology is more efficient and faster. Thus the resources utilization is improved greatly.

6 CONCLUSION

In this paper we research on the Hadoop distributed file system HDFS and MapReduce programming framework. We use the VMware virtual machines to set up cloud data computing and storage platform based on Hadoop. And compared with traditional data processing method, the characteristics of efficient and fast and is proved through experiments. It satisfies the relevant requirements in the field of cloud computing. And by applying virtualization technology to expand the node number, not only the operation efficiency but also the utilization of hardware resources can be improved. It lays the foundation for the future research direction of cloud computing.

REFERENCES

[1] Clark C, Fraser K, Hansen JG, Jul E, Pratt I, Warfield A. Live migration of virtual machines[C]. Proc. Of the 2nd Symp. on Networked Systems Design and Implementation. Berkeley: USENIX Association, 2005, P273–286.

[2] Cui Jie, Li Taoshen, and Lan Hongxing. Design and Development of the Mass Data Storage Platform Based on Hadoop [J]. Journal of Computer Research and Development. 2012(49):12–18.

[3] Gao Jichao. Research on storage strategies and optimization Hadoop platform [D]. Beijing: Beijing Jiaotong University. 2012.6.

[4] Huang Xiaoyun. Research of cloud storage service system based on HDFS [D]. Dalian: Dalian Maritime University. 2010.6.

[5] Konstantin Shvachko, Hairong Kuang, Sanjay Radia, Robert Chansler. The Hadoop Distributed File System. Sunnyvale, California USA, IEEE 2010:1–10.

[6] Taylor R C. An overview of the Hadoop/MapReduce/ HBase framework and its current applications in bioinformatics [C]//BMC Bioinformatics. Washington: BMC Bioinformatics, 2010.

[7] Wang Hongyu. An application of Hadoop platform in cloud computing [J]. Software. 2011, 32(4):36–39.

[8] Wang Yongzhou. Research of Storage Technology Based on HDFS [D]. Nanjing: Nanjing University of Posts and Telecommunications. 2013.2.

[9] Zhang Bo. Research and Optimizing of DataStorage under HDFS [D]. Guangzhou:Guangdong University of Technology. 2013.5.

Computer, Intelligent Computing and Education Technology – Liu, Sung & Yao (Eds)
© 2014 Taylor & Francis Group, London, ISBN 978-1-138-02469-4

Research on modernization construction of troops network thought political education

W.L. Yu

The Campaign and Command Department, Air Force Aviation University, Changchun, Jilin, China

ABSTRACT: Along with development of information network modernization, make use of the network open exhibition troops thought political education work to become brand-new topic to put in front of the whole army thought political education. This article analysis content and characteristics of network thought political education, elaborated the necessity of construction modernization troops network thought political education, basis on problems to put forward valid of solution. It has certain of meaning.

Keywords: troops; network construction; thought political education; information safety

Along with the arrival in network ages, thought political education the mode also face rigorous of challenge. Network thought political education is orientation modernization construction of performance, it have to differ from tradition thought political education of the characteristics is a calculator network technique and thought political education of combine, is thought political education of a kind of modern way. Its ability break time, space and region of restriction, pair of political education of work scope extension arrive conjecture space, control soldiers of thought dynamic state, educate soldiers, make them have firmness of political conviction, classic morals thoughts and feelings, good of mental state character so, troops thought political work have to keep up with a network technique development of step, accommodate new military revolution of request, speed realization thought political work of the network turn.

1 CONTENT AND CHARACTERISTICS OF NETWORK THOUGHT POLITICAL EDUCATION

1.1 *Content*

Network thought political education is catch hold of network essence, aim at network to influence manners education. Network thought political education is new form of thought political education work, and an importance aspect of research thought political education work development.

1.2 *Characteristics*

1. Strong conjecture
   With tradition of thought political education compare, network thought political education of

movable space, corpus and environment all have conjecture. Tradition of thought political education is according to superior unify constitution of education contents from education and drive education pass a certain fix way to open an exhibition in certainly of time and space. Movable space of Network thought political education is an Internet, the form be varied and have vivid. Environment of Network thought political education abundant tradition of thought political education to teach person's environment.

2. Strong technique
   The Internet is a network which deliver an information, not only technique support that need to be been certain, and demand pass change interpersonal information dissemination and interaction way to continuously promote mankind of progress and development. Network thought political education of lie a body is thought political education website, it inevitable meeting along with progress of mankind society technique to continuously development.

3. Strong concealment
   The purpose of Network thought political education has concealment to compare with tradition of thought political education. Thought political education is activity which has stronger purpose and fulfillment. Network thought political education is influenced by network environment complexity, its purpose have certain of concealment.

2 THE NECESSITY OF CONSTRUCTION MODERNIZATION TROOPS NETWORK THOUGHT POLITICAL EDUCATION

The calculator network and thought the political education combine together, make modern thought the political education acquire unprecedented advantage: The information have great capacity and easy to investigate and analytical; Share information, be advantageous to collecting in time with quick dissemination; The information communicate equal, free, overall, be good for carrying on the ego education; Each realm, each layer thought the political educate mutual contact and communication, contribute to carrying on the system integration research, become education to cooperate etc.

2.1 The contents and form of network thought political educational take place variety

First, because network have the super information, can make the education contents become abundant, and have objectivity with selectivity.

Second, the form of network thought the political educational is more novel, the multi-media technical application makes the political educational appearance turn an alignment from the flat surface stereoscopic turn, change into a dynamic state from the static state, incline to a super time-space from the realistic time space.

Third, the carrie of thought political education have a big variety, its political sex essence is implicit in the cultural knowledge and science and technology information.

The topic of the melody, patriotism of the socialism lord is these political contents, it can be exhibited by the modern technique.

2.2 The change of network thought political education method

Traditional thought political education the method regard "infusion" as principle, but the network thought political educational method is lead and illumination, it can provide an information toward the soldier and guide a right choice of information by the available means of the multi-media calculator. Closely-related study from the government troops, work, live to correspond, To establish net top information resources treasure-house from soldiers study work and live. So, we can make use of this high technology of network to designing an education a contents with meticulous care for thought the political work to combine with network to develop valid path.

The troops network thought political educating modern construction is a change that has aggressive meaning, resolving the great problem in the traditional thought education, thoughting a political worker and being educate of can carry on a net up the equal exchanges. Network thought political education the construction broke to thought political educational traditional mode, founding to thought political educational modern way, strengthenning the ages feeling of the political work, strengthenning to pertinence and go-aheadism, attaining to promote the troops construction and raising the troops purpose of battle effectiveness.

3 THE PRINCIPLE THAT THE EDUCATION OF CONSTRUCT THE MODERN TROOPS NETWORK THOUGHT POLITICAL SHOULD FOLLOW

The troops network thought political education construction should with right of the principle and policy for guide. CCP centrality committee <<Concerning some opinions that strengthen to thought political work with improvement>> clarify the policy and principle of thought political educational, the troops network thought political education construction had to be followed strictly.

The first, have to insist with the mark think the Leninism, the thought of MaZedong and Deng Xiaoping's theories for guide, persistence the basic route and basic policy of the party. With the theories of science armed person, with right public opinion leading person, mold a person by classic spirit, grow "four have" a talented person.

The second, have to insist to take economic construction as center, effort is economic the construction serve, paying attention to the coordination benefits relation within network.

The third, have to insist from set out physically, the layer of the attention soldier thought, put advanced request and abroad request together, buildup pertinency and actual effect.

The fourth, have to insist the education and management combine together, building up in time, the network manage of the law laws and system, strengthen the management to the network and the information resources by law.

The fifth, have to insist the leadership of the party, manoeuvre social everyone's enthusiasm by party leading. Become a job to grasp definitely and together total tube, overlay the network of the whole army brigade thought political education work mechanism.

4 THE PROBLEM OF CONSTRUCTING THE MODERN TROOPS NETWORK THOUGHT POLITICAL EDUCATION FOR RESOLVE

The troops network thought political education construction is a huge system engineering, it since need a right value of idea instruction and leadership, need the manpower, material resources and the match of the financial power again.

4.1 To reinforce the new research of the troops network thought political education

We should develop the leading of the network, communicate, serve and manage function actively in the troops network thought political education work, create terrace of the troops network thought political education for soldiers. According to the army camp characteristics construct thought, education, amusement and alternation to integer, made it have characteristic reticulation, to allure soldiers by bright viewpoint and abundant information resource.

Setup item of new format, develop module of ingenious design, create an exquisite article of army camp. For example, establish item of "troops star" on the website, lay out some achievement of elite brilliant scholar, model person, to influence soldiers, develop thought morals cultivated manners of soldiers, set up study for model. Or establishment forum, exert communicate function of leaders and multitudes, this can provide a basis decision, and manoeuvre soldiers enthusiasm. Strengthen consciousness and democracy consciousness of soldiers.

4.2 To reinforce the step up the development virtual politics work troops of politics qualified and high technique

The virtual politics work troops carries mission of the hardware maintenance of the whole system, management and serve for soldiers. We have to the enlargement training strength for establish the online advantage of troops thought work. To develop the virtual politics work troops have a ability of practice experience and innovation. Should to relieve thought, aggressive innovation use person's mechanism, absorb talented person, select excellent person to add importance post, and continuously enhance work troops.

4.3 To establish the efficiently and safely troops thought political education network system

The troops thought political work the safety of the network system is a very important problem, first to ensure the safety of the network system; second, to ensure the safety of the network information resources.

Want to carry out efficiently, perfect network system should establish a safety technique system. This system should adopt forerunner, mature of network technique, have a control interview,

protection data, keep secret correspondence, backup safety, prevention and cure virus, supervision system and report to the police function. Establish correspond of network safety management way, establish accommodation of network safety management system, resolute completely various the occurrence which disobey the rules, enhance the whole network safety. Nation and troops should to draw up strict law system, ensure network thought political work information safety. Or so basis on develop of situation, can draw lessons from abroad lawmaking experience and combine with our army actual of thought political work, establish a safety of network system.

4.4 To reinforce the research of the system safety and keeps secret of the network thought political education

There is no safety of troops network system, have no safety of military, also have no safety of nation. With development of information technique, The troops have to establish a higher safe work. Because of no a network system is an absolute safety, we have to follow close behind the step in ages, continuously perfect, step up a new technique to ensure network information safety, exaltation guard against with examination ability.

First, the troops should value and strengthen the information safety to keep secret the technique work highly, and bring it into science and technology strong soldier development programming. Second, study to draw lessons from technical successful experience of other troops development network information safety, method adopted independence to develop development and cooperation to develop a development to combine together, speed the information safety to keep secret a lately technical application. Third, should study the safe production by oneself. Fourth, should build up and strengthen profession to turn as soon as possible of the national information safety keep secret science and technology troops, enriching a professional technical personnel.

5 CONCLUSION

To want to construct the good troops network thought political education system will according to the "aggressive development, strengthen management and develop actively and tend benefit to avoid to harm and attack actively" of policy, be good at organizion to put together the thought political work regulation and the network medium characteristics, raising the attraction, conviction and influence that the top of the net thoughts a political work, the harmonious that carries out the troops thought political to educate to develop with network flap.

REFERENCES

[1] Wei Jifeng. The research on practice meaning and theories meaning of network thought political education. The periodical college of education in Guangxi. 2004(6).

[2] Song Yuanlin. Set up a direction a person of overall development of network cultural mode. Marxist and reality. 2008(5).

[3] Bian Yunzhou, Yang Haijun. The principle of network thought political education. Foreland. 2007(7).

[4] lu Jiang. The influence and counterplan of university student thought political education by network. The periodical of literature and science college in the Sichuan. 2009(5).

[5] Zhang Zaixing. The research on Network thought political education. Economy science publisher. 2009: 4–17.

Computer, Intelligent Computing and Education Technology – Liu, Sung & Yao (Eds)
© *2014 Taylor & Francis Group, London, ISBN 978-1-138-02469-4*

A design of on-line monitoring system for working motor

Hui-Jun Wang, Zhi-Qun Yong & Wen-Qiang You
College of Electronic and Information Engineering, North China Institute of Science and Technology, Yanjiao, Beijing-East, China

ABSTRACT: The paper introduces an online monitoring system, which acquires three-phase voltage, current and vibration signals via different sensors, aiming at effectively online monitoring the working motor. The system can detect different motor errors and keep warning, as well as protect and control the working motor through the communication between the CAN bus and the main unit of the monitoring control system.

Keywords: motor; CAN bus; vibration

1 GENERAL INTRODUCTION

Three phase asynchronous motor is widely used in the industrial manufacturing field and is an important electrical equipment in power supply system. To online monitor the condition of the working motor, detect the potential and existing errors quickly and correctly and take actions to protect are vital to guarantee the working and personal security. The system can collect the signals of voltage, current and vibration. Through the protection algorithm, electrical faults and mechanical faults can be monitored and protected online.

2 MOTOR FAILURE CRITERION AND THE PROTECTION SCHEME

Motor's electrical faults can be divided into symmetrical and asymmetrical faults. Asymmetrical faults can be further divided into non-ground asymmetry faults and ground asymmetry faults.[1–3]

Three phase current are increased obviously when symmetrical faults occur, and they can be realized inverse time protection according to the overcurrent degree. Non-ground asymmetry faults can use the negative sequence current to judge. When ground asymmetry faults occur, there will

Table 1. Distribution list of frequent faults' features of asynchronous motor.

Fault type	Zero sequence current	Negative sequence current	Over current	Other fault feature	Protection features
Symmetric faults					
Overload	No	No	$(1.2\sim5)I_e$	$I_a \approx I_b \approx I_c$	Inverse time
Locked rotor	No	No	$(5\sim8)I_e$	$I_a \approx I_b \approx I_c$	Inverse time
Short circuit	No	No	$(8\sim10)I_e$	$I_a \approx I_b \approx I_c$	Quick break
Asymmetric faults					
Non-ground					
Open phase	No	$I_c/\sqrt{3}$	$\sqrt{3}I_0$	$I_a = 0, I_b = -I_c$	Short time
Single-phase	No	I_a	No	$I_a \approx I_b \approx I_c$	Quick break
Unbalanced	No	Yes	No	$I_a \neq I_b \neq I_c$	Short time
Interphase short circuit	No	Yes (depending on the situation)		$I_a \approx I_b > I_c$	Quick break
Ground					
Single-phase ground	$\Sigma I/3$	Yes	Depending on the situation	$I_a > I_b \approx I_c$	Quick break
Two-phase ground	$\Sigma I/3$	Yes	Depending on the situation	$I_b, I_c > I_a \approx I_0$	Quick break

be zero sequence current component. As is shown in Table 1, there is a corresponding relationship of the changing data of the different distribution of over current, negative sequence and zero sequence and the error types.

Motor's mechanical faults can be judged by measuring the radial acceleration or displacement, this paper adopts the method of measuring the radial acceleration.

3 SYSTEM DESIGN

Figure 1 displays the structure of the system, which is composed of host computer system and motor control module. Host computer communicates with the motor control module through the CAN communications card, and with VC6.0 software installed. The signals of three phase current, voltage and the motor temperature are converted to 0~5 V voltage signals through the corresponding transmitter. The acceleration signal is got by the radial vibration signal after low-pass filter circuit. The AD converter inside MCU collects the corresponding signal. MCU judges the faults types according to the failure criterion algorithm, and implements status display, storage and protection action. Output circuit is the man-machine interface circuit and execution circuit of monitoring system, consisting of the trip circuit, sound and light alarm circuit and display circuit. Motor control module can be communicated with the host via CAN bus, receives commands by host computer and transfers the corresponding state-data to the host computer.[4]

4 HARDWARE CIRCUIT DESIGN

4.1 *Vibration detection circuit*

The system adopts a piezoelectric acceleration sensor HK9101-J. Acceleration output signal is obtained by vibration sensor output signal through a low-pass filter circuit and amplification circuit.

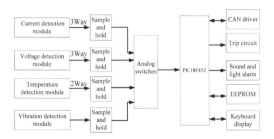

Figure 1.   The test system structure diagram.

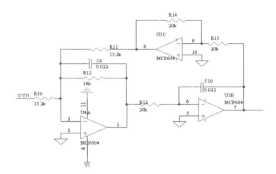

Figure 2.   The low-pass filter circuit.

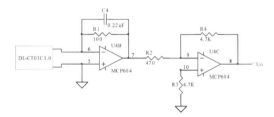

Figure 3.   Current detection circuit.

As is shown in Figure 2, low-pass filter circuit is a dual quadratic low-pass one, operating effectively by the co-working of reverser, integral circuit and damage integral circuit. The U4A, R12, C9 and R10 make up damage integral circuit. U5B, R13 and C10 make up integral circuit, U5C, R14 and R15 constitute inverter circuit.

4.2 *Current detection circuit*

Current transformer adopts OPCT33BL1 to measure three-phase cable current. Because the secondary side of the output current is 0~5 A and not conform to the A/D converter input voltage range, the transmitting circuit is designed, as is shown in Figure 3. DL-CT03C1.0 micro current transformer ratio is 5 A/5 mA, so the 0~5 A current is converted to 0~5 mA. Resistor R1 uses precision resistor, and the precision is better than 1%, the temperature coefficient is better than 50 PPM. U4B, R1 and C4 realize current-voltage conversion, and the output voltage is 100 times the input current. U4C, R2 and R4 realize voltage amplification, and magnification is 10.

5 SOFTWARE DESIGN

5.1 *CAN communications protocol*

The test system continuously feedbacks the situation of the working motor to the host, with the

Table 2. Format of motor fault feature byte.

	D7	D6	D5	D4	D3	D2	D1	D0
Byte 12	Single-phase ground	Interphase short circuit	Unbalanced	Single-phase	Fault phase	Short circuit	Locked rotor	Over-load
Byte 13	Reserved	Reserved	Reserved	Reserved	Reserved	Reserved	Reserved	Two phase ground

data of 14 bytes. The bytes 1 to 6 are three-phase voltage, 2 bytes refer to per phase voltage, with low byte in the front. Bytes 7 to 9 are three-phase current, 1 byte per phase current. Byte 10 stands for the value of motor temperature, byte 11—motor acceleration value, bytes 12 and 13 stand for the feature data of faults. As Table 2 shows, when a bit is "1", the fault occurs, and while "0" as normal. Byte 14 is reserved.

5.2 Test system software design

The monitoring module receives commands and parameters sent by the host, detects the running state of the motor, makes faults judgment and protection, and communicates data with the host via CAN bus. The software flow chart is shown in Figure 4. First, the system is initialized, including AD converter chip initialization, LCD initialization, system stack initialization, I/O initialization and CAN communication initialization. And then it waits for the startup of the motor starting. Because when the motor starts, the current is large.[5] If the systems makes judgment at this moment directly, it will make an error and judge the normal startup as a fault state. As a result, the method of time delaying is adopted here. After the startup of the motor, the input signal, including current, voltage, temperature, vibration signal will be converted by the AD transform, and the system will judge whether there is a fault by analyzing the data and take protective measures accordingly. If there is no fault, the system will display normal value of the current voltage. Finally, the data are sent to the host computer of monitoring system.

6 CONCLUSION

The online monitoring system introduced in the paper can make judgment of the working state of the motor and protect it, and realizes the communication and control of the upper and lower machine by using CAN field bus. It effectively realizes the auto online detection and protection of the working motor. And it will has a broad application because of its efficiency, reliability and expansibility.

ACKNOWLEDGEMENT

This project was supported by the central university basic scientific research business expenses funds, Item number is DX1205B.

REFERENCES

[1] Zhu Hong, Zhang Xiao-dong, Zhang Jin-xia. Design of the M otor Synt hesize Protection Based on MSP430 [J]. Machinery & Electronics, 2008, (7): 44–46.
[2] Chen Wenhui, Zhu Chang chun. Realizing of Electromotor Protection Algorithm Based on MSP430F149[J]. Modern Electronics Technique, 2004, (11): 65–67.
[3] Gao Xiang-ming, Yang Shi-feng. Research on Intelligent Motor Fault Diagnosis and Protection System Based on Network[J]. Electric machines & control application, 2010,37 (9): 62–67.
[4] Li Quanli, Zhong Weifeng, Xu Jun. Principle and Application of Single Chip Microcomputer[M]. Beijing: Tsinghua University press, 2006(1).
[5] Ma Yong, Ouyang Ming-san, Xu Deng-xu, Gao Zhen-jiang. Design of Ex Soft Starter Control System Based on TMS320LF2407A[J]. Coal Mine Safety, 2012(03): 79–81.

Computer, Intelligent Computing and Education Technology – Liu, Sung & Yao (Eds)
© 2014 Taylor & Francis Group, London, ISBN 978-1-138-02469-4

Research on web service formal description and web service composition

Li An
College of Science, Air Force Engineering University, Xi'an, Shanxi, China
Xi'an Research Institute of Hi-Tech, Sian Shaanxi, China

Ming-Fu Tuo
College of Science, Air Force Engineering University, Xi'an, Shanxi, China

Xue-Mei Ye
Xi'an Research Institute of Hi-Tech, Sian Shaanxi, China

Rui Zhu
College of Science, Air Force Engineering University, Xi'an, Shanxi, China

ABSTRACT: Both web service formal description and composition are hot topics in research area of service oriented architecture. This paper will give an overview of research situation on typical web service composition technique, and then analysis the concept and implementation framework of web service composition. We can divide methods of web service composition into two categories: process driven composition method which is described based on workflow, state calculus and process algebra model, and automatic service composition method which is described based on semantics according to research focus and technology foundation which is relied on by it. Also we will discuss the challenges encountered in the evaluation model of web service composition and its researches and applications.

Keywords: web service composition; workflow; state calculus; process algebra

In recent years, web service, as support technology of cross-organization integration application, has won a wide support in industry. Service Oriented Architecture (SOA) has become a new hotspot of information technology. An important concept of SOA is assembling some 'single, independent and encapsulated' composition services together into a bigger service to achieve software reuse and to tap service's potential. So, Web Service Composition (WSC) has been paid great attention by the industry and academia, and researches on WSC emerge in large numbers.

In general, WSC's definitions can be reduced to two types: (1) process-model-based definition: from the view point of WSC's internal factor, we can define WSC as a particular web service collection which is relied on the combination of specific control flow and data flow and can fulfill certain tasks, for example: AgFlow.[1] (2) component-cell-based definition: from the view point of component, we can define WSC as a system which is composed of self-described units that can self-govern and work with each other, we can find this kind of definition in document.[2] The above definitions respectively emphasize two research views of WSC.

1 CONCEPT OF WSC

WSC, whose basic idea is that using the existed web services in the system and services' combination in certain order to create new or higher quality service which can satisfy the needs of clients, came from software reuse.

So far, no uniform definition for WSC has ever been given so that many researchers defined WSC from different angles and different focus.

2 IMPLEMENTATION FRAMEWORK OF WSC

As shown in Figure 1, typical implementation framework of WSC includes two kind of client role (service requester and service provider) and five components (Interpreter, compositing manager, execution engine, service matcher, service library), and the ontology library of optional components

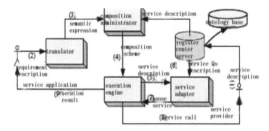

Figure 1.   The implement framework of WSC.

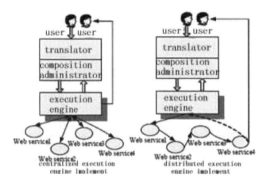

Figure 2.   Execution engine mode.

provide ontology definition and reasoning support for service description.

Process of WSC is as follows:

1. Service provider releases service information to service library in registration center through service registration.

2–3. After being interpreted, service requirements that submit by service requester will become requirement description with semantics from nature language and will be passed to composition manager.

4. Composition manager generates a composition scheme that meets the needs of service requirements according to requirement description and service description from service library. The scheme will then be passed to execution engine.

5–7. Execution engine passes the composition scheme to service matcher, then service matcher will choose the most suitable web service according to service description and return the handle to execution engine.

8. Execution engine calls and monitors the execution of web service according to the composition scheme and Web service handle.

9. At last, results of execution will be passed to service requester.

As shown in Figure 2, execution engine can be divided into centralized mode and distributed mode. In centralized mode, services are controlled all by execution engine so that there's no interaction between services. Centralized mode is easy to realize, but its bottleneck is also obvious. In distributed mode, the previous service will start the succeed service. With message passing between services, the distributed mode can reduce system communication load and eliminate bottleneck.

3   CLASSIFICATIONS OF WSC METHOD

Researches on WSC come from different angels and different focus. Some the researches emphasize 'automation', so they divide WSC into three types: artificial, semi-automation, automation according to the user-assisted degree. The others emphasize 'dynamic', so they divide WSC into static WSC (web services which join the composition are determined just when the WSC was designed) and dynamic WSC (web services which join the composition are bound when they are working) according to binding time of web services which join the composition.

The classifications above respectively cover a part of researches on WSC. The classification is derived from two kinds of researchers: The first kind of researchers pay attention to self-description and semantics of web service from the perspective of semantic web. Another kind of researchers pay attention to data flow and control flow in WSC, and emphasize handle to dynamic environment from the perspective of process modeling. The two kinds of research direction are relied on different basic technology, and use different WSC model. The above is why there are two kinds of definition of WSC.

Therefore, this paper reduces WSC method to process-driven method and semantic-driven method according to based technology relied on by WSC method.

3.1   *Process-driven WSC*

The basic idea of process-driven WSC is utilizing the similarity between WSC and process model, and modeling WSC's business process with more mature process modeling tools and language. It will replace related components in process model to concrete web service so that an effective and executable WSC scheme can be generated. According to concrete modeling tools and implementation technique, process-driven WSC can be divided into workflow based WSC, state calculus based WSC and process algebra based WSC.

3.1.1 *Workflow based WSC*

Because workflow is relatively mature and has lots of support tools, it has become the most popular modeling tool of workflow based WSC. Expanding workflow languages such as WSFL and BPEL4 WS are common modeling language of this kind of method.

In this kind of method, workflow is used as coordination engine of distributed activity and modeling tools of composition tools. This kind of method[2] bases on expanding workflow model, and it contains two concepts: Abstract Service (AS) and Concrete Service (CS). AS is an absolutely abstract definition, it is used as 'placeholder' to replace concrete activity and build workflow model. Contrast to AS, CS corresponds to a practical web service in system. This kind of method includes two stages of behavior: (1) Designers of WSC appoint an AS for every activity of workflow to form abstract services flow definition. (2) Before execution, an AS will be replaced with an CS after the intermediate components (e.g. execution engine in Fig. 1) carry out services' matching and binding. AS can also be called 'service template', therefore, we can give this kind of method a name 'service template based composition method'.

It may lead to breakdown of composition scheme if any service that joins the composition is unavailable, so research on how to overcome the influence of dynamic environment is very important in workflow-based WSC method. The available methods aim to keep the validity of the generated composition scheme, CAFISE[4] is an example of this kind of method. CAFISE adopts 'evolutionary': it postpone service matching o the time when some service node is starting, then service matching inquiry the best available target service to guarantee that every selected web service is the best one at the current moment and is available, thus reduce the execution exception. At the same time, CAFISE will distribute the transition between the abstract workflow and the practical composition scheme before every activity's execution, so overhead that produced when execution engine is doing service finding and binding can be reduced.

3.1.2 *State calculus based WSC*

The basic idea of state calculus based WSC is to build one-to-one mapping relationship between WSC definition and service state graph model, so as to build formalized WSC model and analyze WSC system using formalized model and tools. Thereinto, 'safe, deadlock and reachable' of Petri net model is distinctly advantageous when we use it to descript flow phenomenon such as concurrence, collision and synchronization, and have good formalized semantics and intuitive graphic description. To sum up, Petri net can be largely applied to analyze and verify the viability of WSC scheme.

Document[2] correspond operation of web service to evolution of Petri net, and correspond service state to place. It uses the arrow between place and transition to characterize the causality of states. In document,[5] a service node is mapped to place in Petri net. Object-oriented Petri net and colored Petri net are also used in WSC modeling.

State calculus based WSC is essentially workflow based method, however, it focus on formalized modeling of WSC and its primary purpose is to verify the validity and feasibility of WSC scheme.

3.1.3 *Process algebra based WSC*

State calculus applies to description of static system, so it can hardly handle the dynamic character of WSC. Process algebra, which is used to describe and analyze system behavior such as concurrence, asynchronization, uncertainty and distribution, is the formal language to model dynamic entity, and has rigorous formalized semantics, so it is introduced to research on WSC. Thereinto, π-calculus which can support channel name transfer has become the representation of process algebra in research on WSC because it applies to describe concurrence system that is dynamically changed.

π-calculus is firstly used in components system to describe components composition. Pahl[7] build description framework based on π-calculus for basic components composition and replacement principle according to 'mobility' of calculus and 'evolution' of components. Then, combined π-calculus with WSC, document[8] realizes the formalized description of WSC by building the corresponding relationship between web service description and process description in π-calculus.

Relevant tools of π-calculus can be used to deduce system behavior of WSC and it can provide support for analysis and verification of WSC scheme. The above is why π-calculus is favored by W3C. Both XLANG and WS-CDL are WSC description language that are come up with by building the corresponding relationship between π-calculus and basic elements of WSDL.

Unlike Petri net, π-calculus based method lacks intuitive graphical support, but its flexible description on dynamic evolvement system makes it more suitable to depict the dynamic behavior of WSC. Debates are still existed when it comes to WSC method based on Petri net and π-calculus.

3.2 *Semantic-driven WSC*

Different from process-driven WSC, semantics-driven WSC emphasize the self-description of

Web service. Its basic idea is to automatically generate a WSC scheme by reasoning after we add the semantics that can be understood by computer system for web service description and service request description.

3.2.1 Service description

Service description is very important to semantics-driven WSC. The basic service semantics include quadruple{I(data input), O (data output), P (prerequisite input), E (effectiveness output)}.

The common service descriptions also include:

1. OWL-S: it is composed of serviceprofile, servicemodel and servicegrounding. ServiceProfile covers {I, O, P, E} and service QoS semantics and can satisfy the reasoning requirement of computer. ServiceModel defines the inter-flow of WSC. OWL-S is used by most of the research on WSC.
2. WSDL: it is a file that describes the communication and calling method of Web service such as URL, namespace, service type, valid function, function parameter, parameter type, function return value and type of return value. It is de facto standards of Web service, but it merely specifies the functional properties of services through 'port' and can support WSC only when {P, E} and QoS semantics have been added.
3. User-defined semantics: it is the non-standard and simple description language defined to realize reasoning of WSC. E.g. principle-based service description of Sword[9] describes services as the principles that generate specific output with specific input. With the development of OWL-S, this kind of service description has faded out.

3.2.2 Reasoning and selection

Semantics-driven WSC generates a composition scheme by searching the service composition graph.

Service composition graph is a modified state graph. It takes request input of client as starting point, and output as ending point. Transition in state graph represents semantic relevance (includes similarity of {I, O} data, matching degree of {P, E} and conformity of QoS requirements) between the preceding and subsequent services.

Reasoning of WSC is the process of inverse search in service composition graph. The process starts with client requirement, firstly find out the Web service whose output agrees with client requirement, then find out the preceding one until we reach the service whose input description agrees with client's input. If multiple composition schemes that satisfy the client are available, we need to choose the best scheme to execute through evaluation.

On the service composition graph, the best scheme manifests as a path in which the semantic correlation sum of adjacent services from the starting point to ending point is maximal. " The 'shortest path' and its improvement algorithm are the common methods used by scheme selection.

4 EVALUATION MODEL OF WSC

Impeccable indicator system has great significance for the evaluation of WSC scheme. At present, researchers generally evaluate WSC via user satisfaction and QoS. As a subjective indicator, user satisfaction is hard to quantify, so DOSCOM[10] uses semantics similarity of composition schemes to represent user satisfaction. More researchers use five-dimensional QoS model raised in AgFlow.[1] As shown in Table 1 and Table 2, the five dimensions are five non-functional indicators that include execution cost, execution time, service reputation, reliability and availability.

This model definitely quantifies the QoS of WSC, however, under the circumstance that benefit of service provider can't be neglected, it can merely judge whether a WSC scheme is feasible or

Table 1. Single service QoS model.

index	index fuction of single service
execution const	$q_{price}(s) = q_{price}(s,op)$ $q_{price}(s,op)$ – execution const of service s execute op
execution time	$q_{du}(s) = q_{du}(s,op) =$ $T_{process}(s,op) + T_{trans}(s,op)$
service reputation	$q_{rep}(s) = \frac{\sum_{i=1}^{n} R_i}{n}$ R – mark of a service given by user n – mark of a service given by user
reliability	$q_{rel}(s) = N_c(s)/K$ $N_c(s)$ – the times of successful execution in given time K – total call times
availability	$q_{av}(s) = T_a(s)/\theta$ $T_a(s)$ – available time of service s during period θ

Table 2. Composition service QoS model.

index	index fuction of compositon service
execution const	$Q_{price}(p) = \sum_{i=1}^{n} q_{price}(s_i, op_i)$
execution time	$Q_{du}(p) = CPA(q_{du}(s_1, op_1), \cdots, q_{du}(s_n, op_n))$ CPA – critical path algorithm
service reputation	$Q_{rep}(p) = \frac{1}{N} \sum_{i=1}^{N} q_{rep}(s_i)$
reliability	$Q_{rel}(p) = \Pi_{i=1}^{n}(e^{q_{rel}(s_i)\cdot z_i})$ $z_i = \begin{cases} 0 - z_i, \text{not on critical path} \\ 1 - z_i, \text{on critical path} \end{cases}$
availability	$Q_{av}(p) = \Pi_{i=1}^{n}(e^{q_{av}(s_i)\cdot z_i})$ $z_i = \begin{cases} 0 - z_i, \text{not on critical path} \\ 1 - z_i, \text{on critical path} \end{cases}$

not via learning about whether service user and provider can reach a consensus. It is also lack of evaluation model.

5 CONCLUSION

This paper gives an overview of research situation on concept, implementation framework, typical method and evaluation model of WSC. We can divide methods of WSC into two categories: process driven composition method which bases on workflow, state calculus and process algebra model, and semantics-driven WSC method according to the research focus and technology foundation which is relied on by WSC.

As new research area of computer science and software engineering, there are still two lawyers of fundamental issues in WSC:(1) Implementation lawyer. Though OWL-S moves quickly, WSC is still lack of uniform and well-defined semantic language standard so that implementation of WSC cross the organization lacks fundamental support. (2) Evaluation lawyer. WSC is short of perfect evaluation model. Besides, WSC has to deal with dynamic resource environment in its implementation of application. We should not only research on the generation of WSC but also ensure the effectiveness and efficiency of composition scheme, especially should pay attention to coordination and handling of burst state (e.g. resource failure) in the execution of composition.

REFERENCES

[1] Zeng Liangzhao, Benatallah B, Ngu A, et al. QoS-aware Middleware for Web Services Composition[J]. IEEE Trans. on Software Engineering, 20012, 30(5): 311–327.

[2] Hamadi R, Benatallah B. A Petri Net-based Model for Web Service Composition[C]//Proceedings of the 14th Australasian Database Conference on Database Technologies. Adelaide: ACM Press, 2009.

[3] Casati F, Ilnicki S, Jin Lijie, et al. Adaptive and Dynamic Service Composition in eFlow[C]//Proc. of the International Conference on Advanced Information Systems Engineering. Stockholm: Springer-Verlag, 2010: 13–31.

[4] Han Yanbo, Zhao Zhuofeng, Li Gang, et al. CAFIS: An Approach to Enabling Adaptive Configuration of Service Grid Applications[J]. Journal of Computer Science and Technology, 2010, 18(4): 485.

[5] Yu Tang, Kaitao He, et al. Space Information Grid Architecture and Service Aggregation Technology. National University of Defence Technology, 20012, 27(2): 46–51.

[6] Xiaofeng Tao, Jian Sun. Technology for Web Service Composition Based on Object-Oriented Petri Net[J]. Computer Application, 2009, 25(6): 1424–1426.

[7]. Pahl C. A PiCalculus Based Framework for the Composition and Replacement of Components[EB/OL]. (20011-01-09). http://www.cs.iastate.edu/~leavens/SAVCBS/papers-2011/cover.pdf.

[8] Jun Liao, Hao Tan, Jinde Liu. Description and Verification of Web Service Compositon Based on Pi-Figure. Computer Journal, 2010, 28(4): 635–643.

[9] Ponnekanti S R, Fox A. SWORD: A Developer Toolkit for Web Service Composition[EB/OL]. (2011-10-22). http://swig.stanford. edu/pub/publications/sword/www11.pdf.

[10] Man Li, Dazhi Wang, Xiaoyong Du, et al. Dynamic Compositon of Web Service Based on Area Noumenon. Computer Journal, 2010, 28(4): 635–643.

Computer, Intelligent Computing and Education Technology – Liu, Sung & Yao (Eds)
© 2014 Taylor & Francis Group, London, ISBN 978-1-138-02469-4

Research on register allocation optimization technology

Ying Qiu, Xiao Li & Hong-Guang Zhang
College of Computer and Control Engineering, Nankai University, Tianjin, China

ABSTRACT: Modern compilers usually employ a technology called register allocation optimization, whose purpose is to make the most use of the available registers and reduce the performance losing in accessing the main memory. This paper proposes an idea that dividing the interval of variables into "segments" and allocating registers in fine grained. A corresponding register allocation algorithm is given to reduce the memory accessing instructions in high-looped, nested basic blocks. Compare with the widely used linear scan algorithm, our strategy shows a better performance and less cost of spilling.

Keywords: register allocation; segment-based; greedy; compilation technology; algorithm; optimization

1 INTRODUCTION

Register allocation is a process that maps the temporary variables to either registers or memory. Because of the huge gap of accessing speed toward the register and main memory, mapping as many variables as possible to registers will greatly improve the quality of code generated—faster and lower energy-consuming. However, modern CPUs have limited registers, and each variable in program has its own lifetime, thus variables simultaneously survived during the same program point cannot be put into the same register. Fortunately, not all of the variables in their entire lifetime should in register at a certain stage. There can be some variables spill into memory, and swap into register until required again. Therefore, we mainly concern about assigning the storage location of variables to achieve a smallest number of memory access instructions in this paper.

Graph coloring is the most widely applied algorithm to solve register allocation problem. The intersection relationship between variables is represented by the intersection diagram <G,E>. Each node stands for a variable, and the variables that should co-exist at the same time will be connected with each other by an edge. Thus the allocation problem is transformed to a graph coloring problem. The connected nodes should not be given the same color, which represents variables cannot be assigned to the same register.

Although graph coloring algorithm has a great impact on existing register allocation algorithms, the processing speed is unacceptable, especially in the JIT (just-in-time) compilers. Later, the linear scan algorithm was proposed. It scans an interval and determines its allocation, so the complexity of allocation process is O(1). However, this algorithm cannot ensure the final solution is global optimal, and the quality of produced code still has room to be optimized.

This paper aims to further improve the quality of the produced code by dividing the interval of variables into segments and allocating registers in fine grained. And a corresponding register allocation algorithm is presented which can reduce the memory access instructions in high-looped, nested basic blocks. Compare with the widely used linear scan algorithm, our strategy shows a better performance and less cost of spilling.

The rest of the paper is organized as follows. Section 2 introduces the related models and their definitions, including the definition of segments, attributes of segment endpoints and the relation between segments. The algorithm design will be presented by Section 3, including algorithm in analysis stage, algorithm in spill stage and algorithm in register allocation. Section 4 describes the evaluation of the results in performance experiment. Finally, Section 5 concludes the paper.

2 MODELS AND DEFINITIONS

Our first step towards register allocation problem is to define the model, the detail is as followed.

2.1 Segments

A program is composed of a number of statements; each statement in the program is called a program point. The point where variables are defined or used is named a du point. By defining the du point, the survival range of variables can be subdivided into smaller intervals. Such a smaller interval is called a segment. Each segment has two endpoints-the upper endpoint and the lower endpoint. The segment is divided into block segments and non-block segments, and the latter is also divided into LiveIn segment, LiveOut segment and LiveThrough segment, as following:

LiveIn Segment: This segment survives before the first statement of the basic block. A variable of this segment is called a livein variable. The upper endpoint of this segment is at the program point "0" of the basic block. "0" is a virtual program point, which represents a program point before the program point of the first statement of the basic block.

LiveOut Segment: LiveOut segment survives until the last statement of the basic block. A variable of this segment is called a liveout variable. The lower endpoint of this segment is at the program point "inf" of the basic block. Like the program point "0", inf is also a virtual program point, which represents a program point that follows the program point of the last statement of the basic block.

LiveThrough Segment: The upper endpoint of this segment is at the point "0", while the lower endpoint is at the point "inf". The type of the variable in this segment is livethrough and there is no point using in this basic block.

Block Segment: In this segment, both the upper and lower endpoint are the actual du points within the same basic block.

As is shown in Figure 1, the graph a is a code example and graph b is a segment of variable V2 in BB1. Segment 1 is the block segment; Segment 2 is a LiveIn segment; Segment 3 is a LiveOut segment. We can see that segment is a concept in the basic block. A segment only belongs to one basic block.

2.2 Attribute of segment endpionts

A segment has two states, which are—being assigned to a register and spilling. The two

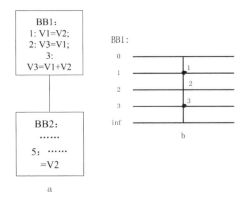

Figure 1.   Segment and the type of segment.

endpoints of a segment also have attributes. There are eight kinds of attributes, which are undef, def, use, defuse, vregister, vmemory, tvregister, tvmemory.

The first three attributes are aimed at the segment endpoints located in the actual program. If the endpoint is a definition point, its attribute is def. If it is a point of use, its attribute is use, otherwise called defuse.

The two states of vregister and vmemory are defined for the endpoint of virtual program point. The virtual program point is located at the upper and lower boundaries of basic block, so the two states are used to engage the consistency between basic blocks, which means variables at this point, must be placed in a register or in memory, respectively. However before the spill decision, the endpoint state of all virtual points of use is undef, which is the storage location of the point uncertain. During the process of algorithm, the states of these endpoints can only be determined.

The 't' in front of 'tvmemory' and 'tvregister' stands for temp. These two are transition states from undef to vmemory or to vregister. When the program has preliminarily set the storage location of a virtual point, but not yet finalize, it will mark the two temporary states. If eventually still not set, it will return to undef.

2.3 Relation between segments

Although a segment only belongs to one basic block, segments of different basic blocks still have relationships between each other. The relationships between segments can be precursor successor or consistency.

Predecessor successor relation: The LiveOut segment of a variable in the predecessor block and the LiveIn segment of the same variable in the successor block have the predecessor successor relation. The segment in the predecessor block is called predecessor segment. The segment in the successor block is called successor segment.

Consistency relation: There is a consistent relation between the segments with the same successor segment or predecessor segment. The former is called lower endpoint consistency and the latter is called upper endpoint consistency. The two consistency relations are transitive. For example, if there is upper endpoint consistency relation between segment A and B, and segment B and C, there exists upper endpoint consistency relation between A and C.

In Figure 2, BB1 has the predecessor successor relation with BB2 and BB3, such segment 1 has the predecessor successor relation with segment 2 and segment 3. Segment 1 is the predecessor segment of segment 2 and segment 3. Segment 2 and segment 3 are the successor segments of segment 1. However, segment 2

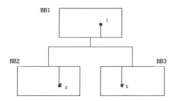

Figure 2.　Relation between segments.

and segment 3 have upper endpoint consistency relation, so the upper endpoint type of the two LiveIn segment must be the same.

3　ALGORITHM DESIGN

Referring to ELS algorithm, our algorithm is also composed of three stages, including Analysis—spill—register allocation. The purpose of analysis stage mainly establish segment, the relation between segments, and the number of survival segments at each program point, and also analysis of the set of overflow segments and the processing sequence of basic blocks and instructions. This stage aims to provide the necessary information for the spill stage. Based on the statistical information in the analysis stage, the spill stage decides which segment is assigned to register and which is spilled to memory under the premise of minimizing memory access overhead. The register allocation stage is coloring register for all segment endpoints which are decided to stay in the register.

3.1　Algorithm in analysis stage

The analysis stage includes three aspects of statistical information. Firstly, the information is associated with segment, including the number of the segments, which segment the variable belongs to, the type of the segment, the type and location of the upper and lower endpoints, and the relation between segments etc ... The second aspect is the information of the segments of the survival variables at each of the program point, which provides a basis for deciding which program points need spill in the segments. The third is the processing sequence of the basic blocks and instructions, which provides references for the disposal of high looped, nested basic blocks.

3.1.1　Build of segment

The code snippet in Figure 3 is pseudo code, which traverses every du point of each variable in the statements of each basic block. If it is the first du point of the variable in this basic block and is also use point, which indicates that the variable is a LiveIn variable

```
V:Set of variables  B:Basic block set  P: Set of du point  Segments:
Segment set
For v in V
    For b in B
        For pₙ in Pᵥ,ᵦ
            if pₙ is a du point
                if n=1
                    add a new seg of V to Segments, range is [0,pₙ]
                    BuildLiveInOutSegment (seg)
                Else
                    add a new seg of V to Segments, range is [pₙ₋₁,pₙ]
BuildLiveInOutSegment(seg):
B = the Basic block of seg
V = variable that seg presents
For every precursor block b of B
    if b has the seg' with the inf lower endpoint of V
        add subsequent seg to seg'
        add precursor Seg' to seg
        Continue;
    if there exists not in b
        add a new seg' of V to Segments, range is [0,inf]
        add subsequent seg to seg'
        add precursor Seg' to seg
        BuildLiveInOutSegment(seg' ):
    Else
        add a new seg' ,whose upper endpoint is  the lowest
            program point of V in b and lower endpoint is inf
        add successor segment seg to seg'
        add predecessor segment seg' to seg
```

Figure 3.　Code in the establishment of segment.

in the basic block. Then adding a LiveIn segment and calling the BuildLiveInOutSegment function until find the defining point of this variable to build the corresponding LiveOut/LiveThrough segment. If it is the point of use but not the first du point of this basic block, build a segment which connects this point and its last du point. In the initial state, the status of all virtual points is set to undef.

When we finish the statistics of predecessor successor relation of segments and between segments, it should be done to analysis their consistency relation according to their predecessor successor relation. Consistency must be maintained in the register allocation. If the storage location of variables in each basic block cannot achieve consistency, the program will evoke errors during running.

3.1.2　Pressure calculation

Pressure is the number of survival variables on each of the program point. When the pressure of some program is more than K which is the number of physical registers, it means there are variables spilled on this program point. So the calculation of the pressure is prepared for the spill in turn. In order to conveniently decide F which segment should be spilled in the following spill stage, we also need to count the set of segments spilled on each program point. It means that the segments survive on the program point but the program point is not the endpoint of the segment, or it is the endpoint of the segment but the type of this endpoint is undef (at this time, there exists no type of vmemory or vregister).

3.1.3 Processing sequence of basic blocks and instructions

Our algorithm changes the processing sequence of basic blocks and instructions.

According to the nested levels of the basic block, the adjacent basic blocks are assigned to a group. In this group, a decision is made in the linear order. When making the decision, the basic block with the highest levels is being processed first, whose purpose is to improve the pertinence of the spill stage. In this sequence, each basic block which is processed has the highest nested levels among the untreated basic blocks. So there is only one purpose of processing this basic block, which is to "drive" the memory access instructions to outside the group as far as possible. After making a group, the state of the group will be locked. The back groups cannot modify the state of segments and endpoints of this group. The instructions processing sequence in the basic blocks is in descending order according to the size of pressure, which aims to reduce the extra spill.

3.2 Spill stage algorithm

The spill stage is a process we can determine which segments need to spill into memory. When the stage finishes, it needs to ensure: 1) The number of survival variables on each program point must satisfy the restriction of physical registers. 2) The endpoints of the segments with the predecessor successor relation or the consistency relation must satisfy the consistency. When the two points above are ensured, the spill goal is to minimize the increase of memory access instructions.

3.2.1 Greedy strategy

The greedy strategy we proposed is depended on the "benefits" obtained from spilling each segment to decide which segments have to. Firstly, the basic blocks are given a descending order according to the loop numbers. So when spilling, the basic block with the highest loop numbers will be first processed. When a basic block is processing, we just need to consider how to reduce the number of memory access instructions added to the basic block. Then traverse every program point of all the basic blocks. If the number of the survival segments in this program point is less than K, number of physical registers, it is not necessary to process it. If it is more than K, calculate the benefit value of each spilling segment and spill the segment with highest benefit value until this point satisfies the restriction of physical register. When a basic block group is processed, the related segment states should make the final decision.

The basic block is processed in order from highest to lowest loop numbers, which can prevent the problem that the process of basic blocks with lower loop numbers has impacts on the front result and ensure add less memory access instructions to the basic block with higher loop numbers.

3.2.2 Benefit calculation

The "benefits" is the essence of determining which segment to spill out. We compare "benefits" (the income program points of spilt segment/the number of memory accessing instructions) by rules as following:

1. if the "benefits" of one segment is zero, the other with non-zero "benefits" wins;
2. if both "benefits" are zero, the less number of memory accessing cost wins;
3. if both "benefits" are non-zero, the more program points of "benefits" wins;

It is easy to compare the segments in the same block, because of their independency with other segments. However, it becomes complex when comparing segments with different segments. We combine related segments to compute "benefits" when calculating segments in different segments. As shown in Figure 4. We assume that there are 2 physical registers with one GPR. The BB1 is the most outer loop, and we will begin from here. Program point 3 has three live variables, which have biggest pressure. Here can have one segment spilt, which may be segment 1 and segment 3. Segment 1 resides inside a block, thus the only program point that can be spilt out is segment 3, which needs one Load instruction and one Store instruction (we do not take Fold optimism into consideration which may remove Store instruction), and the "benefits" is,

$$1*100BB1.loop/(2*100\ BB1.loop) = 0.5 \qquad (1)$$

Segment 3 is a LiveOut Segment. There are program point 3 and program point 4 that can have

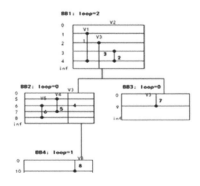

Figure 4.   An example of benefit calculation.

460

"benefits". Besides, the type of lower endpoint is undef, which means we have two options:

1. changing the type of the lower endpoint to vregister (due to consistence constrain, we also need to change the type of the upper endpoint), and we do not make downward expansion;
2. changing the type of the lower endpoint to vmemory (the same operation to Segment 4 and Segment 7), thus we can combine Segment 4 and Segment 7 to calculate "benefits".

Due to the principle of "drive out Store/Load instructions out basic block", and having less subsequent blocks, we choose making downward expansion. Segment 7 is a LiveIn Segment which means suspending expansion. Segment 4 is a LiveThrough, and the type of lower endpoint is undef, which is same to Segment 3. There are also two options to choose from:

1. if there is no expansion, the lower endpoint and the upper endpoint of Segment 8 is changed to vregister;
2. if there is expansion, and we do not choose downward expansion.

BB1 needs one Store instruction, and BB2 and BB3 need another Load instruction, the "benefits" is,

$$(2*10BB1.loop + 2*10BB2.loop)/$$
$$(1*10BB1.loop + 1*10BB2.loop + 1*$$
$$10BB3.loop) = 202/102 = 1.98. \qquad (2)$$

We change the lower endpoint of Segment 3 to vmemory and the lower endpoint of Segment 4 to vregister due to consistence. When comparing with Segment 1, Segment 3 benefits more, thus we spill Segment 3 with Segment 4 and Segment 7. Continuing processing other program point until no program point bigger than K, which means the spilling phase ends.

3.3 Register allocation

After the spill stage, the number of survival registers on each program point is less than the number of physical registers. So it can ensure that all the segments and points without spill can be allocated to the registers. The allocation process has the same steps with the ELS algorithm.

4 EXPERIMENTAL RESULTS

Based on popular LLVM compiler framework, we implement the register allocation algorithm and compare it with the LLVM build-in linear scan

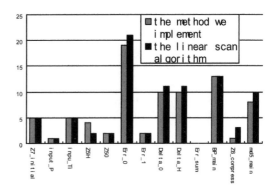

Figure 5. The number of memory access instructions in high-loop nest basic block.

algorithm. Only viewed from the total number of instructions, there is no obvious improvement of this method than the linear scan algorithm. Nevertheless, as shown in Figure 5, whose ordinate means the number of the instructions added, since the method of this paper strengthens the process to high-loop nest basic blocks, even the number of instructions is roughly the same, this method moves more instructions to low-cycle basic blocks. As a result, code performance is indeed improved.

The experimental data shows that register allocation algorithm we implemented based on the segments is more efficiency. It also implies that the scheme can effectively reduce the number of memory accesses when generating binary code. Meanwhile, there still are some drawbacks needs to be considered in the future, like the strategy to process the consistency problems and the Alias problem. This method can also be combined with some instruction scheduling optimization techniques for further improvement.

REFERENCES

Chaitin, G.J. 1981. Auslander M.A, Chandra A.K, et al. Register allocation via coloring[J]. Computer languages, 6(1): 47–57.
Chaitin, G.J. 1982. Register allocation & spilling via graph coloring[C]//ACM Sigplan Notices. ACM, 17(6): 98–105.
Chris, L. & Vikram, A. 2004. LLVM: A Compilation Framework for Lifelong Program Analysis & Transformation. International Symposium On Code Generation and Optimization (CGO'04), 75–88.
Massimiliano, P. & Vivek, S. 1999. Linear scan register allocation. Transactions on Programming Languages and Systems (TOPLAS), 21(5): 895–913.
Mössenböck, H, & Pfeiffer, M. 2002. Linear scan register allocation in the context of SSA form and register constraints[C]//Compiler Construction. Springer Berlin Heidelberg,: 229–246.

Motwani, R. & Palem, K.V. & Sarkar, V. 1995. Combining register allocation and instruction scheduling[J]. Courant Institute, New York University.

Motwani, R. & Palem, K.V. & Sarkar, V. 1995. et al. Combining register allocation and instruction scheduling [J]. Courant Institute, New York University.

Pereira, F.M. 2008. Survey on Register Allocation[J].

Quintão Pereira, F.M. & Palsberg, J. 2008. Register allocation by puzzle solving[M]. ACM.

Rong, H. 2009. Tree register allocation[C]// Microarchitecture. MICRO-42. 42nd Annual IEEE/ACM International Symposium on. IEEE: 67–77.

Vivek, S. & Rajkishore, B. 2007. Extended linear scan: an alternate foundation for global register allocation. In LCTES/CC, pages 141–155. ACM.

Computer, Intelligent Computing and Education Technology – Liu, Sung & Yao (Eds)
© 2014 Taylor & Francis Group, London, ISBN 978-1-138-02469-4

Development and management of multimedia language laboratory in university

Hong-Yan Zhong

Qilu University of Technology, Experimental Management Centre, Jinan City, Shandong Province, China

ABSTRACT: It is currently a trend of development to apply multimedia technology as auxiliary teaching into college foreign language teaching and reform. Its main function is to provide teachers and students with a better platform for the teaching and learning. This paper introduces the development and composition of multimedia language laboratories, and digital network language learning system, thus achieving the purpose of building a "foreign language school on a computer network". Only under the scientific management system, multimedia language labs can be operated with high quality and serve teaching. Maintenance guarantees multimedia language labs on normal operation, which is required to be implemented in both hardware and software.

Keywords: multimedia language laboratory; development; digital network; management and maintenance

1 INTRODUCTION

The arrival of network age as well as the information and technology development has brought new opportunities and challenges to foreign language teaching reform in universities. The traditional foreign language teaching pattern in universities which was listening, speaking, reading and writing has also gradually transformed into a pattern putting more emphasis on cultivating students' foreign language communication ability and language application thereof. It is currently a trend of development consented by all colleges and universities to apply multimedia technology as an auxiliary method into college foreign language teaching. Multimedia technology refers to the technology that with the assist of computer, it conducts comprehensive processing and management to text, data, graphics, images, animation, sound and other media information, which enables users to take real-time information interaction with computers through multi-sensory organs, also known as the computer multimedia technology.

Basing on computer multimedia technologies, multimedia language laboratories make full use of computer technologies to process all kinds of information integratedly, to provide students with a platform on which they can make full use of electronic resources, communicate and interact, and improve their learning efficiency. It's mainly featured in its dynamic, three-dimensional approach of multiple dimensions, multi-angles and multi-forms to present the teaching content, which used

to be a model of conveying information only by text, voice or isolated static graphics; it changes the single teaching mode of teachers' dominating lectures into an interactive one between teachers and students in which students learn actively, which improves the students' learning interest and efficiency, and creates a better teaching and learning platform for teachers and students. Especially with the introduction of network technology into multimedia laboratories, restrictions and constraints on time and place of language teaching have been reduced, which greatly expand the extension of foreign language teaching; meanwhile, massive network resources also set up a more broad space for students to learn foreign languages.

2 DEVELOPMENT OF MULTIMEDIA LANGUAGE LABORATORY

In the 1920s, the name, language laboratory was initiated by Ralph H. Waltz at the University of Hawaii in the United States. The language laboratory was mainly functioned to analyze and study all kinds of physical phenomena of voice at that time. Later it was found in practice that more rapid, high-quality efficiency can be achieved by applying the language lab tape recorders into training listening and speaking abilities; ever since then, language laboratories had boosted all over the world, and become more and more functionally powerful with the development of information and technology.

According to the function, language laboratories generally involve five types: Audio-Passive Language Laboratory, (short for AP type hereinafter), is a kind of language lab only functioning with single-directional voice transmission, where students listen to the recording materials through headphones. It used to be called listening room.

Audio-Active Language Laboratory, (short for AA type hereinafter), is a kind of language lab functioning with bi-directional voice transmission and answering dialogues where both teachers and students take headphones and listening gear, while generally, sound insulation seats are equipped.

Audio-Active Comparative Language Laboratory, (short for AAC type hereinafter). In addition to the interaction between teachers and students, students can make comparative practice by comparing the teacher's recorded materials with their own oral English, while teachers can also check students' work.

Audio-Visual Language Laboratory, (short for AV type hereinafter), can simultaneously play PPT, film, video, or other video materials, to create a vivid and authentic language environment.

Multimedia Language Laboratory, (short for ML type hereinafter). With the rapid development of computer technology and network technology, language labs enter the digital network age, and upgrade their function, which can benefit language teaching more.

3 COMPOSITION OF MULTIMEDIA LANGUAGE LABORATORY

A multimedia language laboratory is generally composed of three parts, the teacher's master part, information integration part and students' terminals.

The teacher's master part is usually made up of indicating equipment, operating and controlling equipment, information-transmission equipment, which is the controlling and decision center of a multimedia language lab. It can convey teaching information, issue commands and conduct integrated processing of media and multimedia information by means of information and computer technology.

Information integration part accomplishes its work mainly through various algorithm tools with all the latest teaching theories, related software developed, and computer media. With the development and maturity of computer technology, efficiency and credibility of the information integration part have also been improved. The output of information processing results facilitates the communication and interaction between teachers and students more and realizes the sharing of teaching resources.

Students' terminal part generally includes students' headset microphones, video displays and playback equipment, and response analysis equipment, etc. Compared with traditional language labs, multimedia language labs have the students' terminal equipment paid more attention to the voice fidelity and information collection methods, and meanwhile, the introduction of video displays enables students not only to listen, and speak, but also watch thus further enhancing imitation and learning effect.

4 DIGITAL NETWORK LANGUAGE LEARNING SYSTEM

On the premise of adhering to classical language teaching concepts, digital network language discipline platform moves preparing, lecturing, assignments, self-study, test management and other procedures of language teaching to the campus network, and has realized the purpose of building a "foreign language school" on a computer network (see the picture). By doing this, it not only preserves the classical teaching concepts and traditional teaching methods of universities, but also takes full advantages of the campus network, which greatly improves the teaching effect. It truly fulfills the implementation of overall system planning and the distribution of preparing, lecturing, homework and exams which transmits the traditional teaching to network teaching smoothly and reduces risks.

At present, the software control system of multimedia language labs meets the three major requirements of foreign language teaching in universities: firstly, a professional language teaching environment. It can realize a basic collaborative teaching mode, and create the best language environment in which everybody can take part in comprehensive listening, speaking, reading and writing activities; being of network learning ability with self-independence, students can use campus network platform for language knowledge learning and language skills training by means of interaction between machines and people; it makes

Figure 1.

large-scale network speaking tests available. The application of advanced network technology to carry out spoken language tests and comprehensive examinations can greatly remove the burden on teachers, and improve examination efficiency.

Multimedia language laboratories have been equipped with advanced teaching mode, and are designed with teaching platforms for listening, speaking, and reading, which not only realizes professional teaching, but also interaction between teachers and students in the teaching process to give timely feedback. This has changed the traditional single-directional "broadcasting teaching" into an interactive, feedback, and bi-directional teaching, which is an exclusive function of the multimedia language laboratories. Teachers can set learning themes according to students' learning and life characteristics to operate teaching procedure in a small class, where each student can get simultaneously interactive training in listening, speaking, reading and writing for motivating the brain, eyes, ears, mouth, hands and other senses to participate in at the same time; in addition to traditional communication between students and teachers, the communication and discussion among students turns easy and convenient. The teacher-dominating class turns into a student-centered class proceeded by means of interactive practice teaching mode, which has greatly promoted the development of students' thinking, stimulated their interest in learning, and improved their learning initiatives. Meanwhile, the application of network technology has not only provided abundant resources for learning, broadened its depth and breadth, but also realized remote teaching in multimedia language laboratories via the Internet. It has broken the traditional boundaries of school, changed the traditional concept of class and the limits of time and space, and provided students with opportunities to communicate directly with the tutors all over the world, to share global information, technology and related materials. It has created conditions for students to get rid of the interference of native languages temporarily, thus prompting students to exchange and communicate in a foreign language thinking mode consciously. This is also a point that multimedia language laboratories are superior to the traditional teaching.

5 MANAGEMENT OF MULTIMEDIA LANGUAGE LABORATORY

The diversity of practical functions in multimedia language labs, the complexity of the management system, and the diversity of participants have higher requirements on the current management work of university language laboratories.

Take Qilu University of Technology for example, its foreign language learning center is equipped with seven digital language laboratories, five computer network laboratories, and total seats more than 1100; the floorage of the center occupies 1600 square meters. The teaching task of college English and more than ten subjects of foreign language majors in the whole university are carried out in this center with the annual workload more than 800,000 hours. Because of the curriculum innovation in the university, the workload of foreign language teaching has increasingly raised. It's necessary to introduce advanced management concept and establish scientific management system, to ensure the language labs functioning always in good dynamic environment.

The most important material base of language teaching is language equipment. The pursuit of maximum benefit of equipment must be guaranteed by a scientific and effective management system. The present language laboratory management system of the university mainly includes laboratory equipment management system, laboratory application management system, laboratory operation procedure system, lab-post administrator system, and laboratory safety management system, etc. In addition to the similarities with general laboratory management systems, particularity of language labs should also be taken into consideration in these systems, to realize the unification of the management system and characteristics of laboratories.

Multimedia language lab management system must be both easy to use for teachers and students, and convenient to control. As most multimedia devices in multimedia language labs are relatively expensive, and easy to be damaged, especially when students don't operate them in accordance with the procedure, they are easy to be damaged. This should be taken full consideration when making rule. For one thing, strengthen the education of students, before the first class of each semester; inform students clearly of the application procedure and cautions of related equipment; ask students to obey the arrangement from managers and teachers. For another, identify the responsibility system; fix seats for students according to the curriculum and student list. Before each class, laboratory managers should take key inspection on the equipment for students' use after being confirmed intact. After class, they should take timely inspection on related equipment. For those damaged, find the reasons in time, identify the one who should take the responsibility, and ask for compensation when necessary. Perfect management system and clear responsibility consciousness, will make students take more care of the equipment.

In addition to having good service consciousness as well as doing well in teaching assistant work, the management personnel of multimedia language labs should also acquire knowledge of the network technology and computer technology, master the basic structure, working principle and characteristics of language equipment, and be able to accomplish the equipment maintenance work with actively correct methods.

The particularity of multimedia language labs makes higher requirements on the quality of foreign language teachers, who should strengthen their related foreign language skills training. After training, for one thing, teachers can understand more completely the management system, equipment performance and operation methods of the language laboratory and know how to operate the equipment in strict accordance with the procedure; for another, updating foreign language teachers' teaching concepts and encouraging them to strengthen the study of foreign language teaching methods, can bring the advanced teaching facilities into full play and improve the effectiveness of foreign language teaching. In addition, in view of some foreign teachers, due to their differences in communication, culture and other aspects, we should pay more attention to their training to avoid various existing loopholes.

Strengthen the management of laboratory equipment. Set up files of improving laboratory instruments and equipments, keep all kinds of information well saved, especially the purchase contracts, product instructions, installation and debugging acceptance reports. Keep spares and accessories of instruments complete. Establish equipment maintenance system, improve the corresponding safety operational regulations, and fill out record forms of equipment application and maintenance for regular filing. Strengthen the management of equipment identification and mark; identify the application state of the equipment. Match equipment numbers, serial numbers, file numbers correspondingly, to realize the four unifications of equipment records in file, entity, mark, and application.

6 MAINTENANCE OF MULTIMEDIA LANGUAGE LABORATORY

The maintenance of multimedia language labs includes active maintenance and emergency maintenance. Maintenance work should be dominated by active maintenance with emergency maintenance as supplement. Good daily maintenance work, is an effective means to ensure the normal operation of multimedia language labs. Daily maintenance mainly involves two aspects, namely, the daily hardware maintenance and daily software maintenance.

Daily hardware maintenance mainly includes regular supervision and inspection on computers, terminals, headphones, lab booths, loudspeakers and other hardware facilities, and making inspection records which should be filled by the language lab manager accompanying with the teacher of the course. Once problems are found, they should be solved in time. Due to the aging problem of computer systems, annual laboratory funds should be increased for the quantity and quality guarantee.

Daily software maintenance mainly refers to ensuring the software of multimedia language labs in good condition, and avoiding interference of viruses and other problems. Do good work in maintenance and upgrade of related systems and software in time, to avoid problems caused by late update, or incompatibility, etc.; according to the openness of multimedia language labs, work of preventing computer viruses should be actively carried out. Install and update anti-virus software and operation systems in time, to reduce system vulnerabilities; make regular backup of related information, and establish a backup system of laboratory information database to avoid losses; when necessary, take physical means to prevent virus attacks.

In the meantime of doing daily maintenance work for labs, we should make a careful analysis on sudden problems and hidden safety dangers existing in labs and establish emergency plans. Emergency maintenance is chiefly designed for equipment failure and personnel accidents. Once there is an unexpected accident in the equipment, the lab manager should be on the scene in the first time to conduct a preliminary inspection in time and make corresponding treatment decisions, or a timely transfer for the equipment to ensure the normal teaching process; when necessary, a language lab shift is required. Language lab accidents involving personnel are mainly caused by fire, electric shock, and other safety accidents due to the line fault and other unpredictable factors. Laboratory management personnel and teachers should be able to handle them correctly and in time and complete each work according to the process. They should do well in simulation exercises of emergency event in daily inspection to improve the ability of related laboratory management personnel in dealing with emergencies.

7 CONCLUSION

Multimedia language labs have provided foreign language teaching in universities with a good teaching and learning platform, whose development and construction is closely related to the scientific research ability and teaching level of universities.

Colleges and universities should attach high importance to the advancement, innovation operating mechanism and management concept of multimedia language labs, make full use of high quality resources and advanced technologies, and integrate the existing resources, to build a more effective platform for the improvement of English teaching quality and cultivation of high-quality talents.

REFERENCES

[1] F. Jiang: Discussion on the Management and Maintenance of Multimedia Language Laboratory in the University. China Modern Educational Equipment, Vol. 8,(2009): 115–117.

[2] Z.H. Pan, X.Q. Zheng, R.H. He and P. Zhang: Development and Management of Multimedia Language Laboratories. Research and Exploration in Laboratory. Vol. 32(4),(2013):190–192.

[3] Y. Zhang: Application of Teaching Management System in Multimedia Speech Laboratory. Modern Electronics Technique. Vol. 34(15), (2011): 183–185.

[4] S.H. Yan: The Quality Construction of the Administrative Personnel of the Language Laboratory. Experiment Science and Technology. Vol. 9 (6), (2011): 154–156.

[5] G.L. Song: Research and Practice of the Open Experimental Teaching Mode. Research and Exploration in Laboratory. Vol. 29(2), (2010): 91–93,123.

[6] X.P. Han: Discussion on the Construction and Management of Laboratories in Ordinary Universities. Sci-Tech Information Development & Economy. Vol. 16(4), (2006): 276–277.

[7] B.Y. Chen and X.L. Chen: Discussion on Experience of Experiment Teaching Reform in Our University. Laboratory Science. Vol. 13(2), (2010): 35–37.

[8] X.L. Shi: Policies of Improving Application Efficiency of Multimedia Language Laboratories. Software Guide. Vol. 10(2), (2011): 70–71.

Computer, Intelligent Computing and Education Technology – Liu, Sung & Yao (Eds)
© 2014 Taylor & Francis Group, London, ISBN 978-1-138-02469-4

Analysis on cleaning chain material wear of steel belt conveyor in coal-fired power plant

Y.D. Wang
Beijing Guodian Futong Science and Technology Development Co. Ltd., Fengtai District, Beijing, China

ABSTRACT: By introducing the working theory of steel belt conveyor, the causes for wear condition of parts of scraper blade, chain and guide roller of running steel belt conveyor have been analyzed. Find out the optimization measure with minimum abrasion loss by corresponding optimization calculation. And through the application demonstration in a some power plant, by implementing the measures for treatment, the equipment defect could be reduced, and the operational reliability of the system could be improved.

Keywords: steel belt conveyor; cleaning chain; wear analysis

1 INTRODUCTION

Steel belt conveyor is widely popularized and applied in thermal power generating unit in recent years because of its obvious technical and economic edges. In China, the dry bottom ash handing system has been applied in hundreds of domestic power plants, which greatly reduced the pollution of coal-fired power plants to the environment and solved the problems of Waterpower Dusting and Slagging System as complex, expensive, high water consumption, high power consumption, over land occupation and expensive operation maintenance. Along with the developing of the dry bottom ash handing system, debug and research of the system in engineering are extremely urgent, of which there's few or no research on cleaning chain. The main content of the paper is to research the reasons of cleaning chain material abrasion, and put forward corresponding solutions, then will be practiced in a power plant. It is expected to pose available methods to solve the abrasion problem of cleaning chain blade, and then optimize the steel belt conveyor.

2 STEEL BELT CONVEYOR

Function brief of Steel belt conveyor. Steel belt conveyor is installed under the boiler furnace of thermal power plant, the slag falls on steel conveyor belt of clinker conveyer from slag shaft; high temperature slag is sent out by steel conveyor belt. The hot slag delivered will be cooled in multistage steel conveyor belt gradually; the air for cooling goes into the equipment through the adjustable air inlet set on the shell of clinker conveyer under the effect of combustion chamber draft, cold air and hot slag would make reverse heat exchange; cold air goes into the combustion chamber after absorbing heat to the appropriate temperature, recycle the heat of furnace slag, so as to reduce the heat loss of boiler, and then been transferred slag storage warehouse through steel belt conveyor.

3 STRUCTURE OF STEEL BELT CONVEYOR

Tank Shell: the head frame of steel belt conveyer is welded by H-shape steel and thick steel plate, and installed with drive unit on top. Braced frame of the center part is welded by H-shape steel and steel plate in structure, and added with reinforcement rib. The tail frame is also welded by H-shape steel and thick steel plate, and installed with stainless steal conveyor tension device on top.

Idler: steel belt conveyor adopts concave tooth, which possesses advantages in case of severe chain abrasion or large pitch deviation as well-adapted to the chain, on off-chain, well guidance, long life and high reliability, etc.

Steel conveyor belt: the transportation steel belt, which made of stainless steel, has excellent heat resistance and well adapted to slag, usually lay out in the form of scale.

Conveyor scraper: steel angle and web plate are adopted for the scraper of dry slag machine, which is of high strength, with no distortion, no bending. The scraper is connected to the chain by rotate-assemble scraper holder through high-strength stainless steel bolt. By using this connection method, the scraper would not fall off in the running process, and the easy to be overhauled.

Steel belt drive mechanism: steel belt drive mechanism of steel machine is mainly composed of motor + BREVINI coaxial gear box, drive roller and transmission roller.

Cleaning chain drive mechanism: cleaning chain drive mechanism is consisted of SEW coaxial gear box, driven sprocket, main gear shaft and driving sprocket. Scraper chain, the main working components, is installed on the driving chain wheel, then through the drive system, the motor drives the driving sprocket rotates, and make scraper driving the slag forward towards incline section.

Tension mechanism: the tension mechanism is consisted of hydraulic system and mechanical tension mechanism. The hydraulic system automatically controls the tensioning system to offer hydraulic oil with certain pressure to the oil cylinder and energy accumulator through a small hydraulic power pack, while two oil cylinders are installed on the tension wheel, so as to control the chain tightness. The mechanical tension mechanism is consisted of tension wheel, axle, track, holder and slide. Through the operation with the oil cylinder, tension wheel could control the chain tension.

Operating principle of Steel belt conveyor cleaning chain: part of furnace slag and ash falls on the floor of box in the extractor, and then been delivered to the head of the extractor (also the slagging direction) by conveyor scraper, and sent out by equipment or truck. At the meantime, scraper chain goes back to the back section of Steel belt conveyor along with the driving wheel. The equipment control cabinet is designed with switch button of on-site operation and remote operation.

4 WEAR MECHANISM AND HAZARD

Wear mechanism: wear refers to diminish of the parts physical dimension (volume); the parts lose the function of the original design; or reliability and security will be lost if continue to use. According to the characteristics of the surface fracture, the form of wear falls into abrasive wear, adhesive wear, contact fatigue wear and fretting wear, etc.

Wear process: Wear can be roughly divided into running-in wear stage, stable wear stage and severe wear stage. Normal use of material is usually in the running-in wear stage and stable wear stage. In the running-in wear stage, as the roughness value of new friction surface is larger, the wear is relative bigger. However, the surface roughness will be reduced along with the running-in process, the wear rate tends to go stabilized, and then entered the stage of stable wear stage. Well running-in wear

can make smooth surface, which is crucial for the whole friction system. After entering into the stable wear stage, wear become relatively slow and stable, and wear rate remain essentially unchanged, so that time of the stage represents the life of the friction surface. Go through long-time stable wear then turn into severe. Due to the change of the gap between friction surfaces, the surface transforms and surface fatigue, the wear rate will sharply increases until the friction surface scraps.

Wear hazard. The wear of cleaning chain of steel belt machine applied in thermal power plant is mainly jointly caused by abrasive wear, adhesive wear and contact fatigue wear between scraper blade or chain and wear-proof base plate of tank. This abrasive action exists in scraper blade, chain and guide pulley, of which the scraper blade wear is the most serious. The scraper blade would deform, bend, and have lining plate up warping or even falling off, which pose a threat to the safety operation of the equipment. When the coal quality is relatively poor, if the operation is not adjusted well, the replacing rate of scraper blade could reach as much as 20% to 30% when the equipment is running every 5000 hours. Steel belt machine is difficult to be tensioned appropriately due to the long chain and plenty of scraper blades. When over-tensioning, the positive pressure on chain increases in power wheel and guide wheel, so the abrasion is intensified; while over-loose, the chain would be dragged at the base plate in descending section, which causes skimming wear. The side of chain where suffered the worse attrition would be stretched gradually, so that the chains are suffered to a varying length, the scraper blade forms a included angle α with axle wire in tensioning wheel when it runs to the tail. While the wear of the chain of loose side under the bottom of tank would get worse, when the hardening coat of thermal treatment is broken by abrasion, it would go into pull-to-loose circle. At this time, the inclination angle α of scraper blade would be larger as the loosen of chain, when the angle α reaches a certain value, scraper blade would be blocked at the tail tensioning wheel or cause the chain coming off the tensioning wheel, thus cause the shut down of steel belt machine.

5 IMPROVEMENT ON WEAR-PROOF CALCULATION OF CLEANING CHAIN

The main wear points of cleaning chain of steel belt machine are the scraper blade and chain.

Reduce frictional resistance. The skimming friction depends on the vertical compression N applied on friction face and coefficient of sliding friction μ, which means f = μN, where f denotes friction, μ denotes coefficient of sliding friction, N represents the vertical compression borne on friction surface of cleaning chain. When steel belt machine is running, given that the abrasion between scraper blade and chain is carried out slowly, the reduction of its quality within a certain time range could be negligible, therefore, the vertical compression N among scraper blade, chain and friction surface within a certain time range could be regarded as constant value. But the value μ has something to do with material and roughness of contact surface. The materials of scraper blade, chain, wear plate and guide pulley of steel belt machine are fixed, to reduce the attrition economically, the only method is to reduce the roughness of all contact surfaces, so as to meet the goal of reducing the friction. After running a certain period, many tiny disintegrating slags will accumulate on the bottom wear plate, if they are not cleaned away in time, the roughness of bottom wear plate would be intensified greatly, and the skimming friction coefficient between scraper blade and wear-resisting plate would be increased greatly, so does the friction force between them, the wear rate of scraper blade would rise perpendicularly. Ash contacts the scraper blade and chain in working, so the wear in this place is inevitable.

Optimum operation speed of chain. When the friction is basically stable, the relative velocity of movement between friction surfaces v becomes determinant factor affecting the wear rate. The abrasion rate k increases as the velocity v, when value v reaches to a certain critical point, the wear rate would progressive increase multiply.

Suppose that when the operation velocity of chain is V_0, the output w_1 of steel belt machine is just equal to the discharge quantity w_2 of boiler, then V_0 is the reference speed of the chain of steel belt machine under the corresponding load, in other words, when the chain velocity is equal to V_0, the following formula could be obtained: $w_1 = w_2$.

According to the actual weigh and empirical analysis, the slag quantity shown in Figure 1 is that of scraper blade when steel belt machine is running normally, its shape could be regarded as tri-prism volume.

Where α denotes the height of working platform of scraper blade, the unit is m; ι denotes the width of that working platform, with the unit m;

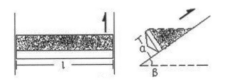

Figure 1.

ρ denotes the density of ash on scraper blade, with the unit of t/m³; β denotes the included angle between inclination section of steel belt machine and horizontal line. L denotes the distance between scraper blades, with the unit m.

Output of steel belt machine $w_1 = V_0 \times 60 \times Q_1/L$.

Discharge quantity of boiler $w_2 = Q \times A \times \phi$.

where Q denotes the coal-burning quantity per hour of boiler, with the unit of t, A denotes the average ash specification of analyzing basic coal, φ denotes the parts shipped out from cleaning chain which turned into coke button from ash specimen after burning, it could be calculated in accordance with the fire coal quantity, ash specimen and slag output per hour. Value φ takes 1% to 3% generally.

Based on $w_1 = w_2$, $V_0 = Q \times A \times \phi \times L \times tg\beta / 30 \times a \times a \times 1 \times \rho$ could be derived.

The reference speed of chain under any boiler load and known coal quality could be obtained from the previous formula. In other words, the wearing capacity of steel belt machine under this velocity suffers the least.

6 APPLICATION OF WEAR-PROOF CALCULATION OF CLEANING CHAIN IN SOME POWER PLANT

The unit boiler capacity of some power plant is 660 MW, the coal burning amount per hour of BMCR operating at full load is 268 t/h, average ash specimen of analyzing base is 36%, value Φ takes 1%, the distance L between scraper plates is 0.8 m, height of working platform of cleaning chain scraper blade is 0.1 m, the width l of working platform of scraper blade is 1.4 m, included angle β between inclination section of steel belt machine and horizontal line is 28°, ash density ρ takes 1.2 t/m³.

$$V_0 = \frac{286 \times 0.36 \times 0.01 \times 0.8 \times tg\,28}{30 \times 0.1 \times 0.1 \times 1.4 \times 1.2}$$

Through calculation, when the reference velocity of chain under corresponding load and coal quality is 0.87 (m/min), the wear amount on scraper blade steel belt machine is the minimum, so the adjustment of operational velocity of cleaning chain from 0.2 (m/min) to 1.7 (m/min) should be the range from 0.6 (m/min) to 1.1 (m/min) accordingly, which is more accurate.

After 5,000 hours operation, the replacement quantity of scraper blade from 2009 to 2010 is 77, after adopting the improved economic operational velocity, that quantity goes down to 38 from 2010 to 2011, which slows down the wear rate and reduce the field overhaul and maintenance cost effectively.

7 SUMMARY

During the daily operation, it is required to lubricate and clean all friction surfaces of steel belt machine, adjust the operational velocity of the chain of steel belt machine carefully, check the wear quantity of chain of steel belt machine regularly, adjust the discharge quantity of boiler in the operational process, the chain should have proper operational velocity, in this way, the rotation of scraper blade, chain and guide pulley could be reduced effectively. Because of that the ash specimen of coal in boiler is uneven, and the roughing slag quantity of boiler varies from time to time under the influence of combustion and coking conditions, in order to deliver the ash discharged from boiler in time, a certain redundancy must be reserved when setting the chain velocity of steel belt machine in practical. The height of working platform of scraper blade would be lowered accordingly, by this time, the theoretical velocity of the chain should be re-calculated.

REFERENCES

[1] Yao Cheng. Operation of Dregs System of Thermal Power Plant. Industrial Press, p. 19.
[2] Yao Wenda, Jiang Fan. Operation and Accident Handling of Boiler in Thermal Power Plant. China Electric Power Press.
[3] Zhang Lei, Lian Genkuan, Technical Q&A on boiler operation; Industrial Press 2007-4–1.

Computer, Intelligent Computing and Education Technology – Liu, Sung & Yao (Eds)
© 2014 Taylor & Francis Group, London, ISBN 978-1-138-02469-4

MEMS-based microsystem for minimally invasive optical monitoring of blood glucose

P.Y. Zhang & Y. Li

School of Physics and Electronics, Henan University, China

ABSTRACT: A new microsystem for minimally invasive monitoring of blood glucose has been proposed. The system proposed here for monitoring of blood glucose is composed of glucose sensors based on minimally invasive optical techniques and integrated microneedle array which is out-of-plane and employs a bi-mask technique to facilitate sharp tips, a cylindric body that has high strength and side ports which minimizes the potential for clogging. This system can sample blood and analyze the sample. The light irradiates the blood sample which is withdrawn by microneedles to assay the concentration of glucose. The microdevice can be used in monitoring blood glucose of diabetes. The needles are small enough in size to prevent user discomfort. It is especially suitability for use by children since it is no pain and requires a less blood sample. Similarly, this device can be used in monitoring of performance enhances in athletes and other biomedical applications.

Keywords: monitoring of blood glucose; microneedles; biosensor; BioMEMS

1 INTRODUCTION

Diabetes mellitus is a mainly cause of death and disability in the world. The World Health Organization expects the number of people with diabetes worldwide to reach 300 million by 2025 [1]. Diabetes mellitus is a chronic disease characterized by varying or persistent hyperglycemia. The body cannot maintain blood glucose levels. Normal levels of blood glucose range between 3–8 mmol/L, for diabetics the range is 2–20 mmol/L [2]. Beyond Normal level can result in long term complications such as blindness, kidney disease and circulatory problems. Frequent and accurate glucose monitoring is needed if the disease is to be effectively brought under control.

The directly method is that the glucose concentration is measured by glucose sensor that directly implanted in the subcutaneous tissue [3]. Since the invasive methods are painful and inconvenient with poor patient compliance, noninvasive method was also proposed using Optical techniques [4]. Optical techniques to monitor glucose are truly noninvasive. The advantages of the method are obviously, painlessness and no tissue trauma.

Recently, the development of glucose sensors based on enzymatic glucose oxidation has been made [5]. The approaches employing glucose oxidize-based sensors possess highly sensitive and specific to the analyte of interes. But these chemicals may be susceptible to degradation over time via consumption, photo-bleaching or denaturation

in long-term use. If the blood sample is measured directly, interfering factors resulted from the skin tissue do not exist. Therefore, high measurement accuracy for glucose sensing may be achieved. In this paper, we propose a minimally invasive optical method for direct monitoring of blood glucose. This method is painless and minimum tissue trauma, minimally invasive, because of employing microneedles. The integrated microsystem for monitoring of blood glucose comprised integrated microneedle array which performed painless sampling with minimally invasion and glucose sensors based on optical techniques.

2 MECHANISM OF MICROSYSTEM

A microsystem for continue monitoring of blood glucose is proposed. The microsystem comprises three parts, chip for monitoring of glucose, control unit and insulin pump. The glucose monitor chip consists of microneedle array and glucose sensor; Existing insulin pump can be adapted to the system. The mechanism of the microsystem is as shown in Figure 1.

The device is placed on the skin and samples some blood by advancing the silicon microneedle under microprocessor control. The skin is punctured and blood is drawn to the micropool by capillary forces to fill the micropool. Then, the microneedle array is retracted, and the assay is performed within the micropool by reagents immobi-

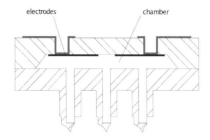

Figure 1. The structure I of chip for monitoring of glucose.

lized on the wafer surface specific for glucose. The assay result either optical or electrochemical can be displayed, stored in memory in the instrument, transmitted by data telemetry, or used in a stored algorithm to allow the microprocessor to provide an indicator that the analyte concentration is abnormal. Finally, the loop could be closed by using an insulin pump to correct deviations from normal values. If the glucose level is abnormal, delivering the drug by insulin pump. If normal, wait for interval, start to sample to enter the next circulation.

3 CHIP FOR MONITORING OF GLUCOSE

Molar absorptivity is certain at every wavelength by the vibrational absorption properties of glucose. Light attenuation passing through the skin is also related to the spectral range. Spectral range is important because glucose absorption properties differ to different wavelengths. The spectral region of 600–1,300 nm called "the optical window" of the skin is allowed considerable penetration through the tissue. Unfortunately, this region contains little specific information for glucose. For the rest regions of near-infrared range above 1,300 nm, glucose absorption at the wavelength band between 1575 and 1700 nm is the greatest. There are three absorption bands of glucose are respectively centered at 6200, 5920 and 5775 cm-1. But the absorptivities are interfered either scattering or absorptions of water, fat and protein [6].

The optimum region through partial least squares regression is from 5975 to 5850 cm^{-1}[6]. Wavelength 1.69 μm (5920 cm^{-1}) is chosen as the probing light. In this wavelength region, the water absorbance relate to glucose is negligible. In order to decrease the inferences of the other blood components except glucose such as, water, hemoglobin and albumin, the reference light is needed. The glucose absorption at the reference light is negligible. The wavelength 1.2 or 1.56 μm is as the reference light.

The microsystem comprises the chip for monitoring of glucose and the optoelectronic instruments what read the optical absorbance of the assay chemistry in the micropool, calculate glucose concentration, and display the result. The packaged microchip (microneedle array and micropool) is assembled in the optoelectronic instruments. The light source and detector unit are needed in the device. The chip for monitoring of glucose includes Microneedle array and a blood pool. An illustration of the chip for monitoring of glucose is shown in Figures 1–3 shows the structure of the micromachined needle array.

The minimally invasive optical method for directly monitoring of blood glucose has not only high measurement accuracy because of avoiding effects of absorption and scattering resulted from the skin tissue due to directly measure to blood sample, by contrast with non-invasive optical method, but also painlessness, minimum tissue trauma and little sample amount because of employing microneedles to sample the blood, by contrast to the tradition finger-prick method.

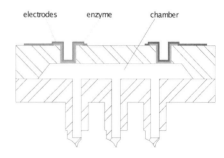

Figure 2. The structure II of chip for monitoring of glucose.

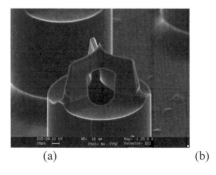

(a)   (b)

Figure 3. Structure of the microneedle array.

4 FABRICATION

The process flow of microsystem for monitoring of blood glucose is shown in Figure 4. In the first step of the process, a silicon wafer is given a thermal growth of oxide and patterned at the upside of the wafer (Fig. 4a). Secondly, the holes are anisotropically etched by RIE from front side of the wafer (Fig. 4b). Those holes are etch-stop holes for the next etching step. Then, the thin film of SiO2 is patterned at the backside of the wafer (Fig. 4c). The holes are anisotropically etched by deep RIE from the backside of the wafer, as shown in Figure 4d. The etching of the holes from backside do not stop till the bottom of etch-stop holes. Those holes are the needle channels. After the SiO2 is removed, the wafer is given a thermal growth of oxide. The next step is patterning a bi-mask (Fig. 4e), and the bi-mask is aligned to the center of the hole on the front side of the wafer. An anisotropic ICP step follows. The body of the needle is formed at this step. Then, the wafer is given a thermal growth of oxide (Fig. 4f). After the upper mask from the bi-mask is removed, the wafer is isotropically etched by ICP (Fig. 4g). Following that, a second anisotropic ICP is carried out. During this step, the side ports are formed (Fig. 4h). In order to acquire the sharp needle tip, a second isotropic ICP is employed (Fig. 4i). After that, the SiO2 is etched (Fig. 4 j), and the structure of needle array is released. Then, a new silicon wafer is thinned by CMP (Fig. 4k). The wafer is given deposit of SiO2 and patterned at the upside of the wafer. Boron doping and diffusion are followed (Fig. 4l). After SiO2 mask is moved, the silicon wafer is given deposit of SiO2 and Si3 N4 on the both of side respectively. After patterning and etching of the SiO2 and Si3 N4 on the backside of the wafer (Fig. 4 m), an anisotropic etch is carried out using KOH (Fig. 4n). Then, the SiO2 and Si3 N4 are moved. Following that, the metal electrodes are evaporated and etched (Fig. 4o). After that, a deposit of SiO2 and pattern are performed, followed by RIE on the front side of the wafer to make grooves (Fig. 4p). After sputtering a metal as contact pads, the metal is patterned and etched (Fig. 4q). Finally, the needle array and biosensor are bonded (Fig. 4r).

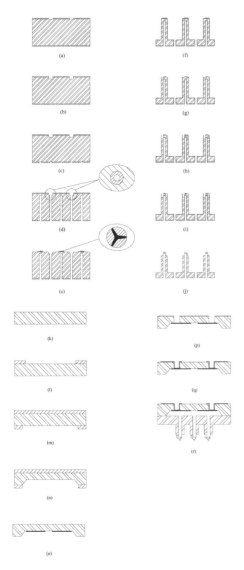

Figure 4.   Process flow of the microsystem.

5 DISCUSSION

The microsystem proposed here is an integrated system of microneedle array and the glucose sensor. The microneedle array employs a bi-mask technique to facilitate sharp tips, a cylindric body that possesses high strength and side ports which minimize the potential for clogging. The microneedle is out-of-plane structure, having high needle density. Moreover, it has a low flow resistance owing to the cylindrical channel and side ports. In addition, the needle array can be easily fabricated. The microneedle has an extremely sharp tip and the knife-like edges allow easy penetration of the skin. The small dimensions of microneedles can provide painless minimal invasion, and reduce damage to the skin. The opportunity of infection is also considerably decreased.

High measurement accuracy for glucose sensing can be achieved through direct sensing blood sample using optical techniques avoiding affects resulted from skin tissue, compared to noninvasive optical method of glucose sensing. Minimally invasive method proposed in the paper is painless and small tissue trauma due to microneedles. This method synthesizes advantages both noninvasive and invasive methods, and compromises the requirements both of measurement accuracy and patients' compliance. Microsystem for directly sensing of blood sampled by microneedles through optical techniques maybe is better choice at present.

This device of glucose sensors has features such as small in size, reliable, inexpensive and easy to fabrication. The device can be used in monitoring blood glucose of diabetes. The needle is small enough in size to prevent user discomfort. It is especially suitability for use by children since it is no pain and requires a less blood sample. Moreover, This device employs a one-step process that is, processes on sampling and analysis are performed in a device, thus minimizing blood required and possible mess and avoiding the demands to transfer blood from a skin puncture to a test strip.

Similarly, this device can be used in monitoring of performance enhances in athletes. The athletes can regulate physical training and food consumption appropriately according to the measurement of indicators through monitoring glucose levels in the blood. This device can be also extended to the other biomedical application, such as monitoring of therapeutic drug levels.

6 CONCLUSION

A novel minimally invasive system for painless blood testing is proposed for assay of blood glucose concentration by diabetics. This microsampling and assay device composed of glucose sensor based on optical techniques and microneedle array capable of reliably taking a very small sample of whole blood painlessly integrated with a micro pool in which the analyte can be analysed. This system has several attractive features including: small in size, reliable, inexpensive and easy to mass fabrication. Besides, the microneedle array has high strength and side ports which minimize the potential for clogging. The microneedles are easy to penetrate the skin painlessly. The glucose sensor has a high accuracy with good patient compliance. Apparently, the miccrosystem can be extended to monitoring of performance enhance in athletes and other biomedical application.

REFERENCES

[1] M. Jones, J.M. Harrison, the future of diabetes technologies and therapeutics, Diabetes Technolp Ther. 2002, 4:p351–359.
[2] M. Lambrechts, W. Sansen, Biosensors: Microelectrochemical Devices. Institute of Physics Publishing Bristol, Philadelphia and New York, 1992.
[3] D.S. Bindra, Y. Zhang, G.S. Wilson et al., Design and in vitro studies of a needle-type glucose sensor for subcutaneous monitoring. Anal Chem, 1991. 63(17): p. 1692–1696.
[4] H.M. Heise, R. Marbach, T. Koschinsky, F.A. Gries, Noninvasive blood glucose sensors based on near-infrared spectroscopy. Artif Organs, 1994. 18(6): p. 439–447.
[5] J. Janata, M. Josowicz, P. Vanysek, D.M. DeVaney, Chemical sensors, Anal. Chem. 70, p179–208, 1998.
[6] K.H. Hazen, M.A. Arnold, G.W. Small. Measurement of Glucose in Water with First-Overtone Near-Infrared Spectra. Applied Spectroscopy, V 52, N12, p1597–1605, 1998.

Computer, Intelligent Computing and Education Technology – Liu, Sung & Yao (Eds)
© 2014 Taylor & Francis Group, London, ISBN 978-1-138-02469-4

Research on visual natural Gas Transmission Pipeline Networks integration model base-on SVG

Y. Gao & M. Yuan
School of Computer and Information Technology, North East Petroleum University, Daqing, Heilongjiang, China

J.S. Yuan
College of Petroleum Engineering, North East Petroleum University, Daqing, Heilongjiang, China

Y. Yu & D.L. Yang
School of Computer and Information Technology, North East Petroleum University, Daqing, Heilongjiang, China

ABSTRACT: During natural gas field development, management of natural Gas Transmission Pipeline Networks (GTPN) is an important task. With the development of gas-field production scale, The GTPN becomes more and more complicated. Therefore, the workers need a platform to display all kinds of space objects of the GTPN, and meanwhile all kinds of information related to the GTPN will be queried. According to these requirements, firstly, a triangle integration model is studied and defined, while the integration algorithm is given. Secondly, a basic WebGIS platform has been constructed based on XML/ SVG/DOM/JS, which can display all kinds of space objects of the GTPN of Daqing recovery gas-field. Finally, According to triangle integration model and the basic WebGIS platform, all kinds of applications are integrated on the platform. Different users are able to obtain information interested on the platform. The triangle integration model proposed and basic WebGIS platform possess common characteristics, these technique can be applied other domains.

Keywords: gas transmission pipeline networks; visualization; WebIGS; SVG; integration

1 INTRODUCTION

Natural gas is one of the foremost high quality and sanitary sources. Gas Transmission Pipeline Networks (GTPN) are the artery connecting natural gas resource and market. In daqing oil field, recovery gas company is responsible for natural gas producing and managing business, the natural gas is recovered from the gas wells, these natural gas recovered will be transported from GTPN. The GTPN includes many space objects, such as gas wells, gathering stations, pipelines and so on. Besides these space objects, it associates with many other space objects, such as railway, road, grassland, farmland and so on. How to manage and maintain the GTPN becomes an important issue. At present, the GTPN is managed by manual work, management efficiency is very low. Technique for GTPN visualization and integration is studied. Considering the GTPN visualization characteristics, it is fit for visualizing on WebGIS. Firstly, all the objects of GTPN can be displayed on the webGIS, and the topology relationship among the space objects related to GTPN can be displayed, while the GTPN is

displayed, all kinds of information either related to space objects, or business is able to query also.

Nowadays, there are many popular commercial GIS software, such as ArcGIS [1], MapInfo, MGE/GeoMedia and so on. These commercial GIS software common characteristics are expensive, and meanwhile these GIS software running efficiency is not ideal on web. In practice, users do not need so complicated WebGIS functions, and it is necessary to provide a light WebGIS, which includes some simple functions, such as map moving, map zooming in, map zooming out and GIS navigation functions. Based on this light WebGIS, many applications can be integrate into the WebGIS [2]. According to these requirements, some key technologies are researched such as GIS technique, XML technique [3], AJAX technique [4], SVG technique [5], metadata technique, information integration [6][7][8], organization technique of space GIS objects, decentralized map loading and some related technologies. A kind of triangle integration mode is proposed, and the algorithm is given. By means of the triangle integration model, the functions for displaying GTPN and querying information of the GTPN are implemented.

2 TRIANGLE INTEGRATION MODEL

The workers hope that they can query all kinds of information interested on the map of natural gas transmission pipeline networks. It is well known that the natural gas transmission networks include many space objects, such as pipeline, gas well, road, gas field and so on. Besides, the networks are related to these space objects, such as river, station, grassland, farmland and so on, these space objects are either covered by networks, or spanned. However, the workers are often interested in some space objects, because of these space objects binding much information, likewise, the workers are only interested in some information too. Therefore, according to these requirements, a triangle integration mode is proposed, which is showed in Figure 1. The triangle integration model defines three primary entities, the first entity is Su, which is the set of users, corresponding to the worker, and the second entity is Se, which is the set of space object, corresponding to all kinds of space objects on the networks. The third entity is the set of applications, corresponding to all kinds of information. Among these entities, the component of Application integration context is a metadata model which is used to describe three entities and relationship among these tree entities. This component is an important component for integrating users, space-objects and applications. In order to understand the triangle integration model more, some definitions will be given below:

2.1 Definitions

1. **Definition 1**: User set, written Su = {Ui (Rua, Ru, Rue)| i∈(the count of user category)}. Ui contains three attributes, Rua, Ru, Rue, they describes applications which the user is interested in, the relationship between users and users category, and space objects which the user is interested in, respectively.

2. **Definition 2**: Space object set, written Se = {Ej, Reu, Re, Rea)| j∈(the count of space objects)}, Ej contains three attributes, Reu, Re, Rea, they describes business domain to which the objects belong, the relationship between space objects and map layers, and object binding applications, respectively.

3. **Definition 3:** Application set, written Sa = {Ak, Rau, Ra, Rae)| k∈(the count of application category)}, Sa contains three attributes, Rau, Ra, Rae, they describes the relationship between application and business domain, all kinds of relationships among different applications, and applications binding space objects, respectively.

In theory, three definitions above give the relationship among the Su, Se and Sa. How to use these entities to implement integration, the integration algorithm will be given below.

2.2 Algorithm for integration

According to definition 1 to 3, the integration algorithm is described in alpha language as follows:

Step 1: Hold Se(Ej) to map ORDER By Ru; //Organizing map layers

Step 2: GET USER(Du, Ru), USER, Ux, Rua, Ru, Rue;)//Obtaining space objects and its applications

Step 3: GET E{E1, E2 ......, En}(Se(Reu)):Ux (Rue)= Ej (Reu)//Finding visual area on map

Step 4: GET A{A1, A2 ......, Am}(Da(Rau)): Ui(Rua)= Ak (Rau); En(Rea)= Ak (Rae); // Deciding applications binding objects in visual area on map

Step 5: According to Step1-step 4, Displaying the map layer and applications binding the objects on the layer.

Step 6: End.

2.3 Underlying metadata model for integration

The theory algorithm is given above, in practice, in order to support concrete applications, a metadata model is constructed, see Figure 2.

Figure 2 describes the important component, Application integration Context in Figure 1. By means of the metadata model, these information can be described and stored, such as the users information, the category information of users, space objects information, the category of space objects, applications information and the category

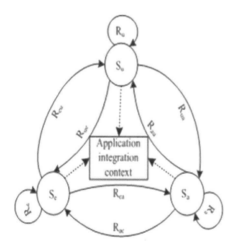

Figure 1. Triangle integration model.

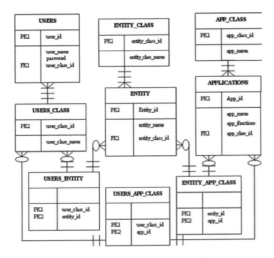

Figure 2. Metadata model of application integration context.

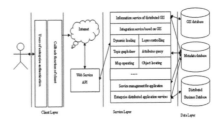

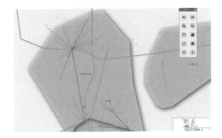

Figure 3. The architecture of distributed integration for WebGIS.

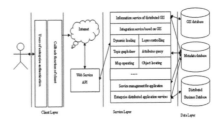

Figure 4. The example of GTPN.

of applications. In fact, although the metadata model is proposed according to oil domain background, the model can be applied to other application domains.

3 APPLICATION CASE

Because gas field spreads widely, the recovery gas data and pipeline transmission networks static data and its operating dynamic data are distributed different sites. Therefore, by means of technique of triangle integration model proposed above, a kind of distributed webGIS integration architecture is defined, see Figure 3.

The architecture contains three primary layers, the data layer which is responsible for storing data, such as GIS data, metadata and static data and dynamic data related to GTPN. The second layer is service layer, which can provide all kinds of services, such as displaying GTPN map, locating interested space objects, moving map, zooming in map, zooming out map, querying static data and dynamic data from the GTPN map and so on.

Figure 4 shows that some gas transmission pipeline networks are visualized, by means of toolbars provided, the users can move or, zoom in, zoom out the map. The information related to the GTPN, both static information and dynamic information are integrated into different space objects. The users only need to click right key on the concrete space object on the map, right key menu will be showed, though this operation mode, the users can obtain the information interested itself.

5 CONCLUSIONS AND NEXT WORK

A common triangle integration model is proposed and given integration algorithm, in order to take these techniques practice, a kind of underlying metadata is constructed. By means of these techniques, a basic WebGIS platform is designed and implemented, during implementation, some advanced techniques are applied, such as XML, SVG, AJAX, JS and so on. Finally, according to Daqing gas-field production, the GTPN displaying system is implemented, now, it has been applied in Daqing. The different workers are able to query information interested. Next, the platform will be continually improved.

ACKNOWLEDGEMENTS

It is project supported by National Undergraduate Innovation Training Planning Project (201310220006): Research on visual application integration model for recovery gas business based on space objects.

REFERENCES

[1] Sun, Xudan, "Research on visualization of spatial data and symbols based on ArcGIS", Applied Mechanics and Materials, v 241–244, p 3107–3111, 2013, Industrial Instrumentation and Control Systems.

[2] Li Ruifang, Yuan Man. "Key techniques for oilfield WebGIS platform based on SVG", Journal of Daqing Petroleum Institute, 2006, 04.

[3] XML standard, 2010, http://www.w3.org/standards/xml/schema.html.

[4] Kris Hadlock, "Ajax for Web Application Developers", Sams, 2006.

[5] Lian, Jianbo, "Study of WebGIS based on XML database and SVG", Proceedings of SPIE—The International Society for Optical Engineering, v 7752, 2011, PIAGENG 2010—Photonics and Imaging for Agricultural Engineering.

[6] N.W. Paton, C.A. Goble, and S. Bechhofer, "Knowledge based information integration systems". Information and Software Technology, 2000 (42); 299–312.

[7] Puligundla Chandrasekhar, Agarwal Rakesh, "COM components on heterogeneous platforms for E-com applications". Inst. of Electronics and Telecommunication Engineers, 2000, 07.

[8] Emmerich Wolfgang, Kaveh Nima, "Component technologies: Java beans, COM, CORBA, RMI, EJB and the CORBA component model", Institute of Electrical and Electronics Engineers Computer Society, 2002, 05: 19–25.

The key installation technology of Shanghai Laohutai pumping station facilities transformation

Y.G. Cao & K.F. Zhang

Department of Construction Engineering, Nantong Radio and Television University, China

ABSTRACT: Laohutai pumping station is located in the Yan Chang Zhong Lu and Peng Yue Pu junction, covers an area of 1339 m², the effluent discharged into the Peng Yue Pu pumping station pump flow 9.2 m³/s, planning of size 9.16 m³/s. The pumping station facilities need to complete the technical transformation and upgrading, key technology of corresponding include the installation of a system of mechanical equipment and electrical installation, the sub-divisional work includes replacement of press, grille decontamination machine, screw conveying squeezing machine, stainless steel floating box door and deodorizing equipment and installation of SCB10-800-10/0.4 type energy saving dry type transformer and high and low pressure switch cabinet equipment. Application of the key technology has solved the quality problems of Laohutai pump installation.

Keywords: Laohutai pumping station; important install technology; replace the press; installation steel tank door

1 KEY TECHNOLOGY OF MECHANICAL EQUIPMENT INSTALLATION

1.1 Main points of press machinery replacement

The model of the new press machinery is RYJ-300, 2 matching garbage crushers and 4 sets of replacing DN1200 doors are provided at the end of press machinery, and the installation requirements are as follows: grille decontamination machine hoisting should be smooth to prevent collision deformation; the connection between the grille decontamination machine and foundation and the connection between all components of the grille decontamination machine must be firmly; the equipment bottom should firmly arranged at the bottom of the groove; the installation angle of the grille decontamination machine should be controlled during installation and should be not more than 5 degrees, the allowed horizontal and longitudinal deviation of base of the grille decontamination machine should be not more than 1/1000; the grille decontamination machine should be connected and fixed to the foundation with bolts and the connecting angle steel; the coincidence degree deviation between the two machine center line and reference line for installation should be not more than 3 mm, transverse inclination should be not more than 1/1000; before operation of the grille decontamination machine the gear box should be added oil; during running of the grille decontamination machine turning, stopping, braking and safety interlocking action, should be correct, sensitive, reliable and meet the design requirements. The transmission system should oriented, continuous, uniform, smooth operation, no abnormal noise; allowable deviation between installation reference line of the grille decontamination machine and building axis, equipment plane position and elevation is in Table 1.

1.2 Main points of screw conveyor pressing machine installation

The screw press, screw conveyor models, specifications approaching must meet the design

Table 1.

Item	Project			Allowable deviation	Test method
1	Installation reference line	Distance to building axis		±20	Metallic tape
2		Distance to equipment	Planimetric position	±10	Metallic tape
3			Elevation	+20–10	Level steel rule

requirements, and has certificates and installation instructions and packing list. Equipments should be no deformation, damage and corrosion. Screw press should be fit to the base of the support surface tightly. Feed hoppers, hoppers, drainage pipe flange connect must be firmly and seamless. The allowable vertical and horizontal degree deviation of screw press should be not more than 1/1000. Forward connecting bolts screwed thread exposed 2–4 pitch.

1.3 Main points of stainless steel floating box door Installation

Preparation before installation includes checking the shipping lists to make sure that the number of goods, fasteners and spare parts meets the list; checking whether the size of the construction size requirements and the plane should be as flat as possible, within a certain angle in elevation; checking whether the preformed holes or pre-buried bolt position is correct, if it is connected by the flange connection, please check whether the door flange matching with; The deformation and damage on the door in the transportation process should be conducted a comprehensive inspection and repair and before installation must be placed horizontally to prevent the casting deformation of sealing.

The door should be directly connected to the pre-embedded bolt connection and fastened after adjusted to the right position. Note the door plane and vertical plane into a certain angle. If the door is made of steel, it should be connected with flanged or direct welding. Pulling the lug in the door, it should be opened and closed flexible, or it should be adjusted. Slot between the frame of the door and the surface of the construction should be filled with concrete. Regularly check the sealing elastic and the sealing effect and replace the invalid sealing ring.

1.4 Main points of deodorization equipment installation

Plant liquid deodorization process installation is simple, which is installed in the pollution source nozzle. Plant liquid is sent to each spray nozzle through pumps and conduits and sprayed to the polluted air. Plant liquid reacts with the harmful substance in the gas. The position and angle of the nozzle should strictly meet the requirements of the manufacture and the design drawings. Construction of the conduit should be conducted by the requirements of the process piping. Other equipments and control boxes should be constructed in accordance with the requirements of the manufacturer's

technical and the corresponding construction specifications.

2 KEY TECHNOLOGY OF ELECTRICAL EQUIPMENT INSTALLATION

2.1 Main points of energy saving dry type transformer installation

In Laohutai pumping station, there are 2 sets of oil immersed transformer SCL-800-10/0.4 which will be replaced by SCB10-800-10/0.4 type energy saving dry type transformer. In order to ensure the normal operation of the pumping station, transformer should be exchanged one by one, required by Taiwan exchange, only in the transformer newly transposed to work properly to replace another transformer. Only after the new exchanged transformer work properly another new transformer can be exchanged. When lifting the power transformer, wire rope should be hanging in the box on the hook, not hanging on the box cover hook or other positions, in order to avoid accident. Translation, mechanical parts should be on the under frame, lifting and translation shall be smooth, attention should be paid to the component of the transformer and the tubing could not hurt. The Withstand voltage experiment test the level of the power transformer foundation with level ruler must conform to the rulers and regulations. Transformer installation axis should be aligned to the transformer center line, deviation should be not more than 10 mm. T The grounding wire should be connected closely and firmly. Antiseptic treatment should be evenly, without missing.

2.2 The points of high and low voltage cabinet installation

The level and verticality degree of the basic channel should meet the requirements of the specification. Ground connections should be not less than 2. Connections between cabinets should be closely, fixed smooth and firm, with clear and complete signs. The second wiring should be fixed firmly and closely, and the connection between appliances or terminal row should be close and neat, with clear and complete mark. Parts of electrical equipment must be complete, insulation device shall not have cracks and defects. Electrical equipment installation and wire arrangement should be neatly. The contact and contact connection of electrical equipment should be reliable. Contact force should meet the requirements of the factory technology. The three-phase contact closing should be synchronized. The connecting wire in the outside of the electric

Table 2.

Item	Project	Allowable deviation (mm)	Test method
1	Counter verticality	(Every meter) ≤1.5	Suspension, ruler
2	*Counter top straightness*		
	Neighboring counters	≤2	Ruler, feeler
	Lined counters top	≤5	Cable, ruler
3	*Counter surface smoothness*		
	Neighboring counters	≤1	Ruler, feeler
	Lined counters surface	≤5	Cable, ruler
4	Connection between counters	≤2	Feeler

appliance box should wear tube protection, opening should be smooth, and the wire should be protected by the retainer. Protection tube shall be arranged in neat and installed firmly. After completion of the low voltage electrical installation, the surface should be clean, fixed bracket and plate should be smooth and firmly installed. The lead of the electrical equipment shall be firmly connected, lashing neat with reliable fixation and good insulation. After switch cabinet installation, all the number and name of the cabinets and the function name of the handle, button, indication should be marked clearly. The façade of the switch cabinet should be aligned to the bottom one. The top surface of the trolley type switch cabinet base frame should be on a level with the ground. Switch cabinet and the bottom frame should be fixed with a screw connection. The allowable deviation and test method of switch cabinet installation should conform to Table 2.

Control cables should not have the middle joint. The two ends of each cable must be marked with signs of number, cable type, specification and start and finish cabinet members. Control cable core line terminals of the casing, and shall indicate the terminal symbol. Control cables should be neatly arranged, with firm binding and fixation and visibility labels. After installation is complete, the control cable should be tested and inspected according to the design circuit function under no load, and must meet the design requirements.

3 SUMMARY

Based on Shanghai old Shanghai pumping station facilities renovation project, combined with specific engineering characteristic and the actual work experience, innovation of complete sets of technical measures are put forward, including: changing the press installation key points, the key points of the installation of the screw conveyor crushing machine, stainless steel tank flap valve installation key points, the key points of deodorization equipment installation technology, energy-saving dry type transformer installation points and key points of high and low voltage cabinet installed achieved good engineering comprehensive benefit, which provides the basis for guiding for the construction of similar projects in the future.

REFERENCES

[1] M. Mery, in: *Diffusion Processes in Advanced Technological Materials*, edtied by D. Gupta Noyes Publications Publising, Norwich, London (2011), in press.
[2] H. Kelman and H. Jónsson, in: Theoretical Methods in Condencsed Phase Chemistry, edited by S.D. Schwartz, volume 4 of Progress in Theoretical Chemistry and Physics, chapter, 9, Academic Publishers (2010).
[3] China steel structure association. Construction steel structure construction manual [M]. Beijing, (2002), in China planning press.
[4] China metallurgical construction research institute. Construction steel structure welding specification. Beijing, (2002), China building industry press.
[5] Guo Zhengxing. Housing construction of prefabricated concrete structure construction technology new tension [J]. Journal of construction technology, 2011, 40(11): 1–2.
[6] Ghaly A, Hanna A, Hanna M. Upliftbehavior of screw anchors in sand [J]. 1998, 117(5): 1300–1317.
[7] Jardine RJ, Overy RF, Chow C. Axial capacity of offshore piles in sense north sea sands[J]. Geotech. Engrg., ASCE, 1998,124(2):171–177.

Computer, Intelligent Computing and Education Technology – Liu, Sung & Yao (Eds)
© 2014 Taylor & Francis Group, London, ISBN 978-1-138-02469-4

Application of web mining in electronic commerce

Z.H. Luo & Y. Yang

School of Electronics and Information, Nanchang Institute of Technology, Nanchang, China

ABSTRACT: Web mining—is the application of data mining techniques to discover patterns from the Web. According to analysis targets, web mining can be divided into three different types, which are Web usage mining, Web content mining and Web structure mining. It is a new area of the dat mining research which combined the traditional data mining and web together to play a role in many ways. Web-based data mining e-commerce recommendation system can meet the e-commerce needs in the future development. This paper firstly introduced the Web mining technology and analyzed the applications of Web Mining in electronic commerce, and then point out that e-business intelligence can be supported through Web mining, excavation laws, patterns and knowledge. The process and method of Web mining in e-commerce application have been discussesed in this paper, and finally described the Web mining in e-commerce in the specific application.

Keywords: e-commerce; web mining; CRM; website; SCM

1 INTRODUCTION

With the development of Internet and Web technology, various types of e-commerce website surging. In addition, the development of the times give a broader meaning of e-commerce, which includes not only e-commerce, and also the Customer Relationship Management (CRM), Enterprise Resource Planning (ERP), Supply Chain Management (SCM) and other business processes, which are forcing the mangers to find some rules from the mass business data to help decision-makers to develop strategies and support these business activities [1].

In order to solve the "data explosion but information poor" phenomenon, data mining came into being. Web mining comes from the activities which to discover and extract interesting, potentially useful patterns and hidden information from the Web documents and Web activities. It is a new area of the dat mining research which combined the traditional data mining and web together to play a role in many ways. Whether EC enterprises to adopt B2B, B2C or B2G e-commerce model, buyers of goods requires to build the interaction of information flow with the suppliers of goods and their partners through the Web, then, on the one hand the buyer can get the information about the desired topics conveniently and efficiently through the Web; on the other hand, based on the integrate information system, the suppliers and their partners through the application of knowledge to transform the data, which the about the visitors and the online buyers, from potential, unknow implication state into

a potential value of information, after extraction, washing, processing, to enhance their core competitiveness [2]. Web Data Mining is a technique which uses data mining technique to find the interested, potentially useful pattern and hidden information automatically from the Web documents and Web services. The log of the WWW server records the information about the interaction and the visit of the user, through Web data mining we can adjust the page structure dynamically according to users' interesting, visit frequency, and visit time, improve service, and carry out targeted e-commerce activities to better meet customer needs.

2 SOURCES OF THE WEB MINING DATA

One of the key steps in data mining is to construct a data set suitable for the target task. The data of Web mining comes from the server, client, and agent, these data types varied. The data generally reflect the visit behavior of single client/multi-site; server-side data is described in a visit behavior of multi-user/single site; the agent's data is recorded in a multi-user/multi-site usage [3].

- *Server-side data.* After the customer visit the e-commerce site, the server will generate a corresponding server data, including log files and query data. And the log file can be divided into server logs, error logs, and cookie logs.
- *Agent-side data.* Web proxy is the mainly traffic arteries between the user's browser and Web server; proxy-side caching will help reduce

the page loading time on the client and server workloads.

3 WEB MINING TECHNIQUES AND METHODS

a. e-commerce web mining method. Different data mining method can be used in different ways for different mining target. There are three categories which are statistical analysis (or data analysis), knowledge discovery, prediction models and the others [4].

- *Statistical analysis.* Statistical analysis is mainly used to check the data in the mathematical laws, and then use the statistical and mathematical models to explain these laws. The methods commonly used are linear and nonlinear analysis, continuous regression analysis and logistic regression analysis, univariate and multivariate analysis, and time series analysis.
- *Knowledge discovery.* Knowledge discovery comes from the artificial intelligence and machine learning, which uses a data-search process, to extract information which shows the relationship and the medoths of these data. The rules and the facts of business can be found by the information. The data visualization tools can be used to help the develops to analyze the data mininged before, and enhance the capabilities of data mining. A graphical analysis of mulivariate data, which helps business analysts doing the knowledge discovery, can be presented from the visualization.

b. the foction of web mining. Through collection, processing and deal with the information, which involves to consumers' behavior, to determine the specific consumer groups or individuals interesting in spending habits, consumers' trends and consumers' demand, and then infer the corresponding behavior of the groups or individual consumer in the future, and then orientated the marketing strategy to the identified consumers with specific content. These can reduce the cost, enhance the efficiency, and make more profits [4].

- *To optimization the Web site and design customized website.* Web designers do not fully rely on qualitative guidance of experts to design websites, but according to the visitor's information to design and modify the site's structure and appearance. To emphasize the personal information, identifying customer preferences, and make the customers can access the site in their own way, targeted personalized banner ads can be provided at the place of which the consumers often visited,

in order to achieve personalized marketing services.

- *To retain old customers, and tap potential customers.* Through Web mining, e-commerce businessmen can learn the visitors' personal preferences, and understand the needs of customers more fully to prolong the residence time of the customers, this helps to improve customer satisfaction and ultimately achieve the purposes of retain the customers.

4 APPLICATION OF WEB MINING METHODS IN E-COMMERCE

a. web mining in e-commerce website design

- *Improving the Site's Structure.* By association rule analysis can identify the group modes of the users who visit the page. To build the associated model, improve the organizational structure of the site, can enable customers to access the pages they want to get, more directly and easily, and minimize the complexity of the user view, so that visitors feel comfortable, and stay long enough to buy. By sequence pattern analysis can explore the page sequence of the users. According to the sequence based on user access patterns which the pattern most visitors search and browse the site to organization or reorganization the e-site, to provide convenience for the most visitors' search and browse [4].
- *Custom personalized interface.* By classification and clustering analysis the customers, the personalized recommendation system can be established based on the behavior of the user visit the site, and the system can provide personalized service and merchandise. According to the association rules the information of the customers to visit the site can be get, and we can get the visit model of the customers to adjustment the structure of the site dynamically, enabling the links of the associated files more direct to provide customers with product recommendations, help customers find the interest commodity easily.

b. application of web mining in crm. *Improve customers' reside time of the site.* Prolong the residence time of the customers on their own web site is the key strategy to keep its resident customers and attract new customers [3]. According to the customer's browsing behavior, we can understand customer interest and demand for clustering, clustering and classification customers, and adjust the Web page dynamically to provide some specific information and advertising of the products to make customer satisfaction, thereby the presence of the time can be extended.

c. applications of web mining in network marketing

- *To develop Internet Marketing Plans.* Before the plan is made, the Web mining should be done from the two sides of time and space. In time of the excavation is analysising the access and sales of products, to gain the regular of the customers visit the site, and then determine the life cycle of consumer spending. Develop appropriate marketing strategies at a specific time for different products, according to the changes of the market. In the space of the mining is that you can analysis the domain of the customers who have purchased the products, and then dig out the area in which the merchandise sales best and develop the strategy to continue these satiation, while digging out the undesirable market area and then expand it.

- *Cross-marketing.* Cross marketing is mainly to sell the new products to the old customers. For existing customers, the information can be much more easily got to the companies. With association rules and sequence pattern analysis, the factor which affect customers buying behavior may be found from the customer information especially the purchase information before and the prediction model of customer buying behavior can be established to predict future purchase behavior [3].

5 CONCLUSIONS

Currently, Web mining in China is still a relatively new area. While some e-commerce sites have begun to try to improve their site design (such as Web Thunder, Taobao, etc.), but there are still many problems to be resolved, such as identify the type of web pages automatically, complete the navigation path. With the study and use of Web mining goes, it will lead the e-commerce system more intelligent and the service more personalized.

REFERENCES

[1] Charu C. Aggarwa and Philip S. Yu: *Data Mining Techniques for Associations, Clustering and Classification*, PAKDD-99, April, 1999.
[2] Cheng Xiao-sheng, Liao Wen-he, Tian Hong, etc. *Research and Application of System Model of E-Commerce Oriented Web Mining Technology [J]*. Journal of Nanjing University Acronautics & Astronautices. Vol. 36 No. 3. Jun. 2004. 322–326.
[3] Huang Jin-feng: *Application of Web Mining Techniques in Electronic-commerce [J]*. Journal of Fujian Education Institute. 2007.1.113–115.
[4] Yu Xiao-bing, Guo Shun-sheng, Huang Xiao-rong: *Intelligent e-commerce based on Web usage mining and its application [J]*. Computer Integrated Manufacturing Systems. Vol. 16. No. 2. Feb. 2010. 439–447.

Computer, Intelligent Computing and Education Technology – Liu, Sung & Yao (Eds)
© 2014 Taylor & Francis Group, London, ISBN 978-1-138-02469-4

Analysis on the evolution of marine innovation collaboration networks

F.X. Qiu

Hebei University of Technology, Tianjin, P.R. China
Hebei Normal University of Science and Technology, Qinhuangdao, P.R. China

ABSTRACT: In this paper, the cooperation networks of marine innovation are drew, which include two stages. Overall, along with evolution of cooperation networks, which scales have expanding continually, the proportions of cooperation innovation have increased, and core nodes have growing up and there exist larger cohesive subgroups in the whole network. Secondly, by using the density, degree, centrality, the networks are analyzed meticulously, and the correlations between the indicators are explored. The aims of the paper are to make the cooperation network for marine innovation in China clear, and provide ideas for further optimization of networks.

Keywords: networks; innovation; marine; cooperation; evolution

1 INTRODUCTION

Nowadays, it is well understood that the creation and application of new knowledge are the primary factors that drive the economic growth. Moreover, it is also commonly accepted that cooperation in the innovation network are important sources of new knowledge. Moreover, it is also commonly accepted that cooperation in the innovation network is important sources of new knowledge[1,2]. Thus, researchers have devoted a great effort to investigate the nature and the importance of collaborations in the network, trying to build a clear picture of which mechanisms may favor the interaction, promoting knowledge transfer and acquisition[3]. Many researchers have mainly centered their attention to identify universities and firms' characteristics promoting collaboration[4,5,6], but some ones investigate the role that both technological and relational aspects, such as technological relatedness, prior collaboration ties, and geographical distance, exert on the value of joint innovations. On the whole, almost all researchers agree that in an industry there is a support value system that includes universities, research institutes, local governments, companies, financial institutions and intermediary organizations of science and technology.

2 DATA SOURCE AND INDICATORS

The data source of current research is about marine industry related winners of marine innovation achievement awards in China from the year of 2000 to 2011. In all, innovation achievement applied by firms, universities, research institutes are collected with the reference period from the two stages, 2000 to 2005, 2006 to 2011. In this research, we used UCINET 5 and Pajek 3 software for network and graph. All winners listed on a project are assumed to have network ties to one another.

This study takes the quantitative approach and social network analysis. The indicators are shown as follows.

The degree of a node (Equation 1) (in this paper, the number of partners) is simply the number of other nodes connected directly to the node. Thus, the degree centrality of node pk is given by:

$$C_D(P_K) = \sum_i a_{ij}(P_i, P_k) \qquad (1)$$

$a(P_i, P_K) = 1$, if node Pi and node Pk are connected. $a(P_i, P_K) = 0$, otherwise. For a weighted network, the strength of a tie (link between two nodes) simply is the weight of the link. In this paper, by considering repeated cooperation in the nodes, the equality degree and weighted degree are used. Equality degree indicates the cooperators one node has, and weighted degree shows the number of cooperation one node has with the partners.

Betweenness centrality (Equation 2) is used to present the concept of point centrality. Betweenness centrality of a node v is given as follows:

$$BC(V) = \sum_{\substack{u,W \in V \\ u \neq W \neq V}} \frac{a_{uw}(v)}{a_{uw}} \qquad (2)$$

where $a_{uw}(v)$ denotes the total number of shortest paths between u and w that pass through node v and a_{uw} denotes the total number of shortest paths between u and w.

Closeness centrality (Equation 3) is the inverse of the sum of geodesic distances from actor i to the g-1 other actors (i.e., the reciprocal of its "farness" score):

$$C_C(n_i) = \left[\sum_{j=1}^{g} d(n_i, n_j) \right]^{-1} \qquad (3)$$

Density can be measured in society between nodes in the network of contacts. The number could be obtained by dividing maximum number of possible total relationship using the number of actual total relationship.

3 STRUCTURE INNOVATOR COOPERATION NETWORKS

During two different stages (Fig. 1), the networks differ in the sizes and structures. Meanwhile, co-operations in networks show different characteristics. During the first stage, with 6 years, there are 147 nodes in the marine system, in which there are 18 independent innovative nodes. The largest connected sub-graph in the network has 106 nodes and its intensity is 0.06, which shows that the cooperation in the sub-graph is intense. During the second stage, although there are 225 nodes in the network, the cooperation shows more obvious and close. Apart from 10 independent innovative nodes, the other nodes have the cooperative partner. During this stage, the largest connected sub-graph expands rapidly to include 179 nodes, that is, 79.6% of the nodes in the network are in the sub-graph, and its intensity is 0.03. Some researchers show that relationship between large networks tends to be sparse and not tight, thus the intensity

Figure 1. Innovation cooperation networks in the marine industry (2000–2005, 2006–2011).

of it is not so large. In contrast, during the two stages, connections in the innovation co-operation network are relatively close, and cooperation among nodes has becoming more and more active.

The degree of a node (Equal. 1) tells us the number of partners of a node has. From Figure 1, we can find that equality degree in the two stages change a lot. During the first stage, 89.1% of the nodes in the network have the equality degree which is no more than 10, and 16.3% of the whole nodes have only two partners. Otherwise, the biggest equality degree in the network is 45. During the second stage, 90% of the nodes in the network have the equality degree which is no more than 8, and 16.9% of the whole nodes have only 3 partners. Otherwise, the biggest equality degree in the network is 53, and the second, third one is 27 and 25 partly. With expansion of the networks, the average quality degree change a little, from 4.88 to 4.9. As for the standard deviations of equality degree, there exists difference. It reduces from 6.1 during the first stage to 5.4 during the second stage, which shows that difference between node equality degrees is decreasing. Considering nodes such as university, firm and research institute in the networks, research institutes have absolute advantage. During the first and the second stages, in the top 10 nodes with large equality degrees, there are 9 research institutes and 1 university.

Because of the repeated cooperation in the networks, weighted degree differs from the equality degree. During the first stage, average weighted degree is 6.95. Second, first and third Institute of Oceanography State Oceanic Administration have equality degree of 45, 31 and 28, which have weighted degree of 78, 64, 54. During the second stage, average weighted degree is up to 9.33. The top first node, second and third Institute of Oceanography State Oceanic Administration, ranks first according to equality and weighted degree, which cooperates with partners for the number of 72. Along with the increase of the networks, the ratio of nodes whose weighted degree is no more than 10 changes from 80.95% to 90.7%, which shows that such nodes grow faster than other nodes. As for average weighted degree, it changes greatly from 6.95 of the first stage to 5.4 of the second stage, and its standard deviations reduce from 11.07 to 7.4. It shows that with the expansion of innovation networks, on the overall, the number of cooperation with partner(s) reduces.

Between degree, which reflects the communication and control capability of a node with other nodes, that is, the ability of the node has in the shortest path between two other nodes. Without such node, the shortest path through it will be changed, and information transferred by the node will be changed. During the first stage, 78.2% of the whole 147 nodes have not between degrees, and 78.7% of the nodes have not between degrees in the second stage. As for the research institutes, there is the node with the biggest between degree and the average between degree in such nodes is the biggest. The firms seldom have between degrees, and the ratio of the nodes with between degrees in the universities and research institutes are 15.8% and 22.6%.

Closeness degree reflects the degree a node has when disseminating information without relying on other nodes. In Pajek, the greater degree a node has, the closer the node stands in the centre of the network. During the first phase, average closeness degree of nodes is 0.19, and its standard deviation is 0.12. With negative skewness, it shows that proportion of the nodes with small closeness degree is more. During the second phase, average closeness degree of nodes is 0.18, and its standard deviation is 0.09.

4 NETWORK CORRELATION

The correlations between the indicators, as shown in Table 1, suggest that partners who have bigger equality degree will also have bigger weighted degree. It tells us the node with more partners will cooperate with the partners more. While this result is not very surprising, Table 1 also suggests that betweenness degree and equality degree have positive correlation, which indicates that the node with more partners could play the role as the bridge of other nodes and the core role in the whole network.

Further, we notice the exits of positive correlation between weighted degree, betweenness degree and closeness degree. This might indicate that with the increase of cooperation in nodes, there are more freedoms when transferring information.

Table 1. Descriptive statistics and correlations.

Variables	1	2	3	4
1. Closeness degree	1			
2. Betweenness degree	0.36** (0.3**)	1		
3. Equality degree	0.55** (0.45**)	0.81** (0.83**)	1	
4. Weighted degree	0.42** (0.42**)	0.72** (0.82**)	0.95** (0.98**)	1

Note: Numbers in the brackets are the ones in the second stage. **p < 0.1, *p < 0.05.

5 SUMMARY

Based on the innovative system of the marine networks, the present study wants to shed further light on the cooperation in the complicated system with multi-agent, exploring the evolution of the network. The analysis of the networks leads us to conclude the following results.

Cooperation network in the marine system has been basically formed and grow rapidly. In the network, cooperation among companies, universities, research institution has been much closer. With the development of the network, the largest connected sub-graph has begun to take shape, which expands faster than the whole network, and the nodes in the sub-graph increase more rapidly than other nodes in the whole network.

There are core nodes in the networks, which act as the bridges between other nodes. Through correlation analysis, we can indicate that nodes with more partners also would have bigger betweenness degree, and the nodes could communicate more freely with other nodes.

In China's marine innovation networks, the research institution nodes occupy the core position. There are many researchers in research institutions in China. During the first stage, there are 34 national marine research institutes in all of the 49 marine research institutes. Apart from the national ones, the number of local marine research institutes expands rapidly from 16 to 31.

In the networks, universities are playing the important role. During the first stage, there are 21 universities, 67% of which are managed by Ministry of Education. But during the second stage, the number of universities has grown to 45, and 53% of the total universities are local ones. In the networks, universities could play as the bridge, that is, act as the intermediary in connecting the firms, research institutions and governments.

During the two stages, the firm nodes grow rapidly, from the number of 31 to 71. But With respect to the core position, firms do not occupy such position in the networks. In all, most firms still have small node degrees and low betweenness degree. It indicates that firms should consolidate innovation and the co-operation with other nodes.

ACKNOWLEDGEMENTS

This work was financially supported by the Science and Technology Project of Hebei Province (No. 13455309D) and Social Science Association Project of Qinhuangdao (No. 201206082).

REFERENCES

[1] Rosenberg, N., Nelson, R. American universities and technical advance in industry. Research Policy, 23(1994), p. 323–348.
[2] Etzkowitz, H., Webster, A., Gebhardt, C., Terra, B.R.C. The future of the university and the University of the Future: evolution of ivory tower to entrepreneurial paradigm. Research Policy, 29(2000), p. 313–330.
[3] Agrawal, A. University-to-industry knowledge transfer: literature review and unanswered questions. International Journal of Management Reviews, 3(2001), p. 285–302.
[4] Antonio Messeni Petruzzelli. The impact of technological relatedness, prior ties, and geographical distance on university–industry collaborations: A joint-patent analysis. Technovation, 31(2011), p. 309–319.
[5] Steven Casper. The spill-over theory reversed: The impact of regional economies on the commercialization of university science. Research Policy, 42(2013), p. 1313–1324.
[6] Xi-Yao Xiang, Hong Cai, Shui Lam, Yun-Long Pei. International knowledge spillover through co-inventors. Technological Forecasting & Social Change, 80(2013) p. 161–174.

Analysis of the collage in fashion design

M.M. Wang, S. Sun & X.C. Chai
Fashion Institute, Shanghai University of Engineering Science, Shanghai, China

ABSTRACT: As an artistic form and decoration, the collage in fashion is being used constantly in the continuous cycle of fashion. In recent years, especially in these years of Fashion Week, the collage in fashion design is used more frequently. This article utilizes the popular with collage in fashion as an object and completely classifies in a system, which starts from the angles it have an effect on fashion and the design elements influence the overall shaping design. Ulteriorly, this article analyzes fashion collage's applications in fashion from the artistic point of design elements through analyzing the reason of this phenomenon of the popular collage in fashion. According to the development of the arty collage in fashion, this article grasps the creation in fashion collage.

Keywords: collage in fashion; artistic design; intrinsic style; application; the trend

1 INTRODUCTION

Collage, derived from the French coller, which can be translated collage technique.[1] It is a long history of the artistic form and decoration phenomenon.[2] Max Ernst (1891–1976) made collage of this artistic form techniques compared to "the two remote object is placed in an unfamiliar plane."[3] Collage is inspired by the streets covered with layers of poster walls in Paris.[4] The European designer Andrzej Klimovski has described collage "collage is one mark of postmodernity by the interception and integration of fragments at the time of various art forms came to an end".[5] Collage is in the name of the resulting from postmodernism based on an angel of methodology.[6]

Fashion collage is a way sparkling a fabric to active and rich, which recombines the change between the positive and negative and the change of color, texture and style in different fabrics after cutting the fabrics of the same or different fabrics.[7]

Collage has been widely used in the field of all kinds of culture and art, and has been a universal and representation technique.[8]

With the development of Dadaism, surrealism and pop art, collage has extended to many other areas, such as architecture, sculpture, design art, film, literature, music, home decoration, packaging, art, even relates to articles for daily life (umbrella, desk lamp), etc.[9]

2 THE CLASSIFICATION OF CLOTHING COLLAGE ART

2.1 Classification in the difference of efficacy in clothing

2.1.1 Aesthetic collage

Aesthetic collage mainly play a decorative ornamental function, which is also known as decorative collage. In ancient China, Paddy cloth had been used of aesthetic collage, which was famous of the fabrics' color interlacing to paddy fields. Aesthetic collage can have the sense of atmosphere and stable with different colors according to certain rules, and it can give a sense of personality or boyish when the colors have no rules to follow.

2.1.2 Functionality collage

Functionality collage plays a functional role in the costumes. The separation of materials (the left and right garment pieces) have to split with zippers, hook, knot and so on, to achieve a complete model; particular parts (the bottom of the sleeve, sleeve elbow, bottom, etc.) have specific request for materials, such as sleeve elbow that needs fabrics with wear-resisting, durable and non-distortion, cuff that requires great endurance in fabrics, and bottom that asks for flat and tidy fabrics. All these need to collage related parts, and this kind of collage becomes a functional collage.

2.2 Classification in an angel of fashion design elements

2.2.1 Color collage

The sensitivity of color is much more than the sensitivity of silhouette. As the impact of the color to person visual sense is great, color is the crucial element in collage design.[10] The three elements of color are hue, lightness and purity. Then make the hue ring as a standard to classify color collage.

2.2.2 Collage in similar colors

Similar colors refer to the same properties and the different purity and brightness, which means two kinds of colors with 15° angle in color hue ring, such as red and vermilion. Collage in similar colors is a collage using the difference of colors' shades in the same properties. Thus the design techniques of this collage are conservative, no strong contagious.

2.2.3 Collage in neighboring colors

Choose a color from the color ring, and the neighboring color is 90° apart. That is called neighboring colors, such as red and yellow-orange. Collage in neighboring colors refers to collage with fabric in neighboring colors. This collage hasn't great visual contrast, but it can reveal a sense of gentle and harmonize.

2.2.4 Collage in contrast colors

The contrast colors refer to two colors from 120° to 180° apart the in hue central, such as yellow and blue, purple and green.[11] The contrast colors collage combine with cold and warm tone, so designers should handle the relationship and proportion between cold with warm tone, and pay attention to the hierarchy from cold and warm tones, otherwise the collage will make the clothing miscellaneous and confusion.

2.2.5 Collage in complementary colors

Complementary colors, which means one color stands 180° apart the color in the color ring, it is the strongest contrast. Combinations of the contrast colors have a sense of rejection and confusion, such as: blue and orange. As the contrast is very high, complementary colors collage will produce strongly visual effects. As a result, be aware of using the collage by accurately grasps of ratio.

3 COLLAGE STYLE IN FASHION

3.1 Minimalism

Minimalism is the pursuit of simple, neat and grace in silhouette.[12] Minimalism pays more attention to the structure and function in fashion, avoids complicated decoration and removes superfluous details, conciseness but not simple.

3.2 Country style

Country Style reflects pure and beautiful in countryside, and it is a spirit of pursuit of nature. As this style is close to nature, it can give people simple and comfortable feeling.[13] Color collage or pattern collage can elaborate the country style.

3.3 Romanticism

Romanticism, is a kind of emotion of the free spirited, and expresses the men' desire of escaping from the real world. Designers usually adopt fantasy or retro to reflect it. All kinds of fashion collage can be romanticism, and there is no need to be a stickler for a type of collage form.

3.4 Hippie

Hippie represents Hippie culture, mostly coming from rebellious teenagers' performance. It embodies unconstraint and unconstraint. Same as romantic, hippie can show in a variety of fashion collage.

3.5 Gothic

Gothic is with mysterious, quirky, terror, bloody atmosphere. Gothic in fashion collage is neutral, exaggerated, and has the stage effect.

3.6 Punk

The spiritual essence of punk is treason, anti-social, anti-traditional. And the expression in fashion is decadent and morbid beauty. Designer can try Collage in *contrast colors and complementary colors to achieve the style.*

3.7 Futurism

Futurism means the leading status, and the pursuit of the future exploration and mysterious space-time. This style obscures boundaries between men

Figure 1. The style of collage in fashion.

and women and possesses a neutral flavor. Futurism subverts the structure traditional costumes.

4 APPLICATION STATUS OF FASHION COLLAGE

Fashion collage can be avant-garde and high profile. Collage cannot only increase the design of texture, but also improve the added value of clothing. Now personalized fashion intensified, while collage gives fashion personality and makes the clothing has the special charm.[14] In recent years, collage in fashion has been applied, which not only enrich the style, also extend a new field for fashion. Designers try to use a variety of texture collage to create a visual on the breakthrough. With more and more diversified in fashion design, collage can produce differences on texture caused by the rich visual texture.[15]

5 SUMMARY

The trend of fashion collage will go on and not just a flash in the pan. It is one of the important techniques designers selected in recent years. Collage is a technique of expression of clothing construction, but also a decomposition and reconstruction technique in secondary design of fabrics.

REFERENCES

[1] Hughes R, Pegram L, et al. The shock of the new[M]. Ambrose Video Pub, 2001.
[2] Xu Hui. Collage in the clothing design of use[D]. Beijing: Beijing Institute of Clothing Technology, 2012,5.
[3] Zheng Yu. Collage of feeling and the feeling of the collage—the reality and surrealism in the art of Dali Paintings[J]. Theory Horizon, 2011 (4):149–151.
[4] Zhang Xuanhan. Collage art—On Ernst collage [D]. Beijing: Central Academy of Fine Arts, 2010,5.
[5] Han Huijun. Theory of the western humanism thought in modern design[D]. Suzhou: Suzhou University, 2008,10.
[6] Yi Zhong. Modern Packaging Art and Jogged Technique[J]. Packaging World, 2001, (3):69–71.
[7] Feng Xiaoran. Introduction to collage in the use of women's clothing design [J]. Modern business, 2012, 15: 193.
[8] Zhang Fei. Talking about the Visual Style and Context of Collage in Graphic design[J]. Art & Design, 2010(6).
[9] Chen Youlin. The Collage Art of Modem Art—From Paintings, Sculptures to Modem Design. Journal of JILIN College of The Arts·Academic Forum, 2011,06 (53):31–34.
[10] Zhao Jia, Guo Fang. From Form to Conception—The Leap of the Collage from Modernism to Postmodernism[J]. Journal of Beihua University (Social Sciences), 2008,09 (3):119–221.
[11] Liu Luan, Li Yiyou. Study on application of stitching design in fashion design[J]. Melliand China, 2008,4: 019.
[12] Zhang Junwei. Minimalist Management: Chinese-style management operating system [M]. China Machine Press, 2013,01.
[13] Zhu Lu. Research on Women's Dress Style from 2000 to 2009[D]. Beijing: Beijing Institute of Clothing Technology, 2009,12.
[14] Su Min. Aesthetic Analytical of the Mix & Match Cultural Style[D]. Shandong: Shandong University, 2011,05.
[15] Xin Xiaoyu, Zhang Yu. On the Negative Texture Effect in Clothing Design[J]. Juornal of Xinjiang Arts University, 2009,07 (1): 65–67.

Optimization methods of report data processing

Li Yan, Yong-Bing Zhu & Ying-Jiang Li
School of Engineering, Honghe University, Mengzi, P.R. China

ABSTRACT: For optimizing the performance of data engine of re-port, we support optimization of Expression structure which can be push-down onto database as possible as we can, but not just be calculated on local. Cause now we support filter, sort and top-N actions in Expression structure, we discuss Set Expression respond to sort or top-N action and Tuple Expression (AND, OR, NOT) respond to filter action push-down onto database.

Keywords: report; database; filter

1 INTRODUCTION

For optimizing the performance of data engine of report, we support optimization of *Expression* structure which can be push-down onto database as possible as we can, but not just be calculated on local. Cause now we support filter, *sort* and *top-N* actions in *Expression* structure, we discuss *Set Expression* respond to *sort* or *top-N* action and *Tuple Expression* (*AND, OR, NOT*) respond to filter action push-down in this paper.

2 FILTER *EXPRESSION* PUSH-DOWN

Filter *Expression* just provide information which tuple in a result set should be accord with or not. That is say, filter *Expression* is a logic *Expression* which contain *AND, OR* and *NOT* logic.

2.1 *AND Expression push-down*

Multi-AND logic can be exchanged in order each other, that's mean A *AND* B equals B *AND* A in logic.

  Multi-AND logic can combine with other *AND* logic, that's mean A *AND* B *AND* C equals (A *AND* B) *AND* C and equals A *AND* (B *AND* C) in logic.

  According upper two basic laws, we get *AND* logic push-down rule: an *AND* logic *Expression* can be push-down if it's all *sub-Expression* can be push-down. A *sub-AND Expression* located in multi-*AND* logic can be push-down, which means all *sub-Expression*s in the *sub-Expression* should be push-down.

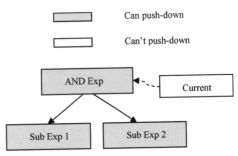

If sub exp1 and sub exp 2 can push-down, AND Exp can be push-down.

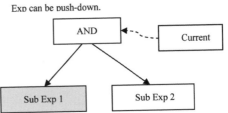

Figure 1. *AND Expression* push-down.

2.2 *OR Expression push-down*

Multi-OR logic can be exchanged in order each other, that's mean A *OR* B equals B *OR* A in logic.

  Multi-AND logic can combine with other *AND* logic, that's mean A *OR* B *OR* C equals (A *OR* B) *OR* C and equals A *OR* (B *OR* C) in logic.

  According upper two basic laws, we get *OR* logic push-down rule: an *OR* logic *Expression* can be push-down if it's all *sub-Expression* can be push-down. If A *sub-OR Expression* located in multi-*OR* logic can't be push-down, the whole *OR* logic cannot be push-down.

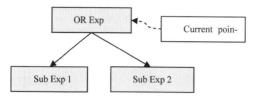

If sub exp1 and sub exp 2 can push-down, OR Exp can push-down.

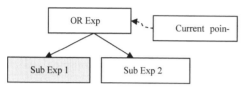

If sub exp1 can push-down but sub exp 2 can't, the whole OR Exp can't push-down.

Figure 2.   *OR Expression* push-down.

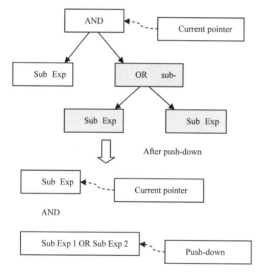

Figure 3.   Complex *Expression* push-down.

2.3   *NOT Expression push-down*

NOT logic is single *Expression*, so *NOT* will have three types *sub-Expression*: direct *sub-Expression* or *AND* logic *Expression* or *OR* logic *Expression*.

- If *NOT* logic *Expression* like this: *NOT* (A > 2), *sub-Expression* "A > 2" is direct *sub-Expression*, if direct *sub-Expression* can push-down, *NOT* logic can push-down.
- If *NOT* logic *Expression* like this: *NOT* (A *AND* B), we can get equivalent as (*NOT* A) *OR* (*NOT* B) in logic according the law of Del

Mogen. If A, or B cannot push-down, the whole *Expression* cannot push-down according upper *OR* logic push-down.

- If *NOT* logic *Expression* like this: *NOT* (A *OR* B), we can transform to (*NOT* A) *AND* (*NOT* B) in logic. *NOT* A push-down if *NOT* B cannot push-down and vice versa. The whole *Expression* push-down if A and B can push-down.

2.4   *Complex Expression partial push-down*

Complex *Expression* means *AND* logic have *OR* logic as *sub-Expression* or vice versa.

If *OR* logic to be *sub-Expression* as *AND* logic, if *OR* sub-logic can push-down, the *AND* logic will remove and local *Expression* will be another *sub-Expression*. The new *Expression* have an *AND* logic with push-down portion.

3   *SORT EXPRESSION* PUSH-DOWN

Sort Expression can have a single *sub-Expression* which is *sort Expression*, *top-N Expression* or filter *Expression*. If *sub-Expression* cannot push-down, *sort Expression* cannot push-down too. If the *Expression* have not *sub-Expression* or *sub-Expression* can push-down wholly and all *sort* references or formulas can push-down, the *sort Expression* can push-down.

4   MAIN ALGORITHM

Expression push-down algorithm will treat as three ways which root type is *AND* or *OR* or *NOT*.

Before we describe main algorithm, we give a clear terms explaining.

- *Tree:* An instance of *Expression* like tree in logic.
- *Root node:* The root of instance of *Expression* which have not any parent node.
- *Current node:* current node in iterating in tree of *Expression*.
- *Equivalent leaf node:* The nodes are not *AND* logic. For example, in *Expression* tree ((A > 2) *AND* (B IS NULL)) *AND* (C *OR* D), sub exp A > 2, B IS NULL and C *OR* D are equivalent leaf nodes.
- *One node can push-down:* All *sub*-node can push-down means all references referred can found in resource container and all formulas and all db fields referred in formulas can found in resource container.
- *Where string:* The result of push-down parsing, format of string conform to ISO-SQL-92 standard.

- *Local Expression:* The result of push-down parsing, which *Expression* cannot push-down in original *Expression* tree instance.

Three steps of main algorithm:

1. Pre-process *Expression* tree, replace all parameter nodes, all redundant *sort* nodes and *NOT* logic nodes.
   1.1 Replace all parameters in *Expression* tree.
   1.2 Iterating from tree root
      1.2.1 if is redundant *sort Expression*, remove
      1.2.2 if is redundant *NOT* logic, remove
         1.2.2.1 If is *NOT* (A *OR* B), replace to *NOT* A *AND NOT* B
         1.2.2.2 If is *NOT* (A *AND* B), replace to *NOT* A *OR NOT* B
2. Distinguish all equivalent leaf nodes, and decide which leaves nodes can be push-down. Collect all push-down nodes input one container, others puts into another container.
3. Gets all push-down nodes from push-down container and parse into strings and connect them by *AND* logic to get where string. Rebuild none push-down nodes from none push-down container with *AND* logic and return a new local *Expression* instance.

5 CONCLUSION

We use these methods to improve the efficiency of database queries, reducing the network data transmission, improving production efficiency reports.

REFERENCES

Abadi DJ, Boncz PA, Harizopoulos S. Column-Oriented database systems. VLDB 2009 Tutorial, 2009. http://cs-www.cs.yale.edu/homes/dna/talks/Column_Store_Tutorial_VLDB09.pdf.

Abraham Silberschatz, 2010, Database System Concepts 6 edition, McGraw-Hill Science/Engineering/Math.

Bakkum P, Skadron K. Accelerating SQL database operations on a GPU with CUDA. In: Kaeli DR, Leeser M, eds. Proc. of the GPGPU 2010. Pittsburgh: ACM Int'l Conf. Proc. Series, 2010. 94–103.

Carlos Coronel, 2012, Database Systems: Design, Implementation, and Management, Cengage Learning.

Computer, Intelligent Computing and Education Technology – Liu, Sung & Yao (Eds)
© 2014 Taylor & Francis Group, London, ISBN 978-1-138-02469-4

Research of mapping XML to non first normal form

Li Yan, Ying-Fang Li & Yong-Bin Zhu
School of Engineering, Honghe University, Mengzi, P.R. China

ABSTRACT: By the customer requirement and reporting-tools development, more and more data resource and been import to report tool. Consequently report tools need support more data resource, For example: XML, POJO, CORBA, SOAP and EJB. So with a unified approach to deal with these is very important, here we introduce N1 NF as a reporting-tools data base model, and describes how to mapping XML to XML N1 NF.

Keywords: XML; database normalization; non first normal form

1 INTRODUCTION

Database normalization is the process of organizing the fields and tables of a relational database to minimize redundancy and dependency. Normalization usually involves dividing large tables into smaller (and less redundant) tables and defining relationships between them.

Edgar F. Codd, the inventor of the relational model, introduced the concept of normalization and what we now know as the First Normal Form (1 NF) in 1970. Codd went on to define the Second Normal Form (2 NF) and Third Normal Form (3 NF) in 1971, and Codd and Raymond F. Boyce defined the Boyce-Codd Normal Form (BCNF) in 1974. Informally, a relational database table is often described as "normalized" if it is in the Third Normal Form. Most 3 NF tables are free of insertion, update, and deletion anomalies.

Denormalization is the opposite of normalization. In recognition that denormalization can be deliberate and useful, the *non-first normal form* is a definition of database designs which do not conform to first normal form, by allowing "sets and sets of sets to be attribute domains" (Schek 1982). The languages used to query and manipulate data in the model must be extended accordingly to support such values.

What is usually meant by non-1 NF models is the approach in which the relational model and the languages used to query it are extended with a general mechanism for such structure; for instance, the nested relational model supports the use of relations as domain values, by adding two additional operators (nest and unnest) to the relational algebra that can create and flatten nested relations, respectively.[5]

2 NON FIRST NORMAL FORM (N1 NF) RELATION DEFINITION

Definition 1: A format is recursively defined by:

1. Let X be a finite string of attributes with no repeated attribute, the X is a *(flat) format* over the set of attributes occurring in X, i.e. set(X), and
2. Let X be non-empty finite string of attributes with no repeated attribute and $f_1, ..., f_n$ some formats over $Y_1, ..., Y_n$, resp., such that the sets set(X), $Y_1, ..., Y_n$ are pair wise disjoint, then the string $X(f_1)^* ... (f_n)^*$ is a *format* over the set set(X)$Y_1 ... Y_n$.

For instance, f = COURSE STUDENT GRAND is a flat format over {COURSE, STUDENT, GRANDE}, and g = COURSE (STUDENT(GRAND)*)* (BOOK)* is a format over {COURSE, STUDENT, GRANDE, BOOK}.

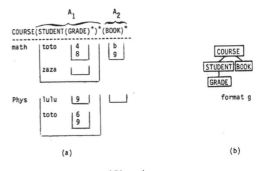

Figure 1. Format and Verso instance.

COURSE TEACHER(BOOK)*(STUDENT GRADE)*

COURSE TEACHER(STUDENT(GRADE)*)*
(BOOK)*

Figure 2. Tree representation of formats.

Definition 2: Let f be a format, The set of all (*Verso*) *instances* over f, denoted inst(f), is recursively defined by:

1. if $f \equiv X$, and X is non empty, the I is in inst(f) iff I is a finite subset of Otup(X), and
2. if $f \equiv X(f_1)^* \dots (f_n)^*, f_1, \dots, f_n$ non empty, then I is in inst(f) iff
a. I is finite subset of Otup(X) × inst(f_1) × ... × inst(f_n), and

If $<u, I_1, \dots I_n>$ and $<u, J_1, \dots, J_n>$ are in I for some $u, I_1, \dots, I_n, J_1, \dots, J_n$ then $J_i = I_i$ for each i in $[1 \dots n]$.

In the previous definition, we assume for 2) that the formats $f_1, \dots, f_n$ are non-empty. Now, if $f \equiv X(f_i)^* \dots (f_n)^*$ with $f_i \equiv \Lambda$ for some i, and $f_j \neq \Lambda$ for $j \neq i$, then by convention, we identify f with $g \equiv X(f_i)^* \dots (f_i-1)^* (f_i+1)^* \dots (f_n)^*$, and the set of all instances over f is obtained from the previous definition by: inst(f) = inst(g).

Intuitively, the 1) condition states that I is atomic over the attributes in X, and not atomic over the "attribute" $f_1, \dots, f_n$. The 2) condition forces X to be a key. It is clear that the mathematical notation for Verso instances is cumbersome and not really readable.

Definition 3: A *Verso database schema* Ω is a finite set of formats, A *Verso database instance* σ of the schema Ω is mapping from Ω to $\bigcup_{f \text{ in } \Omega}$ inst(f) such that is an instance over $\sigma(f)$ for each f in Ω.

We now introduce an inclusion relation on Verso instances. Intuitively, an instance over some schema f is include in another instance over the same format f iff all the information contained in the first instance is also contained in the second one. Formally, we have:

Definition 4: Let f be a format. Let I and J be two instances over f. Then I is include in J (or J contains I), denoted $I \leq J$, iff:

1. if $f \equiv X$, X non empty, the $I \subseteq J$, and
2. if $f \equiv X(f_1)^* \dots (f_n)^*, f_1 \dots f_n$ non empty, then:

$\forall <uI_1 \dots I_n>$ in I, $\exists <uJ_1 \dots J_n>$ in J such that $I_i \leq J_i$ for each i in $[1 \dots n]$.

Definition 5: Let f be a format. Then a subformat g of f is recursively defined by:
1. For each f, Λ is a *subformat* of f,

2. If $f \equiv X(f_1)^* \dots (f_n)^*$, and $g_1 \dots g_n$ are respectively subformats of $f_1 \dots f_n$ then $X(g_1)^* \dots (g_n)^*$ is a *subformat* of f.

3 XML TO N1 NFN

Extensible Markup Language (XML) is a simple, very flexible text format derived from SGML (ISO 8879). Originally designed to meet the challenges of large-scale electronic publishing, XML is also playing an increasingly important role in the exchange of a wide variety of data on the Web and elsewhere. XML quickly became the universal format for publishing and exchanging data on the Web.

Since the structure of XML is hierarchical and N1 NFN is nested relation, then it is easy to implement mapping between XML structure and NFN format. When the element of XML has other attributes or elements, we can convert this element to relation valued in N1 NFN, otherwise convert it to atomic valued in N1 NFN. The attribute of XML only can be converted to atomic valued like Table 1.

Figure 3 gives an example.

When we implement this conversion, we need add primary key information to get correct nested relationship of N1 NF.

Table 1. Mapping rules.

XML nodes in schema	N1 NF value types in format
Element with sub element or attribute	Relation valued
Element without sub element and attribute, but this element is multi-valued	Relation valued
Element without sub element and attribute, and it is not multi-valued	Atomic valued
Attribute	Atomic valued

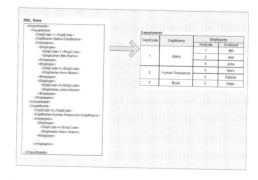

Figure 3. Tree representation of formats.

4 SUMMARY

N1 NF is also a relation module, for someone familiar with classical relation module, it easy understand and study, the learn curve is smooth. Future, we will study all data resource (Include XML POJO CORBA SOAP EJB) can import to N1 NF data module. N1 NF can intuitively map the data source.

REFERENCES

François Yergeau, Tim Bray, Jean Paoli, C.M. Sperberg-McQueen, Eve Maler. Extensible Markup Language (XML) 1.0 (Third Edition) W3C Recommendation 2004.02.

Information on http://en.wikipedia.org/wiki/Database_normalization.

Jump up C.J. Date. An Introduction to Database Systems. Addison-Wesley (1999), p. 290.

Jump up Codd, E.F. "Recent Investigations into Relational Data Base Systems". IBM Research Report RJ1385 (April 23, 1974). Republished in Proc. 1974 Congress (Stockholm, Sweden, 1974)., N.Y.: North-Holland (1974).

Jump up to: a b Codd, E.F. (June 1970). "A Relational Model of Data for Large Shared Data Banks". Communications of the ACM 13 (6): 377–387. doi:10.1145/362384.362685.

Jump up to: a b c Codd, E.F. "Further Normalization of the Data Base Relational Model". (Presented at Courant Computer Science Symposia Series 6, "Data Base Systems", New York City, May 24–25, 1971). IBM Research Report RJ909 (August 31, 1971). Republished in Randall J. Rustin (ed.), Data Base Systems: Courant Computer Science Symposia Series 6. Prentice-Hall, 1972.

Tim Bray, Dave Hollander, Andrew Layman. Namespaces in XML W3C Recommendation 1999.01.

Computer, Intelligent Computing and Education Technology – Liu, Sung & Yao (Eds)
© 2014 Taylor & Francis Group, London, ISBN 978-1-138-02469-4

Answering multiple MAP queries simultaneously using binary jointree

W. Wang
Chinese Flight Test Establishment, Xi'an, Shaanxi, China

Y. Wang
School of Aeronautics, Northwestern Polytechnical University, Xi'an, Shaanxi, China

ABSTRACT: In a Bayesian Network (BN) modeled from a real system often contains several maximum a posteriori hypothesis (MAP) queries and each query corresponds to different MAP variables, which means that one can only solve these multiple queries one by one using variable elimination algorithm. Meanwhile, jointree algorithm is another kind of popular algorithm because it can answer multiple posterior probability queries only after an inward and outward calculation, and then one can extract solution to MAP query from the posterior probability distribution. However, the multiple queries which can be answered using jointree are constrained by the method of constructing the jointree. For now, there is not a formal method to construct a jointree that can answer multiple MAP queries simultaneously. This paper presents a new approach to construct a binary jointree that can answer multiple MAP queries simultaneously just after an inward and outward calculation, which is based on a method proposed by Shenoy, P. P. The paper analyzes the approach in detail and illustrates how to answer multiple MAP queries simultaneously using such a binary jointree. Finally the paper presents two cases to further discuss the method systematically.

Keywords: Bayesian network; binary jointree; MAPs; Shenoy-Shafer propagation

1 INTRODUCTION

In a BN, one may be interested in knowing the most likely values of the some variables, after observing a certain set of symptoms. Such a problem is called MAP problem in Bayesian network inference (Charniak, E. & Shimony, S.E. 1994).

Mainstream, two of the most popular inference algorithms in a Bayesian network are variable elimination algorithm and jointree algorithm (Zhang, L.W. & Guo, H.P. 2006). In essential, there is no much difference between these two algorithms. Jointree can be viewed as some kind of structure derived from Bayesian network, just used for organizing the procedure of calculation. The most outstanding advantage of jointree algorithm lies in that it helps people to know which the shared-procedures between two different inferences are. Hence, one needn't calculate the same procedure once again, improving the inference efficiency.

A Bayesian network can have many different jointrees according to different constructing algorithms, such as the standard construction method (Zhang, L.W. & Guo, H.P. 2006), BuildCT algorithm (Zhang, L.W. & Guo, H.P. 2006), EO2 JT_1

algorithm (Darwiche, A. 2012), EO2JT_2 algorithm (Darwiche, A. 2012) and other algorithms. All these algorithms can calculate the posterior probability over each variable of BN and the posterior probability distribution over each cluster's variables within a time that is just twice than the time spent in calculating one variable's posterior probability distribution using variable elimination algorithm (Darwiche, A. 2012, Zhang, L.W. & Guo, H.P. 2006). However, none of them guarantees to answer multiple MAP queries simultaneously just after an inward and outward inference. Therefore, this paper will propose a jointree that guarantees to answer multiple MAP queries.

In what follows, Section 2 reviews some background and previous work on MAP. Section 3 describes the algorithm for deriving a binary jointree from a Bayesian network and such a binary jointree is used for answering multiple MAP queries simultaneously, and then depicts how to answer multiple MAP queries using such a jointree. Section 4 presents two Bayesian networks modeled from two faulty diagnose cases and discusses how to solve multiple MAP problems using this new method. Section 5 closes this paper with conclusions.

2 BACKGROUND AND PREVIOUS WORK

2.1 The semantics of MAP problems

This part starts with some notation and a formal definition of MAP. Given a Bayesian network that induces a joint probability distribution Pr, all the variables can be divided into three sets: **E**, **S** and **M**. **E** stands for evidence variables that have been known and $\mathbf{E} = \mathbf{e}$ holds; **S** stands for the variables whose values should be summed out that people don't care about; **M** stands for the MAP variables. The MAP probability over variables **M** given evidence **e** is defined as

$$\text{MAP}_p(\mathbf{M}, \mathbf{e})^{\text{def}} = \max_m \Pr(\mathbf{m}, \mathbf{e}) \tag{1}$$

There may be a number of instantiations **m** that attains this maximal probability (Darwiche, A. 2012). Each of these instantiations is then a MAP instantiation which is called a MAP solution, where the set of all such instantiations is defined as

$$\text{MAP}_p(\mathbf{M}, \mathbf{e})^{\text{def}} = \text{argmax}_m \Pr(\mathbf{m}, \mathbf{e}) \tag{2}$$

Generally, calculating MAP needs two steps. First, according to Bayer Conditioning (Zhang, L.W. & Guo, H.P. 2006) calculate Equation 3 to get the posterior probability distribution over MAP variables **M**.

$$\Pr(\mathbf{M} \mid \mathbf{E} = \mathbf{e}) = \frac{\Pr(\mathbf{M}, \mathbf{E} = \mathbf{e})}{\Pr(\mathbf{E} = \mathbf{e})} = \frac{\Pr(\mathbf{M}, \mathbf{E} = \mathbf{e})}{\sum_{\mathbf{M}} \Pr(\mathbf{M}, \mathbf{E} = \mathbf{e})} \tag{3}$$

On the base of Equations 1 and 2, the second step is to choose the max probability and its corresponding instantiation **m** as MAP solution from the first step result $\Pr(\mathbf{M}|\mathbf{E} = \mathbf{e})$. After the two basic steps, one MAP query is answered. Hence, the key problem is to calculate the marginalization probability.

2.2 Computing marginalization probability using jointree

Jointree is a popular method for computing marginalization probability because of its characteristics of data-share compared with variable elimination algorithm (Zhang, L.W. & Guo, H.P. 2006). The part illustrates how to compute marginalization probability using Shenoy-Shafer architecture.

Shenoy-Shafer propagation proceeds as follows. Firstly, set evidence $\mathbf{E} = \mathbf{e}$ in jointree. Secondly, a cluster is chosen as the root and message propagation proceeds in two phases, inward and outward.

In the inward phase, messages are passed toward the root. In the outward phase, messages are passed away from the root. In a jointree, cluster i passes a message to its neighbor cluster j must follow the message passing mechanism (Zhang, L.W. & Guo, H.P. 2006). Figure 1 describes the two-phase process.

In Figure 1, D = y is the evidence and cluster {TLR} is chosen as the root. In the inward phase all the messages from other clusters passes to the root as the virtual arrows labels. After inward phase, $\psi_1(T), \psi_2(R), \psi_3(L,B), \psi_4(R,B), \psi_5(R,L)$ are calculated. In the outward phase, the messages pass away from root {TLR} as the solid arrows label and $\phi_1(T), \phi_2(R), \phi_3(R,L), \phi_4(R,B), \phi_5(L,B)$ are calculated. After the two-phase process, the next step is answer extraction. However, one can only extract the marginalization probability over variables in the same cluster. That's to say, one can get the distribution of Pr(A, T, D = y), Pr(T, L, R, D = y), Pr(R, X, D = y), Pr(L, S, B, D = y), Pr(R, L, B, D = y)

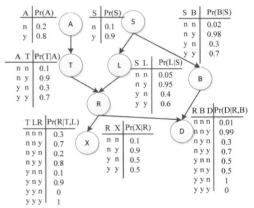

(a) Bayesian network

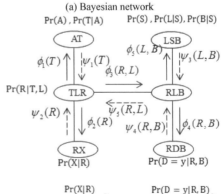

(b) Jointree

Figure 1. Bayesian network and its one corresponding jointree.

and Pr(R, B, D = y). Of course, one can also get Pr(A, D = y) by summing out variable T in Pr(A, T, D = y), Pr(L, R, D = y) by summing out variable T in Pr(T, L, R, D = y) or summing out variable B in Pr(R, L, B, D = y) and so on. However, one cannot calculate marginalization probability over any variables which don't appear in the, same cluster. For instance, one cannot compute Pr(R, A, D = y). For an extreme example, let A and R consist MAP variables. In reference to Equation 3, the MAP problem cannot be solved because Pr(R, A, D = y) cannot be solved in the jointree.

Jointree algorithm's superiority lies in its ability to answer multiply queries after two–phase message passing process (Darwiche, A. 2012). It indeed does. However, the multiply queries must satisfy the condition that the variables in queries must be the set or subset of some cluster of the jointree, as stated preciously.

It is easily can be concluded that there are two problems using jointree algorithm for solving MAP. First, it cannot guarantee solving any MAP problem. Second, even if it can solve some MAP problem, it cannot guarantee to answer multiple MAP problems just after inward and outward calculation process.

3 ANSWERING MULTIPLE MAP QUERIES

3.1 Deriving a binary jointree from a Bayesian network

Different constructing methods lead to different jointree. However, there is not a formal method which can guarantee to solve the two problems proposed in Section 2. This part modifies a fusion algorithm (Lingasubramanian, K. et al. 2011, Shenoy, P.P. 1997), forming a new algorithm presented in Algorithm 1 for answering multiply MAP queries.

The data declaration of Algorithm 1:

a) Λ: A set that contains all the variables of the BN.
b) Γ: A set that is a union set of the following two kinds of sets, which should be presented in the binary jointree.
   i. The first kind of sets contains sets that can denote the CPTs (conditional probability tables) assigned to each variable of the BN. For instance, for node T with its father node A in the BN of Figure 1(a), the set {T, A} is among the set first kind of sets.
   ii. Each set of the second composes of a set of MAP variables. Usually, there are several sets of MAP problems in a fault diagnose model. For example, if {D, S} is a MAP query in Figure 1(a), the set {D, S} is among the second kind of sets.

Algorithm 1. Construct($\Lambda,\Gamma,N,\varepsilon,\pi$).

1: while$|\Gamma| > 1$ do
2:    Choose a variable Y, $Y \in \Lambda$
3:    $\Gamma_Y = \{\gamma_i \in \Gamma | Y \in \gamma_i\}$
4:    while $|\Gamma_Y| > 1$ do
5:       choose $\gamma_i \in \Gamma_Y$, $\gamma_j \in \Gamma_Y$, and $|\gamma_i \cup \gamma_j| \leq |\gamma_m \cup \gamma_n|$
            for all γ_m, $\gamma_n \in \Gamma_Y$
6:       $\gamma_k = \gamma_i \cup \gamma_j$
7:       $N = N \cup \{\gamma_i\} \cup \{\gamma_j\} \cup \{\gamma_k\}$:
8:       $\varepsilon = \varepsilon \cup \{\{\gamma_i, \gamma_k\}, \{\gamma_j, \gamma_k\}\}$
9:       $\Gamma_Y = \Gamma_Y - \{\gamma_i, \gamma_j\}$
10:      $\Gamma_Y = \Gamma_Y \cup \{\gamma_k\}$
11:   end while
12:   if $|\Lambda| > 1$ then
13:      choose γ_i, and $\gamma_i = \Gamma_Y$
14:      $\gamma_j = \gamma_i - \{Y\}$
15:      $N = N \cup \{\gamma_i\} \cup \{\gamma_j\}$
16:      $\varepsilon = \varepsilon \cup \{\{\gamma_i, \gamma_j\}\}$
17:      $\Gamma = \Gamma \cup \{\gamma_j\}$
18:   end if

c) N: A set that contains the nodes of the binary jointree. It is initially null.
d) ε: A set that contains the edges of the binary jointree. It is initially null.
e) π: An order of set Λ. It can be gotten through some heuristic algorithm.
   $|\Gamma_Y|$: The number of the elements in set Γ_Y.

3.2 Computing MAP using binary jointree

Combining with section 2, the process answering multiply MAP queries can be divided into three steps. From now on, assume the number of MAP queries in a model is N_{MAP}.

Step 1. Initialize the binary jointree, which means assign CPT s to their family clusters (Zhang, L.W. & Guo, H.P. 2006);

Step 2. Set evidence $E = e$ and performing an inward and outward message passing calculation (Darwiche, A. 2012) in the binary jointree constructed using Algorithms 1;

Step 3. Chose an arbitrary cluster, multiply all the messages stored in the edges that connect to the cluster, getting a probability distribution and again multiply the distribution with the CPTs stored in the cluster. The result is a probability distribution over variables in the cluster. Then sum out all the variables in the cluster. The final result is $Pr(E_1 = e_1)$;

Step 4. Chose an arbitrary MAP problem among all the MAP queries that is not solved and let M represents the MAP variables of the chosen MAP problem as before;

Step 5. Chose a cluster C_{map} that is the complete set of M;

Step 6. Multiply all the messages stored in the edges that connect to C and get a probability

507

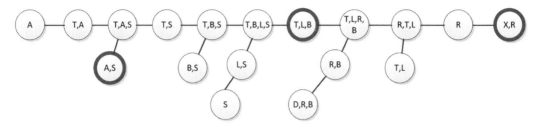

Figure 2. Binary jointree for Bayesian network in Figure 1 (a).

Table 1. MAP solution.

MAP query	M = {S, A}	M = {B, L, T}	M = {X, R}
MAP_P (M,e)	0.153864	0.0439167	0.062268
MAP (M,e)	{S = y, A = y}	{B = n, L = n, T = y}	{X = y, R = n}

distribution ψ_i. Then multiply ψ_i with the CPTs stored in C_{map} to get Pr(**M**, **E**$_1$ = **e**$_1$);

Step 7. Extract the MAP solution: $MAP_P(\mathbf{M}, \mathbf{E}_1 = \mathbf{e}_1) = \max_{\mathbf{m}} Pr(\mathbf{M}, \mathbf{E}_1 = \mathbf{e}_1)$.

Step 8. Store the result in Step 7 and go to step 4 until all the MAP queries in the BN are all solved.

4 CASE STUDY

This part takes the BN in Figure 1(a) for an example. The example is intended to illustrate how multiple MAP queries are answered using the method stated in Section 3.

In Figure 1(a), assume the evidence **E** = {D = y} and there are three MAP queries, {A, S}, {T, L, B} and {R, X}.

First, construct a binary jointree (shown in Fig. 2) using Algorithm 1. Here the construction order is {A, X, D, S, B, R, T, L}, the same one used in standard construction method, shown Figure 1(b).

Second, on the basis of the procedure in Section 3, perform inward and outward calculation. Then to solve each MAP query, choose a cluster in which all the variables compose the complete set of MAP variables. The final solution to each MAP query is shown in Table 1.

From Figure 1(b), one cannot calculate the posterior probability distribution of cluster {S, A} and {B, L, T}, only can calculate the distribution of cluster {X, R}. Above all, it is easy to see that the jointree built by standard construction algorithm doesn't surely contain the cluster which contains MAP variables of a MAP query. From Figure 2, the clusters that contain MAP variables are shown in bold circles. Three MAP queries corresponds three clusters, respectively.

5 CONCLUSIONS

Bayesian network inference algorithm for solving MAP problem in previous has been studies for years. Specifically, almost all the research focuses on answering single MAP query. However, in practice one always needs answering multiple MAP queries. It is obvious that answering MAP query one by one is time expensive. Based on previous search, mainly in view of the data-shared characteristic of jointree, this paper presents a method of answering multiple MAP queries simultaneously. Such a method mainly includes two parts: Algorithm 1 for constructing a special binary jointree and the detailed procedure of how to answer multiple MAP queries using such a jointree. Finally, such a method is validated by one fault case.

REFERENCES

Charniak, E. & Shimony, S.E. 1994. Cost-based Abduction and MAP Explanation. *Artificial Intelligence*, 66(2), 345–374.

Darwiche, A. 2012. *Modeling and Reasoning with Bayesian Networks*. New York: Cambridge University Press.

Lingasubramanian, K., Alam, S.M. & Bhanja, S. 2011. Maximum Error Modeling for Fault-tolerant Computation using Maximum a Posteriori (MAP) Hypothesis. *Microelectronics Reliability*, 51(2), 485–501.

Shenoy, P.P. 1997. Binary Join Trees for Computing Marginals in the Shenoy-Shafer Architecture. *International Journal of Approximate Reasoning*, 17(2), 239–263.

Zhang, L.W. & Guo, H.P. 2006. *An Introduction to Bayesian Networks*. Beijing: Science press (in Chinese).

Analysis of open enterprise-hosted innovative community network based on system dynamics

Min Qin & Liang-Huang Chen
Research Center of Management Science and Engineering, School of Software, Jiangxi Normal University, Nanchang, China

ABSTRACT: Open innovative community has been an important online platform for enterprises to implement the open innovation and users to participate. Employing the feedback mechanism of system dynamics, this paper systematically analyzes the interactive influences and restrictions among the situational factors which appear in both process of implementing open innovative communities and building systemic models for dynamics. Then it explores three key operation factors of the open enterprise innovative community, including the degree of integration communities with enterprises, the cultural construction of communities and the innovative income. The objective of this paper is to give some suggestions for enterprises to improve innovative performance through managing the open innovative community effectively.

Keywords: open innovative community; system dynamics; operation factors

1 INTRODUCTION

The current enterprises are constantly faced with new opportunities and challenges, such as diverse needs of customers, information networking, shorter product life cycle and the allocation and integration of resources. Therefore, enterprises need to predict and respond to the changes of external environment accurately and timely, integrate internal and external resources, develop new products and services rapidly that can meet diverse demands of the market and customers. Some external knowledge, such as market demand, customer review and customer originality, have become more difficult and expensive to obtain and share. And these problems have become the bottleneck of enterprises' development. By the use of open innovation communities, enterprises can communicate with external users in time and collect lots of information and knowledge from different user groups, including market demand, product evaluation, tacit knowledge of experts in specific field, product ideas, etc. Meanwhile, the enterprises can also promote these users to participate in the process of creative design, development and marketing service within the enterprises.

Recently, the theoretical research and the empirical analysis of enterprise open innovation community have attracted more attention of the researchers both at home and abroad. For example, Hau and Kim (2011) researched the factors that may impact users' innovative behavior through

analyzing online game user communities. However, there are lack the analysis of the systematicness of innovation community and the research of causal relationship among each parts and integration of innovation resources in the literatures. System dynamics can seek and research related influencing factors from the perspective of the whole system, and solve complicated problems in the situation of incomplete information by analyzing the dynamic changes and the causal relationship in system. Based on the system dynamics, this paper systematically analyzes enterprise open innovation community network and provides recommendations for enterprises to scientifically manage innovation communities.

2 MODEL BUILDING

2.1 *The confirmation of system boundary and fundamental hypothesis*

1. The confirmation of system boundary

It is considered that the behavior of a system is decided by internal causes, while the external causes are often not crucial. Therefore, choosing a reasonable system boundary is the key to the success of model building. Structurally, enterprise open innovation community network system consist of knowledge activity subsystem, human capital flow subsystem and sales revenue subsystem. After joining in the enterprise open innovation community, the users can provide useful and creative ideas and the enterprise converts these ideas into new products. Then the income from these products can be used to build and manage the community and increase investment in R&D. The key variables, such as user, community and enterprise, are interlinked and manage the innovation system jointly.

2. The fundamental hypothesis of model

H1: Enterprise open innovation community network system is a continuous and gradual process of open innovation activities.

H2: Do not consider the system collapse caused by significant changes in policy and unnatural situation.

H3: The investment in open innovation community includes the construction and management of the community, the investment in human capital and the intellectual capital of users, the awards for users, etc.

H4: Although with research and development ability, the enterprise must integrate external resources and construct open innovation community for the limitation of resources.

2.2 *Analysis of causal relationship model*

Based on the theories and hypothesis mentioned above, the causal relationship in open innovation community network is organized as shown in Figure 1.

In open innovation community network system, there are important components that used to maintain innovation network system, including the user, community culture, knowledge activity and the intensity of adoption. And those also make each network nodes to interact. Then a dynamic cyclical process can be formed through the process of knowledge activities, human capital flow mechanism and the feedback mechanism of sales revenue.

Sales revenue from innovation community network system keeps the sustainable development of the innovative community and enhances incentive effect for users. On the one hand, it can attract more users by strengthening the construction of the community and enhancing the reputation of the community, and the increase of users in turn expands the influence of innovation community and builds a community—enterprise chain structure; On the other hand, the increase of users and their activeness help users to play professional expertise, innovative potential and the sense of cooperation, and achieve self-satisfaction and honor, which in turn enhances the synergy of research and development of the innovative community network.

Once the attractiveness of the innovative community network increased significantly, the innovation-related subjects will provide more material guarantee for the open innovation activities by investing more human, material and financial resources. The growth of funds for innovation, the increase of users and the enhancement of users' cooperative effect jointly promote the generating of new products, while the new products is the most important embodiment forms of knowledge for enterprise innovation activities. New products not only can be converted into the patentability of intangible assets, but also can adapt to the changes

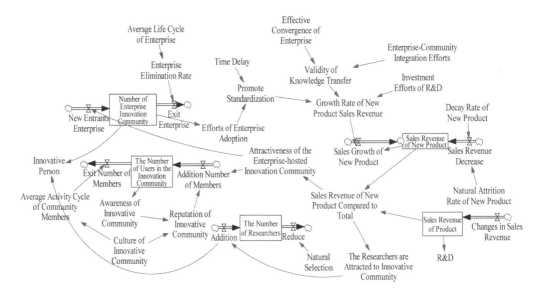

Figure 1.   Enterprise-hosted innovative community system dynamics model of causality.

in market demand and achieve sales revenue to sustain the operation of the entire innovation community network.

2.3 *Analysis of feedback mechanism flow chart*

After analyzing the causal relationship model, we can draw four flow diagrams of feedback mechanism. Limited by space, this paper only takes some examples of the community human capital flow and analyzing. As shown in Figure 2.

Joining new users in the community can bring more knowledge, originality and technologies. And the enterprise can integrate external resources and link to users by building open innovation community. The number of community members mainly depends on the number of new users and users who quit or no longer participate in. New users often are attracted by the content and the reputation of the community and this kind of attraction can help to build good community culture, which in turn attracts more users. The attraction directly affected by the benefit for users, while the benefit for users is indirectly influenced by the sales revenue from the new products converted by originality. The reputation of community is based on the popularity of innovation community, and the popularity is growing as the number of users gradually increasing and directly affected by the community culture. A good innovation community culture helps to create a harmonious atmosphere and enhance a sense of belonging, which is conducive to increase the influence and popularity of the innovation community network. The number of users who quit is mainly restricted by the life cycle of community users, and those who lack understanding of innovation activity, do not make a positive contribution or gradually lost interest will leave the innovation community network with the ending of network life cycle. While the average life cycle of community user affected by community

culture as well. The distribution of income and the community culture from innovative resources is the key to the formation of human capital flow mechanism. If the number of community users can increase continuously and remain stable, more innovative resources, ideas, and opinions for the products will be provided to the innovative subjects. Thus it can be seen that human capital flow provides important guarantee for the innovation community network.

3 DISCUSSION AND SUGGESTIONS

3.1 *Focus on the integrated relationship between enterprises and communities*

Enterprises are the main bodies of the innovation communities building, and also major players. By spending a lot of manpower, material and financial resources to manage the communities, the enterprises can use external resources to develop new products and achieve more benefit. In innovation communities, users continually contribute innovative resources and perform feedback through participating in knowledge activities and achieving benefits, and these behaviors will internalize the external knowledge, decentralize the innovation risk, reduce the cost of innovation and accelerate the speed of development of new technologies for the enterprise. Integrating the relationship between the communities and enterprises is to improve the intensity of adoption and the degree of convergence of enterprises and communities, which can promote the growth of revenue.

3.2 *Strengthen the construction of open innovation community culture*

Enhancing the attractiveness of innovation community network not only need to increase the investment in community environment, innovation funds and other hardware resources, but also need to pay attention to the innovation atmosphere and the construction of open innovation culture. An open and inclusive innovation community culture is the result of the long-term cooperation, mutual trust and respect among the participants of enterprise innovation activities. A healthy innovation community culture helps to reflect human capital value, improve information sharing rate of community users, accelerate the transfer and diffusion of innovation knowledge, and enhance the learning ability of community users and the ability to invert researches into new products. When managing and operating open innovation communities, the enterprises need to play a lead role in actively cultivating all possible social capital, root the innovation

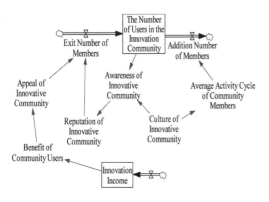

Figure 2.

community culture in the minds of employees and community users, enhance the attractiveness of innovation community and improve the ability of economic growth of open innovation network.

4 CONCLUSION

Open innovation community network is a complex social system that contains multiple loops and a large number of information flows. Based on the analysis of the model, we get that the key to improving economic growth in open innovation community network is to integrate the interactions between all subjects and strengthen the construction of open innovation community cultural, and these also can maintain the healthy operation of open innovation community network.

ACKNOWLEDGMENT

This project is sponsored by following Foundation: ① National Science Foundation of China (71262023); ② Science and Technology Support Project of Jiangxi Province (20121BBE50026); ③ Social Science Plan Project of Jiangxi Province (13GL23); ④ Doctoral Foundation of Jiangxi Normal University.

REFERENCES

[1] Sieg Jan Henrik, Wallin Martin W. Vonkrogh Georg. Managerial challenges in open innovation:a study of innovation intermediation in the chemical industry [J]. R&D Management, 2010, 40(3):281–291.

[2] Boscherini Lorenzo, Chiaonidavide, Chiesavittorio Frattini Federico. How to use pilot projects to implement open innovation [J]. International Journal of Innovation Management, 2010, 14(6):1065–1097.

[3] CHO, et al. An empirical study on the effect of individual factors on knowledge sharing by knowledge type [J]. Journal of Global Business and Technology, 2007, 3(2):1–15.

[4] Xia Enjun, Zhang Ming, Zhu Huaijia. System dynamics model of open innovation community network [J]. Science & Technology Progress and Policy, 2013, 30(8):14–19.

[5] Ulrich Lichtenthaler. Outbound open innovation and its effect on firm performance: examining environmental influences [J]. R&D Management. 2009, 39(4): 317–330.

[6] Hu junyan, Zhu Guilong, Ma Ying. System Dynamic Analysis on Influencing Factors of Industry-University-Research Cooperation in Open Innovation Context [J]. Science of science and management of S. & T, 2011, 32(8):49–57.

[7] DominikMahr, Annouk, Lievens. Virtual lead user communities: Drivers of knowledge creation for innovation [J]. Research Policy, 2012, 41:167–177.

[8] Simard C., & West J. Knowledge networks & the geographic locus of innovation: Open innovation research a new paradigm [M]. Oxford University Press, 2006.

Computer, Intelligent Computing and Education Technology – Liu, Sung & Yao (Eds)
© 2014 Taylor & Francis Group, London, ISBN 978-1-138-02469-4

Study on properties of nonlinear UKF algorithm of information fusion

R.C. Wu
School of Computer Science and Engineering, University of Electronic Science and Technology of China,
Chengdu, China
Police Academy of China, Chengdu, China

F.L. Zhang
School of Computer Science and Engineering, University of Electronic Science and Technology of China,
Chengdu, China

Y. Yang & J.B. Zhang
Police Academy of China, Chengdu, China

ABSTRACT: Kalman filter in linear discrete system optimization when using predictive equations and measurements of system equations, but only consider the most simple linear relationship, that is, prediction equation linearization of the system, because the mean and variance of the variable only for linear operation, so when the prediction equation of nonlinear system, how to calculate the variance of the predicted values? This article thereon UKF filtering algorithm for solving nonlinear discarded when using the system of linear equations of the idea in favor of probability and statistics by approximate methods of calculating the variance and mean. Simulation results show that the algorithm can effectively reduce the impact of errors, real-time, high reliability, easy to calculate, with better tracking accuracy, but also in serious or high-order nonlinear error is introduced, it will postpone or delay filter divergence convenient in practical applications.

Keywords: nonlinear filtering; information fusion; unscented Kalman filter; sensor networks

1 INTRODUCTION

Information fusion filter theory is an important branch of multisensory information fusion, is mainly focused on the study of multisensory information fusion Kalman filters.[1] Main idea is the use of mathematical methods in information integration and integrated technology tools of different sources of information to get high quality useful information.[2] Reference[3] was proposed based on the weighted least squares estimate, optimal linear unbiased estimation of unified optimal fusion rules;[4] is proposed based on linear mean square estimation of the optimal fusion rule, concluded that "using the measured information, the more the optimal fusion estimation of the amount of information is larger, the higher the precision of conclusions;[5] though laser multiplier method and matrix differential operators, respectively is proposed according to the weighted matrix, according to a scalar weighting and according to the scalar weighting of the components in the three kinds of linear minimum variance information fusion estimation criterion; Literature[6] of multi-sensor state of discrete linear time-delay stochastic system, put forward the augmented distributed

optimal weighted fusion Kalman filter. The above documents are not considering nonlinear system integration problems.

Kalman filter method can be applied to a linear system. Modern control objects are often non-linear systems, such as unmanned aircraft vehicle flight control system, inertial navigation systems, tracking systems, and various nonlinear servo systems and so on, some of which are even strongly nonlinear. At present, filtering for nonlinear systems estimation, the most widely used is the use of the extended Kalman filter EKF (Extended Kalman Filter).[7] EKF is the Taylor expansion for nonlinear system of equations or observation equation and took the first-order approximation of filtering algorithms, so the EKF is a suboptimal filter; it inevitably introduces a linear error. When linear assumption does not hold, or that the system is strongly nonlinear systems using EKF will lead to filter performance and even divergent. If applied to the tracking control system which may lead to the safety and reliability of the system as a whole is greatly reduced. And often need to calculate using EKF State equation and observation equations of the Jacobian matrix or matrix of Hessians, which undoubtedly is increased computation and computational complexity of the algorithm, that high real-time requirements of tracking system is not practical. In order to solve problems in the EKF, aiming to the Julier and Uhlmann made suitable for nonlinear systems with no trace of Kalman (Unscented Kalman Filter, UKF).[8] UKF was a group of Sigma points through deterministic sampling, so that they can get more observation assumes that increased the mean and covariance estimation accuracy of the system state. UKF without linear approximation of nonlinear systems, thus avoiding the linearization errors, and reduce the amount of intermediate computations. Because the UKF filter parameters are not sensitive, robust, high reliability.[9] Compare with EKF, UKF filter computation smaller estimates more accurate. For nonlinear systems, the UKF filter method based on information fusion filtering algorithm to further improve estimation accuracy.

2 THE DESCRIPTION OF THE SIMULATION PROBLEM

Consider a particle in two-dimensional $x - y$ movement M, k at some point the position, velocity, and Acceleration vectors available $\mathbf{x}(k) = [x_k, y_k, \dot{x}_k, \dot{y}_k, \ddot{x}_k, \ddot{y}_k]^T$ says. Suppose M in the horizontal direction (x) approximate linear motion with constant acceleration, the vertical direction (y), are also similar to linear motion with constant acceleration. Two upward motion with additive noise $\mathbf{w}(k)$, then the motion of a particle in a Cartesian coordinate system state equations for $\mathbf{x}(k+1) = \mathbf{f}_k(\mathbf{x}(k)) + \mathbf{w}(k) = \mathbf{F}_k\mathbf{x}(k) + \mathbf{w}(k)$. Among

$$\mathbf{F}_k = \begin{bmatrix} 1 & 0 & t & 0 & \frac{t^2}{2} & 0 \\ 0 & 1 & 0 & t & 0 & \frac{t^2}{2} \\ 0 & 0 & 1 & 0 & t & 0 \\ 0 & 0 & 0 & 1 & 0 & t \\ 0 & 0 & 0 & 0 & 1 & 0 \\ 0 & 0 & 0 & 0 & 0 & 1 \end{bmatrix} \quad (1)$$

Assuming a coordinate location (0,0) radar ranging r_k and angular φ_k of M, the actual radar with additive measure noise measurement in c, then the sensor under the polar coordinate system and observation equations for

$$\mathbf{z}(k) = \mathbf{h}_k(\mathbf{x}(k)) + \mathbf{v}(k) = \begin{bmatrix} r_k + v_r(k) \\ \varphi_k + v_\varphi(k) \end{bmatrix}$$

$$= \begin{bmatrix} \sqrt{x_k^2 + y_k^2} + v_r(k) \\ \tan^{-1}\dfrac{y_k}{x_k} + v_\varphi(k) \end{bmatrix} \quad (2)$$

In Cartesian coordinates, the observation equation is nonlinear model sport. Our goal by using UKF algorithm based on radar measurement tracking, and compares the results with EKF algorithm.

3 PROBLEM ANALYSIS

3.1 The UKF filter tracking

For nonlinear system $\begin{cases} \mathbf{x}(k+1) = \mathbf{f}_k\mathbf{x}(k) + \mathbf{w}(k) \\ \mathbf{z}(k) = \mathbf{h}_k(\mathbf{x}(k)) + \mathbf{v}(k) \end{cases}$, set $\mathbf{w}(k)$ with covariance matrix $\mathbf{Q}_k$, $\mathbf{v}(k)$ with covariance matrix $\mathbf{R}_k$. UKF algorithm steps are as follows:

Step 1, Calculate the point σ to point $\boldsymbol{\xi}_{k-1|k-1}^i$, under points $\mathbf{x}_{k-1|k-1}$ and $\mathbf{p}_{k-1|k-1}$ produce 2n+1 a σ point $\boldsymbol{\xi}_{k-1|k-1}^i$, $i = 0, 1, 2, \ldots 2n$. At UT time, take the scale parameter $\alpha = 0.01$, $\kappa = 0$, $\beta = 2$.

Step 2, Calculate the point σ to point $\boldsymbol{\xi}_{k|k}^i$, that is:

$$\begin{cases} \boldsymbol{\xi}_{k|k}^i = \mathbf{f}_k(\boldsymbol{\xi}_{k-1|k-1}^i), i = 0, 1, 2, \ldots 2n \\ \hat{\mathbf{x}}_{k|k-1} = \sum_{i=0}^{2n} \omega_i^m \boldsymbol{\xi}_{k|k}^i \\ \mathbf{P}_{k|k-1} = \sum_{i=0}^{2n} \omega_i^c (\boldsymbol{\xi}_{k|k}^i - \hat{\mathbf{x}}_{k|k-1})(\omega\boldsymbol{\xi}_{k|k}^i - \hat{\mathbf{x}}_{k|k-1})^T + \mathbf{Q}_{k-1} \end{cases}$$

Step 3, the Calculate σ point $\hat{\mathbf{x}}_{k|k-1}\mathbf{P}_{k|k-1}$, by measuring equation for the spread of $\mathbf{x}_k$, that is:

$$\begin{cases} \eta_k^{(0)} = \hat{\mathbf{x}}_{k|k-1}; \\ \eta_k^{(i)} = \hat{\mathbf{x}}_{k|k-1} + (\sqrt{(n+\lambda)\mathbf{P}_{k|k-1}})_i, \quad i = 1, 2, \ldots, n; \\ \eta_k^{(i)} = \hat{\mathbf{x}}_{k|k-1} - (\sqrt{(n+\lambda)\mathbf{P}_{k|k-1}})_{i-n}, \\ \quad i = n+1, n+2, \ldots, 2n; \end{cases}$$

Step 4, calculation one step ahead of the output, that is:

$$\begin{cases} \boldsymbol{\zeta}_k^{(i)} = \mathbf{h}_k(\eta_k^{(i)}), \quad i = 0, 1, \ldots, 2n; \\ \hat{\mathbf{z}}_{k|k-1} = \sum_{i=0}^{2n} \omega_i^{(m)} \boldsymbol{\zeta}_k^{(i)}; \\ \mathbf{P}_{\hat{z}_k} = \sum_{i=0}^{2n} \omega_i^{(c)} (\boldsymbol{\zeta}_k^{(i)} - \hat{\mathbf{z}}_{k|k-1})(\boldsymbol{\zeta}_k^{(i)} - \hat{\mathbf{z}}_{k|k-1})^T + \mathbf{R}_k \\ \mathbf{P}_{\hat{x}_k\hat{z}_k} = \sum_{i=0}^{2n} \omega_i^{(c)} (\eta_k^{(i)} - \hat{\mathbf{x}}_{k|k-1})(\boldsymbol{\zeta}_k^{(i)} - \hat{\mathbf{z}}_{k|k-1})^T; \end{cases}$$

Step 5, after obtaining a new measurement, filter updates:

$$\begin{cases} \hat{\mathbf{x}}_{k|k} = \hat{\mathbf{x}}_{k|k-1} + \mathbf{K}_k(\mathbf{z}_k - \hat{\mathbf{z}}_{k|k-1}); \\ \mathbf{K}_k = \mathbf{P}_{\hat{x}_k\hat{z}_k}\mathbf{P}_{\hat{z}_k}^{-1}; \\ \mathbf{P}_{k|k} = \mathbf{P}_{k|k-1} - \mathbf{P}_{\hat{x}_k\hat{z}_k}\mathbf{P}_{\hat{z}_k}^{-1}(\mathbf{P}_{\hat{x}_k\hat{z}_k})^T \end{cases}$$

3.2 Analysis of extended Kalman filtering algorithm

For discussion of non-linear system a, because of State equations for linear, defined:

$$\mathbf{f}_k^x = \left.\frac{\partial \mathbf{f}_k(\mathbf{x}_k)}{\partial \mathbf{x}}\right|_{\mathbf{x}_k = \hat{\mathbf{x}}_{k|k-1}} \tag{3}$$

$$\mathbf{h}_k^x = \left.\frac{\partial \mathbf{h}_k(\mathbf{x}_k)}{\partial \mathbf{x}}\right|_{\mathbf{x}_k = \hat{\mathbf{x}}_{k|k-1}} \tag{4}$$

Due to the system state equations for linear, that is $\mathbf{f}_k^x = \mathbf{F}_k$, and measurement equation is nonlinear, the partial derivatives of $\mathbf{x}_k$, get it:

$$
\mathbf{h}_k^x = \left.\frac{\partial \mathbf{h}_k(\mathbf{x}_k)}{\partial \mathbf{x}}\right|_{\mathbf{x}_k = \hat{\mathbf{x}}_{k|k-1}}
$$

$$
= \begin{bmatrix} \dfrac{x_k}{\sqrt{x_k^2 + y_k^2}} & \dfrac{y_k}{\sqrt{x_k^2 + y_k^2}} & 0 & 0 & 0 & 0 \\[3mm] \dfrac{-y_k}{x_k^2 + y_k^2} & \dfrac{-x_k}{x_k^2 + y_k^2} & 0 & 0 & 0 & 0 \end{bmatrix} \tag{5}
$$

EKF algorithm steps are as follows:
K-step ahead of time for

$$\hat{\mathbf{x}}_{k|k-1} \approx \mathbf{f}_{k-1}(\hat{\mathbf{x}}_{k-1|k-1})$$

Forecast error covariance

$$\mathbf{p}_{k|k-1} \approx \mathbf{f}_k^x \mathbf{p}_{k-1|k-1}(\mathbf{f}_k^x)^T + \mathbf{Q}_{k-1} = \mathbf{F}_k \mathbf{p}_{k-1|k-1}(\mathbf{F}_k)^T + \mathbf{Q}_{k-1}$$

The Kalman filter gain is:

$$K_k = \mathbf{p}_{k|k-1}\mathbf{h}_k^{xT}(\mathbf{h}_k^x \mathbf{p}_{k|k-1}\mathbf{h}_k^{xT} + \mathbf{R}_k)$$

In the K moments after getting the new measure, status filter updates the formula is:

$$\hat{\mathbf{x}}_{k|k} = \hat{\mathbf{x}}_{k|k-1} + K_k(\mathbf{z}_k - \mathbf{h}_k(\hat{\mathbf{x}}_{k|k-1}))$$

Filtering the covariance matrix is:

$$\mathbf{p}_{k|k} = (\mathbf{I} - K_k \mathbf{h}_k^x)\mathbf{p}_{k|k-1}$$

4 SIMULATION AND EXPERIMENTAL RESULT ANALYSIS

Suppose $\mathbf{w}(k)$ system noise covariance matrix

$$\mathbf{Q}_k = \begin{bmatrix} 1 & 0 & 0 & 0 & 0 & 0 \\ 0 & 1 & 0 & 0 & 0 & 0 \\ 0 & 0 & 0.1^2 & 0 & 0 & 0 \\ 0 & 0 & 0 & 0.1^2 & 0 & 0 \\ 0 & 0 & 0 & 0 & 0.01^2 & 0 \\ 0 & 0 & 0 & 0 & 0 & 0.01^2 \end{bmatrix}, \quad \mathbf{v}(k) \text{ has}$$

covariance matrix $\mathbf{R}_k = \begin{bmatrix} 5^2 & 0 \\ 0 & 0.01^2 \end{bmatrix}$, both unrelated. Number of observations $N = 50$, sampling time for $t = 0.5$. The initial state is $\mathbf{x}(0) = [1000, 5000, 10, 50, 2, -4]^T$. The generated trajectory is shown in Figure 1.

1. $t = 0.5$ UKF and EKF filter comparison

We compare the UKF and EKF algorithm, as shown in Figure 2. In order to facilitate comparison, we will measure the worth of distance and angle measurement value conversion to Cartesian coordinates in the x–y, intuitive UKF algorithm for filtering the results can be seen over the EKF algorithm.

Quantitative analysis of the filtering results below. First calculate the EKF and UKF filter is worth to the location of the (x_{ukf}, y_{ukf}), (x_{ekf}, y_{ekf}) and the moment the distance of the actual location of the (x, y) is $d_{ukf} = \sqrt{(x_{ukf} - x)^2 + (y_{ukf} - y)^2}$, $d_{ekf} = \sqrt{(x_{ekf} - x)^2 + (y_{ekf} - y)^2}$. To do it 50 times in Monte Carlo simulation of the model, various measuring points (times) the distance root mean square error, as shown in Figure 3. UKF filter at all measurement results superior to the EKF.

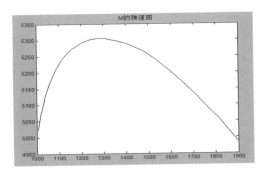

Figure 1. M the trajectory of figure.

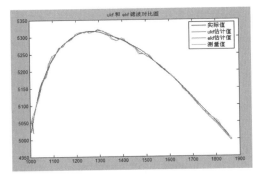

Figure 2. Filtering results comparison chart.

515

2. The sampling interval t impact on filtering results

Below discuss the effects of different sampling interval t on filtering results. Each take $t = 0.1$, 1.0, 1.5 get filtered results with RMSE. As shown in Figures 4–6.

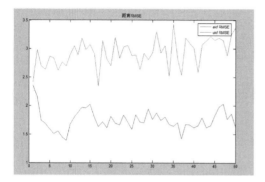

Figure 3. $T = 0.5$ all measurement points from the RMSE comparison chart.

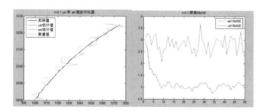

Figure 4. Sampling time results when $t = 0.1$.

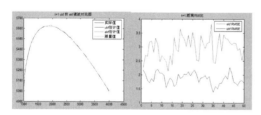

Figure 5. Sampling time results when $t = 1.0$.

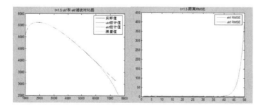

Figure 6. Sampling time results when $t = 1.5$.

3 pictures you can see from above, at the time of the sampling interval t is not too big (0.1,1.0), the UKF and EKF algorithm have been able to track the target and accuracies of EKF UKF algorithm for filtering algorithm. And when $t = 1.5$ is even greater, and EKF algorithm for filtering does not converge, UKF algorithm keeps track of little change in accuracy. UKF and EKF algorithm, when different t, we each take their filtering covariance matrix diagonals of the second element (the variance in y direction), made variance change maps (Fig. 7).

This behavior occurs because when the sampling interval t increases, Taylor expansions of the nonlinear function of higher-order items cannot

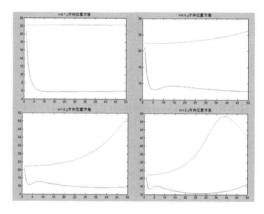

Figure 7. Location filtering variance in Y direction change of different sampling intervals.

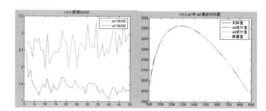

Figure 8. When measurement error for R_{1k} filtering results.

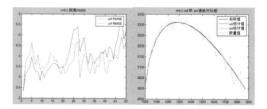

Figure 9. Measurement error for R_{2k} filtering results.

516

be ignored, EKF algorithm for linear (first-order) systems have a greater margin of error, leading to instability in the filter. Because the UKF algorithm to within a second or third-order Taylor expansion, this phenomenon is not obvious, but when greater t, especially when tracking state changes are severe, more higher-order errors cannot be ignored, UKF algorithm will be the divergence cannot track the target.

3. The effect of measurement error on filtering results

Take the sampling interval is not changed, such as $t = 0.5$ s, for measurement error of different $\mathbf{R}_k$, analyzing their impact on UKF and EKF algorithm for filtering the results. Take

$$\mathbf{R}_{1k} = \begin{bmatrix} 10 & 0 \\ 0 & 0.001^2 \end{bmatrix} \mathbf{R}_{2k} = \begin{bmatrix} 500 & 0 \\ 0 & 0.001^2 \end{bmatrix}, \quad \text{respec-}$$

tively, with Figures 8 and 9.

From the above comparison of Figures 8 and 9 indicate that when measurement error, UKF filter accuracies of EKF; when measurement error is large, the UKF and EKF filtering accuracy's not that far away.

5 CONCLUSIONS

Based on the above analysis, we can see, UKF algorithm for solving non-linear model of filter questions, relative to the EKF algorithm, it does not need to compute the Jacobian matrix, with better tracking accuracy, and when serious or higher-order nonlinear errors introduced, could delay or slow filter divergence, therefore has been widely used in practice.

ACKNOWLEDGMENT

This work was supported by the National Science Foundation (Grant No. 61133016), and the National High Technology Joint Research Program of China (863 Program, Grant No. 2011 AA010706), thank for the help.

REFERENCES

[1] Pan Quan, Yu Xin, Cheng Yong-Mei, Zhang Hong-Cai. Essential methods and progress of information fusion theory[J]. Acta Automatic a Sinica, 2010, 29(4):599–615.

[2] Li X.R, Zhu Y.M, Wang J, Han C.Z. Optimal linear estimation fusion—part I: unfiled fusion rules[J]. IEEE Transactions on Information Theory, 2003, 49(9):2192–2208.

[3] Zhou Jun, Wang Zhi-Sheng, Zhou Feng-Qi. The theory of multi-sensor system data fusion based on linear least estimation[J]. Journal of Astronautics, 2011, 24(4):364–367.

[4] S.L. Sun, Multi-sensor optimal information fusion Kalman filter with application[J]. Aerospace Science and Technology, 2011, 8(1):57–62.

[5] S.J. Julier and J.K. Uhlman. A New Approach for Filtering Nonlinear Systems[C]. In Proceedings of the 1995 American Control Conference, Seattle, WA, 1995, 1628–1632.

[6] Zhang Ximin, Li Jiangdong, Chen Shi. Stability of the networked control systems with time-delay and data packet dropout[J]. Control Theory & Applications, 2007, 24(3):494–498.

[7] S.L. Sun, L.H. Xie, W.D. Xiao, and Y.C. Soh, "Optimal linear estimation for systems with multiple packet dropout," Automatica 44, 2008, pp. 1333–1342.

[8] S.L. Sun, "Optimal Estimators for Systems With Finite Consecutive Packet Dropouts," IEEE Signal Processing Letters, vol. 16, no. 7, pp. 557–560, 2009.

[9] S.J. Julier and J.K. Uhlmann. Unscented filtering and nonlinear estimation[J]. Proceedings of the IEEE, 2012, 92(3):401–422.

Computer, Intelligent Computing and Education Technology – Liu, Sung & Yao (Eds)
© 2014 Taylor & Francis Group, London, ISBN 978-1-138-02469-4

Design and implementation of college physics demonstration experiment network aided teaching platform

R. Jiang, H.Q. Liu & C.-X. Zheng
School of Physics and Microelectronic Science, Hunan University, Changsha, Hunan, China

ABSTRACT: This article embarks from the college physics demonstration experiment teaching, to interview the students who chose the physics demonstration experiment courses and the teachers who teach these courses, and analysis the result. Fully consider the various factors of teachers' teaching process and students learning process, design and develop a teaching system which plays a supporting role in college physics demonstration experiments. Trying to improve the effectiveness of physics demonstration experiment through this network aided teaching platform.

Keywords: University physics; demonstration experiments; network-assisted teaching

1 THE REQUIREMENTS ANALYSIS OF COLLEGE PHYSICS DEMONSTRATION EXPERIMENT NETWORK AIDED TEACHING SYSTEM

1.1 *Necessity analysis of system*

1. The necessity of teaching and learning environment: As teachers' teaching and students' learning activities need a platform, so need to set up a teaching support subsystem.
2. The necessity of the support of teaching resources: As Network Aided Teaching system advocated cooperative learning and inquiry learning, teaching resources support is essential. And teachers' teaching also needs teaching resources to support.
3. The necessity of the entire system management: A complete system needs.
   Administrators to manage and maintain, collate data, and therefore need to set a management subsystem.
4. The necessity of setting of users: Currently, College physics Demonstrational Experiment is a basic course for engineering students in Hunan University, so the large number of classroom teachers and students to participate in learning. The whole Network Aided Teaching system can set five user identities: teachers, students, assistants, visitors and administrators. Teachers, students, assistants, visitors are the users of the aided teaching subsystem, all teaching and learning activities in the system. The system administrators control the teaching support system and teaching resources through the management subsystem.

1.2 *Feasibility analysis of system*

1.2.1 *Hardware conditions are ripe*
According to the actual situation of the school, the establishment of a network aided teaching system is entirely feasible.

At present, Hunan University campus network has taken shape, the wireless network has covered the entire campus. Students and teachers can access to the Internet by the client or to pay a variety of ways to use Wi-Fi in school rooms, classrooms, laboratories, dormitories.

1.2.2 *Technical conditions are ripe*
Before the system design, I have mastered related technologies that Network Aided Teaching system needs, such as .net, asp, html, css, xml, front page, edit plus and so on. By using these techniques basic knowledge that system design needed to fully realize the necessity of the development of Network Aided Teaching system.

1.2.3 *Economic conditions are ripe*
College physics demonstration experiments in addition to theoretical courses allow students to have sufficient time to clear knowledge and understand the physical world through other mean. Hunan University has always been the pursuit of efficiency in the undergraduate teaching quality, so also invested heavily in the improvement of teaching equipment and teaching resources. Network Aided Teaching is the reform of teaching methods in the direction of a large. This subject also received strong support from school and departments, that we could put all energy on research topics.

1.3 *Analysis of user requirement*

College physics demonstration experiment course is a required course for science and engineering students in Hunan University, teachers usually use multimedia or blackboard to explain physics knowledge to students. But students can understand physics concepts, physical processes and physical phenomena from sensory by allowing themselves to operate experiment instruments. Limited experimental equipment cannot meet the huge student repeated experimental operation. Network Aided Teaching system can help schools and students to solve this problem. Students can analyze their own achievements, then log into the network Aided Teaching system according to their own learning problems to choose a different way of learning.

2 DESIGN AND DEVELOPMENT OF COLLEGE PHYSICS DEMONSTRATION EXPERIMENTS NETWORK AIDED TEACHING SYSTEM

The choice of system development tools and key technologies.

2.1 *Web design*

By using Dreamweaver CS5 or FrontPage 2003 Web design and other tools to achieve web design.

2.2 *B/S framework*

B/S (Browser/Server) structure, also known as the Browser and Server structure. With the rapid of development of the Internet technology, it is a variation or improve structure on the C/S. Under this structure, the user interface is implemented via the WWW Browser, few transaction logic in the front-end (Browser), But the main transaction logic on the Server side (Server), forming the so-called three layer structure. This greatly simplifies the client computer loads, reduce the workload of system maintenance and upgrade costs and, reduce the overall cost of users.

2.3 *ASP technology*

ASP (Active Server Pages) is a WEB application development technology which was launched by Microsoft in November 1996, it is a technical framework. It can be used to produce and implement dynamic, interactive and efficient WEB services applications. ASP is similar to combination which is from HTML, Script which was developed by Microsoft combined with CGI (common network management interface), which allows the user to use many existing scripting languages, including VBScript, java Script, etc. to written ASP applications. ASP programming is more convenient and more flexible than HTML, which is running in the WEB server, then send the results in HTML to the client's browser. Therefore, ASP is more safe than the general scripting language. ASP is a more developed web application development technology, its core technology is the full support of the establishment and object technology. By using the ASP formation and object technology, users can directly use ActiveX controls, calling object methods and properties, to achieve powerful functions in a simple way.

2.4 *Access database technology*

Access is application-oriented database management system, which provides a number of tools and wizards, even without any programming experience, also can finish most of the database management and development work through the operation. Access also provides a programming language (Visual Basic for Application, VBA), can be used to develop high-performance, high-quality desktop database system. It can manage all types of data from a simple text, numeric characters to complex images, animations, sound, video, etc. In Access, can store and archive data through the visual way or structure applications; Can use a variety of ways for data screening, classification and query; Can view the data which is displayed on the screen of the form; can also access the page by creating a database to publish data to the Internet or an intranet. Access can also be used as the front-end access on the host and other network database to store data, provide relevant information for a number of large organizations.

3 THE BASIC STRUCTURE OF COLLEGE PHYSICS DEMONSTRATION EXPERIMENT NETWORK AIDED TEACHING SYSTEM

There are big differences about the orientation of network aided teaching system no matter domestic or abroad. And orientation directly affects the network-assisted platform functions and modules. At present the orientation of network aided teaching system forces on the course of learning, aid learning, a certain teaching function. This network aided teaching platform positioned in college physics demonstration experiment, based on Hunan University college physics experiment course. To improve the teaching quality of Hunan university physics demonstration experiment as the guidance. Considering all the necessary function of auxiliary teaching to design ten modules, each function module desgins the corresponding sub-module, Structure is shown in Figure 1.

Under each module, designing the corresponding sub-module, give full consideration to the needs of the teaching process.

News includes two sub-modules which are the latest physical and news announcement. Course description module includes the commencement of the form, teaching characteristics, assessment methods, experimental content. Teaching team sets up three sub-modules, they are the excellent teacher team, assist teachers team and the elite teacher team. Syllabus includes general of science, liberal arts general and technology explore. Experiment instruction sets up four sub-modules, they are heat, optics, electricity, magnetism. Experimental class includes video presentation, animation, simulation programs and teaching video. Experiment provides students with online self-booking an appointment to attend the experiment. Download includes software download, courseware download, download papers. Online Q&A provides a platform for teachers to answer the questions that students ask. Physical BBS is a platform for students and teachers to communicate.

3.1 News

To release of the latest news physics community, and to help the students to keep abreast of the latest physical dynamics, broaden their knowledge

and horizons. Notice published module includes experimental classroom equipment upgrades and maintenance of unexpected changes, curriculum, the experimental teachers transfer courses, the special requirements of experimental teachers before class. Teachers and students can know the corresponding situation in time, adjust the time for experimental operation.

3.2 Course introduction

Provide the main form of course, teaching characteristics, evaluation method and the experiment content. Students can read and understand the process of teaching and the mode of test before and after school, prepare for studying and test.

3.3 Teaching team

Teaching teams are divided into teams of outstanding teachers, support team of teachers, and the elite team of teachers. Provides each teacher's teaching style, resume and introduction. Students can choose their own interest of teachers according to their own learning styles. Can also in touch with teachers by using the contact information which were provided in this module, or discuss and exchange with the teacher after class.

3.4 Syllabus

Given detailed description for the syllabus of general education, liberal arts general and technology explore. Including the nature of the experiment, task, purpose, course credits, experiment method, the basic requirements and the method of grading.

3.5 Experimental guidance

Covering mechanical, optical, electrical, magnetic chunks and each module has a corresponding description of each experiment. Including the description of physical phenomenon, the introduction of demonstration equipment, of the demonstrate methods, the explanation of physical principle and exploration of the question after class.

3.6 Experimental classroom

The classroom experiments module, includes video presentations, animation, simulation programs and teaching videos. Video presentations which include mechanical, thermal, electromagnetic, optical, relativity, and wave, atomic physics experiments demo video. Students can watch the concrete operation process before or after class. Animation provides

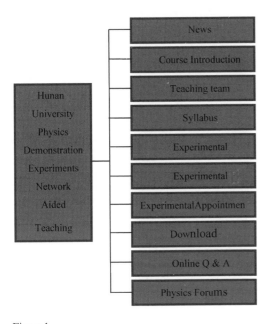

Figure 1.

optical, electromagnetic, mechanical vibration, thermodynamics and modern physics Flash animation, students can clearly observe physical phenomena and principles. Simulation program includes simulation experiment, and matlab simulation. Students can operate the simulation experiments instrument through the simulation experiment module. Also can import experimental data in matlab simulation interface, then use the results to observe and analyze physical phenomena and laws. Teaching videos are live videos that recorded teachers taught physical theory knowledge in class. Students can watch the videos repeatedly for the understanding physical theory, with theoretical knowledge into the classroom experiments to operate experiments. Give full consideration to the needs of the teachers, also provides some software courses for teachers to learn and encourage teachers reference to the construction of the physical resources platform.

3.7 Experimental appointment

Students can enter the experimental platform, booking experiments which they are interested in. Teachers can prepare according to the situation of students' experimental booking before class.

3.8 Download

The download module includes download courseware, teachers questions in class, in addition to the physical software. Teachers and students can download special software for learning, enrich our resources platform.

3.9 Online Q&A

Online Q&A major is a main platform for the exchange of teachers and students. In this platform, if students have any problems in their process of learning, they could ask any questions through online FAQS module. Teachers will give timely reply to the questions from students. Students can also ask questions which they can't understand when previewed before class. Teachers collect and explain the questions from students in the experimental classroom.

3.10 Physical BBS

Students can communicate through physical BBS; also can share their learning materials and learning experience.

4 CONCLUSION

The network aided teaching system can be used as a generic model of other engineering experiment course, also can be used in secondary schools. Both can exercise their self-learning ability, but also can reduce the burden of teachers and schools. Improve the overall quality of experimental teaching curriculum.

REFERENCES

Jiang. y.q. 2008. *The Research on Web-based Teaching in Physical Demonstration Experiment and the Development of Teaching Website*. Masterthesis: Shandong Normal University.
Li, Q. 2006. *The Design of Online Inquiry Learning System for College physics Demonstrational Experiment*. Master thesis: Hunan University.
Xu, J.P. 2008. *Design and implementation of network aided teaching system based on web*. Masterthesis: Ocean University of China.

Computer, Intelligent Computing and Education Technology – Liu, Sung & Yao (Eds)
© 2014 Taylor & Francis Group, London, ISBN 978-1-138-02469-4

A novel algorithm of contour initialization

P. Zang & L. Wang

Shandong Transport Vocational College, Weifang, China

ABSTRACT: We proposed an improved algorithm of Contour Initialization in GVF Snake Model based on detailed analysis of the problems in current active contour models: poor performance under interference, large computational cost, inability to converge to complex or rough contours and difficulty for setting initial contour, etc. Our method efficiently solved the problems in complex or rough contours initialization by connecting the initial points of different resolutions obtained by multi-scale edge detection methods based on wavelet transform and suitably controlling the number of GVF force field iterations. Experiments show that the initial contour can be accurately set close to the objective contour and successfully extract the objective contours with interferential edges and points. Simultaneously the new contour initialization algorithm has further reduced computational cost.

Keywords: GVF snake model; edge-detection; wavelet transformation

1 GVF VECTOR FLOW DEFORMABLE MODEL

1.1 GVF snake model

GVF Snake model is also called the gradient vector flow deformable model. From the force-balance equation

$$X_t(s,t) = \alpha X''(s,t) - \beta X''''(s,t) - \nabla E_{\text{ext}} \quad (1)$$

We design the GVF force field. The potential force $-\nabla E_{\text{ext}}$ is replaced with $V(x, y) = [u(x, y), v(x, y)]$, yielding

$$X_t(s,t) = \alpha X''(s,t) - \beta X''''(s,t) - V \quad (2)$$

where α and β are weighting parameters that control the contour's tension and rigidity respectively, and $X''(s,t)$ and $X''''(s,t)$ denote the second and fourth derivatives of $X(s,t)$ with respect to s and t. Given $f(x,y)$ is the edge map derived from a gray-level image $I(x,y)$, and the gradient vector field of $f(x,y)$ is $\nabla f(x,y)$, which expands toward the edges from the gradient vector flow field $V(x,y) = [u(x,y),v(x,y)]$ which is formed by minimizing the following energy functional:

$$E = \iint \mu \left(u_x^2 + u_y^2 + v_x^2 + v_y^2 \right)$$
$$+ |\nabla f|^2 |V - \nabla f|^2 \, \mathrm{d}x\mathrm{d}y \quad (3)$$

where μ is a parameter and ∇^2 is the Laplacian operator. When $|\nabla f|$ is small, the energy is domi-nated by the first term, yielding a slow-varying field. On the other hand, when $|\nabla f|$ is large, the second term dominates the integrand and is mini-mized by setting $V = \nabla f$. This produces the desired effect of keeping V nearly equal to the gradient of the edge map when it is large, but forcing the field to be slow-varying in homogeneous regions. To minimize the energy functional, V must satisfy the following Euler equation

$$\mu \nabla^2 u - (u - f_x)\left(f_x^2 + f_y^2\right) = 0$$
$$\mu \nabla^2 v - (v - f_y)\left(f_x^2 + f_y^2\right) = 0 \quad (4)$$

The iterative equations for GVF force field are

$$u_t(x,y,t) = \mu \nabla^2 u(x,y,t) - (u(x,y,t)$$
$$- f_x(x,y)(f_x^2(x,y) + f_y^2(x,y)) \quad (5.\text{a})$$

$$v_t(x,y,t) = \mu \nabla^2 v(x,y,t) - (v(x,y,t)$$
$$- f_y(x,y)(f_x^2(x,y) + f_y^2(x,y)) \quad (5.\text{b})$$

The initial GVF force field is usually set to the gradient of the edge map. Xu Chenyang used the GVF force field $V(x,y)$ as static external force field in snake model. Thus the iterative equations for active contour deformation in GVF snake model are

$$x = inv \times \left(\gamma \times x + \kappa \times \mu\right) \quad (6.\text{a})$$

$$y = inv \times \left(\gamma \times y + \kappa \times \mu\right) \quad (6.\text{b})$$

1.2 Problems of GVF snake model and our method

Figure 1(a), (b), (c) shows the results of contour extraction using GVF snake model and Figure 1(d), (e) shows the results of our method.

Figure 1(a) shows that the initial contour is usually set by hand far away from the objective edges. In this way, the capture range is expended and the interference of burr noise is avoided. But the larger capture range is at the cost of more iterations and larger GVF force field, which increases complexity of time and calculation. What's more, it's difficult to set the initial contour near the true contour just by interactive method.

Figure 1(b) shows the GVF force field after 80 iterations using equations (5.a) and (5.b). GVF force field is asymmetric. Areas with high density of force lines are where the true edges are. Blank areas are where the force is zero and the energy functional is minimized. Fake contours are formed when the active contour falls into the blank areas during convergence process as in Figure 1(c).

Figure 1(c) shows the extracted contour after 90 GVF force field iterations. As the analysis, more iterations will not result in further changes of the contour. GVF snake can't converge to complex contours such as Ω-shaped and narrow U-shaped contours. What's more, because of the existence of burr noise and interferential points, the GVF Snake model can't extract the objective contour, which indicates GVF snake model is sensitive to noise and interference.

From the Figure 1(d), we can see our L's initial contour is closed to the objective contour and this can reduce the times of calculation of GVF force field and extraction of objective contour. However, it can't overcome the burr noise as in the left of the figure and can't extract the objective contour with rough surface. In Figure 1(d), if the initial contour

can overcome the burr noise and interferential points, it can successfully extract the objective contour with less GVF force field.

For GVF Snake model, the 80 iterations to obtain GVF force field took 17.5350s. The 90 iterations for contour convergence took 25.3260s. The computational cost is high. For the method of Caixia L's, computing GVF force field took about 0.07s. So if the initial contour can overcome the interference and be closed the objective contour, the time cost will be certainly low.

2 IMPROVED CONTOUR INITIALIZATION ALGORITHM

In most cases, the contours of areas of interest have the features of edges, as well as noise, such as interferential points and burr noise. So if the method can overcome the noise, the initial contour can be set closed to the true contour. In this paper, we first use multi-scale edge detection algorithm based on wavelet transform to obtain edge points of areas of interest. Then we improved the method of link algorithm to overcome the interference.

2.1 Connecting edge points into continuous segments

Choosing initial reference points. The initial reference points must lie outside the true edges of interested areas and in counter-clockwise direction. For each continuous segment, two reference points should be selected, such as point A and B in Figure 2(a). Here the dashed line is the objective contour in Figure 2(a).

Establishing searching direction. As shown in Figue 2(a), A and B are reference points. Define searching angle ω as the angle between vector $\overrightarrow{AB}$ and x-axis. There are eight directions for searching which respectively locate at the 8 connected area of some point.

Obtaining the first edge point. Start from point A, search along the reverse direction of

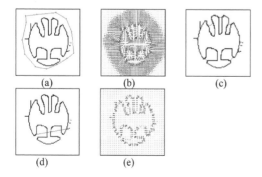

(a)   (b)

(d)   (e)

Figure 1. (a) Initial contour of GVF Snake model. (b) GVF force field of GVF Snake model. (c) Contour extraction results with GVF Snake model. (d) Initial contour of our method. (e) GVF force field of our method.

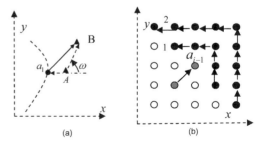

(a)   (b)

Figure 2. (a) The setting of initial points and searching angle. (b) Searching algorithm of our method.

initial searching direction to obtain the first edge point a1. Calculate the new searching angle ω as the angle between $\overline{a_1B}$ and x-axis. Establish new searching direction according to the new searching angle.

For each point ai, search along current searching direction for n layers of points around point ai in counter-clockwise direction. We use $n = 2$ in our algorithm. Here we adopt arrow shape searching area along the direction of tangent as shown in Figure 2(b). Make the point a_{i-1} as the center point and along the searching angle ω we search n layers of points around point a_{i-1} in counter-clockwise direction. The search stops when the first edge point ai is encountered. New searching angle ω is calculated as the angle between aiai-1 and x-axis and new searching direction is established. Following this method, we search for the next edge point.

Step 4 is repeated until no edge point can be found or edge point that was already processed is encountered.

Searching for ending point a_N. After we found nth (n>=3) points starting from the first point, we mark the points of sixteenth connected area as the ending points. After that, when we find a new edge point, we judge that whether it is the ending point first.

2.2 *Contours with multiple segments*

Assume the true contour consists of N continuous segments. Two initial reference points in counter-clockwise order on the outside are needed for each segment, as shown in Figure 2. Thus a total of 2 N initial reference points in counter-clockwise order are needed for the entire contour. We obtain each segment using algorithms described above and link them up to form a closed contour.

3 RESULT DISCUSSION

3.1 *Result analysis*

The above algorithm is used to extract contours from several images. The results are shown in Figure 3.

Results show that the initial contours calculated with our initialization algorithm are very close to the true contours and can converge to the true contour with just a few numbers of iterations. Conventional GVF snake model can not converge to such complex shapes and the approach can not extract the contours with much noise. With the help of our contour initialization algorithm, it now can converge to these complex shapes.

3.2 *Time complexity*

In the original GVF model proposed by Xu Chenyang, the number of GVF force field

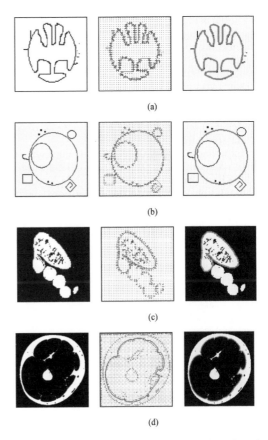

Figure 3. (a) Image with several Ω-shaped and U-shaped contours. (b) Image with contours consisting of burr noise and interferential points. (c) Slice of foot. (d) Slice of leg.

iterations usually ranges from tens to hundreds. After the initial contour is set, tens to hundreds of iterations are also needed for contour convergence. Typically, completing a contour extraction process takes from 20 to 155 seconds. Then it can set the initial contour very close to the rough objective contour. Thus the effective area of GVF force field does not need to be very large and few GVF force field iterations are needed. This also leads few number of contour convergence iterations. Typically, only one or two GVF force field iterations and no more than 10 convergence iterations are needed to obtain good contour extraction results. These can be completed in less than 10 seconds.

4 CONCLUSION

The key to solve some of the convergence problems associated with the original GVF snake model is to set initial contour inside "effective area" and make the "effective area" as small as possible [4]. The method proposed in [4] realizes this aim and on the basis of it, our approach can process the rough contour. Initial contour set according to our algorithm is very close to the true rough contour with some interferential points and burr noise. This not only reduces the "effectual area" needed but also makes it easier for the active contour to converge to the true edges.

Experiment results show that our contour initialization method greatly increases the accuracy of GVF snake model. At the mean while, it reduces computational cost and time complexity, extend its application rang while maintaining all the merits of GVF snake model.

REFERENCES

Liu, C.X. & Fan, Y.B. 2006. A new algorithm of contour initialization in GVF Snake model, Computer Application.

Stephane Mallat. 1999. A Wavelet Tour of Signal Processing, Second Edition. Academic Press.

Xu, C.Y. & Prince, J.L. 1997. Gradient Vector Flow: A New External Force for Snakes, Proceedings of the 1997 Conference on Computer Vision and Pattern Recognition (CVPR '97), IEEE Computer Society.

Xu, J. & Huang, Z.H.Y. 2002. Detection and recognition or aeral targets based on the Bubblew avelet function and GVF Snake model. Electronics optics and control. 11(4):32–35.

Computer, Intelligent Computing and Education Technology – Liu, Sung & Yao (Eds)
© 2014 Taylor & Francis Group, London, ISBN 978-1-138-02469-4

H-beam rolling schedule influence on the microstructure

J.H. Ma, S.B. Zheng & B. Tao
College of Metallurgy and Energy, Hebei Polytechnical University, Hebei Province, China

ABSTRACT: Cross section structure has significant effect on the mechanical properties of H-beam. Based on the site rolling conditions, FEM model is established. Microstructure module in DEFORM-3D is used to simulate microstructure of the web, flange and the conjunction of web and flange. By simulation results, the influence of and deformation amount, rolling speed, blooming temperature and finishing temperature on microstructure and grain size has been analyzed. Metallurgical structure of actual production was observed.

Keywords: in order to; MS Word microstructure; grain refinement; uniform cross section; rolling schedule; numerical simulation

1 INTRODUCTION

With the H-beam gradually accepted by domestic market, sales and output continue to expand. There is increasing user requirement about product performance. It is requirement of that H-beam has comprehensive mechanical properties, which is decided by the raw material and rolling process. The hot rolling process will produce different physical metallurgical phenomena such as work hardening, dynamic recovery and recrystallization. This metallurgy changes decide microstructure and mechanical properties of the final product, which determines the performance of products in a certain extent[1–3]. Therefore, It is necessary that according to the raw material and rolling process, microstructural evolution of rolling process is simulated and analyzed, thus the microstructures and properties are accurately controlled.

2 FEM MODEL

2.1 *Taking the finish product dimension*

200 mm × 200 mm × 12 mm × 8 mm of Jinxi Steel co.ltd as for example. The rolling process

and recrystallization process are simulated by FEM software DEFORM-3D. The billet dimension is 294 mm × 218 mm × 59 mm × 32 mm after rolled by BD cogging. The length of rolling piece is 1000 mm, the diameter of horizontal roller is 1000 mm, that of vertical roller is 800 mm, the continuous rolling method is used. To simplified the computation, the 1/4 sectionis used to model, the material is 25 steel, the FEM model is shown as Figure 1.

3 SIMULATION RESULT ANALYSIS

Deformation degree, deformation velocity, temperature and microstructure evolution are coupled with DEFORM-3D software. Rolling schedules are consistent with the rolling procedure of site. Rolling procedure of site is shown as Table 1. The rolling speed of each pass roller is shown as Table 2. The initial temperature of billet is 1050 °C. P1, P2, P3 are three points selected from the same

Figure 1. The continuous rolling model of H-beam.

Table 1. The rolling schedule.

Pass		Roll gap (mm)	Pass		Roll gap (mm)
1	Horizontal	25.20	5	Horizontal	12.5
	Vertical	46.40	6	Horizontal	9.90
2	Horizontal	19.90		Vertical	16.20
	Vertical	35.70	7	Horizontal	8.50
3	Horizontal	15.80		Vertical	13.20
	Vertical	27.40	8	Horizontal	8.5
4	Horizontal	12.50	9	Horizontal	8.00
	Vertical	21.10		Vertical	12.00

Table 2.　The roll velocity of each pass.

Pass	Rolling speed (mm/s)	Pass	Rolling speed (mm/s)
1	635	6	1620
2	720	7	1960
3	920	8	2000
4	1190	9	2200
5	1250		

Table 3.　The chemical compositions of sample in experiment.

Element	C	Si	Mn	P	S
Content (%)	0.190	0.220	0.570	0.032	0.021

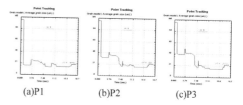

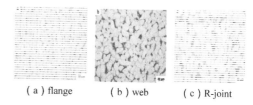

(a)P1　　　　　　(b)P2　　　　　　(c)P3

Figure 3.　Grain size.

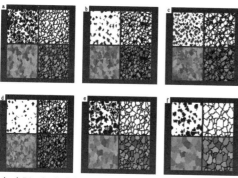

(a) flange　　　　(b) web　　　　(c) R-joint

Figure 4.　Different parts of the microstructure.

(a) P1point in deformation (b) P1point between passes (c) P2 point in deformation (d) P2point between passes (e) P3 point in deformation (f) P3between passes

Figure 2.　Changes in the process of rolling grain.

section of H-beam, P1 point is in the web, P2 is in the flange and P3 in the junction of web and flange. Microstructure of three points were simulated by Microstructure module of DEFORM-3D. The grain size change is shown Figure 3. Four kinds of microscopic characteristics is displayed in Figure 4.

As can be seen from Figure 2, dislocation density of P1 is bigger, more grain boundary, and smaller grain compared with that of P2 and P3. For the same point, there is bigger dislocation density, more grain boundary and smaller grain in the process of deformation than that of between the passes.

Main physical metallurgical phenomena of metal hot plastic deformation process includes in the process of including work hardening, dynamic recovery and dynamic recrystallization. The typical

organizational changes between rolling passes are static recovery, static recrystallization and grain growth. As can be seen from this, in the rolling process of rolling piece, microstructure and properties of metal materials is affected by the hardening and softening process and this process is affected by deformation temperature, strain rate, deformation degree and the metal itself properties.

When bigger deformation degree and lower heating temperature, the hardening process caused by the deformation is dominant. With the manufacturing process, the strength and hardness of metal rise but plastic gradually decreases. The lattice distortion of internal metal can not be resorted and cannot be soften. In this condition, deformation resistance is more and more bigger, even leading to metal fracture. Conversely, if smaller metal deformation and higher deformation temperature, because the recrystallization and grain growth take advantage, metal grain will become coarser and coarser. In this process, metals can not be broken down, but the performance of metal can be worse.

In the metal thermoplastic change process, whether the grain is refined depends on the factors, such as deformation amount, rolling speed, rolling temperature, final rolling temperature and cooling after rolling. Increasement of deformation is beneficial to obtain finer grain. But bigger deformation amount can cause uneven deformation degree. In the rolling process, grain size is not uniform, but also will cause uneven deformation degree, deformation is too large, then the rolling process of grain size is not uniform, non uniform grain especially appear in flange and web of H-beam. This direct consequence is that uneven section machinery property increases. In the rolling process, the deformation temperature is higher and recovery degree will be greater.

Thus, the energy storage after deformation reduces and grain becomes coarse. But the deformation temperature is too low to cause the work hardening and make metal plastic and toughness decrease.

In order to better illustrate the above, microstructure and sectional average grain size of final product after rolling are simulated as shown in Figure 3. Four small figures in Figure 3 respectively represent crystal orientation, dislocation density, grain boundary and the crystal orientation and grain boundary. It can be seen from Figure 3 that the grain size of P1 is 19.6 μm, the grain size of P2 was 22 μm, and the grain size of P3 is 23.1 μm. In contrast of structure grain of web, flange and R-joint, the grain of web is smallest and flange is following.

In the rolling process of H-beam, the reduction of web is maximum, therefore, the the web deformation is the biggest. Web deformation is the biggest, the web grain is so small that the strength and plastic and toughness increase. The deformation of the flange and web of the junction of the minimum, so the grain maximum. The deformation of R-joint is the smallest, therefore, the structure grain is the biggest. Grain size distribution of section is uneven, leading to uneven mechanical properties of H-beam section.

As can be seen from Figure 3, the grain refinement of P1 points is the fastest, but after the grain size change of grain size is relatively gentle. Grain of P2 and P3 point is continuous refinement at the back of the passes. This is main reason that at the former pass the web reduction is the biggest and equivalent strain is relatively the biggest. But after bloom, the rolling piece flange is thicker, in order to get the product size, the equivalent strain of flange began to take advantage, the grain of the flanges are constantly more refined.

4 EXPERIMENT

In order to test the simulation results of H-beam rolling process with FEM software, taking samples from Jinxi Steel co.ltd, the microstructure is observed and grain size is rated and that are compared with simulation results.

The sample from Jinxi Steel co.ltd, whose specifications is H200 × 200 × 12 × 8 mm. The small size H-beam production line has 9 finishing mill, 7 out of 9 are universal mill and two are edged mill. Rolling rule is shown in Table 1.

Three positions are cut from sample with line cutting machine and observed. There parts are respectively web, flange and R-joint. The sample size is 10 × 10 mm. Microstructures are observed.

And grain size of organization is measured and compared with the simulation result, this provide the basis for validation of FEM simulation.

Metallographic microstructure are respectively observed on the flange, web and R-joint and average grain size is determined, as shown in Figure 4. As can be seen from the Figure 4 that the organization of flange, web and R-joint are white ferrite and black pearlite. Their grain size are different (b > a > c) and grain fineness number is determined. The results show that b is 10.5 level, a 9.0 level and c 8.3 level. This result is consistent with simulation result, indicating simulation result is accurate.

In the hot plastic deformation of metal, with the increase of the plastic deformation, yield strength and tensile strength of rolling piece were increased, but the plasticity decreases. Comparison with Figure 4(a), 4(b) and 4(c). It shows that in the rolling process of H-beam, because the reduction of web is bigger and web deformation is bigger, microstructural organization is smaller and web strength is higher. The deformation rate of web and flange are almost equal. But in the actual production process of H-beam, because of the non uniform reduction of web and flange, deformation amount of the flange and the web is not consistent. The reduction of web is obviously bigger than that of flange, thus, the grain of web is finer and grain of flange is coarser, this is the reason that the properties of web and flange are different.

5 CONCLUSION

Increase of deformation is beneficial to obtain fine grain, but too big deformation will cause uneven deformation degree, therefore, the grain size is uneven in the rolling process, especially flange and web of H-beam will appear the phenomenon of uneven grain. Slower rolling speed is helpful for the dynamic recrystallization. Dynamic recrystallization can obviously refine the grain. Lower rolling temperature is helpful to improve the mechanical properties of the products.

Reasonable distribution of reduction, rolling speed, rolling temperature, not only can refine grain, but also can make uniform microstructure.

REFERENCES

[1] Xu Feng, HE Cai-Hong, Xu Yong. Characteristics of Hot Rolled H-beam Process in China. Research on Iron & Steel. 2009,(4):59–61.
[2] Tian Jian. Development of H-beam Rolling Process. Tanjin Metallurgy. 2010,1:17–19.
[3] Jin Xiao-guang. Theory and Experimental Investigation into the Universal Tandem Rolling Process of H-beam. Qinghuangdao: Yanshan University, 1995.
[4] Mao Wei-min, Zhao Xin-bing. Recrystallization and Grain Growth of Metal. Beijing: Metallurgy Industry Press, 1994.

Computer, Intelligent Computing and Education Technology – Liu, Sung & Yao (Eds)
© 2014 Taylor & Francis Group, London, ISBN 978-1-138-02469-4

Multi-objective fuzzy optimal design of hot rolling strip mill housing

J.H. Ma, B. Tao & X.H. Yao
College of Metallurgy and Energy, Hebei Polytechnical University, Hebei Province, China

ABSTRACT: Mill housing vibration influents the T strip thickness fluctuation. The longitudinal deformation of rolling mill will directly affect plate thickness difference. The longitudinal deformation should be reduced, improving the mill stiffness. Hot rolling mill is seen as is as subject investigated. The weighting function of housing weight, stiffness and first-order natural frequency is seen as multi-objective function. The weighting coefficient closest to ideal solution is obtained through the choose close principle of fuzzy nearness degree. The optimal result is analyzed. The housing stiffness improves. Low order natural frequency improves after optimization, avoiding resonance and improving the housing dynamic stability.

Keywords: mill housing; multi-objective; fuzzy nearness degree; mill vibration; stiffness

1 INTRODUCTION

Optimal design of machinery, there are often multiple objectives and decision scheme. Optimal goal hopes that more objective or decision scheme can simultaneously achieve the most optimal in the constraints. But due to the complexity of system problems, multiple targets can not often achieve the most optimal value at the same time, some contradictory each other, even conflicts. So in the process of optimal design, in order to make the scheme more reasonable, we often give the corresponding weight coefficients in the front of targets according to the important degree of targets to the unified into a target. Then non inferior solution closest to the ideal solution of total target is obtained. In the past, weighted coefficient of each objective function of multi-objective function are often obtained by experience. Because the relationship between multiple targets is complicated, it is difficult to determine the weighted coefficient, and even to consider many factors, even human factor and the performance factors.[1,2] In this paper, the fuzzy mathematics method is introduced to determine the weight coefficient. Weight coefficient obtained fromfuzzy nearness degree of each objective function, optimization result of each goal is more close to the ideal solution.

2 PLATE AND STRIP MILL HOUSING VIBRATION AND STIFFNESS ANALYSIS

2.1 Vibration analysis of plate and strip mill housing

Mill vibration seriously affects the mill accuracy, affects the longitudinal thickness difference, shorten the service life of the mill parts, increase the cost of production, but also easily produce quality problem such as the strip thickness fluctuation and the surface grinding crack. So in the rolling process, the mill vibration should be reduced, the stability of mill system increased, thereby reduce the thickness fluctuation of plate and improve the rolling quality of plate. In order to avoid the low order resonance of frame in the rolling process, the first-order natural frequency of vibration of the housing is seen as the research object.[3]

2.2 Stiffness analysis of plate and strip mill housing

Plate and strip mill housing stiffness has a direct impact on steel longitudinal thickness difference, the greater is stiffness of housing, the smaller is elastic deformation, the longitudinal thickness difference of rolling plate is smaller. Housing stiffness is inversely proportional to longitudinal deformation. It can increase the stiffness of mill housing to reduce the plate longitudinal thickness difference.

2.3 FE analysis of plate and strip mill housing

In this paper, the hot rolling plate mill housing is seen as the research object. The housing diagram is shown in Figure 1, the size of each part is $B_1 = 850, B_2 = 1100, H_1 = 900, H_2 = 1270, W = 760$. Solid model of housing is shown in Figure 2. Rolling force of hot rolling plate is 30000 kN, so rolling force of single frame is 15000 kN. Modal analysis of the housing is carried out by the finite element software ANSYS, first order vibration is shown in Figure 3, the first-order natural

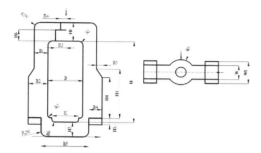

Figure 1. Housing dimension of diagrammatic sketch.

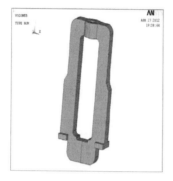

Figure 2. Stereogram of housing.

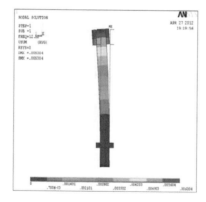

Figure 3. First order vibration of housing.

frequency is 12.120 Hz. Longitudinal deformation is maximum deformation difference between the upper and lower beam. It can be seen from that the biggest longitudinal deformation of upper beam is 0.918 mm and the biggest longitudinal deformation of lower beam is −0.217 mm. Therefore, the longitudinal deformation of housing f_v is deformation difference between upper and lower beam, as 1.135 mm.

3 MULTI-OBJECTIVE FUZZY OPTIMIZATION ANALYSIS OF HOUSING

3.1 Design variables

$$X = [X_1, X_2, X_3, X_4, X_5]^T = [B_1, B_2, H_1, H_2, W]^T \quad (1)$$

where, B_1, B_2—the width of column(mm); H_1—the height of upper beam(mm); H_2—the height of lower beam(mm); W—thickness of housing(mm).

3.2 The constraints

1. Stress constraint of housing
   The maximum stress of upper an lower beam is expressed as $\sigma_{e\max}$, allowable stress is $[\sigma] \le 50 \sim 90\,\mathrm{MPa}$, i.e. $g_1(x) = \sigma_{e\max} - 90 \le 0$.
   The maximum stress of column is expressed as $\sigma_{\max}$, allowable stress is $[\sigma] \le 40 \sim 50$ MPa, i.e. $g_2(x) = \sigma_{\max} - 50 \le 0$.
2. Boundary constraints
   Boundary constraints are geometry limit condition to housing $X_{i\min} \le X_i \le X_{i\max}$, $i = 1,2,3,4,5$, i.e.

$$\begin{cases} g_3(x) = 700 - B_1 \le 0 \\ g_4(x) = B_1 - 1000 \le 0 \\ g_5(x) = 1000 - B_2 \le 0 \\ g_6(x) = B_2 - 1200 \le 0 \\ g_7(x) = 800 - H_1 \le 0 \end{cases} \begin{cases} g_{11}(x) = H_1 - 1000 \le 0 \\ g_{12}(x) = 1200 - H_2 \le 0 \\ g_{13}(x) = H_2 - 1300 \le 0 \\ g_{14}(x) = 750 - W \le 0 \\ g_{15}(x) = W - 900 \le 0 \end{cases}$$

$$(2)$$

3.3 Multi-objective function establishment

The housing stiffness, first order natural frequency and the weight are unified into single function, then optimization is carried out by finite element software ANSYS. Because of the weight is proportional to volume and the product of stiffness and longitudinal deformation is constant. So the weight total volume, longitudinal deformation

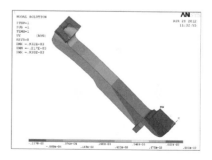

Figure 4. Longitudinal displacement of housing.

and first-order natural frequency are unified as the objective function, considering the magnitude of unity, the objective function is established as formula (3).

$$F = \omega_1 * volume + \omega_2 * y * 1000 + \omega_3 * 100/freq \quad (3)$$

where, *volume*—total volume of housing(m³); *y*—longitudinal deformation of housing(mm); *freq*-first-order natural frequency of housing(Hz); $\omega_1, \omega_2, \omega_3$,—weight parameters of each sub target.

4 OPTIMIZATION METHODS

The advantages of the zero order method uses only the objective function and constraint conditions value, which is solved by penalty function method, instead of obtaining partial derivative of the objective function and constraints, providing convenient for the majority of the objective function and constraint function not good derivative problems.

The housing is a large and complex part, after meshing element number is more. Stress at the corner changes a lot. Constraint condition and objective function is relatively complex, not easy to calculate the derivative. Therefore, the zero order method is used to solve the optimization, in order to ensure the successful optimization process.

5 OPTIMIZATION ANALYSIS

In this paper, housing stiffness and stability of vibration is mainly considered. So weight parameters before the volume is fixed as 0.2 to facilitate the calculation. Thus, the following five groups of parameters are combined as flowing formula (4).

$$\begin{cases} f = 0.2 * volume + 0.2 * y * 1000 + 0.6 * 100/freq \\ f = 0.2 * volume + 0.3 * y * 1000 + 0.5 * 100/freq \\ f = 0.2 * volume + 0.4 * y * 1000 + 0.4 * 100/freq \\ f = 0.2 * volume + 0.5 * y * 1000 + 0.3 * 100/freq \\ f = 0.2 * volume + 0.6 * y * 1000 + 0.2 * 100/freq \end{cases} \quad (4)$$

Multi-objective above groups after optimization is optimized with the zero order optimization method with ANSYS software. Non inferior solution of each weight of multi-objective is shown as Table 1.

According to fuzzy nearness degree the the ideal solution of three sub targets is as formula (5).

$$F(x^*) = [f_1^*, f_2^*, f_3^*] = [volume^*, y^*, freq^*]$$
$$= [7.2494E + 9, 1.133, 15.892] \quad (5)$$

Table 1. Noninferior solution of each scheme.

Scheme	ω_1	ω_2	ω_3	Volume/mm³	y/mm	freq/H$_Z$
1	0.2	0.2	0.6	8.2475E+9	1.0730	15.947
2	0.2	0.3	0.5	8.2124E+9	1.0693	15.907
3	0.2	0.4	0.4	8.2054E+9	1.0691	15.845
4	0.2	0.5	0.3	8.2246E+9	1.0633	15.860
5	0.2	0.6	0.2	8.0254E+9	1.0754	15.596

Table 2. Nearness degree of non inferior with ideal solution at normal distribution.

Scheme	1	2	3	4	5
Nearness degree	0.4616	0.5663	0.4969	0.5433	0.2618

Non inferior solutions of sub target and each ideal solution of groups obtained from formula (5) are substituted into formula (6), this can find the membership of the non inferior solution corresponding to ideal solution of sub target. The membership is substituted into formula (7). The nearness degree of non inferior solution to ideal solution is shown as Table 2.

$$\mu(f_{rj}) = \exp\left[-(f_{rj} - f_j^*)\Big/ \left(1/k \sum_{i=1}^{k} |f_{rj} - f_j^*|\right)^2\right] \quad (6)$$

$$\sigma(F_r^*, F_r) = 1 - \frac{1}{q}\left[\sum_{j=1}^{q} |1 - \mu(f_{rj})|^p\right]^{1/p} \quad (7)$$

As can be seen from Table 2, the membership of non inferior solution corresponding to ideal solution of sub target is obtained from normal distribution. The nearness degree of the second groups result is maximum. Therefore, in accordance with the preferred principle, selecting second group weight coefficient of as the optimal weight coefficient of multi-objective optimization of housing, non inferior solution of second groups is the optimum solution of the multi-objective optimization. The mass, stiffness and natural frequency of three objective optimization of housing is the most optimal solution is as formula (8).

$$F(x^*) = F_2 = [volume^*, y^*, freq^*]$$
$$= [8.2124E + 9, 1.0693, 15.907] \quad (8)$$

The optimization results are shown in Table 3. It can be seen from Table 3, although the volume increases from the initial value 7.2494E+9 mm³ to

Table 3. Optimization result.

Parameters	Before optimization	After optimization	Parameters	Before optimization	After optimization
B_1 (mm)	850	700.61	σ_{emax} (MPa)	53.38	48.303
B_2 (mm)	1100	1199.6	σ_{emax} (MPa)	90.84	89.631
H_1 (mm)	900	848.52	volume (mm³)	7.2494E+9	8.2124E+9
H_2 (mm)	1270	1216.0	y (mm)	1.133	1.0693
W (mm)	760	899.70	freq/Hz	12.133	15.907

8.1224E+9 mm³ and increases 13.2%. The longitudinal deformation reduces from 1.33 mm to 1.0693 mm, and decreases 5.6%, housing stiffness after optimization is 14027.87 kN/mm, the stiffness before optimization is 13215.86 kN/mm, and increases 6.1%. Therefore, the longitudinal stiffness increases. The most obvious change is that the first-order natural frequency increases before optimization from 12.133 Hz to 15.907 Hz, and increases of 31.1%. Therefore, effectively improves the low order natural frequency to avoid resonance and improve the dynamic stability of housing.

6 CONCLUSION

1. Multi-objective function as the mass, stiffness and natural frequency of the housing is established. Weight coefficient closest to the ideal solution is obtained from the nearness principle of fuzzy nearness degree. Optimum analysis is made by zero order optimization method with ANSYS.

2. Longitudinal stiffness of housing after optimization increases. The low order natural frequency of housing effectively improves to avoid the resonance and improve the dynamic stability of housing.

REFERENCES

[1] Cadenas JM, Verdegay JL. Using Ranking Functions in Multi-objective Fuzzy Linear Programming[J]. Fuzzy Sets and Systems, 2000, 111:47–53.
[2] Maleki HR, Tata M. Linear Programming with Fuzzy Variables[J]. Fuzzy Sets and Systems, 2000, 109:21–33.
[3] QIN Chenwei. Vibration analysis and multi-objective fuzzy optimization design of hot rolled steel plate mill[D]. Qinhuangdao, Master dissertation of Zhejiang University, 2012:30–61

Computer, Intelligent Computing and Education Technology – Liu, Sung & Yao (Eds)
© 2014 Taylor & Francis Group, London, ISBN 978-1-138-02469-4

Optimal design roller of Y-type mill

J.H. Ma, B. Tao & X.H. Yao
College of Metallurgy and Energy, Hebei Polytechnical University, Hebei Province, China

ABSTRACT: Y-type rolling mill with three roller is a new kind of wire mill. Because of its unique advantage, It is very important to optimize structure. Roller is important part of the rolling mill, whose size effects the strength, stiffness, as well as the rolling piece quality and service life of the rolling mill. Therefore, It is important to optimize the roller structure dimension of Y-type mill. The roller model is set up referring to first pass roller dimension of ϕ 250 Y type mill with three roller. The stress and deformation of roller is analysed by the finite element software ANSYS. The optimal mathematic model is established. Objective function is established by three kinds of scheme. The optimal result is evaluated by one-order comprehensive fuzzy evaluation method. In conclusion, the multi-objective scheme is the most optimal.

Keywords: Y-type rolling mill; roller; optimal design; fuzzy evaluation

1 INTRODUCTION

Wire production has developed very fast in recent years, from small mill to continuous mill and semi—continuous. High speed wire mill has now become mainstream, Capacity and production are 50% more than that of total amount. The urgent demand for wire production in view of the market, the requirement of wire mill increases. Three rollers Y type mill is shown in Figure 1. Because of its special deformation way can make the workpiece maintaining high precision and high surface smoothness[1].

Y type mill is a new kind of high speed wire mill, because of its unique advantages, It is necessary to further optimize structure size[2]. Roller is the main part of the mill. It is more stringent requirements about rollers. Roller strength, stiffness, weight, the amplitude of the vibration and fatigue limit will affect the quality and service life of rolling mill.

In order to meet the needs of the market and design more efficient mill, it is important to optimize structure dimensions of Y type mill roller.

2 FE ANALYSIS OF ROLLER

Roller designed in this paper is based on the roller size given on the relevant dimensions of φ 250 Y type mill of Tongchuan aluminum plant. The roller size is optimized in the condition of the maximum rolling force, so initial size of roller model is adopt the first pass size. The roller structure sketch is shown in Figure 2. The initial roller values of main parameters are $B = 13$, $H = 18$, $L_1 = 20$, $L_2 = 43$, $R = 125$. Material parameters and rolling parameters are shown in Table 1. Y direction deformation diagram analysed by finite element software ANSYS is shown in Figure 3. It can be seen from Figure 3, Y direction maximum deformation

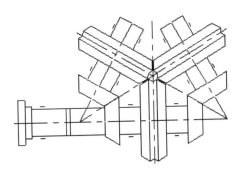

Figure 1. Y rolling mill.

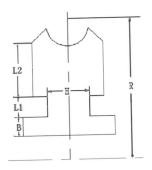

Figure 2. The section of roller.

Table 1. Material and parameters of roller.

Parameters	Value	Parameters	Value
Material	40 Cr	Modulus of elasticity	2.1*10⁵ MPa
Allowable stress	160 MPa	Density	7.82*10³/m³
Maximum rolling force	30 KN	Nominal diameter of roller	ϕ 250

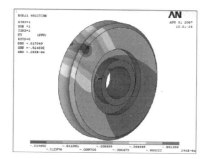

Figure 3. The deformation of the roller along Y-direction.

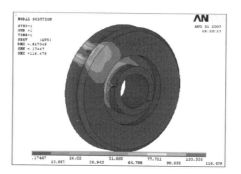

Figur 4. Von-Mises stress of the roller.

Table 2. Initial results data about roller.

Parameters	σ (MPa)	WT (kg)	y (mm)
Value	116.47880	12.180640	1.4631532E-2

value is 0.0000295 and Y direction minimum deformation value is −0.0146021. Y direction deformation is difference between the maximum deformation value and the minimum deformation value, i.e. Y direction deformation of roller is y = (0.0000295) − (0.0146021) = 0.0146315 mm. Equivalent stress contour of contact surface between roller and workpiece is shown in Figure 4.

It can be seen the danger point of roll location from Figure 4. Initial computing results of roller is shown in Table 2.

3 Y TYPE ROLLER OPTIMIZATION ANALYSIS

In this paper, the roller size is optimized. Depending on change the size to meet the strength and stiffness, service life of the roller is improved and materials is saved.

3.1 Design variable

The roller designed in this paper is based on the given roller size of φ 250 Y type mill. According to the stress and shape features of the roller, referring to Figure 2, the design variables are selected as $X = [X_1, X_2, X_3, X_4, X_5]^T = [B, H, L_1, L_2, R]^T$.

3.2 Constraint conditions

1. Strengthen condition: Through finite element analysis of the roller, maximum stress point exists in the contact surface between the roller and rolling piece, the equivalent stress of this point value is seen as constraint conditions[4]. The roller material is selected as alloy steel 40 Cr. Taking into account the important role of roller in mill. It must give the larger reserve strength. The allowable stress is $[\sigma] \leq 160$ MPa. Therefore, constraint function is expressed as $g_1(x) = \sigma_{u\,max} - 160 \leq 0$.
2. Boundary contraints: The range of design variables (the maximum value and the minimum allowed value) is limited as $X_{i\,min} \leq X_i \leq X_{i\,max}$. The constraints range of design variables are $8 \leq B \leq 15; 16 \leq H \leq 26; 10 \leq L_1 \leq 20; 35 \leq L_2 \leq 45; 115 \leq R \leq 130$.

Therefore, The constraints function of design variables are expressed as the following formula:

$$g_2(X) = 8 - B \leq 0 \qquad g_3(X) = B - 15 \leq 0$$
$$g_4(X) = 16 - H \leq 0 \qquad g_5(X) = H - 26 \leq 0$$
$$g_6(X) = 10 - L_1 \leq 0 \qquad g_7(X) = L_1 - 20 \leq 0$$
$$g_8(X) = 35 - L_2 \leq 0 \qquad g_9(X) = L_2 - 45 \leq 0$$
$$g_{10}(X) = 115 - R \leq 0 \qquad g_{11}(X) = R - 130 \leq 0$$

3.3 Objective function

1. Scheme one: The minimum weight is seen as the objective function, in satisfying with the conditions of strength and stiffness to pursuit lightest roller, i.e. $F_1(X) = WT$.
2. Scheme two: In order to improve the quality of performance of roller and ensure the frame stiffness.

536

Table 3. Optimization result comparison of three kinds optimal scheme.

Parameters	Initial value	Single objective WT	Single objectivey	Multi-objective
B (mm)	13	8.2068658	13.848376	8.8277342
H (mm)	18	17.550828	16.062298	23.589103
L_1 (mm)	20	19.282070	19.960689	17.136493
L_2 (mm)	43	36.694182	35.132813	40.908625
R (mm)	125	115.24375	115.04201	115.95247
σ (MP)	116.4778	118.04270	113.69372	117.32568
WT (kg)	12.180640	9.6391845	9.6373464	10.32745
y (mm)	1.4631532 E-2	1.2249376 E-2	1.1728435 E-2	1.2034726 E-2

Stiffness can be expressed as the deformation and the main index is the radial deformation. Therefore, the minimum radial deformation is seen as the objective function, i.e. $F_2(X) = y$.

3. Scheme three: The roller sizes influence on the roller weight and stiffness are comprehensively taken into account. Because the radial deformation can reflect the stiffness. Therefore, in this paper, the weight and the radial deformation are combined into a united objective function, which can be optimized with ANSYS software. The objective function of optimization is $F_3(X) = \omega_1 * WT + \omega_2 * y$.

The objective function is expressed as following formula (1).

$$\min F(X)$$
$$X = [X_1, X_2, X_3, X_4, X_5]^T$$
$$s.t.\ g_u(x) \leq 0\ (u = 1, 2, 3, \ldots 11) \tag{1}$$

The zero order optimization method with ANSYS software is used for optimization analysis. Three kinds of scheme optimization results are shown in Table 3.

4 OPTIMAL RESULTS ANALYSIS

Roller is comprehensively evaluated with the first level comprehensive fuzzy evaluation from single objective results and multi-objective optimization results to verify the advantage of the multi-objective optimization results[3–5].

1. Determining weight of each evaluation factors
   Multi-objective optimization of weight and stiffness are united as single objective function, considering the stiffness more, which accounts for 70% and weigh 30%. Therefore the weight set is $A = (0.3, 0.7)$.
2. Determining the schemes membership degree of the factors Weight factors and stiffness membership degree are $u_{WT,y} = e^{-x^2}$, the and the

Table 4. Weight and subodinate degree of appraisal factors.

Appraisal factors	Scheme 1	Scheme 2	Scheme 3
WT (0.3)	0.44647	4.60684	4.78334
y (0.7)	0.99985	0.99986	0.99986

membership degree of evaluation factors, such as weight and stiffness, are obtained by calculating as shown in Table 4. The fuzzy relation matrix R is shown as Table 4.

$$R = \begin{bmatrix} 4.44647 & 4.60684 & 4.78334 \\ 0.99985 & 0.99986 & 0.99986 \end{bmatrix}$$

3. Matrix calculation: According to the B element size, the schemes quality are compared and selected by the principle of maximum membership.

$$B = A \bullet R = (0.3, 0.7) \begin{bmatrix} 4.44647 & 4.60684 & 4.78334 \\ 0.99985 & 0.99986 & 0.99986 \end{bmatrix}$$
$$= (2.033836, 2.081954, 2.134904)$$

Through a comprehensive evaluation, the scheme three is the best one set of data, compared with the initial data, the parameter B is reduced by 32.09%, H increased by 31.05%, L_1 decreased by 14.32%, L_2 decreased by 4.86%, R decreased by 7.24%, equivalent stress increases 0.73%, the weight is reduced by 15.21%, Y direction displacement decreased by 1.77%, the stiffness increases by 1.77% and the numerical value is within the allowable range. It meet the demands of the lightest weight and largest stiffness optimal objective.

5 CONCLUSION

Finite element model of Y type mill roller is established. The stress and deformation of roller is analysed using ANSYS software. Single objective and multi-objective function are respectively set up. The roller is optimized using zero order optimization method with ANSYS software. Optimization results are evaluated using first-level fuzzy comprehensive evaluation method. The multi-objective optimization data is the most optimal.

REFERENCES

[1] Hu Haiping, Sun Jixian, Zhu Weizhang. Deformation Simulation of 3-Roll Rolling with Finite Element Method and Visual-plasticity Approach[J]. Journal of university of science and technology Beijing. 1999,21(4):372–375.

[2] Li Liming. Finite element analysis of ANSYS tutorial[M]. Beijing: Tsinghua university press, 2005: 322–339.

[3] Yan Gai, Zheng Yanping, Zhang Wenyan, et al. Process parameters optimization of sheet stamping forming based on orthogonal experiment[J]. Hot working technology, 2013,42(17):94–97.

[4] Liu Yangsong, Li Wenfang. Fuzzy optimization method in machine design[M]. Beijing: Mechanical Engineering press, 1996, 22–33:130–148.

[5] Yang Wei, Guang Dejuan. Development of fuzzy methodology and review of its application in machinery industry[J]. Journal of Kunming university of science and technology, 2001:427–430.

Computer, Intelligent Computing and Education Technology – Liu, Sung & Yao (Eds)
© 2014 Taylor & Francis Group, London, ISBN 978-1-138-02469-4

Structure optimization of the corrugated web rail using SA combined with FEM

J.H. Ma, B. Tao & X.H. Yao
College of Metallurgy and Energy, Hebei Polytechnical University, Hebei Province, China

ABSTRACT: The corrugated web rail has been successfully rolled. This new kind of rail structure is superior to traditional rail on mechanical properties. Because wave parameters of the corrugated web rail directly affects the mechanical properties, It is necessary to optimize the wave parameters. In this paper, the Simulated Annealing algorithm (SA) combined with Finite Element Method (FEM), a new kind of structural optimization method is established. MATLAB language is used to compile the program combined on the SA with FEM to optimize sine curve parameters of the corrugated web rail. Compared with the zero order and first order optimization method of ANSYS program, the result of this optimal method is better.

Keywords: corrugated web rail; genetic algorithm; FEM; wave parameters; optimum design

1 INTRODUCTION

With the continuously increasing train speed and flow, It is of increasingly stringent requirements about heavy rail. At present, have large iron and steel enterprise production of heavy rail universal law. In order to improve the performance and

Figure 1.   The corrugated web rail.

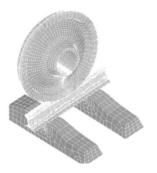

Figure 2.   The model of wheel-rail.

service life of the rail, a new kind of rail structure, corrugated web rail, is developed. The corrugated waist rail has been successfully rolled in the Mill Research Institute of Yanshan University,[1] the rolled product is shown in Figure 1, to make the rail waist structure shown clearly, the longitudinal section of rail waist is shown in Figure 2. It has been already tested that the mechanical properties of this kind of special structure rail are better than those of the ordinary structure rail. The new structure heavy rail is superior to the ordinary rail on rail waist lateral bending and longitudinal stability.[2] The dynamic properties are also improved. In consideration of the rolling process, the curve of the rail waist is replace by the sinusoid. However, the mechanical properties are directly affected by the parameters of the sinusoid, so it is necessary to optimize the parameters of the sinusoid in order to improve the mechanical properties of the corrugated waist rail.

2 THE BASIC THEORY SIMULATED ANNEALING ALGORITHM

The idea of Simulated Annealing algorithm (SA) was first proposed by Metropolis in 1953.[3] In 1983, Kirkpatric had successfully applied it to combinatorial optimization problems, and later spread it to the function optimization problem, thus, it become a general optimization algorithm. At present, SA has been widely applied in engineering.[4–5]

The physical process of solid annealing and the statistical properties is the physical background of the simulated annealing algorithm. Solid annealing is a thermodynamic process, firstly heating the solids above the melting temperature, then slowly cooling to solidify into rules crystal. This process consists of three parts. Heating process, namely the enhancement of thermal motion of molecules, which deviates from the equilibrium position, with the increase of temperature, particle and its equilibrium position deviation is more and more bigger. Isothermal process, when the temperature rises to the melting temperature, regular solids is thoroughly destructed. Solid melts into liquid, now heat exchange with the surrounding environment, but the temperature is unchanged. The purpose of this process is to eliminate the possible existence of previous non uniform state in the system. This is a kind of high free energy equilibrium state and this is the starting point for the next process, i.e. cooling process. Cooling process, namely, with the decrease of temperature, the thermal motion of molecules is weakened and is in a different states. When the temperature is the lowest, molecular is rearranged in a certain structure, so as to obtain the the the minimal energy crystal structure, namely the new equilibrium state.

The basic idea of the simulated annealing algorithm is constructed as following. Starting from a high initial temperature (choosing a point with a large value of the objective function (high energy) in the solution space). According to the random sampling strategy with probabilistic jumping property (importance sampling), random search is carried out in the solution domain. With temperature decreasing, repeats sampling process, achieving the minimum energy state, namely the global optimal solution of the equivalent energy function. In fact, this optimization method is a random search zero order algorithm based on Monte-Carlo iterative solution strategy.

3 SA-FEM COMBINED OPTIMIZATION METHOD

With he computing power increased, the finite element analysis combined with several kinds of mathematic programming methods, a kind of systemic and mature method has been set up step by step making the technique of structure optimization rapidly developing. Besides, the simulated annealing algorithms search the global optimum and find the global optimal solution at large probability.[1] Finite element is integrated with simulated annealing algorithms, can make computer aided design actual, more importantly, can gain the best ratio of the product property and cost. The method combined FEM with SA, taking full advantage of the feature of FEM that computes precisely and

the feature of SA that search the optimal solution globally and rapidly, will play important role in the mechanical engineering applications.

In the procedure combined SA with FEM, it is key that SA procedure uses the FEM procedure and realizes the data transmission between the two kinds of procedures.

In the ANSYS commercial software, it provides two kinds of optimizing methods, i.e. the zero order method and first order method, which can solve most of the optimizing problems.[2] Although Zero order method randomly searches solution in the design space, it adopts the traditional methods that the initial point will influences the optimization result, this reflects the disadvantages of the traditional optimizing methods. First order method is time-consuming indirect method, which needs to compute the one order derivative. Therefore, for optimizing problems that one order partial derivatives do not exist and complex non-linear problems, the one order optimizing method can not solve them.

APDL stands for ANSYS Parametric Design Language, a scripting language that you can use to automate common tasks, (such as parameters; macros; branching, looping, and repeating; and array parameters; and technology of ANSYS connection with MATLAB), or even build your model in terms of parameters (variables). For the system enclosed by APDL, it is required that the operators input the parameters for preprocessing, then, automatic solution will run. Therefore, in this paper, parameters model is set up and the common tasks are written by APDL, making up the text file and model setting up, meshing, loading, solving and post processing automatically.

In the optimizing process, takes the design variables as the independent variables of the individuals of SA, transmitting them to the text file written in APDL. The solution results are obtained from the ANSYS program are looked as the individual objective values of SA, thus the datum transmission is achieved. In order to combine SA with FEM, the MATLAB program must automatically use the ANSYS program. ANSYS 5.7 provides a kind of batch mode that is as following, "ansys57-b-p ansys_product_feature-i input_file-o output_file" where the input_file is the name of the input file, output_file is the name of the output file. The explanation of the format can be found in 'Interactive Versus Batch Mode' in the ANSYS help file. 'ansys_product_feature' is the ANSYS product feature code. During the MATLAB program applying the ANSYS program, it is necessary that the judge sentence should be added to make certain if the ANSYS program finishes or not. The applying method is shown as following, result=system ('d:/ANSYS57/BIN/INTEL/ANSYS57-b-p ansys_product_feature-i input_file-o output_file').

4 COMPUTATION STEPS OF THE PROGRAM GA COMBINED WITH FEM

APDL language is used to establish the ANSYS command file, The computation steps of SA combined with FEM are as following:

Step 1: The wheel and rail model is established with CAD software, then saved as IGES format files, easy to be used by ANSYS.

Step 2: ANSYS IGES format file produced by step 1 is analysed and file is called by ANSYS. And the design variables are defined.

Step 3: MATLAB program will write variable result in to a file, then use the APDL language reading this file data into preprocessing program of ANSYS software.

Step 4: Finite element using ANSYS software is calculated, the corresponding results are obtained by post processing function of ANSYS software and output the result data to a file.

Step 5: MATLAB program read the file data for calculation.

Step 6: Repeating step 3 to step 6 until output the final results.

5 CALCULATION EXAMPLE

5.1 FEM model of optimization

FEM model adopted is shown in Figure 2. This FEM model simulates the true contact condition of the wheel and rail. A classical bilinear elastic–plastic constitutive material model with kinematical strain hardening is used for the rail and wheel in the numerical analysis. The physical properties of the relevant material are listed in Table 1. The material of sleeper is high property reinforcing

Table 1. Material properties of ordinary rail and corrugated waist rail model.

Properties	Value
Young's modulus (GPa)	210
Poisson ratio	0.3
Density (kg/m³)	7820
Yield stress (MPa)	883
Tangent modulus (GPa)	88.3

Table 2. Material properties of wheel model.

Properties	Young's modulus (GPa)	Poisson ratio	Density (kg/m³)
Value	210	0.3	7820

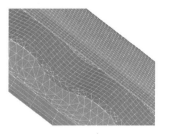

Figure 3.   FEM model of corrugated web rail.

steel bar concrete, the physical properties of the relevant material are listed in Table 2.

Axle load, which is 150 KN, is suffered by the single wheel. The dimensions of the corrugated waist rail refer on the ordinary heavy rail of 60 kg/m, the length of the rail is 1 m. To ensure the computational precision, on the contact zone of the wheel with the rail, the elements are meshed finer, while on the non contact zone of the wheel with the rail, elements are meshed coarse. Elements of wheel are meshed by the sweeping manner. Due to the complex shape of the corrugated waist rail, elements on the regular shape are meshed by the sweeping manner, while elements on irregular shape are meshed by free manner. The elements of rail on the contact zone are shown in Figure 3.

5.2 Optimization methods

In order to compare the combined method with the optimization methods companied with the ANSYS software, In this paper, three kinds of the optimization methods are adopted, the first, the zero order optimization method is companied with ANSYS software, the second, the first order optimization method is companied with ANSYS software, the last, the optimization method of improve SA combined with FEM is developed by the MATLAB.

The ANSYS command files of three kinds of optimizing methods are all written in APDL. In the third method, the command file in APDL is written by the MATLAB program, this file is transmitted to the ANSYS program, the solution result of ANSYS program is also transmitted to the MATLAB program.

5.3 Optimization mathematical methods

The mathematical model of the optimization of the corrugated waist rail is as following:

$$\begin{cases} \min W = \rho V + 30y \\ s.t.\sigma_{max} \leq \overline{\sigma} \\ \underline{x_i} \leq x_i \leq \overline{x_i}\,(i=1,2,3) \end{cases} \quad (1)$$

541

Table 3. Comparison of three kinds of optimization results.

	Zero order method	One order method	Combined method
Wave length λ (mm)	99.679	56.735	58.339
Wave amplitude H (mm)	7.5074	9.6127	7.6670
Thichness d (mm)	5.6952	5.6324	5.1264
Weight M (kg)	52.371	52.339	51.233
Deflection (mm)	1.1592	1.0185	0.9482

where, ρ is the material dense, v the rail volume, σ_{max} effective Von-Mises stress of element, obtained from the post process, $\bar{\sigma}$ is maximum allowable stress of the rail material. x_i stands for three design variables $\lambda, H, d, \underline{x_i}$ and $\overline{x_i}$ respectively the upper limits and lower limits of the three design variables.

6 CONCLUSION

1. From the Table 3, It can be seen, the result of method of SA combined with FEM is 51.233 kg, it is reduced by 14.62%, apparently is better than result of the zero order optimization methods, which is 52.371 kg, and at the same time, better than the result of the first order optimization methods, which is 52.339 kg.

2. The optimizing method SA combined with FEM, provides a kind of method for solving the complex and large engineering problem.

REFERENCES

[1] Xu Xiumei, Zhang Wenzhi, Xie Hongbiao. Simulation and experimental study on rolling process of corrugated rail waist rail. China mechanical engineering, 2005, 16(12):1103–1106.

[2] Wu Bo, Chang Fuqing, Zhang Wenzhi. Stress analysis for corrugated waist rail. Journal of Yanshan University, 2003, 27(3):278–282.

[3] MetroPolis N, Rosenbluth A, Rosenbluth M, Teller A and Teller E. Equations of state Calculation by Fast Computing Machines. The Journal of Chemical Physics, 1953, (21):1087–1092.

[4] Aarts E and Korst J. Simulated Annealing and Boltsmann Machines: A StochasticApproach to Combinatorial Optimization and Neural Computing, 1989.

[5] Deek G, Scheuer T. Threshold accepting: A general Purpose optimization algorithm appearing uperior to simulated annealing. Journal of Computational Physics, 1990, 90(1):161–175.

Computer, Intelligent Computing and Education Technology – Liu, Sung & Yao (Eds)
© 2014 Taylor & Francis Group, London, ISBN 978-1-138-02469-4

The multi-object optimal pass design based on improved GA

J.H. Ma, B. Tao & X.H. Yao
College of Metallurgy and Energy, Hebei Polytechnical University, Hebei Province, China

ABSTRACT: In this paper, the standard genetic algorithm is modified based on the deduction of Rolle theory. A kind of genetic algorithms is set up. This method can solve multi-objective problems with more complex constraints in the engineering. The optimal pass design is based on improved Genetic Algorithm (GA) with the objective of the least of total energy consumption and loads balance on bar mill. By optimization, in condition of normal rolling, the less total energy consumption and relative balanced bar mill loads. Genetic Algorithm Toolbox with Matlab software is adopted to search optimum parameters, which is a new kinds of method for the multi-object optimal pass design.

Keywords: improved GA; pass design; multi-object optimal design; total energy consumption; load balance

1 INTRODUCTION

Recently, the presentation of genetic algorithms and development is a large progress, which are evolutionary algorithms based on the nature biology evolution. The advantage of this method is not necessary to compute the function gradient and not dependent on the problems self. Besides, the algorithms search the global optimum and find the global optimal solution at large probability.[1]

Continuous rolling is generally used in bar production, the process is divided into three stage, which is rough rolling, intermediate rolling and finishing rolling. According to commonly used pass design method of rolling bar, it is difficult to make balance loads between the mills and make the least total energy consume. With the objective of least energy consumption and mill loads balance, the passes of bars are optimized by the improved Genetic Algorithm compiled by Matlab language, thus, the reasonable rolling process is obtained.

Taking continuous rolling alloy steel 40Cr of the bar factory in a steel company as example, the main rolling line is made up by 22 stands, which is divided into rough group, inter-mediate group and finishing group. Each strand is driven by a direct current motor respectively. Mills are layout with flat vertical alternate arrangement. Billets 180 mm square are used. The train is composed by 4–6–6–6 strands, i.e rough rolling group is composed by four stands, intermediate rolling group by six stands, the first finishing rolling group by six strands and the second finishing group by six stands.

The method of changing pass size or adjusting rolling gap is adopted to achieve the least energy consumption and the rolling loads balance[2]. Adjusting roller gap has to adjust gap range, however, the size of the rolling piece is greatly altered, only the method of changing the pass size is used to reduce the total energy consumption and balance the mill loads. In this paper, the former method is used.

2 THE MODIFIED GA

GA is a new kind of structural optimizing design method, which can avoid the many disadvantages of the traditional optimizing methods. It can effectively solve the problems that the traditional optimizing methods, such as direct method and analysis method, can not solve, for example, the discrete design variable, and multi optimal values and nonlinear objective problems.

Although, GA has many advantages in searching for the optimal values and many experts and scholars research on the GA continually, too many problems still exist.[3] The global search ability of the standard GA comes from the random creation of the initial population and the crossover operation. But due to contrast the limitation of the population with more dimension of the solution space, this makes the global search is limited, cannot find the global optimal value and computational precision is low. The mutation operator is small in the SGA, a few new mutated individuals are easily assimilated by the many old individuals. Close relative propagate and premature convergence exist in SGA, and near the optimal solution, the solution sways near the optimal solution and converge speed is slow.

3 OPTIMIZATION MODEL

3.1 Design variables

$$X = [B, H, R, r]^T \tag{1}$$

where, $B = [B_1, B_2, \ldots, B_{22}]$, $H = [H_1, H_2, \ldots, H_{22}]$, $R = [R_4, R_5, \ldots, R_{22}]$, $r = [r_4, r_2, \ldots r_{22}]$.
Therefore, $X = [x_1, x_2, \ldots, x_{22}]$.

3.2 Objective function

3.2.1 Minimum rolling energy consumption
Rolling process is consisted by n passes, therefore, the total energy is shown as formula (2).

$$Q = \sum_{i=1}^{n} q_i = \sum_{i=1}^{n} M_i v_i \tau_i / D_i \to \min \tag{2}$$

3.2.2 Relative equal load distribution
When the motor power is not equal, if load is distributed according to equal load, equal load distribution power may be lead to small capacity motor inadequacy, however, the big capacity motor not give full play to its ability. In this kind of circumstance, the rolling rules is according to relative equal energy consumption of each mill, i.e, big capacity motor consumes more, however, the small capacity motor consumes less, thus, the equipment ability can be full played and can avoid load uneven distribution and produces rolling accidents.

The objective function of bar mill load distribution is expressed as formula (3).

$$\min S = \sum_{i=1}^{n} (N_i - \lambda N_{hi})^2 \to \min \tag{3}$$

3.3 Boundary conditions

Taking into accounting of the pass design and optimal practical problems, the following boundary conditions are introduced.

1. Bite condition. In order to guarantee the rolling-piece into roller smoothly and ensure normal and stable rolling process, bite condition must be considered into rolling condition. Rolling angle is usually used to measure the rolling conditions when rolling piece into roller, namely bite angle of the actual rolling piece should be less than that of maximum pass of mill.

2. Stable condition of rolling piece in the pass. The stable condition of rolling piece in the pass can be shown as following formula (4).

$$a_{\min} < a < a_{\max} \tag{4}$$

3. Motor capability. Main motor of mill is not overheating and overload.
4. Mill capability. The maximum allowable rolling force, maximum allowed torque, minimum allow rolling speed and maximum allowable rolling speed requirements are meet, and roller, transmission system strength and mill speed range should be meet.
5. The rolling-piece filled pass condition. To meet the demand of filled pass degrees to ensure the rolled-piece cross-section shape correct.

4 MATHEMATICAL MODEL

4.1 Rolling temperature model

a. и LeonKeFu method is adopted to calculate rolling temperature, temperature changes is calculated by the formula (5).

$$\Delta T = t_0 - \cfrac{1000}{\sqrt[3]{\cfrac{0.0255\Pi t_1}{\omega} + \left(\cfrac{1000}{t_0 + \Delta t_b + 273}\right)^3}} + 273 \tag{5}$$

Δt_b is determined by formula (6).

$$\Delta t_b = 0.183\sigma \ln \mu \tag{6}$$

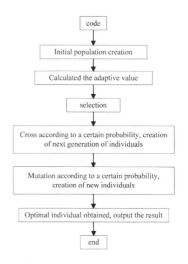

Figure 1. Flowchart of program designing.

4.2 Deformation resistance model

According to ZhouJiHua's research[3], the deformation resistance mathematical model is repressed as following formula, which formula shows the relationship between the deformation resistance and deformation temperature, and the relationship of the deformation speed and deformation degree. With each unit of the various kind of steel, nonlinear regression used, each regression coefficient values are obtained by formula (7).

$$\sigma = \sigma_0 \exp(a_1 T + a_2)\left(\frac{u}{10}\right)^{a_3 T + a_4}$$

$$\times \left[a_6\left(\frac{\gamma}{0.4}\right)^{a_5} - (a_6 - 1)\frac{\gamma}{0.4}\right] \qquad (7)$$

Table 1. Pass dimension before and after optimization.

Passes	Pass	Pass dimension before optimization		Pass dimension after optimization	
		B	H	B	H
1	Box	204.32	135.00	205.80	141.03
2	Box	161.44	145.00	166.18	145.47
3	Oval	195.00	108.00	196.50	108.00
4	Circle	130.55	125.00	130.55	125.00
5	Oval	178.00	82.00	147.36	87.67
6	Circle	104.44	100.00	104.44	98.37
7	Oval	138.79	68.00	124.16	71.11
8	Circle	84.81	81.00	84.81	79.49
9	Oval	120.00	48.00	102.87	53.94
10	Circle	65.17	62.00	65.17	60.62
11	Oval	90.51	39.00	85.90	43.33
12	Circle	51.11	48.50	51.11	47.31
13	Oval	75.26	30.00	67.50	33.53
14	Circle	40.08	38.00	40.08	37.04
15	Oval	55.24	24.00	52.87	24.36
16	Circle	31.57	30.00	31.57	29.30
17	Oval	45.14	19.00	43.68	20.85
18	Circle	25.10	24.00	25.10	23.58
19	Oval	37.92	16.00	36.08	16.98
20	Circle	20.54	19.50	20.54	19.03
21	Oval	24.82	14.00	26.15	12.66
22	Circle	16.79	16.19	16.79	16.03

Table 2. Mill load before and after optimization.

Pass	Mill load % Original pass	Optimal pass	Comparison with original pass %	Pass	Mill load % Original pass	Optimal pass	Comparison with original pass %
1	46.3	45.33	−2.10	12	66.14	63.69	−3.70
2	46.14	50.91	10.33	13	67.18	67.33	0.22
3	52.81	54.39	1.99	14	70.52	68.84	−2.38
4	70.53	66.17	−6.18	15	71.8	65	−9.47
5	56.67	58.26	2.81	16	71.93	67.15	−6.65
6	46.14	52.47	13.72	17	64.87	67.59	4.19
7	55.44	62.5	12.73	18	71.93	68.23	−5.14
8	45.26	53.27	17.70	19	64.87	70.02	7.94
9	64.74	64.2	−0.83	20	68.07	68.46	0.57
10	66.32	57.44	−13.39	21	52.44	60.2	14.80
11	61.28	60.64	−1.04	22	62.81	63.91	1.75

where, $T = \dfrac{t+273}{1000}$.

4.3 *Mechanical parameters model*

SiMiErNuoFu method is adopted to calculate rolling force and rolling torque, although this method is trival, its accuracy is high and it is close to actual measurement.

5 OPTIMAL RESULTS

Genetic algorithm program compiled by Matlab language is operated. The passes dimensions are obtained, which can reduce total energy consumption in the rolling process of bar and balance the mill loads. Taking the bar mill of a steel company as example, 180 mm × 180 mm continuous casting slab is used for rolling Φ16 mm bar, the type of steel is 40Cr. The pass is optimized, taking the minimum total energy consumption and mill loads equilibrium as objective and Weight coefficient 0.5.

The program diagram is shown as Figure 1. The dimensions of pass before and after optimization are shown in Table 1, mill loads are seen as Table 2 before and after optimization. Based on genetic algorithm by Matlab optimization design, bar mill units realize that the total energy consumption is relatively small and mill load relative balance. The optimization results show that the total energy

consumption is reduced 9.8% after optimized, The original load of tenth mill, which load is highest, compared with the original design rolling power drop nearly 13.4%, therefore, rolling load distribution is more reasonable, the roller rings collapse accident is no longer happen.

6 CONCLUSION

Multi-objective optimization based on the genetic algorithm is adopted in this paper, although its programming process is complicated, calculations is quickly and accurately and drawing is handy and it can quickly and accurately output the result for a specific rolling process. This has a very important role in shortening the design cycle, improving product quality, reducing accident and improving efficiency. The genetic algorithm used in optimization of pass is not very broad, so more thorough research is necessary.

REFERENCES

[1] S.Y, Zhao, W.L, Tang. Shaped steel pass design. Peking:Metallurgical Industry Press, 2000:276–295.
[2] Kalyanmoy Deb. Chichester: JohnWiley & Sons, Ltd. 2001:12–38.
[3] J.H, Zhou, K.Z, Guang. Metal plastic deformation resistance. Peking: Machinery industry press, 1989:211–229.

Computer, Intelligent Computing and Education Technology – Liu, Sung & Yao (Eds)
© 2014 Taylor & Francis Group, London, ISBN 978-1-138-02469-4

Based on interpolating windowed FFT to achieve the data acquisition module in electricity network monitoring meter

Yan-Feng Liu

College of Physics and Electronic Information, Yan'an University, Yan'an, China

ABSTRACT: This paper have made improvements on the traditional electricity network monitor data acquisition module. Due to spectral leakage and barrier effect in FFT, the thesis chose interpolating windowed FFT to process the data, and transplant the algorithm to microcontroller LPC2138. Every frequency harmonic wave's amplitude and frequency were calculated precisely, including the total harmonic distortion.

Keywords: interpolating windowed FFT; electric network monitoring system

1 INTRODUCTION

Network monitor is usually used for intelligent switchboard, variable power distribution and energy management system, to realize the remote data acquisition and control.[1] At present, most of power parameter measurement instrument for measuring use chip and DSP chip as the core, because of these chips generally do not have the harmonic function, and poor portability, which is not conducive to further expand and upgrade;[2] while the high-end monitor integrated ADC + DSP + ARM structure, although the measuring accuracy is improved, but also increase the hardware cost and complexity, which is not conducive to the further application of digital monitor. Network monitor is designed in this paper uses ADC and ARM high accuracy combination model, a LPC2138 chip with high performance multi-resource, realize the high accurate analysis of measurement of electric parameters and real-time harmonic.

2 WINDOWED INTERPOLATION BASED-2FFT ALGORITHM

The Hanning window for the time domain expression is:[3]

$$w(n) = \left[0.5 - 0.5\cos\left(\frac{2\pi n}{N-1}\right) \right] \cdot R_N(n)$$
$$\text{(where } n = 0, 1, ..., N) \tag{1}$$

In a continuous period of time, the voltage (or current) uniform synchronous sampling sampling sequence, signal through the Hanning window is N sequence, where is:

$$x_w(n) = x(n) \cdot w(n) \tag{2}$$

Transform the formula (2) as Fu Liye transform (DFT), the resulting frequency shows that:

$$X(k) = \text{DFT}[x_w(n)]$$
$$= \sum_{n=0}^{N-1} x_w(n) W_N^{nk} \quad k = 0, 1, ..., N-1 \tag{3}$$

where $W_N^{nk} = e^{-j\frac{2\pi}{N}nk}$, because the W_N^{nk} and $x_w(n)$ are all complex numbers. Calculation of a N DFT needs N^2 complex multiplication, so the calculation is very large. Because of this, FFT algorithm emerge as the times require. FFT is an improvement on DFT, which use periodic, reducible and symmetry for butterfly operation, so as to reduce

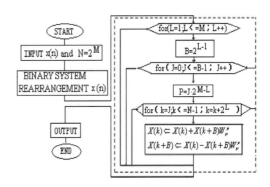

Figure 1. FFT operational flowchart.

the amount of computation.[4] When the length of the sequence $N = 2^M$ (M is an integer), called based –2FFT algorithm. The FFT operation is very regular, usually consists of two parts: binary reverse rearrangement and three nested loops to complete the iteration. Three layer circulation function is: the innermost layer of circular complete butterfly operation of the same factor; the middle layer of circular complete factor changes and the outer loop is to complete the M iteration process. FFT algorithm flow chart is shown in Figure 1.

3　THE HARDWARE DESIGN OF DATA PROCESSING MODULE

DFT or FFT are based on synchronous sampling conditions on existence, synchronous deviation, harmonic DFT or FFT analysis will create if synchronization error based on. To reduce or eliminate the synchronous error is the use of synchronous sampling technology. The system uses synchronous sampling, the sampling points evenly distributed in a whole cycle power system, the synchronous sampling.

4　THE OVERALL SYSTEM STRUCTURE DESIGN

The hardware structure of power network monitor is composed of four main parts: power supply board, main board, CPU board and liquid crystal display module. As shown in Figure 2.

The power supply board is mainly realized by AC to DC switching power supply voltage, to meet the different devices required; CPU board mainly completes the voltage current value corresponding to the collected data calculation and harmonic analysis and complete the corresponding data storage; motherboard adopts PLL frequency doubling technology realizing the AC synchronous sampling, and through the serial port to communicate with PC. Implementation of synchronization and sampling used PLL technology, namely hardware synchronous sampling method.

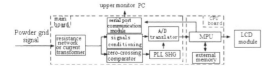

Figure 2.　Power network monitor system structure diagram.

5　PLL FREQUENCY TRACKING CIRCUIT

The circuit shown in Figure 3 is a typical PLL frequency tracking circuit which uses a generic CMOS PLL IC CD4046. In order to meet the requirements of high precision data acquisition module, using A/D converter CS5451 16 6 channel, synchronous acquisition of three-phase voltage and three-phase current value. Phase locked loop is a phase feedback control system. It consists of three basic components: a phase comparator, filter and oscillator.

6　THE SOFTWARE DESIGN OF DATA PROCESSING UNIT

The description of the algorithm is transplanted to the ARM microprocessor LPC2138, procedures for the preparation of the general process are: (1) the sequential sampled were handled with Hanning window truncation, getting a new set of sequence, a sequence of length $N = 2^n$. (2) FFT transform is per-

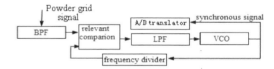

Figure 3.　PLL frequency tracking circuit principle diagram.

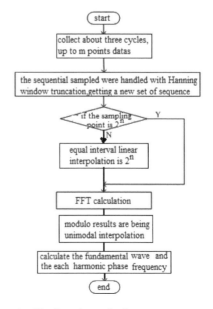

Figure 4.　The flow chart of software.

548

formed on the new sequence window. (3) Modulo results are being unimodal interpolation. The coefficients of fundamental and harmonics, find the discrete spectrum line frequency point near the left and right sides of the maximum amplitude and the maximum spectrum line interpolation, amplitude, phase and frequency of the fundamental and harmonics are obtained. The specific software process is shown in Figure 4.

7 CONCLUSION

The data acquisition module of traditional power network monitor has been improved by the engineering application of FFT harmonic measurement. The 6 channel 16 bit precision A/D conversion chip CS5451, joined the PLL frequency tracking circuit, windowed interpolation based on the improved FFT algorithm, in the engineering application of the harmonic analysis precision is improved greatly. The function modularization, easy function expansion and upgrade the software, have certain reference value for similar instruments.

REFERENCES

[1] Lobos T, Kozina T, Koglin HJ. Power system harmonics estimation using linear least squares method and SVD [J]. IEE Proceedings-Generation, Transmission and distribution, 2001, 148(6):567–572.

[2] Zhang Lin-li, Wang Guang-zhu. New Artificial Neural Network Approach for Measuring Harmonics [J]. Proceedings of the EPSA, 2004, 16(2):40–43.

[3] Hu Guang shu. Digital signal processing: theory, algorithm and Implementation. [M]. Beijing: Tsinghua University press, 1997.

[4] Zhang F, Geng Z, Yuan W. The algorithm of interpolating windowed FFT for harmonic analysis of electric power system [J]. IEEE Trans on Power Delivery, 2001, 16(2):160–164.

Parametric planting design in landscape architecture

J. Ling & S. Lu
Landscape Department, Beijing University of Agriculture, Beijing, China

ABSTRACT: Parametric planting design is an important aspect of CAD field. With this method, the landscape architecture can be designed quickly and efficiently with a high quality. This paper presents the parametric design process, consisting of four sub-systems (input, processing, evaluation, and output system), the construction and connection methods of each part. Based on the control elements of traditional planting design method, the paper generalizes the parameter system of parametric planting design and discusses the possibility of their quantification. Finally, the author emphasizes the huge potential and significant status of parametric planting design in incorporate design practice. Meantime, it is faced with obstacles due to the limitation and complexity of plant ecology study. This paper is a general guide for the construction of parametric planting design theory system and the programming of associated software platforms.

Keywords: parametric design; planting; landscape architecture

1 PREFACE

Planting design in landscape architecture is a process of coordinating plants, environment and human activities in multidimensional space.

The factors such as ecological habitus and visual features of plants, human's demands for the environment and the sustainability the environment needs, altogether impact the outcome of the design, which have a great possibility of being quantified. At the same time, the process of modeling for plant on landscape consists of a series of ordered procedures. The above two conditions have made it possible to build-up a parametric system for planting design.

The traditional planting design mode usually translates the multidimensional space into 2D drawings. The design presentations are limited to describing words and plan, elevation, section, and all projection drawings as auxiliary layouts, and then, 2D drawings are used to instruct the construction in real world. Moreover, most decisions in planning and design process in practice relies on experience, lacking specific process and procedure, which is far behind the manufactory industry and architecture industry. Thereby, the problems in landscape design industry today mainly lie on the lack of systematic, scientific and technical methods. The discordance between drawings and real site condition, results in information delay, inaccuracy, or even disconnection.

On the other hand, without databases, each part of the traditional drawings is relatively isolated rather than related. The lack of topology makes the form modification and optimization job complex and inconvenient for designers. Somewhile, in a project, repeated modification operations may cover more than 2/3 of the total design schedule, which—wastes designers lots of time and energy.

If we apply the parametric method in building the planting design system and manage our design process modularizely, for one thing, we can strongly enhance the visual ability, scientificalness and systematicness for the benefit of developing our industry. For another thing, we can offer more alternative ways for their design, liberate their mechanical labor, when concerning about designer's benefit. In the aspect of the benefits of the design companies, we can improve their efficiency and quality of the design.

2 GENERAL INSTRUCTION OF PARAMETRIC DESIGN

2.1 Background

The development of the Internet, computer hardware and software, and cloud computing has created unprecedented developing opportunities for parametric planting design.

After the Industrial Revolution, environment problems emerge gradually. Saving our planet through the ways of planting is a mostly agreed solution for the environmental crisis for the sake of scientific and artistic planting ensuring us the cheap and sustainable ecological service.

Moreover, what we should be aware of is that more social responsibility and professional capability requirement have been packed on the back of every planting design practitioners. Low carbon design, LID (Low Influence Development), more scientific and efficient work are not only new challenges but also new opportunities for each planting designers. Furthermore, the existing experientialism and low-efficiency have made the parametric design more competitive.

2.2 *Advantage*

When compared with traditional planting design method, the parametric design method has the following advantages:

1. 3D design
   Parametric design closely incorporates with 3D simulation platform and allows designers to conduct their design with 3D model which is visible, and accurately reveals the real condition. Any modifications of the model can be seen on screen when you alter it, more importantly, making the result more applicable.
2. More efficient work
   The highly associated logical parametric system simplifies the process of modification, and minimize the repeated labor, saving designers more time for creative thinking.
3. Alternative solutions
   The multiple choices of parameter combination brings the alternative plans, which greatly enriches the design results, enhances the possibility of winning the bid in a fierce commercial competition.
4. Coordination
   Digital plants database and GIS provide a sharing platform for designers, enhancing the coordination and cooperation practice.
5. Maximum benefit
   The accurate and comprehensive control of ecological factors, along with the efficient working ability, maximizes both the ecological benefit and the economic benefit of the company.

2.3 *Main difficulties*

Plants, as nature beings, are more difficult to parameterize their properties than the architectures or the machines. Because some parameters, such as the parameters of culture preference, are not so sure and always fluctuate with the time or conditions. Another obstacle is that studies on plant ecological factor quantization are more superficial than sophisticate, which make parametric design lack theoretic base.

3 PLANTING PARAMETRIC SYSTEM AND THEIR QUANTIZATION POSSIBILITIES

Planting design was constrained by the morphology, ecological habit, planting form, function we need, and public preference etc, which have a great possibility to be quantified. Due to limitations on space, the paper mainly discusses the parametric system for tree planting (Fig. 1).

3.1 *Morphology parameters*

Plant morphology parameters are used to describe plant profiles. It includes two parts: the individual morphology parameters and the group morphology parameters. The individual morphology parameters consist of stem diameter, height, height of crown, leaf shape, leaf color, etc. The group morphology includes the quantity and kind of member trees in the group, height, wide, outline curvature of crown canopy of the plants group, etc. These parameters can be defined by length or ratio, and are relatively easy to be quantified.

3.2 *Location parameters*

Location parameters are the information of location defining as the place plants located in the

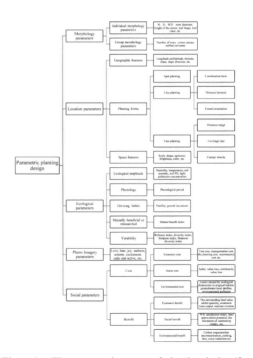

Figure 1. The parametric system of planting design (for tree).

552

coordinate system, which include the relative location and the absolute location. The relative location defines the distance and orientation relationship between the plant and the other entity (another tree, another group of trees or other landscape elements on site). For example, a tree is 10M far from a house to the northwest. The absolute location is the place where the plant planted or distributed in an absolute coordinate system. For example, a pine is planted with the planting point at coordinate (100, 48). These parameters can be defined by coordinate, vector and constrain functions. Spatial relation directly influenced the ecological habitat. Considering the inadequacy of studies on it, it seems difficult to quantify the relation between space location and plants adaptation features accurately. Further studies are needed to determine ecological habitat.

3.3 Ecological parameters

Ecological parameters are the plants ecological habitat information, including ecological amplitude, reproductive capacity, diversity, phonological phenomenon, stress resistance etc. This kind of parameters can be defined by ecological index.

3.4 Plants imagery parameters

Imagery is usually defined as the reflection of an image of a thing that is not in your sight. The Chinese culture is of long standing and well established. In Chinese culture system, a certain kind of plants may implicate a special profound meaning which can call up people's imagery. The imagery also can strongly stimulate people's emotions such as happiness, sadness, love or hate and so on. For instance, pines give us the feeling of solemnity and respectfulness, while an *ormosia hosiei* may bring a feeling of missing someone. The imagery effects of plants are always used to bring up visitor's vibration in planting design. So, the plants imagery can influent the choice of plants indirectly, and should be taken into consideration. This kind of parameters has to be classified and be assigned to a certain weight value in order to be quantified.

3.5 Social parameters

Ian Mcharg said that the best plan brings the maximum social benefit while take the minimum social cost. So we can evaluate the planting design with the social benefit parameters and the social cost parameters and build-up the structure of evaluation parameter system of planting design in the serve of function evaluation process. The social parameters are used to define the construction cost and benefit, which can be sub-divided into

3 categories: economic benefit/cost, social benefit/cost, environment benefit/cost. This kind of parameters has to be classified first and then be assigned to a certain weight value before it can be quantified.

4 THE PROCESS OF PARAMETRIC PLANTING DESIGN

Parametric planting design is a comprehensive information system and a decision-making system, which depends on the database of digital plants and GIS. Constrained by the restriction functions, it filters combines, matches, locates, evaluates the plants and space data in the databases, and finally output the result. The process can be summarized as Figure 2.

4.1 Parametric input system

Parameters input system includes two part, the project information collecting and transforming system and two databases—digital plants database and GIS. The first step of parametric design is to collect basic data of the project (site condition, users' needs, investor's opinions, etc.). The basic data will be transformed into organized data with a special format, constructing the design mission database. In addition, the attribute data of available plants stored in the digital plants database and GIS takes the responsibility of record the geographic information of the site. There exist corresponding relationships between the project basic data and the digital plants database and the GIS. So, when they match each other, the suitable plants which can both adapt to the local environment and meet people's needs are picked out. For example, the solar radiation intensity data of the site correspond with the requirement for radiation intensity index, the height of a billboard on the street corresponds with the height of branching-point attribute.

4.1.1 Digital plants database
The digital plants database includes the individual attribute data and the environment attribute

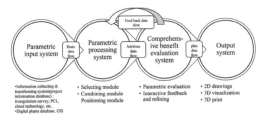

Figure 2. The process of parametric planting design.

data which can be classified into the following 6 categories: general attribute, growing attribute, visual attribute, ecological adaptation attribute, ecological amplitude attribute and application attribute (Fig. 3).

4.1.2 GIS information

GIS contains the geographic information of the project, such as slope, aspect, radiation distribution, contamination distribution, etc. All of them support the selecting system with data in 3D space.

4.2 Parametric processing system

The parametric processing system consist of 3 modules: the selecting module, the combination module and the positioning module.

Selecting module is a matching program used for matching the site condition, functions needed

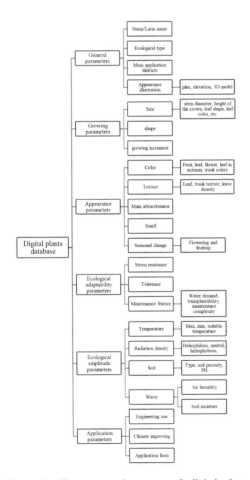

Figure 3. The parametric system of digital plants database.

and the attribute data of the plants in digital plants database, and then, output the suitable plants. The final fruits are an available plants table for the positioning use. It is possible that the amount of available trees is more than wanted, so we got alternative combinations. But if less than wanted, negotiation should be made to compromise with our demands or change the site condition until reaching the demanded amount and quality for plants.

Combination and positioning module take the responsibility of determining the planting form of the selected plants and locating them in space coordinate system or time line. As a result, the system is able to generate various form of planting closely accorded with the site condition. We may take tree planting design as an example: the combining forms of trees in the same layer, and the single layer structure can be defined by the kind, size, quantity, distance between each other, vectors linking two nearest planting point, etc. Thus, we get various planting forms. Furthermore, the multilayer structure plant community can be viewed as the overlaying of several single layers (usually not more than 3). In addition, since the factor of the minimum amount is the solar radiation under the upper layer plants, we also have to match the illumination value in the wood with the shade-endurance value of the sub layer plants, in order to keep the sub layer plants alive according to the theory of Liebig's Law of Minimum.

There are two kinds of positioning, the space positioning and the time positioning. Space positioning means locating the plants or plants group in 3D coordinate system according to the ecological habit of the plant and the needs for human. The time positioning is to add planting, maintaining, removing and replacing attribute information to the plants and applying them to the plans and maintaining system; in other words, locate the plants in the time line of the project life cycle from the beginning of planting to the removing.

4.3 Comprehensive benefit evaluation system

Every biocoenosis of built plants has a certain function, i.e. it gets a capability of realizing a function. Due to the flexibility of parameters, the output plans are always alternative and are ready to alter according to the designer's decision or a new consideration. Depending on a comprehensive evaluation standard group, the system evaluates the primary design results (usually more than one), and then output the evaluation report. The evaluation reports contain a lot of evaluation indexes of the plan. These indexes are aimed at assisting the designers, owners and experts with their comparison work between different plans, and helping them decide the adjusting plan as a feedback transferring back to the parametric processing system, through which the result can be renewed and refined. After coming to the ultimate plan, the system transfers the primary 3D model to the output system for advanced rendering.

4.4 Output system

The output system convert the primary model altogether with its economic and technical index from comprehensive benefit evaluation system to 2D drawings or multimedia display work which are used for construction and presentation. 2D drawing usually includes the plan, elevation, section, all projection drawings, as well as all kinds of investment budget table, etc. With talented multi-sensory stimulation capability, the multimedia display method is widely used in project presentation nowadays. It makes you feel personally on the scene. In addition, 3D printer is also powerful tools for outputting real model directly. The virtual reality technology makes it possible for man to interact with the design works.

5 PARAMETRIC PLANTING DESIGN OF INCORPORATE DESIGN STRATEGY

The incorporate design strategy is a systematic method of design that is supported by the concepts of concurrent design, cooperative design, and optimization of multiple branches of learning and so on. According to this method, designers from different subjects cooperate with each other and make overall decision after considering the multidiscipline relationship and interactive influence of different stages in project lifecycle, to undertake extremely complicated and integrated design tasks. It values the integration of a design, aims at obtaining the optimum, makes comprehensive analysis and keeps harmonious balance on structure, function, arrangement, reliability, maintainability, life cycle cost and so on. After that, we can improve the quality, efficiency of design, shorten the design cycle, and lower the expense. The L.A. design is a complicated system which needs cooperation of many different professions. Obviously, L.A., architecture, city planning, the 3 industries have got a tendency of incorporation nowadays. If we apply the incorporate design strategy to L.A. design, we can reach an equal or higher status in multidiscipline cooperations.

Parametric design is the core method of incorporate design. Due to the big information model

with restriction algorithm, it possesses the powerful capability of coordinating the professions and stages in project life cycle. L.A. parametric design is a node of the whole parametric design web. It coordinates and manages the relationship between plants and its growing environment.

Plants are the most significant element of L.A. for its high proportion. Compared with other element of L.A., plant has much more complex interconnections with the other L.A. elements, and has got more restriction from other elements. At the same time, when we do the planting design prior, it dominates the other elements more heavily. So the parametric planting design will become the main and the hardest point of the future incorporate design research. However, more researches should be made on the connections between the ecological adaptability and the quantified description of the geographic space, and the logic based on engineering requirement included. In particular, how to apply the achievement of complex system and nonlinear science into parametric planting design will be the hot point in the future.

6 SUMMARY

Parametric planting design is a comprehensive decision-making system based on database and restriction model. It makes the design process visible, efficient and the design results alternative, accordant and beneficial. The parameters of parametric planting design can be subdivided into 5 categories: morphology parameters, location parameters, ecological parameters, plants imagery parameters and social parameters. These parameters motivated by algorithm flow through the process chain involving input system, processing system, functional evaluation system and output system in order. Finally, the system output the ultimate plan after decision-makers' comparison and optimizing. But, we should squarely tackle that the key point of parametric planting design is based on the study of plants biocoenosis adaptability which need more extensive and deeper research.

ACKNOWLEDGEMENTS

I would like to express my warmest gratitude to Lusheng, my corresponding author (ls@bua.edu.cn), for his instructive suggestions and valuable comments on the writing of this thesis. Without his invaluable help and generous encouragement, the present thesis would not have been accomplished.

REFERENCES

Changli, Yuan & Lei, Hu. 2012. The thinking about building density calculation in plan, architecture and landscape architecture integrated design. ChengShi Jianshe LiLun Yan Jiu 2012(36).

Ian, Lennox Mcharg. 2006. Design with nature: 41. Tianjin: Tianjin university publishing house.

Jianjun, Zhu. Who am I—imagery dialogue and psychological treatment. Beijing: Beijing Medical University publishing house.

Jianjun, Zhu. 2006. Who am I—Imagery dialogue and psychotherapy.

Jimin, Liu thory of incorporate design and its advance. Journal of machine design 23(3):4–6.

Wen, Liu. 2012. A study on scientific and digital decision-making in planning boundaries of scenic sites based on bem-taking three gorges scenic area planning in wushan for example: 1 Beijing: Beijing forestry university.

Xiangxu, Meng & Yanning Xu. 2002. A survey of the research works on parametric design 14(11).

Computer, Intelligent Computing and Education Technology – Liu, Sung & Yao (Eds)
© *2014 Taylor & Francis Group, London, ISBN 978-1-138-02469-4*

Interpretable rule-based knowledge acquisition for characterizing fungal virulence factors

Wen-Lin Huang
Department of Management Information System, Asia Pacific Institute of Creativity, Miaoli, Taiwan

ABSTRACT: Fungal virulence factors are molecules expressed and secreted by fungal pathogens that cause many serious diseases in plants and animals. Targeting virulence factors is helpful for vaccine development to combat fungal infections. However, few methods pay attention to characterize virulence factors and advance to understand their reverent functions. This study proposes a knowledge acquisition method based on if-then rules for predicting fungal virulence factors (called FuVF). FuVF identifies non-virulent and four types of virulence factors, adhesion, toxin, secretion, and biofilm by using top-ranked Gene Ontology terms (GO) with amino acid composition. The top-ranked GO terms are selected by according to their numbers of annotated proteins in the dataset. Based on these features, FuVF generates several if-then rules by using the decision tree mechanism for characterizing fungal virulence factors. The top-ranked informative rules with high certainty grades reveal that five terms and three amino acid compositions of T, Y and S are effective in distinguishing virulence factors in fungi. The five terms comprise GO:0009405 (pathogenesis), GO:0005886 (plasma membrane), GO:0006508 (proteolysis), GO:0016757 (transferase activity) and GO:0016021 (integral to membrane).

Keywords: support vector; gene ontology; if-then rule; amino acid composition; adhesion; toxin; secretion; biofilm

1 INTRODUCTION

Pathogenic fungi cause many diseases in humans or other organisms (San-Blas and Calderone 2008). Virulence factors are molecules expressed and secreted by pathogens, such as toxin synthetic enzymes and secreted biodegradation enzymes (Yike 2011), that cause diseases in the host as they inhibit certain host functions. These molecules have several functions which are reverent to virulence factors, adhesion, toxin, secretion, biofilm and etc (Bhatnagar et al. 2002). Adhesion constitutes one of the initial stages of infection in microbial diseases. Biofilm formation further contributes to increased drug resistance and persistence of infections (Ramana and Gupta 2010). Microbial toxins that damaged the host caused toxicity, whereby aggressiveness was a complex trait that included the ability of a microbe to survive and multiply in tissue (Kolmer 1924). Plant infection by pathogenic fungi requires polarized secretion of enzymes (Schuster et al. 2012). Targeting these virulence factors in vaccine development can help efficiently combat fungal infections by blocking their functions and preventing adherence to host cells.

Some methods focus on predicting fungal adhesins and adhesin-like proteins. For example, FungalRV (Chaudhuri et al. 2011) is a fungal adhesin predictor and an immunoinformatics database with predicted adhesins; and FaaPred (Ramana and Gupta 2010) is a Support Vector Machine (SVM) based method for the prediction of fungal adhesins and adhesin-like proteins. Additionally, DFVF (Lu et al. 2012) is a disease-based database of fungal virulence factors. However, the knowledge about fungal virulence factors is rudimentary compared to that of bacterial virulence factors. Therefore, this work proposes a knowledge acquisition method based on if-then rules for predicting fungal virulence factors (called FuVF). The knowledge can be revealed from three aspects: 1) characterizing four types of virulence factors, adhesion, toxin, secretion, and biofilm, 2) identifying a feature subset with top-ranked Gene Ontology (Ashburner et al. 2000) terms with Amino Acid Composition (AAC), 3) if-then rules for distinguishing between non-virulent proteins and the above-mentioned four types of virulence factors. Accordingly, FuVF identifies a feature subset with 95 top-ranked GO terms, and yields test accuracy of 77.8%. The top-ranked informative rules with high certainty grades reveal that five terms and three amino acid compositions of T, Y and S are effective in distinguishing virulence factors in fungi. The five terms comprise GO:0009405 (pathogenesis), GO:0005886 (plasma membrane), GO:0006508 (proteolysis), GO:0016757 (transferase activity) and GO:0016021 (integral to membrane).

2 MATERIALS AND METHODS

Figure 1 shows that FuVF consists of five steps to characterize the functions of virulence factors: 1) collecting fungal protein sequences, 2) developing a GO-module for retrieving GO terms, 3) using a GO-grouping scheme for ranking the retrieved GO terms, 4) developing the FuVF predictor, and 5) interpreting if-then rules for knowledge acquisition about fungal virulence factors.

2.1 Collecting fungal protein sequences

This work creates one new fungal protein dataset, namely FuP, to evaluate this proposed FuVF method. The fungal proteins in the FuP dataset are obtained from the DFVF (Lu et al. 2012) and FungalRV (Chaudhuri et al. 2011) databases and using four keywords, "adhesion", "toxin", "secretion" and "biofilm". The FuP dataset has 171 virulent proteins (79 adhesion, 31 toxin, 43 secretion, and 18 biofilm) with a sequence identity of 40% by using a culling program PISECS (Wang and Dunbrack Jr. 2003) to avoid homolog bias and overestimation. Additionally, 170 non-virulent proteins are collected from the FungalRV database. Table 1 shows the numbers of protein sequences within the five classes.

2.2 Developing a GO-module for retrieving GO terms

For a novel fungal protein that may not correspond to an accession number, FuVF straightly uses the protein sequence to find one representative homolog of the query protein from the UniProt/Swiss-Prot database (released on April 3, 2013). Then, the accession number of the representative homolog is used to retrieve the associated GO terms from the UniProtKB-GOA database (released on May 1, 2013, at http://www.ebi.ac.uk/GOA/). Two candidate homologous proteins are first obtained by applying BLAST with the number of homologies $h = 2$, where h is the number of homologies. The first homology that has a sequence identity <100% to the query sequence is the representative homology (Huang 2012).

2.3 Using a GO-grouping scheme for ranking the retrieved GO terms

FuVF uses a GO-grouping (Huang et al. 2013) mechanism to determine a small number of GO terms for designing classifier. The detailed description is followed.

Step 1: Let n be the number of GO terms that are obtained by using all proteins. For each of the n GO terms, calculate the number t of annotating proteins in the training set.

Step 2: Rank all GO terms in order of decreasing annotation number t.

Step 3: Group all the GO terms that have the same value of t into a group g_t, where $t = 1, 2 \ldots N$. In this work, the largest annotation number is $t = 76$ and thus $N = 76$.

Step 4: Gather each group $\Psi_t = g_t \cup g_{t+1} \cup \ldots g_N$ such that each of the GO terms annotate at least t proteins, where $t = 1, 2 \ldots 10$. For instance, $\Psi_{10} = g_{10} \cup g_{11} \ldots \cup g_N$.

Step 5: Calculate the percentage of GO terms, $\varphi_t = m_t / n$, where $m_t (=|g_t| + |g_{t+1}| + \ldots, |g_N|)$.

In this study, SVM is used with five-fold cross-validation (5-CV). The best set of m top-grouped GO terms is the one has the highest accuracy. The SVM

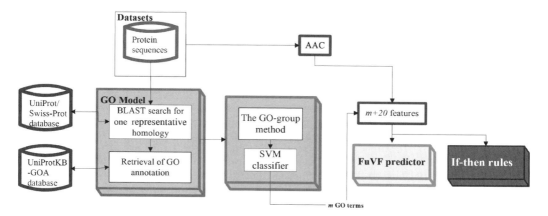

Figure 1. The block diagram of the proposed FuVF method.

Table 1. Prediction accuracies of FuVF on the FuP dataset.

Class	No. of samples	SN	SP	MCC	OA(%)
Non-virulent	170	0.824	0.731	0.557	82.4%
Adhesin	79	0.747	0.786	0.476	74.7%
Toxin	31	0.613	0.794	0.272	61.3%
Secreted	43	0.907	0.758	0.471	90.7%
Biofilm	18	0.444	0.796	0.130	44.4%
FuVF	OA (MCC)		77.8% (0.381)		
SVM-GO	(718 GO terms)		74.3%		
SVM-AAC			67.0%		

classification problem is solved by using an SVM with a radial basis kernel function $\exp(-\gamma \|x^i - x^j\|^2)$ from LIBSVM (Chang and Lin 2001), where x^i and x^j are training samples, and γ is a kernel parameter. The parameters γ and a cost parameter C are to be tuned using a similar grid (Chang and Lin 2001) approach from $\gamma \in \{2^{-15}, 2^{-14}, ..., 2^{15}\}$ and $C \in \{2^{-15}, 2^{-14}, ..., 2^{15}\}$. This work uses Overall Accuracy (OA), Sensitivity (SN), Specificity (SP), and Matthew's Correlation Coefficient (MCC) to measure prediction performance. They are derived as follows.

$$OA = (TP_c + TN_c)/(TP_c + FP_c + TN_c + FN_c),$$
$$c = 1, 2, ..5$$
$$SN_c = TP_c/(TP_c + FN_c)$$
$$SP_c = TN_c/(TN_c + FP_c) \qquad (1)$$

$$MCC_c = (TP_c * TN_c + FP_c * FN_c)/$$
$$\sqrt{(TP_c + FP_c)*(TP_c + FN_c)*(TN_c + FP_c)*(TN_c + FN_c)}$$

where TP_c is the number of sequences of class c that are predicted correctly; TN_c is the number of sequences not in class c that are predicted correctly; FP_c is the number of under-predicted sequences, and FN_c is the number of over-predicted sequences. Moreover), the MCC in the range $[-1, 1]$ is recorded. A coefficient of 1.0 denotes a perfect prediction; 0 represents an average random prediction, and −1.0 represents.

2.4 Developing the FuVF predictor

The input of this FuVF predictor is a fungal protein sequence P with FASTA format. The outputs are the predicted virulence-factor labels. The prediction procedure is described below.

Step 1: When using BLAST with $h = 2$ is performed to obtain two homologies. The first homology that has a sequence identity <100% to the query sequence is the representative homology.

Step 2: The obtained accession number of the representative homology is used to retrieve the corresponding GO terms from the UniProtKB-GOA database. Let the total number of obtained GO terms obtained be κ.

Step 3: The query sequence P is represented by using 20 AAC features and the m GO terms (called AAC-GO) i.e., $P = [p_1, p_2, ..., p_{20}, ... p_{m+20}]$.

Step 4: Verify whether the κ GO terms exist in the m GO terms. If the j-th GO term is in the set of the m GO terms, then the element $p_j = 1$; otherwise, $p_j = 0$, where $j = 21, ..., m+20$ and $j = 1, 2, ..., \kappa$.

Step 5: The query sequence $P = [p_1, p_2, ..., p_{20}, ... p_{m+20}]$ are the input to a SVM predictor. The output label is one of non-virulent, adhesion, toxin, secretion, and biofilm.

2.5 Interpreting if-then rules

This work presents a knowledge acquisition method based on if-then rules for insight of fungal virulent factor prediction mechanism. This rule-based knowledge acquisition method uses decision tree method C5.0 (Quinlan 2003) to develop if-then rules of the $m+20$ GO-AAC features. Each if-then rule has five types, Ri-ω, where i is the rule number index and ω is the class label (N: non-virulent, A: adhesion, T: toxin, S: secretion, and B: biofilm). For example, R1-N is the first rule for predicting non-virulent proteins.

3 RESULTS AND DISCUSSIONS

3.1 Evaluation of top-grouped GO terms

This work uses the GO-grouping scheme to assemble all $n = 718$ GO terms into several groups and then advances to measure which groups of GO terms are efficient in discriminating fungal virulence factors. Figure 2 shows the distribution of

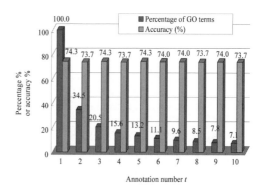

Figure 2. Distribution of the annotation numbers of n GO terms.

Table 2. The rule-based knowledge of tungal VF prediction.

	Rule-based knowledge			CF	Rules	Accuracy
R1-N:	If GO:0009405 = 0	then	Non-virulent	0.551	1	50.0%
R2-A:	If AAC$_T$ > 0.349994 and GO:0009405 = 0 and GO:0005886 = 0	then	Adhesion	0.872	1-2	59.4%
R3-T:	If AAC$_Y$ > 0.052656 and GO:0016787 = 0 and GO:0009405 = 1	then	Toxin	0.952	1-3	64.9%
R4-S:	If GO:0005739 = 0 and GO:0006508 = 1	then	Secreted	0.864	1-4	70.2%
R5-A:	If AAC$_S$ > 0.313665 and GO:0016301 = 0 and GO:0016021 = 0 and GO:0005576 = 0 and GO:0006508 = 0 and GO:0003700 = 0 and GO:0051301 = 0	then	Adhesion	0.833	1-5	73.1%
R11-B:	If GO:0016021 = 1 and GO:0016757 = 1		Biofilm		1-11	82.5%

the annotation numbers t from 1, 2 to 10. The percentage of GO terms ϕ_{10} = 7.1% means there are 7.1% of the GO terms annotate over 10 training protein sequences; i.e., 51(= 7.1% × 718) GO terms have association with more than 10 MCK proteins. Successively, 10 SVM-based classifiers are implemented by using the 10 subsets with 51, ... 718 GO terms. Accordingly, the SVM-based classifier using m_5 = 95 (= 13.2% × 718) GO terms yields the highest accuracy of 74.3%, where each of 95 GO terms annotates at least five protein sequences for t = 5 and ϕ_5 = 9.4%.

3.2 Prediction performance

The FuVF predictor is thus implemented using the group of 95 GO terms and 20 AAC features with the SVM classifier, where $(C, \gamma) = (2^3, 2^{-1})$. This predictor obtains a prediction accuracy of 77.8%, better than that of SVM-GO (74.3%) and SVM-AAC (67.0%). Additionally, a low value of MCC = 0.381 reveals little unbalanced within classes due to the fact that the number of samples are not balanced, for example, 170 (non-virulent) vs. 18 (biofilm).

3.3 Rule-based knowledge

This work presents a knowledge acquisition method based on if-then rule for insight of fungal virulence factors. The knowledge can be revealed from three aspects: 1) identified informative 115 AAC-GO features, 2) if-then rules of distinguishing between non-virulent proteins, and virulent proteins with adhesion, toxin, secretion, and biofilm functions, and 3) further analysis of distinguishable mechanism using AAC-GO features. Table 2 shows the interpretable rules as follows. The CF is a certainty grade of this rule in the unit interval [0, 1].

The R1-N rule has a certainty grade of 0.551 to predict 935 (= 50% × 341) fungal non-virulent

proteins by using the GO:0009405 term. In addition to the same GO:0009405 (pathogenesis) term, the second rule, R2-A, using GO:0005886 and AAC$_T$ (amino acid composition of T), has a certainty grade of 0.872 to identify 32(=(59.4%− 50%)× 341) fungal proteins that are associated with adhesin virulence factor. When applied these two rules, the rule-based classifier yields a prediction accuracy of 59.4%, reconfirming that the GO:0009405 (pathogenesis) and GO:0005886 (plasma membrane) terms, the amino acid composition of T, are efficient features in distinguishing from non-virulent proteins and adhesion virulent proteins in fungal pathogens. When adding the third rule, FuVF further enhances the prediction accuracy up to 64.9%. For example, a query sequence P has normalized values of 0.3, 0.06, 1, 1, 0 for AAC$_T$, AAC$_Y$, GO:0009405, GO:0005886 and GO:0016787, respectively. The classification procedure using the third rule R3-T (0.3 < 0.349994, 0.06 > 0.052656, GO:0009405 = 1, GO:0005886 = 1, and GO:0016787 = 0) predicts this query sequence to be a toxin protein. Accordingly, the five top-ranked informative rules with high certainty grades reveal that five terms and three amino acid compositions of T, Y and S are effective in distinguishing virulence factors in fungi. The five terms comprise GO:0009405 (pathogenesis), GO:0005886 (plasma membrane), GO:0006508 (proteolysis), GO:0016757 (transferase activity) and GO:0016021 (integral to membrane).

4 CONCLUSIONS

This work proposes a knowledge acquisition method based on if-then rules for characterizing four types F fungal virulence factors, adhesion, toxin, secretion, and biofilm. This proposed FuVF method identified 115 AAC-GO features by using a simple ranking scheme. Based on these features, FuVF acquires if-then rules using decision tree algorithm. The top 5 rules show that five GO terms, GO:0009405 (pathogenesis), GO:0005886 (plasma membrane), GO:0006508 (proteolysis), GO:0016757 (transferase activity) and GO:0016021 (integral to membrane), and three amino acid compositions of T, Y and S are effective in distinguishing virulence factors in fungi. Moreover, we believe that this proposed method will also be effective in designing prediction methods for other sequence-based applications.

REFERENCES

Ashburner, M., Ball, C.A., Blake, J.A., Botstein, D., Butler, H., Cherry, J.M., Davis, A.P., Dolinski, K., Dwight, S.S., Eppig, J.T., Harris, M.A., Hill, D.P., Issel-Tarver, L., Kasarskis, A., Lewis, S., Matese, J.C., Richardson, J.E., Ringwald, M., Rubin, G.M., Sherlock, G., 2000. Gene ontology: tool for the unification of biology. The Gene Ontology Consortium. *Nat Genet.*, 25–29.

Bhatnagar, D., Yu, J., Ehrlich, K.C., 2002. Toxins of filamentous fungi. *Chem. Immunol*, 81, 167–206.

Chang, C.C., Lin, C.J., 2001. LIBSVM: a library for support vector machines, Software available at http://www.csie.ntu.edu.tw/~cjlin/libsvm.

Chaudhuri, R., Ansari, F., Raghunandanan, M., Ramachandran, S., 2011. FungalRV: adhesin prediction and immunoinformatics portal for human fungal pathogens. *BMC Genomics C7-192*, 12, 1–14.

Huang, W.-L., 2012. Ranking Gene Ontology terms for predicting non-classical secretory proteins in eukaryotes and prokaryotes. *Journal of Theoretical Biology*, 312, 105–113.

Huang, W.-L., Liaw, C., Tsai, C.-T., Ho, S.-Y., 2013. Identification and Analysis of Single- and Multiple-region Mitotic Protein Complexes by Grouping Gene Ontology Terms. *Applied Mechanics and Materials*, 421, 277–285.

Kolmer, J.A., 1924. Infection. 58–83.

Lu, T., Yao, B., Zhang, C., 2012. DFVF: database of fungal virulence factors. *Database*, 2012: bas032.

Quinlan, J.R., 2003. C5.0 Online Tutorial. *http://www.rulequest.com.*

Ramana, J., Gupta, D., 2010. FaaPred: A SVM-Based Prediction Method for Fungal Adhesins and Adhesin-Like Proteins. *PLoS ONE*, 5.

San-Blas, G., Calderone, R.A., 2008. Pathogenic Fungi: Insights in Molecular Biology. *Caister Academic Press.*

Schuster, M., Treitschke, S., Kilaru, S., Molloy, J., Harmer, N.J., Steinberg, G., 2012. Myosin-5, kinesin-1 and myosin-17 cooperate in secretion of fungal chitin synthase. *The EMBO Journal*, 31(1), 214–227.

Wang, G.L., Dunbrack Jr., R.L., 2003. PISCES: a protein sequence culling server. *Bioinformatics*, 19, 1589–1591.

Yike, I., 2011. Fungal Proteases and their pathophysiological effects. *Mycopathologia*, 171, 299–323.

Computer, Intelligent Computing and Education Technology – Liu, Sung & Yao (Eds)
© 2014 Taylor & Francis Group, London, ISBN 978-1-138-02469-4

Research on power management methods for airborne fire-control radar

Jian Ou, Feng Zhao, Jian-Hua Yang, Jin Liu & Guo-Yu Wang
Key Laboratory of Complex Electromagnetic Environment Effects on Electronics and Information System,
National University of Defense Technology, Changsha, Hunan, China

ABSTRACT: Power management is an important method to LPI. The fundamentals of power management on airborne radar are firstly discussed. And then a set of processes to design the parameters in power management is given, based on the background of technique and tactics application. Finally, taking typical Air-to-Air situation of airborne radar as a model, the simulation of power management is given. The result shows that the methods of power management are feasible and effective.

Keywords: airborne radar; power management; LPI; RF stealth

1 INTRODUCTION

Modern warfare has lead to more highly demand to the Low Probability of Intercept (LPI) on airborne fire-control radar. Power management is one of the most fundamental and intuitive realization ways of LPI. Power management is the ability to control the power level emitted by the antenna, and limit the power to the appropriate range/RCS detection requirement. The basic idea is to control the parameters in real time according to the difference between sensitivity of the intercept probability is to parameters, to achieve the balance between detecting capability and LPI.

The majority of existing research results is not sufficiently connected with actual weapon equipment and combat environment. The methods, modeling and simulation of power management which consider various factors are still rarely reported.

An implementation method of power management is given in this paper, using four-step process to achieve the optimal design of radar parameters. It applies to various working modes and radar systems, improves the airborne radar model system and provides support to the relevant simulation and evaluation system.

2 FUNDAMENTALS OF POWER MANAGEMENT

The best solution for LPI is no radiation, for example, radar will keep radio silence in early stage of low altitude penetration. But at some point, radar must be turned on to satisfy the demands of high precision and anti-jamming capability. So the suboptimal solution is adjusting wave parameters dynamically to decrease intercept probability to an acceptable level.

2.1 Analysis of interception conditions

The interception of radar signal must possess the "five-domain" condition: being intercepted in time domain, space domain, frequency domain, energy domain and polarization domain simultaneously. In addition, the cumulative effect of multiple radiations should also be taken into account.

- *Frequency-domain interception*: It means that the frequency range of radar and interception receivers is overlapped partly. The bandwidth of interception receivers is usually wide (larger than 4 GHz), which can almost cover the frequency range of the mainstream airborne radar. So we can consider the frequency-domain interception probability $p_{If} = 1$.
- *Time-domain interception*: That is the probability of the interception receiver is working when radar signal arrives at its antenna. We assume that the receiver is always working, so this probability is equal to irradiation time in unit time, namely duty ratio. $p_{It} = \tau \cdot f_r$, τ is pulse width, f_r is PRF.
- *Space-domain interception*: It means the beams of radar and receiver aim at each other. In tracking state, the probability is related to the beam width of interception receiver, $p_{Is} = B_i/2\pi$, B_i is beam width; while in searching state, it should be $p_{Is} = (\beta/\Omega) \cdot (B_i/2\pi)$, Ω and β are the solid angles of scan window and antenna beam, $\beta = 4\pi/G$, G is the gain of radar antenna.

− *Energy-domain interception*: It means the radar signal is detected by interception receiver. Two cases should be considered: one is for aerial targets, which must have carried an interception receiver, and the Energy-domain interception probability is the detection probability of interception receiver. Another case is for the ground or sea surface targets. In this case, receivers are distributed as an array. So $p_{Ie} = p_{dl} \cdot A_I \rho$, A_I is size of the area where the power density is larger than the sensibility of receivers, ρ is array density.

− *Polarization-domain interception*: The polarization direction of interception receivers and radar signal must be basically the same. A receiver usually uses several circularly polarized antennas. It is almost impossible for polarization mismatching, and we can assume that $p_{Ip} = 1$.

So the interception probability for a single pulse is

$$p_{I0} = p_{If} \cdot p_{Ie} \cdot p_{It} \cdot p_{Is} \cdot p_{Ip} \tag{1}$$

− *Pulse accumulation*: High SNR of radar is usually achieved by pulse accumulation. Within the dwell time in the target direction, every pulse will increase the interception probability. So the final interception probability should be an accumulation form for n pulses.

Above all, the general formula to calculate the interception probability is

$$p_I = 1 - \left(1 - p_{If} \cdot p_{Ie} \cdot p_{It} \cdot p_{Is} \cdot p_{Ip}\right)^n \tag{2}$$

2.2 *Key factors for power management strategies*

It can be seen from (2), the biggest impact comes from the exponent n, the number of pulses. The value of n is closely linked to radar systems: $n = 1$ for monopulse system, $n > 10^2$ for PD system, and $n > 10^4$ for SAR system. The big difference of n will cause the different power management strategies.

On the other hand, the combat mission background is another key point. As detecting capability and LPI is a pair of contradictions, an appropriate tradeoff is necessary. The principles should be the cost between failing to detect targets and being intercepted by receivers. In air-to-ground missions, the task for aircrafts is usually breaking through the enemy blockade secretly, in order to attack the targets in deeper enemy area, and the main threats are radar networks, receiver arrays and ARMs. So it is very critical to keep covert during the whole process. Here "survival first" is a proper strategy: increasing detection probability on the premise of LPI. While in air-to-air missions, if enemy target was not been detected timely, our aircraft may be locked by the fire-control system firstly due to the lack of maneuvers. So "combat first" strategy should be used: ensuring effective target detection before decreasing the interception probability.

3 IMPLEMENTATION PROCESS OF POWER MANAGEMENT

Power management for airborne radar can be achieved by a four-step process: ①Delimit a general range of radar parameters from the inherent constrains. ②Calculate the constrain of getting enough SNR by radar equation. ③Calculate the constrain of LPI by the general formula for interception probability. ④Optimize the parameter combinations according to the combat circumstance.

3.1 *Delimit the general range of parameters*

A general parameter range should be limited firstly to reduce the quantity of calculation. The constraints for parameters are as follows.

a. Upper limit of P_t: Maximal peak power for radar transmitter.
b. Upper limit of $\tau \cdot f_r$: Maximal duty ratio D_{max} for radar transmitter.
c. Upper limit of τ: Avoiding targets falling into the first ranging blind region for monopulse system.
d. Lower limit of τ: Minimal pulse width limited by the index of radar transmitter.
e. Upper limit of t_r: Limited by tracking data rate and tracking capability for multiple targets.
f. Limits of variations: The current unclassified LPI emitter parameters that are variable are as Table 1, and parameters shall not exceed these ranges.
g. Parameter classification: As continuous adjustment of parameters is unavailable for the existing radar transmitters, the parameters should be classified. We assume P_t, τ and t_r will vary by twice.

A general parameter range is calculated after being screened by the restrictions above, while the following conditions will give an exact range.

Table 1. Parameter ranges for LPI transmitters.

Parameters	Peak power (P_t)	PRF (f_r)	Pulse width (τ)	Dwell time (t_r)
Range	10^7:1	1000:1	8000:1	10:1

3.2 Requirements for high generalized SNR

The minimum requirement for radar detection is that the SNR equals to theoretical detection threshold $\text{SNR}_{\min}$:

$$\frac{P_t \tau f_r t_r \cdot G_R^2 \lambda^2 \sigma}{(4\pi)^3 R^4 L_R \cdot KTF_n} = \text{SNR}_{\min} \qquad (3)$$

where K is the Boltzmann constant, T is temperature, F_n is noise coefficient, σ is RCS of the target, L_R is the total loss.

A T_a-P_t plane is constructed in Figure 1. The abscissa and ordinate are cumulative time and peak power of radar respectively, both of which use the logarithm expression. The requirement of SNR and other conditions are expressed with lines. The shadow represents the range of parameters which can reach the SNR requirement.

The oblique line represents the parameters that can reach the minimum SNR; The range of peak power is shown between two horizontal lines; The cumulative time of three different radar systems are expressed with three vertical lines. Every point in the plane represents a set of parameters. Actually, the alternative parameters should be some discrete points considering the stepped value of parameters classified.

3.3 Requirements for LPI

The exact formula of interception probability is different for different radar systems and working modes. But the key point is the same that is calculating energy-domain interception probability. When P_t is the peak power, G_{RI} and G_I are the antenna gain in the direction of receiver and the interception receiver gain respectively. Then the received SNR is:

$$\text{SNR}_I = \frac{P_t G_{RI} G_I \lambda^2}{(4\pi)^2 R^2 L_I \cdot P_{nI}} \qquad (4)$$

where the noise power P_{nI} can be calculated from intercept sensibility S_I:

$$P_{nI} = \frac{S_I G_I G_{IP}}{\text{SNR}_{Ig}} \qquad (5)$$

$\text{SNR}_{Ig} \approx 14.39$ dB, which is a SNR threshold for interception calculated when false alarming probability is 10^{-8} and the detection probability is 0.9.

For aerial targets, the detection probability of receiver equals to the energy-domain interception probability. It can be calculated according to the Rice formula for liner detectors and expressed with MarcumQ function:

$$Q(\alpha,\beta) = \int_\beta^\infty \zeta I_0(\alpha\zeta) e^{-(\zeta^2 + \alpha^2)/2} d\zeta \qquad (6)$$

where $I_0(\cdot)$ is zero order Bessel function. So the energy-domain interception probability is:

$$p_{Ie} = p_{dI} = 2 \cdot \int_{\sqrt{-\ln p_f}}^\infty y I_0\left(2y\sqrt{\text{SNR}_I}\right) \cdot e^{-\left(y^2 + \text{SNR}_I\right)} dy$$

$$= Q\left(\sqrt{2\text{SNR}_I}, \sqrt{-\ln p_f}\right) \qquad (7)$$

In air-to-ground mode, there should be another factor $A_I \cdot \rho$ in (7). ρ is receiver array density, A_I is size of the area where the power density is larger than the sensibility of receivers, which is related to peak power, antenna pattern and the geometric relationship among beam, target and the surface. Then the total interception probability can be calculated according to (2):

$$p_I = 1 - \left(1 - p_{Ie} \cdot \frac{B_i \cdot \tau f_r}{2\pi}\right)^{f_r \cdot t_r} \qquad (8)$$

Let the LPI threshold be p_{Ilim}, so the parameters that satisfy the condition of $p_I < p_{Ilim}$ can be expressed as the shadow part in Figure 2.

The meanings of two horizontal solid lines and three vertical lines are the same with Figure 1. The horizontal dash line is the interception sensibility boundary and the curve is the LPI boundary. Conditions of LPI are calculated taking the example of PD radar system. As the pulse numbers of monopulse, PD and SAR system increase, more

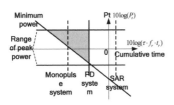

Figure 1. Limits of parameters from SNR.

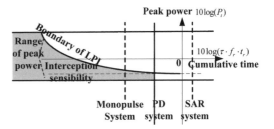

Figure 2. Limits of parameters from LPI.

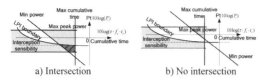

a) Intersection   b) No intersection

Figure 3.　Two situations of parameter optimization.

sensitive the total interception probability is to the single pulse interception probability. So the curve should be steeper for monopulse and gentler for SAR system.

3.4　*Parameter optimization strategy*

The final parameters range has been determined by the front three steps. The optimal parameters will be selected in this step. Overlapping the two T_a-P_t planes above, either of the following two situations may occur.

For the situation of a), the shadow represents the parameters that satisfy both the conditions of SNR and LPI. While in b), there is no such parameter. So a balance must be kept between the strategy of "survival first" and "combat first".

Assume that A is the set for the SNR condition and B is for the LPI condition. Any element in the set is a combination of parameters related to power management. The parameter optimization processes for two strategies are summarized as follows:

– "Survival first" strategy for ground targets
 If $A \cap B \neq \varphi$, choose the element has the lowest interception probability in the intersection; if $A \cap B = \varphi$, choose the element has the highest SNR in B.
– "Combat first" strategy for ground targets
 If $A \cap B \neq \varphi$, choose the element has the highest SNR in the intersection; if $A \cap B = \varphi$, choose the element has the lowest interception probability in A.

The final optimal parameter of power management will be selected after the four-step process for different situations.

4　SIMULATION AND VERIFICATION

The process of power management will be simulated taking a simple air-to-air mission as an example. Assume that two aircraft fly towards each other, considering the distance from 250 km to 15 km. Parameters are set as Table 2 based on relevant references.

The airborne radar will work in monopulse system and up-view mode, $n = f_r \cdot t_r = 1$, so only P_t and

Table 2.　Parameters for power management simulation in air-to-air mission.

Parameters	Symbols	Value
Radar and signal		
Maximum peak power	P_{tmax}	10 kw
Main gain of radar	G_R	40 dB
Center frequency	f_0	10 GHz
Maximum duty ratio	D_{max}	0.25
SNR threshold	SNR_{min}	16 dB
PRF	f_r	1000 Hz
Interception receiver		
Beam width	B_I	10°
Frame period of scanning	T_s	60 s
Sensitivity	S_I	−70 dBm
Antenna gain	G_I	30 dB
Process gain	G_{IP}	25 dB
Others		
RCS of target	σ	2 m²
Interception probability for LPI	p_{Ilim}	0.0001

τ are related to power management. For the right moment of the distance is 40 km, the parameter range after power management is:

The solid box is the parameter range limited in the first step. The dotted line is SNR boundary, and the asterisks on its upper right are the parameters that can provide enough SNR. The dash line is LPI boundary, and the circles on its lower left are the parameters that satisfy the LPI condition. The distance between any two adjacent points is 3 dB. As we can see there is intersection in Figure 4, the alternative parameters are listed as follows according to step 4.

According to the principle of "combat first", the optimal parameters should be No. 6 for its highest SNR as well as good LPI performance.

The power management simulation result for the whole process is shown in Figures 5 and 6.

The meanings of lines have been noted. Several conclusions can be summarized from the trend of lines:

Firstly, power management is effective comparing the interception probability lines. Before power management, the interception probability is above the LPI threshold the whole process. While after power management, the interception probability reduces to lower than 10^{-4} and satisfy the LPI condition.

Secondly, because of the difference of antenna gain and process gain between radars and interception receivers, radars usually dominate at short distance and on the contrary for receivers. So the interception probability decreases in the trend after power management in Figure 5, which is consistent

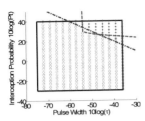

Figure 4. Radar parameters when target distance is 40 km.

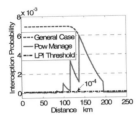

Figure 5. LPI performance.

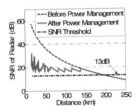

Figure 6. Detection performance.

with our analyses. The sawteeth of the lines are due to parameter classification.

Thirdly, three lines intersect at 194 km in Figure 6, which is the largest operation range of radar in theory. And the radar SNR line is above the SNR threshold. It shows that power management can reduce peak power to an acceptable level, without any negative impact on the regular detection.

Fourthly, the real radar SNR is at least 3 dB larger than the SNR threshold. This is the spare set aside in case of the factors like target maneuver or RCS fluctuation.

Table 3. Alternative parameters when target distance is 40 km.

No.	Peak power (w)	Pulse width (s)	SNR (dB)	Interception probability
1	10000	1.9531E-6	19.368	5.4253E-5
2	5000	1.9531E-6	16.358	5.4253E-5
3	312.5	6.2500E-5	19.368	6.6930E-5
4	312.5	3.1250E-5	16.368	3.3465E-5
5	156.25	1.2500E-4	19.368	2.8253E-6
6	156.25	2.5000E-4	22.379	5.6506E-6

Lastly, in Figure 6, if the distance is more than 80 km, high SNR can be obtained to keep tracking the targets even not satisfying the LPI conditions. It is consistent with the principle of "combat first".

In summary, the method of power management is effective in reducing the interception probability, meets actual requirement, and almost no negative impact on the regular detection of radar. It provides a feasible and effective way of power management in airborne fire-control systems.

5 CONCLUSIONS

Starting from the fundamentals of power management, the conditions of interception and factors of power management are analyzed. Then, a four-step process is proposed to optimize the radar parameters and apply to various working modes and radar systems. Simulated and verified in a typical air-to-air mission, the method is proved to be feasible and effective. It is of certain significance in applying power management in airborne radars and improving the model system of airborne fire-control radar.

REFERENCES

David Lynch, Jr. Introduction to RF Stealth. Charlotte: North Carolina Science Technology Publishing Inc, 2004.

Phillip E. Pace. Detecting and Classifying Low Probability of Intercept Radar. Boston: Artech House, Inc, 2003.

Design and implement of data integrity verify service under cloud environment

Q.L. Wu

College of Computer Science and Technology, Chongqing University of Posts and Telecommunications, China

ABSTRACT: Cloud Service Providers (CSP) is facing more and more challenges from data security and privacy protection. During the process of data communication and data storage and data integrity verify in the open authentication schemes, user must do many complex computing work which is not reasonable. In this article, we analyzed current data integrity verify schemes, then design and implement the data integrity verify service under cloud environment which called DIVS. We have tested it under the Aliyun OSS, and the result demonstrates DIVS can be a service and do a good job.

Keywords: cloud; data security; integrity verify; DIVS

1   INTRODUCTION

1.1   *General introduction*

Cloud computing improve computing efficiency but brings huge challenges about user informations and privacy protection.[1] Current, Cloud service providers have difficulties to provide effect methods for data security and privacy protection. The famous IT company Google and Amazon have declared that they can't guarantee use's data security in their user agreements. Meanwhile, in cloud environment, data is outsourced to the server, which leads user cannot manage his data directly as local storage. However, cloud service provider manage data from different users, but user can't trust cloud service providers absolutely. Physical storage equipments or servers in CSP may count some troubles and it is skeptical that integrity and usability of data in CSP. When data stored locally, we just care about potential errors and verification efficiency[7] when we validate data integrity directly, but in cloud environment, we do't have backup file locally.

According to different application scenarios and requirements, data can be divided into archives of static storage data and operation dynamic storage data. In cloud environment, static data verification[1] can be realize in the constant communication costs and dynamic storage date verification[2–5] must be $O(\log(n))$ at least (n stands for count of data object). Researchers devote to solve open authentication, further, they want to fuse dynamic operation include insertion, deletion, update and so on and make data integrity verification closer to practice application.

Merkle hash tree[6] is a widely research structure and it can be used to prove that a set of elements is not damaged and has not changed efficiently and safely. In the Wang et al.,[2] data block label is treated as the basic data of certification, then the data block signature is bind to data block and its label, so as to support efficient dynamic data operation.

Relatively speaking, the signature schemes based on the BLS[8] can use shorter homomorphic signature mechanism (e.g., 160 bits), which has the shorter query and response information, But the reference [2] corresponds to BLS signature scheme (referred to the Wang et al.) of MHT validation data block size is the same as the length of the signature.

Privacy protection is an important problem. In wang scheme, MHT manage data block tags can avoid upload data itself, at the same time, homomorphism authentication information of data can be further randomized.

In the Wang et al., user have to do some precomputing and the process of verification need CSP compute and offer some data, so TPA[2] can finish integrity verification. Therefore, current cloud storage don't have obligation to offer these computation and TPA is a virtual conception. If pre-computation and data integrity verification can delegate to a service-side, user will be liberated from the complex computation. What's more, service-side can finish all special computation in the process of verification. At all, all computation can be done by service-side, and this scheme is adapted to current cloud environment. In this article, we design and implement the service: DIVS.

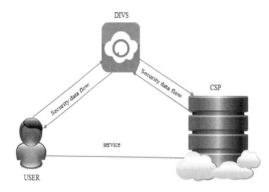

Figure 1.　The model: user, DIVS and CSP.

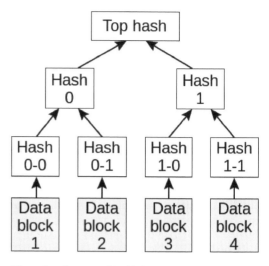

Figure 2.　Construct Merkle hash tree.

1.2　*DIVS description*

DIVS stands fo data integrity verify service. It is a kind of data integrity verify service under cloud environment. When user use some cloud storage service, they care about data security and data integrity, but they have no professional skills to verify wether their data is safe. So DIVS comes into being. Under current cloud environment, user can delegate DIVS to all computation in data verification, include pre-computing, construct Merkle hash tree, verify operation and so on.

2　BASIC KNOWLEDGE

2.1　*Bilinear map and Merkle hash tree*

Bilinear map.[2,4] A bilinear map is a mape: $G \times G \rightarrow G_T$, where G is a Gap Diffie-Hellman (GDH) group and G_T is another multiplicative cyclic group of prime order with the following properties: (1) Effective computing: there is an efficiently computable algorithm for computing for computing e; (2) Bilinear: for all $h_1, h_2 \in G$ and a, b $\in Z_p$, $e(h_1^a, h_2^b) = e(h_1, h_2)^{ab}$; (3) Nondegenerate: $e(g, g) \neq 1$, where g is a generator of G.

Merkle hash tree is a tree in which every non-leaf node is labeled with the hash of the labels of its children nodes. Hash trees are useful because they allow efficient and secure verification of the contents of larger data structures. Hash trees are a generalization of hash lists and hash chains.

So, a Merkle hash tree is a tree of hashes in which the leaves are hashes of data blocks in, for instance, a file or set of files. Nodes further up in the tree are the hashes of their respective children. For example, in the picture hash 0 is the result of hashing the result of concatenating hash 0–0 and hash 0–1. That is, hash 0 = hash (hash 0–0 || hash 0–1) where "||" denotes concatenation.

3　DESIGN AND IMPLEMENT

3.1　*Pre-computing*

When user want to use cloud storage service, they need to upload file F, so they can use DIVS. They just need authorized DIVS to upload file F, so DIVS use KeyGen(.) to get public key and security key, and then DIVS run SigGen(.) to process File F. The following is the concrete implementation of these two method.

We have a number set:

$I = \{1,2,3 \dots n\}$

KeyGen(.):run random algorithm get a number $\alpha \in Z_p$, and compute $\upsilon = g^\alpha$. The key pair is (spk, ssk), so there are $pk = (\upsilon, spk)$ and the $sk = (\alpha, ssk)$. The algorithm as follows:

SigGen(.):file File divide into n block,

so the tag of file F is:

$(m_1, m_2, \dots, m_n), m_i \in Z_p$

There is a signature set should be compute as

$Tag = name \parallel u \mid SSig(name \parallel u)$

bellow:

metaSize = 16 M bytes
blockNum = fileSize/metaSize
For each block in F
i is from 0 to blockNum

$\sigma_i = (H(m_i) \cdot u^{m_i})^\alpha$

So the signature set is as below:

$\Phi = \{\sigma_i\}, 1 \leq i \leq n$

Construct MHT: DIVS compute MHT based on F. The leave node of MHT is $H(m_i)$. Algorithm is as follows:

$$Sig_{sk}(H(R)) \leftarrow (H(R))^\alpha$$

For each block in set m:

do
$m_i = H(H(m_i) \| H(m_{i+1}))$
remove m_{i+1}
untile $\text{len}(m) = 1$

So we get the result of root Hash: H(R) and result of root hash is R, DIVS use sk to make a signature for it.

After finish, DIVS send

$$\{F', T, \Phi, sig_{sk}(H(R))\}$$

to CSP, and for privacy protection, DIVS must delete without delay locally.

$$\{F', \Phi, sig_{sk}(H(R))\}$$

3.2 Data integrity verify

Once user need to check whether his data is integrity, he will delegate the work to DIVS. Therefore, DIVS gets the authority, and it will prepare for data integrity verification. Firstly, DIVS verify the signature T, if verification can't pass, we can conclude that the file is not integrity, else, we resume u. In order to determine which block will be verified, DIVS select c items from set I randomly, which consists set s $I = \{s_1, s_2, s_3 \dots s_c\}$. For every item among the set I, we select a random number. We use "chal" indicate location of block which will participates in verification.

After finished the "chal", DIVS will run Gen-Proof to generate proof. So, DIVS need to do some computation as follows:

$$\sigma = \prod_{i=s_1}^{s_c} \sigma_i^{y_i} \in G \qquad \mu = \sum_{i=s_1}^{s_c} v_i m_i \in Z_p$$

After finish these computation, DIVS compute the result of root hash R, and then verify the equation as below:

$$e(\sigma, g) \overset{?}{=} e\left(\prod_{i=s_1}^{s_c} H(m_i)^{v_i} \cdot u^{\mu}, v\right)$$

If result of the equation is false, then verification is over and the data is not integrity, else, further verify:

$$e(Sig_{sk}(H(R)), g) \overset{?}{=} e(H(R), v)$$

DIVS   CSP

1. Generate a random set

$$\{(i, v_i)\}_{i \in I};$$

$$\underrightarrow{\{(i, v_i)\}_{i \in I}}$$
Challenge request chal

2. compute $\mu = \Sigma_i v_i m_i;$

3. compute $\sigma = \prod_i \sigma^{v_i};$

$$\underleftarrow{\{\mu, \sigma, \{H(m_i), \Omega_i\}_{i \in I}, sig_{sk}(H(R))\}}$$

4. compute R using

$\{H(m_i), \Omega_i\}_{i \in I};$

5. Verify $sig_{sk}(H(R))$

6. Verify $\{m_i\}_{i \in I}$

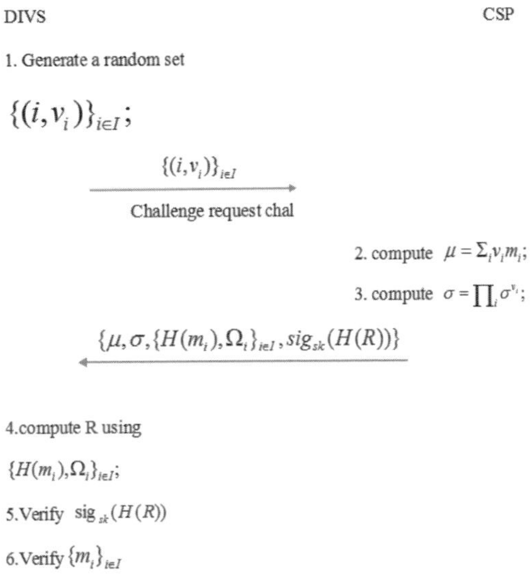

Figure 3. Default integrity verification.

	Pre-computing	Construct MHT
256M	99s	98s
512M	195s	189s
1G	398s	383s

Figure 4. Compare different size file run time.

If equation is not true, then data is not integrity, else, data is integrity and usability. After all, the process of verification is over.

4 TEST DIVS

We use Aliyun OSS as our cloud storage service. In the process of test, we use Charm to construct crypto model (Charm is a framework for rapidly prototyping advanced crypto systems based on the Python language, it was designed from the ground up to minimize development time and code complexity while promoting the reuse of components). And we need GMP, PBC, pyparsing, openssl to support and we use OSS Python SDK to develop DIVS. The test computer hardware configuration is: 2G RAM, Intel core 2.

We use three different size files to test: 256 M, 512 M, 1 G.

The test result is as follows in Figure 4.

5 CONCLUSION

In this article, we research and analyze data integrity verify schemes, design and implement a data integrity verify service under cloud environment. We just test the service named DIVS based aliyun OSS, and the result express DIVS can be a stable service to offer data integrity verify in current cloud environment.

But DIVS, as a data integrity verify service, just support for Aliyun, so, in the future, we want to develop DIVS as a higher software abstract level and make it to support more cloud storage service. Because of data integrity verification, DIVS will make some data redundancy, which may increase user's storage costs, meanwhile, that also may increase CSP's storage burden. The result of test show that int the pre-computing, construct Merkle hash tree cost too much time which is bad for user experience. So, in the next, we will further research and improve the schemes to make DIVS faster and simpler.

REFERENCES

[1] Feng Deng-guo, Zhang Min, Zhang Yan, et al. Study on Cloud Computing Security[J]. Journal of Software, 2011, 22(1):71–83.

[2] Qian Wang, Cong Wang, Kui Ren, et al. Enabling Public Auditability and Data Dynamics for Storage Security in Cloud Computing[J]. IEEE Transactions on Parallel and Distributed Systems, 2011,22(5): 847–859.

[3] H. Shacham, B. Waters. Compact Proofs of retrievability [J]. Advances in Cryptology Asiacrypt, 2008, LNCS 5350: 90–107.

[4] Cong Wang, Qian Wang, Kui Ren, et al. Privacy-preserving Public Auditing for Data Storage Security in Cloud Computing[C]//InfoCom2010, IEEE, 2010.

[5] Chris Erway C, Alptekin Küpçü, Charalampos Papamanthou, et al. Dynamic Provable Data Possession [C]//Proc of CCS'09. Chicago, IL: ACM, 2009:213–222.

[6] Merkle R.C. Protocols for public key cryptosystems [C]//Proc of IEEE Symposium on Security and Privacy'80, 1980.122–133.

[7] Chen Long, Wang Guo-yin. An Efficient Integrity Check Method for Fine-Grained Data over Galois Field[J]. Chinese Journal of Computers, 2011, 34(5): 847–855.

[8] D. Boneh, B. Lynn, H. Shacham. Short Signatures from the Weil Pairing [C]//Proc of Cryptology-Asiacrypt'2001. London, UK: Springer-Verlag, 2001: 514–532.

Computer, Intelligent Computing and Education Technology – Liu, Sung & Yao (Eds)
© 2014 Taylor & Francis Group, London, ISBN 978-1-138-02469-4

Study on control of artificial intelligence on swarm intelligence

Philip F. Yuan, T. Xiao & L.M. Zhang
College of Architecture and Urban Planning at Tongji University, Shanghai, China

ABSTRACT: Swarm intelligence is a decentralizing self-organization system based on information collection, which provides a new way for management and control on artificial intelligence. This paper analyzes the design, practice and application of swarm intelligence for robot. The achievement demonstrates that the swarm intelligence shall have positive meaning for optimization of robot cost and intelligence level, as well as a conclusion of further application of swarm intelligence in artificial intelligence.

Keywords: artificial intelligence; swarm intelligence; robot control; miniaturization; low-cost; emotive robot

1 INTRODUCTION

Intelligent control technology is raised for the complexity and uncertainty of the controlled object, the environment and complex task.

Based on the computer science, artificial intelligence, information science, thinking science, cognitive science and artificial neural networks Cross and other disciplines, laid the theoretical foundation of intelligent control from different aspects. Intelligent control is the core of high-level control. Its mission is to carry out the actual environment or decision making and planning process to achieve the generalized problem solving. Intelligent control is in the process of development, there are many issues to be further studied and improved.

2 FROM SWARM INTELLIGENCE TO SWARM ROBOTICS

2.1 Swarm intelligence

With the development of the society, there is necessary for people to make multi-agent system tackle optimization the mass, unordered and automatic data or some sequence event.

We definite the swarm intelligence with the characters as follows.

The group compounds with majority individuals.

The individuals are homogeneous.

The interactions among the individuals are on the condition of the simple rules.

The behavior of group is self-organized.

Artificial Intelligence of different levels of sophistication is used to endow agents with the capacity to reason about what they sense and decide how to act. These reasoning capacities may range from simple reactive abilities (if stimulus X is sensed then do Y) to more complex ones involving the anticipation of future stimuli and the planning of adequate responses.

2.2 Swarm robots

When the swarm intelligence approach is applied to robotic systems, it is called "swarm robotics".

Swarm robotics systems are made up of swarms of relatively simple and cooperating devices rather than of a single and powerful robot. The main idea is that a system of many simple devices that exploit distributed control and self-organization to coordinate their activities might be more robust to failures than a monolithic system such as a humanoid robot. In other words, the lack of a central controller—none of the robots is in charge of directing the swarm activity—and the redundancy in the robot swarm—individuals are interchangeable as they all have the same or very similar capabilities—makes a swarm robotics system very robust to failures. In fact, should one or a few individuals fail, the others can take over

Figure 1. The scene photo & situation simulation.

and the overall system would show only a limited degradation of its performance.

Another potential advantage of a swarm robotic system is that, if properly designed, it can be scalable. In other words, the amount of work carried out by a robotic swarm can be increased simply by adding new robots to the swarm.

3 PRACTICE OF SWARM INTELLIGENCE DESIGN—EMOTIVE ROBOT

In the summer of the year 2013, the third session of "Shanghai Digital Future" themed on "Interaction" held a series of events in Tongji University. Taking on this opportunity, we did experiments on artificial intelligence and robot cluster named "Mechanic Carnival". By grouping nine low-intelligent robots, complicated robot movements were realized, and the total costs of experiment and manufacturing were less than 10,000 yuan.

3.1 Control system design

3.1.1 Motion rules

With the robots as vehicles, the experiment aims to test intelligent system (low intelligence system) that brings simple and specific attributes to individual robot's motions so as to study motion properties of collective intelligent robots.

Robot motions can be divided into several levels, the first level is the properties shown as of a "living" individual and motions. The robot group emulates mammal's motions of leg joints and can move forward, backward and make turns by motion differences between the two leg groups; when they meet obstacles, they are able to make decisions on whether to retreat or to turn and to keep away from obstacles by judging position of the obstacles. We placed distance sensors at three directions of the robot cluster so they are able to make accurate judgment on obstacle position relying on multiple feedbacks.

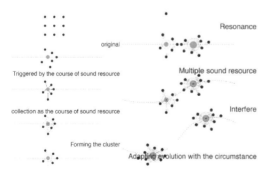

Figure 2. Diagram of group's motion rules.

We define robot species through control of leg motions, paces, motion speed differences between left and right legs and dodging motions in front of obstacles. To study collective artificial intelligence, we define a group as the same species.

In respect to this level, we provide individual sense system to individual robots. The robot individuals are designed to have only the ability of sound judgment. Sound directions keep controlling motion directions of individual robots, and acceleration rate of the legs is controlled at a given coefficient. Sound is similar to pheromone which is distributed in the space as an abstract fluid; therefore we are able to control robot's personality by the effect of sound as a kind of pheromone upon robot "brain".

We control robot personality by controlling scope of sound perception and the extent to which the sound elements impact on movement rate of robots. Similarly, to study collective artificial intelligence, we define a group as the same species.

The second level is the collective properties of a "living" group (sociality). The relative robot motion rules is that two individuals judge motion differences to decide whether to keep still or to make turns in a given relative spacing, so that smooth collective motion is achieved. The sound serves as the information source in this experiment, sound volume serves as information capacity of pheromones, robot group speeds up to gather as a way to exchange pheromones and when spacing between individuals is less than a given value, this signifies that they successfully realize exchange of pheromones. The robots are able to judge only one pheromone source at a given place, that is, the place where the sound volume reaches the greatest within the scope of perception is the place for information exchange.

We define robots' collective characters by controlling scope of sound perception, robots' different judgments on place of information exchange and relative motions.

3.1.2 Motion simulation

In the actual problem, we cannot use the same number of robot agent to represent the various problems in the real scene. Under this condition, we may use movement route arithmetic to analogue the movement of swarm robotics. The movement route arithmetic of a robot is used to solve other complicated problem.

In swarm robotics intelligence, there are already many types of basic arithmetic. Particle Swarm optimization, PSO (Bird swarm preying) and Ant Colony Optimization, ACO (ants looking for food) are typical ones.

Two algorithms sum up the most direct and concise movement rules, by observing the

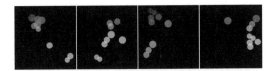

Figure 3.   Free points simulation in processing.

Figure 4.   Physical agents simulation in processing.

Figure 5.   Physical agents simulation with sound factors in processing.

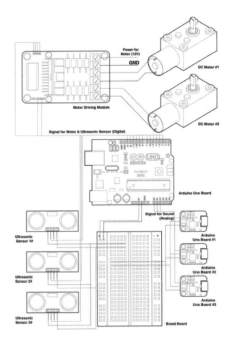

Figure 6.   Diagram of sensor and controller.

characteristics of the cluster, form the algorithm in the computer, to simulate the evolutionary optimization.

The experiment of the swarm robotics is a gradual process. We increase the attached condshengyiitions to the robot and study the route of swarm robotics. Under primary state, we set each robot as one movement agent, searching the next agent beyond the safe range. This way for searching is a roaming without rules.

When combined with physical conditions, path algorithm simulation has the effectiveness to face the physical characteristics of special tasks and the environment. Here, we designed agents roaming way by factors as follow: roaming rates, the avoid ways facing the obstacles without a safe distance.

In the swarm intelligence research, we set sound for information communication, the robot itself as a source of pheromone carry again. We give the launch of a variable value to the agent when the path simulation. At the same time, the agent chooses the next direction through collecting all the data of the sound values in the area of the maximum, forming a purposeful way of roaming.

In this route analogue, the changeable factors cover the basic behavior of independent robot and the definition of information factor in swarm intelligence, to get the new optimization simulation.

3.1.3   Sensor and controller

Control system is composed of sensor and controller. For sensing, we use three ultrasonic ranging modules (HC-SR04) to detect the surrounding space of an independent unit. We also use sound detecting modules (DFR0034) on the right and left sides to collect surrounding sound source.

For controlling, each independent unit is set with a module of Arduino Uno to realize digital processing and feedback. Arduino Uno shall analyze the data of three groups that collected by the three ultrasonic modules and complete the corresponding behavior to avoiding obstacle, thus to complete the first behavior process.

At the same time, two sound detection modules (DFR0034) are used to collect surrounding sound and give feedback signal to the two analogue inlets of the Arduino Uno. By comparing the sizes of the data collected by the module, the independent unit shall decide which behavior to do under the different sound circumstance and complete sound control behavior, thus to complete the second behavior principle.

3.1.4   Mechanical system

We chose the Beach Beast as the swarm independent unit, which movement principle has been relatively mature. The Beach Beast simulates the limb movement through the linear interaction and can walk under the driving of external force.

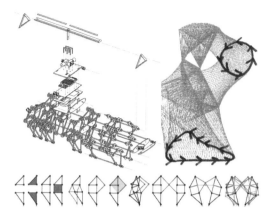

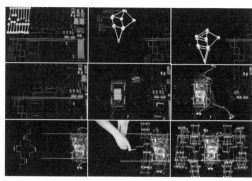

Figure 9. Photos of fabrication processing.

Figure 7. Diagram of mechanical motion.

Figure 8. Photo of mechanical details.

In this project, we keep the mechanical movement principle of a Beach Beast. Aero wood, bearing and smooth iron shaft are used as the mechanical materials. "Legs" of each independent unit are composed of 32 mechanical rods. Each pair of "Legs" is combined with two rods by 180⁰ turning and crossing, which may complete a complete leg movement. Each Beach Beast is composed of six legs and each side is arranged with three. Each leg unit has a phase difference of 360⁰/leg number. Therefore, the more the legs, the smaller the phase difference shall be, and the more continuous the leg movement will have.

In consideration of the width of Beach Beast that shall influences the flexibility of turning, six Beach Beast leg units are adopted in this project, with the phase difference of 120⁰. It ensures rather smooth movement.

3.2 Outline of movement

The project is completed with low-intelligence design and low-cost fabrication. The two expected behavior principles are been initially realized. The robotic unit has completed the behavior of getting back or turning when it meets obstacle. The swarm robotics have realized grouping—disassembly—assembly

driven by the sound of cicada. At the same time, it also shows the uncertain movement that cannot be defined simply as assembly or disassembly because of the uncertainty of cicada sound.

There are still some problems in movement process, such as following:

1. The information transfer mechanism in the group basing on sound transfer is not reliable enough, which will be influenced easily by outside noise. More reliable mechanism is required.
2. The movement mechanism of this swarm robotics is driven by cicada sound. Biologic intelligence is partially used to reduce the cost of man power intelligence design. Furthermore, because of the complication and uncertainty of biologic movement, this shall not be a complete final solution. It is unknown that a complete man power intelligence robot unit shall have the character of low cost of intelligence design when realizing movement of higher degree.

4 CONCLUSION

Based on the simple principle and swarm interaction, low intelligence robot completes complicated swarm interaction, which provides rich experience support for complicated behavior with higher level.

The fabrication cost of each independent robotic very low. Movement of higher level is realized by combination. So, it provides a solution for cost optimization of swarm robotics.

As a field developed from biology, it means a field crossing when the swarm intelligence and robot are combined for application. The behavior principle of swarm robotics in this project is obtained from development of cicada sound. The successful experiment of this project demonstrates that this field crossing experiment is very interesting, which develops a new space for the study on control of robot.

REFERENCES

Beni, G. & Wang, J. 1989. Swarm Intelligence in Cellular Robotic Systems, Proceed. NATO Advanced Workshop on Robots and Biological Systems, Tuscany, Italy.

Lewis, M. Anthony & Bekey, George. A. 1992. The Behavioral Self-Organization of Nano robots Using Local Rules. *IEEE/RSJ International Conference on Intelligent Robots and Systems.*

Martens, D., Baesens, B. & Fawcett, T. 2011. Editorial Survey: Swarm Intelligence for Data Mining. *Machine Learning.*

Rifaie, M.M. & Aber, A. 2012. Identifying metastasis in bone scans with Stochastic Diffusion Search, Proc. *IEEE Information Technology in Medicine and Education, ITME*: 519–523.

Rifaie, M.M, Ahmed A. & Ahmed M.O. 2012. Utilizing Stochastic Diffusion Search to identify metastasis in bone scans and micro-calcifications on mammography. *In Bioinformatics and Biomedicine Workshops (BIBMW), 2012 IEEE International Conference on IEEE*: 280–287.

Computer, Intelligent Computing and Education Technology – Liu, Sung & Yao (Eds)
© 2014 Taylor & Francis Group, London, ISBN 978-1-138-02469-4

Application practice of artificial intelligence in interactive architecture

Philip F. Yuan & L.M. Zhang
College of Architecture and Urban Planning at Tongji University, Shanghai, China

ABSTRACT: Artificial intelligence is applied in more and more fields, but seldom in Architecture. With the wide and deep application of computer technology in Architecture, intelligent and interactive architecture emerges and the application potential of artificial intelligence is gradually releasing in architectural field. The necessity and feasibility of artificial intelligence in reactive architecture are discussed in this paper and its feasibility is verified in a installation design project "Social Forest". The experiences drawn from this project provides basis and direction for the application research of Artificial Intelligence in reactive architecture field.

Keywords: artificial intelligence; interactive architecture; social forest; A* search algorithm

1   INTRODUCTION—APPLICATION POTENTIAL OF ARTIFICIAL INTELLIGENCE UNDER THE NEW BACKGROUND OF ARCHITECTURAL DEMAND

Artificial intelligence has been deeply researched and widely applied in electronic equipment research and development, mechanical design and industrial design, and is applied in Architecture field in recent years. With the development and wide application of artificial intelligence, operations research, mathematical logic, artificial intelligence and other technologies are widely used in building construction and management. The building site management system developed based on C/S (Client/Server) architecture covers every aspect of construction site management; computer-aided design, many intelligent and visual assistance softwares are widely used by architects; with the application of artificial intelligent technology, structure system identification method based on artificial neural network is invented to utilize the powerful nonlinear mapping and leaning capacity of fuzzy neural network for establishing the dynamic property model based on the actually measured structural dynamic data. However, these applications are only reflected in the assistance to architectural design and construction, but not influence and boost the architectural design method.

Nowadays, architectural design method is transformed from simple architectural form creation to paying close attention to the relationship between architectural form and users' behavior and the environmental performance. Holographic images and 3D animation applied in 2010 Shanghai Expo turn visitors into participants; sustainability requirement of building becomes more and more stringent, how to reduce energy consumption, how to make building adapt to environment and the conditioning of lighting, sunshine and interior micro-climate being transformed from conventional solid components to dynamic mechanism adapting to environment. The application and development of new building material (high polymer material, photosensitive and heat sensitive material, etc.) and process technology (3D printing, laser cutting, CNC sculpture technology, etc.) make building more intelligent and acclimation. New interdisciplinary study is required under these new demands in architecture field—architectural design and artificial intelligent technology, which deeply influences architectural design method and generates new architectural form, space and functions. Its application potential is inestimable.

2   APPLICATION PRACTICE OF ARTIFICIAL INTELLIGENCE IN INTERACTIVE ARCHITECTURE

2.1   *Project background*

In recent years, the application of many artificial intelligence techniques in interactive architecture has been practiced through university workshop. Through the design and construction of experimental intelligent interactive installations, provide technical and experience base for the study of interactive architecture. Such approach is low-cost and quite suitable to interactive architecture in the stage of study and experiment.

Figure 1. Social forest.

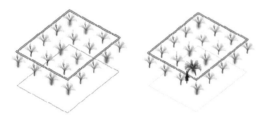

Figure 2. Diagram of the first interaction system: interaction between people and installation.

In third-term "Digital Future" activity with "interactive architecture" as theme in 2013, we have completed a spatial installation cluster named "Social Forest", try to design an installation cluster to achieve communication through interaction between people and installations based on artificial intelligence technology, creating new social space. Finally, one installation cluster composed of 20 small installations is completed, forming 5 m. *5 m. *3 m. small social space.

2.2 Intelligent system

2.2.1 Rules for interaction

Design concept of "Social Forest" includes interaction at two levels—interaction between people and installation and interaction between people. Thus, two interaction systems are required to actualize interaction at two aspects. The first system is point-to-point interaction between human and installation, i.e., installation adjusts its form through perceiving distance between people and installation. In the design, if there are no people

Figure 3. Diagram of the second interaction system: interaction among multiple people through installation.

around installation, "branch" disperses and gathers regularly in small extent, and if action around installation are perceived, "branch" will disperse totally and breathing lamp lights normally. The second system is point-to-point to point-to-multipoint interaction between humans. It occurs when two persons get close to installation cluster. A* search algorithm is used to get the shortest line between two points through installation, and installations on the line will have "branch" disperse and breathing lamp light, to connect the two points where the two persons are through installation cluster so that they can see each other to promote interaction between them.

2.2.2 Core algorithm

To actualize the second system—multi-point connection between humans, we have adopted the widely-used shortest path algorithm—A* search algorithm, the process of finding least-cost path between points in plan. It is often used in NPC mobile computing in games or BOT mobile computing in on-line games.

A* search algorithm is one of Heuristic algorithms. It evaluates the point for every proceeding to find the best point, and then to find next point till target point. The evaluation formula of point is:

$$f(n) = g(n) + h(n), \tag{1}$$

f(n) is the estimate cost function from initial point, through point N to target point. g(n) is the actual cost from initial point to point N in state space. h(n) is the estimate cost of best path from Point n to target point. The key to find shortest (beat) path is the selection of h(n). Much closer the value of h(n) is to actual value, more actuate the path is. We use "Manhattan distance" to calculate the value of h(n), i.e., calculate the quantity of points covered in horizontal and vertical move to target point. We write A* search algorithm into Mega Arduino board with Arduino as the control core of our second system.

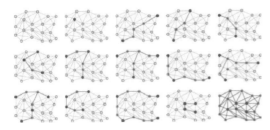

Figure 4. Caption of a typical figure. Photographs will be scanned by the printer. Always supply original photographs.

Figure 5. Form left to right: sensor (infrared sensor), controller (Arduino Mega board) and servo.

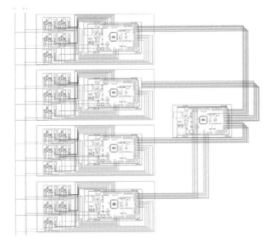

Figure 6. Connection of Arduino boards: two-level structure.

2.2.3 Sensor, controller & servo

The intelligent system consists of sensor, controller and servo. For sensing, we use infrared sensors (GP2Y0A21) to detect the surrounding space. Arduino Mega board based on Arduino programming language is used as controller to analyze the data collected by sensor and to control servo (DF15MG) to drive the individual installation.

In "Social Forest", there are 20 individual installations. In A* search algorithm, we need to collect all signals received by sensor into one controller which will process the signals and give orders.

Due to limitations of Arduino board, even Mega Arduino board cannot provide sufficient interfaces in one board, and therefore 4 Mega Arbuino boards are used to control at two levels. At the first level, one Mega Arduino board is used to collect all data, and one Mega Arduino board can provide sufficient data input ports. But there are not sufficient output ports. At the second level, after the first Arduino board collects and processes all data, the data are sent to another Arduino boards which will send the data to connected installations. Since there are several installations and two-level data management structure, simulation, refinement and adjustment is required in circuit design to achieve highest reliability and simplest wiring.

2.3 Mechanical system

Mechanical design is mainly composed of two parts, namely design controlling opening and closing types of "branch" (Part I) and design of gear connecting motor and mechanical part (Part II). In Part I, as restricted by capacity of motor, "branch" needs to realize large opening and closing range in small moving scope. Finally, we obtain the solution of "rotating control panel" through continuous geometric diagram and optimization on mechanical motion. In Part II, we obtain detailed dimensions of required gear by professional gear calculation software and cross-section shape of gear based on those dimensions to guide gear processing and design.

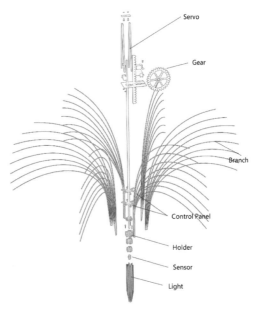

Figure 7. Structure of the installation unit.

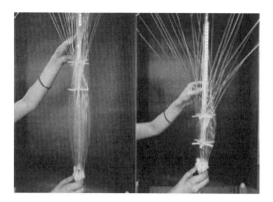

Figure 8. Action of the installation unit.

2.4 *Running condition*

Two interactions are basically completed in the whole spatial installation. Installation can successfully complete "opening" and "closing" and the installation cluster completes the point-to-point interaction, which creates unique spatial effect. Design goal is basically achieved, but some problems still occur.

In the whole spatial installation cluster, in case more than two installations are activated simultaneously, there is problem when completing the second interactive action. In calculation of the shortest distance from multi-points by control code based on A* search algorithm, it is a challenge to determine point sequence, which is not solved in this installation cluster. Therefore, correct result can be obtained in point-to-point, but the result is largely different from the optimal solution in point-to-multipoint interaction.

As material, equipment and construction method of the whole installation cluster are experimental, it turns out that durability of installation is poor, servo is stuck within an hour's running.

3 CONCLUSIONS AND FUTURE RESEARCH DIRECTION

Positive results brought by this project, namely unprecedented space perception brought by artificial intelligence technology, profoundly inspire new building forms and spatial design. Meanwhile, problems occurring show the direction of research and development urgently required by interdisciplinary artificial intelligence technology and architectural design.

Interdisciplinary education and practice are insufficient. Due to lack of related technologies and experiences of artificial intelligence, we meet up with many challenges from design to construction during implementation of project. These issues which are simple in single discipline turn to problematic problems in interdiscipline, which is caused by lack of related education and practice.

Industrial products related to building intelligence are far from developed. During implementation of project, twice and thrice processing and design is required for many components and parts after being bought, which increases labor cost and adversely affect application expansion of artificial intelligence technology in building industry. Therefore, toolkit of R&D of supporting facilities related to building will be the key direction of future research and development.

The application of artificial intelligence on sustainable architecture is another potential research direction. The interactivity brought by artificial intelligence between environment and architecture could lead to the dynamic adaption of architecture to environment, which can improve the performance of architecture to better realize the sustainability.

REFERENCES

Grove, A.T. 1980. Geomorphic evolution of the Sahara and the Nile. In M.A.J. Williams & H. Faure (eds), *The Sahara and the Nile*: 21–35. Rotterdam: Balkema.

Jappelli, R. & Marconi, N. 1997. Recommendations and prejudices in the realm of foundation engineering in Italy: A historical review. In Carlo Viggiani (ed.), *Geotechnical engineering for the preservation of monuments and historical sites*; *Proc. intern. symp., Napoli, 3–4 October 1996.* Rotterdam: Balkema.

Johnson, H.L. 1965. Artistic development in autistic children. *Child Development* 65(1): 13–16.

Polhill, R.M. 1982. *Crotalaria in Africa and Madagascar.* Rotterdam: Balkema.

Computer, Intelligent Computing and Education Technology – Liu, Sung & Yao (Eds)
© 2014 Taylor & Francis Group, London, ISBN 978-1-138-02469-4

Innovation research on personnel training of undergraduates on communication engineering

Guang-Ming Li & Zhen-Zhen Li
School of Mechanical, Electrical and Information Engineering, Shandong University, Weihai, China

ABSTRACT: The importance of cultivating the high quality personnel of undergraduates with innovation capability has been widely recognized worldwide. To change the students from the traditional passive acceptance to active exploration, strengthen their practical innovation abilities, this paper mainly makes comprehensive design and research from teaching and practice modes, taking Department of Communication Engineering, Shandong University at Weihai, as an example. Among them, the teaching mode of the integrated design mainly includes three aspects, namely teaching content, teaching method and examination mode respectively. Practice model of integrated design mainly contains experiments of theory courses, practice of professional courses and instruction of professional practice.

Keywords: education reform; innovation; communication engineering; personnel training

1 GENERAL BACKGROUND

In June 2008, Department of Communication Engineering, Shandong University at Weihai, was established on the basis of Department of Electronics in the college of information engineering. Through sharing the resources of the information engineering college it established the talents training target according to its own actual situation and the requirement of informatization in Shandong province. The talent cultivating mode was constructed which should pay equal attention to the knowledge, ability and quality. It also developed the scientific and reasonable course system, and then the teaching content and teaching method reform are gradually deepening. At present, communication engineering department share all the 25 various laboratories of the information engineering college. All laboratories are open to undergraduates, which provide experimental conditions for experimental instruction of basic courses and professional courses for under-graduate. All above create a good environment for cultivating students' innovative ability and creative ability.

2 CURRENT STATUS

Innovation is the soul of a nation's progress and the unceasing power of a country's prosperity. The importance of innovation capability of the quality of the training of personnel has been recognized worldwide. Many colleges and universities have various modes to cultivate the students' innovative spirit and ability. Many foreign universities introduce innovative education into the teaching system and carry out a variety of creative activities in the engineering disciplines of electronic information. Moreover, many companies and research institutes carry out exchanges and cooperation to promote the cultivation of students' practical ability and innovative thinking [1]. There are also many universities setting up a research center with the theme of innovation or innovative curriculum. For example, the Massachusetts Institute of Technology set up Undergraduate Research Opportunities Program (UROP). To participate in the UROP project, students can participate in actual scientific research. They can start with developing a research plan, writing the proposal, the implementation of the research program, finishing the analysis of data and final publication of the research results. Through these exercises, students further cultivate the practical ability and innovation ability, but also stimulate their interest in research and innovation [2].

Many colleges and universities in China also recognize the importance of cultivating creative talents, and treat innovative ability as the core objective of training of highly qualified students. For example, Peking University launched an undergraduate education reform plan named "YuanpeiPlan", following the principle of "enhancing fundamentals, indistinct majors, individualized quality instruction", in order to adapt to the development needs of the high-quality creative talents with international competition in the 21st century. Tsinghua University has set up a special class focusing on fundamental science. Zhejiang University has set up "Chu Kochen College", to create top creative talents cultivation mode which realizes educating "high-quality, high-level, diverse, creative" talents for the society [3]. Unfortunately, the range of knowledge of our students at present is narrow, practical ability and innovation capability is inferior. Synthesizing the advanced innovative education and training mode worldwide and the advanced experience of other famous universities based on the characteristics of Communication Engineering, to strengthen the cultivation of students' practical innovation ability has become an important issue worth exploring in order to meet the needs of the employer and society [4].

3 THE DESIGN AND STUDY OF TEACHING MODE

The cultivation of innovative and high quality talent is one of the basic missions of higher colleges and universities. The state council and the Ministry of Education have published a series of documents to stress the importance of college students' innovative abilities since the 17th Party Congress.

Communication Engineering is a major with wide knowledge and wide employment directions. Students have both a solid theory foundation of basic skills and very strong practical abilities so that they can undertake the work of design, manufacture and research of communication system. However, technologies in communication engineering have distinct characteristics: technologies develop rapidly, new device equipments update quickly, basic theories are mature and systemic background is strong. Traditional passive force-feeding teaching mode will only make students struggle to cope with examination. It is hard to stimulate students learning enthusiasm and initiative and can't meet society's need for innovative talents with high quality [5]. Nowadays, with rapid growth of information, technologies change quickly and the frequency of talent flow accelerates. Those companies put forward higher requirements to the talents for their own survival and development. How to improve the students' theoretical and practical ability and cultivate innovative talents to meet the needs of society is worth studying.

In order to make the students turn from the traditional passive acceptance into active exploration, we must do comprehensive design from teaching content, teaching methods and examination mode [6]. To meet the requirement of cultivating high-quality innovative talents, the design of teaching content should promote the integration of courses to strengthen the basic ability of students and reflect the latest technology and academic progress to stimulate students' interest.

In the teaching methods, we combine many teaching methods such as exploring heuristic and discussion to cultivate students' innovation consciousness and innovation ability. As for the inspection way, we explore an effective mode to pay attention to the learning process and learning effect to avoid the high score low skills phenomenon of traditional exam oriented education.

3.1 Design on teaching content

In the process of constructing the characteristic professional curriculum system, we treat the foreign university of high level as the reference target, we have a thorough investigation into the needs of communication field and establish the professional curriculum system with wide level. Curriculum system mainly consists of five parts general educational curricula, disciplinary basic courses, specialized backbone courses, specialized elective courses and practical skills training courses: firstly, the general education courses are mainly composed of the humanities, mathematical and natural science foundation course; secondly, the subject foundation courses are divided into level one, level two and across the secondary discipline course three parts; thirdly, professional backbone courses are the several key professional courses set by communication professional; fourthly, professional elective courses provide students with a free space where students are free to fully develop their own hobbies; fifthly, practical skills training courses cultivate students' practical abilities and development abilities of related engineering.

In the teaching process, we strengthen the development of the research-oriented teaching, carried on many kinds of teaching modes such as the discussion teaching and case type teaching. We centered on research and development project to guide students' course selection and study, to cultivate students' abilities to analyze and solve problems and to improve their abilities to learn initiatively. In the recent revision of teaching plan, we strengthen the construction of professional backbone courses, elective courses and practical skills training courses. To adapt to the rapid demand of development of communication technology for the knowledge structure of talents, students involved in at least two professional directions of the teaching content, mastered the knowledge of communication engineering, microwave, circuit, information and information security, and other disciplines of knowledge.

3.2 Design on teaching method

Treat social need as the goal, the cultivation of application ability as the main line when we design communication technology professional training scheme. Based on discipline development, with the reform of course system as the core and ability training as the main line, we combine teaching and scientific research to improve the teaching quality.

In the process of teaching we attach great importance to the teaching means of computer aided analysis and design, such as EDA software and DSP (Digital Signal Processing), communication MATLAB system analysis and simulation software. At the same time, the circuit design of FPGA (Field Programmable Gate Array) and application of embedded system is introduced into the curriculum system of teaching reform.

In teaching process, we stimulate students' interests in learning and guide students to learning actively. Teaching primarily such as cramming one-way infusion and a piece of chalk and a blackboard in the traditional teaching mode gives priority to self-study, heuristic teaching methods are adopted gradually, when teachers given learning tasks, learning progress and arrangement, students are required to write notes and finish assignments to train their creative ability. Teaching forms such as the seminar, answer questions, class discussion can cultivate the students' learning interest and learning ability. Students' self-study ability is the core of the reform of teaching methods and teaching means; and self-study ability is the basis of creativity and other abilities.

3.3 Design on assessment model

Assessment process and examination results are aim to inspire students to work hard, improve the learning enthusiasm and self-esteem, help students develop in an all-around way. In the design of assessment mode, especially the assessment content, attention should be paid to all sidedness, theory with practice, set aside enough development space for students, encourage students to carry on the innovation and exploration. In addition to the traditional final exam, test scores also include the course of practice part and peacetime grade. In the practice part, the experimental teaching is very important because for engineering students solving practical problems is ultimate purpose [7]. We assess students' experiment effect, as well as the degree of students' understanding of basic knowledge through the experiment actual operation ability, independent innovation ability and experiment examination report. Usual course evaluation includes the students' attendance, assignments, and class performance in various learning activities, in order to understand the teaching process, guide the interaction in the process of teaching, arouse student's study initiatively, establish good study style, and evaluate students' knowledge, ability and style of study in a comprehensive way.

In order to overcome the limitations of traditional exam or a certain specific exam form, course assessment adopts a variety of forms, which can assess students' abilities of knowledge level from many aspects and angles.

4 DESIGN AND RESEARCH OF PRACTICE MODE

Practice is the source of innovation. To cultivate the high-quality talents in the field of communication engineering, we must strengthen training of students' practical ability and innovation ability. This topic mainly contains two aspects, practice teaching and practice innovation, to study the effective cultivation mode. To cultivate students' comprehensive quality and innovative ability as the goal, guided by the market demand and social development, we establish a new teaching mode, "theory, practice, application", to optimize the experiment content and create effective professional practice teaching system.

4.1 Experiment on theory courses

Theoretical courses include public basic course, professional basic course, professional required courses and professional elective courses. Students are organized to take an active part in all kinds of competitions to cultivate their practical innovation abilities. Some course includes some experiments. Through these experiments, theoretical knowledge can be verified. Students can deepen the understanding of theoretical knowledge and improve the comprehensive analysis ability. Their skills in experimental equipment and instrument can be cultivated as well.

4.2 Professional course practice

Professional practice and training base provide practice platform for students. These activities dig the school and the market with the characteristics of "zero distance". Through visiting external communication equipment and network equipment manufacturers, as well as the campus network management center, students can get a comprehensive understanding of the main technological process and production lines of communication equipment manufacturing enterprises. Students may get general knowledge of the master communication equipment production and the actual application of communication engineering in various fields. Through visit and study the communication equipment manufacturing company, students can understand the characteristics of the production and main process of modern communication electronics industry. They can deepen the understanding of professional knowledge, turn the abstract concepts in the books into the specific understanding, consolidate the theoretical knowledge and adapt to the job well when they graduate from the school.

4.3 *Professional practical training teaching*

The instruction of professional training in communication engineering is orientated in making students contact with various techniques and skills related to this professional by stages. On the basis of theory teaching, expansion of large amounts of systematic practice teaching, the perceptual understanding of theoretical knowledge is enhanced. Students may strengthen the understanding and using of knowledge. They can form a systematic understanding of communication engineering specialty, reach a certain theoretical level, and have good ability of professional talents, also strengthen the competitive power during the process of seeking opportunities of employment.

We set up a long-term off-campus practice base with outstanding high-tech enterprises in Jinan, Weihai, Qingdao and other places as well as the engineering training center of Shandong University. In the process of practice, students can learn advanced technologies, study the principle, function and usage method of advanced equipment. At the same time their practice ability, professional quality as engineer, innovative consciousness and spirit of cooperation can also get trained.

5 CONCLUSION

Teaching reform is not a castle in the air. It needs to do a lot of exploration and practice. In the process of summarizing experience and lessons, it advances gradually. This paper, summing up many years of experience in teaching practice, put forward some idea and scheme design. Of course it still need some support in details and refining principles to be implemented. This needs the support and cooperation from the teaching functional departments in the institution. We believe that through these reform, the innovation ability of talents in communication engineering will have large improvement.

ACKNOWLEDGEMENT

This work was supported by Education & Research Foundation of Shandong University at Weihai (Grant No. A2012002).

REFERENCES

[1] Farr, J.V. 1997. Education reform: pros and cons. *Journal of Management in Engineering* 13(6): 34–36.
[2] Aburas, A.A. & Rustempasic, I. 2012. New proposed structure for communication engineering curriculum. *9th International Symposium on Tele communication*, 25–27, October, Sarajevo, Bosnia and herzegovina.
[3] Spang D. & Genis, V. 2010. Opportunities for students and faculty stemming from engineering technology program reform. *ASEE Annual Conference and Exposition*, 20–23, June, Louisville, KY, United States.
[4] Zhang, Y. 2010. Study on foreign language teaching reform in higher engineering education. *4th International Conference on Distance Learning and Education*, 3–5 October, San Juan, PR, United states.
[5] Liu, Y.Z. & Ji, C.P. 2010. Teaching reform and practice of computer communication and network. *5th International Conference on Computer Science and Education*, 24–27, August, Hefei, China.
[6] Fontenot, D. & Chandler, J.R. 2007. The Texas High School Initiative aims at STEM education reform. *37th ASEE/IEEE Frontiers in Education Conference*, 10–13 October, Milwaukee, WI, United states.
[7] Lu, J.S. & Ding, Y.P. 2012. Capstone course reform in a Chinese University. *International Journal of Engineering Education* 28(4): 831–844.

Computer, Intelligent Computing and Education Technology – Liu, Sung & Yao (Eds)
© 2014 Taylor & Francis Group, London, ISBN 978-1-138-02469-4

Research of assessing system in environmental experiment course based on working process in colleges: A case study of operation management course of secondary sewage treatment plants

Hai-Yun Qi, Hai-Bo Lun & Li Ta
Environmental Management College of China (EMCC), Qinhuangdao, Hebei, China

ABSTRACT: Experiment teaching is a main part of the vocational education. The assessment is an important part of experiment teaching, and also an important means to check the effectiveness, consolidate the knowledge, and reform the teaching method. Based on the study of literatures and expert opinions who has rich experiences of sewage treatment plants, refered to staff performance appraisal methods of sewage treatment plants, this paper studies and formulates a assessing system in environmental experiment course based on working process in colleges.

Keywords: base on working process; environmental experiment course; assessing system

1 GENERAL INTRODUCTION

The traditional assessment methods of experiment course is to mark the student's test report, but not attach importance to the basic operation in the process of experiments. That leads to students only pay attention to the experiment report, but do not pay attention to their own experimental quality and operational skills. It is difficult to mobilize the enthusiasm of the students to do experiments. This is not scientific and standard for comprehensive test students' ability.

Based on years of teaching experience of environmental experiment course, Environmental Management College of China (EMCC) reformed the original experiment teaching mode, and put forward environmental experiment course based on working process. In this course, students learn in practice and practice in learning. It is a teaching mode that truly reflects the integration of teaching, learning, and practicing.

In order to better implementation of environmental experiment course system based on working process, as an important supplementary means of teaching, assessment is also need to carry on the corresponding reform. The experiment teaching is a teaching behavior of multi factor, multi link, and multi-level, so, the assessing of students need to consider all aspects of student learning, including experiment preparation, experiment process, experimental report and final basic operation skill examination.

2 PROCEDURE OF ASSESSING SYSTEM DEVELOPMENT

The assessing system development should analyse corresponding jobs and learning goals, what is the basis of test analysis. The assessing system includes assessing methods and their weight, assessing contents and their weight.

After determining the preliminary assessing system, we should consult the professional experts who have practical technology and management experience, and preliminary correct and improve it. And then, in the application of the system, there will have continuous feedback, amendment and supplement.

The procedure of assessing system development in environmental experiment course based on working process is shown in Figure 1.

3 ASSESSING SYSTEM IN ENVIRONMENTAL EXPERIMENT COURSE BASED ON WORKING PROCESS

Based on in-depth analysis of typical tasks and occupation ability in secondary sewage treatment plants of the city, we use modularized teaching method, and propose four learning areas in order to train students' ability. They are learning area A: basic knowledge of secondary sewage treatment plants; learning area B: monitoring and analy-

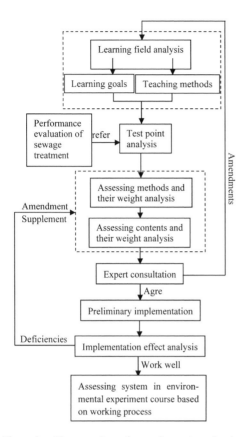

Figure 1. The procedure of assessing system development in environmental experiment course based on working process.

sis of indicators in secondary sewage treatment plants; learning area C: operation and regulation of Sewage treatment system; learning area D: treatment of excess sludge. Learning area B as an example, we give a demonstration of assessing system development.

The four learning areas' assessing methods and their weight in score of student are shown in Table 1.

3.1 Learning area analysis

In learning area B, students need to can do:

– Correct sampling of various monitoring items according to the type of industry requirements;
– Field test;
– Laboratory analysis;
– Correct operation;
– The experimental data accurately;
– Analysis of the data;
– Monitoring report.

Table 1. Four learning areas assessing methods and their weight in score of student.

	Weight	Assessment at ordinary times	Operation skills assessment	Written examination
Learning area A	20%	√		√
Learning area B	35%	√	√	
Learning area C	25%	√	√	
Learning area D	20%	√	√	

3.2 Test analysis

– Student's attitude and ability of experiment;
– Student's monitoring method for different monitoring project;
– Student's ability to analyse data and write monitoring report.

3.3 Assessing methods and their weight

Corresponding 3.2, the assessing methods are:
– Assessment at ordinary times
  The teacher determines individual score according to the performance of each student's. The performance including the preparation before experimental subject, experiment ability, experimental attitude, experimental effect, experimental report and other aspects. At last, each student's regular score is to take the arithmetic mean value.
– Operation skills assessment
  At the end of term, students need to take an examination of operation skills assessment. The experimental project can choose the typical project. It is need to the establishment of specific assessment indicators to assess performance.
– It is same as above
  At last, the two assessing methods each accounted for 50% of student's last score in learning area B.

3.4 Assessment indicators and evaluation standards

Assessment indicators at ordinary times are shown in Table 2. Each primary indicators can be divided into a plurality of secondary indicators. The score of each indicator are different.

Operation skills assessment includes 6 basic operation unit, what is COD determination, BOD_5 determination, total nitrogen determination, ammonia nitrogen determination, total phosphorus determination and aerobic biological treatment of

Table 2. Assessment indicators at ordinary times in learning area B.

Primary indicators	Secondary indicators	Evaluation criteria	Points
Preparation before experimental subject (10 points)	Preview report (4 points)	Submit on time	2
		Contents intact	2
	Preview effect (6 points)	Basic understand of the objective, principle and procedure	3
		Answer questions correctly	3
Experimental ability (40 points)	Practical ability (8 points)	Participate in the experiment	4
		Operation regulation	4
	Observation ability (8 points)	Observe and record the experimental phenomena	4
		Discover the problems existing in the experiment	4
	Ability to analyze and solve problems (8 points)	Positive thinking	4
		Solve problems	4
	Apply knowledge (8 points)	Combine knowledge and practical	8
	Cooperative ability (8 points)	Work in cooperation	4
		Encourage each other but not against each other when have problems	4
Experimental attitude (20 points)	Learning attitude (14 points)	Do not be late	2
		Do not leave early	2
		Attendance seriously, and feedback to teacher	10
	Operating attitude (6 points)	Receive the teacher's advice to correct errors	6
Experimental effect (10 points)	Successful experiment	Summarize the problems what should be pay attention to	10
	Failure of the experiment	Find out the reasons for the failure, and redo	
After the experiment (20 points)	Glassware and equipment (4 points)	Clean the glassware and put them into place	2
		Without damage	2
	Cleaning (3 points)	Make the lab and equipment be cleanliness	3
	Experimental report (13 points)	Submit on time	5
		Contents intact	3
		The experimental results correctly	5
Total score			

Table 3. Assessment indicators and evaluation standards of COD determination.

Primary indicators	Evaluation criteria	Points	Score	Remarks
Stationing and sampling (10 points)	From the place of sewage treatment system where the water inlet and outlet are evenly mixed	5		
	Mixed samples according to the time	5		
Specimen removement (30 points)	Clean glassware correctly	5		
	Dry the lower end of the pipet outer wall after remove with with filter paper	5		
	Level adjustment correctly	10		
	Remove the solution into the container correctly	10		
Condensation operation (10 points)	Connect the condensation reflux device correctly	2		
	Open the condensed water and then heat	4		
	Stop heating and then condensed water	4		
Titration (30 points)	Clean and check the buret correctly	5		
	Solution filled and level adjustment correctly	10		
	Correct titration	10		
	Read results correctly	5		
Data processing and the results of calculation (20 points)	Accurate recording of raw data	10		
	Correct calculation	10		

*The remarks column is for teachers to fill out the reason of deduction.

wastewater. As an example, the assessment indicators and evaluation standards of COD determination are shown in Table 3.

4 FEATURE OF THE ASSESSING SYSTEM BASED ON WORKING PROCESS

4.1 *Practical and targeted assessing content*

The assessing content covers all aspects of knowledge and ability requirements in sewage treatment plant, including the analysis and test skills, pretreatment, activated sludge system, sludge and sewage treatment plant operation and management.

4.2 *Multi-level, fair and reasonable assessing methods*

The assessing methods contain assessment at ordinary times, operation skills assessment, and written examination. It is a multi-level system. Teacher chooses different methods according to different learning area. Assessment at ordinary times can enable students to maintain a correct learning attitude, and stimulate their enthusiasm. Operation skills assessment pays attention to the students' practical ability. Written examination can assess the theory of knowledge. It is a comprehensive assessment of students.

4.3 *Accurate and objective evaluation criteria*

There are accurate and objective evaluation criteria, what make the assessment becomes feasible.

4.4 *Transparency scoring process*

This assessing system must be transparent to students. Students can clearly see their own mistakes from the tables. That is why we design the remarks column in Table 3.

ACKNOWLEDGEMENT

Fund Support: this study is the scientific research fund project of Environmental Management College of China named *research on the problems and countermeasures of discipline construction in the process of appling for undergraduate education (No. 2013006)*.

REFERENCES

[1] M.H. Cao & C.S. Chen & Z.S. Xu. Exploration and reform of organic chemistry testing method[J]. Experimental Technology and Management, 2007,24 (2):117–119.
[2] D.M. Lu & X.M. Chen. Application of AHP in analog electronic experiment course assessment[J]. Journal of Baise University, 2009, 22(3):65~70.
[3] W.W. Li. Research on staff performance appraisal of Zaozhuang city sewage treatment plant[D]. Kunming, Yunnan. Kunming University of Science and Technology. 2006.
[4] Z.L. Wang & M.D. Lin etc. A preliminary attempt to establish experimental physiological science curriculum examination system[J]. China Higher Medical Education, 1999,(5):46~47.

Computer, Intelligent Computing and Education Technology – Liu, Sung & Yao (Eds)
© 2014 Taylor & Francis Group, London, ISBN 978-1-138-02469-4

Research on mobile Home-School Communication System

Jie Fan
DaXing Number One Middle School, Beijing, China

ABSTRACT: The home-school cooperation is both an integrated model of education and a basic approach to enhancing education quality. Characterized by mobility and interconnection, the mobile Home-School Communication System builds a convenient connection between home and school, and offers instant concentration and care to students. The paper analyzes the mobile Home-School Communication System's application environment in China, and compares the differences between traditional and mobile Home-School Communication System. After that, a detailed description of the composition of mobile Home-School Communication System is given. The application of the System contributes to the improvement of home-school cooperation and enriches the information education concept to a large extent.

Keywords: home-school cooperation; mobile; Home-School Communication System

1 INTRODUCTION

In the administration management of primary and secondary education, the home-school cooperation is an integrated model of education and a basic approach of enhancing education quality [1]. It emphasizes student-centered concept, proposes to solve specific conflicts and problems in the educational practice by the cooperation of school, family and community. Therefore it achieves the goal of comprehensive development of individual student. The first level of home-school cooperation including home visits, home-school meetings, school opening day, students' homework exhibition, Home-School pamphlet, and etc [2]. With the development of communication and internet technology, a new method of home-school cooperation has been introduced into the Chinese educational practice since 2002: Home-School Communication System [3]. It is an application of communication and internet technology in the field of home-school cooperation, establishes a flexible, convenient and efficiency platform for teachers and parents to connect with each other. In this paper, it is named "traditional Home-School Communication System".

Mobile use changes ways of life. With the thriving of mobile internet and popularity of smart devices, the information technology and educational practice have been integrated gradually. It not only provides a strong technological support to solve problems in the educational practice, but also provides a new idea, a new model, and a new approach to reveal the evolutionary effect of the information technology in the educational practice.

In the age of mobile internet, the traditional Home-School Communication System meets a fleshing new development opportunity. The prevalence of smart mobile devices provides an even more flexible terminal platform to create an even more agile, instantly responsible connection between family and school. The research and investigation of mobile Home-School Communication System, which is based on the combination of mobile internet and smart devices, is becoming one of the direction deserving focus in the near future.

2 THE MATURITY OF MOBILE HOME-SCHOOL COMMUNICATION SYSTEM APPLICATION ENVIRONMENT IN CHINA

2.1 *The construction of mobile internet infrastructure*

Chinese government strengthens policy support for mobile Internet, which lead to comprehensive upgrades for its information networks and extraordinarily boosts the development of third-generation technology (3G), especially homegrown TD variants of 3G and LTE (long-term evolution) technology. According to CNNIC's data, the quantity of 3G users is up to 234 million by the end of 2012. Meanwhile, China Telecomm, China Mobile and China Unicom aim to improve mobile internet user experiences, such as to achieve seamless Wi-Fi coverage, to improve connection speed and quality, and to reduce data usage cost.

2.2 The expansion of mobile terminal users

In China, more and more people use mobile terminals to access internet. According to CNNIC's data, released by CNNIC in Jan 2013, there are 420 million cell phone internet users. Among these users, about 74.5% are using mobile internet and about 300 million (about 63.4%) end users access internet through smart devices. Internet Queen Mary Meeker predicts that mobile terminals will replace PC to become the dominant internet access devices by the end of 2013. With the increasing sales forecast of smart phones, tablets, laptops and electronics readers, a tremendous growth of mobile internet users can be estimated.

3 COMPARATIVE ANALYSIS OF TRADITIONAL AND MOBILE HOME-SCHOOL COMMUNICATION SYSTEM

3.1 Disadvantages of traditional Home-School Communication System

In year 2002, the traditional Home-School Communication System announced and introduced to Chinese primary and secondary education and gradually implemented to practice usage among school, family and community. It undeniably contributes to enhancing education quality and establishing connections between families and schools, as well as plays a major role in home-school cooperation [3].

However, the traditional Home-School Communication System still has some disadvantages in practice which need further investigation and advancement [4].

Objectively speaking, the major factors are including:

- Ignorance to the importance of home-school connection between teachers and parents.
- Limitation of skills and knowledge of teachers and parents in information technology.
- Limitation of students' household financial capability.

The solutions to the problems mentioned above majorly depend on improving the whole society information level, which requires additional efforts and long-term development.

Subjectively speaking, the major deficiencies of the traditional Home-School Communication System relate to systematic design and technical application. According to the investigation, criticisms focus on the following four aspects:

- Additional financial burden due to service charge of the system.
- The restriction from communication service providers, such as China Telecomm, China Mobile and China Unicom, forces parents who use different service provider to add or change cell phone number.
- Lack of personalized instruction and mentoring in information handout, which only focuses on assignments, schedule, and fee collections, etc.
- Connections among different students' parents not established.

3.2 Characteristic analysis of mobile Home-School Communication System application

As characterized by mobility and interconnection, mobile Home-School Communication System can solve the problems mentioned above.

- No additional service charge, parents only need pay the data usage charged by communication provider. Specifically, internet data services are almost free under Wi-Fi environments and worthwhile through 3G or GPRS connection by using monthly data package.
- No specific requirements for service providers since the system works once internet connected.
- Personalized instruction for students become practical and convenient, as mobile terminals can provide abundant contents and expressions.
- Establishing a convenient, efficiency, interactive communication platform for all parents.

4 COMPOSITION OF MOBILE HOME-SCHOOL COMMUNICATION SYSTEM

Framework of the system is as Figure 1. There are two kinds of roles in the system: One is class teacher (teacher in charge of the class), the other is parents. It also provides two kinds of logins: through mobile app and website. The system consists of four major modules: Information Bulletin, Examination Performance, Information Exchange Center, and Students' Growing-up Files.

The Information Bulletin module shows public notices, such as news of school, notification of class, assignments, and etc.

Examination Performance module offers score inquiry, study performance and strategy analysis, etc.

Information Exchange Center module provides an interactive platform for teachers and parents of all students. The ways of sharing information among them could be one-to-one, one-to-many or many-to-many synchronously and asynchronously.

Students' Growing-up Files module keeps overall records for every student from enrollment to graduation. These files guide parents and teachers to track the students' progress and shortages at

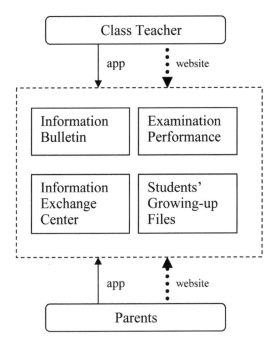

Figure 1. Framework of mobile Home-School Communication System.

different stage, and to assess students' comprehensive development subjectively.

5 BENEFIT ANALYSIS ON THE APPLICATION OF MOBILE HOME-SCHOOL COMMUNICATION SYSTEM

The application of mobile Home-School Communication System will create a brand new pattern of home-school cooperation, and propel educational practice by the creation of harmonious home-school relationship, the full involvement of parents, and the combination of conventional education and modern technological concept.

- With application of the system, it improves personalized development of all students. Students' interests, habits, and specialties are varied from one to another. For each student, connections between teachers and parents should be different in content and method. The system could provide personalized teaching package to different student individuals.
- With application of the system, it helps to build up an equal, cooperative relationship between

parents and teachers, and to establish the interactive educational instruction mode. The conventional cooperation pattern, which represent by passive parents involvement in the school leading educational practice, will be changed. The awareness of parents about actively participate in educational practice is largely enhanced.

- With application of the system, it provides technological services for the Parents Committee to promote home-school cooperation in deep. Information and resources could be exchanged between the members of Parents Committee flexibly, and opinions and feedback from parents could be collected in time and handled instantly.

6 CONCLUSION

In the mobile internet age, new technology influences the education industry strongly. Characterized by mobility and interconnection, the mobile Home-School Communication System builds a convenient connection between home and school, removes the barriers between home and school effectively, and offers instant concentration and care to students. The mobile Home-School Communication System makes contribution to the personalized educational method and enriches the information education concept to a large extent.

ACKNOWLEDGEMENTS

The paper is supported by the project of Beijing Education Sciences the Twelfth Five-Year Planning 2012 under grant CJA12136.

REFERENCES

[1] Xue Guo-feng, Liu Wei-ping. The Comparative Study on Parent-School Cooperation in England America and China. *Journal of Hebei University (Philosophy and Social Science)* 2011, 36(6):7–10.
[2] Zhou Yue-lang. Research and Practice on Family-School Cooperation in American in Recent Years. *Journal of Educational Science of Hunan Normal University* 2006, 5(4):81–83.
[3] Pan Ke-ming. Study on Application of EduToHome. *CET China Educational Technology* 2007, (2):76–78.
[4] Wang Xiao-hui. Exploration of Problems in School-family Connect System. *Shanghai Research on Education.* 2010, (4):39–41.

Computer, Intelligent Computing and Education Technology – Liu, Sung & Yao (Eds)
© 2014 Taylor & Francis Group, London, ISBN 978-1-138-02469-4

The design and analysis of management information system for nuclear disease specimens of Zunyi medical university

Y. Sima & X. Zeng
Zunyi Medical University, Guizhou, Zunyi, China

ABSTRACT: Combined with the Nuclear disease specimens management information system which respiratory medicine laboratory of affiliated hospital of Zunyi medical university is now running, this paper introduces the designing process of the Nuclear disease specimens management information system, and expounds the higher efficiency which in the management of Nuclear disease specimens management information system that based on B/S scheme.

Keywords: MIS; B/S; Nuclear disease specimens; NET

1 INTRODUCTION

1.1 *Current situation*

Medical and health work belongs to the experimental science, usually in order to track the efficacy of certain drugs or in order to determine the development of some kind of virus and need to do a lot of experiments. The consequent need to have a lot of experimental data and efficient preservation and statistics, but at present, most laboratory experiments on data processing in manually fill out paper documents and artificial statistical way, even if is to use the office software of Excel, also only has realized the automation in the limited scope. Traditional way of experimental data sorting cost a lot of manpower and work efficiency is low, in order to make the experiment personnel from heavy data arrangement work, Zunyi medical college affiliated hospital respiratory medicine laboratory specimens of nuclear disease management information system design was carried out.

1.2 *The current situation of the development of MIS*

Management Information System (Management Information System, MIS for short) is a people-oriented, using computer hardware, software, network communication equipment and other office equipment, Information collection, transmission, processing, storage, updating and maintaining integrated man-machine System. The system can improve the work efficiency and data sorting, will people free from the complicated manual operation. Advanced management information system, and even can use the auxiliary decision-making data sorting result.

1.3 *B/S structure*

The structure of B/S namely the Browser and Server structure. It is with the rise of the Internet technology, the C/S structure of a change or improve structure. Work under this structure, the user interface is implemented via the WWW Browser, few transaction logic in the front-end (Browser), but the main transaction logic on the Server side (Server), forming the so-called three layer structure. This greatly simplifies the client computer load, reduce the workload of system maintenance and upgrade costs and, reduces the overall cost of ownership of the user. Look at the current technology, local area network based B/S structure of network applications, database applications, and through the Internet/Intranet mode is relatively easy to grasp, cost is low.

2 MANAGEMENT INFORMATION SYSTEM FOR NUCLEAR DISEASE SPECIMENS

This article is based on "specimens of nuclear disease management information system" of actual development as the background, in view of the present experimental data management, and combining the current MIS management information system of technology development.

2.1 *Demand analysis*

Tuberculosis specimens during the overall design of management information system, and to process experimental data of several respiratory made a careful investigation, as much as possible in order to accurately grasp the respiratory comprehensive business characteristics, finally design a good solution. Specimens according to the current research situation of nuclear disease management information system is divided into user login, experimental data management, comprehensive query, statistics, report forms printing, and user management of six modules, the design of overall framework as shown in Figure 1.

In the legal user login system at the same time, the system also according to user's identity to endow them with appropriate permissions, each page will be according to the user's identity selective block certain function module. Respiratory specimens for tuberculosis of information management mainly includes clinical data management, microbial molecular biology information management, information management, management of tuberculosis specimens, DNA and management, and follow-up outcome management. System of the whole design process are around the table 6 pieces of information for design.

2.2 Development platform and development tools

2.2.1 Development platform
Specimens of NUCLEAR DISEASE management information system hardware configuration requirements need not too high, this design USES the workstation is the lenovo brand computer: cpu faster 2.8 ghz and 2 gb memory, hard disk 200 gb. Operating system for windows server 2003.

2.2.2 Development tools
With Visual Studio 2008 as development tool, SQL Server 2005 database, use Microsoft.NET Framework 3.5 as a development Framework for development.

2.3 The detailed design

The whole system is mainly divided into six modules: user login, experimental data management,

comprehensive query, statistics, report printing and user management, the design of detailed information is as follows.

2.3.1 The user login module
In the user login module, the user can try to input the user name and password three times, if a match is smoothly into the system; If the user is success is not locked within three information, request the system administrator.

2.3.2 The experimental data management module
Combined with respiratory business characteristics, design of experiment data management module mainly includes clinical data management, microbial molecular biology information management, information management, management of tuberculosis specimens, DNA and management, and follow-up outcome management a total of six information input, modify, and delete data tables. All the specimens are numbered to nuclear disease samples as a keyword input, 6 table entry sequence begins with a clinical data management, strictly can selectively in the process of the next input other information management.

2.3.3 Integrated query module
Integrated query module can be 6 to meet the need of retrieval table of federated query, also can single table query. Query keywords can be processed for precise query, fuzzy query and range query and query filtering, etc.

2.3.4 Data statistics module
Data statistics module can be showed according to the selected keyword statistics data histograms and

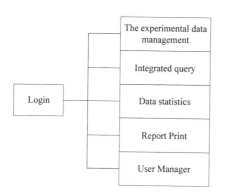

Figure 1. Whole frame.

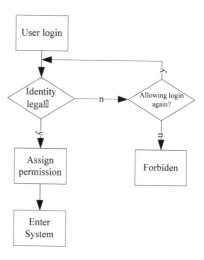

Figure 2. Login process.

pie charts. For example: in the random access and natural selection "access" results, results in a new page.

2.3.5 *Report print module*
Print module can according to user's need to be selective printing or exporting some form, or batch export all forms.

2.3.6 *The user management module*
The user management module system administrator privileges the user action by the user, the system administrator can add users, delete users in this module, and reset user passwords, etc.

3 SECURITY DESIGN

Specimens of tuberculosis in order to ensure that data will not be in the process of management information system using malicious modified or deleted, in the design process introduced two ways to protect the experimental data.

3.1 *Permissions*

Permissions is according to the characteristics of the user itself to the limitation of access control, the system used the permissions set mainly comes from three aspects: 1, the database level permissions Settings, is in the process of database design by system developers to set specific data table, and even specific data fields such as add, delete, update operation; 2, view, level of permissions that is in the process of user access to data, using the view some of the data block up, so that a secret; Level 3, roles, permissions Settings, which is based on the system administrator to give the user's role to allocate corresponding permissions, the user login system, the system automatically according to the role of the user block certain function module.

3.2 *The encryption algorithm*

In order to ensure the user account and password is not used by theft or even by the system administrator users, the system introduced cryptography MD5 one-way hash algorithm. One-way hash algorithm make the real database is not the user account and password itself, but using the MD5 algorithm to calculate the 256-bit binary data. Users can use the correct account number and password generated by a 256 bit binary data and to match the data stored in the database, if the match succeeds is legitimate users, allowed to login, otherwise it is illegal to users. And even let the cat out of the data stored in the database of 256 bit hash,

is hard to find the corresponding user account and password.

Introduced cryptography algorithm to deal with key fields, to a certain extent also guarantee the security of the system.

4 CONCLUSION

Specimens of nuclear disease management information system in operation, has produced obvious economic benefits and social benefits. Is based on the demand while the system is a part of the department to carry on the design, but its practicability is not confined to the respiratory, can according to the actual situation of the hospital and flexible to expand investment scale, meet the needs of different types of department.

With the rapid development of management information systems and technology, the system in such aspects as auxiliary decision still need further perfect, the system of the late version will be dedicated to developing data mining aspects of the auxiliary decision-making.

ACKNOWLEDGEMENTS

Grateful Corresponding author X. Zeng who put time and effort for the papers and information system, also thinks to QIAN KE HE J ZI LKZ [2011] 22 and ZUNYI MEDICAL UNIVERSITY J-1-1 for their support and sponsorship.

REFERENCES

Cai C.A. 2006. Design and implementation of student information management system based on B/S model, China. Computer Engineering and Design. 27:2585~2587.
Dai W., M. Zhu. 2011. Data Mining and Utilization of Outpatient Service Information on Basis of HIS, China. Chinese Medical Equipment Journal. 32:43~46.
Deng Y.Q., J. Gong, H. Shi. 2012. Concise Guide to Cryptography, China. Tsinghua University Press.
Huang Y.F., D. Wu. 2012. Web application security situation and protection, China. Science & Technology Information. 35:16~16.
Hu X.D., Q.F. Wei, R. Hu. 2012. Applied Cryptography, China. Publishing House of Electronics Industry.
Wan Y.X. 2001. Legal Issues Relating to Electronic Signatures, China. People's Court Press.
Wang B. 2011. Realization of Hospital Online Appointment Registration System Based on B/S Scheme, China. Journal of Medical Informatics. 32:23~25.
Zhang L.M. 2010. ASP.NET development paradigm real book (using C#), China. Science Press.

Computer, Intelligent Computing and Education Technology – Liu, Sung & Yao (Eds)
© *2014 Taylor & Francis Group, London, ISBN 978-1-138-02469-4*

A new notion to test unit root for the LSTAR model

Chun-Yan Zhao & Shi-Jing Nan
Xi'an Jiaotong University, Xi'an, Shaanxi, China

ABSTRACT: This paper proposes a new notion to test unit root for the LSTAR model, which is absolutely different from the traditional unit root test. The test is run in the nonlinear LSTAR model's third-order Taylor expansion where the linear test can also be run at the same time. We also provide the rationalities for the notion. Based on the new notion, we present the t statistic and derive the specific distribution of the statistic according to wiener process and functional central limit theorem.

Keywords: Unit root test; LSTAR model; statistic; Taylor expansion

1 INTRODUCTION

The Smooth Transition Autoregressive (STAR) model is one of the most widely used non-linear time series models, in which the Logistic Smooth Transition Autoregressive (LSTAR) model is a an important form. The STAR modeling is a challenging job, and linear test is a necessary step for the STAR modeling. In the earlier literature, many scholars assume that the series is stationary before STAR modeling (Luukkonen, 1988; Teräsvirta, 1994). Recently, some scholars recognize that the statistic of the linear test is non-standard, so that people should implement unit root test before linear test for the STAR models (Kapetanios et al., 2003; Kilic, 2004; Sandberg, 2008). However, the unit root tests which are proposed by them are either linear test or detached from the linear test. This paper proposes a new notion of unit root test for LSTAR model which is run in the nonlinear LSTAR model's third-order Taylor expansion where the linear test can also be done at the same time.

The remaining of the paper is organized as follows: Section 2 introduces the LSTAR model. Section 3 presents some unit root tests for STAR model and introduces the new test notion. Section 4 derives the specific distribution of the statistic. Section 5 concludes.

2 THE LSTAR MODEL

The LSTAR model is a kind of STAR model. The general STAR form is given by:

$$y_t = \sum_{i=1}^{p} \alpha_i y_{t-i} + \left(\sum_{j=1}^{p} \beta_j y_{t-j} \right) G(s_t, \gamma, c) + \varepsilon_t,$$
$$t = 1, ..., T \qquad (1)$$

where $\varepsilon_t \sim iid(0, \sigma^2)$ and $G(s_t, \gamma, c)$ is the transition function. The choice of the transition function is various. For instance, we have LSTAR model where $G(s_t, \gamma, c)$ follows a logistic function:

$$G(s_t, \gamma, c) = \{1 + \exp[-\gamma(s_t - c)]\}^{-1}, \quad \gamma > 0 \qquad (2)$$

or an ESTAR model where $G(s_t, \gamma, c)$ follows an exponential function:

$$G(S_t, \gamma, c) = 1 - \exp\{-\gamma(s_t - c)^2\}, \quad \gamma > 0 \qquad (3)$$

With these parameterizations, γ measures the smoothness of the transition which has to be positive; s_t is the transition variable which can be simply chosen as lagged-endogenous variables or a point on the time axis, while exogenous variables also can be included; c is the threshold parameter to be estimated.

The primary goal of this paper is to study the first type of STAR model, i.e. LSTAR model, focusing on its unit root test problem.

3 UNIT ROOT TEST FOR THE LSTAR MODEL

We assume y_t is demeaned and in order to simplify the problem, we use LSTAR(1) model with transition variable y_{t-1} as an example.

Previously, people use the traditional unit root test for the LSTAR model (Luukkonen, 1988; Teräsvirta, 1994). Take LSTAR(1) for example, testing whether the nonlinear series is stationary is equivalent to test if the β_1 equals to 1 in the following formula (4).

$$y_t = \beta_1 y_{t-1} + \varepsilon_t \qquad (4)$$

However, recently, people recognize that using the traditional unit root test is not suitable for the LSTAR model because its characteristics are obvious different from the linear AR model. Thus, researchers begin to consider running the LSTAR model's unit root test in nonlinear model. However, the presence of unidentified nuisance parameters γ and c in the nonlinear part of the LSTAR model makes the unit root test and linear test difficult to run (Teräsvirta, 1994). Fortunately, in mathematics, the nonlinear expression can be asymptotically substituted by its Taylor expansion. Assuming the transition variable is y_{t-1}, Luukkonen, Saikkonen and Teräsvirta (1988) suggested that the transition function $G(s_t, \gamma, c)$ in LSTAR(1) can be substituted by its third-order Taylor expansion, then the LSTAR(1) model yields the following auxiliary regression:

$$y_t = \beta_1 y_{t-1} + \beta_2 y_{t-1}^2 + \beta_3 y_{t-1}^3 + \beta_4 y_{t-1}^4 + \varepsilon_t \tag{5}$$

Based on this idea, Kapetanios (2003) recommended that the ESTAR model's unit root test should also be run in the ESTAR model. Take ESTAR(1) model as an example, the model formula is expressed as:

$$y_t = \alpha y_{t-1} + \beta y_{t-1}[1 - \exp(-\gamma y_{t-1}^2)] + \varepsilon_t \tag{6}$$

when $\alpha = 1$, the unit root test is running in its first Taylor expansion in the following model:

$$\Delta y_t = \delta y_{t-1}^3 + \text{error} \tag{7}$$

And the unit root test's hypothesis is specified as:

$$H_0 : \delta = 0; \; H_1 : \delta < 0 \tag{8}$$

The statistic of the unit root test is given as:

$$t = \frac{\hat{\delta}}{se(\hat{\delta})} \tag{9}$$

Accepting H_0 means y_t is a linear unit root process, while accepting H_1 stands for y_t follows a nonlinear but globally stationary process provided that $-2 < \beta < 0$.

He and Sandberg (2006) also proposed that the STAR model's stationary test should be implemented in the nonlinear STAR model. Unlike Kapetanios (2003), the model they select is given as:

$$y_t = \alpha_0 + \alpha_1 y_{t-1} + (\beta_0 + \beta_1 y_{t-1}) F(t, \gamma, c) + \varepsilon_t \tag{10}$$

where $F(t, \gamma, c)$ is the transition function with the transition variable t. The unit root test's null hypothesis is specified as:

$$H_0 : \gamma = 0, \; \alpha_0 = 0, \; \alpha_1 = 1 \tag{11}$$

Actually, the unit root test can be implemented in its third Taylor expansion in the following model:

$$y_t = \lambda_{10} + \lambda_{11}t + \lambda_{12}t^2 + \lambda_{13}t^3 + \varphi_{10} y_{t-1} \\ + \varphi_{11} y_{t-1}t + \varphi_{12} y_{t-1}t^2 + \varphi_{13} y_{t-1}t^3 + \varepsilon_t \tag{12}$$

And the null hypothesis is correspondingly changed as following:

$$H_0 : \lambda_{1i} = 0, \; \varphi_{10} = 1, \; \varphi_{1j} = 0 \; (j \geq 1) \tag{13}$$

Then the statistic of the test is

$$t = \frac{\hat{\varphi}_{10} - 1}{se(\hat{\varphi}_{10})} \tag{14}$$

Accepting H_0 means the series is a random walk, while rejecting H_0 means y_t is nonlinear stationary.

From the above STAR's unit root test analysis of the traditional unit root test, Kapetanios (2003) and He and Sandberg (2006), we can obviously find that there are some caveats in their studies. The traditional linear unit root test is based on the linear model, and if the series is nonlinear, the traditional unit root test is inefficient. In Kapetanios (2003), the unit root test is relied on the assumption of $\alpha = 1$, so there exists two issues here: First, the unit root test Kapetanios proposed is actually nonlinear test conditioning on the existence of unit root. Second the assumption of $\alpha = 1$ does not always hold, and we should test the reasonability of the hypothesis before we make the conclusion. In He and Sandberg (2006), the null hypothesis is formula (13), indicating the unit root test statistic and the critical value are relied on the condition that the nonlinearity does not exist, and the unit root test here is actually unit root test in the linear model.

Based on the above analysis, it can be concluded that the LSTAR model's unit root test and its linear test is correlated. Running the LSTAR's unit root test without considering its nonlinearity and running LSTAR's linear test without considering its stationary are both problematic. Therefore, we propose that LSTAR's unit root test and linear test should be implemented like model (5), and the hypotheses of unit root test and linear test are specified as:

$$H_{01} : \beta_1 = 1; \; H_{11} : \beta_1 < 1 \tag{15}$$

600

$H_{02} : \beta_2 = \beta_3 = \beta_4 = 0;$
$H_{12} : \beta_2, \beta_3, \beta_4$ at least one non-zero (16)

Formula (15) is the unit root test hypothesis, and formula (16) is the linear test hypothesis. We should run the unit root test first, because the statistic of the linear test is determined by the result of the unit root test. In this paper, we mainly discuss the unit root test. In practice, after fitting the model (5), we should first run the unit root test, that is to test if β_1 equals to one. And here we propose the t statistic whose distribution is different from the traditional distribution of DF test, because there is a nonlinear part in model (5). Of course, the significance of the nonlinear part needs to be test. The expression of t statistic is expressed as:

$$t = \frac{\hat{\beta}_1 - 1}{\eta} \tag{17}$$

$\hat{\beta}_1$ is the estimator of β_1, η is the standard error of $\hat{\beta}_1$.

4 THE DISTRIBUTION OF THE T STATISTIC

The t statistic doesn't have an asymptotic standard normal distribution under the null hypothesis. In order to obtain the t statistic distribution, we denote the parameters and the variables in model (5) as vectors β and x_t as below:

$$\beta = (\beta_1 \ \beta_2 \ \beta_3 \ \beta_4)', \ x_t = \left(y_{t-1} \ y_{t-1}^2 \ y_{t-1}^3 \ y_{t-1}^4 \right)'$$

$\hat{\beta} - \beta$ can be obtained by model (5)'s OLS as:

$$\hat{\beta} - \beta = \left[\sum x_t x_t' \right]^{-1} \sum x_t \varepsilon_t \tag{18}$$

To facilitate our analysis, we provide all the $\hat{\beta} - \beta$ estimator. The first row of matrix (18) is the estimator of $\hat{\beta} - 1$, where

$$\sum x_t x_t' = \begin{pmatrix} \sum y_{t-1}^2 & \sum y_{t-1}^3 & \sum y_{t-1}^4 & \sum y_{t-1}^5 \\ \sum y_{t-1}^3 & \sum y_{t-1}^4 & \sum y_{t-1}^5 & \sum y_{t-1}^6 \\ \sum y_{t-1}^4 & \sum y_{t-1}^5 & \sum y_{t-1}^6 & \sum y_{t-1}^7 \\ \sum y_{t-1}^5 & \sum y_{t-1}^6 & \sum y_{t-1}^7 & \sum y_{t-1}^8 \end{pmatrix} \tag{19}$$

$$\sum x_t \varepsilon_t = \begin{pmatrix} \sum y_{t-1} \varepsilon_t \\ \sum y_{t-1}^2 \varepsilon_t \\ \sum y_{t-1}^3 \varepsilon_t \\ \sum y_{t-1}^4 \varepsilon_t \end{pmatrix} \tag{20}$$

Next, we obtain the standard error of $\hat{\beta}_1$, it is easy to show that $E(\hat{\beta}_1) = \beta_1$, so $D(\hat{\beta}_1) = \sigma^2 / \Sigma y_{t-1}^2$, where σ^2 is the standard error of model (5)'s disturbance ε_t. Then the expression of t statistic is as below:

$$t = \frac{\hat{\beta}_1 - 1}{\eta} = \frac{(\hat{\beta}_1 - 1) \left(\sum y_{t-1}^2 \right)^{1/2}}{\hat{\sigma}} \tag{21}$$

where $\hat{\sigma}^2$ is the least-squares estimate of σ^2 from the auxiliary regression model (5).

It is difficult to derive the distribution of the t statistic directly, thus we can decompose the derivation into two steps. First deriving the distribution of $\hat{\beta}_1 - 1$, and next deriving the distribution of $(\Sigma y_{t-1}^2)^{1/2}$. Composing the two part's distribution will help to get the distribution of t statistic.

$\hat{\beta}_1 - 1$ is the first element of the vector $\hat{\beta} - \beta$, so we can get the distribution of $\hat{\beta}_1 - 1$ by deriving the distribution of $\hat{\beta} - \beta$. In order to derive the distribution of $\hat{\beta} - \beta$, we define the 4×4 data diagonal matrix S as below:

$$S = \begin{pmatrix} 1 & & & \\ & T^{\frac{1}{2}} & & \\ & & T & \\ & & & T^{\frac{3}{2}} \end{pmatrix} \tag{22}$$

let us pre-multiply $\hat{\beta} - \beta$ by ST, it is easy to show that:

$$ST(\hat{\beta} - \beta) = [(S^{-1}T^{-1} \sum x_t x_t')S^{-1}T^{-1}]^{-1} \\ \times (S^{-1}T^{-1} \sum x_t \varepsilon_t) \tag{23}$$

where we denote $(S^{-1}T^{-1} \sum x_t x_t')S^{-1}T^{-1}$ as Q, denote $S^{-1}T^{-1} \sum x_t \varepsilon_t$ as H. Meanwhile it is easy to show that

$$Q(\cdot) = \begin{pmatrix} T^{-2} \sum y_{t-1}^2 & T^{-\frac{5}{2}} \sum y_{t-1}^3 & T^{-3} \sum y_{t-1}^4 & T^{-\frac{7}{2}} \sum y_{t-1}^5 \\ T^{-\frac{5}{2}} \sum y_{t-1}^3 & T^{-3} \sum y_{t-1}^4 & T^{-\frac{7}{2}} \sum y_{t-1}^5 & T^{-4} \sum y_{t-1}^6 \\ T^{-3} \sum y_{t-1}^4 & T^{-\frac{7}{2}} \sum y_{t-1}^5 & T^{-4} \sum y_{t-1}^6 & T^{-\frac{9}{2}} \sum y_{t-1}^7 \\ T^{-\frac{7}{2}} \sum y_{t-1}^5 & T^{-4} \sum y_{t-1}^6 & T^{-\frac{9}{2}} \sum y_{t-1}^7 & T^{-5} \sum y_{t-1}^8 \end{pmatrix} \tag{24}$$

According to wiener process and functional central limit theorem, we can derive each element's asymptotic distribution of the matrix Q. It shows that:

$$T^{-2}\sum y_{t-1}^2 \Rightarrow \sigma^2 \int_0^1 w(r)^2 dr; \quad T^{-3}\sum y_{t-1}^4 \Rightarrow \sigma^4 \int_0^1 w(r)^4 dr;$$

$$T^{-4}\sum y_{t-1}^6 \Rightarrow \sigma^6 \int_0^1 w(r)^6 dr; \quad T^{-\frac{5}{2}}\sum y_{t-1}^3 \Rightarrow \sigma^3 \int_0^1 w(r)^3 dr;$$

$$T^{-\frac{7}{2}}\sum y_{t-1}^5 \Rightarrow \sigma^5 \int_0^1 w(r)^5 dr; \quad T^{-\frac{9}{2}}\sum y_{t-1}^7 \Rightarrow \sigma^7 \int_0^1 w(r)^7 dr;$$

$$T^{-5}\sum y_{t-1}^8 \Rightarrow \sigma^8 \int_0^1 w(r)^8 dr. \tag{25}$$

Once the distribution of Q is obtained, denote it as $Q(\cdot)$. Next, we attempt to derive the distribution of H whose expression is as below:

$$H(\cdot)=\begin{pmatrix} 1 & & & \\ & T^{\frac{1}{2}} & & \\ & & T & \\ & & & T^{\frac{3}{2}} \end{pmatrix}^{-1} \begin{pmatrix} \sum y_{t-1}\varepsilon_t \\ \sum y_{t-1}^2\varepsilon_t \\ \sum y_{t-1}^3\varepsilon_t \\ \sum y_{t-1}^4\varepsilon_t \end{pmatrix} = \begin{pmatrix} T^{-1}\sum y_{t-1}\varepsilon_t \\ T^{-\frac{3}{2}}\sum y_{t-1}^2\varepsilon_t \\ T^{-2}\sum y_{t-1}^3\varepsilon_t \\ T^{-\frac{5}{2}}\sum y_{t-1}^4\varepsilon_t \end{pmatrix} \tag{26}$$

And similarly we can also derive each element's asymptotic distribution of the matrix H as below.

$$T^{-1}\sum y_{t-1}\varepsilon_t \Rightarrow \frac{1}{2}\sigma^2(w^2(1)-1);$$

$$T^{-\frac{3}{2}}\sum y_{t-1}^2\varepsilon_t \Rightarrow \frac{1}{3}\sigma^3(w^3(1));$$

$$T^{-2}\sum y_{t-1}^3\varepsilon_t \Rightarrow \sigma^4\left[\frac{1}{4}w^4(1)-\frac{3}{2}\int_0^1 w(r)^2 dr\right];$$

$$T^{-\frac{5}{2}}\sum y_{t-1}^4\varepsilon_t \Rightarrow \sigma^5\left(\frac{1}{5}w^5(1)-2\int_0^1 w(r)^3 dr\right). \tag{27}$$

Once the distribution of H is ready, denote it as $H(\cdot)$. As the distributions of $Q(\cdot)$ and $H(\cdot)$ are known, then the distribution of $ST(\hat{\beta}-\beta)$ can be expressed as $Q^{-1}(\cdot)H(\cdot)$. The first row of matrix $Q^{-1}(\cdot)H(\cdot)$ is the distribution of $\hat{\beta}_1-1$.

Next, the distribution of $(\Sigma y_{t-1}^2)^{1/2}$ is derived as follows. Using formula (20) to show that

$$t = \frac{\hat{\beta}_1-1}{\eta} = \frac{(\hat{\beta}_1-1)\left(\sum y_{t-1}^2\right)^{1/2}}{\hat{\sigma}}$$

$$= \frac{ST(\hat{\beta}_1-1)\left(\dfrac{1}{S^2T^2}\sum y_{t-1}^2\right)^{1/2}}{\hat{\sigma}} \tag{28}$$

The first row of matrix $1/s_t^2T^2\ \Sigma y_{t-1}^2$ is our objective. As the first row of the diagonal matrix S is one, then

$$\frac{1}{S^2T^2}\sum y_{t-1}^2 \Rightarrow \frac{1}{T^2}\sum y_{t-1}^2 \Rightarrow \sigma^2 \int_0^1 w^2(r)dr \tag{29}$$

Now, we present the distribution of t statistic as below:

$$t = \frac{ST(\hat{\beta}_1-1)\left(\dfrac{1}{S^2T^2}\sum y_{t-1}^2\right)^{1/2}}{\hat{\sigma}}$$

$$\Rightarrow \frac{Q^{-1}(\cdot)H(\cdot)(\sigma^2\int_0^1 w^2(r)dr)}{\hat{\sigma}} \Rightarrow Q^{-1}(\cdot)H(\cdot)\int_0^1 w^2(r)dr \tag{30}$$

where we only fetch the first row of the matrix $Q^{-1}(\cdot)$ multiply $H(\cdot)$.

5 CONCLUSION

Univariate analysis of nonstationarity against stationarity has become an integral part of time series econometrics, and many scholars proved that nonlinear stationary is different from linear stationary. However, most of the existing literature still uses traditional unit root test to check the stationary of the nonlinear time series when they face nonlinear models. Although a few scholars consider the nonlinear unit root test, their studies are mainly relied on: either nonlinear test conditioning on the existence of unit root or unit root test when the nonlinearity does not exist. Nothing has been discussed in the sense that the linear test and unit root test can be implemented in the same model simultaneously. In this paper, taking LSTAR(1) as an example, we propose a new notion to test unit root in the nonlinear models: linear test and stationary test are run in the same model. Based on the new notion, this paper provides t statistic for the unit root test of the nonlinear LSTAR(1) model. According to wiener process and functional central limit theorem, we obtain the asymptotic distribution of t statistic.

Finally, although we provide a new notion to test unit root for the LSTAR model and our test is univariate, there are also some limitations in the study. First, we propose the unit root test statistic for the LSTAR(1) model, but the application of statistic maybe narrow, it is probably not suitable for the unit root test of other nonlinear models. Second, although we obtain the distribution of the statistic, we cannot derive the exact expression of the statistic and its critical value, which restricts its application. Third, nonlinear test and stationary test are run in the same model, but we only obtain the unit root test statistic for the LSTAR model, not for the linear test statistic. These gaps will be fitted in my further studies.

REFERENCES

Changli He, Rickard Sandberg. 2006. Dickey-Fuller type of tests against nonlinear dynamic models. Oxford Bulletin of Economics and Statistics 68:835–861.

George Kapetanios, Yongcheol Shin, Andy Snell. 2003. Testing for a unit root in the nonlinear STAR framework. Journal of Econometrics 112:359–379.

Luukkonen, R., Saikkonen, P., Teräsvirta, T. 1988. Testing linearity against smooth transition autoregressive models. Biometrica 75:491–499.

Rehim Kilic. 2004. Linearity tests and stationarity. Econometrics Journal 7:55–62.

Rickard Sandberg. 2008. Critical values for linearity tests in time-varying smooth transition autoregressive models when data are highly persistent. Econometrics Journal 11:638–647.

Teräsvirta, T. 1994. Sepecification, estimation and evaluation of smooth transition autoregressive models. Journal of the American Statistical Association 89:208–218.

Computer, Intelligent Computing and Education Technology – Liu, Sung & Yao (Eds)
© *2014 Taylor & Francis Group, London, ISBN 978-1-138-02469-4*

Fruit quality evaluation based on surface color and SVM

Y.H. Wu

*College of Electronic Information and Automation, Tianjin University of Science and Technology,
Tianjin, China*

Y.Y. Wang

School of Technology, Beijing Forestry University, Beijing, China

C. Wang, Q.J. Liu & Y.Z. Wang

*College of Electronic Information and Automation, Tianjin University of Science and Technology,
Tianjin, China*

G.Q. Huang

*Department of Industrial and Manufacturing Systems Engineering, The University of Hong Kong,
Hong Kong, China*

ABSTRACT: Machine vision is one of non-invasive and nondestructive methods for evaluating the quality of agricultural products. In this paper, a fruit evaluation method is proposed and implemented based on color processing and Support Vector Machine (SVM). In this method, the image of a fruit is taken with the RGB color model. After converted into the HSI color model, its simplified H histogram is calculated as the feature vector, which is inputted into one-against-all SVMs. The output is the evaluation result. Experiments are conducted with satisfied results for evaluating the qualities of bananas, which show the feasibility and reliability of the proposed and implemented method.

Keywords: fruit quality; evaluation; color identification; Support Vector Machine

1 INTRODUCTION

Food safety has recently been focused on widely and is also affecting agricultural products. This trend makes fast, non-invasive, and efficient inspection methods of food safety significant. In particular, the technologies such as near infrared spectrum, sound waves, x-rays, and machine vision are much more popular (Song et al. 2004).

As one of the most important characters, surface color can be used to identify the quality of some fruits. In this paper, a fruit quality evaluation method is proposed based on color identification and support vector machine. In this method, an image of a fruit is firstly taken by a CCD camera with the RGB (Red-Green-Blue) color model. Secondly, the image is converted into the HSI (Hue-Saturation-Intensity) color model. Then, the simplified histogram of hue (H) of the image is calculated, which is taken as the feature vector and inputted into a SVM (Support Vector Machine) classifier. The output of the SVM classifier is the evaluation result of the fruit, which has four levels.

2 COLOR MODELS AND COLOR HISTOGRAMS

2.1 *Color models*

When an image of a fruit is taken by a CCD camera, it is in the RGB color model, which is an additive color model and supported by commonly used tools (Verikas & Bacauskiene. 2008). But, the RGB color model is not suitable for color identification as it is hard to extract the hue and saturation information from an image with the RGB color model. Therefore, the HSI color model is adopted in this paper.

The HSI color model can be described using the terms hue, saturation, and intensity, which represents colors within a double-cone space (Sanchez-Cuevas et al. 2013), as shown in Figure 1. Hue represents various colors in RGB, saturation stands for colorfulness of a stimulus relative to its own brightness, and intensity is the total amount of light passing through a particular area, which makes no contribution to the color. It is clear that the information in hue is suitable for color identification because hue makes great

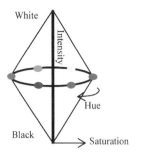

Figure 1.   The HSI color model.

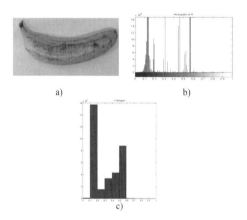

a)

b)

c)

Figure 2.   The image of a banana and its H histogram.

contribution to the color in the HSI color model. The RGB color model is easily transferred into the HSI color model with formulas (Tang et al. 2013).

2.2   Color histograms

In image processing, a color histogram is a representation of the distribution of colors in an image, which is derived by counting the number of pixels of each given set of color ranges in a color space. The histogram of H is used in this paper for fruit quality evaluation. As an example, the normalized H histogram of the banana image shown in Figure 2(a) is given in Figure 2(b). If Figure 2(b) is directly used, there will be a lot of input points for evaluation. Thus, simplified color histogram of H is used in this paper. As illustrated in Figure 2(c), H is divided into ten levels.

3   SUPPORT VECTOR MACHINE

3.1   Support vector machine

Support Vector Machine (SVM) is a supervised learning method based on the statistical learning

theory (Huang et al. 2014). The basic idea of SVM is to convert linear inalienable issues within a low-dimensional space into linear alienable issues within a high-dimensional space by inner product operation, and determine the optimal classifier plane within a linear alienable space to implement classification. Inner product operation is conducted based on the selected kernel function. The most common kernel functions include Polynomial Function, Radial Basis Function, and Sigmoid Function, etc. (Camps-Valls et al. 2004).

3.2   Multiclass classification strategies

SVM is essentially a two-class classifier. However, multiclass classification is required in most cases. The basic method of implementing multiclass classification is to construct multiple SVMs. There are generally two kinds of multiclass classification SVMs: one-against-one SVMs, and one-against-all SVMs (Kumar & Gopal. 2011).

The calculation amount of one-against-one classifier is large and its accuracy is low. In this paper, the number of samples is small and the differences between features are distinct. Therefore one-against-all classifier is selected. The number of binary classifiers depends on the ranks of fruit to be evaluated.

4   FRUIT QUALITY EVALUATION WITH SVM

4.1   Training SVMs

SVMs must be trained to determine appropriate parameters after selecting the kernel function that is polynomial function in this paper. SVMs are trained using simplified H histograms of fruits as the feature vectors. The number of SVMs equals to the levels of fruit qualities.

The output of the SVMs is the evaluation result, which is represented using a vector that consists of 1 and 0, i.e. [1, 0, …, 0].

4.2   Evaluation process

After training, SVMs can be used to evaluate the quality of fruit. The whole working process is depicted in Figure 3.

5   CASE STUDY

In order to verify the proposed fruit quality evaluation method, experiments are conducted using bananas, some of them are given in Figure 4. The qualities of bananas are divided into four levels from 1 to 4 to represent the range from good to bad.

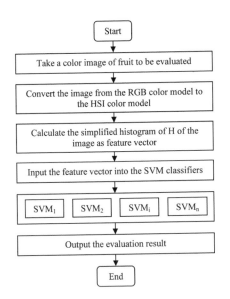

Figure 3. The flowchart of evaluation process.

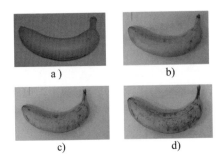

Figure 4. Some banana images in different quality levels.

Therefore, four SVMs classifiers are employed. Their outputs are [1, 0, 0, 0] or [0, 1, 0, 0] or [0, 0, 1, 0] or [0, 0, 0, 1] to represent the quality from good to bad, respectively.

After training, the SVMs are used to evaluate the qualities of bananas with their images. Some of experiment results are tabulated in Table 1. It shows that all evaluation results are correct.

6 CONCLUSION

Fast non-invasive and nondestructive methods are useful for fruit quality evaluation. One of such methods is proposed and implemented in this paper based on color identification and Support Vector Machine (SVM). In this method, a fruit's image is taken with the RGB color model. The simplified H histogram of the image is calculated after converted into the HSI color model. The simplified H histogram is used as the feature vector to be inputted into one-against-all SVMs. The output is the evaluation result. Experiments are conducted for evaluating the qualities of bananas, which are divided into four levels. Four SVM classifiers are used with satisfied results, which show the feasibility and reliability of the proposed fruit quality evaluation method.

ACKNOWLEDGEMENT

The corresponding author is Y.Z. Wang.

REFERENCES

Camps-Valls, G., Martı́n-Guerrero, J.D., Rojo-Álvarez, J.L., Soria-Olivas, E. 2004. Fuzzy sigmoid kernel for support vector classifiers. *Neurocomputing* 62: 501–506.

Huang, X.L., Shi, L., Suykens, J.A.K. 2014. Asymmetric least squares support vector machine classifiers. *Computational Statistics and Data Analysis* 70: 395–405.

Kumar, M.A. & Gopal, M. 2011. Reduced one-against-all method for multiclass SVM classification. *Expert Systems with Applications* 38: 14238–14248.

Sanchez-Cuevas, M.C., Aguilar-Ponce, R.M., Tecpanecatl-Xihuitl, J.L. 2013. A Comparison of Color Models for Color Face Segmentation. *Procedia Technology* 7: 134–141.

Song, L.M., Qu, X.H., Xu, K.X., Lv, L.N. 2005. Novel SFS-NDT in the field of defect detection. *NDT&E International* 38: 381–386.

Tang, Z.J., Zhang, X.Q., Dai, X., Yang, J.Z., Wu, T.X. 2013. Robust image hash function using local color features. *In. J. Electron. Commun.* 67: 717–722.

Verikas, A. & Bacauskiene, M. 2008. Estimating ink density from color camera RGB values by the local kernel ridge regression. *Engineering Applications of Artificial Intelligence* 21: 35–42.

Table 1. Some experiment results.

Number	1	2	3	4
Image				
Input				
SVM output	[1, 0, 0, 0]	[0, 1, 0, 0]	[0, 0, 1, 0]	[0, 0, 0, 1]
Evaluated quality level	1	2	3	4
Actual quality level	1	2	3	4

Computer, Intelligent Computing and Education Technology – Liu, Sung & Yao (Eds)
© *2014 Taylor & Francis Group, London, ISBN 978-1-138-02469-4*

Based on MB JPEG image analysis algorithms secret

Hui-Fen Huang

Shandong Yingcai University, Shandong, China

ABSTRACT: In this paper, digital image forensics integrity perspective, conducted secret research targeted analytical methods proposed MBl secret (JPEG images) analysis algorithms secret, whether the carrier image can contain secret information to make reliable judgments, and in the case of a known secret method can determine the length and location of the secret information.

Keywords: digital forensics; privacy analysis; JPEG

1 INTRODUCTION

JPEG images are currently on the network the most common image formats, JPEG image carrier based on secret algorithms endless. From the initial J-StegShell, JPHide & Seek[1–3] and OutGuess to later F5, etc., for the secret analysis in JPEG there is also a more effective detection of ideas, is a secret method for a first analysis to identify closely with the secret embedding rate relevant statistics, and then try to estimate the former secret deal with the statistics of the original value, by comparing the difference between the original value and the value was seized to determine whether or not and estimates the embedded hidden capacity. Of course, the main difficulty of this approach is to find an appropriate statistic, another method by which to more accurately estimate the amount of the original value statistics also need to be explored.

Since the secret is embedded in the JPEG[4–6] image block adjacent to the operation is not relevant, so the operation will exacerbate JPEG discreet block effect of the image, and the operation to remove the above-described four and left at 4 rows offset secret operation block effect caused by the thus obtained reference image with the original image will be relatively close to the statistical characteristics.

2 MB1 SECRET ALGORITHM PRINCIPLE

Model based on the idea of information hiding and compression from the similarity between a compressor is ideal for nature after a scene diagram any compressed output is a string of compression, absolutely random[7] (does not contain any statistical information) bitstream. Conversely,

the random bit stream is input to the compression decompressor can recover the image. Ideal base compressor is established: the compressor must be complete statistical model natural images. In this case, if the sender of an encrypted communication (encrypted stream is a string of random bits), then the compressor is obtained by solving a normal image. In the receiver have the same condition compressor; you can get secret information transmission, which is a perfect steganography program. However, due to a statistical model to get the full picture of the current nature is impossible, so a viable approach is to select a model that contains part of the statistical characteristics of the image. Steganography thus obtained can only be broken Steganography than those who have it good model. So Steganography model model established safety depends on the extent to which said cover image information.

JPEG image as an example is given below to MB1[8,9] algorithm. MB1 algorithm selected model is generalized Cauchy distribution with parameters describe the distribution $P(\mu)$ of AC DCT coefficients.

$$P(\mu) = \frac{p-1}{2s}\left(\left|\frac{\mu}{s}\right|+1\right)^{-p} \tag{1}$$

where μ in the quantized DCT coefficients, $p > 1$ and $s > 1$. Corresponding cumulative probability function

$$D(\mu) = \begin{cases} \dfrac{1}{2}\left(1+\left|\dfrac{\mu}{s}\right|\right)^{1-p} & \mu \le 0 \\[2ex] 1-\dfrac{1}{2}\left(1+\left|\dfrac{\mu}{s}\right|\right)^{1-p} & \mu > 0 \end{cases} \tag{2}$$

Before operations begin embedding low precision DCT coefficients need to calculate the histogram. Accuracy refers to the so-called low-step histogram channel grew at a histogram. Each low-precision coefficient consists of two parts: the histogram channel index and channel offset. Histogram channel index composed MB algorithm $\mathcal{X}_\alpha$ is not being modified. Channel $\mathcal{X}_\beta$ offset constitute the model is modified according to a secret letter. Model parameters s and p make adjustments based on low-precision coefficients and solution. Because only the offset $\mathcal{X}_\beta$ is modified in the embedding process, so low-precision coefficient histogram is maintained, so that the extraction operation can be resumed s and p.

3 MB1 STEGANALYSIS ALGORITHM

Steganography according MB1, assuming $h_k^{(i,j)}$ a given number of said (i,j) DCT coefficients of the image position of the first coefficient is equal to &, the histogram $h_k^{(i,j)}$ will be referred to as channel level precision k. In contrast, the low-precision $b_k^{(i,j)}$ accuracy histogram channel contains multiple channels. MB1 algorithm used is a low-precision accuracy histogram histogram channel contains two channels:

$$b_k^{(i,j)} = \begin{cases} h_{2k+1}^{(i,j)} + h_{2k}^{(i,j)} & k < 0 \\ h_0^{(i,j)} & k = 0 \\ h_{2k-1}^{(i,j)} + h_{2k}^{(i,j)} & k > 0 \end{cases} \quad (3)$$

Each 8×8 DCT coefficient block relationship $(2,2)$ channel low-accuracy position of the histogram of histograms between the channels and high-precision 8. For simplicity, we only discuss the situation $k > 0$.

MB1 low accuracy histogram $b_k^{(i,j)}$ algorithm channel size is determined as part of the model $\mathcal{X}_\alpha$, the coefficients of each low precision in the distribution of the histogram for each channel coefficient precision can not be determined as part of the model $\mathcal{X}_\beta$.

So MB1 practice is to modify a factor, $2k-1$ and $2k$ vice versa. With respect to the simple LSB inverted from the conditional probability model $P(X_\beta | X_\alpha = \mathcal{X}_\alpha)$ is dependent on the accuracy of the low probability of all histogram channel $P\left(h_{2k-1}^{(i,j)} | b_k^{(i,j)}\right)$ precision of the histogram is a channel 1.

$$P\left(h_{2k-1}^{(i,j)} | b_k^{(i,j)}\right) + P\left(h_{2k}^{(i,j)} | b_k^{(i,j)}\right) = 1, \ \forall i,j,k \quad (4)$$

The following analysis $P\left(h_{2k-1}^{(i,j)} | b_k^{(i,j)}\right)$ algorithms will be expressed as $P_k^{(i,j)}$. In the embedding process

$P_k^{(i,j)}$ needs to be adjusted to meet the generalized Cauchy distribution after correction (MGC) form.

$$P_k^{(i,j)} = \frac{f(2k-1,\pi,s)}{f(2k-1,\pi,s) + f(k-1,\pi,s)} \quad (5)$$

Which is the probability density function of the generalized Cauchy distribution

$$f(k-1,\pi,s) = \frac{p-1}{2s}\left(\left|k/s\right| + 1\right)^{-\pi} \quad (6)$$

Although the DCT coefficients obey Cauchy distribution histogram probably, but there are some natural images exist outside this volume. After embedding secret information, which is inconsistent with the model histogram channel was adjusted to fit the model of the distribution histogram channel. This is the main idea of steganalysis algorithm.

Analysis of a total of two-step method: first, the histogram is consistent and inconsistent channel histogram channel separately. This process is the operation of the JPEG image histogram of all of the low accuracy of the channel. Second step, the threshold value obtained in Step experiences cover image with the result, and if a suspect "non-uniform" histogram contains the number of channels is less than the cover picture, it is reasonable to suspect that it is embedded using MB1 the cover image of secret information secret.

There are obvious outsiders DCT coefficients in low-precision b_{-1} coefficient histogram channel. Original frequency, frequency h_{-1} and expectations h_{-2} there is a difference. Expected frequency and steganographic images corresponding frequency is matched.

This difference can be used to lower the observed and expected frequencies of the two high-precision accuracy histogram channel frequency channels between the possibility to measure the number of tests. To calculate the desired frequency, we will use the output of the arithmetic decoder Bernoulli random variables found to modeling $Y(p)$ wherein the masking precision $p = p_k^{(i,j)}$ density histogram of the image $\hat{h}^{(i,j)}$ subject to the Bernoulli distribution channel.

$$\begin{cases} \hat{h}_{2k-1}^{(i,j)} - B(b_k^{(i,j)}, p_k^{(i,j)}) \\ \hat{h}_{2k-1}^{(i,j)} - B(b_k^{(i,j)}, 1 - p_k^{(i,j)}) \end{cases} \quad (7)$$

$h^{-(i,j)}$ B is the mean number of expected frequency of $h^{-(i,j)}$.

$$h_{2k-1}^{-(i,j)} = E\left(B(b_k^{(i,j)}, p_k^{(i,j)})\right) = b_k^{(i,j)} \cdot p_k^{(i,j)} \quad (8)$$

Table 1. Steganalysis tool test results.

Order	Average embedding capacity	Detector threshold	Correct classification
1	0%	10	488
2	50%	10	496
3	75%	10	584
4	100%	10	625

Order	Misclassification	Correct rate	Detection time
1	141	77.6%	25 min
2	132	79.0%	30 min
3	44	93%	32 min
4	3	99.5%	28 min

Note: The detector threshold referred to herein refers to the technique of quantizing said statistical characteristic quantities, dimensionless.

Because after embedding secret information, the histogram is low accuracy is not changed, so steganalysis $p_k^{(i,j)}$ who can get through to regain the model and then calculate the various frequencies above x^2. Pearson x^2 then test to complete the test $Q(x^2, df)$, the distribution function is given by the distribution of the error rate analysis.

4 MB1 SECRET ANALYSIS OF EXPERIMENTAL

Images used in the experiment were: JPEG image with 629 Nikon E5700 camera directly taken, the size of 1280×960 of 24 bits true color images of natural scenery and characters; then use the network to download MB1 program, select a different random number embedding rate (experiment were selected by 50%, 75% and 100%) to the random number embedded in the image, the generation of different embedded JPEG image density carrying capacity test. Testing and test data forms the image type is shown in Table 1.

After testing, the secret method of analysis methods to embed hidden secret information MB1 different amounts, for embedding in more than 50% of the full amount of the capacity of the embedded image and the original image steganography detector false alarm rate of 23.4%, less than 30% for image steganography detection rate of a minimum of 79.0%, greater than 70%.

5 CONCLUSIONS

This article will examine the hidden secret analysis extended to the analysis of the range of forensics research, summed up the direction of development of analytical techniques based on secret evidence in court for the purpose of providing covert forensic analysis techniques. According to the framework of secret evidence before analysis system, introduced secret research status of digital image forensics analysis technology and solve the image is hidden from the general analysis of secret information secret and to determine the hidden secrets in the case of the known methods targeted analysis methods secret message length position paper puts forward an effective targeted analysis of the most popular occult secret method of compressing images (JPEG format) MB1 secret hidden digital images such as common carriers undermine efforts to secret research to analyze forensic analysis to extract the hidden secret letter to the goal of advancing research evidence.

ACKNOWLEDGMENT

This work is supported by Shandong Yingcai University key issues (13YCZDZR01).

REFERENCES

[1] J. Fridrich, M. Goljan, D. Soukal, T. Holotyak. Froensic Steganalysis: Determining the Stego Keyin Spatial Domain Steganography [A], Edward J. Delp, Ping WahWong (Eds.): Security, Steganography, and Watermarking of Multimedia Contents-VII [C], SanJose, California, USA, January 17–20, 2005, Proceedings. Proceedings of SPIE 5681 SPIE2005:631–642.

[2] Gary C. Kessler. An Overview of Steganography for the Computer Forensics Examiner [J]. Forensic Science Communications, Vol. 6 Number July 2004.

[3] Guo Yunbiao, You Xingang, Zhang Chuntian, Hu Lan and Zhou Linna, Steganalysis of Facsimile ICACT2005 2005, 2.

[4] Guo Yunbiao, Lin daimao, Nu xiamu, Hu Lan and Zhou linna, A Secure Steganographic Scheme in Binary Image, IIHMSP'05, Lecture notes in computer science. 2005, 9.

[5] Wong PW. A watermark for image integrity and ownership verification. Portland OR: Proc. Of IS & PIC Conf., 2005.

[6] Fridrich J, Goljan M and Baldoza AC. New fragile authentication watermark for images. Proc. ICIP, Vancouver, Canada, Sep, 2007:446~449.

[7] Nopporn and Sangiamkun W. Digital watermarking technique for image authentication by neighboring block similarity measure. Proc. IEEE Region 10 International on Electrical and Electronic Technology:734~747.

[8] Li D-T. Oblivious fragile watermarking scheme for image authentication. IEEE, 2010: 3445~ 3448.

[9] Yao-Jen Chang Shih-Kai Tsai, Li-Der Chou, Tsen-Yung Wang, "An Indoor Wayfinding System Based on Geo-coded QR Codes for Individuals with Cognitive Impairments", JCIT, Vol. 2, No. 4, 71 ~77, 2011.

Computer, Intelligent Computing and Education Technology – Liu, Sung & Yao (Eds)
© 2014 Taylor & Francis Group, London, ISBN 978-1-138-02469-4

Digital image authentication algorithm based on the source characteristics of higher-order statistics

Hui-Fen Huang
Shandong Computing Science Center, Shandong, China
Shandong University of Science and Technology, Shandong, China

Xiao-Shi Zheng
Shandong Computing Science Center, Shandong, China

Yong-Guo Zheng
Shandong University of Science and Technology, Shandong, China

ABSTRACT: From the mathematical statistical point of view, the study of natural digital photos digital cameras available, the impact generated route scanned images and computer-generated images on their respective properties, from multi-scale analysis of the angle of the image, study images from different sources in a transform domain presented individual characteristics, higher-order statistical feature extraction digital image wavelet domain.

Keywords: digital forensics; privacy analysis; JPEG

1 EXTRACTION OF HIGHER-ORDER STATISTICS FEATURES

First, the wavelet decomposition of the digital image shown in Figure 1, the decomposition of the image is decomposed into a frequency domain and a plurality of multistage direction. Were shown from top to bottom section 0, Level 1, Level 2; details were left to right, vertical, horizontal and diagonal components. Wavelet decomposition can take advantage of the low-pass and high-pass filter along the axis of the picture image is decomposed into detail, vertical, horizontal and diagonal components. Each successive level of decomposition is higher level of detail components of recursive filtering through the formation.[1] Here, for a true color image, the i-level, c color channel vertical, horizontal, and diagonal components are represented by $V_i^c(x,y), H_i^c(x,y)$ and $D_i^c(x,y)$. Figure 2 is a schematic diagram lena three wavelet coefficients of the amplitude.

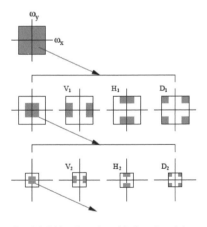

Figure 1. Multi-level and multi-directional image frequency domain decomposition.

Figures 2 and 3. Lena. Schematic amplitude wavelet coefficients.

In this paper, four wavelet decomposition ($i = 4$). Wherein the first set of image statistics obtained by the wavelet decomposition of each stage ($i = 1, 2, 3$), the mean, variance, skewness and kurtosis coefficients in each direction component of the composition of these statistics. These statistics demonstrated wavelet coefficients of basic statistical distributions. For example a factor in the vertical direction:

$$F\_V_{1-9} = mean(V_i^c(x,y)) \tag{1}$$

$$F\_V_{10-18} = variance(V_i^c(x,y)) \tag{2}$$

$$F\_V_{19-27} = skewness(V_i^c(x,y)) \tag{3}$$

$$F\_V_{28-36} = kurtosis(V_i^c(x,y)) \tag{4}$$

Decomposition statistical characteristics of the other three directions perpendicular direction with the same calculation method, thus obtaining a first set of classification of the characteristic dimension $36 \times 3 = 108$ (dimension for gray scale $12 \times 3 = 36$ images).

In order to extract the wavelet decomposition coefficients of each decomposition level and the correlation between the direction, the paper introduces a second set of classification features: linear prediction error statistical characteristics of wavelet coefficients. This set of characteristics extraction method follows.

The vertical component of the image G channels, for example, the decomposition coefficients can be used adjacent the decomposition level, the direction of the decomposition, a linear relationship between the color channels and the resolution factor in the same position adjacent to the decomposition level in the same direction prediction decomposition:

$$\begin{aligned}
\left|V_i^g(x,y)\right| = &\, \omega_1\left|V_i^g(x-1,y)\right| + \omega_2\left|V_i^g(x+1,y)\right| \\
&+ \omega_3\left|V_i^g(x,y-1)\right| + \omega_4\left|V_i^g(x,y+1)\right| \\
&+ \omega_5\left|V_{i+1}^g(x/2,y/2)\right| + \omega_6\left|V_i^g(x,y)\right| \\
&+ \omega_7\left|D_{i+1}^g(x/2,y/2)\right| + \omega_8\left|V_i^r(x,y)\right| \\
&+ \omega_9\left|V_i^b(x,y)\right|
\end{aligned} \tag{5}$$

Said linear relationship can be expressed in matrix form simpler out:

$$\vec{v} = Q\vec{\omega} \tag{6}$$

Which $|\cdot|$ represents the amplitude $|\cdot|$ is the amplitude $\left|V_i^g(x,y)\right|$ of the sheets $\vec{\omega}$ into a column vector $\vec{\omega} = \{\omega_1, \omega_2, \cdots \omega_9\}$ for the right value.

By following a minimum mean square error function to give weight $\vec{\omega}$:

$$E(\vec{\omega}) = [\vec{v} - Q\vec{\omega}]^2 \tag{7}$$

Taking the derivative of the above equation to get:

$$\frac{dE(\vec{\omega})}{d\vec{\omega}} = 2Q^T(\vec{v} - Q\vec{\omega}) \tag{8}$$

So the formula result is 0, the solution out $\vec{\omega}$ as follows:

$$\vec{\omega} = (Q^TQ)^{-1}Q^T\vec{v} \tag{9}$$

So you can get the value of linear prediction coefficients of the wavelet decomposition amplitude. Then calculate the true value and prediction error log value decomposition coefficients:

$$\vec{p} = \log(\vec{v}) - \log(|Q\vec{\omega}|) \tag{10}$$

Finally, calculate the mean, variance, skewness and kurtosis of linear prediction error log. Similarly calculate the vertical component of the above statistical features of the other two color channels, as well as horizontal and diagonal components of the three color channels, three decomposition levels above statistical features, so get a second set of classification characteristic dimension (for gray for the dimension $12 \times 3 = 36$ of the image, $\vec{\omega} = \{\omega_1, \omega_2, \cdots \omega_7\}$). Finally get 216 Victoria (such as the 72-dimensional grayscale) image for high-level statistical characteristics of the image source authentication.

2 CLASSIFIER DESIGN AND CLASSIFICATION RULING

Digital image source authentication process based on higher order statistical features are as follows. First, high-level training samples extracted statistical features for multi-class classifier training.

This article uses a multi-class support vector machine classifier using commonly used in the experiment SVM toolkit.[2] Assuming, x_i, $i = 1, 2, \ldots, N$ in the training X set is a feature vector. These vectors from the class, ω_1 and ω_2 assuming that these two are linearly separable. So the purpose of classification is to design an ultra-flat, all the training vectors correctly classified:

Where in a hyperplane ω coefficient vector, the input vector is x, the offset ω_0. Obviously, such a hyperplane is not unique. However, given the versatility of the classifier, i.e., the capacity of the classifier should be chosen so that the hyperplane:

hyperplane in that direction with each class, each class in the same distance from the nearest point, ω_1 and ω_2 spacing as large as possible. This problem is represented by the equation:

There is a gap to meet $1/\|\omega\| + 1/\|\omega\| = 2/\|\omega\|$

Required to meet

$$\omega^T x + \omega_0 \geq 1, \quad \forall x \in \omega_1$$
$$\omega^T x + \omega_0 \leq -1, \quad \forall x \in \omega_2 \qquad (11)$$

The problem now is to solve the parameters of the hyperplane ω, ω_0:

Minimize

$$J(\omega) \equiv \frac{1}{2}\|\omega\|^2 \qquad (12)$$

Limited conditions

$$y_i(\omega^T x_i + \omega_0) \geq 1, \quad i = 1, 2, \ldots, N \qquad (13)$$

where in for ω_1, y_i is $+1$; for ω_2, y_i is -1.

This is a non-linear series of linear inequalities satisfy the conditions of the optimization problem. Assuming $(\lambda_1, \lambda_2, \ldots, \lambda_N)$ a Lagrange multiplier, then from (12) and (13) can be calculated:

$$\omega = \sum_{i=1}^{N} \lambda_i y_i x_i \qquad (14)$$

Such a final decision function can be expressed as:

$$f(x) = \text{sgn}\left(\sum_{i=1}^{N} \lambda_i y_i x_i^T x_i + \omega_0\right) \qquad (15)$$

In fact, support vector machine, this feature vector is called "Support Vector."[3–5]

When the two types of data can be time-sharing in the current space is not linear, SVM feature space by function $K(x_i, x)$ to be mapped to a higher dimensional space, where the mapping function $K(x_i, x)$ satisfies Mercer theorem. Such a final decision function can be expressed as:

$$f(x) = \text{sgn}\left(\sum_{i=1}^{N} \lambda_i y_i K(x_i, x) + \omega_0\right) \qquad (16)$$

Described above is SVM classification model for two types of data. Multi-class SVM is determined by pairwise hyperplane for data classification, and finally get the final verdict by voting or probabilistic estimation methods.

Select-SVC in our system, the non-linear Radial Basis Function (RBF) as the kernel function. RBF kernel function is defined as:

$$K(x_i, x) = \exp\left(-\gamma \|x_i - x\|^2\right) \qquad (17)$$

Under the proposed [2], the optimal parameters (C, γ) can be obtained by grid search. Grid search parameter C to the grid search parameter is $\{2^{-5}, 2^{-4}, \ldots, 2^5\}$. This completes γ the multi-class classifier design $\{2^{-5}, 2^{-4}, \ldots, 2^5\}$.

Finally, classification feature extraction test samples have been trained with multi-class classifier to classify the decision to get recognition system output.

Enter the SVM feature data preprocessing needed in our experiments the characteristic data normalized between [0,1].

3 BASED ON THE STATISTICAL CHARACTERISTICS OF THE HIGH-END DIGITAL IMAGE SOURCE TO ACHIEVE CERTIFICATION

3.1 The feature extraction process

1. Reads an image file, the image file format to read the information, determines whether the image is a true color image or a grayscale image;
2. To re-set the image size, length and width of the image are integer powers of 2;
3. The image wavelet transform, wavelet decomposition coefficients in each direction at all levels;
4. To extract higher-order statistics features of images according to Section 2.1 of the method;
5. High-level statistical characteristics of the image obtained by writing to the file.

3.2 Classifier design and classification decision process

1. Select the saved file feature of training samples;
2. On the characteristics of the training sample data were normalized;
3. With a cross-check to get the optimal parameters of support vector machine and save the training results (model file) for testing;
4. Select the test specimen signature files;
5. The characteristic data test samples were normalized;
6. The use of the training was to test samples for classification decision and save the test results.

4 SIMULATION

4.1 Image files used in the experiment

Training images:[6–8]

Scan images: 238 images using HP C7710A scanner and scanner Epson Perfection 1200 photo obtained (scan resolution is set between 150–300).

615

Table 1. Test accuracy.

Image	Natural images	Computer image
Natural	296	2
Computer	8	287
Scanned	0	2

Image	Scanned image	Correct rate
Natural	2	98.7%
Computer	5	95.7%
Scanned	236	99.2%

4.2 Test results

See Table 1.

4.3 Experimental results

Best classification performance of the scanned image, reaching 99.2%; For the computer-generated image of a lower classification performance among the three, but also reached 95.7%. In addition to the reasons for the algorithm itself, the choice of image samples may also affect the results. Natural selection of images and scanned images are more concentrated, and computer-generated images to select more widely.[9]

As can be seen from the experimental results, the source of a digital image authentication system basically meet the requirements of this article source authentication system, has good validity and reliability.

5 CONCLUSIONS

In this paper, the use of higher-order wavelet domain statistical characteristics as classification features images of sources, using support vector machine as classifier, build a digital image source authentication system based on higher-order statistical features. Experimental results show that the source of this image authentication system has a high recognition accuracy and reliability certification.

ACKNOWLEDGMENT

This work is supported by Shandong Yingcai University key issues (13YCZDZR01).

REFERENCES

[1] S. Lyu, H. Farid. How realistic is photorealistic? IEEE Transactions on Signal Processing, 53(2):845–850, 2005.
[2] C.-C. Chang and C.-J. Lin. LIBSVM: a library for support vector machines. 2001. Software available at http://www.csie.ntu.edu.tw/~cjlin/libsvm.
[3] Guo Yunbiao, You Xingang, Zhang Chuntian, Hu Lan and Zhou Linna, Steganalysis of Facsimile ICACT2005 2005, 2.
[4] Guo Yunbiao, Lin daimao, Nu xiamu, Hu Lan and Zhou linna, A Secure Steganographic Scheme in Binary Image, IIHMSP'05, Lecture notes in computer science. 2005, 9.
[5] Wong PW. A watermark for image integrity and ownership verification. Portland OR: Proc. Of IS & PIC Conf., 2005.
[6] Fridrich J, Goljan M and Baldoza AC. New fragile authentication watermark for images. Proc. ICIP, Vancouver, Canada, Sep, 2007:446 ~ 449.
[7] Nopporn and Sangiamkun W. Digital watermarking technique for image authentication by neighboring block similarity measure. Proc. IEEE Region 10 International on Electrical and Electronic Technology: 734~747.
[8] Li D-T. Oblivious fragile watermarking scheme for image authentication. IEEE, 2010: 3445~3448.
[9] Yao-Jen Chang Shih-Kai Tsai, Li-Der Chou, Tsen-Yung Wang, "An Indoor Wayfinding System Based on Geo-coded QR Codes for Individuals with Cognitive Impairments", JCIT, Vol. 2, No. 4, 71~77, 2011.

Computer, Intelligent Computing and Education Technology – Liu, Sung & Yao (Eds)
© *2014 Taylor & Francis Group, London, ISBN 978-1-138-02469-4*

How to do confidential work of electronic archives

Feng-Li Zhang

Environmental Management College of China, Qinhuangdao, Hebei, China

ABSTRACT: Along with the continuous development of science and digital communication technology, confidential work suffers from a rigorous test to some great extent. Various leaks have adversely affected or caused great losses for many enterprises and people's personal life. The traditional file management mode has gradually been replaced by modern electronic pattern due to the improvement of information technology. It remains an inevitable part for the confidential work of electronic files.

Keywords: file management; classified files; electronic information technology; secrecy

1   FEATURES OF TRADITIONAL CLASSIFIED FILES MANAGEMENT

The storage location is the essential component of secrecy work. Taking the characteristics of traditional files into consideration, the proper storage must be provided with moderate temperature and humidity. In accordance with the Archives Law of the People's Republic of China, the storage sites must formulate and implement a strict access control and management system to ensure the confidentiality and security of the archive files.

Lay stress on the vocational training for staff. The archives law stipulates that institutions, organizations and enterprises must have their dedicated file management personnel to strictly implement all the management regulations. In recent years, most provinces have developed a strict qualification system for archivists and regularly organize professional training for archivists. The professionalism of the archivists guarantees that the confidential work goes smoothly. Organize regular archivists learning the Secrets Act and related knowledge, do archives management strictly in accordance with the requirements of Secrets Act.

Reasonably carry on hierarchical management according to the confidential class of the files. In accordance with the relevant regulations, the traditional files are divided into top secret, classified and secret on the basis of degree of secrets. In the traditional file management system, different categories of files proceeded centralized management. Detailed provisions for management and inspection of the files are provided. At the same time, the decryption standard, the decryption time and the decryption methods of all the files are strictly and respectively limited. By this, the protections for the secrecy of the files are maximized.

With the continuous development of information technology, the traditional paper-based archives management mode will be replaced by electronic information-based management system. Compared with the traditional confidentiality mode, electronic information mode has its special features. The traditional file management mode has been unable to meet the requirements of informationization. Further more, several egregious leaks utilizing electronic information have brought tremendous influence on the constriction of China's socialistic modernization. How to do the confidential work of electronic files well needs great efforts from archivists.

2   THE ADVANTAGES AND DISADVANTAGES OF THE CONFIDENTIALITY MANAGEMENT FOR ELECTRONIC ARCHIVES

2.1   *The advantages of confidentiality management for electronic archives*

First, it is relatively easy to manage and maintain the electronic files. With the digital technology of file compression, the electronic archives need minimal space and the requirements for the storage sites are relatively low. Secondly, the electronic files are convenient to read or transfer. Owing to the high transfer speed, data upload, download and transmit managements are quite convenient. The ability to serve the community of file management has been greatly improved. Electronic archives are composed of a variety of information media, convenient to manage, and can greatly improve the work efficiency and realize the network share.

2.2 The disadvantages of confidentiality management for electronic archives

It is true that the disadvantages of confidentiality management for electronic archives are obvious as the advantages. For electronic information technology's own characteristics, classified files are more likely to be changed its existence forms of information, data loss, storage medium material is easy damaged, the save time is shorter, more dependent on computer hardware and software environment, at the same time there is a greater risk of network access. After disclosure, the characteristics of diversity transmission bodies result in difficulties to make up for the loss in a short period. Therefore, electronic archives secrecy confidentiality is more important than paper files.

3 HOW TO DO THE CONFIDENTIAL WORK FOR CLASSIFIED ELECTRONIC ARCHIVES

The author thinks that the main principle to do the confidential work for classified electronic archives well is to make full use of the advantages of electronic information technology, combining with the traditional management experience. Drawing upon each other's strength and trying to overcome the problems and shortcomings. Specifically, we should pay attention to the following aspects.

3.1 Firmly establish the service consciousness for achieves management and secrecy

Either for the archives management or confidential work, the original intention is to provide information service for the social and economic development. The utilization of electronic information technology to maintain secrecy can serve the society better. Therefore, service consciousness is the guiding ideology for archives management.

3.2 Establish a sound inquiry system for electronic archives to ensure the security of confidential information

The utilization regulations of archives generally contain reading system, confidential system, lending system and replication system.

1. According to the practical situation, different usage access and approval procedurals for the archives should be classified for the user. While vigorously developing the utilization of the archives, we should assure the confidentiality and intactness of them. All the utilization regulations should be tight, concise and easy to perform. On the basis of the traditional management system, we should develop a more comprehensive management system combining with the features of electronic archives.

2. Fully guarantee the security of the storage medium for the electronic confidential archives. The storage medium for the electronic confidential archives generally refers to CD, soft disk or hard drive. Based on the characteristics of electronic archives storage medium to take effective measures to make it play a role. Mainly control the suitable temperature and humidity environment. Keep the ideal temperature of the electronic file for 17°C~20°C, relative humidity is 35%~45%. Prevent dust damage to electronic archives carrier, mainly including the physical damage, chemical damage, and biological damage. Prevent external magnetic field and mechanical vibration, external magnetic field effect on the magnetic carrier, can make the magnetic coating degaussing or magnetization, causing signal loss, destruction of records information, influence, speaking, reading and writing effect. Mechanical wear and tear or strong vibration also can cause damage to electronic files. So the electronic file storage medium must be far away from the magnetic field and against a strong shock. On the one hand, we should propose fireproof and waterproof measures to ensure the hardware security; on the other hand, corresponding backup should be provided timely to prevent the loss of important data from storage medium failure. As for electronic files for long-term preservation, the carrier s to be sampled once every two years. The sampling ratio is not less than 10%. The electronic files of magnetic carrier need to be copied once every four years, electronic archives at least once every five years archived or migration, the original carrier and retention time is not less than two years. (3) The use of electronic classified archives, besides according to the general use of paper files, must also be: Every seal save CD cannot be checked out. Any copy of electronic archives shall be with the approval of the archives department heads, without the approval of any unit or individual anyone are not allowed to copy the electronic files. Every online classified electronic archives, reliable security measures should be taken, and shall strictly abide by the relevant security regulations of the state and the units. Control the use permissions for the use of electronic files at different levels. Also, record the environment and climate change, timely adjust the temperature and humidity. Regularly check the quality of electronic archives, make after-inspection records at any time. Set the scope of authorization referring to archive electronic files, ensure the security and confidentiality of the electronic files.

3.3 *Further improve the professionalism and service quality of the archivists*

The archivists who are in charge of the utilization service are the direct implementers of the utilization regulations. They have direct liability for the files' security. In the future work, apart from the training on the electronic information management technology and archives management skills for the archivists, professional awareness should be strengthened. The high degree of political responsibility, the spirit of serving the people heart and soul and the passion for their career are also important. Possessing a higher educational level can help them summarize and analyze the experience and problems in their work so as to master the regular pattern of their work.

3.4 *Well manage the warehouse of electronic files*

The management of temperature and humidity of the durable storage in the archives: (1) it is inappropriate to implement a same temperature and humidity standard all over the country. Carrying out a more practical standard adapting to local conditions is more reasonable. The current standard for temperature and humidity of the archives is a little high theoretically. (2) "Prevention first, combining prevention with controlling" is the basic idea of the file protection technology. In order to maintain a low temperature and low humidity environment, firstly we should start from containment structures of thermal protection, moisture barrier and waterproof. Then control the temperature and humidity into a suitable condition by utilizing the equipments and technology of airtight, aeration and air-conditioning.

3.5 *The confidentiality for electronic files in digital archives*

Digital archives are the data distribution center for the information resources, also are the final destination of e-government resources. The combination and systematical study of the relationship between the two are rare both practically and theoretically. Therefore, the study on the construction of local governments' digital archives based on the concept of e-government is conducive to the digital archive research, to the smooth development of digital archive project, to the construction of e-government and to the text research on science of administrative, archival science, management and information engineering. In particular, the e-government conception focuses on the way of digital archives construction for local government.

3.6 *Strengthen the information security management in the unit*

Firstly, carry out the regulation of physical isolation, stick to the principle that classified files cannot be online. Secondly, protect the computer from virus invasion: Refuse to use piracy management software. In order to prevent the computer from virus invasion, and to ensure the safety of the archives information confidential, archives management departments should use the original file management software. Be careful to use floppy disk. Electronic information files are usually kept with CD, floppy and hard disks for storage medium, a computer virus is spread easily through these media. The computers of archive department should use the special designed plate as far as possible, don't use other floppy disks. Don't download files and software at random. Archives department do not use the internet to download files and software as far as possible especially visit unknown sites, prevent the invasion of the virus. Use genuine antivirus software. Archives department should choose legitimate anti-virus software as far as possible and update and upgrade anti-virus software.

4 CONCLUSION

The confidential regulations are the primary means to protect the classified files from violation. Electronic information confidentiality is a very complicated systematic project, which calls for all the social forces to participate into it. Only by this can we form a positive interaction mode of "secrecy drives management, management drives service" and effectively improve the archive management of our country to a new level.

ACKNOWLEDGEMENT

Corresponding author: Yan-Xia LIU, Environmental Management College of China, E-mail: 109483131@qq.com.

REFERENCES

[1] Long Zhang. Promote the Regulationization and Standardization of Archive Management Work[J]. Journal of Innermongolia Radio and TV University, 2007(12):112–113.

[2] Yingchun Wen. Exploration on the New Thinking of Security Work of Enterprise Archives[J]. Technology and Enterprise, 2012(22).

[3] Lingling Zhou. How to do well in archive security work[J]. Science and Technology Information, 2006(5).

[4] Chonghua LI. How to do well in archive security work[J]. Modern Communication, 2011(5).

[5] Yan Zhao, Ning Chang. Primary Discussion on Archive Security in the New Period[J]. Heilongjiang Historical Record, 2010(3).

[6] Xiujuan Zhang. Some problems that should arouse attention in archive information construction of the office[J]. Electronic Information and Technology, 2004(5).

Computer, Intelligent Computing and Education Technology – Liu, Sung & Yao (Eds)
© *2014 Taylor & Francis Group, London, ISBN 978-1-138-02469-4*

Data mining techniques for customer analysis and management in banking industry

J.Y. Wang & C.X. Zhao
Nanjing University of Science and Technology, Nanjing, China

ABSTRACT: With the development of information systems, the banking industry has already stored large amounts of data. How to use these data effectively and improve the service level becomes an essential problem. Data Mining can collect potentially valuable information and data, reveal the existing rules and predict the future trend, which can help the bank make the decision and improve competitiveness. This article discussed the implementation of customer analysis and management in the banking industry by data mining.

Keywords: commercial bank; customer relationship management; data mining; decision tree

1 GENERAL INTRODUCTION

Customer Relationship Management (CRM) is also known as Customer Asset Management or Customer Interaction Management.[1] CRM is the scope of the bank's strategy, it distinguish different kinds of customers by customer segmentation and optimize business processes. In order to meet customer demand and maximize bank profitability, CRM enhances customer satisfaction by connection customers and banking products. Base on Romano,[2] CMR attracts and maintain valuable customers and banish worthless customers. Gartner[3] think that CMR organized the enterprise through customer classification, encourage behaviors that meet the customers' needs and bridge customers and vendors to improve revenue and satisfaction.

A pressing issue facing us is that how to use data warehouse and data mining technology in customer relationship management, including the construction of CRM system, the research on data warehouse and data mining technology, more effective design and other aspects of mining algorithm.

The banking industry currently focuses on the difficulties of how to integrate customer information with large amount of data, mine the customers' value and understand the business process rules. Customer information will be used for decision-making. It appears that data mining techniques can be used in all phases for Customers' life cycle management. Data mining can help banks identify customers' characteristics and found customers' common ground, which can expand the customer group and prevent the

losing by taking specific measures for customers who have similar characteristics with losing group. In summary, data mining will receive increasing attention in banking industry based on increasing demands for knowledge discovery and decision support systems.

This article discussed the implementation of customer analysis and management in the banking industry in different aspects including: Customers classification method, classification model and decision tree method for bad debt prediction.

2 THE IMPLEMENTATION OF DATA MINING IN THE BANKING INDUSTRY

Data mining is a new business information processing technology, its main feature is using commercial database to get data extraction, transformation, analysis, and model processing to search the key element of business decisions.

Collection and processing of financial transactions need a lot of complicated data, most banks' financial institutions provide a variety of banking services (such as personal savings), credit services (such as Loans, personal credit cards) and investment services (such as mutual funds). Financial data mining can find useful information to help banks predict the future trend by analysis customers' demand trends in the past and distinguish the potential customers and poor reputation customers by clustering methods.

The main data mining techniques using for banking industry are data warehouse and Online Analytical Processing (OLAP). As a platform, with massive data owned by the bank, through feature extraction, cleansing, integration, transformation, mining, pattern evaluation, data processing methods such as knowledge representation, found the association between large amounts of data and trends, explore the unique business rules and models that cannot discover by other ways. Nowadays statistical methods including linear and nonlinear regression analysis, discriminant Analysis, cluster analysis, principal component analysis and time series analysis are widely used. The use of specific analysis methods includes Decision Tree, Association Detection, Neural Network, Genetic Algorithms and so on.

3 BANK'S CUSTOMERS CLASSIFICATION

Each client of the bank has different characters; however the company does not need to concern about all the differences for each one. Whether to meet their needs should be carefully considered for the banks. If base on a larger colony, lower cost services will be provided to the client, if base on a small colony, the services will cost much. In order to analyze the problem, the model for customers' value gives as following:

$$V = \sum_{i=0}^{n} (G_i \times R_i - C_i)$$

G_i represents the customer group.
R_i represents group contribution rate.
C_i represents cost that the bank pays for the group.

Because of the fierce competition for the same service with other banks, Crouhy[4] thinks that the profit rate for a mature group begin to drop as time went by. So the whole revenue for the bank will decline. In order to avoid this situation, the bank should provide new services, divide one group into two customer groups: G_m, G_n, for the group G_m, still provide the original service, whereas provide new services to G_n. Because of the new service have less competition, profit rate becomes higher, but by offering a new service, the cost will also increase, so if:

$$(G_{mn} \times R_{mn} - C_{mn}) > (G_m \times R_m - C_m) + (G_n \times R_n - C_n)$$

If so, this classification is valuable.

4 BANK'S CUSTOMER CLASSIFICATION MODEL

To identify and distinguish the data accurately, finding proper model is a vertical process for data

mining. Derived model is based on analysis of the training data set, use classification rules, neural networks and mathematical formula. Currently, classification is widely used in business, especially in the banking area.

To construct the classifier, we need input data set as training sample. Training set consists of database records or tuples, each tuple is an eigenvector consisting of attributes. The form of a concrete sample can be: $S(V_1, V_2 \dots V_n, C)$; V means field value, C means category. Different classifiers have different characteristics. We evaluate the accuracy of prediction, complexity of calculation and simplicity degree of classification models. The accuracy of general classification related to the characteristics of data, such as data noise and missing values.

Based on Berry,[5] there is no certain method that suitable for different kind of data with various characteristics. Data classification process mainly consists of two steps: firstly, shown in Figure 1, established a conceptual model to describe existing data set that has already been classified, this model is obtained by analyses the content for data recording, therefore, this classification learning is also called supervising

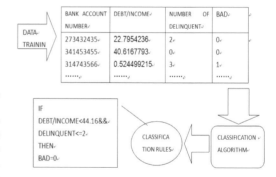

Figure 1. Model learning.

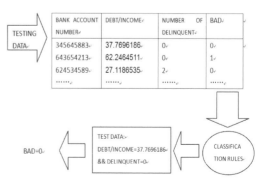

Figure 2. Classification testing.

learning. As it is shown in Figure 1, the data set has been classified into two groups by credit rating: 1 (BAD) and 0 (GOOD).

Secondly, shown in Figure 2, use obtained model to estimate the classification accuracy. Use a set of samples with a classification type to test, testing samples and training samples were independent. If the accuracy of learning model obtained by the test is considered acceptable, then you can use this model to classify the unknown data. For example: Figure 1 use training data set to learn and get classification rules. Figure 2 uses to obtain learning classification rules to test the accuracy of the model, as well as classify new customers for prediction.

5 DECISION TREE METHOD AND BAD DEBT PREDICTION

Decision tree learning is a method commonly uses in data mining. The goal is to use information gain to identify the strongest ability to distinguish the properties of the database and divided it into multiple sub-sets. Then recursive call until each subset contains the same type of data. Finally, use decision trees to classify new samples. The most influential decision tree method is ID3 method developed by J. Ross. Quiulan.[6] In 1986, based on ID3, Schlimmer and Fisher designed ID4 algorithm. In 1988, P.E. designed the ID5 algorithm, which developed ID4 algorithm.

In the decision tree method, we used property with the highest information gain as the current test node, so that minimum the need for devide training samples to subset.

The expectations of the sample information are calculated as follows:

Suppose S is a set of instances

$$entropy(S) = -\sum_{i=1}^{n} p_i \log_2 p_i$$

The data set is S, n means the number of samples, C_i means classification (for $i = 1 \ldots n$), Pi is the probability of C_i,

A divided by the entropy of the subset is calculated as follows:

$$entropy(S, A) = -\sum_{i=1}^{m} \frac{|S_i|}{|S|} entropy(S_i)$$

Information gain is calculated as follows:

$$gain(S, A) = entropy(S) - en$$

For personal loan business, customers can be divided into two categories, bad debt group and the loan paid group. To forecast bad debt, we use the information with customers' characteristics by decision tree method. Figure 3 shows a domestic bank's customer database as training samples. The attribute is: "BAD", this property has two different values, which is, {0, 1}, 0 means good debt and 1 means bad debt. Suppose category Cl correspond to 0, category C2 correspond to 1. As is shown in Figure 3, based on decision tree algorithm, delinquency and debit/income rate are the most two important factors for bad debt.

Using the ID3 algorithm, we get a decision tree shown in Figure 4.

We can see from Figure 4, using the decision tree algorithm, segmentation analysis can be done for customer data. We can determine customer who has less than 44 debit/income rate and 2 times of delinquency will have low bad debit rates. Therefore, the bank can distinguish between valuable customers and worthless customers which help the bank avoid losing and improve profit rate.

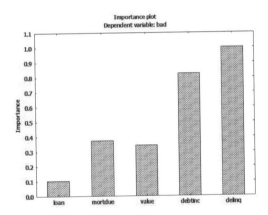

Figure 3. Importance of attributes.

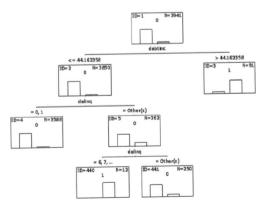

Figure 4. Decision tree model.

623

6 CONCLUSION

Customer relationship management is essential for banking industry which helps the company identify potential customers and allocate resource for valuable customers. Data Mining technique collects valuable information among a large number of data from bank's information system, reveal the existing rules and predict the future trend. This article elaborates customer classification model in the banking industry, and analyze a practical example using a decision tree method for bad debt prediction.

REFERENCES

[1] Carter, C. & Catlett, J. 1987. Assessing credit card applications using machine learning[J]. IEEE Expert, 2(3): 71–79.

[2] Hunt, M. 1987. The process of translating research findings into nursing practice[J]. Journal of advanced nursing, 12(1): 101–110.

[3] Rombel, A. CRM Shifts to Data Mining to Keep Customers[J]. Global Finance, 11, 15.

[4] Crouhy, M. & Galai, D. & Mark, A.R. 2000. Comparative Analysis of Current Credit Risk Models. Journal of Banking and Finance, 1/2, 24.

[5] Berry, M.J.A. 2000. Mastering Data Mining: the Art and Seienee Of Customer Relationship Management. NewYork: Wiley Cmoputer Publishing.

[6] Berry, M.J.A. & G. Linoff. 2004. Data Mining Techniques: For Marketing, Sales, and Customer Relationship Management. Wiley Computer Publishing.

Computer, Intelligent Computing and Education Technology – Liu, Sung & Yao (Eds)
© 2014 Taylor & Francis Group, London, ISBN 978-1-138-02469-4

Design of words similarity based message router in enterprise service bus

X. Sui
Henan Key Laboratory for Machinery Design and Transmission System, Luoyang, Henan, China

C.Y. Liu, J.S. Li & H.B. Han
School of Mechatronics Engineering, Henan University of Science and Technology, Luoyang, Henan, China

ABSTRACT: In order to change the poor adaptability and low efficiency of the message router in enterprise service bus, this paper proposed a natural language processing based semantic-level message routing algorithm and design an intelligent message router which is suitable for large-scale business integration. The designed message router is designed to imply high-efficient, dynamic and intelligent message routing and improve the ability of service integration bus by expanding its adaptation and reducing the cost of maintenance of business collaboration.

Keywords: enterprise service bus; concept auto clustering; natural language processing; word similarity based message routing

1 PROPOSAL

In many existed SOA solutions, the Enterprise Service Bus (ESB) has already become an essential core infrastructure for its ability to transport and exchange data between heterogeneous systems. As the kernel of ESB, the message router's performance largely decides the efficiency and validity of the entire service integration environment. Further more, the message router, which uses Web Service Description Language (WSDL) to describe integrated service, has already exposed the shortcomings in its key functions in the aspects like services registration, services search and services matching and led to low accuracy in services search and increasing cost of maintenance.

Figure 1 shows the brief scenario of message routing in ESB environment. The main function of a message router is to choose a proper service provider out of many candidates when receives a service request sent by service consumer. The existing message routers normally use definite service address in service request as the main certification to complete the message routing process, which is easy to understand and control in simple scenarios but poorly respond to complicated enterprise environment. To date, many researchers studied advanced message routing mechanism, like content-based message routing, to improve the efficiency in ESB. Gulnoza Ziyaeva and Dugki Min [1] studied the content-based message routing to dynamically select proper service consumer in complicated environment. Yan Liu and Ian Groton [2] studied the message routing in ESB environment. Sun Yao [3] proposed a dynamic reliable model-DRRSR to modify the path contents in the routing table and the analysis of the DRSR and DRESR model to relocate service providers. These entire content-based message routing mechanism are not utilized widely because they involve the sensitive information in enterprise environment, which is kept secret to infrastructure utilizing the service integration.

In order to solve this problem, this paper tries to present semantic-level, word similarity based message routine method from a new perspective. The rest of this paper is organized as follows: Section 2 presents a word similarity based message routing algorithm on the study of an automatic concept clustering method. Section 3 gives the design of message router on base of the proposed new message routing algorithm. Section 4 shows the experiment result to testify the effectiveness and accuracy of the new designed message router.

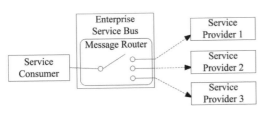

Figure 1. Message routing scenario in ESB environment.

Section 5 summarized the advantages of this new message router in ESB and shows the possible direction for future research.

2 DESIGN OF THE WORD SIMILARITY BASED MESSAGE ROUTER

The existed message routing method, which normally relies on the keywords in service address in WSDL, has already shown poor applicability and will fail when participated services' addresses changes. In order to improve accuracy and applicability in message routing, this paper presents a word similarity based message routing method which is constructed on the study of an automatic retrieval and clustering of similar words [4]. After a brief introduction of this automatic clustering algorithm, we will design and implement a word similarity based message routing algorithm for web service integration.

2.1 Automatic retrieval and clustering of similar words

2.1.1 Natural language processing of corpus
Firstly, this paper chooses Stanford Parser [5] to parse corpus and extract dependency triples. A dependency triple consists of two words and the grammatical relationship between them in the input sentence. For example, an input sentence "It's a sendup of the old model …" will be parsed into dependency triples as:

nsubj(sendup-4, It-1)
cop(sendup-4, 's-2)
det(sendup-4, a-3)
det(model-8, the-6)
amod(model-8, old-7)
prep_of(sendup-4, model-8)
…

In this paper, we use the notation "$r(g–n1, d–n2)$" to denote these dependency triples, where g is the governor word, d is the dependent word, r is the grammar relationship between g and d, $n1$ (or $n2$) is the g (or d)'s index (start from 1) in the input sentence. Furthermore, $n1$ and $n2$ will be omitted in the following calculation for they are irrelevant to the computation of word similarity.

2.1.2 Calculating the information of dependency triples
This paper follows the information measurement algorithm of dependency triples in paper [4]: notation "$\|g,r,d\| = c$" means a certain dependency triple, (g, r)'s frequency count in the given corpus is c. To measure the information contained in the statement $\|g,r,d\| = c$, we: 1. Measure the amount

of information in the statement that a randomly selected dependency triple is (g,r,d) when the value of $\|g,r,d\|$ is not known. 2. Measure the amount of information in the same state when the value of $\|g,r,d\|$ is obtained. The difference between these two number is taken to the information contained in $\|g,r,d\| = c$. Let $I(g,r,d)$ denote the amount information contained in $\|g,r,d\| = c$. Its value can be computed as follows:

$$I(g,r,d) = \log \frac{\| g,r,d \| \cdot \| *,r,* \|}{\| g,r,* \| \cdot \| *,r,d \|} \tag{1}$$

In equation (1), "*" is the wildcard means any word can be applied into its position.

2.1.3 Generate the similarity words set
This paper uses equation(2) to measure the similarity between two governor words:

$$
\begin{aligned}
Sim(g_1,g_2) \\
= \sum_{(r,d)\subset(T(g_1)\cap T(g_2))} I(g_1,r,d)*I(g_2,r,d) \\
\div (\sum_{(r,d)\subset T(g_1)} I(g_1,r,d)^2 + \sum_{(r,d)\subset T(g_2)} I(g_2,r,d)^2 \\
- \sum_{(r,d)\subset(T(g_1)\cap T(g_2))} I(g_1,r,d)*I(g_2,r,d)
\end{aligned}
$$

$$\tag{2}$$

For a certain governor word g, a thesaurus entry which contains the top-N most similar words can be constructed. The thesaurus entry for governor word g could be like:

$g(pos): g_1, s_1, g_2, s_2, …., g_n, s_n.$

where pos is a part of speech, g_i is a similar word, $s_i = sim(g,gi)$ and s_i's are ordered in descending order.

In order to enlarge the similar words' range of a given governor word g and increase the query hit rate in the message routing process, we expand the concept of RNNs (Respective Nearest Neighbors) in paper [4] to n-RNNs: two words are a pair of respective top-N nearest neighbors if each is the other's top-N most similar words. Next, a word's similar words set can be constructed the concept of n-RNNs.

2.2 Words similarity based message routing algorithm

For the convenience reason, this paper present definition 1 and 2 as following:
Def. 1: we call an web service's operation which can receive and process message as Message Function (MF), and choose the MF's belonging web

service's endpoint name, service name, operation name and the input, output arguments of this MF to identity it, which is denoted as MF = {MF^{EP}, MF^S, MF^{OP}, MF^I, MF^O}.

Def. 2: for a given web-service request, R, we choose its endpoint name, service name, operation name, input and output name as its identity, which can be denoted as R = {R^{ep}, R^s, R^{op}, R^I, R^O}.

The reason why we choose MF's input and output arguments to identify a MF is to avoid the operation override situation in which two different operations may use same operation names but different arguments.

The whole words similarity based message routing algorithm is shown as follows in Table 1.

In this algorithm, all pre-registered web services in message router forms the Web Service Registry (WSR) and we combine all its MFs as the Message Function Matrix (MFM). When a given service request, R, is received, the algorithm compute its similarity to all MFs in WSR's MFM and put the qualified MF, whose similarity to the request R is higher than a pre-defined threshold (MF_SIM_THRES), into the Candidate MF set (CMFSet). After all MFs in MFM is processed, this algorithm will sort the MFs in CMFSet by their similarity to the given request and the most similar one will be selected as the message routing destination. Here, we compute the similarity between a MF and service request as following:

$$MFMatch(MF_i, R)$$
$$= g1 * Sim(MF_i^{ep}, R^{ep}) + g2 * Sim(MF_i^s, R^s)$$
$$+ g3 * Sim(MF_i^{op}, R^{op}) + g4 * Sim(MF_i^I, R^I)$$
$$+ g5 * Sim(MF_i^O, R^O)$$
$$(3)$$

In which the similarity between two key address words (endpoint name, service name, etc.) follows

equation (3) and g_i is the weight for certain type of key address words which meets:

$$g_i \in (0,1) \text{ and } \sum_{i=1}^{5} g_i = 1 \qquad (4)$$

According to the common principle in message routing, the choose for the value of g_i should follow the priority order between different types of key address words, $g_1 > g_2 > g_3 > g_4 > g_5$, which means that the endpoint name plays more important roles than the service name or any other kind of key address words in message destination location process, etc.

2.3 Architecture of word similarity based message router in ESB

Based on the architecture presented in paper [6], this paper designs a new word similarity based message router, which is illustrated in Figure 2.

This new message router contains 8 modules as its main components, these modules are:

Message routing service: this is the core component in message router which encapsulates all the details in message routing process and provides all its functions in a service form to all the other components in enterprise service bus environment, these functions includes: message endpoint register/unregister, endpoint lookup, add/remove message routing channel and of course, message routing.

Service endpoint registry: in ESB's runtime, service providers will dynamically summit the information of service endpoints to message router and it is service endpoint registry's responsibility to register these info in its in-memory database. Furthermore, service endpoint registry will index these endpoints by their endpoint name, service name, operation

---

Table 1. The process of words similarity based message routing algorithm.

MessageRoutingProcess(R)
  Foreach MFi in WRS.MFM
  //Compute the similarity between service request
    R and MF
    If(CalMFSim(R, MFi)> = MF_SIM_THRES)
      CMFSet.add(MFi)
    End
  IF CMFSet.size = = 0 Throw RoutingFailedException
  //sort all the candidate MF by its similarity
    to request R
  Sort (CMFSet)
  DeliveryMessage(R, CMFSet [0].EP)
End

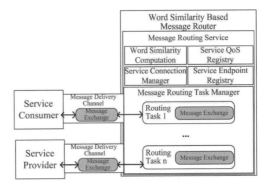

Figure 2. The architecture of word similarity based message router.

name, input and output arguments to enhance runtime endpoint lookup performances.

Service connection manager: ESB end users may decline service connection in their service integration description file to use direct, definite service connection between service consumer and service provider. The service connection manager in message router is responsible to add, remove and query service connection info in runtime situation.

Message delivery channel: all the service integration participants use their message delivery channels to complete their asyn-/synchronous message delivery task with message router. And, when a proper service endpoint is located, message routing service will buffer the delivering message to this endpoint's belonging message delivery channel and the channel's owner, a service provider, will periodically poll its message delivery channel to check and process received message in a FIFO way.

Routing task manager: in order to increase its efficiency, message router service utilizes concurrent mode to finish message routing tasks. Considering the high reusability of these routing tasks, routing task manager maintains certain number of sleeping routing task threads in its thread pool and randomly active one to route arriving service request.

Message routing task: it is an independent thread which can receive, transfer and delivery message like a postman in ESB environment. When routing job is finished, this task will automatically return to routing task manager for next round of calling.

Words similarity computation: this model executes the word similarity algorithm in eq.3. It will compute and compare the similarity between incoming service request and registered message functions in service endpoint registry.

Service QoS registry: its job is to collect, count and register the runtime quality of integrated services. The message router may use these statistic data to filter endpoints as the final, suitable one to process receiving service request when multiple endpoints are selected according to word similarity computation.

3 EXPERIMENTS

This paper implements the word similarity algorithm in Eclipse 3.6 and run all computation on a dual-core 2.8 Pentium CPU with 2 gigabytes memory. The experiment is fulfilled in two stages.

3.1 *Experiment on word similarity calculation*

We choose part of American National Corpus [7], Open American National Corpus (OANC), as the proceeding corpus for word similarity calculation.

The OANC contains 2,300 documents and the Stanford parser extracts 63,806 content words, 60 relationship words and about 1,636,991 dependency triples. In order to fasten process speed, the algorithm performs dictionary-based semantic disambiguation on these dependency triples and reduces the number down to 942,735. The whole words counting process takes 56 seconds.

In the process of experiment, we found that the dependency triples which appear too few times will not affect the final result significantly but increase the counting time consuming apparently. Furthermore, the n of n-RNNs and the length of thesaurus entry can affect the experiment performance as well. We choose different threshold values of these parameters to testify their impact on experiment, which is shown in Table 2.

From Table 2 we can see that: 1. Lower the dependency triples appearance; 2. Shorter length of thesaurus entry and 3. Smaller n of n-RNNs, will take more time in computation while obtain more similarity words. Considering the real-time requirement for message router in ESB environment, this paper tries to carefully choose the values of the thresholds to strike a balance between time consuming and the number of similarity words.

3.2 *Message routing experiment based on word similarity computation*

This paper utilizes Apache Axis 2.0 to design a number of web service models, which are integrated with the help of BPEL modeling tools. Next, while keeping a copy of these service integration models with accurate web-service address keywords (Set A), we manually edit a few of the description files of WSDL by changing the original keywords with similar words (Set B). The experiment will testify both the traditional accurate keywords based message routing strategy and word similarity based

Table 2. Experiment on different threshold values' effect on word similarity computation.

Times of dependency triples appeareance	Length of thesaurus entry	n of n-RNNs	Time cost (ms)	Similar words number
10	10	5	127,297	197
10	10	3	101,640	108
10	10	1	101,359	36
7	10	5	141,656	379
5	10	5	230,844	674
10	7	5	102,016	344
10	5	5	102,515	559
5	5	5	237,938	1533

Table 3. Comparison of two message routing strategies.

	Accurate keywords based message routing		Word similarity based message routing	
	Success/time	Fail/time	Success/time	Fail/time
Set A	100/340 ms	0/0 ms	98/627 ms	2/20 ms
Set B	32/110 ms	68/1,823 ms	82/495 ms	18/543 ms

message routing strategy to shows the validity of this new designed message router. The result of this experiment is shown in Table 3.

From the comparison in Table 3, we can find that when set A is used, both algorithms show equal performance (100 times vs. 98 times) while accurate keywords based message routing consumes less time because it directly uses the relationship "equal" between keywords in service address and service request and simply ignore those potential "semantic equal" situation. The experiment result changes apparently when set B of web-service integration models are tested: the accurate keywords based message routing algorithm fails for 68 times when it cannot find proper service providers under the constraint of relationship "equal", while the word similarity based message router success for 82 times. This experiment shows that the word similarity based message router achieves higher accuracy but takes more time expenses in message routing process.

4 CONCLUSIONS

In order to meet the actual requirement for ESB solution in enterprise environment in which the keywords of the address of integrated web service change as time goes by, this paper designs a word similarity based message router on the study of an automatic retrieval and clustering algorithm of similar words. The proposed experiments demonstrate the validity of this new designed message router. On the same time, we found that the word similarity computation, which includes natural language process on the corpus and word thesaurus generation, consumes more time than the accurate word based message routing algorithm and leads to low effectiveness, this is the problem we have to solve in the future study.

ACKNOWLEDGEMENT

This paper is supported by HAUST Youth Grand: NLP-based word similarity algorithm in ESB environment (2012QN021).

REFERENCES

[1] Ziyaeva, G. & Choi, E. & Min, D. 2008. Content-Based Intelligent Routing and Message Processing in Enterprise Service Bus. International Conference on Convergence and Hybrid Information Technology.
[2] Liu, Y. & Gorton, I. & Zhu, L.M. 2007. Performace Prediction of Service-Oriented Applications based on an Enterprise Service Bus. Annual International Computer Software and Applications Conference.
[3] Sun, Y. & Lian, D.B. An Efficient and Reliable Dynamic Routing Model in ESB. Computer Systems & Applications, 2011,20(2).
[4] Lin, D.K. Automatic Retrieval and Clustering of Similar words.
[5] The Stanford Parser: A statistical parser. http://nlp.stanford.edu/software/lex-parser.shtml#Sample [EB/OL].
[6] Sui, X. & Zhu, Y.L. & Nan, L. Design and Implementation of Message Router in Enterprise Service Bus. Computer Engineering, 2011, 37(21).
[7] American National Corpus[EB/OL]. http://www.americannationalcorpus.org/.

Computer, Intelligent Computing and Education Technology – Liu, Sung & Yao (Eds)
© 2014 Taylor & Francis Group, London, ISBN 978-1-138-02469-4

Proper guidance to mobile phone culture on campus

Ya-Li Wang
Editorial Department, Environmental Management College of China, Qinhuangdao, Hebei, China

ABSTRACT: College students have become more and more dependent on the mobile phone, which poses a new challenge to the training and education of college students and meanwhile puts forward a new problem to college student management. Therefore, the positive roles of mobile phone culture in ideological and Political Education deserve full exploration and it is essential to provide students proper guidance and meanwhile avoid the negative influence.

Keywords: ideological and political education; college students; mobile phone culture; guidance

With the development of modern communication technology, mobile phones have become increasingly multifunctional, starting to transform to smart phones. Besides the original function, some other functions have been added, such as 3G network and various games. As a result, mobile phones have turned into a must for college students. However, some students are overly dependent on cell phones and develop psychological problems. Without the phones at hand, they will become anxious, perplexed, depressed and even annoyed, which not only affects their daily interpersonal relationship, but also interferes in their health and growth. It poses a new challenge to the training and education of college students and meanwhile puts forward a new problem to college student management.

1 PRESENT CONDITION OF MOBILE PHONES ON CAMPUS

The popularity of mobile phones among college students has led to the phone craze on campus and almost every class is disturbed or interrupted by keypad tones or warning tones, which especially becomes worse in those crowded selective courses. Particularly, in some assemblies or meetings, ringtones rise here and there and never cease. It has become a common sight that fingers dance on the phones in the classroom, canteen, corridor, playground and wherever.

College students have become over-dependent on cell phones and therefore develop various psychological problems. Psychologists give it a name—mobile phone dependence and this is a mental illness with its typical feature—mentally addicted. This dependence indicates some people choose mobile phones as their most important communicative approach in their interpersonal communication and remain strongly dependent on mobile phones both mentally and physically.

This is a hard nut for colleges and universities to deal with the problem of mobile phone dependence among college students. Whether a student suffers from this dependence is judged not simply by how many times he uses a mobile phone, but by for what he uses it. Even if a student becomes mentally dependent on a mobile phone, he does not necessarily have psychological problems. What matters is that if he is able to use the phone in a healthy and correct way. According to our investigation, research and analysis, we have concluded three standards as judging criteria: firstly, excessive use of the mobile phone has produced a harmful effect on daily work and life; secondly, spend much time playing with the mobile phone without doing anything helpful or useful; lastly, when the phone is out of service or powered off, the owner will have both mental and physical reactions, restless, nervous, dizzy, feeble, even with the heart beating much faster.

In order to better know the present condition of mobile phones on campus, we have made a questionnaire survey among the students in Qinhuangdao's vocational schools. In March, 2012, we chose the students in Qinhuangdao's vocational schools as the survey objects and did a test with each class as a group. The test took 35 minutes and a total of 800 questionnaires were delivered and 753 returned. With 5 questionnaires invalid, the rest of 748 questionnaires were valid. Of the 748 respondents, 3 of them did not have cell phones and 687 of them admitted that mobile phones became indispensable in their life, taking up 91.8% of the respondents. Besides, monthly phone charge amounted to 50.04 yuan averagely and daily phone-on time covered 19.55 hours. 43.9% of the students chose to have their phones on around the clock.

The survey shows that a majority of students have developed both physical and mental problems because of their excessive using of mobile phones. They are labeled with the symptoms of mobile phone dependence. Overdependence on cell phones not only affects daily life and work, but exerts a negative impact on mental health and what is worse is that it may lead to mental problems. Therefore, it is essential that schools attach great importance to this issue and take some effective measures to control and even interfere.

2 NEGATIVE IMPACTS OF MOBILE PHONE DEPENDENCE

2.1 *Impact on mental health*

A working cell phone is able to produce electromagnetic radiation and it has a harmful effect on eyes, heart and nervous system. Constant texting and surfing on the phone also does great physical harm, arms sour and numb, neck aching and eyes dry and tired.

Some students power on their phones around the clock and put them in their pockets anytime and anywhere and even leave the phones beside their pillows when they are sleeping. These bad habits have done great harm to their health.

Excessive use of mobile phones makes students addicted and over-dependent. Some students even have auditory hallucinations. When a phone rings, they always mistakenly feel that it is their phones are ringing and sometimes they even feel that their phones are ringing when actually they are not. If they forget to take their phones or their phones are out of service, they will be very afraid to miss any calls and become very anxious and restless.

2.2 *Impact on teaching*

Quite a few students are not able to be well-disciplined in class and they text, chat, play games or read novels and news on the phone. As a result, students cannot concentrate on the class and teaching quality has been greatly affected. Sometimes ringtones rise in class, teachers and students are disturbed and even interrupted, which has produces a very harmful effect on class teaching.

2.3 *Impact on students*

Some students use the mobile phones to send messages to other students on the quiet and inform them if the teachers will take attendance and help them skip the class. In addition, some students use mobile phones to cheat in the exams, exchanging and even sharing the answers, which has posed a challenge to the honesty and responsibility of college students.

2.4 *Impact on interpersonal relationship*

Some students have been indulged in the unreal world of phone network. They make friends by texts and network but ignore those friends in the real world. They even have difficulty communicating with those people around and sometime they contact their dorm mates by texts. Overdependence on cell phones has severely affected their communication with others, but also set barriers to their interpersonal relationships. Consequently, they feel lonely and isolated.

2.5 *Impact on values*

Messages involving sex, politics and fraud are potential dangers to college students, because most of the students are simple and short of self-protection awareness. Some students do not take obscene messages seriously and even share with others. They are not capable enough to distinguish the right from the wrong and therefore are likely to be cheated and get lost, deviating from the right path.

2.6 *Impact on consumption concept*

With the advance of technology, mobile phones have been updated in appearance, style and function as fast as possible. Together with this, the prices range from hundred to thousand and students are prone to compare with each other to feed their vanity but bring burden to their families.

3 APPROACHES TO THIS PROBLEM

Culture of mobile phones is a kind of modern and open culture, an essential part of campus culture. It is a double-edged sword, having both advantages and disadvantages. It is necessary that we actively offer proper guidance not interfere or interrupt in a violent way.

3.1 *Give a full play to the positive aspect of the culture of mobile phones*

3.1.1 *Meet the needs of college students to communicate with others*
Each college student is eager to have a favorable interpersonal relationship and the appearance of mobile phones shortens interpersonal distance,

making interpersonal communication fast and convenient. Teachers send messages to students by means of mobile phones or QQ, helping students acquire the exact information without any delay and really facilitating the communication between teachers and students. With the help of mobile phones, embarrassment or nervousness resulting from face-to-face communication has been avoided. Besides, words about thanks or apologies can be conveyed by phone messages and the same apply to festival greetings and wishes, which greatly contributes to interpersonal communication.

3.1.2 *Help college students acquire knowledge*

This is an information age and the age to acquire knowledge through books, magazines and newspapers has been replaced by the age of internet. There is a popular saying among college students: if you don't know it, baidu it. The 3G network provided by the mobile phones help students get the answers to their questions. In addition, the network provides with the latest news at home and abroad. Novels, blogs and forums are also available on the network. Mobile phones are small and inexpensive and easy to take, especially the wide use of smart phones; all these advantages have met the information needs of college students.

3.2 *Eliminate the negative impact of mobile phone dependence on college students*

3.2.1 *Strengthen social supervision and improve the legal system*

It is crucial that China's legislation in standardizing the dissemination of mobile phone text messages be improved and China further standardize the information services through legal means. Chinese government should strengthen the supervision of mobile phone culture, formulate corresponding laws and regulations and ensure that there are laws to abide by so that mobile phone operators, web services and mobile phone users' personal behavior can be effectively supervised and restrained.

At the same time, strengthen the filter function of text messaging on mobile phones. It is necessary that cooperation and communication with mobile communication operators be enhanced so as to set up a function similar to filter or firewall. This function can intervene and control the content of the text messages received by college students and delete those unsuitable messages for students. In this way, students can directly shield those unwelcome senders' numbers on their phones. The filtering function will effectively prevent the invasion of bad information, which is conducive to the civilized dissemination of text messages.

3.2.2 *Offer proper guidance and promote healthy mobile phone culture*

3.2.2.1 Strengthen moral instructions and help students develop good habits

Take mobile phone culture as a moral instruction platform and help students form proper values. Students are expected to be aware that the proper use of mobile phones contributes to social ethics as well as the atmosphere for study. Make the negative impacts of mobile phones known to the students and they are required to reject vulgar and trash messages and join hands to create a pleasant atmosphere for mobile phone culture.

3.2.2.2 Rules are to be made to restrain students from their improper using of mobile phones

Mobile phones are not allowed to use in class and they are adjusted to silence or vibration. Teachers are required to take the lead and in this way they are qualified to be strict with the students. Anyone who does not obey the rule will be punished according to their actual fault. Mobile phone are strictly forbidden in exams and anyone who does not obey will be regarded as cheated in the exam. Rules help teachers have something to follow when dealing with such problems and it really plays a positive role to class teaching and school learning.

3.2.2.3 A variety of campus activities are to be held to enhance communication and improve interpersonal relationship

Healthy and positive campus activities are encouraged by the schools, bringing individual student to the group activity and this involvement may help students feel the happiness of group work and stay away from loneliness. In this way, students are able to build up communication and confidence and become less and less dependent on mobile phones and at last get rid of their addiction to mobile phone culture.

A variety of campus activities such as photo exhibition, dancing party, model competition and singing contest may enrich campus life and distract students from mobile phones, helping create a civilized and healthy campus atmosphere.

3.2.2.4 Hold mobile phone cultural festival and promote healthy mobile phone culture

College is the cradle of knowledge and it is essential to demonstrate the cultural aspects of mobile phones so as to help students better know the culture of mobile phones, because college students are usually blind and passive to the culture of mobile phones and they need to be properly guided to perceive the richness and colorfulness of mobile phone culture.

Schools are expected to set up a text message platform and expose the latest news about campus life to students. Current news as well as good articles is well selected and excellent websites are recommended. As a result, phone messages are enriched and bad messages are removed.

Literature contests on mobile phones are held and novels and poems are encouraged. Those award-winning ones are picked out for students to read and share. Mobile phones have become a crucial platform for the communication and creation of literature, greatly uplifting the cultural level of mobile phones.

3.2.2.5 Provide psychological counseling and help students adjust mood

The school psychological counseling center measures up students' dependence on mobile phones by means of mental measurement. To those who are overly dependent on mobile phones, the center offers psychological counseling and treatment, helping them adjust mood, relax and get rid of their addiction to mobile phones.

Psychological counseling websites are widely used to provide college students with proper psychological guidance, especially by group assistance or friend assistance, helping more students learn how to relax, adjust mood and communicate with others.

Mobile phone culture is a burgeoning culture appearing in the information age and it is an irresistible cultural trend. It is important that educators in universities and colleges guide and control in an objective way, promote the diversity of mobile phone culture, enrich the content of mobile phone culture and uplift the level of mobile phone culture. Mobile phone is an access to ideological and political education. It is of great importance to provide college students with proper guidance give a full play to the positive aspects of mobile phones and make mobile phone culture an essential part of campus culture.

ACKNOWLEDGEMENT

Fund Support: This project is the scientific research fund project of Environmental Management College of China "Investigation and analysis of status quo of college students psychological causes of mobile phone dependence" (No. 2014012).

REFERENCES

[1] Liang Na, Yang Shuo. 80 students mobile phone dependence degree investigation report [J]. Southwest communication, 2009, (3): 99–101.
[2] Ning Niya. Mass communication context under the mobile phone mobile phone media audience research. [Master's academic dissertation. Jinan University].
[3] Fang Min. students "mobile phone dependence" phenomenon of rational analysis [J]. Shanxi Youth Administrative Cadres College, 2010,1 (24):35–37.
[4] Li Qiaoyi. On their mobile phone dependence and debugging psychology [J]. Journal of Chengdu Polytechnic, 2008, 2(2): 75–76.
[5] Alastair C. van Heerden, M.Sc., et czl., Using Mobile Phones for Adolescent Research in Low and Middle Income Countries: Preliminary Findings From the Birth to Twenty Cohort, South Africa [J]. Journal of Adolescent Health, 2010, 46: 302–304.
[6] Mizuko Ito, et al. Mobile phones: Japanese youth and the replacement of social contact. http://www.emarkets.grm.hia.no/semoc/.

Computer, Intelligent Computing and Education Technology – Liu, Sung & Yao (Eds)
© *2014 Taylor & Francis Group, London, ISBN 978-1-138-02469-4*

Research on multiple attribute decision making of graduate students comprehensive quality assessment

Yan-Hong Dong, Chun-Sheng Sun & Jin-Shu Wang
Navy Submarine Academy, Shandong Qingdao, China

ABSTRACT: This paper analyzes the present situation of research on comprehensive quality evaluation of graduate students, and puts forward the graduate student's comprehensive quality evaluation index system, evaluation method and evaluation procedure for TOPSIS method based on multiple attributes decision analysis. The result shows that TOPSIS method applied to evaluate the comprehensive quality of graduate students has the advantage of simple calculation, strong operability, and intuitively reflecting the relative gap between different evaluation objects.

Keywords: multi attributes decision making; TOPSIS method; comprehensive quality evaluation

1 INTRODUCTION

In recent years, with the rapid development of Chinese higher education, in order to meet the social demand for talents of high level, number of graduate students greatly enhanced. The Ministry of Education stand out the guidance of selecting outstanding talent, encouraging the innovation spirit, and paying attention to quality and ability at the same time of expanding the postgraduate enrollment. Evaluation of comprehensive quality of graduate students has become a research focus in the educational field. There have been a large number of research results on the evaluation index system and evaluation method. Some research uses the theory of fuzzy mathematics, considering the impact of different evaluation sources and evaluation target on evaluation results, construct twice quantitative models based on the fuzzy comprehensive evaluation to evaluate the data, getting more specific results. Some research use the rough set theory to reduce the index and calculate the index weight without prior information, uses fractional standardization method to convert the original scores to standard scores, in order to overcome the raw score's poor addition. Some research puts forward a set of comparatively objective evaluation index system aiming at postgraduates majoring in economy and management, use the AHP method to determine the weight of each index, propose a new method to evaluate the comprehensive quality of postgraduates majoring in economy and management.

The main problems of existing research are: the calculation method is complex, operability is poor, evaluate result could not reflect the relative difference among evaluation objects. Aiming at these problems, this paper analyze the TOPSIS method based on multi-attribute decision making, and applies it to the evaluation on the comprehensive quality of postgraduates.

2 TOPSIS METHOD BASED ON MULTI ATTRIBUTES DECISION MAKING

Multiple Attributes Decision Making (MADM) is the preferred order by limited properties of finite samples, and get an important position in the modern decision science. Research on multiple attributes decision making focuses on the basic factor, decision matrix, analysis method, nondimensionalization and attribute weight. The basic factor is the attribute affecting decision and revenue function reacting effect. Decision matrix refers to the basis which is selected for optimal decision method, generally refers to the original data used to evaluate. Analysis methods generally include linear weighting, the ideal solution, efficacy coefficient method. Nondimensionalization refers to the process of data standardization and normalization. Attribute weight is calculated weight of each attribute in the decision. The rationality greatly effects the decision reliability and stability. Copying old text onto new file.

It is an effective method that is commonly used in multiple target decision analysis, also is known as the optimal and worst solution distance method. The basic principle of TOPSIS method is to sort by the distance between the object and the optimal solution, and the distance between the object and the worst solution.

The TOPSIS method can fully reveal the gap among the targets, and has the advantages of the real, intuitive, reliable, and has no special requirements to the sample data. It has been widely used in university academic performance evaluation, subway construction risk analysis, evaluation of water quality, project management staff performance appraisal, product life cycle impact assessment and many other decision analysis areas.

2.1 Standardized data processing

With the original matrix is:

$$x = \left[x_{ij} \right]_{m \times n} \tag{1}$$

where m is the number of evaluation index, n is the number of evaluation object, the original matrix is converted to standardization decision matrix

$$y = \left[y_{ij} \right]_{m \times n} \tag{2}$$

$$y_{ij} = \frac{x_{ij}}{\sqrt{\sum_{j=1}^{n} x_{ij}^2}} (i = 1,2 \ldots\ldots m; j = 1,2 \ldots\ldots n;) \tag{3}$$

2.2 Use the variation coefficient to determine index weight

The index weight include subjective and objective determination. This paper uses the variation system to objectively determine index weight, the solution process is as follows:

Calculate means of each index.

$$x_i = \frac{\sum_{j=1}^{n} y_{ij}}{n} \tag{4}$$

Calculate Standard deviation of each index.

$$S_i = \sqrt{\sum_{j=1}^{n} (yi_j - x_i)^2} \tag{5}$$

Calculate variation number of each index.

$$v_i = \frac{S_i}{x_i} \tag{6}$$

Calculate the weight of each index.

$$w_i = \frac{v_i}{\sum_{i=1}^{m} v_i} \tag{7}$$

2.3 Calculate weighted attribute matrix

$$Z_{ij} = w_i * y_{ij} \tag{8}$$

2.4 Determine the positive ideal solution and negative ideal solution

Positive ideal solution is the maximum value of each line.

$$Z_i^+ = \max_j \left[Z_{ij} \right], i = 1,2 \ldots m \tag{9}$$

The negative ideal solution is the minimum value for each line.

$$Z_i^- = \min_j \left[Z_{ij} \right], i = 1,2 \ldots m \tag{10}$$

2.5 Calculate positive ideal solution distance and negative ideal solution distance

Positive ideal solution distance:

$$d_j^* = \sqrt{\sum_{i=1}^{m} (z_{ij} - \max Z_i)^2}, \quad j = 1,2 \ldots n \tag{11}$$

Negative ideal solution distance:

$$d_j^0 = \sqrt{\sum_{i=1}^{m} (z_{ij} - \min Z_i)^2}, \quad j = 1,2 \ldots n \tag{12}$$

2.6 Solving sort value

$$c_j^* = \frac{d_j^0}{d_j^0 + d_j^*}, \quad j = 1,2 \ldots n \tag{13}$$

2.7 Sort

Sort According to the calculation of ranking values, the greater the value the bigger the ordering, the smaller the contrary.

3 GRADUATE STUDENTS COMPREHENSIVE QUALITY EVALUATION INDEX SYSTEM

Index system refers to the overall of the evaluation object index, object index complements each other, and become a complete combination. The process of establishing postgraduate comprehensive quality evaluation index system is also the analysis on graduate students comprehensive quality requirements.

Based on the graduate students training objectives of PLA Navy Submarine Academy, this paper established comprehensive quality evaluation index system that consists of three first level indexes, which are basic quality, learning ability, practice and innovation. And there are nine two level indexes in this system, which are physical and mental health, political morality, military quality, degree courses score, professional courses score, self-learning ability, published papers, research projects, coordination and cooperation ability.

3.1 Basic quality index

Basic quality indexes include three two level index, which are physical and mental health, political morality, military quality. Physical and mental health includes physical health and mental health. Physical health requires students to have certain sports, do physical exercise, participate in sports activities, up to the military academy fitness test standard, and have no serious physical disease. The mental health requires students have good psychological adjustment ability, strong psychological endurance, strong adaptability, and have no serious psychological disorder. Political morality refers to the student's political position and social morality. Students should adhere to the political study, have no improper comments, and have a correct view of personal gain or loss. Military quality mainly examines how the students executive rules and regulations, daily life system, daily habit, and military discipline.

These three indexes implement centesimal system. The evaluation method is to do weight calculation from the team leaders score and the students democratic evaluation results based on individual daily performance and related work record.

3.2 Learning ability index

Learning ability indexes include three two level index, namely degree courses score, professional courses score and self-learning ability. Because the degree courses and professional courses are different in different majors, degree courses score should take average from the student's all degree courses score, professional courses score should take average from the student's all professional courses score.

3.3 Practice and innovation index

Practice and innovation indexes include 3 two level index, which are participation in scientific research projects, publish papers, coordination and cooperation.

Table 1. Scientific research project score sheet.

Project scale	Key personnel bonus	General staff bonus	Restriction
National project	18	15	No more than 100
Provincial project	15	10	No more than 95
Municipal project	10	8	No more than 85
Academic project	8	5	No more than 75

Table 2. Published papers score sheet.

Grade	Author 1	Author 2	Other	Total score limit
SCI	20	15	10	No more than 100
EI	15	10	5	No more than 95
SSCI	10	8	5	No more than 85
Core journals	8	5	3	No more than 75
Open access journal	6	4	2	No more than 65
International conference	4	2	0	No more than 65
Domestic academic	2	0	0	No more than 65

Participation in scientific research is calculated mainly by number and grade of the project. The calculation method is given in Table 1.

The published papers index is calculated according to the number, author sort and grade of the paper. Specific calculation method is given in Table 2.

Coordination and cooperation ability mainly test the student's ability of language expression, coordination, cooperation consciousness etc. It uses centesimal system. The evaluation method is to do weight calculation for the team leader's score and the students' democratic evaluation results based on the condition how the students participate in group activities, in management activities, and in the collective scientific research work.

4 EVALUATION STEPS

We select A random sample of 4 graduate students, and obtain the original evaluation data based on the proposed evaluation index system and calculation method in this paper. See Table 3.

4.1 Standardized data processing

Standardize data according to the formula 1, the results is in Table 4.

4.2 Determine the index weight by using variation coefficient method

Calculate variation coefficient value according to the formula 2–4. See Table 5.

Calculate index weight value according to the formula 5. The results is in Table 6.

Calculate weight attribute matrix according to the formula 6, the results is in Table 7.

4.3 Sort valuation

Calculate positive and negative ideal distance, and ranking values according to the formula 7–11, the results is in Table 8.

Analysis of result: According to the "Table 3 original evaluation data", we can not directly determine the overall quality of students.

Table 3. The original evaluation data.

Index	Student 1	Student 2	Student 3	Student 4
Physical and mental health	95	98	93	95
Political thought	90	93	85	88
Military quality	90	95	90	90
Degree courses score	95	95	88	92
Professional courses score	85	89	75	70
Self-learning ability	75	80	85	90
Research project	85	90	88	90
Published papers	80	88	90	78
Coordination and cooperation ability	90	90	95	90

Table 4. Standardization decision matrix data.

Index	Student 1	Student 2	Student 3	Student 4	Student 5
Physical and mental health	0.4508	0.4651	0.4508	0.4413	0.4271
Political thought	0.4561	0.4713	0.4307	0.4459	0.4307
Moral character	0.4403	0.4647	0.4403	0.4403	0.4500
Common course score	0.4616	0.4616	0.4276	0.4470	0.4373
Professional courses score	0.4711	0.4932	0.4156	0.3879	0.4600
Published papers	0.3932	0.4195	0.4457	0.4719	0.4981
Research project	0.4385	0.4643	0.4540	0.4643	0.4127
Students work	0.4477	0.4925	0.5037	0.4365	0.3358
Social activities	0.4422	0.4422	0.4668	0.4422	0.4422

Table 5. Variation coefficient value.

Index	Variation coefficient value
Physical and mental health	0.0626
Political thought	0.0776
Military quality	0.0479
Degree courses score	0.0670
Professional courses score	0.1924
Self-learning ability	0.1860
Research project	0.0974
Published papers	0.3001
Coordination and cooperation ability	0.0491

Table 6. Weight value.

Index	Weight
Physical and mental health	0.0580
Political thought	0.0718
Military quality	0.0444
Degree courses score	0.0620
Professional courses score	0.1781
Self-learning ability	0.1722
Research project	0.0902
Published papers	0.2778
Coordination and cooperation ability	0.0455

Table 7. Weight attribute matrix.

Index	Student 1	Student 2	Student 3	Student 4	Student 5
Physical and mental health	0.0261	0.0270	0.0261	0.0256	0.0248
Political thought	0.0327	0.0338	0.0309	0.0320	0.0309
Moral character	0.0195	0.0206	0.0195	0.0195	0.0200
Common course score	0.0286	0.0286	0.0265	0.0277	0.0271
Professional courses	0.0839	0.0878	0.0740	0.0691	0.0819
Published papers	0.0677	0.0722	0.0768	0.0813	0.0858
Research project	0.0396	0.0419	0.0410	0.0419	0.0372
Students work	0.1244	0.1368	0.1399	0.1213	0.0933
Social activities	0.0201	0.0201	0.0212	0.0201	0.0201

Table 8. Positive and negative ideal distance, ranking values.

Student name	d_j^*	d_j^0	c_j^*	Result
Student 1	0.0244	0.0347	0.5873	3
Student 2	0.0139	0.0480	0.7751	1
Student 3	0.0170	0.0479	0.7385	2
Student 4	0.0270	0.0315	0.5385	4
Student 5	0.0474	0.0222	0.3185	5

Using the TOPSIS method to analyze and evaluate, we finally can sort the overall quality of the students, and can see the relative gap between students.

5 CONCLUSION

This paper established the evaluation index system that consists of three first level indexes and nine two level indexes, and used the multi-attribute decision making TOPSIS method to evaluate. Practice shows that TOPSIS method has no strict limits on data distribution, sample size and index number. Mathematical calculation is not complex. It is suitable for small sample data, and also suitable for the multi sample big system. To determine the index factors weight by using variation coefficient method, we can weaken the subjective factors of the evaluation, and improve the scientificalness of evaluation.

REFERENCES

Chen Quancheng, Chen Dongqing, 2011. The research on The comprehensive quality evaluation of Economics and management graduate students. *Journal of Changchun University of Science and Technology (SOCIAL SCIENCE EDITION)*): 132–147.

Guo Yingling, Liu Hongqi, Guo Ruifeng, 2010. Evaluation method of life cycle impact based on TOPSIS. *Mechanical design and manufacturing*: 187–188.

Jia Lianxia, Huang Feng, Zhang Jiangshui, 2010. Thinking of graduate student quality education. *The contemporary education theory and Practice*: 39–41. Beijing: China.

Jiang Delong, Yin Shuping, Shi Li, 2011. Evaluation study of The comprehensive quality of graduate students based on fuzzy synthetic discrimination. *Computer engineering and design*: 3208–3210. Beijing: China.

Qi Wei, Chen Xiaojian, 2010. Study on evaluation method of Academic performance of China Research University based on TOPSIS. *Chinese higher education research*: 15–19.

Wang Jinshan, Wang lei, 2011. The use of Rough set theory on military academy postgraduate's comprehensive quality Evaluation. *Journal of Chongqing University of Technology (Natural Science)*: 107–112.

Yu Jianxing, Tan Zhendong, 2005. Research on quantificational performance evaluation based on combination weighting and TOPSIS. *Systems engineering theory & Practice*: 46–50.

Zhang Xianqi, Liang Chuan, Liu Huiqing, 2007. Application of improved TOPSIS method based on entropy weight in water quality assessment. *Journal of Harbin Institute of Technology*: 1670–1672.

Zhang Yijun, Rong Xiaoli, Qian Qi Hu, 2010. Application of TOPSIS method in the risk analysis of subway construction. *Chinese Journal of underground space and Engineering*: 856–860.

Computer, Intelligent Computing and Education Technology – Liu, Sung & Yao (Eds)
© 2014 Taylor & Francis Group, London, ISBN 978-1-138-02469-4

Research mode for constructing internal information office platform for small scale government units

Y.G. Wei, S.Y. Yu & X.M. Zhu
College of Information Science and Technology, Beijing Normal University, China

J.Y. Liao
Beijing Xiao Ji Tong Information Technology Ltd., China

ABSTRACT: This paper summarizes the mode for constructing a small scale government's internal information office platform characterized by a document flow based approach. In this mode, the platform supports all functions of the document life cycle. This solution is proposed for use in small-scale government units with approval by the users.

Keywords: document flow; document lifecycle; online office; document collaboration

1 INTRODUCTION

With the development of computer and network technology driven by relevant national policies such as "three networks and one data base", e-government[1] has gradually spread. Governments have implemented electronic and networked office configurations such as information portals and the web office, but they differ greatly in the development and utilization of information technology in the various levels of government agencies. Usually, offices of the core business, which have adequate funding and technical support, have a greater degree of office information technology. The small-scale government units, however, generally use the information office platform configuration of their superiors, which is not of their own design and construction. Because of this, some of their daily office work is still stuck in the traditional way of working offline and then submitting online, even when they do "web office" work.

The offline work obviously is not enjoying the benefits brought by information technology; with further development of the information office, offline work will enjoy these benefits. This article addresses work in the area of the information office platform and explores the configuration of an actual project.

2 PRESENT

Currently, almost all office staff have a work computer, and their daily work involves document processing. Based on operational needs, staff draft documents as requested per supervisory instructions, eventually creating a file that can be added to classified files or can be published. From the document perspective, the work is to create documents, modify documents, finalize documents and publish or archive documents. Small government units use advanced information technology functions, such as e-document approval, but these advanced functions are not particularly strong. The figure below shows the document view of daily work:

The figure also reflects the document's life cycle.[2] In general, there are two common modes[3][4] for these small government units for the use of information technology in daily work.

2.1 Building an internal information issemination network

Generally, through the construction of a Content Management System platform, unit announcements of the latest developments and company rules and activity data will be posted to this platform. Because small government units usually have fewer employees, i.e., smaller scale, the audience for information dissemination is fewer, the level of enthusiasm when the CMS is released is not high, and over time, the system status is rarely updated.

Figure 1. Document perspective of daily work.

2.2 Building an internal information work platform

Another approach is based on creating a customized business information work platform for the unit; the platform covers almost all aspects of work, and each type of work corresponds to a working module or subsystem, which can include instant messaging, BBS, electronic signature and so on. This comprehensive system is more complex than the CMS and is conducive to document filing. However, we found that this platform was ineffective because we still needed to post to the platform when we completed our computer work and this task gradually became a workload. Finally, this system also slid into the status of rarely being updated.

The first mode—a simple introduction of website publishers—was met with little interest; the second mode encountered resistance due to the increased workload. When a certain government unit encountered these problems, the first phase of platform used the first mode, and the second phase of platform used the second mode. Reflecting on these issues, we find that due to the special characteristics of small government unit work with office information technology, e.g., small staff as well as personnel changes, we cannot simply copy other approaches to constructing an office information technology platform.

3 EXPLORATION

In light of the special characteristics of small government units, we abandoned the publishing-centric construction mode, instead focusing on the document life cycle, and built a workspace as the core of the internal information platform mode and solicited user approval. In this paper, some ancillary modules for the workspace, such as an announcement module, work plan module, document template printing module, etc., are not described.

3.1 Workspace

This refinement to Figure 1 shows the staff's work from the perspective of the document life cycle, which combined with detailed user requirements, yields the following document flow logical figure.

Document flow includes document creation, collaboration, modification, finalization, use, sharing and destruction; staff members initiates these document flow actions. The workspace approach strongly supports all aspects of the document flow life cycle and achieves internal office information management for documents. Specifically, the

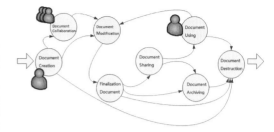

Figure 2. Document flow schematic diagram.

features required to implement the workspace approach include the following:

Online Document Creation and Modification: including Office (e.g., Word, Excel, PPT, etc.), web documents, pictures and other multimedia file uploads.

Online Document Collaboration: to support collaboration on single-author and multi-author documents, to achieve synergistic modification of documents through an online platform and to keep revision history.

Personal Document Management: to enable staff to manage their document directory, drafts and trash and to monitor the collaboration status of documents.

Online Document Sharing: to share documents with single or multiple persons, the department or the entire unit.

3.2 Core objects

From the perspective of an object-oriented workspace, the core objects include Documentation Directory (for users to manage), Content of Document (the specific documentation), Temporary Documents (temporary files), Document Attachments (document associated attachments), Document Collaboration (recorded document collaboration process) and Document Template (document initialization content).

3.3 System implementation

In the workspace, our platform will list the user's own document directory, including trash, recycle bin, etc. If the user is a department or unit leader, our platform will list the department's or unit's staff, by clicking on the name of the staff, the user can obtain further documentation; staffs' drafts and trash will not be listed to guarantee a certain degree of privacy. In addition, there are several auxiliary functions, such as search by time periods or keywords, and some flags such as some documents require collaboration or have a request for collaboration.

Table 1. System core objects.

Objects	Primary attributes
Documentation directory	Directory ID, whether a draft catalog, whether trash directory, the directory path tree, creator, creation date, modification by, modification time, has been deleted, who deleted, deletion time, directory name, description, parent directory, sorting index by type, owner ID
Content of document	Document ID, creator, creation time, modification by, modified, deleted, who deleted, deletion time, title, content, content type, content files, content length, the extension
Temporary documents	Document ID, catalog ID, creator, creation time, file name, file path
Document attachments	Attachment ID, attachment name, file size, creation time, modification time, document ID, length, width, thumbnail file path, sort index
Document collaboration	Collaboration ID, catalog ID, document ID, request collaborators, collaborators, status, collaboration date, received date, finish date, collaboration requests, whether the file can be modified, collaboration results
Document template	Template ID, catalog ID, title, content, content type, content files, sorting index

Figure 3. Workspace.

3.3.1 Document online creation

Staff can select the type of document to be created online, including Word, PPT, Excel and several web-types; every 10 minutes the system will automatically save the document to the server. So that staff do not need to upload documents

Figure 4. Create new document.

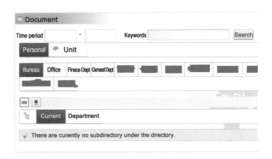

Figure 5. Department and unit catalog.

manually, these documents will be managed in the work process. Some document templates can also be built to facilitate daily office work.

3.3.2 Individuals, departments and unit documents

For ease of management, document types include three categories: individual, department and unit. For an individual document, only the owner can create, revise, use and destroy and department heads can browse; department level documents could be browsed by the department members while authorization is required to modify and delete; unit level documents would be visible to all members of the unit, while only the administrator could modify and delete.

3.3.3 Documents and directory collaboration

In daily work, newly created documents often require collaboration with colleagues. Staff can enter the collaborative process after they create a document, set up their collaboration needs and select collaboration colleagues. Colleagues who were selected will get tips in the Documents Collaboration module. They also can view the collaborative process by themselves. When tasks include more than one document and require more colleagues contributing, the staff can use the directory collaboration function. The Task Leader creates a directory, initiates collaboration and chooses relevant colleagues, and then these colleagues can add documents in that directory. The person responsible for the document can see the progress of collaboration

643

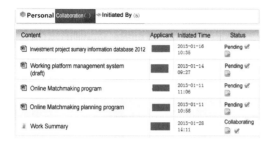

Figure 6. Documents and directory collaboration.

Figure 7. Documents publishing.

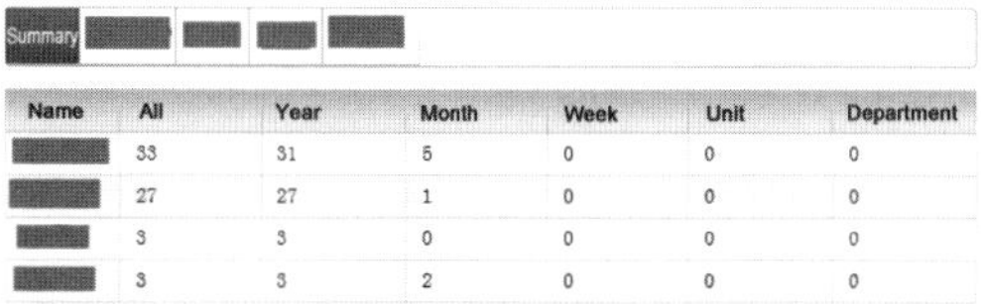

Name	All	Year	Month	Week	Unit	Department
	33	31	5	0	0	0
	27	27	1	0	0	0
	3	3	0	0	0	0
	3	3	2	0	0	0

Figure 8. Document statistics.

and can end the collaboration when all tasks have been completed, after that, other people will not be able to modify the document.

3.3.4 Documents and directory publishing
Staff can publish their personal directory's documents, such as Edited Documents, Collaborated Documents and Directories or Collaborated Directories to the department's and unit's directory to achieve document archiving and sharing.

3.3.5 Document statistics
Users can view statistics of the number of documents per person according to department, day, week, month and annual. This capability will help leaders understand the work of each staff and of the department as a whole.

4 CONCLUSION AND FUTURE

An online workspace based on the document flow approach that supports all functions of the document lifecycle and converts traditional, separate document creation and use brings the following benefits:

1. In the work process, the document has already entered the platform when it is created; this facilitates collaboration and ease of use, and the staff author is not required to re-upload the document.
2. Transfer of work when a staff member leaves or jobs are transferred is greatly facilitated because the daily work documents are on the platform.
3. Because the life cycle of documents and the revision of history are managed, a foundation for subsequent deep data mining applications is established.

The construction of the workspace approach that has been described requires server stability, higher data storage and data security. The application requires hot back up, and the data require redundant storage.

REFERENCES

[1] Long Jian, Comparison of E-government Research. J. Information Science. Vol. 29 No. 2 (2011).
[2] Yin Junjun, Archives Information Management Platform. D. Sichuan University Master Thesis. pp. 1–2 (2005).
[3] Li Hui, Government Information Technology Research At Home and Abroad—Concurrently Talk about the recommendations of Beijing Government Information. J. Information Studies: Theory & Application. pp. 47–50 (2011).
[4] He Shaohua, Huang Jing, Building Information Resources Management System Base On Integrated Perspective of Government. J. Library and Information Service Online. pp. 64–70 (2012).
[5] Yu Baojun, Research on the Growth Process and Evolution Mechanism of Enterprise Information Systems. D. Jilin University Doctoral thesis. (2008).
[6] Wu Jiang, Hu Bin, Multi-agent simulation for interaction of IT implementation and group behavior. J. Journal of Systems Engineering. pp. 92–99 (2009).
[7] Wang Weiying, Research on Local government departments to promote information sharing model and mechanism. D. East China University of Political Science and Law Master Thesis. Vol. 29 No. 2 (2012).

Computer, Intelligent Computing and Education Technology – Liu, Sung & Yao (Eds)
© 2014 Taylor & Francis Group, London, ISBN 978-1-138-02469-4

Application of network protocol teaching system in computer network courses teaching

L.P. Feng, T. Li, K. Xie & H.Q. Liu
Beijing Institute of Graphic Communication, Beijing, China

ABSTRACT: Computer networking has become ubiquitous. We developed a laboratory-based course on computer network. Through a computer network experimental simulation environment, we can motivate the interest of the students to learn computer network, enhance their understanding of network knowledge and improve their comprehensive quality and ability. In this paper, with an experimental example of FTP protocol, we describes SimpleNPTS Protocol Analysis System and our work to enhance computer network courses teaching and learning through hands-on practice and immersive experience.

Keywords: network protocol analysis systems; simulation tools; computer network courses; experimental design

1 INTRODUCTION

Computer networking has become so ubiquitous that every computer system of any importance is networked to others. Computer network courses are essential parts of college computer science curriculum. The ACM/IEEE Computer Science Curriculum 2008 lists Computer Networking as a required course under the "Net Centric Computing" body of knowledge[1]. Based on the social demands analyses and discussion with the teachers, we divided computer network courses into three modules: computer network infrastructure, computer network technology and computer network programming. The computer network infrastructure modules is composed of Internet Technology and Applications, Computer Networking, Network Security, Computer Networking Design.

These courses not only contains abstract and profound theoretical knowledge such as the principles of network communication, TCP/IP protocols, etc., but also involves a large number of network technologies such as operation and configuration of networking equipment. All these make it difficult for students to fully comprehend and appreciate the intricacies regarding network communication without implementing some portion of the network logic[2]. Through the use of a network simulator, students are able to obtain the benefits of actually implementing network without the degradation of network performance, and active learning in networks gives students experience in the subtleties of the design of a complex system, as well as prepare them for the networking industry.

This paper describes SimpleNPTS Protocol Analysis System and our work to enhance computer network courses teaching and learning through hands-on practice and immersive experience.

2 NETWORK PROTOCOL ANALYSIS AND SIMULATION PLATFORM

2.1 *Network experiment simulation platform*

As the network experiments involved in the underlying implementation of the system, it is difficult to implement experiment in the real environment. Experiment simulation platforms are widely used in the teaching of computer network courses because of their low cost and high efficient. Generally, there is a lot of network equipments and tools in the simulation environment, students can implement various experiments conveniently.

Network protocol analysis tool (also known as sniffer) is a computer network interface to intercept network data, that can be used in many aspects of network management and network security. In network attack and defense technology, sniffer technology is the most basic kind of technology. From the perspective of the attack, the hacker can use sniffer program illegally get a lot of sensitive information transmitted over the network, such as account numbers and passwords. Sniffer technology is basic part of a network intrusion detection system, the data source of the entire system. Tcpdump and Ethereal are well-known sniffers.

2.2 SimpleNPTS network protocol teaching system

SimpleNPTS Network Protocol Teaching System[3] is a network experiment simulation platform developed by Beijing Simpleware Technology Co., Ltd. Because of the GUI as well as the opportunity to create operations, SimpleNPTS provides much more flexibility than other network sniffing programs. Through SimpleNPTS, students have access to a complete set of network data—all layers in the TCP/IP network model stack.

SimpleNPTS Network Protocol Teaching System combines the actual situation of university education, realizes the theoretical knowledge of networks through software. Students can know the basic network theoretical knowledge well, understand the internal structures and protocols of network clearly in the process of practice. SimpleNPTS Network Protocol Teaching System makes students to understand internal network principle clearly and aid network programming debugging by editing the various protocol packets.

In the teaching of computer network courses, the Interactive process of network protocol is complex and difficult to understand that the network experiments are necessary and essential. Experimental teaching is complement and enhancement of theoretical teaching. It Plays a very important role in training students to solve the practical problems using knowledge comprehensively.

SimpleNPTS Network Protocol Teaching System is an effective tool for students to do protocol analysis and network experimentation. It allows students to construct TCP/IP protocol packets and analyze network data. The experiments can broaden perspectives of the students, emphasize initiative learning and designing, and achieve true interactive teaching.

3 APPLICATION OF NETWORK PROTOCOL TEACHING SYSTEM

3.1 Experiments design

More and more colleges and universities across the country are turning to authentic learning practices and are putting the focus back on the learner in an effort to improve the way students absorb, retain, and transfer knowledge[4].

Our experiments will facilitate the computer network theory and concept learning to overcome the lack of hands-on practices in traditional teaching and learning environment.

The main objectives of the proposed experiments are: (1) using SimpleNPTS Network Protocol Teaching System to help students better understand network core concepts, the layered architecture of network protocols; (2) facilitating students learning of network knowledge and skills; and (3) encouraging students to exploring computer network.

With the above objectives, our experiments based SimpleNPTS Network Protocol Teaching System are designed as follows. The experiments adopt a modular structure that organizes the learning materials into a sequence of modules.

Each module is designed as a building blocks that can be combined together into a single experiment. Each module covers a specific fundamental networking concept subject.

In this paper, as an example of how the network experimental teaching carried out using SimpleNPTS Network Protocol Teaching, FTP protocol analysis is illustrated. Compared to other application layer protocols, FTP is more complex relatively. It uses two ports, one is control port 21, and the other is data port 20. How does FTP protocol transfer files? It is difficult for students to understand the working process of the FTP protocol only with lectures in the classroom.

3.2 Experimental procedure

In the experiment part, the lab instructs students on using SimpleNPTS Network Protocol Teaching to understand FTP file transfer process with four modules. Two students as a group, A is server, and B is client.

1. Capture and analyze FTP packets
   A starts the FTP server. B lands the server, and open the protocol analyzer before. To capture and analyze FTP packets, students can see the FTP interactive process and the format of FTP packets. From the captured data packets, students can also see the FTP USER command and its parameters (user name), PASS command and password as shown in Figure 1. These not only stimulate the learning interest of the students, but also so make the students to realize network insecurity furtherly.

2. Use the TCP tool to connect the FTP server
   In this modular, the students can fill IP address and the port number (21) of control connection in "TCP connection tool" to connect to the FTP server, and establish the connection between the client with the FTP server. With the protocol analyzer, the students can view the three way handshake interactive process of the control connection established.

3. Use the FTP commands
   Input the FTP commands in the sending area to interact with the FTP server (Fig. 2), students can deepen their understanding of the FTP commands.

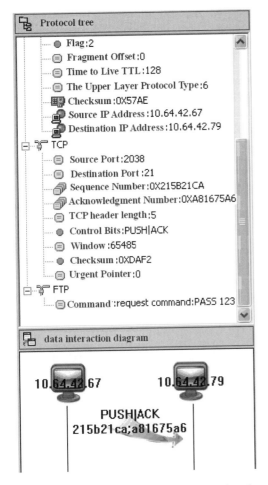

Figure 1. Interaction with the FTP server and packet analysis.

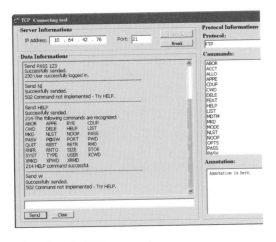

Figure 2. The FTP commands.

4. Construct FTP packet

Using protocol Editing software, the students can edit a FTP packet, fill in the Ethernet frame header, IP header, TCP header and data, and send the edited FTP packet. The student can capture the FTP packet with the protocol analyzer. These practices can provide the students with further knowledge on the format of FTP protocol and the relationship between the FTP protocol and the lower layer protocol (Fig. 3).

Network Protocol Teaching System can makes the students to understand the real situation of data transfer in the network environment and operational aspects of network protocols.

These enable students have lively and vivid understanding on the data exchange, transmission process in the network environment, and stimulate the interest of the students in learning computer network courses.

3.3 Teaching manner

Network Protocol Teaching System provide a more complex learning scenario that the students can carry on a deeper exploration. Experiments are supportment of classroom teaching behavior and the key to the implementation of the curriculum. Using virtual experiment technology such as SimpleNPTS, we can optimize computer network teaching and learning behavior. In the experiments, students and teachers are driven by a series of tasks as above, they would have greater flexibility. To accomplish the tasks, they analyze, explore in the ocean of knowledge, and share the teaching and learning experience with each other. Through discussion and cooperation, students achieve their efficient learning experience and construct their own knowledge.

To consolidate the knowledge points, teacher and students should summarize and make a

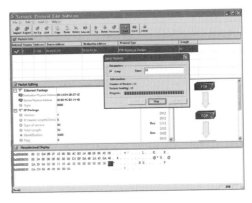

Figure 3. Edit and send the FTP packet.

review[2]. Course evaluations by students indicate that they value the course highly. Most of the students felt the experiments were interesting and helpful, and obtained immerse experience in learning. Most students felt that the experiences with our experiments gave them confidence and motivation to learn more about networking concepts and to try projects that are more ambitious in the future.

4 CONCLUSION

In this paper we have considered the emerging problem of computer network teaching: how to motivate the students to learn network knowledge. Our research shows that many students need additional motivation to study.

With the description above we can see, using Network Protocol Teaching System not only makes the students to have a deeper understanding on network knowledge and principle through experiments, but also inspires the interest of the students better learning and cultivates ability through the protocol analysis experiments.

With the research and practice of the teaching reform of undergraduate computer network in recent years, the interest of the students in learning computer network courses is improved greatly. Computer network is no longer boring but challenging and fun. Their sense of team have been enhanced, the comprehensive quality and ability have been greatly improved.

Network technology changes rapidly, the computer network curriculum should be closely integrated with practice. It will be a trend that the simulation tools participate and play its role in the computer network teaching.

ACKNOWLEDGMENTS

This paper is supported by the course construction project of Beijing Institute of Graphic Communication (No. 22150113077).

REFERENCES

[1] K. Qian, M. Yang, M.Z. Guo, et al. Authentic Learning for Computer Network with Mobile Device-Based Hands-On Labware. World Academy of Science, Engineering and Technology, 2013:318–313.
[2] X.H. Li, R.L. Zhang, L. Yang, et al. Optimization of Computer Network Teaching and Learning Behavior Using Virtual Experiment Technology. International Conference on Information, Business and Education Technology, 2013:1058–1061.
[3] SimpleNPTS Network Protocol Teaching System Experiment Guidbook. Beijing simpleware Technology Co., Ltd., 2010.
[4] M. Lombardi. Authentic Learning for the 21st Century: An Overview. ELI White Papers, EDUCAUSE Learning Initiative (ELI), 2007.

Computer, Intelligent Computing and Education Technology – Liu, Sung & Yao (Eds)
© *2014 Taylor & Francis Group, London, ISBN 978-1-138-02469-4*

Research on the motivation status and stimulus strategies for sports volunteer activity of college students

Qi-Jun Lai

Department of Physical Education, North China Electric Power University, Baoding, China

ABSTRACT: By the methods of documentary and investigation, the current situation of college students' sports volunteer activity is analyzed and the motivation strategies are revealed which include: supporting university sports volunteer service to strengthen their participation; enhancing the value education; focusing on sports volunteer training quality; emphasis on college sports volunteer's performance appraise; and enhancing promotion and guiding of sports voluntary activity.

Keywords: college students; sports volunteer; motivation; stimulus strategy

1 GENERAL INTRODUCTION

Youth volunteer action is a promising career.[1] Through sports volunteer activities, college students get more personal all-round development and promote the social development. In recent years the successful experience of large-scale sports events in our country proves the key role of sports volunteer. At present, China's institutions of higher learning have a total scale of 31.05 million students.[2] College students volunteer participating in sports bring advantages of human resources and promote the development of physical culture. But the reality is that volunteers erosion has become a noticeable problem on the non-profit organizations development path.[3] There is a gap between theory and practice of the motivation of college students volunteer service, therefore, it becomes an important subject to explore the motivation of sports volunteer and offer the incentive strategy to promote their participation.

2 SUBJECTS AND METHODS

2.1 Study subject

The subject is incentive strategies for college sports voluntary participants in our country.

2.2 Research methods

2.2.1 Literature
China Academic Journals database, VIP Chinese technical full-text database, Wanfang Database and other websites and related books, and over 200 literature both domestic and abroad have been retrieved.

2.2.2 Questionnaire
Questionnaire is prepared after reading a lot of literature. Firstly a small-scale test measurements is conducted in a class of 30 people. Then the questionnaire is perfected with a consideration of the problems emerging in the test. Finally ten experts in the field of college sports management are hired to detect the content validity and structure validity, in which three experts think very well (30%). Seven experts believe it is relatively perfect (70%); The questionnaire is inspected with a method of test-retest reliability in an interval of two weeks. In Jinan City, the test-retest reliability was conducted in a small sample of 50 people. Test-retest reliability was $r = 0.86$, $P < 0.01$, which illustrates the questionnaire has high stability and reliability.

The motivation of the first and second year college sports voluntary participants in our country are taken as research subjects covering areas such as North China, South China, Central China, Northeast region, including 19 universities in 6 cities ranging from Beijing, Shanghai, Guangzhou, Nanjing, Shenyang, to Jinan. Four universities in Beijing were surveyed, three in each other city, a total of 19. There were 175 questionnaires for boys, 125 for girls, 150 for freshmen, and 150 for sophomores relatively. 5700 copies were distributed, and 5130 were recovered, with the recovery rate of 90%. There were 4514 copies of valid questionnaires, with an efficiency of 88%.

2.2.3 Mathematical analysis
Statistical analyses of the collected data are conducted with the aid of the statistical software SPSS17.0.

Table 1. The distribution of respondents number of college sports volunteers.

	Beijing	Shanghai	Guangzhou	Nanjing	Shenyang	Jinan	Total
Grade one	600	450	450	450	450	450	2850
Grade two	600	450	450	450	450	450	2850
Boy	700	525	525	525	525	525	3325
Girl	500	375	375	375	375	375	2375
Total	1200	900	900	900	900	900	5700

3 RESULTS AND ANALYSIS

3.1 Analysis of college sports volunteering motivation

3.1.1 Contents of college sports volunteering motivation of different genders

Research on college sports volunteering motivation shows that China's college students' participation in volunteer activities aims to enrich life experiences, exercise capacity, accumulate experience, enhance the resume, acquire the glory, shoulder obligations and get rewards. (The motives of the seven areas are illustrated in Table 2). Overall, China's college students basically have a right and positive motive to participate in sports volunteering activities, but a considerable proportion of college students have a cognitive bias towards sports volunteering activities. They participate just for the rewards or glories or with an unclear attitude. Besides, there are gender differences ($p < 0.05$) in the needs of shouldering obligations, enhancing the resume and acquiring the glory. The perception of boys is an honor, and a recognition of their values whereas the perception of girls is a means of exercise, and a contributor of their resume. This suggests that gender differences should be taken into account in motivating volunteers to participate in the sports activities.

3.1.2 Content of different grades of college sports volunteering motivation

Survey (see Table 3) shows that college students in different grades differ ($p < 0.05$) in motives of exercising capacity, enriching the resume, acquiring the glory, and so on.

In general, the freshmen value glory over others, seeing such obligation as a reflection of his own value. In contrast, the sophomore put more emphasis on practical benefits, such as enriching the resume, accumulating experience, and exercising ability and so on.

3.1.3 Intensity of college sports volunteering motivation

Students' interest in sports volunteering is a reflection of the core indicators of their motivation, and interest is also an important indicator to measure the intensity of motivation. The results showed that only 31.84 percent of male college students are interested in sports volunteering, while female students accounted for 26.13% (Table 4); first year students' interest are stronger, accounting for 63.8%, as compared to 52.7% in the sophomore. This result is in line with the reality that the number of volunteers of all kinds in our country accounts for only 5% of the total population and registered volunteers are even less. 20% of citizens participate in voluntary organizations in our country, which is a large gap compared with developed countries who have a percentage of 40%–60% of the citizens participating in volunteer services.[4]

3.1.4 Influence factors of the motivation of undergraduate voluntary activities

The result indicates that the first four problems in the voluntary process are social support (21.8%), time conflict (19.2%), personal security (17.9%) and fund injection (15.1%) (Table 4). Under the test of the statistics, male and female undergraduates have gender difference in personal security ($p < 0.05$). Female undergraduates are concerned more about their personal security relatively. However, No grade difference ($p > 0.05$) is shown since the listed problems are confronted by both freshmen and sophomore.

3.2 The incentive strategic analysis of undergraduate voluntary activities in sports

3.2.1 Attaching great important to and supporting undergraduate voluntary activity in sports

Though Chinese governments at all levels and relevant organizations advocate voluntary activities, there is a lack of measurements such as institutional arrangement, fund support, examination and evaluation and process control. Moreover, some enterprises, ignoring voluntary experience, view undergraduate volunteers as free labor force, causing their confrontation with capital, property, court and security barriers. According to the investigation, the lack of "social support" is viewed as the primary difficulty by 21.8 percent of

Table 2. Results of motives of different gender of college sports volunteer (%).

Variable	Obligation	Capacity	Experience	Resume	Life	Rewards	Glory
Agree percent	Boy: 34.1 Girl: 14.2	Boy: 40.1 Girl: 41.4	Boy: 39.4 Girl: 42.2	Boy: 28.4 Girl: 40.6	Boy: 38.5 Girl: 44.2	Boy: 19.1 Girl: 22.0	Boy: 42.12 Girl: 21.12
P	0.048*	0.686	0.754	0.025*	0.578	0.898	0.048*
Disagree percent	Boy: 8.5 Girl: 13.0	Boy: 6.6 Girl: 6.0	Boy: 7.3 Girl: 8.4	Boy: 7.4 Girl: 3.0	Boy: 5.3 Girl: 5.2	Boy: 21.3 Girl: 22.2	Boy: 1.9 Girl: 11.1
P	0.038*	0.678	0.545	0.038*	0.698	0.789	0.039*
Indifferent	Boy: 19.1 Girl: 11.1	Boy: 2.8 Girl: 3.0	Boy: 6.5 Girl: 6.1	Boy: 11.8 Girl: 9.1	Boy: 3.9 Girl: 3.0	Boy: 7.4 Girl: 8.0	Boy: 11.8 Girl: 13.0
P	0.575	0.579	0.687	0.378	0.845	0.745	0.143
Total	100	100	100	100	100	100	100

Table 3. Results of motivation of different grade of sports volunteer.

Variable	Obligation	Capacity	Experience	Resume	Life	Rewards	Glory
Agree percent	One: 33.22 Two: 30.00	One: 33.23 Two: 55.30	One: 38.35 Two: 45.33	One: 22.32 Two: 46.34	One: 41.27 Two: 43.50	One: 20.2 Two: 22.0	One: 54.22 Two: 20.20
P	0.048*	0.686	0.754	0.025*	0.578	0.898	0.048*

Table 4. Results of the problems of college sports volunteer.

Variable	Personal loss	Ability display	Fund injection	Social support	Job value	Personal security	Time conflict	Others
Order	6	7	4	1	5	3	2	8

undergraduates. So the implement of "support" theory should be the priority of organizers by creating specific supporting strategy.

3.2.2 Enhancing the value guidance of undergraduate voluntary activities

The investigation shows that 41.1% of undergraduates "wishing for material reward", which calls for the proper measurements on the host's part to give correct value guidance for basically voluntary activities is the participation of one's own accord and little care about personal material gain and loss. Material motivation is ever and never the requirement.

3.2.3 Laying emphasis on the training quality of the undergraduate voluntary activities in sports

Training of voluntary activities in sports is in need of knowledge, professional skills, qualities and management methods. 32.25% of the investigated undergraduates are willing to participate in the training, which should be paid high attention by relevant organizations in the selection part, especially the quality cultivation.

3.2.4 Paying attention to the performance evaluation of the undergraduate voluntary activities in sports

The investigation shows that the longer undergraduates enter a university, the less enthusiasm to the voluntary activities in sports. Organizers are required to reinforce the voluntary project evaluation, enact normal quantitative evaluation and examination standards, establish intermediaries of evaluation and supervisory, perfect voluntary projects and implement supervisor system. Furthermore, the exploration of the statistical indicator system should be deepened, and the commend incentive mechanism taking spiritual motivation as the principal thing and material reward as the complementary should be perfected.

3.2.5 Reinforcing the propaganda guidance of the undergraduate voluntary activities in sports

According to the investigation, voluntary activities in sports, amounting to apportion due to the lack of autonomy and selectivity, are far from the basic principle of "voluntary". Only 10% of undergraduates are fully aware of the current activity compared with the 90% of the less comprehended

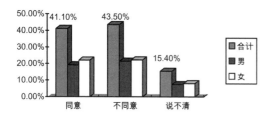

Figure 1. The statistical results of college students' perceptions to get material reward.

ones. Consequently, the priority is to increase the propaganda and recruit undergraduate volunteers by adopting more promoting approaches as possible to engage more undergraduates in voluntary activities.

4 CONCLUSIONS AND RECOMMENDATIONS

4.1 *Conclusions*

The motivation of college sports volunteer activities aims to enrich experiences, exercise capacity, accumulate experience, enhance the resume, acquire the glory, shoulder obligations and get rewards. The whole, China's college students to serve as a sports volunteer have nearer positive and correct values; College students' subjective motive for sports volunteer activity is relatively insufficient, which are influenced by such factors with social support, time, personal protection and funds investment; College sports volunteer incentive

strategies include great importance and support for the college sports volunteer activity, the guidance of the value orientation, intensive training to be a sports volunteer, more attention to the performance evaluation and the publicity to guide sports volunteer activities.

4.2 *Advice*

To guide college students volunteer correctly to strengthen the motivation to participate in sports activities to form the correct cognition; To intensify propaganda and education to create a positive and enthusiastic atmosphere; To train related knowledge and develop sports volunteer's ability; To establish reasonable incentive policy and introduce specific assessment standard system; To interfere with physical voluntary behavior in the form of practice credit.

REFERENCES

[1] The important instructions for youth volunteer of the central authorities. http://www.people.com.cn/GB/shizheng/252/6135/20010820.html. January 16, 2000.
[2] Theory of China's central propaganda bureau[M]. From how to see to how to do—hot issues face to face, Beijing: Press of learning, People's publishing house, 2011.
[3] Y. Ch Li. Research on the volunteer management mode and evaluation system of 2008 Beijing Olympic Games [M]. Beijing: Beijing sport university press. 2007.
[4] China's volunteer service survey: the plight "before and when and after the use of volunteer" [N]. People's Daily, May 5, 2010.

Computer, Intelligent Computing and Education Technology – Liu, Sung & Yao (Eds)
© 2014 Taylor & Francis Group, London, ISBN 978-1-138-02469-4

GenBank data management based on Hadoop

Y.L. Zhao, Z.Q. Sun & H.J. Li
Shandong Provincial Key Laboratory of Computer Network, Shandong Computer Science Center,
Shandong, Jinan, China

S.S. Xuan Yuan
Shandong Academy of Information and Communication Technology, Jinan, China

ABSTRACT: GenBank is a most popular DNA sequence database founded by National Center for Biotechnology Information. It is big and rapid growing. In order to make use of GenBank data efficiently, data management becomes more and more important. With the development of information science and technology, distributed computing plays a key role in many fields. Based on Hadoop (a famous distributed computing framework), we proposed a method of processing Genbank data. First, we divided GenBank sequence file into sequence items. Second, sequence items were analyzed into key/value pairs by BioJava Tools. At last, Hbase table was designed to store key/value pairs. The experiments show it is efficient and accurate. GenBank data stored in Hbase should be applied in data searching, contrasting and managing rapidly and efficiently.

Keywords: GenBank; key/value pairs; Hadoop; Hbase

1 INTRODUCTION

GenBank is a comprehensive public database of nucleotide sequences and supporting bibliographic and biological annotation. It is an open-obtained sequence database, and produced by National Center for Biotechnology Information (NCBI). GenBank receives sequences produced in laboratories throughout the world. In the more than 30 years, GenBank has become the most important and most influential database for research in almost all biological fields, whose data are accessed and cited by millions of researchers around the world. GenBank is fast growing at an exponential rate, doubling every 18 months. GenBank Release 199.0, produced in December 10 2013 contains over 150 billion nucleotide bases in more than 169 million reported sequences. Uncompressed, the Release 199.0 flat files require roughly 618 GB (sequence files only).[1] Managing such a huge database becomes more and more difficult.

Hadoop is an Apache Software Foundation project, and it is an open-source framework that allows for the distributed processing of large data sets across clusters of computers using simple programming models.[2] It is designed to scale up from single servers to thousands of machines, each offering local computation and storage. In our work,

we download GenBank sequence files suffixed with '.seq' from website, then analysis them into items and stored in Hbase based on Hadoop.

2 SEQUENCE FILE ANALYSIS

In GenBank database, sequence file is familiar, including many sequence items separated by '//'. To manage these GenBank files, we need to divide them into separate sequence items automatically. In Hadoop, we adopt MapReduce model to separate Genbank files into lots of items.

2.1 *MapReduce model*

MapReduce model is a programming framework, and it is applied widely in a parallel, distributed algorithm on a cluster for extreme scale data sets.[3] The main idea of MapReduce is 'map' and 'reduce'.

Figure 1 is the representation of MapReduce working. Once we submit our code to the cluster, the only JobTracker determines the execution plan by determining which files to process, assigns nodes to different tasks, and monitors all tasks as they are running.

'Map' function takes a series of key/value pairs, processes each, and generates new and more out-

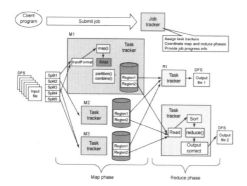

Figure 1. MapReduce structure and data flow.

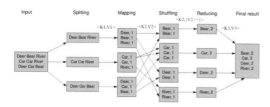

Figure 2. A MapReduce example in a word-count application.

```
public static class SeqFileInputFormat extends
    FileInputFormat<LongWritable, Text> {
  @Override
  public RecordReader<LongWritable, Text> createRecordReader(
    InputSplit split, TaskAttemptContext context) {
    return new IsearchRecordReader("//");
  }

  @Override
  protected boolean isSplitable(JobContext context, Path file) {
    //
    return false;
  }
}
```

Figure 3. SeqFileInputFormat code.

put key/value pairs. The input and output types of a 'map' function often are different from each other.

For example in Figure 2, during a word-count application, the map function would break the line into words and output a key/value pair for each word. Each output pair would contain the word as the key and the number of instances of that word in the line as the value.

2.2 Customized input format

Before MapReduce running, Hadoop will split files and read according to the definition format. All these jobs will be done in InputFormat.

As one of abstract class of InutFormt, FileInputFormat class is especially for splitting and reading information of ordinary files. It includes two methods, getSplits() and RecordReader(). Whether splits or not and split rules are drafted in getSplits(). And RecordReader() determines the way in which to read the file.

Through FileInputFormat, input files are divided into logic InputSplits, and one for one single Mapper task. And lots of Key/value pairs will be as input of Mapper, after RecordReader.

In our work, we custom a new class SeqFileInputFormat and define '//' as the special separator in RecordReader (seen in Fig. 3).

3 SEQUENCE ITEM ANALYSIS

After obtaining sequence items, we will analysis each item into key-value pairs. Sequence items are in a fixed regular format.

A sequence item is consisted of several fixed fields, and every field is beginning with key word, ending with definitions of this field. Some field can be divided into several sub-fields, beginning with sub-key-words or specifications. Key words in sequence items include LOCUS, DEFINITION, FEATURES, NID, KEYWORDS, SOURCE, REFERENCE, BASE COUNT, ORIGIN, etc.

In order to extract key/value pairs, we use Biojava libraries to analysis sequence items.

3.1 BioJava

BioJava is an open-source project designed to providing a Java framework for processing biological data. The goal of it is to facilitate rapid application development for bioinformatics.[4]

To use BioJava, add the required JAR files to your CLASSPATH environment variable. In main() method, BioJava jar files should be add directly, as seen in Figure 4. We download biojava1.5 from website, and place it in local directory.

3.2 Hbase

It is not our final results to analysis keywords and their definitions. What we want is storing the key/value pairs into Hbase for further management.

Apache HBase is an open-source, distributed, versioned, column-oriented store modeled after Google's Bigtable.[5] And it provides Bigtable-like

```
addTmpJar("D:\\biojava\\BioJava1.5-bin\\bytecode.jar", conf);
addTmpJar("D:\\biojava\\BioJava1.5-bin\\apps-1.5.jar", conf);
addTmpJar("D:\\biojava\\BioJava1.5-bin\\biojava-1.5.jar", conf);
addTmpJar("D:\\biojava\\BioJava1.5-bin\\commons-cli.jar", conf);
```

Figure 4. Adding BioJava jar files.

capabilities on top of Hadoop and HDFS. Data is stored in Hbase through table. A Hbase table is comprised of rows and columns. And columns can be divided into several column families. Every column in a Hbase table belongs to some column family. While row key is major key for indexing records.

4 EXPERIMENTAL RESULTS

In our experiments, we uploaded GenBank sequence files onto HDFS based on Eclipse platform. And development environments are JDK 6.0. Distributed environments based on Hadoop–1.0.3 with a namenode and three datanodes.

1. Genbank data key/value pairs by BioJava
   In order to verify BioJava Tools, we read and analysis sequence files through a single node. The major code is seen in Figure 5. The analyzed key/value pairs are shown in output window in Figure 6. From these results, key/value pairs are obtained by BioJava efficiently.
2. Genbank data storage in Hbase
   According to the practical demands, we design a Hbase table with the following structure. We take 'ACCESSION' as row key, and define 'info', 'fea', 'ref', 'seq' as four column families. The structure can be seen in Table 1. And Figure 7 displays a sequence item data stored in Hbase table.

```
/**** read the GenBank File          *******/

  //iterate through the sequences
  while(iter.hasNext()){

    try {
      Sequence seq = iter.nextSequence();
        //do stuff with the sequence
      Annotation anno = seq.getAnnotation();
       for( Iterator i = anno.keys().iterator();i.hasNext(); ) {
          Object key = i.next();
          System.out.println(key + " is:" + anno.getProperty(key));
       }

    } catch (BioException ex) {
      //not in GenBank format
      ex.printStackTrace();
        }catch (NoSuchElementException ex) {
      //request for more sequence when there isn't any
      ex.printStackTrace();
        }
  }
```

Figure 5. Analyzing key/value pairs code.

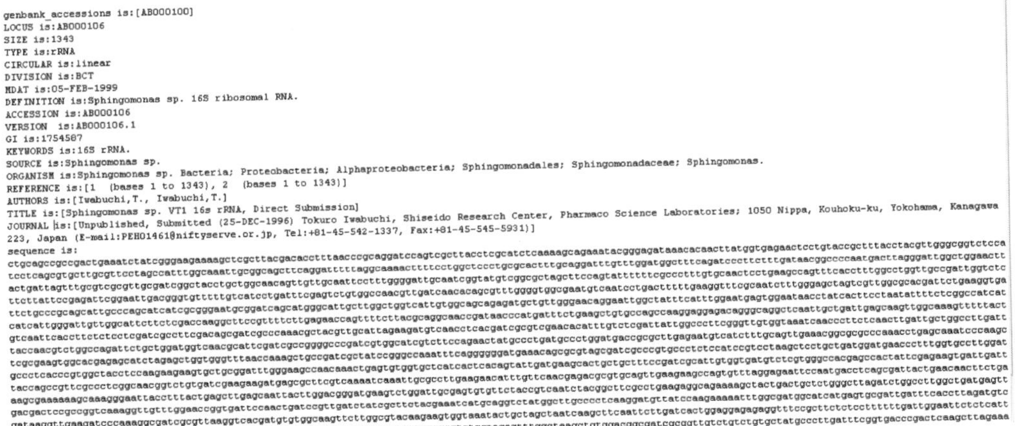
genbank_accessions is:[AB000100]
LOCUS is:AB000106
SIZE is:1343
TYPE is:rRNA
CIRCULAR is:linear
DIVISION is:BCT
MDAT is:05-FEB-1999
DEFINITION is:Sphingomonas sp. 16S ribosomal RNA.
ACCESSION is:AB000106
VERSION is:AB000106.1
GI is:1754587
KEYWORDS is:16S rRNA.
SOURCE is:Sphingomonas sp.
ORGANISM is:Sphingomonas sp. Bacteria; Proteobacteria; Alphaproteobacteria; Sphingomonadales; Sphingomonadaceae; Sphingomonas.
REFERENCE is:[1 (bases 1 to 1343), 2 (bases 1 to 1343)]
AUTHORS is:[Iwabuchi,T., Iwabuchi,T.]
TITLE is:[Sphingomonas sp. VT1 16s rRNA, Direct Submission]
JOURNAL is:[Unpublished, Submitted (25-DEC-1996) Tokuro Iwabuchi, Shiseido Research Center, Pharmaco Science Laboratories; 1050 Nippa, Kouhoku-ku, Yokohama, Kanagawa 223, Japan (E-mail:PEH01461@niftyserve.or.jp, Tel:+81-45-542-1337, Fax:+81-45-545-5931)]
sequence is:

Figure 6. Analyzed key/value representation.

Table 1. Hbase table structure.

Row-key	Column	Column-family Column-family 1 Info	Column-family 2 Fea	Column-family 3 Ref	Column-family 4 Seq
ACCESSION	Column1	SIZE	DEFINITION	REFERENCE	ORIGIN
	Column2	CIRCULAR	KEYWORDS	AUTHORS	
	Column3	DIVISION	SOURCE	TITLE	
	Column4	MDAT	ORGANISM	JOURNAL	
	Column5	VERSION		PUBMED	
	Column6	GI		COMMENT	
	Column7	TYPE			

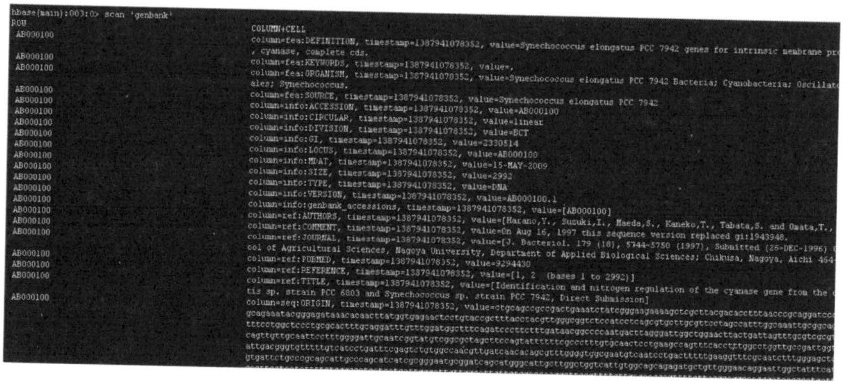

Figure 7. A sequence item data stored in Hbase table.

5 CONCLUSION

With the development of internet and bioscience, GenBank database is growing rapidly. How to store, manage and retrieve sequence items efficiently becomes more and more important. Distributed computing enables computers to coordinate their activities and to share the resources of the system hardware, software, and data. Users of a distributed system should be more cost-efficient and reliable to perceive a single, integrated computing facility, even though it may be implemented by many computers in different locations. Hadoop implements a distributed file system referred to HDFS.

Based on Hadoop, we divided GenBank sequence files into sequence items. Then analyzed sequence items into key/value pairs and stored in a pre-defined Hbase table. The experiments show it is faster and more efficient than a single high-end computer. Users could search, contrast and manage DNA data stored in Hbase.

ACKNOWLEDGEMENTS

This work is partially supported by national youth science foundation (No. 61004115, No. 61303199), Provincial Outstanding Research Award Fund for young scientist (No. BS2009DX016).

REFERENCES

[1] GenBank release 199 now available: December 13 2013. http://www.ncbi.nlm.nih.gov/news/12-16-2013-genbank-199-available/.
[2] Tom White. Hadoop: The Definitive Guide (Second Edition). 2011.07. O'Reilly Media.
[3] Dean and S. Ghemawat. MapReduce: Simplified Data Processing on Large Clusters. 6th Symposium on Operating Systems Design and Implementation. 2004. pp: 137–150.
[4] Andrew Yates, Spencer E. Bliven, Peter W. Rose, etc. BioJava: an open-source framework for bioinformatics in 2012. Bioinformatics Applications Note. Vol. 28 no. 20 2012, pp: 2693–2695. doi:10.1093/bioinformatics/bts494.
[5] Apache HBase Project. http://Hbase.apache.org/.

Computer, Intelligent Computing and Education Technology – Liu, Sung & Yao (Eds)
© *2014 Taylor & Francis Group, London, ISBN 978-1-138-02469-4*

Research on the information technology course teaching in middle school in Western China

Y.F. Zhang
Education and Science College, Yan'an University, Yan'an, China

ABSTRACT: With the rapid development of information technology, China has begun in the popularization of information technology education in middle and primary schools, focusing on training students to adapt to the modern information society and to be the people with lifelong learning abilities. Because of information technology education development time is not long; the information technology course teaching environment has large gaps in different areas in China, especially in the undeveloped areas in Western China. There are still many problems in the information technology course teaching practice, which affect the quality of teaching seriously. This paper reports on a study of investigation into the information technology course teaching in Western China. The results show that the present IT course teaching situation in that area is far from being satisfactory. There are six essential problems in the teaching practice: value judgement, the students' individual differences, inconformity between the instructional objective and the teaching practice, lack of sufficient qualified teachers, the distribution of media resources, evaluation and feedback in the class. And then the paper puts forward corresponding strategies and methods to the problems.

Keywords: Western China; information technology course; teaching; IT

1 INTRODUCTION

With the rapid development of information technology, China has begun in the popularization of information technology education in middle and primary schools, focusing on training students to adapt to the modern information society and to be the people with lifelong learning abilities. Because of information technology education development time is not long; the information technology curriculum teaching environment has large gaps in different areas in China, especially in the undeveloped areas in Western China. So it is urgent to research on the present situation of IT curriculum teaching in those areas, and realize the balanced development of information technology education.

2 SUMMARY OF INFORMATION TECHNOLOGY CURRICULUM TEACHING IN MIDDLE SCHOOL IN CHINA

In the drive of international information tide, China began to open the Basic Language optional course at the Affiliated High Schools of Tsinghua University, Peking University in 1982. It is the beginning of China's information technology education in middle school.

China formally promulgated the "Guidance of Computer Course Teaching Outline in Middle and Primary Schools (Revised Draft)" file In 1997, clearly shows the course's objective: cultivating students' interest and awareness of information technology; making the students understand and master the basic knowledge and basic skills of information technology, have the ability to obtain, transmit, process, and applying information, and understand information technology theory and relevant cultural and social problems; to foster students' good information literacy. Let the students take information technology as a support method for lifelong learning and cooperative learning, and construct necessary foundation of modern information society.

At present Chinese information technology course teaching has achieved initial results. The majority of middle and primary schools have set up courses of information technology. They have the professional information technology course teaching materials, form their own special academic system. Information technology has become an indispensable basic subject in middle school education. However, due to the uneven geographical development of education in Western-China underdeveloped area, the information technology course teaching still have many problems compared with the eastern China developing area.

3 MAIN PROBLEMS EXISTING IN THE MIDDLE SCHOOL INFORMATION TECHNOLOGY COURSE TEACHING PROCESS IN WESTERN CHINA

3.1 Having a misunderstanding value judgement of information technology course

Affected by geographical environment and economic factors, people's awareness of information technology is relatively backward. Through education to change their own destiny becomes the good wishes of students. The selection standard of senior and high school entrance is the test scores. The entrance examination courses to students are the "life-giver". But the information technology course is often seen by them as "the minor subject"; it is not to be one of the "life-giver" courses. So the students take the course as relaxing class, some teachers and parents also do not understand the value of information technology, think the students do not need spend more time and effort in it.

What's more, information technology teachers in the school's status is not high and is low-paid than other course teachers, they tend to be marginalized. Some teachers only take the information technology course as a means to live; they are lack of enthusiasm and initiative in teaching IT course. Some schools also do not pay attention to the teaching of IT course under the guidance in the college entrance examination, and do the evaluation on the IT teaching situation rarely. Because the students, teachers, parents, schools all have the deviation of IT course value judgement, the IT course becomes unimportant and more and more marginal in some middle schools in the Western China area.

3.2 Overall the students' basic information technology knowledge is poorer than other areas

At present, the development of economy and education in all areas of Chinese is unbalanced; the Western-China area is relatively backward in teaching conditions of information technology. The students' information technology awareness and ability is poorer than those in the Eastern Area.

3.3 Inconformity between the instructional objective and the teaching practice

3.3.1 Shortage of class hours
According to the Ministry of Education promulgated China "Information Technology Curriculum Guidelines (Trial)", the class hours of "information technology" course provides not less than 68 hours in the middle school stage, the real time in using computer should not be less than 70% of the total hours.

But at present in many center city schools offer "information technology" course only one class time weekly, 20 hours per term, and 40 hours a year. In the vast rural areas, because of the lack of special teachers and the time to give to other "life-giver" courses, the IT course hour number is even lower. Shortage of class hours has weakened the effect of teaching.

3.3.2 Thinking highly of practicing IT skills and ignoring the training of the information literacy
In the teaching process of information technology course, some teachers take over emphasis on skilled operation, neglect the cultivation of students' comprehensive quality and the emotion and value education objectives. Some local students are to practice typing throughout the term; the information technology course has become only a typing class. Some schools take the course only as a computer skill training class, teaching content only concluding the operation skills of Word and Excel programs; take more emphasis on the skill training. While the students' need for information acquisition, processing, management, expression, application and related laws and regulations of moral education is not enough.

3.4 Lack of sufficient qualified teachers

3.4.1 At present most middle school information technology teachers in this area are not majoring in the professional education technical
Relevant data shows that less than 3% full-time undergraduates with the background of Educational Technology specialty are in middle school information technology teachers. More of them are transferred from other disciplines, with lower degree of specialization, lacking appropriate modern educational theory of information technology teaching and professional teaching experience.

Some teachers do not regulate the operation. They echo what the books say, spend little time in the research of information technology teaching, instructional system design, and the preparation of lesson plans. These facts affect the quality of classroom teaching seriously.

3.4.2 The problem of teaching method
The teacher's teaching methods relatively simple. The main method of Teaching is combining training and explaining. They often adopt a

teacher-centered instruction; students are passive recipients of knowledge, their practice basically is to stay on imitating teachers. It is not good for developing students' exploring and creative spirit, ignores the learning autonomy of students.

Some teachers seldom design their own teaching in a systematic way; often casually organize teaching according to their own experience. The teaching knowledge structure is loosely organized, and is not reasonable.

3.4.3 *The teacher-student interaction problems*

In the area's secondary schools, an information technology teacher usually teaches many classes' IT course. Some teachers understand their students too little. The classroom interaction is based on the teacher's questioning and observation on individual students. There is nearly no other opportunity for teachers and students to interact with each other under the class.

3.4.4 *The problems of classroom management*

There are often some students in information technology class without shoe-covers, without textbooks, playing games, chatting with net friends, going to sleep. The IT course teaching environment mostly is in the computer lab, with many computers to support the students to learn IT course. The computer lab room environment is more complex than ordinary classroom, with more interference factors. The teacher in the room is very difficult to control the learning status of students, and grasp the teaching or learning process. Students easily escape form the teachers' supervision, and do not do as the teacher told. Teaching state will easily fall into chaos.

3.5 *The distribution of media resources*

In the teaching of information technology, the teaching media is an important platform for the teaching information dissemination; this requires schools to have enough resources to support the teaching media. Problems on allocation of media resources exist in current middle school is mainly reflected in two aspects: hardware and software. In terms of hardware, the problems are that the number of computers is not enough, the configuration is too low, the computer is running slowly, the slow network speed, or simply not connected to the Internet, even with the phenomenon of having computer without internet.

Teachers sometimes have to teach class, and in the same time, troubleshooting, process and effect of, students sometimes because of outdated equipment faults and stop learning, it is difficult to use media resources to expand the autonomous learning. The teacher is teaching, at the same time,

the computer machines crash frequently, he or she has to solve the computer fault. Because of outdated equipment faults students sometimes have to stop learning, it is difficult to use media resources to expand the autonomous learning.

In terms of software, the problems are that learning resource database construction is not enough. The resources construction attaches importance to hardware than software, resource classification and management is not uniform. Lack of teaching materials, animation, pictures, video tutorials, appreciation, courseware, Webpage, website, outstanding cases and other media resources needed in the class. The students themselves are difficult to find complementary resources associated with the teaching contents.

3.6 *Lack of effective evaluation and feedback in the class*

Most middle schools of Western China area have not good evaluation mechanism for the information technology curriculum, lack effective assessment and incentive system. Some schools have no mid-term and final exam for the "information technology" course, no evaluation on teachers.

Teachers in the teaching process is often teacher-centered, rarely gives students opportunities for feedback. Classroom questioning sometimes becomes just a formality, feedback link is ignored, or only pays attention to the feedback information of special students. Feedback information is lack of extensive representative. The majority of students can't know the evaluation from their teacher, thus they can't judge their own learning. This has seriously affected the enthusiasm of students.

4 SOLUTION STRATEGIES FOR THE EXISTING PROBLEMS IN THE IT COURSE IN WESTERN CHINA AREA

4.1 *To establish a correct value of information technology course*

The China Ministry of Education promulgated "Guideline for 10 Years Education Informatization (2011–2020)" pointed out that: Education Informatization is intended to promote the modernization of education, is the strategic choice for the development of education in China. Aim to build a covering education information system in both in urban and rural schools, promote sharing of high quality education resources.

Information Technology course should have very important status; it is of great significance to construct Chinese modern education system. It is the main and important way to cultivate human resources with rich information literacy, which will tell the students how to learn and live in the present society.

4.2 Reform of teaching methods and content

Because the student information technology ability foundation of this area are relatively poor, students are differences in the starting point of learning, ability, interest, motivation, environment and so on. The instruction design of the course should give full consideration to the different situation of students, encourage their strengths, maintain the students' confidence, and stimulate their interest. According to the differences of students' information technology level and ability, teacher should take graded teaching method.

The teacher should give some real-life tasks relevant to the course content to stimulate students' interest in learning process.

Strengthen the education of information ethics. It's urgent to cultivate the students' information ethics. Let the students understand the unique culture, the ethical demand, social responsibility, legal and occupation moral in information society; cultivate students' law-abiding ideas and information security knowledge; respect other people's intellectual property rights, the privacy of the individual; and not publish and disseminate false, harmful information.

4.3 To strengthen the integration of information technology course and other courses

In information technology course teaching, the teacher can take the information technology as a tool, let students to construct knowledge actively, promote the student take it as a means of receiving autonomous learning, to construct their own disciplines of learning. Try to combine the IT course practical exercises with other courses content in order to develop the students' ability to use information technology to solve practical problems in all courses, even after graduation.

4.4 To reinforce information technology teachers team construction

Teachers play a decisive role in the information technology teaching. Try to choose the teachers with professional background of educational technology in teaching IT course so as to make the teachers more professional. To provide information technology teachers with extracurricular training opportunities, establish certain incentive mechanism, encourage the teachers to engage in teaching research, encourage teachers to absorb the new educational ideas, constantly sum up experience, enhance the teachers teaching and research capacity, improve the information technology teachers' status and benefits.

The teacher can establish IT course electronic portfolio, which will record students learning process and collect students' works in subjects. The students can evaluate their own work with their peers each other.

Communication and evaluation channels between teachers and students should be diversiform, face to face in the classroom or asynchronously through the internet programs after class.

5 CONCLUSION

The study found that there are most serious problems affecting "Information Technology" course teaching in Western China: acute shortage of qualified teachers, neglected by schools, and lacking of funds. Here only gives the strategies and methods to improve the performance of IT course teaching, applying these into the teaching practice will require much more effort from the local education department and teachers, and it will be a long-term process. Hope that more colleagues can pay attention to the Information Technology course teaching in the Western China area together, and so as to improve the education and economic development level in the area.

REFERENCES

He, K.K. & Wu, J. 2007. *The Integration of Information Technology and Curriculum*. Beijing: Higher Education Press.
Jie, L. & Wang, Y. 2011. Study on construction and application of ecological school information teaching resources. *China Educational Technology*. 289:73–76.
Li, Y. et al. 2005. *Information Technology Curriculum and Teaching*. Beijing: Higher Education Press.
Mu, L.Y. & Lu, Q.J. 2011. Strategies to solve the problems of middle school information technology class. *China Educational Technology & Equipment*. 225:60–61.
Zhang, Q. 2013. Reflection on the information technology teaching in the middle school under the new curriculum reform. *Journal of Guizhou Normal College*. 29:76–78.

Computer, Intelligent Computing and Education Technology – Liu, Sung & Yao (Eds)
© 2014 Taylor & Francis Group, London, ISBN 978-1-138-02469-4

A smart visualization system for vessel tank layout configuration

Dae Geon Kwon, Bo Kuk Park, Haesung Tak & Hwan Gue Chos
Department of Computer Science, Pusan National University, Busan, Republic of Korea

ABSTRACT: In order to prepare factory construction, it is very important to simulate the physical placement of manufacturing components and verify that the design structure does not violate the construction constraints. In large ships, the vessel tank system consists of numerous pipes, valves and pumps over a set of large tanks. It is crucial to simulate the whole layout of tanks, pumps and other basic components in terms of their stability and ensure safe operations. In this paper, we propose a new automated tool to visualize the vessel tank configuration from a set of layout specification files, consisting of all connection rules for tanks, pumps and valves in the form of formal grammar. One advantage of our system is that it provides an automated procedure which links the real-time database on vessel components to show the real-time values to the visualization system. We propose a simple verification system to ensure vessel components conform to construction rules such that two different tanks should be separated more than a specified distance. Our system enables us to fast and easily construct a prototype of the vessel visualization system while minimizing human interventions.

Keywords: remote monitoring; web-based visualization; ballast tank; design constraints

1 INTRODUCTION

A fast and reliable monitoring system is very important for remote sensing and management. It is difficult, however, to describe a complicated vessel tank system where lots of tanks, pumps, valves, and pipes are interconnected in a large field under working and layout constraints.

When loading and unloading items, ballast system is used to balance a ship and lower its center of gravity in order to provide stability. For this reason, vessel's balance system needs monitoring system. The existing monitoring system is managed in the bridge.

In this paper, we propose a web-based monitoring platform. Our platform is implemented in web, so manager is no need to check system in bridge. If the manager has permissions, he can check system on other places. The manager can control visualization using functions saved in text files. These files can define or remove devices and control the web design for each user. It means monitoring web page is not fixed, and this platform can adapt to different vessel tank control systems.

This paper is organized as follows. In Section 2, we describe the vessel tank control system. In Section 3, we discuss our web platform. In this section, we define the file function and grid space to use web visualization. In Section 4, we implement a web-based monitoring system using our platform and provide an example. Finally, in Section 5, we draw conclusions and discuss our future work.

2 OVERVIEW OF THE VESSEL TANK CONTROL SYSTEM

In this paper, we propose a platform for display on the web the overall system design. Before proposing our monitoring platform, we analyzed the balance control system [1, 2]. There is little difference in each system, but it follows the structure shown in Figure 1.

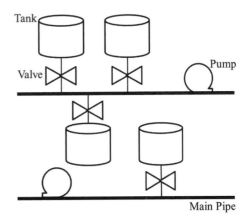

Figure 1. Tank control system for vessel.

There are three device types: tank, valve, and pump. Each device is capable of connecting each other. The main pipe is in whole system. Water flows through this pipe to the ballast tank.

Sensor data is stored in a database which follows a form defined by the water tank monitoring and visualization system with smart phone previously announced [3].

3 SMART MONITORING PLATFORM

3.1 System overview

Virtual design and factory layout simulation is a key issue in intelligent manufacturing. We can easily find some previous papers considering the main issues of this paper. Related study [4, 5] introduced an integrated and synthetic environment and composed software tools and systems such as Virtual Reality and Simulation to support such processes. They presented the Virtual Manufacturing (VM) environment focusing on potential application areas and the resulting benefits. Furthermore, another study [6] described the results of recent and ongoing major European projects about the virtual factory design topic, especially on the networked collaborative design of factory's layout and configuration.

We suggest a web-based monitoring platform for monitoring the balance control system. This platform visualized the functions located in files and a database described in Chapter 2. The architecture of the visualization platform is shown in Figure 2.

Sensor data obtained from each device is stored in the database server. When a web page is called, read the function for visualization from an UI function file and check each function. After reading the functions, Web page visualizes the balance system structure and then, web page loads the latest sensor data from the database and displays this information. We explain the function defined in the file in the next subsection.

3.2 File function

The function for the visualization was saved in the file because of working well, even if vessel's balance system has different structure of each ship. Web page loads the visualization information from the files. These files contain function information for visualizing the balance system. A description for each function can be found in Table 1.

Function is stored metadata in each format. DEVICE and LINE functions define the device and position identification. The LABEL function determines which sensor data, from the database, are shown in the webpage. The LOC function sets the device location in the web page by using position identification. The RELATION function defines a connection between two devices, and the PIPEJOINT function defines a connection between a device and the main pipeline.

Web master writes this function file. He can control information on the web page and modify which visualization devices follow the balance system structure. Even if a web developer modifies a visualization algorithm, it is still possible to visualize the web interface that matches the file function definition. This means that the platform can reduce modification costs when the web design or balance system is changed.

3.3 Grid method

In order to easily locate a device on the web page, we define the Grid Space. Grid Space is shown in Figure 3.

We can set the position of the device using this space. For example, Tank information can be as follows:

- DEVICE DEVICE_TYPE DEVICE_ID
- LINE LINE_TYPE LINE_ID POSITION
- LOC DEVICE_ID VERTICAL HORIZONTAL

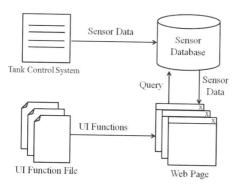

Figure 2. The architecture of web-based monitoring and visualization platform.

Table 1. File format and descriptions of each function. This table shows function and description each function in each file format.

Format	Function	Description
.dev	DEVICE	Define Device Identification
.dcd	LABEL	Set component's data display
.grd	LINE	Define Position Identification
.loc	LOC	Set device location to use position ID
.rel	RELATION	Connection between Source & Destination
.pip	PIPEJOINT	Connection between Device & Main pipeline

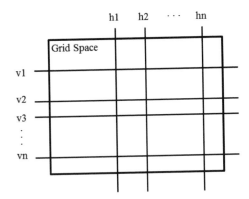

Figure 3.   Grid space. In this space, we can set the location using vertical and horizontal line such as v1 and h1, respectively.

User can set the vertical or horizontal position using LINE function. Administrator can be positioning devices efficiently using this space.

3.4   Function error detection

Prior to visualization, file functions are checked to determine if any design errors. This error detection process checks design rules such as assuring a proper gap between devices and checking whether each device is connected correctly and has the proper number of connections.

4   IMPLEMENTATION

To implement the platform which we previously proposed in Section 3, we used JavaScript and PHP language, and considered various web-browsers such as Chrome and Internet Explorer.

First we define the device and label them based on the following conditions:

- Tank contains five sensors.
- The pump and valve only display ID. Do not use any labels.
- The pump and valve must consider the direction.

Next, we write the DEVICE and LABEL functions. The LABEL function controls what is shown to the user. The DEVICE and LABEL functions of the tank are written as follows:

- LABEL COT-01 LEVEL TEMP PRESSURE

As shown in Figure 4, devices are visualized based on their definitions. After device components are set, the relationship of each device in the *rel* file and location of device in the *loc* file and implement all functions. After setting all UI control files, we

a. Tank Component

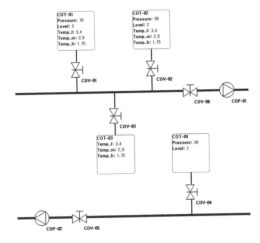

b. Pump Component   c. Valve Component

Figure 4.   Visualization of device components. Pumps and valves have no label and Tank has five labels.

Figure 5.   This result is visualized Figure 1. Tank sensor data obtained from the database.

connect database to receive sensor data. The result of this process is implemented in Figure 5.

The two tanks at the top of Figure 5 show all sensor data and the two tanks at the bottom display only temperature or pressure and level. All device locations are defined in Grid Space.

As shown in Figure 6, we can change the design by using LINE and LOC functions. Furthermore, the file functions make it possible to visualize more complex design such as shown in Figure 7.

Prior to visualization, error detection is performed to check for file function error, if the detection system detects an error, the web page displays a warning as show in Figure 8. The manager uses this error information to modify the design.

663

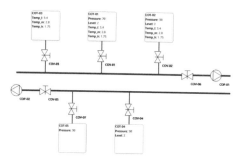

Figure 6. This result is same structure Figure 5. Function file can control device position.

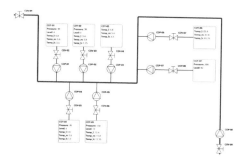

Figure 7. File function can show more complex design.

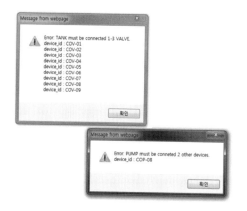

Figure 8. File function error detection. This detection can be check simple design error likes exceeding of connections.

5 CONCLUSION AND FUTUREWORK

In this paper, we proposed a monitoring visualization platform and implemented in web page. This platform has the following advantages:

– A manager can change the system's structure without modifying the actual code by only changing the function file.

– Developer can easily change visualization algorithm without modifying the file function.
– This platform can reduce the cost of remotely monitoring the balance control system.
– Error detection can check for design errors and help design or visualize the balance system.

A manager can easily change the system structure by changing the file without modifying the code. This benefit said that our platform can apply most changes to the balance system without considering its architecture. As expected, administrative costs of the balance control systems is reduced.

In this paper, we proposed a web-based monitoring platform for monitoring vessel balance system architecture. In the future we will analyze device sensor data and research about determining failures and predictions. This system can analyze the sensor data from the server and find the device which will be suspicion of failure.

ACKNOWLEDGEMENT

This research was financially supported by the Ministry Of Trade, Industry & Energy (MOTIE), Korea Institute for Advancement of Technology (KIAT) and DongNam Institute For Regional Program Evaluation (IRPE) through the Leading Industry Development for Economic Region.

REFERENCES

[1] Celik M. 2008. Managing the Operational Constraints in Ship Machinery Design and Installation: Synthesis of Design-Based Failures for Improving the Structural Quality of Shipboard Systems, *Naval Engineers Journal* 120:67–76.
[2] Harries S., Tillig F., Wilken, M. & Zaraphonitis G. 2011. An Integrated Approach for Simulation in the Early Ship Design of a Tanker, *in Proc, 10th International Conference on Computer and IT Applications in the Maritime Industrie (Berlin, May 2011)* 411–425.
[3] Tak H.S., Kwon D.G. & Cho H.G. 2013. Water Tank Monitoring and Visualization System Using Smart Phones. *International Journal of Machine Learning and Computing* 3(1): 142–146.
[4] Iqbal M. and Hashmi M.S.J. 2001. Design and analysis of a virtual factory layout *Journal of Materials Processing Technology* 118: 403–410.
[5] Souza M.C.F., Sacco M. & Porto A.J.V., 2006. Virtual manufacturing as a way for the factory of the future, *Journal of Intelligent Manufacturing* 17(6): 725–735.
[6] Mottura S., Vigano G. and et al. 2008. New challenges in collaborative virtual factory design *Innovation in Manufacturing Networks* 266: 17–24.

Study on psychology electronic teaching environment based on E-Learning of groupware technology

Dian-Zhe Xu

School of Economic Management, Beihua University, Jilin City, China

ABSTRACT: E-Learning is a new learning mode with the continuous development of the growing popularity of Internet and information and communication technologies. On the basis of groupware technology and E-Learning networked learning environment were analyzed. The system framework model was described based groupware technology B/S mode, architecture, function modules, and its features.

Keywords: E-Learning; psychology electronic teaching environment; groupware technology; collaboration

1 INTRODUCTION

E-Learning is the development of computer network technology. Distributed open architecture, communication collaboration, resource sharing, updates and other learning environment characterized by rapid network teaching system, which has changed the mode of transmission of information from the fundamental education, becoming constructed lifelong education system, building the future learning society need to learn platform. The first step in the completion of E-Learning: After the core curriculum courses resource sharing, how to break the boundaries of a single course, create interactive psychology interconnected electronic teaching environment, take advantage of the openness of the network, media diversity, virtual, cross-regional, abundant resources and other characteristics, the teachers, learners and researchers connected to a common platform to provide personalized, real-time, reasonable cost, effective training and continuous learning to become E-Learning further development of the urgent problems.

2 GROUPWARE TECHNOLOGY AND E-LEARNING DEVELOPMENT OVERVIEW

2.1 Groupware technology overview

Groupware is AC (Communication), coordination (Coordination), collaboration (Collaboration) and information sharing (Information Sharing) aim to support the application software group work needed. Currently, according to the main functions of groupware products division, roughly: e-mail support, represented by the transmission of information (Messaging Passing) class to the workflow (Workflows), spreadsheet (Spreadsheet) as the representative of the support process automation Process Automation) class to video meeting, sharing, co-edit documents and other types of database software groups emphasized the promotion of cooperation and includes workflow management, messaging and integrated database functionality, users have integrated development environment with a high degree of safety, represents the development direction of groupware type integrated groupware development platform, such as Figure 1.

Groupware largely solved the problem of space constraints when working in collaborative work groups among members faced improve interpersonal communication, coordination, cooperation and information sharing situation, strongly supports and fully representative the future direction of collaborative computing.

2.2 E-Learning development overview

Education is the first step to electronic resources, such as the existing course materials published

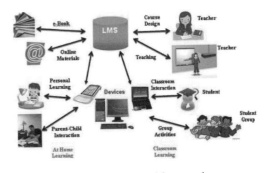

Figure 1. E-Learning structural framework map.

online. 1998 Blackboard products come first, which is derived from Cornell University Blackboard-CourseInf0. Blackboard—Blackboard and follow the development path of some other software—are used as the core of the problem with the concept of Blackboard courses concern is: How can I make not a technical expert teachers quickly and easily to the existing curriculum published online today? Most colleges only use a certain program or certain kinds of management tools, and is gradually integrating multiple systems on campus, unify them. Gaynor 2002 survey showed that 73 percent of U.S. colleges and universities have been locked up only a teaching course management system. In the current is technical background. Courses online problem has been basically solved, such as Figure 2.

E-Learning challenges facing today is how to jump out of bound course, many other educational resources will be integrated into online learning, whether these resources are the traditional form or in digital form. How can we achieve the various courses and off campus libraries, research institutes, instructors, students, alumni, parents, brothers and institutions as well as other types of connections between learning resources and integrate it? There. With the expansion of the learning environment, how can we maintain the system, management of resources? Both establish order for a large number of digital data, and further accumulate more resources?

Students feel free to cooperate with education experts by creating electronic teaching psychology environment, ready to be found in academic achievement, ready access to learning resources. Advanced electronic teaching environmental psychology of the people and resources not only a school organically connected as one, but also extended to other institutions or organizations. Teachers and students do not have to learn new software, not familiar with the new interface, do

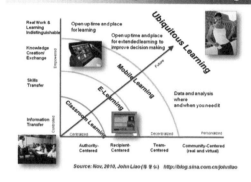

Figure 3. From M-Learning to U-Learning.

not need to remember a new password, you can easily complete the learning task in this integrated environment, such as Figure 3.

3 PSYCHOLOGY ELECTRONIC TEACHING ENVIRONMENT ANALYSIS

3.1 *Psychology electronic teaching platform model analysis*

Electronic teaching psychology is an Internet-based technical support, open, new ways of learning: a learner active, autonomous, non-linear, and interactive, in order to obtain and understand the information—based, multimedia as a means of expression. Establish learning network support above. For the prospect of electronic teaching psychology as the "digital era missionaries," the Negroponte wrote in his famous book "Being Digital", a book wrote: "The ability to invest time and wisdom of people on the Internet will be more and more, the Internet will become a human exchange of knowledge and mutual assistance network ...."

Through the network, the e-mail, document management, workflow application combined with wow can be dispersed in communication between members of different places. It can not only share information, but also provide a shared space and multimedia information. As a collaborator provides management and control mechanisms. Building a psychology electronic teaching environment through information technology, making people's minds will bring together tacit knowledge becomes easier. And enable knowledge clarity, so that members can work together to produce new knowledge. An excellent platform for electronic is teaching psychology model.

In psychology electronic teaching platform: management and results through teaching courses

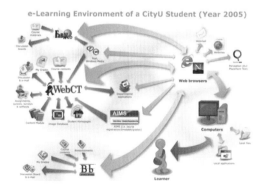

Figure 2. E-Learning environment of a cityU Student (Year 2005).

feedback, curriculum resources and centralized management to achieve learning outcomes reported: self through a variety of learning styles, collaboration, real-time communication and face to face learning on the one hand to achieve the team's tacit personal knowledge into explicit knowledge to tacit knowledge other team to achieve the team's explicit knowledge conversion: by tracking real-time learning and assessment tests mastery learning progress and learning outcomes: by the relevant participants/experts query from a practice experience to acquire knowledge.

3.2 Psychological characteristics of electronic teaching environment convenience

1. Learning resources (including people and content) to get. Psychology electronic is teaching environment to accommodate a convenient and practical knowledge base for all kinds of readers to students, institutions and organizations, such as browsing. Users do not need to register a door specific courses will be able to exchange, store and update the contents of that part of their interest: Meanwhile, other institutions can access the psychology of learning resources through electronic teaching environment. With more and more schools have their own electronic teaching environmental psychology? Form a super network. Joint so that each school, communication, in order to achieve a real sense of sharing.

2. Rapid transmission of information. Psychology electronic teaching environment, rapid transmission of information is necessary for effective learning aspects of the organization. One feature of electronic teaching psychology is different from the individual learning: mastery of the information is not stagnant in the hands of individuals but to be shared throughout the organization. Only in this way can the organization is far greater than the individual ability to produce force. The first time access to information in order to make the correct response for the first time, thereby increasing the speed of information transfer is a key to improve electronic teaching psychology. In psychology, electronic teaching environment, knowledge and personal problems encountered by the master, can pass through the network in real time, and get feedback.

3. Collaborative space free discussion. From personal knowledge to grasp the organization needs to master a certain time delay, in order to achieve improved knowledge and awareness of unity, the need for adequate communication. In psychology, electronic teaching environment is via email, whiteboard, file and screen sharing, short messaging, audio, video sessions and

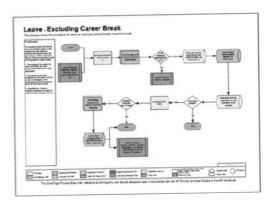

Figure 4.   Leave Excluding Career Break.

other networking tools. Makes the nature of communication and exchange between people becomes more democratic, it promotes various concepts and ideas passed in the network, but also to promote the development of high-level organizational knowledge.

4. Effective collaborative awareness and management. Collaborative awareness for the organization is to provide a good learning atmosphere. Collaborators need to know the existence of other users in the same group, to keep abreast of the status of the other members of the organization, behavior, and identity can be confirmed, select partnership. There is a synergistic conflict, such as: Midway attend meetings or exit, voice, etc. to compete for the meeting, discussed the necessary coordination within the organization, providing safe and reliable system environment.

5. Through the learning process of evaluation and tracking. Psychology electronic is teaching environments to provide cross-curricular, cross-semester entire profession or tracking and statistical tools throughout the study period.

6. Can be customized multi-role environment. Member of the role is identity psychology electronic teaching environment is different, but no matter for which one (or more) is role or identity of all operational processes are around this expanded role or identity.

4   PSYCHOLOGY ELECTRONIC TEACHING ENVIRONMENT FRAMEWORK MODEL BASED GROUPWARE TECHNOLOGY

4.1   System architecture

The traditional E-Learning Learning Framework uses a Client/Server (C/S) mode, using a shared text database, the lack of mutual exchange between members, making it difficult to meet the requirements of practical use. L8l Therefore, we propose to build electronic teaching environment based on psychology groupware technology, Browser/Server (B/S) mode. B/S mode simplifies the client software; simply install the browser as a client application running platform, while all the development, maintenance and upgrade work has focused on the server side. Users collaborate using a browser to access the Psychology electronic teaching environment framework model based groupware technology System Architecture.

The traditional E-Learning Learning Framework uses a Client/Server (C/S) mode, using a shared text database, the lack of mutual exchange between members, making it difficult to meet the requirements of practical use. L8l Therefore, we propose to build electronic teaching environment based on psychology groupware technology, Browser/Server (B/S) mode. B/S mode simplifies the client software; simply install the browser as a client application running platform, while all the development, maintenance and upgrade work has focused on the server side. Users collaborate using a browser to access the server module. The appropriate workspace is database server database module through collaboration. And applications (Java applets) downloaded to the client, and by starting the application server provides a variety of services to interact. Achieve collaborative learning function. This mode uses flexible and can provide various forms of communication to members of the organization; greatly facilitate the application of the system.

Psychology electronic teaching environment constructed function of the system can be divided into three parts: the client application, collaboration services and database management. Creating the appropriate workspace is database server database module through collaboration. And applications (Java applets) downloaded to the client, and by starting the application server provides a variety of services to interact. Achieve collaborative learning function. This mode uses flexible and can provide various forms of communication to members of the organization; greatly facilitate the application of the system.

4.2 Functional structure

Psychology electronic teaching environment constructed function of the system can be divided into three parts: the client application, collaboration services and database management.

Client applications. According to a browser running different users can be divided into modules: chat clients, meeting clients, customers,

and mobile radio customers. Customers can directly talk to the network real-time information exchange; by way of online text chat function can be invited to talk to one or more users from online users. Meeting customers in the form of meetings and screen sharing, whiteboard, audio and video tools for collaborative learning, meetings may be scheduled can be immediate. Broadcast customers can watch as a spectator event, but you can not interact with the personnel participating in the meeting. Mobile customers using Podcasting (Personal Optional Digital casting, personalized freely selectable digital broadcasting) and Void casting (video podcasts) technology and will no longer need to tightly connect to their computers and networks, they can learn while climbing. Stroll on the beach learning, or learning in the city streets jogging.

5 CONCLUSION

At present, the researches on E-Learning in theory have made many achievements and get a preliminary application in practice. With the extensive application of the further development of economic globalization and modern information technology, everyone will become a small global node tissue. The exchange of information between people will become more frequent and widespread. We constructed based electronic teaching environment psychology groupware technology is based on a detailed consideration of the future of this trend, the use of network support provided by the environment, efficient learning, knowledge, foster innovation and promote knowledge a broader range of information sharing. In the socialization process to achieve different organizations have tacit knowledge, so as to achieve the maximum benefit of learning, providing support for the blended learning environment.

REFERENCES

Cheng Peng-Fei, Yan Hao-Wen, Han Zhen-Hui, 2008. An Algorithm for Computing the Minimum Area Bounding Rectangle of an Arbitrary Polygon.
Gabrielidesa N.C., A.I. Ginnisa, P.D. Kaklisa, 2007. Smooth branching surface construction from cross sections.
Guo Furong, 2004. Enjoy the value of modern ideological and political education of China.
Yi-Jun Yang, Jun-Hai Yong, Hui Zhang, 2006. A rational extension of Piegl's method for flling n-sided holes.
Yong Jun, 2005. A piecewise hole filling algorithm in reverse engineering.

Computer, Intelligent Computing and Education Technology – Liu, Sung & Yao (Eds)
© *2014 Taylor & Francis Group, London, ISBN 978-1-138-02469-4*

Research on the fatigue strength of self-piercing riveting by computer simulation

Rui-Jun Liu, Jian Zhang, Xing Wang & Xiang-Wen Dang
Automotive and Architectural Engineering College, Beihua University, Jilin City, China

ABSTRACT: The burr around the edge of self-piercing riveting joints is the source of crack growth. So it is more important to research the fatigue life growth of self-piercing riveting joints in order to improve the fatigue life of riveted points, especially to the defective joints. The factors of fatigue strength in self-piercing riveting were analyzed by computer simulation, and the fatigue mechanism of self-piercing riveting was revealed.

Keywords: SPR; improve; fatigue life; computer simulation

1 INTRODUCTION

With increasingly fierce competition in the automobile industry, automobile manufacturers continue to market new models, new models in addition to outstanding safety, cost-effective, fashionable, and other characteristics, mainly directed at competitive economy car driving. In the past 20 years, car manufacturers have been looking for ways to solve the problem; the test proved that the use of new light metal materials to achieve lightweight body, to improve the economy of cars is effective. At the same time, reduce the quality of vehicle can make a variety of performance vehicles to improve and improve. Studies have shown that when the vehicle mass reduced by 10%, the fuel economy is improved by 3.8%, accelerating time to reduce 8%, CO emissions by 4.5%, 5% reduction in braking distance, tire life increased by 7% 6% reduction in steering effort. This shows the importance of lightweight vehicles.

Self-pierce riveting process to overcome the drawbacks of traditional riveting, riveting punch once achieved, is connected to the car body opened up new avenues. Foreign auto manufacturers have applied this technology, such as Jaguar has applied X350 series, XJ luxury sedan aluminum car body HSPR, at least 3,000 vehicle applications rivets, UK series are also expected to apply Audi sedan car company in the aluminum car body applications at least 1,400 rivets. Volvo Car Corporation will not only have their own self-pierce riveting vehicle production line, also built self-piercing riveting and rivet lines, and first in the Volvo FH12 Series heavy-duty truck cab application of self-pierce riveting technology, the weight ratio of the previous 30% reduction in annual savings of $ 244,000 production costs.

2 SELF-PIERCING RIVETING RESEARCH STATUS AND INTENSITY OF FATIGUE FAILURE

Compared with the resistance spot welding process, the main advantages of self-pierce riveting process is fast connection, without pre-drilling, step, easy to automate, to facilitate monitoring equipment; welding material and can not be used to connect different materials; able to connect two or more sheets; coating materials no damage or minimal damage; do not emit smoke and heat, low noise, environmental compliance; mold long life (usually number more than 20,000); energy consumption is low; unilateral remain formation and so on.

Compared with the resistance spot welding process, the main drawback of self-pierce riveting process that requires a higher pressure, which means that there must be placed punch and rivets C-shaped frame to maintain accuracy; only be used for lap connected with the edge of; presence rivet consumables; the bosses formed on the side of the die, the self-piercing riveting limits in some cases used. 1993 Audi HENROB and the first time HSPR Audi A8 for aluminum car body manufacturing, self-pierce riveting technology to solve the welding technology can not meet the performance requirements of the connection problem, not enough to overcome the fatigue strength, painted rivets layer and the aluminum and steel rivets and aluminum incompatible incompatibility issues, so the Audi A8 automobile assembly process to a new level.

Study load and punch stroke curve helps to understand riveting process and quality control. Self-pierce riveting process initially due between rivets and sheet metal between the sheet and the sheet, there is a gap between the sheet and the mold, so there is a process of eliminating the gap by pressing start before riveting. Pierce the upper sheet in the process, nearly linear increase in the load gently until completely through the upper sheet metal, rivets leg into the lower sheet. Rivet legs carried along with the lower plate material deformation under the effect of the punch, blank holder and die, the pressure began to rise rapidly, when the leg is fully open after the rivet into the pier forging stage, the pressure starts to increase until the riveting dramatic completed.

1993 Audi HENROB and the first time HSPR Audi A8 for aluminum car body manufacturing, self-pierce riveting technology to solve the welding technology can not meet the performance requirements of the connection problem, not enough to overcome the fatigue strength, painted rivets layer and the aluminum and steel rivets and aluminum incompatible incompatibility issues,

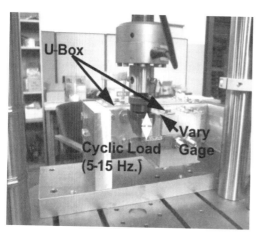

Figure 1.   HSPR test equipment.

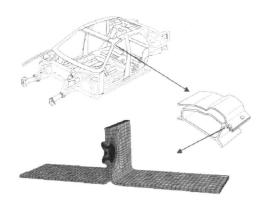

Figure 2.   Audi A8 all-aluminum body.

so the Audi A8 automobile assembly process to a new level.

3   PUNCH RIVETING FAILURE

Punching load is supplied by the punch, which requires a high punch strength, fixed and reliable, neutral good. Using a punch to punch fixing plate fixed on the template, while the use of two positioning pins to ensure that the punch. Blank holder main role is pressed sheet metal in the process of self-pierce riveting, riveting sheet to avoid the subject because of the pressure to produce large red curly deformation. Use the four screws on the blank holder fixed to the lower template, while taking advantage of the two locating pins to ensure the blank circle in the center of the hole. Die by the upper and lower mold base oriented guide pins and bushings to ensure punch and rivets, coaxial positioning sleeve to avoid punches and positioning in the riveting process generates sets of lateral offset. A displacement sensor fixed to the vicinity of the punch, punch riveting measuring stroke. Millivolt voltage signal of the pressure sensor is installed on the host pipe, the sensor output is amplified by the signal conditioning, filtering, by the A/D Analog to digital conversion; computer calibrated digital converting the real-time the obtained test data payload. Data acquisition is system theory and composition of the test shown in Figure 4.

In order to improve the accuracy of the test system, the software system uses a piecewise linear interpolation method sensor calibration. Consider the nonlinear characteristics of sensors and other parts of the test system; the test range is divided into several sections, with each line segment approximation. Piecewise linear interpolation

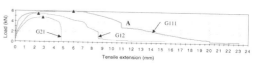

Figure 3.   The resulting tensile test specimens fail.

Figure 4.   Shear load versus tensile extension for the three groups of samples.

calibration method can significantly improve the accuracy of the test system, and can appropriately reduce the sensor linearity requirements.

4 SELF-PIERCE RIVETING PROCESS ANALYSIS OF FATIGUE

In order to improve system reliability, design and development of a dedicated integrated signal conditioning + ADC will be integrated into both the test card directly into the computer's motherboard expansion slots, due to increased system integration, improved system operational reliability and stability. Measurement accuracy specifications of automatic test system: better than 1% relative error (a precision). Self-pierce riveting process test equipment system works as follows: On the WE-30 hydraulic universal testing machine to punch controlled by the experimenter to set a speed value during the experiment, the pressure value is reflected in the universal testing machine console, obtained by the same pressure sensor; LVDT-5 by displacement of the displacement sensor to obtain, via the data acquisition for both signal acquisition, and then converted from an analog signal/digital signal converter to a digital signal finally transmitted to the microcomputer system obtain each data collection point and load displacement corresponding experimental data.

5 HSPR FATIGUE STRENGTH FATIGUE MODEL & SIMULATION

MSC.SuperForm calculated using finite element analysis software. Due to the geometry of the model and load cases are the axis of symmetry, we can use 2D axis symmetric algorithm, the 3D model into 2D model, will greatly reduce the computing time and improve efficiency. Riveting process simulation are ax symmetric nonlinear large deformation elastic-plastic mechanical analysis. Below bosses height of 0.25 D4 mold an example simulation.

Meshing is an important part of the impact analysis accuracy, the mesh should be noted that the rules directly from the surface of the work piece can be transformed into a grid element, the shape of complex plane, may first line segments,

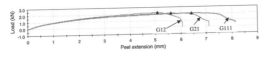

Figure 5. Peel load versus peel extension for the three groups of samples.

Figure 6. Static load and variable load.

and then carried out separately for each of the segments treatment as a basis to generate the grid.

$$\sigma_{rN}^m \bullet N = \sigma_r^m \bullet N_0 = c$$

$$\sigma_{rN}^m = \sigma_r \bullet \sqrt[m]{\frac{N_0}{N}} = \sigma_r k_N$$

$$k_N = \sqrt[m]{\frac{N_0}{N}}, k_N > 1,$$

Will directly affect the density of the grid computing, complex shape, large deformation of thin section should be appropriately zoned in the simulation process takes place, but not be too small, too small will make the computation time is too long, when the mesh reaches a certain density when, the results with mesh refinement levels did not change significantly. The shape of the analysis process is simple and a small portion can be appropriately modified to increase the grid size. Sheet metal rivets and mold geometry dimensions shown in Figure 24. The upper layer sheet having a thickness of 1 mm, the lower plate material having a thickness of 2 mm, the mold inner diameter D1 = 6.16 mm, D2 = 9.22 mm, mold depth h = 1.95 mm, the projection height t = 0.25 mm, R = 0.7 mm.

1. Each $\sigma > \sigma_r$ cycle of the material has damage, injury rate for each $1/N$
2. The damage is cumulative total injury rate

$$\frac{n_1}{N_1} + \frac{n_2}{N_2} + \ldots + \frac{n_z}{N_z} = \sum_{i=1}^{z} \frac{n_i}{N_i}$$

3. When fatigue damage, damage rate of 100%, that err.M.N. Theorem $\sum_{i=1}^{z} \frac{n_i}{N_i} = 1$ Among

$$N_1 = N \left(\frac{\sigma_r}{\sigma_1} \right)^m, N_2 = N \left(\frac{\sigma_r}{\sigma_2} \right)^m, N_i = N \left(\frac{\sigma_r}{\sigma_i} \right)^m,$$

and

$$\frac{\sum_{i=1}^{z} n_i \sigma_i^m}{N \sigma_r^m} = 1$$

4. When the parts are not damaged, the

$$\frac{\sum_{i=1}^{z} n_i \sigma_i^m}{N \sigma_r^m} < 1$$

Meshing is an important part of the impact analysis accuracy, the mesh should be noted that the rules directly from the surface of the work piece can be transformed into a grid element, the shape of complex plane, may first line segments, and then carried out separately for each of the segments treatment as a basis to generate the grid.

Riveting simulation, the upper sheet metal piercing rivets make the lower sheet large plastic deformation occurs; a direct result of the calculation grid appears distorted. In order to ensure the normal calculation process and get more accurate calculations, you must set the standard two-sheet redistricting grid.

To prevent intrusion caused severe lower grid computing accuracy remeshing criteria must be adjusted to ensure that the initiative to contact the body more than passive exposure grid mesh body should ensure that breakage occurs mesh size larger than the contact body fracture criteria.

Self-pierce riveting machines work process includes binder and punching two parts. Binder is achieved by the blank holder, the main role is blank holder riveted sheet metal pressing in self-piercing riveting process, limiting sheet too much, too fast cause wrinkling flow into the die, while avoiding sheet in the process of self-pierce riveting punch due to the greater pressure to produce curling deformation. Because the mold is not designed

rivet guide, designed so blank holder height slightly higher than the maximum thickness of the rivets, which can punch holes on the implementation of the blank holder rivet positioning and orientation, to ensure that the process of punching rivets vertically downward. To test the operation is simple, easy to mold processing, testing manual binder ways: blank circle with four locking screws on the lower template, using two locating pins to ensure the blank holder and the die center hole in the center of. In the course of the trial due to the different thickness in each sheet, so long locking screw design, which ensures that each time you replace the sheet metal blank without completely removing the ring, as long as the four locking clamping ring Loosen the screws can be replaced uniform sheet, using an auxiliary positioning pin can not guarantee each test blank holder center hole and the center of the die. Stamping process is mainly punch downward push rivets, which requires a higher intensity punch, to be firmly fixed on the neutral better.

6 CONCLUSION

HSPR fatigue crack easily extend the riveting hole, because here there is stress concentration, and where the hole wall roughness. Through the hole in the center and perpendicular to the surface of the load, the crack tip stress suffered greatly. Although the material inside the average ultimate strength of the material (which is usually said that the ultimate strength) is not reached. However, the ultimate strength of the material at the micro-local has reached, and closed when the crack is loaded sheets, resulting in the accumulation of dislocations and other cutting-edge micro-damage accumulation, cracks in the local load exceeds a certain point where the ultimate strength of the expansion, which led to lower fatigue limit on the ultimate strength. Due to the dynamic load fatigue loads, with some impact, deformation of the components inside the material will be inconsistent, inadequate, etc., to achieve the ultimate strength of the material microscopic part of the local coordination of the yield will be difficult, but also conducive to the expansion of micro-cracks, which also fatigue strength of the material is less than the ultimate strength.

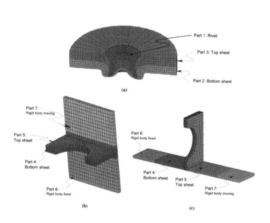

Figure 7.   Fatigue life simulation model.

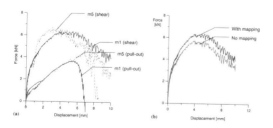

Figure 8.   Fatigue failure stress map.

ACKNOWLEDGEMENTS

1. Jilin Province Department of Education "twelfth-five" scientific and technological research projects [2013–166]
2. National Natural Science Foundation of China [51178001]

REFERENCES

Hana L. & A. Chrysanthou. 2006. Mechanical behaviour of self-piercing riveted multi-layer joints under different specimen configurations.

Li B. & A. Fatemi. 2005. An experimental investigation of deformation and fatigue behavior of coach peel riveted joints.

Porcaroa R. & M. Langsethb. 2007. Crashworthiness of self-piercing riveted connections.

Porcaroa R. & A.G. Hanssen. 2005. The behaviour of a self-piercing riveted connection under quasi-static loading conditions.

Computer, Intelligent Computing and Education Technology – Liu, Sung & Yao (Eds)
© *2014 Taylor & Francis Group, London, ISBN 978-1-138-02469-4*

The popularization of english education based on internet platform

Min Zhang
Foreign Languages' College, Beihua University, Jilin, China

ABSTRACT: With the rapidly development of political globalization and the Internet technology, online education in promoting the process of popularization of English has occupied a very important position. The popularity of online education English meaning features was discussed briefly in this paper. And a network of education, topology and other hardware components, and promote the construction of English popularization of online education system was build through the network platform.

Keywords: network platform; english popularization; topology; educational approach

1 INTRODUCTION

Dry country the attention of the Ministry of Education in recent years, public colleges and universities Englishman towel also varying degrees of development and attention to different professions have the opportunity to wash Optional English public course, by doing so opened the public taught scenario translation teaching prohibited from the following aspects introduced the college public English lessons translation teaching:

It is understood that, in many colleges and universities translation of public English lessons teaching is only concerned voice and skills training to the neglect of the translation theoretical knowledge to explain the many students will only open date to sing, but I do not know why there is such as. Ban that explanation can join in the translation teaching theoretical knowledge to stimulate students' curiosity and innovation u knowledge. To join in the theory to explain a living knowledge such as: copies of legato into a "light bulb", the quadruplets can sing "bright" light bulb, crotchet Road spiciness such as the scenario of children, quavers running spiciness, etc., so that the students very easy to understand and easy to remember. Prior to the start of the scenario translation training, the students talk about the line a variety of "ensemble" training. Teachers can be the first to write a 2/4 beat simple rhythm, first joint training after grouping, respectively, with the stomping beat flat twist refers, Paiute to complete. Then the student can own choreography rhythm spectrum, sub-part speaking line training, the students develop a sense of rhythm, coordination, training of harmony feel so boring rhythm becomes, to enhance the spirit of cooperation and collective consciousness of the students.

2 AUDITORY TRAINING TO IMPROVE STUDENTS DISCRIMINATIVE POWER OF ENGLISH

English learning, feelings and appreciation is the most basic towel 'is the most important area, students recite discussion listening to English to improve the translation Ai surgery accomplishment. Teachers live in scenario translation teaching when the wash Optional original English single melodic songs and song scenario translation speaking line contrast appreciate, to enable students to fully feel the translation of spider force, and further cultivate the spirit of the students love the translation, scenario translation training and lay a solid foundation. To appreciate the high level scenario translation English can help students to establish a correct concept of scenario. How to train the right scenario, the author introduced from the following children respect the line: the breath is the basis and driving force of the singing, the breath of use can be issued only by mastering the correct scenario nice voice. Translation of teaching is how to equip student with the correct breathing? Let all students to maintain the correct posture before practice scenario: Fit maintain Xiao—established, two in front of the head, shoulders relaxed and slightly back, even natural droop. Aspiratory mention hips twisting the chest and abdomen then use the date the nose slowly smooth and uniform, with the date of breath slowly. Exhale like to blow out the candles, ring to maintain a uniform suction. The inhale activity available "smell the flowers" to experience the feeling of suction. The breathing training including slow call slow absorption, fast absorption slow call, the fast absorption fast call, slow suck fast call, in which the focus is slow suck slow respiratory and fast absorption slow call. Each student must maintain while breathing to the injection point coordination. Nose and mouth while breathing, excited nostrils open. Hum, the scenario is uniform, soft sighing out from the nasal cavity, in the sighing feeling for scenario chant Chang, the diaphragm support point. Hum mouth like closed non-closed, and the upper and lower teeth do not killed, the tongue flat sinking throat. Voice issued from more than catchy cover, between the eyebrows and the bridge of the nose at a slight sense of vibration and each tone hum from the same location. Usually at the beginning of the vocalization, the first and thought "M" is beneficial, because the send this scenario easy to achieve the high position and the front, and bright, concentrated effect. First BU lower lip exercises hum naturally close inside the mouth to open, if closed yawn feeling, feel the scenario expansion to the high, frontal sinuses at, but never the scenario blocking Walled nasal, otherwise will issue a twang.

3 TO STRENGTHEN VOICES OF BASIC TRAINING TO CULTIVATE SCENARIO OF TRANSLATION

This vocalist from bass to treble attack to keep the combination of breath and throat stability, especially behind the treble to keep the throat stable, uniform breath, do not arbitrarily change the position. This vocalization is a combination of vowels to alternating exercises, breath control to be smooth, bass; midrange and treble scenario area resonate throughout unified. Between each different vowel scenarios and to keep the same singing state concert scenario vertical in "singing channel," scenario effects with ease, stretch, fullness, coherent, smooth. The more vowels exercises, single vowel exercises, such as a, i, o, u, e, can also be used to line the mixed vowels exercises such as ma, me, mi, mo, mu, and so in terms of vocal voice training.

Nose and mouth while breathing, excited nostrils open. Hum, the scenario is uniform, soft sighing out from the nasal cavity, in the sighing feeling for scenario chant Chang, the diaphragm support point. Hum mouth like closed non-closed, and the upper and lower teeth do not killed, the tongue flat sinking throat. Voice issued from more than catchy cover, between the eyebrows and the bridge of the nose at a slight sense of vibration and each tone hum from the same location. Usually at the beginning of the vocalization, the first and thought "M" is beneficial, because the send this scenario easy to achieve the high position and the front, and bright, concentrated effect. First BU lower lip exercises hum naturally close inside the mouth to open, if closed yawn feeling, feel the scenario expansion

to the high, frontal sinuses at, but never the scenario blocking Walled nasal, otherwise will issue a twang.

As we all know, scenario translation teaching art colleges in China has made considerable development in recent years has been comprehensively push forward with education reform and the deepening of the quality of education, has achieved a high degree of perfection and popularity of scenario translation teaching art colleges data show that the number of China's institutions of higher learning scenario translation teachers accounted for 8.97% of the entire art teachers, and art colleges this year in the number of students in the translation learning an increase of 24.8% over last year, enough to see on our art colleges emphasis in scenario translation teaching building. Compared with the translation of ordinary institutions of higher education teaching scenario translation teaching art colleges are more abundant in the faculty and professional Equipment more perfect, more professional and standardized teaching scenario translation teaching these characteristics to students play a certain role in emotional infection, and thus enhance the taste of art colleges campus there is a certain amount of influence. Art colleges must constantly improve translation teaching, to play an important role in Improving Students' Humane qualities, build good campus cultural tastes.

The so-called campus culture is built in various schools of their own culture, it has the school's own cultural characteristics, is an important part of the school building of spiritual civilization. Build the main campus culture students, humanities students directly determines the taste of campus culture, campus culture to enhance the taste, the most important to improve students' humanistic qualities. Translation teaching its unique nature, in enhancing the method of Students' Humanistic Quality plays a huge role, and thus plays an important role in improving the taste of campus culture. The translation needs of all members of the co-operation in order to carry people whenever they hear the noise when listening to the translation will feel uncomfortable, when the translation of discord, will ensure the teachers during the translation teaching part harmony between this senses, the translation teaching can promote a harmonious relationship between the students. Teachers during the translation teaching requires each student to participate in scenario translation work together in the unity of the request of the commander-in-chief, and joint efforts to sing part responsible Translation able to demonstrate the effect of the application. The same time the students responsible for their own part, while taking care of the other part, to regulate themselves and the overall relationship, so to achieve harmony.

Translation teaching students through mutual cooperation with each other mutual understanding, mutual trust; enhance mutual feelings so translation with smoother. Middle school students in this process, not only in the translation exercise their singing skills, and also to enable students to understand through their own personal practice between people in real life should also be in harmony, thereby enhancing the humanities students, help construction of campus cultural tastes.

4 TRANSLATION TEACHING POSITIVE ROLE TO ENHANCE THE TASTE OF CAMPUS CULTURE

In society, a lot of things are people collaborate to be able to complete, so with a sense of collaboration are the basic requirements for students in the humanities. In translation practice, some students often ignore the voice of the translation requirements, the volume is very casual, suddenly big and small, some part volume is too strong too weak, the volume of some part owe clearly part coordination level, resulting in volume imbalance phenomenon, volume imbalance will affect the entire translation of harmonious relations. How to overcome such a phenomenon? Translation volume balance like a car, uniform and uniformly accelerated uniform deceleration sitting would not surprise. Scenario translation scenario awareness of crescendo and diminuendo are belong to smooth. Scenario translation teaching by teaching students breathe control and vocal skills singing to enable students to be able to control their own volume, so that the translation becomes smooth and improve the overall volume balance. Scenario translation teaching through this teaching method can not only improve the students' own scenario volume control, to improve their singing skills. And high school students in the learning process gradually understand that to control the performance of desire, to have a sense of collaboration and collective consciousness, the individual must be subordinated to the collective arrangement, only mutual cooperation among the students to good things.

5 MEANING OF ENGLISH POPULARITY OF ONLINE EDUCATION

In order to better understand the meaning of English popularization of online education, let us understand the meaning of the popularization of English; it has broad and narrow sense. Popularization of English, including broad popularity and the popularity of contemporary Chinese English basic principles of English, English popularity narrowly mainly refers to the popular Contemporary Chinese English is now mainly in terms of academics to study and narrow explore the popularization of English, namely the theoretical system of socialism with Chinese characteristics.

Development of network technology in the ascendant, along with online education is also becoming increasingly popular and popular, online education is the use of modern network technology and computer technology, and modern teaching philosophy as a guide, to provide learners with an across time and space constraints maximize the use of computer resources and educational resources to facilitate autonomous learning, creative learning new educational model. However, if English does not occupy this position, then a variety of non-Marxist or anti-Marxist bound to occupy. Therefore, we should make full use of modern network technology, to further promote the popularization of English. Meaning of English popularization of online education is an excellent resource for the shared use of online education, individualized instruction, and other interactive features to promote the basic principles of English and English of contemporary China, to make these ideas and theories popularity, popularization, specific, action guide masses become conscious identity, the people transform nature into a material force of society and transformation, to play its due role in the great practice of socialism.

6 CHARACTERISTICS OF ENGLISH POPULARIZATION OF ONLINE EDUCATION

6.1 *The rapid integration of resources*

Since the party's congress report of contemporary Chinese English since the research on this new topic after another, how will the outcome of the Marxist theory of the rapid popularization of research focused integration is a critical issue, network media become a powerful tool that goal, the network media have unlimited capacity, high-speed concentration, it can be a variety of research results popularization of English, literature materials to electronic journals, e-books and other forms of highly concentrated form special education sites, achieve the rapid integration of resources, such as Figure 1.

6.2 *Popular theory of propaganda*

As Mao Zedong said, "Any ideas, and if not linked to the objective reality of things, if there is no need for an objective reality, if not the master of the people, even the best of things, even English-Leninism,

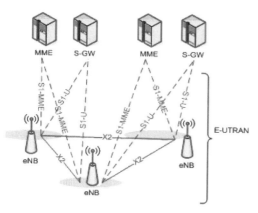

Figure 1.   Network structure.

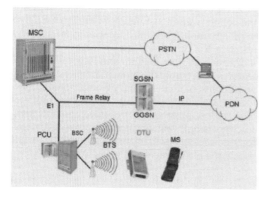

Figure 2.   Network topology.

it is not play a role." With the development of computer network information technology, China's computer users has surpassed the U.S. as the most in the world, online media has entered every household, online education is widely publicize the popularization of English provides a platform guarantee, whether government officials, businessmen hawkers, professors and scholars, students, or the general public more access to the Internet and enjoy the speed and convenience it brings, popular with English during network popularization process is illuminated can say for sure: online education to promote theoretical propaganda become popular.

6.3 *Interactive forms of learning*

In the online education environment, the Macross and multimedia nature of the network, learning is no longer adhere to the traditional one-way form of communication, but in the context of equal dialogue and exchange of information dissemination,

which gives Marxist theory learner brings unprecedented convenience and positive factors, both theoretical researchers, or ordinary people, can take advantage of online education in the form of English popularization of this proposition for interactive discussion and research, and then crash out more ideological spark that theory tends to improve and mature.

6.4 *Lifelong learning theory*

With the advent of the era of knowledge explosion, stunning speed of updating knowledge, the concept of lifelong learning as more and more people have accepted, while the Marxist Popular Education is a complex system engineering, which requires us to constantly explore learning, broaden horizons Marxist theory to explore its theoretical meaning, so that the times. Learning as a lifestyle trend of social development, online education is an effective way to achieve lifelong learning, the stage, China is gradually building an open network education system, compared with traditional education, for those who desire it people to continue their education and an open window.

7 SUMMARY

Obviously, art colleges, "Scenario translation" is not only an important cultural and recreational activities enrich students' classroom, it is the interpretation of the teachers and students the individual image of temperament, the the show college team spirit of collaboration and effective way to render the entire campus culture; translation teaching more perfect interpretation of the connotation of scenario translation art as a the personalized campus culture carrier has been the leading art colleges campus culture, to enhance the functionality of the campus cultural tastes full demonstration, art colleges, it reflects the charismatic profound aesthetic pursuit of idealistic principles, college civilization value showed a strong and positive signal. Art colleges have ushered in the emphasis on the effect of the scenario translation teaching, enhance transition of scenario translation teaching quality, and we are seeing these changes constantly.

REFERENCES

Deng Guofeng, 2009. Issues Network Media era popularization of English.

Feng Y.Q. 2001. Strengthen the the english aesthetic education cultivate Students sentiment.

Luo Huide, 2008. Historical process of popularization of English and basic experience—30 years of review and summary.

Mame. 2002. Translation angle on aesthetic value orientation.

Man P.D., C. Peng 2007. Normal Translation Teaching Reform in the context of new curriculum.

Suxing Hong, 2009. Network cultural situation in the popularization of English.

Wu Keming, 2005. "Network civilization education theory": Hunan Normal University Press.

Zhang Guoqi, 2009. Era connotation popularization of English and practical dimensions.

Computer, Intelligent Computing and Education Technology – Liu, Sung & Yao (Eds)
© 2014 Taylor & Francis Group, London, ISBN 978-1-138-02469-4

BIM technology application in the field of construction engineering research

Y. Peng
Master of Environmental Art and Design in Reading, Tianjin Polytechnic University, Tianjin, China

B.S. Ruan
Level 2 of Secondary Education, The Eighth Middle School in Taihe County, Anhui Province, China

ABSTRACT: Following Computer-Aided Design CAD (Computer Aided Design) technology in Building Information model of the BIM (Building Information Modeling) is the revolutionary technology of the Computer application in the field of construction engineering once again. The informatization reform has been promoting the development of architectural engineering field. Realize information exchange and the information integration can avoid the waste of resources effectively in the architectural design and achieve efficient operation. Building information model can integrate information in the whole project life cycle and exchange and share information among the different application systems. The features of BIM make BIM quickly become an important research direction and development trend of informatization in the field of the construction project. This paper introduces the countermeasures and the key problems of the application of BIM in the field of construction engineering at home and abroad in our country.

Keywords: building information modeling; construction project; building model; the management of the construction engineering in the entire life cycle

1 INTRODUCTION

Building information modeling is the model of construction project which is based on the relevant information data of each construction project. Through the simulation of digital information technology to simulate the real building, the traditional two-dimensional building information expressions of virtual architecture transform to include all the information of a real building.

The five major characteristics of the BIM, respectively is the predictability and controllability, visualization and charting, coordination and sharing. Predictability and controllability of BIM is embodied in which can be used in the construction preparatory to planning to design construction, management and maintenance of the whole building life cycle through a digital method, which can realize the virtual design, virtual construction, management, and the whole life period. A full range of forecasting and controlling can improve efficiency and reduce risk significantly in the process of its construction project in the entire life cycle. BIM is based on the 3D digital technology, integrated engineering data construction project related information model. BIM is an entity project facilities and features of digital expression. Therefore, visualization and charting

of BIM is unmatched by other techniques. BIM support building environment, economy, energy consumption, safety aspects of the analysis and simulation. The application of BIM can be implemented to enable all participants of the projects work together and share building information in the entire life cycle. It can organically integrate, share and manage relevant engineering information in different stages of the project, support process definition various participants of the project, so as to realize integrate the information of the construction engineering project in the whole life period[1].

2 THE APPLICATION OF BIM TECHNOLOGY IN DOMESTIC

As early as in 2004, the relevant BIM application technology has entered the field of construction project in China. BIM technology in construction project at present is mainly construction the professional design software to get a degree of application. But the use of BIM technology road is not flat. BIM technology is too early to large-scale applications. The causes of this situation are considered to have two factors: the one is that the designer. It is not easy to accept the

3D model design. The other is the product of manufacturer of foreign software have the difference with the Chinese specification degree[2]. At present, Chinese development of BIM can be seen as the vacuum period of change[3]. Although there is a gap in popularity in China, but the frequency in the use of BIM technology in Chinese enterprises as same as that is in abroad. Furthermore proficiency in the use of BIM technology in Chinese enterprises are alike that is in the developed countries[4].

BIM supports the state greatly. The first is reflected in the national science and technology support plan. The building housing and the department of technology as the main organizational units has been supported the related research projects of BIM vigorously as early as in the "fifteenth five-year plan", "eleventh five-year plan", "Twelfth five-year plan" key science and technology programs. In recent years, the national natural science foundation of China "863" project in varying degrees, also support the related research projects of BIM. For example, recently launched a "863" project for the whole life period of green residential transition digital development technology is mainly based on the research and application projects of BIM. The research object is the green residential products, for the entire life period of product design, construction, production and management. Another institute is built based on the design of the building information model of three-dimensional construction engineering the application of software development. In addition, the national natural science funds also made a number of projects about BIM.

After all, after so many years of state support, BIM has now formed a group of about research results, these results include standard research. One factor is the framework of Chinese BIM standard. The other factor is industrial base class platform specification in national standards, this standard is being compiled by the "fifteenth five-year plan" the outcome of the research program of science and technology. In addition, the construction of the IFC data description standards, this is the result of some standard research[5]. What is more, the project construction management system based on BIM twice won the China construction science and technology awards, "fifteenth five-year plan", "eleventh five-year plan" science and technology research project technical support has been successfully used in Kunming new airport, Qingdao bay bridge, the national stadium—"the Bird's Nest" and other large engineering. It is BIM technology in the application results of the study are successfully used in the field of architectural design.

3 RESEARCH AND APPLICATION ABOUT BIM TECHNOLOGY IN FOREIGN COUNTRIES

In 2002, Autodesk company using Building Information Modeling in propaganda initials "BIM", the abbreviation got a widely accepted and used today[6]. The application and research of BIM technology, compared to domestic research fields of construction engineering, construction engineering field abroad started early, and the development of application started early too. Thus, foreign architectural engineering field covered a wide field and had a large number both in theory, application and case analysis. And all participants in the construction projects such as government agencies, private enterprises and academic circles and other construction, involved actively in the research activities on BIM technology.

Construction industry is an important domain in the United States, which is viewed as bellwether of economic growth. In 2012, the U.S. building industry gross value of production is approximately 1.2 trillion dollars, accounting for 9% of GDP, of which 7 million people in the construction industry, accounting for 5.5% of labor population. Operating conditions of the construction industry and national economic conditions basic synchronization, particularly non-residential investment, by the impact of the economic environment is more obvious. In the U.S. construction industry nearly saturated condition, the control China and South Korea rapid productivity growth in the construction industry, the EU, Japan to maintain a normal level, compared to the United States over the past 10 years, agricultural productivity has grown exponentially, the U.S. construction industry decreased productivity becomes more prominent, currently, the U.S. construction industry is considered to be a backward industry.

Faced with this situation, the United States is committed to the use of BIM technology to build the whole life cycle of the building information model, full use of electronic information systems and parametric analysis of the implementation of the construction industry to promote the development of the industry, to change this phenomenon, the U.S. construction industry low profits, the profits of around 2%, but profitable, the industry return on investment increased year by year, project management is particularly important. Currently, the U.S. government vigorously promotes the construction industry within the next half of companies use BIM or BIM-related tools, in the past two years, an increase of 75% utilization rate, now 1/3 of the companies in more than 60% of the project using BIM. Over the next two years, the usage is expected to triple. BIM applications in the U.S. construction industry point of view, the integration of information management resource management project life cycle, so that the project design 3D visualization, engineering and construction details of the concrete can be implemented, the introduction of time parameters and cost parameters, the whole process of construction and implementation of 4D or 5D project cost management, project management of the whole process of quality, schedule, safety, and cost- and post-project maintenance objectives can be implemented. The use of BIM technology has changed the original project management model, a 50% reduction in the number of design changes, reducing errors and collision detection, save resources and improve industry productivity has advanced in the construction industry.

Hungary Graph soft company launched Computer Aided Design, CAD in short, in 1984. It has a powerful graphics engine library, the programmer can be used for the application of visualization, provided by function can create, edit, management, export and import, and print the 2D and 3D graphics and graphics files. In software, and puts forward with BIM technology as the core of "virtual building" design concept. But due to the limited by the technology behind the level of computer hardware, the technology is not widely used. Starting in the 90's, some foreign universities and scientific research of the season had started for the further research of BIM technology, and gradually began to promote and use in the field of architectural design. At present in the field of computer aided architectural design, some European countries, especially as Finland, Norway, Germany, the penetration of BIM application software has reached 60~70%.

The international application case: New York Queens community psychiatric services center Creedmoor, founded in 1912, is located in Queens, New York. This is USA engaged in building design and city planning and design of Architectural Resources application of the company BIM as the basic architectural design development. This is the Architectural design and urban planning and design of Architectural Resources company based on the application of BIM in architecture design, the service center is a 45000—square-foot education, rehabilitation institutions. FKA application of BIM technology for Eureka building and the introduction of the three-dimensional CAD instead of 2D CAD, most of the construction documents including about 1000 A1 size drawings, are from the direct generation of 3D model based on BIM. With it, save a lot of time cost, and at the same time reduce the mistakes in a large number of construction documents. Green-minded Germany PULS and the famous green building management consulting company BMP (Shanghai) Co. Ltd., with creative ideas and the latest technology, the pursuit of energy and economic optimization scheme, Suzhou industrial park in September 2009 in China, the application of BIM technology building green ecological PULS Plus Electronics (Suzhou) Co. Ltd.

4 CONCLUSION

Although the application of BIM technology in China already has a number of years, the BIM application and popularization in China is still uneven, not plain sailing. But we must be profoundly aware that if not deep application of BIM technology popularization, it is impossible to realize the fundamental transformation and upgrading of enterprises. Without the spread of further application of BIM technology, it is impossible to realize information management of the core business. It should be said that BIM design contest with the national development strategy, for the meaning of modern design is also very important. BIM is changing the pattern in the field of design, not only in the field of design, but also in a broader field in the future. BIM will be able to expand, provide perfect technical support for the innovation of the Chinese design.

REFERENCES

[1] L.X. Fang & Q. Zhou & W. Dong. Building the holographic model based on the IFC standard [J]. Architectural technology, 2005, 32 (2): 98–98.
[2] Z.L. Ma. The problems and countermeasure of BIM application in China [D]. Information technology in civil engineering and construction, 2010 (2): 12–15.
[3] J.M. Wu. Building information model (BIM) localization strategy research [D]. Beijing: Tsinghua university school of architecture, 2011.
[4] X.T. Wang. China enterprise proficiency in the use of BIM comparable developed countries [N]. Chinese economic report, 2013.
[5] J.P. Zhang. BIM technology application situation and development direction of [C] / /. Commercial real estate projects research conference. The risk of BIM technology application commercial real estate projects research conference, 2013.
[6] X. Wang. The history of t BIM application. Information technology in civil engineering and construction [J], 2011 (4): 146–150.

Computer, Intelligent Computing and Education Technology – Liu, Sung & Yao (Eds)
© *2014 Taylor & Francis Group, London, ISBN 978-1-138-02469-4*

Based on multiple DBMS aircraft black box data decoding technology research

Q.L. Yang, L.C. Zhang & W.B. Jiang
Information Engineering College, Haikou College of Economics, Hainan, China

H.G. Liang
Hainan Airlines, Hainan, China

ABSTRACT: The "black box" is one of the electronic recording equipment dedicated aircraft, called aviation flight recorders. In this paper, according to the characteristics of the Boeing 787 aircraft black box data, we propose a variety of database management systems based on the aircraft black box decoding technology. We elaborate separately from Boeing 787 airplane black box data coding theory, Research and design of aircraft black box decoder analysis system, compatible with a variety of database management systems design, flight data analysis layer design, Research and Design of three-dimensional animation of flying, etc.

Keywords: black box; decoding; research

1 INTRODUCTION

Inside aircraft black box is equipped with the flight data recorder and the cabin voice recorder, each aircraft mechanical parts and electronic instruments are equipped with sensors connected to it. It can record relevant technical parameters or cockpit voice, when aircraft stopped working and crashed half an hour ago. The argument put out re-recorded, can be used for flight test or accident analysis. Black Box has a strong anti-fire, pressure, shock and vibration resistant, water-resistant (or kerosene) soaked, anti-magnetic interference capability, even if the aircraft has been completely damaged in the black box recording data can also be preserved. Most of the causes of the crash of the world is through the black box to find out.

Flight Data Recorder (FDR) of the black box, which tracks the flight of a variety of data, such as flight time, speed, altitude, skewness aircraft rudder surfaces, engine speed, temperature, etc., a total of 30 kinds of data, and cumulative record 25 hours. Before takeoff, simply open the black box of the switch, while flying to all these data will be income in the black box.

Quick Access Recorder (QAR) finger protection device with onboard flight data recorder, which records a capacity of 128 MB, continuous recording time up to 600 h, can simultaneously capture hundreds of data, covering the quality control of the aircraft flight control vast some parameters.

FDR and QAR record information is the state of the airline to get planes, aircraft troubleshooting and other important sources of data to work, so Civil Aviation Administration of China provides that any airline must establish FDR/QAR decoder analysis system. However, due to the FDR/QAR decoding technology is monopolized foreign companies, China's civil aviation purchased from Western aviation industry in developed countries, purchase-related decoder analysis system, not only buy expensive, more important is the difficult to maintain; same time, when there is a serious flight safety incident investigations carried out, if there is no decoding system and corresponding decoder database, you can only rely on foreign companies to decode and investigations, not only lead to leakage of confidential, but also make the people lack the right to speak in this regard. Therefore, to have a significant economic value and safety implications for FDR/QAR decoder decodes related research and design analysis systems.

2 AIRCRAFT BLACK BOX DATA ENCODING RELATED TECHNOLOGIES

2.1 *Aircraft black box data coding theory*

The introduction of the Boeing 787 aircraft is the traditional aviation technology subversive change, which FDR data format is completely different to conventional aircraft. Traditional aircraft

ARINC573 and ARINC717 format and Boeing 787 FDR data format used is standard type ARINC647A-1 record. The most important feature of the system is breaking the previous frame length and a fixed order of seconds recorded flight data features, instead of using the recording feature are not fixed length frames, which has led to the existing domestic and international decoding system can not be decoded on Boeing 787.

FDR data formats Boeing 787 aircraft with a traditional data format has revolutionized the change through research, we found FDR will generate recording parameters and frame types text XML document database simultaneously recorded data. Recording raw data encoded as follows: sampling frequency of the same parameter is placed in the same frame or the same type of frame, the same frame to ensure that the sampling frequency is the same parameter. The parameters specified in the frame of the bit position in the XML document. When the original data read frame, it can be decoded parameters corresponding reference to the provisions of XML document.

At the same time, the study found Boeing 787 data frame encoding as follows: Each frame consists of Frame Header, Frame Data and Frame Trailer three parts. Thus, the decoding system should first read the label and description Frame Header information for the entire frame, including the length of the frame, time stamps, frame type, frame ID and the like. Then the next Frame Data to interpret the contents of this information, the end of the last frame has been determined based on Frame Trailer information.

2.2 Research and design of aircraft black box decoder analysis system

All sectors critical index data systems QAR decode analysis will be placed in the background server. Select server database, database capacity issues should be considered, and should therefore choose a larger capacity database management system, currently the database industry, SQL Server and Oracle is an ideal database management system. The system is running, there is capacity is relatively small database forms which similar to aircraft database or airport database, using stored on the local workstation manner, this will help speed up access to the database. These small database forms can also be stored separately in a small database such as Access, used alone like a small example Access database storage, so not only easy to maintain, and quick system access speed.

Backend server database for write, modify, delete frequent commands to set the appropriate stored procedure, such reception system decode critical data only need to handle their own backend server database can be, this can greatly speed up your system to avoid in order to seize resources among multiple workstations which led to the phenomenon of mutual lock.

The following is a stored procedure program about insert flight schedules:

```
CREATE PROCEDURE pro_InsertFlt
(

    @ Reg istration char (10),
    @ Aircraft_type char (10),
    @ Flight_date char (10),
    @ Remove_date char (10),
    @ Replay_date char (10),
    @ Replay_time char (10),
    @ To_time char (10),
    @ Ld_time char (10),
    @ To_airport char (10),
    @ Ld_airport char (10),
    @ To_runway char (10),
    @ Ld_runway char (10),
    @ To_weight int,
    @ Ld_weight int,
    @ Vref int,
    @ Vr int,
    @ V2 int,
    @ Flight_No char (10)

)
as
begin
    INSERT INTO [FOQA].[Dbo].[FLIGHT]
([registration], [aircraft_type], [flight_date],
[remove_date], [replay_date], [replay_time],
[to_time], [ld_time], [to_airport], [ ld_airport],
[to_runway], [ld_runway], [to_weight], [ld_weight],
[Vref], [Vr], [V2], [flight_No]) VALUES (@
registration, @ aircraft_type, @ flight_date, @
remove_date, @ replay_date, @ replay_time, @
to_time, @ ld_time, @ to_airport, @ ld_airport, @
to_runway, @ ld_runway, @ to_weight, @
ld_weight, @ Vref, @ Vr, @ V2, @ flight_No)
    return 0
end
```

Field explanation:

"Registration" means aircraft registration number

"Flight_date" means aircraft flight date

"Replay_date" means system decoding analysis replay date

"Replay_time" means system decoding analysis replay time

"To_airport" means aircraft landing took off airport

"Ld_airport" means aircraft landing airport.

2.3 The main advantage of the aircraft black box to decode analysis

1. The reliability of information
   Because of the special importance of the aircraft black box, which is based on the flight accident investigation, and the most important parts of aircraft manufacturing, so starting from the aircraft design stage, a variety of telex systems on the aircraft, sensor systems, data systems must take into account black box shall seek to ensure that the black box recording data reliability. Therefore, by decoding the aircraft black box and black box analysis system derived from QAR decoded data is very reliable, qualitative basis for various events.
2. Completeness of information
   Data collected by sensors on the aircraft will be sent by electronic signals inside the aircraft to aircraft data acquisition components, data acquisition module and then save the data to the black box. According to the relevant provisions of the world aviation, not just any aircraft black box must be installed, and must meet at least 88 other types of parameters are saved, and provides for the use of frequency data, using some parameters of frequency up to 16 times per second. This high density stream data used ensure the integrity and continuity of the data.
3. Diverse manifestations
   Form of the data after decoding, in addition to the ordinary display data in tabular form, but also uses a graph display, in addition to using three-dimensional simulation of the way state aircraft performance, flight data will have a more intuitive way to display it.

2.4 Aircraft black box decoder analysis system platform module

Each module of aircraft black box and QAR data decoder analysis system platform integrates a complete decoding and analysis system, which decodes the analysis of information system development will include the following 12 modules:

1. The original data of black box decoding module;
2. Unsafe event query module;
3. The flight data query module;
4. Black box and QAR data tables display module;
5. Black box and QAR data graphic display module;
6. Basic information management;
7. Decoding database editing module;
8. Query format Managing Editor module;
9. The system management module;
10. Statistical reporting module;
11. Analysis program module;
12. 3D flight simulation module.

These modules support each other, and independent of each other, a lot of modules can be run independently. Which analyzes program module is open source modules to user, the user through simple training, analytical procedures can be modified according to the needs of actual work setting, the system will not produce results output. This open source module will develop secondary users tremendous freedom, the user can modify the program as necessary or use the original system program.

2.5 Compatible with a variety of database management systems design

System underlying decoder needs to deal directly with QAR raw data files after encoded, and to achieve decoding, requiring the system to run fast and smooth. Accordingly, this part is best performed using the C++ programming, it is a good system to run fast and smooth. Since each data word of aircraft black box is a way of using the 12-bit encoded, and the computer byte is only 8-bit. For the reason, when read/write the black box byte, make the appropriate conversion.

For decoding the specific parameters, usually divided into the switch parameter, polynomial parameter, discrete parameter, multi-discrete parameter, multi-simulation parameter and so on. After parameters classification needed design for each type of parameters corresponding function to invoke the decoder. For nonlinear curve should calculate the value of its associated works by interpolation or differential method, curve fitting; numerical point aircraft manufacturer provided interpolate the entire curve fitting; manufacturers do not provide a value range of numerical point, but merely provide numerical boundary conditions, curve at each point project value should be calculate by difference algorithm.

2.6 Flight data analysis layer design

After the decoder decodes, flight parameter data will be sent to the data analysis layer, then to discover security risks aircraft running through data analysis. For example, through analyzing the aircraft manipulate data to find the pilot operating aircraft technical defects, through engine parametric analysis to find the aircraft fault and troubleshooting. Analysis methods often used in data analysis are integral method and differential method. For example, the monitoring algorithm for the case of aircraft grounded distance longer, the core of the algorithm is: from the aircraft entered the runway began to differential treatment for displacement of aircraft, and projected onto level ground, then calculated the distance by integrating from the ground of aircraft to the runway endpoint, in order to determine the time when the aircraft is grounded, whether parallel drift distance is too long.

2.7 Research and design of three-dimensional animation of flying

Interface displays using the common Windows interface components display data, including the commonly used grid components, documents show management component, progress bars, toolbars, pop-up menus, etc. The underlying raw data sent through the decoder decodes the interface layer, forming a user can understand the engineering data.

User about interface data manipulation command transmitted to the underlying raw data processing, for a large number of QAR warning record processing command, if the data of interface directly sort operation within grid records component, it will cause the processing speed is very slow, can not meet the actual job requirements. Therefore, the user commands to the underlying C++ data processing, in C++ underlying using the STL sorting, filtering and other processing, then the user command will the processed data displayed on the interface layer. This will greatly accelerate the speed of the user command to reflect.

3D graphically reproduce the aircraft using the time of flight, including topography, the flight path of aircraft takeoff/landing time, etc., so that the aircraft was done visually reproduce the flight state, the black box and QAR flight data obtained after decoding fully used.

3 CONCLUSION

Based on multiple database management systems aircraft black box data decoding technology research and analysis system design, we design successfully aircraft black box decoder analysis software in a large airline—FDAS software systems. The software system to fill the gaps in research of this area, through the identification of scientific and technological achievements of the Civil Aviation Administration of China, it has a certain value.

ACKNOWLEDGEMENTS

It is a Hainan Natural Science Foundation project by the Hainan Provincial Science and Technology Agency supported (613168). The corresponding author is Wen-Bo Jiang.

REFERENCES

[1] Lan-Chun Zhang. Based on C++ aircraft black box decoder analysis system design. The computer system, 2009.
[2] Hua-Gang Xiong. Advanced avionics technology. National defense industry press, 2012.
[3] Jun Liu. Aircraft parts aerodynamics. National defense industry press, 2012.
[4] Herbert Schildt and Greg Guntle. Borland C++ Builder: The Complete Reference.

Computer, Intelligent Computing and Education Technology – Liu, Sung & Yao (Eds)
© 2014 Taylor & Francis Group, London, ISBN 978-1-138-02469-4

Artificial neural network-based boiler optimal combustion guide system and its application

Hai-Shan Li, Yong-Jun Xia & Xiao-Fei Mao
Jiangxi Province Electric Power Research Institute, Nanchang, China

Gang Ju
School of Energy and Environmental Engineering, Southeast University, Nanjing, China

Ting-Fang Yu
School of Mechanical and Electronic Engineering, Nanchang University, Nanchang, Jiangxi Province, China

ABSTRACT: A real-time optimal combustion guide system for coal-fired boiler based on artificial intelligence technology was proposed in this paper. This system combined the data of coal-fired boiler combustion adjustment test data and historical operation data. Back Propagation (BP) neural network was adopted to construct a mathematical model predicting the functional relationship between outputs (NOx emissions and the overall heat loss of the boiler) and inputs (operational parameters of the boiler) of a coal-fired boiler. The results from combustion adjustment tests and the operational experience from stokers were modelled; the expert combustion operation knowledge and experience were also extracted by the NSGA-II mathematical model. Under the aid of computer program, this system can guide real-time combustion adjustment which can lead to lower NOx emissions and higher boiler efficiency.

Keywords: boiler combustion; guidance system; artificial intelligence; neural network; boiler efficiency

1 INTRODUCTION

Energy conservation and emission reduction is the context in which China's power enterprises are operating. For coal-fired boilers, how to improve boiler efficiency while reducing gas NOx emissions to achieve economical and environmentally friendly operation of the boilers, is a practical issue that power plants need to address.

The parameters that have significant impact on the boiler combustion optimization objectives in the modern large coal-fired power plant can be grouped into three types: 1) the equipment parameters, such as the coal-fired boiler structure, and the coal burner structure and layout. These parameters are not adjustable after the boiler is designed and installed, and can be changed only through equipment modification; 2) non-adjustable parameters, which are parameters subject to the external conditions, such as load, ambient temperature, coal burning data parameters. Load is determined according to the user's instructions or the central command, and is also an non-adjustable factor for a specified working condition that needs optimizing; 3) parameters that the operator can adjust, which include air distribution, oxygen content, and the way milling system operates. Depending on the objectives of the combustion optimization adjustment, the optimization can be classified into single-objective optimization and multi-objective optimization. Early boiler combustion optimization generally aimed to improve boiler efficiency, and optimization objectives could be the lowest carbon content of fly ash and minimum heat loss in emission[1–3]; in order to achieve the minimum nitride emission, the lowest concentration of nitrogen oxides in the boiler exhaust could be identified as the optimum objective[4,5]. As a result of the dual requirements of energy conservation and emission reduction, increasing attention is given to the multi-objective optimization, i.e., boiler efficiency and NOx emissions, in modern large-scale power plants[6–8].

The boiler combustion optimization approach currently adopted by coal-fired power plants is primarily based on combustion optimization test results from the Jiangxi Electric Power Research Institute (EPRI), China, and combustion adjustment is made by the boiler operation technicians according to their own operating experience. As EPRI's combustion optimization adjustment test results cannot guide the operation online, these test results are not fully taken advantage of.

Moreover, operators have different levels of competence in operating a boiler; even the same stoker may be affected by subjective factors, therefore may present different levels of competence in their operation at different times. As a result, boiler combustion adjustment operation based on operational experience alone may be subjective and arbitrary to a certain extent, and may affect the safe operation of the boiler.

The boiler optimal combustion guide system based on artificial intelligence technology introduced in this paper took advantage of the combustion adjustment test data from the EPRI and the boiler's historical operation data, and the most advanced artificial neural network technology to construct a mathematical model of optimal combustion, thus modelling the EPRI's combustion optimization adjustment test results and the stoker's daily operating experience. Meanwhile, genetic algorithm optimization techniques were adopted to extract expert combustion operation knowledge and experience from the model. A computer program was used to guide online the operator's adjustment of the combustion operation regarding the air distribution and coal blending, and meet the goal of improving the boiler's thermal efficiency while reducing the NOx emissions.

2 COMBUSTION OPTIMIZATION SYSTEM PRINCIPLES

2.1 Neural network modelling

2.1.1 The neural network selection
In the engineering field, artificial neural network has been widely used in the modelling process of input and output objects in a variety of complex systems. The artificial neural network extracts effective knowledge and rules through learning the typical sample set given, and realizes the black box modelling of the complex systems through correcting the weights and threshold[9,10]. Currently, the most widely used are the BP neural network and RBF neural network, both of which have a relatively good function approximation. While the convergence rate of the BP network training is slower than that of the RBF network convergence, the BP network is more capable of generalization than the RBF network. Therefore, the system proposed in this study selected the BP network to construct the combustion optimization model.

2.1.2 Combustion optimization model
The boiler's combustion characteristics and the stoker's operation experience are always contained in the boiler's combustion historical data. The BP neural network-based combustion optimization mathematical model was constructed by adopting the neural network technology and making use of the EPRI combustion adjustment test data and historical data of the boiler operation (Fig. 1).

The model contains the site combustion adjustment test results and everyday operational experience of a stoker. For any given load, coal quality, and performance, the model can be used to make comparisons of a boiler's combustion efficiency and NOx emissions in a variety of operating modes with different air distribution and coal blending, to find the optimal combustion operation mode of air distribution and coal blending, making the boiler more economical while low in NOx emissions.

Other variables can also be selected for the model outputs according to the requirements in specific applications.

2.2 Multi-objective genetic algorithm optimization

Combustion optimization is a multi-objective nonlinear optimization issue that the genetic algorithm can effectively address. Typical multi-objective genetic algorithms are NSGA-II[11] and SPEA2[12], with both advantages and disadvantages: NSGA-II algorithm has high operating efficiency and good convergence, but poor distribution of Pareto solution set obtained in optimizing the high-dimensional objective function; SPEA2 algorithm is able to obtain a well distributed Pareto optimal set, but is low in running efficiency, and time-consuming.

In order to improve the performance of the optimization algorithm, the system proposed an improved multi-objective genetic algorithm based

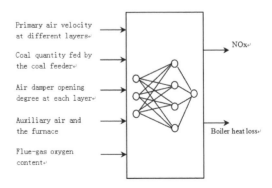

Figure 1. The boiler's combustion characteristics model.

690

on adaptive mesh refinement, which is characterized by the use of adaptive mesh refinement to adjust the distribution of individuals in population, so that the Pareto set obtained has a good distribution and also a faster computational efficiency. The algorithm procedure is as follows:

1. Population initialization. A population of size N was randomly generated, and the value of each individual in the population on the m-dimensional objective function was evaluated using fitness function;
2. The fast non-dominated sorting algorithm was adopted to calculate non-dominated individuals among them, forming the dominating population P_1, and the rest were dominated individuals, forming population P_2;
3. For all individuals in P_1, the length of its grid side on a certain target was calculated using the adaptive mesh refinement, determining the number of individuals in each grid of the m-dimensional spatial mesh; for any individual x_i in P_2, the sum $n(i)$ of all individuals dominated by individuals dominating x_i in P_2 was calculated, and $n(i)$ is expressed as in the following equation:

$$n(i) = \sum_{x_j \prec x_i}^{j} |\{x_k \mid x_j \prec x_k\}| \qquad (1)$$

错误！未找到引用源。

The greater the $n(i)$ is, the greater the number of individuals dominating individual xi, then the greater probability of that individual being eliminated in the evolution.

4. Selection operation. The two-dimensional tournament selection method was used: Two individuals were randomly selected from P. If both these individuals were from P_1, then by comparing the numbers of individuals in the grids where these two individuals were located, the individuals with the smaller number in the grid would be selected; if one individual was from P_1, and the other from P_2, then the non-dominated individual from P_1 would be selected; If both individuals were from P_2, their $n(i)$ values would be compared, and the individual with the smaller $n(i)$ value would be selected. The new population Q with size N would be selected by using this method repeatedly.
5. Genetic operation was undertaken on population Q. Progeny population Q_0 was formed by adopting simulated binary crossover and polynomial mutation.
6. A new population P_0 was formed by combining Q_0 and P. The non-dominated set P_{01} and dominated

set P_{02} were identified by using non-dominated sorting method. If the size of P_{01} exceeded N, then the most crowded individuals in P_{01} mesh would be pinned down according to the distribution evaluation method provided by the adaptive mesh refinement, and deleted. This method was repeated until the size of the P_{01} reached N, forming P'. If the size of P_{01} was less than N, then proceed to step (7), otherwise to step (8).
7. Let the size of P_{02} be N_0, then the $n(i)$ value corresponding to each individual in P_{02} was calculated. $N–N_0$ individuals were selected in ascending order of $n(i)$ to form a new population P' combined with P_{01}.
8. P' was taken as population P. Return to step (2) until the end of iterations.

3 FIELD APPLICATION

The 300 MW unit boiler in a power plant was a tangentially fired, natural circulation drum boiler manufactured by Dongfang Boiler Works, with the DG-1025/17.5-II type 4 sub-critical parameters. The system was a direct-fired pulverizing system which consisted of five medium-speed mills and five coal feeders. Each medium-speed mill corresponded to one layer of primary air, and four mills were being operated under rated load. The boiler was equipped with seven layers of auxiliary air, and one layer of OFA.

3.1 Combustion optimization model

The model input variables included: unit power, coal quality (calorific value, volatile matter, ash, moisture), flue-gas oxygen content, secondary air/furnace differential pressure, the seven-layer auxiliary air damper opening degree, the one-layer OFA damper opening degree, five primary air volume, and amount of coal by five coal feeders.

Considering the plant's operating requirements and the actual unit operation conditions, the project identified improving cost-effectiveness as the main optimization objective, and the boiler thermal efficiency, reheat steam temperature, and superheater attemperating water flow as the outputs for the model.

3.2 Training samples

The samples for training were mainly the boiler combustion adjustment test data. In order to reduce the size and workload of the test, the system also collected some of the real-time historical operation data of the boiler as a supplement to the model samples, so as to ensure that the training

691

Table 1. Test parameters and results.

Operating mode	Load/MW	The amount of coal feed (t/h)					Secondary air damper opening command (%)							OFA Degree of opening EF (%)
		A	B	C	D	E	AA	AB	BC	CC	DD	DE	EE	
3	180	20.1	26.1	24	24	0	30	20	30	34	38	50	60	65
4	240	18.9	26.6	23.6	19.4	23.7	30	25	30	35	40	50	60	68
5	180	0	24.7	24.2	21.2	21.9	30	40	40	40	40	40	40	60
6	180		24	25.2	19.8	19.9	40	60	50	40	35	30	40	60
7	240	24.3	28.4	28.8	29.2	28.5	40	40	40	40	40	40	40	45
8	300	26.2	28.7	29.3	29.5	30.3	50	40	40	40	40	40	40	45
9	300	24.1	31.7	31.1	30.2	29.9	65	60	50	40	40	40	40	60
10	240	17.3	27	25.8	24.2	23.8	65	60	50	40	35	30	20	45
11	300	24.3	30.2	28.2	26.2	26.8	40	20	30	35	40	50	60	68

Operating mode	Load/MW	Super-heater steam temperature /°C	Reheat steam temperature/°C	Oxygen content (dial)/%	Primary parental pipe air pressure KPa	Superheater attempering water flow (t/h)	Reheater attempering water flow (t/h)	Post correction flue gas temperature /°C	Flue gas oxygen content /%	Fly ash combustibles /%	Slag combustibles /%	Post modification flue gas heat loss/%	Incomplete combustion of solid heat loss/%	Flue gas temperature Post modification flue gas thermal efficiency /%
3	180	538	530	3.85	10.1	45	0	129	6.48	1.76	3.07	6.1	0.99	91.88
4	240	540	536	3.37	11	42	0	137	5.87	0.89	1.82	6.3	0.53	92.32
5	180	540	535	5.11	10.5	61	0	131	7.96	1.36	1.54	6.88	0.72	91.36
6	180	541	537	3.41	10.9	40	0	133	6.18	1.33	1.07	6.21	0.67	92.07
7	240	541	541	3.99	12	58	0	140	6.36	1.8	2.06	6.63	1.88	90.41
8	300	542	540	2.86	11.4	12	0	135	5.49	1.88	0.1	6.06	0.7	92.62
9	300	540	542	3.33	11.7	34	16	142	5.77	2.23	1.34	6.52	1.27	91.48
10	240	542	541	4.66	10.5	68	8.7	138	7.09	3.07	1.65	6.85	1.75	90.55
11	300	540	539	3.88	12	12	1.9	144	6.32	2.01	1.99	6.82	1.18	91.28

samples contained enough information regarding the boiler operation characteristics.

The combustion adjustment tests adopted orthogonal method for test condition arrangements. Combustion adjustment parameters and the level of parameters were selected according to the actual site conditions (mainly load, oxygen amount, air distribution, and primary air pressure), and L9 (34) orthogonal table was used in test arrangement. Part of the test conditions and test results are presented in Table 1.

3.3 Combustion optimization

Based on the combustion optimization neural network model, the system set the maximum boiler efficiency, deviation of the reheat steam temperature from the set value, and the minimum superheater attemperating water flow as the optimization objectives, and optimized the following combustion parameters by adopting multi-objective genetic algorithm optimization technology:

1. The coal amount by five coal mills;
2. The primary air volume of five coal mills;
3. Flue-gas oxygen content;
4. The auxiliary bellows and the furnace differential pressure;

5. The average auxiliary air damper opening degree at each layer in the seven-layer auxiliary air;
6. The average opening degree of the one-layer OFA air damper.

The results of the multi-objective optimization were a Pareto solution set. The system determined the best optimized variables solution by the following steps: First select from the Pareto solution set the deviation of the reheat steam temperature from the set value and the solution of the superheater attemperating water flow within a present range, and then select the maximum solution to the boiler efficiency as the optimal combustion parameter value.

3.4 System optimization results

Nearly a year has passed since the system was applied in the power plant and the test results indicated that the system not only has improved the operational safety of the boiler, but has lifted the boiler thermal efficiency by an average of 0.68% compared with that before the optimization. Figure 2 is the system's combustion optimization monitor interface, while Figure 3 shows the comparison of boiler efficiency curves before and after the optimization.

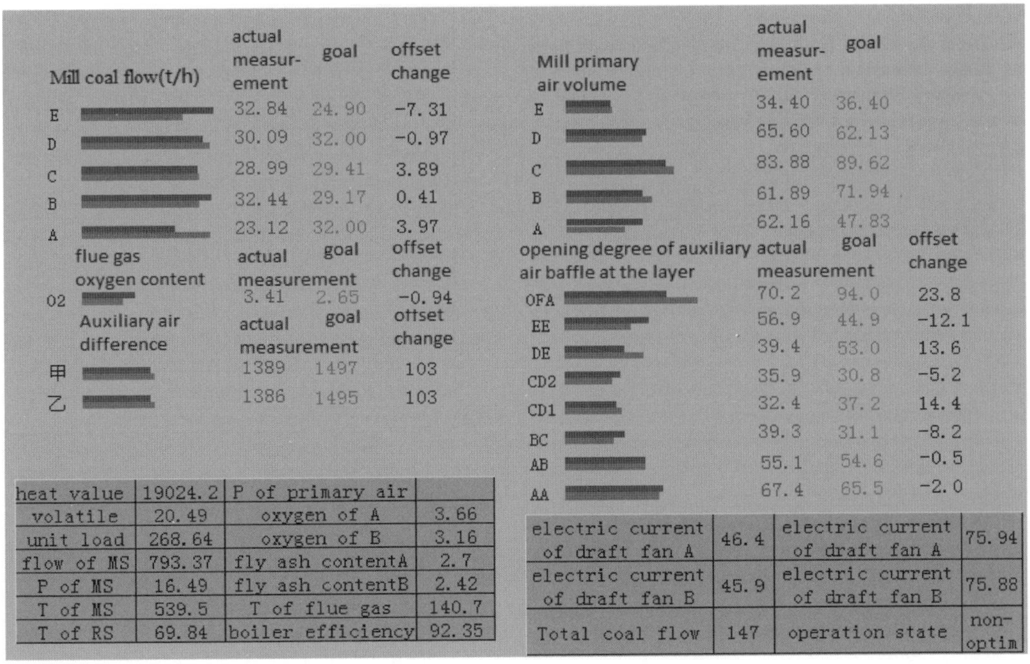

Mill coal flow(t/h)	actual measurement	goal	offset change		Mill primary air volume	actual measurement	goal
E	32.84	24.90	−7.31		E	34.40	36.40
D	30.09	32.00	−0.97		D	65.60	62.13
C	28.99	29.41	3.89		C	83.88	89.62
B	32.44	29.17	0.41		B	61.89	71.94
A	23.12	32.00	3.97		A	62.16	47.83

flue gas oxygen content	actual measurement	goal	offset change		opening degree of auxiliary air baffle at the layer	actual measurement	goal	offset change
O2	3.41	2.65	−0.94		OFA	70.2	94.0	23.8
Auxiliary air difference	actual measurement	goal	offset change		EE	56.9	44.9	−12.1
甲	1389	1497	103		DE	39.4	53.0	13.6
乙	1386	1495	103		CD2	35.9	30.8	−5.2
					CD1	32.4	37.2	14.4
					BC	39.3	31.1	−8.2
					AB	55.1	54.6	−0.5
					AA	67.4	65.5	−2.0

heat value	19024.2	P of primary air	
volatile	20.49	oxygen of A	3.66
unit load	268.64	oxygen of B	3.16
flow of MS	793.37	fly ash contentA	2.7
P of MS	16.49	fly ash contentB	2.42
T of MS	539.5	T of flue gas	140.7
T of RS	69.84	boiler efficiency	92.35

electric current of draft fan A	46.4	electric current of draft fan A	75.94
electric current of draft fan B	45.9	electric current of draft fan B	75.88
Total coal flow	147	operation state	non-optim

Figure 2.   Main interface in optimal combustion system for boiler.

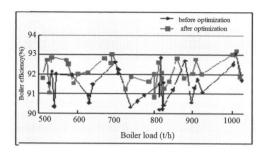

Figure 3. Comparison of combustion efficiency curves before and after the optimization.

4 CONCLUSION

The operation of thermal power boilers in China mainly depends on the EPRI's combustion adjustment test results; however, the results of such tests can only guide the boiler operation offline, and are far from playing their proper role. Based on the EPRI field combustion adjustment tests, the present study adopted neural network technology to construct a mathematical model of combustion optimization, and realized online optimal combustion guide by applying the multi-objective genetic optimization technology. It has significant practical value.

REFERENCES

[1] Zhen, Z., Chen, H., Li, Y., et al. Optimization of boiler efficiency based on genetic algorithm and its application in the energy-loss analysis system in thermal power plants. Electric Power, 2003, 36(10): 21–24.

[2] Huang, B., Luo, Z., & Zhou, H. Optimization of Combustion Based on Introducing Radiant Energy Signal in Pulverized Coal-fired Boiler, Fuel Processing Technology [J]. 2010.

[3] Lu, G. Optimization operation technology and its application of large blending coal-fired boiler. Electric Power, 2010, 43(12).

[4] Zheng L-G., Zhou, H., Wang, C., & C, K-F. Application of scaleable chaotic ant colony algorithm in NOχ emissions optimization. Proceedings of the Chinese society for electrical engineering, 2008, 28(11).

[5] Zheng L-G., Zhou, H., Cen, K-F, Wang, C-L. A Comparative Study of Optimization Algorithms for Low NOx Combustion Modification at a Coal-fired Utility Boiler [J]. 2009, 23(36):2780–2793.

[6] Wang, P., Li, L., Chen, Q., & Dong, Y. Research on applications of artificial intelligence to combustion optimization in a coal-fired boiler, Proceedings of the Chinese Society for Electrical Engineering, 2004, 24(4).

[7] Gao, Z., Guo, Z., Hu, J. et al. Multip-objective combustion optimization and flame reconstruction for W shaped boiler based on support vector regression and numerical simulation. Proceedings of the CSEE, 2011, 31(5):13–19.

[8] Xu, C., Lv, J., & Zheng, Y. The efficiency-and NOx emission-based boiler combustion optimization test and analysis. Boiler Technology, 2006, 37(5):69–74.

[9] Liu, F., Zhang, D., & Zhao, W. Neural network modelling of utility boiler combustion system. Electric Power Science and Engineering, 2010, 6:33–37.

[10] Li, Z., Cai, J., Zhao, D. et al. Construction of a boiler combustion optimization model. Thermal Electricity Generation, 2012, 41(3):62–65.

[11] Kalyanmoy Deb, Amrit Pratap, Sameer Agarwal, et al. A Fast and Elitist Multiobjective Genetic Algorithm: NSGA-II [J]. IEEE Transactions on Evolutionary Computation, 2002, 6(2):182–197.

[12] Eckart Zitzler, Marco Laumanns, Lothar Thiele. SPEA2: Improving the Strength Pareto Evolutionary Algorithm for Multiobjective Optimization. Evolutionary Methods for Design, Optimization, and Control [J]. CIMNE, Barcelona, Spain, 2002:95–100.

Computer, Intelligent Computing and Education Technology – Liu, Sung & Yao (Eds)
© 2014 Taylor & Francis Group, London, ISBN 978-1-138-02469-4

Improvement of approach to detect sinkhole attacks in Wireless Sensor Networks

Feng-Jun Shang, Cheng Li & Jiang-Ling Qin
School of Computer Science and Technology, Chongqing University of Posts and Telecommunications,
Chongqing, China

ABSTRACT: Characteristics of wireless sensor networks sinkhole attack were analyzed. Based on the investigation of various critical shortcomings that the recently proposed works on sinkhole intrusion detection in WSN have, this paper improves the sinkhole detection approach based on link quality. The Castalia simulation based on OMNet++ shows that the approach has a low rate of false positives, and the energy consumption is relatively low, so the approach is suitable for large-scale sensor network.

Keywords: WSN security; intrusion detection in WSN; sinkhole detection

1 INTRODUCTION

In many WSN application scenarios, the security is a very important factor, especially in a hostile environment or business environment [1]. Due to the dynamic characteristics of wireless sensor networks, nodes' routes to the base station are continuously updated, which sinkhole attack launch through. Karlof C. who is the first proposed the sinkhole attack, and pointed out that the threat caused by sinkhole attack was the worst compared to the others types of attacks [1]. The main purpose of sinkhole attack is to attract flows in the network via forging or modifying the routing packets passing by, to make the malicious node more attractive to routing algorithm; causing neighbor nodes choose improperly the malicious nodes as the next hop in the path to reach the destination node [1–5]. Sinkhole attack can also be used as a platform for launching other attacks, such as selectively forwarding attacks, black hole attacks, and data tampering and so on. Sinkhole attack resulted in the data stream flows through malicious nodes, making the implementation of other attacks become more effective or easier to implement.

2 RELATED WORKS

Edith CH et al proposed a sinkhole attack detection method [2]. The method first finds a list of suspected nodes through checking data consistency, and then effectively identifies the intruder in the list through analyzing the network flow information. By analysis, however, due to the complexity of the sensor network deployment environment,

the station often cannot distinguish properly the difference between data tampering caused by malicious node or selectively forwarding and changes caused by a result of environmental changes, so this method will have false positives. And the message to the base station to report the messages is bound to cause an additional burden of communication in the network.

Ioannis Krontiris etc. are the first to describe the conditions WSN IDS should satisfy [3,4]. And based on the assumption that the amount of normal nodes is larger than malicious nodes, they proposed a basic architecture of distributed IDS. But the proposed local detection technology is not suitable for constantly updated network. But it is instructive when to design a new detection method based on collaboration between neighbour nodes.

H. Shafiei et al proposed two methods to detect sinkhole attacks [5], one of which is based on the geographical statistical sampling methods, using the energy consumption model of each region in the network to detect the occurrence possibility of sinkhole attack. The second is attack mitigation strategy; it will be used to prevent traffic flow through the attackers. Finally, the two methods were verified on Castalia simulator.

S. Rajasegarar et al proposed a WSN anomaly detection technique based on distributed hypersphere clustering algorithm and KNN strategy [6]. Claims it can be used to detect sinkhole attack. But according to the analysis, when launching a sinkhole attack, the data stream is hijacked, so there is little possibility of attacks in the network.

Based on the analysis above, and motivated by the approach proposed by Edith CH et al, and we improved the approach by introducing the link quality in the network and we name it CUSUM-based intrusion detection approach. The method improved was compared with the approach based on cluster proposed by S. Rajasegarar, et al. on the detection rate and false alarm rate.

3 CTP ROUTING PROTOCOL AND SINKHOLE ATTACK ANALYSIS

CTP (Collection Tree Protocol) is a widely-known routing protocol that provides reliable data aggregation service for the sensor network [8]. In the published version of the TinyOS, CTP have been provided for the realization of its standard implementation, which has three main components: Routing Engine (RE), Forwarding Engine (FE) and Link Evaluation Engine (LE). CTP RE periodically sent the routing information (beacon) to build and maintain a routing tree. The LE is responsible for the maintenance and updates of link table. When there exits data to be sent, FE always access the routing table, to choose the node with best link quality as the next hop node for packet forwarding.

The next hop selection process in CTP agrees the criteria: 1) periodically; 2) beacon request routing updates; 3) the current parent node congested; 4) a neighbor node unreachable; 5) a neighbor node is no longer congested; 5) the current node cannot find a route to the base station. Only those who have a legitimate path to the base station, without congesting, not the current child node and have been stored in the routing table neighbor nodes, are eligible to be selected as a parent node.

Most of the time, sinkhole attackers either pretended to be having a good link quality to base station, or slander other nodes link quality is poor [4]. For CTP, sinkhole attack primarily pretended the ETX to base to be the minimum, causing the attacker to be the parent node of the majority of nodes in the attack area, just as Figure 1. In which the multi-hop ETX to base station is a key factor in launching sinkhole attacks. Attacker can impersonate other nodes to send routing beacons, setting C flag to 1, leading to its child nodes to update the current parent node. You can also send a large number of invalid data to the network, resulting in network conflict; triggering

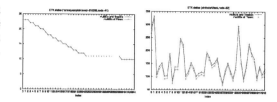

Figure 2.   Changes of link quality.

nodes in the network continuously update the parent node. Sending routing updates with frequency Higher than normal to the network, and the network packet P flag is set to 1, requesting the node within the region to updates routes.

As a sensor network routing protocol for data aggregation, CTP does not provide any security measures, even if the deployment of authentication and other security protocols on its nodes t due to its characteristics of spontaneous choosing the route o the base station based on the link quality, it cannot resist any intrusion, especially sinkhole attack [1–5]. Once the attacker successfully hijacked the sinkhole network traffic, it will continue to destroy the network environment: maliciously tamper data, selectively forwarding, the black hole attack, and so on.

According to the characteristics of sinkhole attack, it can be summarized as follows: traffic collapse may occur in the affected area (Fig. 1, the attacker uses the powerful equipment to launch sinkhole attack, making the traffic flow near the attacker convergence); reverse direction traffic flows may occur; flow pressure near the attacker nodes increases, while increasing the energy consumption, the conflict increased. Nodes near attacker may find network behavior of the area to a sink node and the behavior of the other nodes in the network are inconsistent: packet loss rate, large deviations of data values, routing beacon sends frequent, large deviations of link quality, network packet transmission frequencies inconsistent.

The multi-hop link quality and link quality estimation of the nodes randomly selected from the network show in Figure 2. It be seen from the figure, the link quality has stabilized gradually within an initial stage of the network until sinkhole attack occurs. When attack occurs, abnormal fluctuations appear in the link quality changes as Figure 2 shows.

4 INTRUSION DETECTION SYSTEM

This article assumes that during the initial deployment phase of the network, the attack does not exist, and this phase last until a steady state. Multiple attackers are not considered in the current network

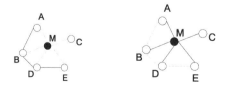

Figure 1.   Sinkhole attack by node M.

environment. An attacker will always try to avoid being detected within the region. This article aims to discover attacks, and the response of attack is not within the scope of research. Nodes can collect information on neighbor nodes in 2hops.

Based on the analysis of the above study, when the sinkhole attack occurs, attacked node will send all message to the attack source, resulting in information to be hijacked, so the base station cannot receive valid information. So the base station periodically send beacon frames, and the first three bytes of CTP routing frame header (D domain) is set to 1 (to be labeled as intrusion detection information frames, referred to as the Information Frame IF), which means that the base station is gathering the exception information. Node A receives the broadcast IF, if an abnormality is detected locally, then the abnormality information will be transmitted to the base station hop by hop in reverse direction of IF.

Each node has a promiscuous listening mode, intrusion detection module periodically collect information as follows: 1) D_{ij}, packet loss rate of node j observed by node i; 2) LQ_{ij}, link quality of node j observed by node i; 3) CN_{ij} child node of j observed by node i.

Gives the following definition:

Definition 1: A reverse link appears when the node in child nodes list is found in the current node's parent list; Definition 2: aggregation C_{ij} defined as the ratio $C_{ij} = CN_{ij}/n$ of j observed by node i.

If one node find the abnormality on the above statics through CUSUM change point detection, it will transmit the abnormality information to the base station via the data packet (if within a certain time, no data will be transmitted, sent separately). After modified, the CTP data frame is as shown bellow. Respectively, the 6 bits of the original header are utilized. LQ, C and RD attributes associated domains are labeled without exception, if the corresponding bit field is 0, otherwise indicates an abnormality occurs, wherein RD domain marked the current node's reverse degrees. The node ID suspected domain SuspectedID is added to the CTP data frame end, occupies 16 bits. 8 bits for LinkEtx which is hop link quality estimation to the SuspectedID.

4.1 Sinkhole attack detection

When the base station CTP collect sufficient data frame, each field of intrusion detection information d, sq, RD, SuspectedID, LinkEtx can be extracted, and be used to construct a local area network topology which contains all the node in the anomaly area. Then the structure of a Sinkhole attacker may be deemed to be the root of the tree. As shows in Figure 4, the sinkhole node launched a attack, abnormal information gathered from the base station bs form a tree, nodes d and node e are malicious nodes, the nodes who testify ma are node a, b, c, and the node who testify b are d, e, ma.

Analyzing the method proposed by Edith CH Ngai, link quality was introduced instead of the hops to the Sink node to use as the detection information. The principles of detection technology are: 1) if the malicious node ma launch an attack, due to the aggregation affects of flow, sinkhole attacks nodes will form a tree network structure and the malicious node is the root within the suspicious area. 2) Because there may be false positives in anomaly detection phase or malicious nodes might be libel, resulting in chaos in the abnormal area topology, making it difficult to identify root, so it is necessary to introduce recognition mechanism. 3) There is a rule in the network, if the node a is the parent of node b then we have:

$$multiETX_a + linkETX_{(a,b)} = multiETX_b$$

If the abnormal area exceeds the detection index ρ (set by detecting the intensity of the requirements), and the root is a node a, then the node a will be considered the source of sinkhole attacks. Malicious nodes may testify the normal node or forge single hop link quality information, so test, if found not to comply with the above formula, then that testify will not be legitimate, and will be automatically ignored. In Figure 4, for example, the detection algorithm loops through suspicious nodes (in figure, they are mal and b), refers to the proportion of legitimate nodes. If the maximum number of nodes to testify one node excess of the permit ρ, it will be believed that the attack has took place.

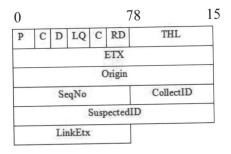

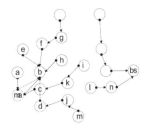

Figure 3.   Topology information of abnormal area.

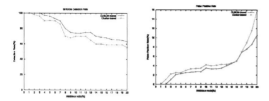

Figures 4 and 5.   Detection rate. False positive rate.

Gives the following definition:

Definition 1: Node a is legitimate to testify, which means that testify a the exception message frame sent to all children of a node in the $linkETX$ And $multiETX$ Satisfies the equation. Definition 2: mal_1 is the first suspected node, mal_1^n is the suspected node count of mal_1, that node Refers mal_1 to the total number of permits to be legal for all nodes of all child nodes; and mal_1 is one of the multiple root nodes currently suspicious area.

Assume that m is the total number of suspicious nodes and C is the number of all nodes in suspect areas. If $\max mal_j^n / C > \rho$, we believe that a attack has been launched. In order to avoid excessive false alarm rate, it is recommended ρ values is greater than 0.5.

5   SIMULATION AND ANALYSIS

Castalia is a framework designed for Wireless Sensor Networks (WSN) network simulation, based on OMNet + + platform that can be used to test the proposed new distributed algorithms and wireless communication protocols [7]. Ugo Colesanti et al developed the CTP routing protocol [8] based Castalia wireless sensor network simulator. Simulation environment: experimental scenario is to deploy 100 WSN nodes evenly within a rectangular area of 200 m * 300 m. The data delivery rate is 0.333/s. MAC layer module is the IEEE802.15.4 standard CC2420 MAC module jointly issued with CTP Castalia-based routing module, and already has provided with promiscuous listening mode. Radio parameter file is cc2440.txt. TxOutputPower is—3dBm. Initial energy for each node is 18720 Joules. Attack sensor nodes are randomly deployed in a network environment, and initiate sinkhole attack sensor network after a period of operation.

Detection rate is the ratio of the number of malicious nodes detected in a network environment to the amount of malicious node. The higher the ratio, the better the performance is. It can be seen that with the increase of malicious nodes in the network, difficulty of the attacker detection become more and more great. When the proportion of malicious nodes up to a certain value, there is no need to study. False alarm rate is defined as the ratio of node detected as malicious node improperly to the actual amount of nodes in the network. And it can be seen that with the increase of malicious nodes in the network, the difficulty distinguishing the malicious nodes from normal nodes increasingly, so the false positive rate rises.

6   CONCLUSION

We will continue to improve the detection algorithm, and to further enhance its detection rate, lower the false alarm rate, make it more suitable for the sensor network. Besides, it will be the next study content to extend the algorithm able to detect other types of attacks.

ACKNOWLEDGEMENTS

The author would like to thank the Chongqing Natural Science Foundation under Grant No. cstc2012 jjA40038. The work presented in this paper was supported in part by the Ministry of Industry and Information Technology of the Peoples Republic of China for the special funds of Development of the Internet of things (2012-583) and the College Students Scientific Research Training Program.

REFERENCES

[1] Karlof C, Wagner D. Secure routing in wireless sensor networks: attacks and countermeasures [C] IEEE International Workshop on Sensor Network Protocols and Applications, (5)2003, pp.113–127.
[2] Edith CH Ngai, et al. An efficient intruder detection algorithm against sinkhole attacks in wireless sensor networks, Elsevier, Computer Communications 30 (2007), pp. 2353–2364.
[3] Ioannis Krontiris, TD, et al. Intrusion Detection of Sinkhole Attacks in Wireless Sensor Networks, Springer, 2008, pp. 150–161.
[4] I. Krontiris, T. Giannetsos, T. Dimitriou. Launching a sinkhole attack in wireless sensor networks; the intruder side, Proceedings of the 2008 IEEE International Conference on Wireless and Mobile Computing, Networking and Communication, 2008, pp. 526–531.
[5] H. Shafiei, et al. Detection and mitigation of sinkhole attacks in wireless sensor networks, J. Comput. System Sci. 2013.
[6] S. Rajasegarar, et al. Hyperspherical cluster based distributed anomaly detection in wireless sensor networks, J. Parallel Distrib. Comput, (2013).
[7] Athanassios Boulis. A simulator for Wireless Sensor Networks and Body Area Networks Version 3.2 User's Manual, NICTA.
[8] Ugo Colesanti, et al. The Collection Tree Protocol for the Castalia Wireless Sensor Networks Simulator, Technical Report Nr. 729 Department of Computer Science ETH Zurich.

Application of multi-media technology on the sports website in China—a case study on Li Ning

J.M. Sun, H.T. Yang, Y. Wang & T.J. Ge
Harbin Engineering University, Harbin, China

ABSTRACT: As a sports company, Li Ning has become the leader of the sports market in China, which now is one of the biggest sports enterprise. With its development, Li Ning builded its online website for consumers. Previous studies pay no attention to multi-media technology's application on the sports website. However, this paper analyzed how Li Ning apply flexible multi-media technology on its own website and then gain great success. This research will provide some advice about the application of multi-media technology for other sports company's online selling, which is of great significance.

Keywords: sports website; multi-media technology; case study

1 INTRODUCTION

Nowadays people hardly can live without the Internet, according to the statistics, Chinese net citizens has been up to 600 million. Internet's online selling has been shaped with the development of the technology, so a lot of offline companys open its own online websites. The emergence of sports online website illustrates the big attraction of the Internet market. Shopping online volume has been over 1000 billion in 2012, which shows the huge business value. At present, Chinese sports develops rapidly, so many sports company emerge one after another, and more and more people select sports online platform to achieve varieties of trade needs. Most people choose sports platform purchase sports products, such as Nike, Anta and Li Ning etc. In the meanwhile, companys take a variety of ways to attract consumers, so their competition among is very heat. The companys realize that it is extremely important to design the online website of sports activities, and they are paying attention to the multi-media's application in their website.

There are many sports online websites in China, whereas most of them stuck in the crisis or fails to expend up. R. Xiaojian and S. Yan (2004) consider that the key of solving the problems is to improve the searching system of the website besides the combination of the multi-media. Li Ning makes big breakthrough since its establishment in online selling field. The authors believe that it plays an important role to use flexible multi-media technology. As a result, the paper intended to analyze the success of Li Ning and expect to summarize practical suggestions to other online sports websites.

2 MULTI-MEDIA TECHONOLOGY'S FORM ON SPORTS WEBSITE

Interface multi-media: Under the condition of WEB, the consumers are no longer the passive receiver of traditional multi-media in the online shopping, instead, they take part in the message as a volunteering person. Web designer can change and mild according to company's targets and strategies (Luo, W., 2008).

Voice media: Voice is one of the most convenient and familiar way, people send information and communication, if you have grace and pleasant music suits the theme of the electronic commerce in scanning, it is sure to attract the interest of consumers, so consumers will spend more time on the site, so that we can bring more information to consumers. (Luo, W., 2008).

The main characteristic of the application of multimedia on sports website: 1. The integration. It can get, save, organization and integration of information from many aspects. 2. Control. Multimedia technology integrated multimedia information processing and control center computer, as people order, it affects the sensory organ of people. Three nonlinear. The nonlinear characteristics of multimedia technology can change people's traditional pattern of reading and writing. In the past, people took the article, page to get knowledge, whereas will use HyperTextLink, make the content more flexible and variable to the reader (Luo, W, 2008).

In order to use the online resource in the 21st century, the best choice for consumers need combination of e-commerce and highly interactive multimedia technology integrated sports website system.

3 MULTI-MEDIA TECHNOLOGY'S APPLICATION ON SPORTS WEBSITE

Multi-media is a kind of technology that conducts two more different type information at the same time, which includes image, text, audio and video, etc. From the way that people sense the information, media can be divided into visual, auditory, tactus and taste media. It is sure that the present sports website focus on the visual and audio, which have a large number of data, and the audio-visual and interaction is better.

Sports is a business process that takes advantage of the electric media to make a deal on the basis of the Internet environment. It is a new business transaction model that emerged in western countries in 1990s. Sports makes the transaction go on efficiently and automatically without paper using, which transfers the traditional indirect material transaction into direct economy that is based on bit form. Sports is generally divided into four parts: sports website, consumer, bank and logistic company.

From the situation of the multi-media application on the website, the potential of multi-media technology on website still needs to be digged. It should be studied more about how multi-media technology can attract more consumers, and then produce more profit to sports company. Visual media: Visual media contains words, figures and images, etc. which is the basic element of e-commerce website. Text is the fundamental form of the release of e-commerce information, text can deliver more information to consumers about the product simply (Luo, W., 2008).

4 DISCUSSION OF THE APPLICATION OF MULTI-MEDIA TECHNOLOGY ON LI NING WEBSITE

Li Ning's group-buying model not only provide information for consumers, and provide a platform for B2C sales campaign. In the first year of Li Ning, the total income of more than 100 million, and 1 billion in three years. Competitive sports in China, the success of Li Ning should discuss and research.

Framework and structure of website: From the consumers' point of view, they are willing to buy commodity with complete information beautiful website compared to the simple and less information website. People can combine these goods with media, which helps consumers to receive these information. As a result, the quality of website design has direct influence on the quality of website. The design should make vivid, harmonious and beautiful page according to the theme, which

can make the users enter the sports world in a relaxing and pleasant mood, catch more information with little time.

When you enter the Li Ning's home page, we can see in the video above, Li Ning's advertising page, click after can see the ads. Small area of the page to become a bright spot, attract many customers. Successful advertising to capture customer's eyes, they like it. Plug-in module is a vice President of Li Ning, the chief executive and photos, very young, according to the company's confidence and courage to seize the customer heart, especially to the young lady. In this picture, "glory, I speak of myself" to express the features of Li Ning, provides customers with a deep impression.

Then it is the navigation bar, including "today's deals, sporting goods stores, discount famous brand, sports words—of—expressions using mobile Li Ning". Although just in black as the background, it expresses functional group buying activity, emphasize its sports goods and its quality is very good.

Product Introduction: Compared with other on-line shopping websites, Li Ning's page is more professional. Generally, the product name is composed of "brand+function+name+product number". Apart from the product image and price, discount percentage and keywords are given. Product introduction: compared with other online shopping websites, Li Ning page more professional. In general, the product name by "brand + + name + product number". In addition to product pictures and price, discount and keywords.

Next to the widespread use of words and pictures, Li Ning company to set up a "luck" section free trial fee and micro-comic desire stimulation test. Also, the use of language is very stylish, like "in the cold, no emotional and hatred of the world, xiaomei (Li Ning brand personalized name) warm you. Instant classic! Li Ning products!" These interesting customer focused and energetic indeed example, Li Ning concerned about customers, and because of that, in the rapid development.

The above analysis shows that the importance of correct language environment. Exquisite fashion network language will contact the heart of consumers.

Li Ning's media marketing: with the widespread use of Internet, involves network media interactive and high embrace more and more consumers. Micro—the birth of the film and advertising of the shape of the incredible: implantable advertising products into the film high—involving and emotional arousal, rather than a simple scenario. With better story lines, film technology, micro film advertising can express the brand image and brand concept. The point of view of communication, micro film advertising is a new communication method, with the traditional film and advertising. Its differentiation production, broadcast and distribution of a new method in all communications.

A successful advertisement should make full use of communication resources, the combination of multimedia and art, not just rely on the traditional way. In the case of Li Ning, plays an important role in the new media. Through the Internet media criticism and column as well as the personnel promotion, brand exposure and attraction is insurmountable. In the process of integrated marketing communication is to achieve the overall strategy, by makeup, an interactive modification and execute marketing plan, should be adjustable, measurable and persuasive (Wang, q. L and the sun, S.J., 2013). Its goal is to cover the current consumers and the potential ones, external internal ones and other targets. The successful marketing of Li Ning is an excellent example of good integrated marketing.

Interactive interface design of Li Ning: Interactive feature of sports guarantees the free communication between communicators and receivers via media platform. Providing more information and problem-solving solutions, interactive sites definitely help minimize the customer gap, offer better shopping experience and customer satisfaction, ultimately enhancing the buying motives. Based on that, we built a mutual-trust communication mode (Tang, J.G., 2006). See Figure 1.

Sports interactive target to any consumers want to know the information, customer interaction is in the process of the subject and the company's web site platform. Smartly on the lower right corner of the screen, the Java script driven Li Ning "online services" section of the page active and fresh consumers. Its convenience and availability at any time greatly improve the function of interaction and access to credit.

As consumers, on the company website browse to collect product information and services related products. Therefore, stationary and user friendly page is required. Personalized design content and features, consumer products and services can be found in a quick and convenient way. Li Ning's home page provides a great attempt to integrate resources, provide the interactive platform.

Different efficiencies of communication tools have various results. The interaction based on the prevalent messaging tool and mail well-preserves the interactive feature of Internet in during customer communication (Yang, L.M. and Li, T., 2012). On the other hand, due to inefficient feature of customer feedback, interactions based on message board yield a lousy result. The interaction methods adopted by Li Ning are live800 on-line service hotline and mail box, which bridges the customer and website, combining the on-line and off-line service. Thanks to that, most of the consumer questions and problems are solved in time. In addition to instant messaging, the feedback of consumer is another engine driven interactive. According to the China Internet network information center: 43% of buyers believe that comment is a great purchase factor, 41% of the buyers comments before each purchase another 26% see comments before purchase. Li Ning center to build a good word-of-mouth, provide consumers with a full review platform, and evoke potential purchase desire.

5 CONCLUSION

All in all, from the overall analysis of the above, through the use of multimedia technology correctly, Li Ning sports websites realize the aesthetic value and the marketing effect, and made a great breakthrough in the application of multimedia in China. Li Ning company makes full use of current technology, combined with audio, visual, and interface methods, which leads to improve its web site. Therefore, consumers are willing to spend more time on this site. The author thinks that the flexible use of multimedia technology to help Li Ning win more and more market share in the field of sports. The author also believes that other sports sites in China should learn from Li Ning's model, which will help them in this fierce market so that they can grow faster, stronger.

ACKNOWLEDGEMENT

This paper is funded by Fundamental Research Funds for the Central Universities. The project No. is HEUCF14601.

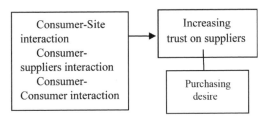

Figure 1.

REFERENCES

Luo, W., 2008. The application of multi-media technology on the sports website. sports 5,154.
Shen, Y. and Ren, X.J., 2004. Application of multi-media technology on the sports website. Information Studies: Theory & Application. 2, 215.

Tang, J.G., 2006. The research of influence of interaction on trust and purchasing intention under B2C environment. Fu Dan university.

Wang, Q.L. and Sun, S.J. 2013. Analysis of the spread of integrated marketing of micro-movie. Media of Today 7, 74–75.

Wang, W. 2013. On the application of multi-media in the construction of sports Website. Journal of Liao Ning Higher Vocational 15, 85–86.

Yang, L.M. and Li, T., 2012. The interactivity strategy of B2C sports site. China soft science magazine (supplement) 141–143.

Computer, Intelligent Computing and Education Technology – Liu, Sung & Yao (Eds)
© 2014 Taylor & Francis Group, London, ISBN 978-1-138-02469-4

Investigation report about talent demand in Mechanical Manufacturing and Automation specialty

L. Wang & K. Zhang
School of Mechanical Engineering, Shenyang University of Technology, Shenyang, China

ABSTRACT: In order to adapt to the training objectives and training standards of Mechanical Manufacturing and Automation specialty in colleges and universities, comprehensively understand the business demand for talent, highlight the practical ability and professional skills training of students. Some teachers, major in Mechanical Manufacturing and Automation of Shenyang University of Technology, perform the investigation on how to highlight the specialty skill training, standardize the course content and structure, and how to increase the employment rate for graduates.

Keywords: investigation report; talent demand; Mechanical Manufacturing and Automation specialty

1 INTRODUCTION

In order to better implement the "taking the service as the aim, the employment as the direction, the post ability training as the emphasis" education philosophy, strengthen the specialty construction, and promote the specialty reform, we carried out the investigation on talent demand for mechanical manufacturing and automation specialty [1–3]. The purpose of the survey is to provide a comprehensive understanding of the market demand trend of this specialty, the post links, the requirements of the knowledge, skills, and quality of professionals, explore the direction of professional development, and formulate a scientific and reasonable training program [4–6].

2 ORGANISATION AND IMPLEMENTATION

The research was done by the teachers majored in mechanical manufacturing and automation, and takes the state-owned, joint venture, and private companies in electro-mechanical manufacturing industry of Liaoning old industrial base which employ many graduates engaged in this specialty in recent years as research objects. The research was carried out mainly in the form of surveys and employer visits, and achieved in the face-to-face discussion and communication with some directors of enterprises and graduates. In addition, the research was complemented by informal conversations and telephone exchanges. The survey questionnaires were issued 300 copies and recycled 252 copies. Among them, 152 and 100 copies were from graduates and enterprises separately, and the recovery rate is 84%.

3 RESEARCH CONTENTS

The research contents are designed based on the objective of this investigation.

1. The hierarchy and planning of needs for enterprise talents.
2. The main channel and source of technicians employed by enterprise.
3. The main jobs of recruiting talents.
4. A number of factors in employing.
5. The nature, size and condition of the graduates' units.
6. The ability and knowledge needed most by the employment at present, and in 2 or 3 years later.

The following problems are investigated in the employing units.

1. The nature, size and condition of the units.
2. The status quo of technologist.
3. The demand degree in the mechanical manufacturing specialty in recent years.
4. The jobs most in need at present, and in 2 or 3 years later.
5. The suggestions to the school personnel training.

The graduates get some information mainly through internet and questionnaire. Focus on investigate the following questions.

1. The nature, size and condition of the students' units.

2. The working conditions of the students' individuals, which mainly reflect the graduates' information including professional counterparts, the adapt degree of working, the competent level of working and the job satisfaction.
3. The graduates' job situation in recent years. The degree of demand and the difficulty of employment are reflected by the difficulties and the number of times to apply for a job in this specialty.
4. The ability and knowledge needed most by the employment at present, and in 2 or 3 years later.
5. The courses and practice should be strengthened by the colleges.
6. The jobs you want to choose.

4 RESULTS ANALYSIS OF INVESTIGATION

The investigation has been supported and cooperated by the graduates and units who could fill in the questionnaire items seriously and objectively. The text feedback information is larger, which fully embodies the graduates' feelings to the college, the concern for the college work, the unit's support for the college and the serious and responsible attitude. The statistical results of the questionnaire achieve the research purpose, which provide an important basis for the teaching and research section in the professional building, the course system reform, the students' quality education, the employment education and guidance and so on. Both the graduates and enterprise personnel under investigation think it is necessary to carry out such activities in the college. The investigation is beneficial to strengthen the relation between the college and the enterprise or the graduates. The investigation is beneficial to the combination of the talent cultivation and production, enterprise and society. The investigation is beneficial to the education teaching reform and development in college.

Among the 100 copies of retrieved questionnaires of employing unit, 52% of the enterprises have high demand for talents of Mechanical Manufacturing and Automation specialty in college. The working posts are basically classified as the following four kinds: The first is the technical position in production line, which is engaged in the compilation and implementation of mechanical manufacturing process specification and the design and manufacture of mechanical processing equipment. This category accounted for 47.3%; The second is the operation and maintenance status, which is engaged in the operation, commissioning, running and maintenance of mechanical and electrical equipment. This category accounted for 27.2%;

The third is engaged in the quality inspection and supervision work with mechanical products, which accounted for 13.8%; The fourth is engaged in product marketing, after-sales technical service and administrative work, which accounted for 11.7%. The proportional allocation situation is shown in Figure 1.

Among the main channel and source of technical personnel employed in production line, 61% of them were the graduates recruited from college by companies, and 28% of them were recruited from the labor market. The other was mainly recruited from businesses cultivation and acquaintance recommendation, as well as in online recruitment. The proportional distribution condition is illustrated in Figure 2.

Among the most important factors that were emphasized by enterprises in the process of recruitment, about 92% of enterprises pay attention to the conscientious and meticulous working attitudes, work ethic, safe and civilized production ability, the consciousness to think and solve technical problems, communication and team collaboration skills, self-learning ability, quality and safety, efficiency and environmental consciousness. Only 8% of them don't think these qualities are needed. This situation was depicted in Figure 3.

In the 152 copies of recovered survey questionnaires from graduates, the distributions of graduates of the institution system are as follows: state-owned 15.8%, foreign-funded 14.6%, private 64.8%, and others 4.8%. From the statistical data of research table, at present the graduates work

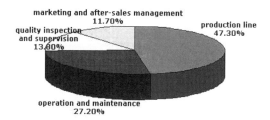

Figure 1. Post demand research on the talents in Mechanical Manufacturing and Automation specialty.

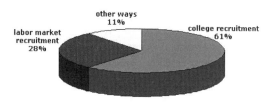

Figure 2. Main channel of enterprise recruitment for talents of production line.

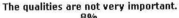

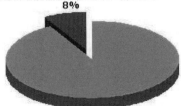

The qualities are not very important.
8%

The qualities, such as conscientious and meticulous working attitudes, are very important.
92%

Figure 3. Requirements of enterprises for the overall qualities of talents.

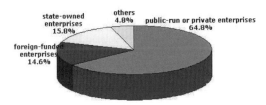

state-owned enterprises 15.8%　others 4.8%　public-run or private enterprises 64.8%

foreign-funded enterprises 14.6%

Figure 4. Distributions of graduates in Mechanical Manufacturing and Automation specialty of the institution system.

mainly in small and medium sized public-run or private enterprises, and this section accounts for 64.8% of investigated graduates.

This situation is more in line with the economic characteristics in our country and the cultivation direction of talents in our school. The survey proves that at least 82% of the graduates in our specialty are engaged in the job in their professional field. The ones who quickly adapt to current work occupy 85%, and 93% of the graduates could be qualified for their post. They have the all capacities of the corresponding status, and are more satisfied with current work. This case is exhibited in Figure 4.

5 RESEARCH CONCLUSIONS

Based on the above statistics, the following judgments can be basically made:

1. There is heavy demand for graduates majoring in mechanical manufacturing and automation. The number of graduates graduated from mechanical related major of colleges and universities every year is approximately 800,000. Due to the importance and large scale of the machinery industry, it requires a large team of

professionals. Every year the market demand for mechanical engineering application talents is about 5 million people, so there is still greater need of mechanical talents over a period of time in the future. According to survey of demand for all kinds of talents of Liaoning province in 2013, the demand for talents majoring in mechanical manufacturing and automation ranks in the top two in all undergraduate. Therefore, the task of the cultivation of high-quality mechanical manufacture applied talents with is significant and urgent.

2. The position of our specialty is primarily accurate. The enterprise requirements for technical applied ability of high-skilled talents in machinery industry mainly reflect in the process of the technological process planning, the operation and maintenance of machining equipment, fixture design, CNC programming, and quality testing. They need a large number of front line operation type high-skilled talents who have strong first-post ability and high comprehensive quality, as well as a large number of front line technology or management type high-skilled talents who have process implementation ability and multiple post adaptability. In addition, they put forward the higher expectation for graduates at other areas, such as professional integrity and humanism diathesis, so as to adapt to technical and management requirements for small and medium-sized enterprise. The graduates generally agree that these courses, such as machinery processes, tooling design, mechanical design, mechanical drawing, machine tool electric control, software applications and foreign language, are very important in the mechanical manufacturing and automation specialty of our school. The graduates wish to enhance their professional knowledge and skills. At the same time, they are fully aware of the significance to improve comprehensive quality.

3. The reform of our specialty meets enterprise demands for talents. In order to adapt to the demand for highly skilled talents in machinery manufacturing enterprise, the Mechanical Manufacturing and Automation specialty in our school takes the technical talent of production line as the goals, and the on-site process implementation ability as the main line. Our specialty should be collaborated with the industrial enterprises, design work-integrated learning, task-driven and project-oriented teaching pattern, and construct practice-oriented curriculum system based on the process of the implementation process. Moreover, it should strengthen process implementation skill, innovate talent training mode, and achieve the cultivation goal, namely the firm first-post qualification ability,

the outstanding job adaptability, and the strong sustainable development ability. The research shows that the teaching reform of our specialty coincide with the company's demand for talents.

6 PROBLEM AND THINKING

Found during the investigation, many enterprises lack talent, especially the ones who work in production line and understand processes and operation. This situation seriously restricts the economic development and growth, and becomes the main "bottleneck" to build advanced manufacturing industry base of Liaoning province. The companies generally agreed that after entering the 21st century, the graduates recruiting from our college and other universities have high expectations, and don't try their best to engage in front-line operations in the enterprise. They usually leave their job 1 to 1.5 years later, which affects the normal production of enterprises, and is disadvantageous to the development of graduates and companies. As for the graduates born in 1990s, they don't grasp the basic knowledge well, and haven't enough ability to fulfill the process. In addition, they lack of ability to solve practical problems by looking for information. They have many certificates, but practise poorly and lack of hard-working spirit.

According to the survey, the education and teaching work in mechanical manufacturing and automation major of our school can enhance the following links:

1. The general requirement for graduates is a broad base of knowledge, and they can be engaged in machine work, process implementation, and mechanical and electrical equipment maintenance in production line.
2. The college should further strengthen the construction of practice base inside and outside school, deepen the cooperation with enterprises, and introduce the advanced processing technology and corporate culture. Moreover, it should also construct entirely new curriculum system which is oriented to engineering science and combined with the talent cultivation model in higher education, and determine and refine the main schema of practice-oriented curriculum system based on the working process of the technology implementation.
3. In appropriate period (for example, during recognition or production practice), the relative school leader should introduce the corporate high-tech talents to teach students in class, and further strengthen the teaching of advanced manufacturing technologies, such as CNC machining techniques, CAD/M, Pro/E, and so on.
4. The graduates should improve their foreign languages and computer skills, so that they can better master the CNC machine tool performance, be familiar with the operation, and meet the requirement foreign-funded enterprises.
5. The practical marketing should be established as the elective courses. At present, the corporate marketers have the machinery industry background. The students of Mechanical Manufacturing and Automation specialty possess specialized knowledge, such as marketing approach, which are the company's much-needed personnel.
6. The corresponding courses, such as business management and quality management, should be set up, and the certification cultivation of ISO9000 quality system should be performed. Enterprises have higher expectations for the recruited college graduates, and hope that they have a certain workshop integrated management capacity. As a result, the students master the basic knowledge of business and quality management, which is beneficial to the common development of graduates and enterprises.

ACKNOWLEDGMENT

This research is supported by the General Program of Education and Science of Liaoning Province during the 12th Five-Year Plan Period, No. JG11DB207.

REFERENCES

[1] Y.K. Chen. Teaching Evaluation, Beijing: People's Education Press, 1999.
[2] L. Yu. Classroom Teaching Assessment, Beijing: People's Education Press, 2007.
[3] Z.R. Du, W.W. Liao. Higher Education, Shanghai: Fudan University Press, 2003.
[4] Shi Congji, Sun Lipeng. Mechanical design course design teaching reform practice. Journal of the national mechanical design teaching conference, 2009.
[5] Wang Guihe, Lv Jianguo. Connotation and cultivation way of engineering consciousness of engineering college students. Chinese geological education, 2006, 4: 62–64.
[6] Chang Zhibin, Gui Dingyi, Ren Bailin, Zhang Chenyang. Cultivation of students' engineering consciousness and innovation ability combined with the engineering practice. Higher education research of mechanical industry, 2001, 2: 61–63.

Computer, Intelligent Computing and Education Technology – Liu, Sung & Yao (Eds)
© 2014 Taylor & Francis Group, London, ISBN 978-1-138-02469-4

Numerical study on rolling characteristics of canard-controlled missile with a free-spinning tail

Z.H. Lan, Y.G. Ji, C.Y. Tian & L. Zhang
Department of Campaign and Command, Air Force Aviation University, Changchun, China

H. Mei
Changchun Yuheng Optics Co., Ltd., China

ABSTRACT: To investigate the rolling control characteristics of canard-controlled missile with a free-spinning tail, we have adopted a numerical simulation method. Three dimensional compressible Reynolds averaged Navier Strokes numerical simulations were carried out to predict the flowfield characteristics and the SST $k–w$ two equation turbulence model was used for the numerical simulations here. Through the numerical simulation, we have got a function curve which indicates the rolling moment coefficient is positive when the mach number changes. So the canards are effective as rolling control devices for canard missiles with free-spinning tails. We have compared the numerical simulation result with experiment result which is consistent. So the theory model in the paper is very good for dealing with the similar problems.

Keywords: rolling characteristics; canard-controlled missile; free-spinning tail

1 INTRODUCTION

The canard configuration is a common form of layout in tactical missile, such as Russia's "red" terminal guidance ammunition, "basij aung" gun, "gecko" air defense missiles, American paveway I, paveway II, paveway III, laser-guided bombs, France's "magic" air-to-air missile and so on. The reason is that it has many advantages such as high efficiency rudder steering, a smaller power of steering engine, short connecting cables and easy lay. But the main disadvantage of this arrangement is that when the ailerons of missiles carry roll control, large reverse roll moment are produced on the tail because an asymmetric downwash flow field near the tail fins was induced, producing a so-called reversed rolling moment. So that the missile roll control efficiency is greatly reduced. Aiming at the problem, a lot of researches in two aspects of theory and experiment were carried to improve roll control efficiency of canard missiles. The measures of reduction induced roll torque of duck rudder are that reducing the wingspan of tail wings; using ring tail; with T blade on the tail in Figure 1; using ring tail in Figure 2; the free rotation tail.

Due to the limitation of the test conditions, the phenomenon of mechanism research data is less. With the CFD (Computational Fluid Dynamics) in real international engineering design application

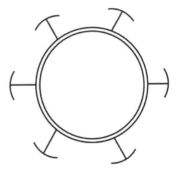

Figure 1. T blade on the tail of missile.

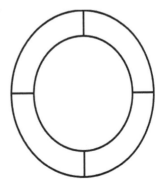

Figure 2. Ring tail of missile.

gradually thorough, flow around objects of many things Phenomenon, interact with each other, the mechanism of flow field in the flow structure flow characteristics, change rule also gradually through numerical simulation and simulation analysis. In this paper, the numerical simulation method, CFD currently widely applied to study the rolling characteristics.

2 BASIC EQUATIONS

2.1 Control equations

By using three-dimensional viscous flow field of spoiler, the control equation is the reynolds averaged navier-stokes equations and its form is as follows:

$$\frac{\partial Q}{\partial t} + \frac{\partial F}{\partial X} + \frac{\partial G}{\partial Y} + \frac{\partial H}{\partial Z} = \frac{1}{Re}\left(\frac{\partial F_v}{\partial X} + \frac{\partial G_v}{\partial Y} + \frac{\partial H_v}{\partial Z}\right)$$
(1)

In the type : Q is the Conserved variable vector; F, G, H are no sticky pass vectors; F_v, G_v, H_v are sticky pass vectors. We solve this equation using the finite volume method and the time advance by using implicit format. The discrete equations are solved by the coupled algebraic multigrid method proposed by the Raw.

2.2 The turbulence model

The turbulence model is a set of describing the average amount of turbulence closure equations under the premise of a series of assumptions which base on the average Reynolds equation of motion and rulsating motion equation and rely on the combination of theory and experience. In this paper, the $k-\omega$ SST two-equation model which describes the eddy viscosity turbulence is relatively mature to deal with engineering problems.

In the type, μ_t is the turbulent viscosity; k is the turbulent kinetic energy and ω is the frequency of turbulence. These parameters have the following relationship:

$$\mu_t = \frac{\rho a_1 k}{\max(a_1\omega, \Omega F_2)}$$
(2)

$$\frac{\partial(\rho k)}{\partial t} + \frac{\partial(\rho u_j k)}{\partial t} = P - \beta^* \rho\omega k$$
$$+ \frac{\partial}{\partial x_j}\left[(\mu + \sigma_k\mu_t)\frac{\partial k}{\partial x_j}\right]$$
(3)

$$\frac{\partial(\rho\omega)}{\partial t} + \frac{\partial(\rho u_j\omega)}{\partial t} = \frac{\gamma}{v_t}P - \beta\rho\omega^2$$
$$+ \frac{\partial}{\partial x_j}\left[(\mu + \sigma_\omega\mu_t)\frac{\partial\omega}{\partial x_j}\right]$$
$$+ 2(1 - F_1)\frac{\rho\sigma_\omega}{\omega}\frac{\partial k}{\partial x_j}\frac{\partial\omega}{\partial x_j}$$
(4)

The meanings of parameters in (3) and (4) refer to the third references.

3 CALCULATION RESULTS AND ANALYSIS

3.1 Missile shape

It is calculated by using canard-controlled missiles with a free-spinning tail. The shape of missiles is shown in Figure 3 which has 4 pieces of rudder surface and 4 pieces of wing surface that appear a "++" layout. The missile head is vertebral and the body of missile is a cylinder with a large slenderness ratio.

3.2 Calculation conditions

In the numerical calculation, we have thought that the flow field area boundary include two parts. They are the wall of missile and outer boundary. The condition of wall no-slip insulating solid wall boundary condition. It's outer boundary takes far-field boundary conditions that is no reflection boundary conditions.

$H = 10$ km

$\alpha = 0^\circ$

$\delta_x = -5^\circ$

3.3 Rolling characteristics

The change curve of rolling moment coefficient m_{x_0} acting on the body of missile with the mach number is shown in Figure 2, when a canard as aileron deflection is -5° ($\delta_x = -5^\circ$) to carry forward roll control.

It can be seen from Figure 4 that when the mach number changes, the rolling moment coefficient

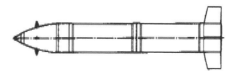

Figure 3. The shape of duck type layout missile with a free-spinning tail.

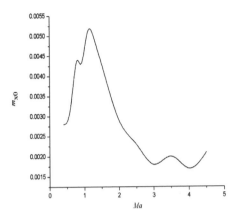

Figure 4. The change curve of m_{x_0} with Ma.

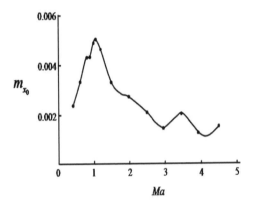

Figure 5. The change curve of m_{x_0} with Ma in the experiment.

m_{x_0} is always positive which is consistent with the canard roll force in direction. It indicates that the canard wing of missiles with a free-spinning tail is capable of normal roll control. The result is accordant with experimental results.

Duck missile of the layout, when the duck rudder roll do aileron deflection control, the rudder surface drag the trailing edge vortex formed in the tail of asymmetry of flow field, induce a duck with the direction of the rudder roll control moment. The torque decreases even can completely offset the duck rudder rolling control moment, so that the roll on the surface of the rudder control efficiency is greatly reduced, in order to produce in contrast to the rudder deflection control effect of roll torque, the duck rudder all loss of roll control. So generally cannot duck type layout missile.

Duck rudder roll of the aileron deflection control of missile, the backward induction of roll torque will make the tail tube around the longitudinal axis of missile body to roll, not passed on to the former projectile, former projectile in duck rudder roll only Turn control torque under the action of roll, thereby eliminating the duck rudder/tail gas. Dynamic coupling, roll decoupling is realized. Spin the tail has been applied on missile models in several countries, such as Russia's SA an 8 Gecko surface-to-air missile, French R. 550 Magic air-to-air missiles, etc., by using spin tail to eliminate the backward induction, roll moments to duck rudder roll control of missile.

4 SUMMARY

The rolling moment characteristics of canard missiles are studied, and the influence of downwash of canard was analyzed. As a result of canard fin deflections, an asymmetric downwash flow field near the tail fins was induced producing a so-called reversed rolling moment. It can be seen in Figure 2 that the rolling moment coefficient of canard missiles with free-spinning tails is always positive when the mach number changes. It indicates that the direction of the control moment is same as the control force. So the free-spinning tails can reduce the downwash which is caused by the canard fin's rolling controllation and is an effective way.

To investigate the rolling control characteristics of canard-controlled missile with a free-spinning tail, we have adopted a numerical simulation method. Three dimensional compressible Reynolds averaged Navier Strokes numerical simulations were carried out to predict the flowfield characteristics and The SST $k - w$ two equation turbulence model was used for the numerical simulations in this article. By comparing the the numerical simulation result with experiment result, we found that they are accordant. So we can get the conclusion that theory model is very good for dealing with the similar problems.

Through the numerical simulation method to research the rolling control characteristics and analyze the roll coupling mechanism of canard missile, we can get a good approach to improve the controllation efficiency.

REFERENCES

[1] Liu Tonglin. 1998. Complete collection of world guided missile. Beijing: Military Science Press.
[2] Wu jiasheng. Lei juanmian. 2003. Trends in the development of acrodymanic configuration of guided weapons and relevant aerodynamic techniques. Transactions of Beijing Institute of Technology. Vol. 23: p. 665.

[3] Burt J R. 1974. An experimental investigation of the aerodynamic characteristics of several nose-mounted canard configurations at transonic mach numbers. AD/A: p. 006484.

[4] Blait A B. 1978. Wind tunnel investigation at supersonic speeds of a controlled canard missile with fixed and free-rolling tail fins. NASA. Vol. 78: p. 32067.

[5] Liu Tonglin. 1991. Winged missiles aerodynamic design. Beijing: Aerospace Press.

[6] Qi Zaikang. 2002. Guided ammunition technology. Beijing: Beijing Institute of Technology Press.

[7] Burt J R. 2002. The effectiveness of canards for roll control, Vol. 98: p. 897.

[8] Lei Juanmian. Ju Xianming. 2004. Wu Jiasheng. Rolling Characteristics of Canard-Controlled Missiles with a Free-Spinning Tail. Transactions of Beijing Institute of Technology. Vol. 24: p. 657.

Computer, Intelligent Computing and Education Technology – Liu, Sung & Yao (Eds)
© 2014 Taylor & Francis Group, London, ISBN 978-1-138-02469-4

The challenges of social media technology to management engineering courses

H. Xie
Department of Technology, Illinois State University, Normal, Illinois, USA

Y. Shi
Department of Computer and Information Science, Xi'an Technological University, Shaanxi, China

T. Liang
Department of Systems Engineering, University of Arkansas at Little Rock, AR, USA

S. Li
School of Management, Xi'an University of Architecture and Technology, Xi'an, China

ABSTRACT: The use of social media involves employing web and mobile technologies to support interactive dialogue and mediate human communication. With the influence of social media in political, economic, and recreational fields, higher educational institutions start to recognize and utilize the idea of adopting the emerging technology in education processes. This paper highlights the difficulty that educators face in the age of social media. The paper discusses how to teach an increasingly networked generation that is ready to search for the opinions of their peers (who may be anonymous) on the internet besides what they learn from classroom teaching. Particularly, this paper discusses the challenges, opportunities, and possible practice of using social media in management engineering courses. The paper suggests using Cooperative Learning as the instructional method to let students work together in small groups to enable and organize students to participate the authentic and focused learning activities.

Keywords: social media; mobile technology; Cooperative Learning

1 INTRODUCTION

Social media has been adopted into enterprise product sales, customer service, product innovation, education, and many other fields. The features of social media include wide participation, sharing, communication through user-generated contents, frequency, accessibility, usability, immediacy, and permanence (Morgan, et al., 2013). The various forms of social media, such as blog, forum, social networking, etc., have been used by millions of people daily. As admitted by media mogul Keith Rupert Murdoch, it will be difficult and dangerous to underestimate the impact and the power of social media (Mackay, 2011). Social media has changed the traditional teaching and learning approaches as well. Teaching methods and Learning styles undergone profound changes. For example, student interactions happen frequently in asynchronous learning environments, including social media uses (Blanchette, 2012). During the interactive learning process, students use social media to exchange communication contents and build dialogues. The use of social media among students caught the attention of educators. The new technology brought in opportunities as well as challenges to management engineering education. Implementing social media to build relationships with students is not easy (Pan, 2013). For those educators who are not familiar with social media, communication through blogs may seem to be time-consuming. Sometimes, students may not completely understand the meaning of a post and would not want to follow. If that is the case, the two-way communication is not carried on properly. Social media also brings a question to educators about how to evaluate student performance. The new and diverse student evaluation methods should not only reflect academic achievement, but also assess collaboration skills and self-reflection ability. The paper suggests using Cooperative Learning as the instructional method to let students work together in small groups, with each member of the group participating in a clearly assigned and collective task, to enable and organize students to participate the authentic and focused learning activities using social media technology.

2 LITERATURE REVIEW

As noted by Jarvis (2006) and McGill (2013), students understand information commonly by relating to the events of their past. Students can also gain knowledge or skills by relating them with commonly accepted facts and events. Using the connection between events and the external world, an individual can build experiences and transform perspectives, perceptions, or frame of reference; this is experiential learning (Jarvis, 2012). For the current generation of students, instructors can integrate the traditional way (e.g. classroom teaching) with the network way (e.g. Facebook activities) to deliver the valuable information to students.

In a traditional classroom learning environment, teacher's explanations, class discussion, and class exercises are used to help students to achieve the goal of acquiring and consolidating knowledge. The weakness of classroom learning is that it is difficult for every student to have active engagement, collaboration, and participation in class activities. Using social media, instructors can disseminate information dissemination with measurable results and monitor and evaluate collaborative and independent efforts and activities of students (Okoro, 2012). Another limitation of classroom learning is that students only learn the knowledge listed in the syllabus. The range of knowledge that students can learn is restricted (Runesson, 2006). However, with the development of the information age, network becomes a new way for students to acquire knowledge. Internet gradually becomes the main way for students to access information outside of classrooms due to its abundant resources and fast searching speed. Learning with the aid of informal online groups can help students to perform Cooperative Learning or experiential learning. But some issues with social-media-assisted learning should also be noticed. Pike, Kuh, and McCormick (2011) noticed that under the network environment, students can get the information they need and engage with others to exchange and share learning resources. However, compared with the traditional classroom learning, the quality assurance of the information or resources obtained from social media network is imperfect.

Through the investigation on how students surfing Internet, people find that students make use of network environment and resources to learn theories, practices and improve their knowledge and skills according to their own interests and hobbies. A sizable minority of students experience problems related to Internet use. In addition, the use of Facebook may contribute to the severity of symptoms associated with Internet addiction (Kittinger, Correia, & Irons, 2012). Students lack the understanding and skills of organizing the information

obtained from Internet. Social media network can enrich student's knowledge and promote the students' learning autonomy. Used properly, social media network can reach a large capacity of students with high efficiency. But the rich contents of the social network world could make students distracted and lost (Hakverdi-Can & Sonmez, 2012).

Social media has been a critical channel to deliver information in daily life. With the huge convenience it brings in transmitting and sharing information, it becomes very popular in all kinds of communities. Organizations of various business sectors are eager to exploit this new tool to promote the market development. Governments use it to know the public voice and make the policy-decision more practical. With the influence of social media in political, economic, and recreational fields, higher educational institutions start to recognize and utilize the idea of adopting the emerging technology in education processes. In order to understand the different uses of social media in various fields, e.g. political, economic, recreational, and educational uses of social media, this paper discusses 4 case studies.

Many Americans use social media for political and civic engagements. Around 60% of American adults use social networking sites, mainly Facebook or Twitter. A survey by the Pew Research Center's Internet & American Life Project found that 66% of the social media users (or 39% of all American adults) had done at least one civic or political activity with social media (Brenner, 2013). Thirty eight percent of those used Social Networking Sites (SNS) or Twitter to "like" or promote materials related to politics or social issues that others had posted. Fifty two percent of Liberal Democrats who used social media were particularly likely to use the "like" button. Forty two percent of conservative Republicans have also done so.

Companies and organizations become more creative as they compete to attract customers and stimulate local economies. Many local economic development agencies have turned to social media tools and tactics to enhance their efforts nationally and locally. According to a 2009 survey conducted by the International Economic Development Council (IEDC) and marketing agency Development Counselors International, 57% of IEDC members surveyed said they were using social media tools (Sherman, 2010). Developers are using blogs, Twitter, Facebook and YouTube to attract and interact with site selectors and company decision makers nationally and globally. For example, when Orlando, Florida, was trying to attract a New York City based company, it heard a concern from the company. The impression was that Orlando wasn't considered a place famous for its high-tech development, but rather a city with a lot of theme parks.

To demonstrate an image with high-tech focus, the Metro Orlando Economic Development Commission created a microsite with a YouTube and Flickr presence. The city also sourced stories from their members as well as testimonials about why they loved living and working in Orlando through Facebook, Twitter and its e-newsletter. As a result, Orlando was shortlisted and matched against the target company's home base of Manhattan. The company decided not to relocate. But the Metro Orlando Economic Development Commission credited social media as part of what helped rebrand their city and made a strong demonstration of its recruiting efforts.

3 CONCEPTUAL MODEL

How college students interact and socialize today is different from the students in 5 or 10 years ago. They are now hanging out online and often texting or interacting via their social-networking profiles. While these activities can be time-wasting, they can also be productive, helping them define their identities, reinforce offline social relationships and express themselves in a variety of way (Boyd, 2008). This study was carried out with a class of sixty (n = 60) first year undergraduate students in Engineering Management major. The overall aim is to understand the skills of the students for independent learning and social interaction, while keeping a foundation for developing critical thinking skills. At the outset a social media account was set up. Account details included instructor's name and a logo of the university. Contents were carried out using the web interface, Short Message Service (SMS) and Smartphone application. Students were voluntary to decide on the participation in the study.

Most of the students were very familiar with the social media uses in recreation or searching for news. But to use social media in learning was fairly new to them. The students were required to either set up an account for this use or use their existing ones. To encourage student participation, the instructor revised the lectures for the course to include a variety of materials and teaching methods. Each lecture contained a) PowerPoint presentations, b) video clips with pre and post questions, c) short classroom discussion for 15–20 minutes, d) questions and answers, and e) explanation of homework assignment. Students were encouraged to express their opinions, feelings and experiences through either classroom discussion or social media group discussion. The online discussions were displayed to the group using the instructor's account, which remained open for the entirety of the class. For instance, video clips were posted before class. Students were encouraged to bring questions to class after viewing the videos. During class discussion, the online discussion was also displayed on the projector screen. The teaching strategy used was Cooperative Learning. In the Cooperative Learning environment, activities were based on groups as the units. The instructor made sure that groups were target oriented. Students in the groups were from different backgrounds. Each of the heterogeneous groups was made up of 2–6 students. Together, those students were engaged in a variety of discussions. The classroom instruction to team learning was the main organizational form. The instructor, according to certain procedures and methods of cooperation, encouraged students to study together in the heterogeneous groups.

4 IMPLEMENTATION OF THE MODEL AND CONCLUSION

To select the appropriate tool to use for social media communication, the author did a comparison among some commonly used social media systems. The comparison of different social media was provided in Table 1. In the designed class, students also simulated a communication process in the Architecture/Engineering/Construction (AEC) industry. The stakeholders communicated with each other during the construction of the project. Every participant has a social media account and plays different roles in the project. Social media groups were created to make the communication more easily. In Figure 1, the solid line circles represent the participants, i.e. business owners. The arrows represent the flow of the communications.

During the research, the instructor and the students had discussions about the drawbacks of social media tools. For example, using social media can help people to promote business, communicate with customers, and even recruit or check-up on employees. However, careless use of social media may cause leakage of important personal information, such as social security numbers, bank account information, etc. Intellectual property was another issue that the students were interested with. Students exchanged the ideas on how to correctly include the information in the content created by others. For example, there is risk when using contents created by others to promote one's own business without getting permission. In the study, students also discussed the best practice of learning in a network environment. Relaxed learning atmosphere can help to inspire students to participate in learning activities. Class time may not always be enough to allow students to thoroughly

Table 1. The comparison of different social media systems.*

	Blogs	Microblog	BBS	SNS
User group	Large	Large	Medium	Large
Transparency	Open	Open	Register	Register
Communication	Review	Review & message	Review & message	Message
Dependency	2	4	2	2
Connectivity	5	5	5	5
	Wikis	Youtube	Online community	
User group	Large	Large	Medium	
Transparency	Open	Open	Partial open	
Communication	Browse	Review	Review	
Dependency	3	5	2	
Connectivity	5	5	5	

*In the table, the rank is from worst to best with 1 indicates worst and 5 indicates best.

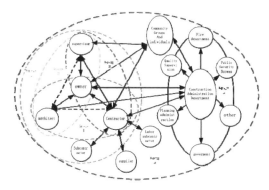

Figure 1. The communication among social network participants.

understand the provided knowledge. Students need to learn more knowledge after class. Social media network can be used to discuss homework questions.

In order to understand how the students used social media tools to assist academic study, a questionnaire was designed and a survey was performed. The questionnaire included 12 questions. This survey issued 50 questionnaires totally and 45 questionnaires were recovered. Excluding 3 invalid questionnaires, the effective recovery rate was 84%. The following are the results of the present investigation: In the 42 valid questionnaires, 42% were from male students, 58% were from female students. 24% of the respondents did not use social media to complete daily work, 76% of the respondents usually used social media to complete daily work, including 12% who occasionally used the tools, 42% frequently used the tools, 34% used the tools every day. 8.16% of

the students surveyed believed social media security management system is very satisfactory. 28% of them were satisfied with social media security management system. 34% considered that social security management system was fair. 8.16% of the people was not satisfied with the social security management system. 6% of them were very dissatisfied with social media security management system. 4% of the people thought that the update speed of social media information was very slow. 30% agreed the update speed was slow. 38% considered the update speed was OK. 22% believed the update speed was quickly. 6% ranked the update speed as very quickly.

In the survey, only 8% of the people surveyed completely trusted the reliability of the information obtained from the social media. 50% of them partially trusted the reliability of the information, and the rest did not trust the information obtained from social media. 64% of the people surveyed would validate the authenticity of the information obtained from the social media. 36% of the people would not validate the information authenticity. As for the people who don't use social media, 20% of them were because that social media contents were not serious. 26% considered the social media contents were not complete. 12% believed that social media was too complex for operation. 6% considered that the social media cost was high. 16% of people who don't use social media were because they didn't understand social media.

Therefore, from what has been surveyed above, the functions and the uses of social media are not perfect at present. How to improve the model to meet the demands of students will be the key issue in the future research on using social media for education.

REFERENCES

Blanchette, J. (2012). Participant interaction in asynchronous learning environments: Evaluating interaction analysis methods. Linguistics and Education: An International Research Journal, 23(1), 77–87 doi:10.1016/j.linged.2011.02.007.

Boyd, D.M. (2008). Taken out of context: American teen sociality in networked publics. ProQuest.

Brenner, J. (2013). Pew Internet: Social Networking (full detail) http://pewinternet.org/Commentary/2012/March/Pew-Internet-Social-Networking-full-detail.aspx.

Hakverdi-Can, M., & Sonmez, D. (2012). Learning How to Design a Technology Supported Inquiry-Based Learning Environment. Science Education International, 23(4), 338–352.

Jarvis, P. (2006). Towards a comprehensive theory of human learning. Routledge. Pages 13, 70, 82, 87.

Jarvis, P. (2012). Adult learning in the social context (Vol. 78). Routledge.

Kittinger, R., Correia, C.J., & Irons, J.G. (2012). Relationship Between Facebook Use and Problematic Internet Use Among College Students. Cyberpsychology, Behavior & Social Networking, 15(6), 324–327. doi:10.1089/cyber.2010.0410.

Mackay, D. (2011). Social media campaign takes on Rupert Murdoch's News Corp <http://thenextweb.com/socialmedia/2011/07/08/social-media-campaign-takes-on-rupert-murdochs-news-corp/>. Retrieved August 15, 2013.

McGill, S. (2013). The social network and the legal environment of business: An opportunity for Student-Centered learning. Journal of Legal Studies Education, 30(1), 45–97. doi:10.1111/j.1744–1722.2013.01114.x

Morgan, N., Jones, G., & Hodges, A. (2013). The Complete Guide to Social Media: From The Social Media Guys. <http://www.scribd.com/doc/135022820/Complete-Guide-to-Social-Media> Retrieved August 15, 2013.

Okoro, E. (2012). Social Networking And Pedagogical Variations: An Integrated Approach For Effective Interpersonal And Group Communications Skills Development. American Journal Of Business Education, 5(2), 219.

Pan, Z. (2013). Transactions on edutainment X. New York: Springer; 2013. Page 10–23.

Pike, G., Kuh, G., & McCormick, A. (2011). An Investigation of the Contingent Relationships Between Learning Community Participation and Student Engagement. Research In Higher Education, 52(3), 300–322. doi:10.1007/s11162-010-9192-1.

Runesson, U. (2006). What is it Possible to Learn? On Variation as a Necessary Condition for Learning. Scandinavian Journal Of Educational Research, 50(4), 397–410.

Sherman, A. (2010). 5 Ways Cities Are Using Social Media to Reverse Economic Downturn http://mashable.com/2010/12/16/cities-social-media-recession/.

Computer, Intelligent Computing and Education Technology – Liu, Sung & Yao (Eds)
© 2014 Taylor & Francis Group, London, ISBN 978-1-138-02469-4

Similar region search: A distribution-aware approach based on Zernike moments

Chang-Qing Zhang & Min Hua
School of Computer Science, Xinyang College of Agriculture and Forestry, Xinyang, P.R. China

Yuan Sun
School of Computer, Northwestern Polytechnical University, Xi'an, P.R. China

ABSTRACT: Increasingly generated spatial data provides us with the opportunity to make similar region search possible. However, due to region's scale or rotation transform, it is difficult to find similar regions effectively. To deal with this problem, we introduce modified Zernike moments and use them to define region's distribution feature. On the basis of these, we propose a quadtree based approach to search similar regions. The proposed approach employs two kinds of pruning strategy in order to achieve efficient query. Experiment results show that our approach is both effective and efficient, and outperforms existing approach.

Keywords: similar region search; Zernike moments; quadtree

1 INTRODUCTION

With an increasing number of locations sensing systems integrated into mobile devices, more and more geo-reference data, such as trajectory, geo-tagged media, Point of Interest (POI), become available. This continuously generated spatial data provides us with the opportunity to make similar region search possible. We hold the opinions that similar region search can play an important role in many scenarios, such as improving traditional map search engines and identifying susceptible areas to certain infectious disease. As we known, traditional map search engines response to us with one or more locations, according to the text which we give to them. But under certain circumstance, finding similar regions on the basis of a given one is desirable.

In general speaking, region similarity means the combinations of two kinds of similarity: representative categories similarity and local distribution similarity. To measure representative categories similarity, a concept of CF-IRF modified from TF-IDF (Salton et al., 1975) was introduced (Sheng et al., 2010). We consider this approach practical, and further improvement to it may not be needed. For local distribution similarity, however, few satisfying measurements were proposed due to complexity of local distribution of POIs. We are aware of that we often run into trouble when comparing two regions which are just different in scale or rotation angle. That is to say, by proper scale or

rotation transform, those dissimilar regions can become similar ones.

In this paper, the above-mentioned problem is firstly dealt with. We adopt modified Zernike moments to define local distribution similarity. The distribution feature of a region is denoted as a vector which is composed by a series of modified Zernike moments with different repetitions and orders. We also provide a quadtree based approach in order to speedup the very time-consuming search on spatial map. We partition the whole map into many cells with identical width and length, and then a quadtree is employed to hierarchically cluster all the cells. To achieve efficient searching, category based pruning and PCA based pruning is adopted to eliminate as many dissimilar clusters as possible.

The rest of this paper is organized as follows. We first present the related work. Next, distribution feature is introduced, and then we describe the approach to query similar region in detail. Afterwards, we conduct experiments and analyze the effectiveness and efficiency by comparing with other methods. Finally we conclude our paper.

2 RELATED WORK

Zernike Moments (ZMs) are the first related issue, since we introduce them into the definition of POI distribution similarity. ZMs are based on Zernike polynomials, which were firstly proposed for diffraction theory in Optics (Zernike et al., 1934).

As complex moments, ZMs also feature rotational invariants, because their magnitude remains unchanged under arbitrary rotation. Therefore, ZMs have been employed as feature sets in applications such as pattern recognition (Kim et al., 1994), content-based image retrieval (Kim et al., 1998), and other image analysis systems (Kim et al., 1999).

Efficient index structure is also related to our work, since our top-k similar region search is analogue to the k-nearest neighbor (k-NN) search in high-dimensional data space. For achieving efficient and accurate searches, many index structures and corresponding query algorithms has been proposed, such as the Pyramid technique (Berchtold et al., 1998), the iDistance (Yu et al., 2001), the pcDistance (Cui et al., 2010), etc. When handling top-k similar region search, however, we must consider the regions' spatial relations, so the proposed structures cannot be employed. Yet, the prune strategy in the proposed algorithms can be utilized in our work.

3 DISTRIBUTION FEATURE

Distribution feature denotes the local distribution of POIs in region. If we treat region and POI as image and pixel respectively, existing image features can be borrowed to define distribution feature of region. In this section, we firstly introduce Zernike moments, and then we detail the definition of distribution feature.

We can define Zernike moments of the nth order with repetition m as

$$Z_{nm} = \frac{n+1}{\pi} \int_0^1 \int_{-\pi}^{\pi} R_{nm}(r) e^{-jm\theta} f(r,\theta) r \, dr \, d\theta, \quad (1)$$

where r, θ are polar coordinates, f is image function, $R_{nm}(r)e^{-jm\theta}$ is Zernike polynomial.

Due to the discontinuity of digital image, we cannot use the above formula to compute Zernike moments. A discrete form of Zernike moments (Hwang et al., 2006) is denoted as

$$Z_{nm} = \frac{n+1}{\lambda_N} \sum_{x=0}^{N-1} \sum_{y=0}^{N-1} f(x,y) R_{nm}(r_{xy}) e^{-jm\theta_{xy}}, \quad (2)$$

where $f(x,y)$ is gray value at the pixel of (x,y). The coordinates of image must be normalized to $[0, 1]$ by mapping transformation, so r_{xy} and θ_{xy} is the transformed polar coordinates, and λ_N refers to the number of pixels located in the unit circle after transformation.

Although POIs in region are also discrete, (2) cannot be used directly. It is because that POIs fall into many categories while pixels have no categories, and pixels have their gray values while POIs have no corresponding attribute. In order to use (2), we believe that transforming original regions with POIs into a corresponding image is an effective solution.

We first partition a region into many square cells with same edge length. If the region is N meters long and N meters wide, and cell's edge length is w meters, a $(N/w)*(N/w)$ image is generated. The square cells correspond to the pixels of the image. The "gray values" of pixels of the image is equal to the flag values of the corresponding cells in the region. Flag value is adopted to distinguish different categories, POIs and cells. Each category is assigned a flag value in advance. With category's flag value, we can get flag value of POI and cell.

We know that a POI can be labeled with multiple categories. For example, a building is labeled both as "Cinema" and "Restaurant" if it houses a cinema and has at least one restaurant inside. Therefore, the flag value of a POI labeled with multiple categories is summation of the flag value of its categories. Suppose that VC_i denotes a category C_i's flag value. For a POI O_i labeled with a category C_j and a category C_k, O_i's flag value VO_i is equal to $VC_j + VC_k$. A cell's flag value is the summation of flag value of all POIs in it. If there is no POI located in the cell, the cell's flag value is zero.

We illustrate the transformation process by the following example. The original region is 125 meters long and 125 meters wide, and cells' edge length is 25 meters. There are three categories: restaurant, mall and cinema, which are denoted as C_1, C_2 and C_3 respectively. Suppose $VC_1 = 20$, $VC_2 = 200$ and $VC_3 = 2000$. Table 1 gives the relative location, categories and flag value of all the POIs in the region.

Table 1. POIs.

	POI								
	1	2	3	4	5	6	7	8	9
Relative	63 m	56 m	70 m	38 m	88 m	13 m	113 m	56 m	70 m
Location	32 m	43 m	43 m	37 m	63 m	88 m	113 m	83 m	93 m
Categories	$C_1 C_2$	C_3	C_1	C_1	C_2	$C_2 C_3$	$C_1 C_3$	C_3	C_2
Flag value	220	2000	20	20	200	2200	2020	2000	200

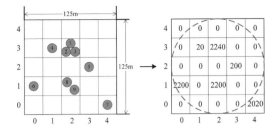

Figure 1. The distribution of all the POIs and the generated image.

Figure 1 depicts the distribution of all the POIs and the generated image.

Once we obtain the generated image and the "gray values" of all the pixels of it, we can employ (2) to compute a series of Zernike moments. Since these Zernike moments are generated from an unreal image, we can call them Modified Zernike Moments (MZMs). On the basis of these MZMs, the distribution feature of a region R_j can be denoted as

$$\overline{DF_j} = \left(MZM_{1,j},\ MZM_{2,j}, \cdots,\ MZM_{T,j} \right), \qquad (3)$$

where T is number of MZMs used to define distribution feature.

4 PROPOSED APPROACH

Our approach comprises offline process and online process. In offline process, we first partition the whole map into many square cells with same edge length. Second, we extract the category features and distribution features of all regions with different sizes. Smaller regions occupy less square cells, while bigger regions occupy more square cells. Third, we use a quadtree to hierarchically cluster all regions. Fourth, we construct an efficient index with two kinds of pruning strategy, which will be detailed in the next subsection. In online process, we first determine the size range of regions that we want to query. Then we begin search from smallest size inside the size range. On the basis of the quadtree index and two kinds of pruning strategy, we can effectively prune dissimilar regions and efficiently obtain the top-k most similar regions.

Pruning Strategy. In order to achieve efficient query, we employ two kinds of pruning strategy: category based pruning and PCA based pruning. The main idea of category based pruning is that more similar regions must have more common representative categories. Given a threshold m, if a region has less than m common representative

categories with the query region, the region must be dissimilar with the query region. Category based pruning is implemented by Representative Categories Bounds Vector ($RCBV$) which is maintained by all nodes in the quadtree. Like category feature vector, $RCBV$ is also a boolean vector. We know that a node in the quadtree indicates a region cluster, and $RCBV$ is just based on the very region cluster. The element of $RCBV$ is either 0, if no region in the cluster has the corresponding category as its representative category, or 1, if not.

PCA based pruning is based on the fact that in PCA space, first principal component of a vector takes most important role in computing Euclidean distance. Given a distance threshold H and the query region q, for each region r, before we completely compute Euclidean distance between their distribution feature vectors, we can first compute the distance dl between first principal components of their distribution feature vectors in PCA space. If dl is already large than H, the region must be not similar with q. In order to implement this pruning strategy, first principal components range is maintained by all nodes in the quadtree. For all the regions in the cluster, the lower bound ($FPCL$) is the minimum first principal component of their distribution feature vectors in PCA space, and the upper bound ($FPCU$) is the maximum one. With this range, many time-consuming float operations can be avoid when comparing two distribution feature vector.

Query Algorithm. Algorithm 1 and Algorithm 2 shows the two key algorithm used in our approach. Algorithm 1 gives a sketch of query process. From line 1 to line 4, we compute the size range of answer regions, and extract query region's category feature and distribution feature. Line 5 indicates that the result set is initially empty and the threshold is initialized to a maximum value. In the future, the threshold will be gradually updated to smaller value. From line 6 to Line 8, we can see that if this round of query doesn't obtain adequate answer regions, we will lower our demand to the common representative categories.

Algorithm 2 recursively searches and prunes the candidate regions in quadtree. Line 1 and Line 2 show the category based pruning. For each node, we first determine its common representative categories between with the query region. If the number of common representative categories is less then the threshold, this node will not be handled further. From line 3 to line 7, PCA-based pruning is employed. If the node is not pruned by the two pruning strategy, it will be dealt with further. If it is an unleaf node, recursive search begins for each of its child nodes (line 8 to line 10). If it is a leaf node, we accurately compare all the regions belonging to this leaf node (line 11 to line 15).

Algorithm 1. RegionSearch(q, T, k, m)	Algorithm 2. SearchQuadTree(N, cm)
Input: q, query region; T, quadtree; k, number of answer regions; m, number of common representative categories	Input: N, node of quadtree; cm, number of common representative categories

	1 n = CommonCategory($N.RBCV$, CF_Q)
	2 if ($n >= cm$) {
	3 $fpcq$ = FirstPrincipalComponentOf(DF_Q)
1 SL = MinSizeOfAnswerRegions(q)	4 if ($N.FPCL < fpcq$ - sqrt(H) or
2 SU = MaxSizeOfAnswerRegions(q)	5 $N.FPCU > fpcq$ + sqrt(H)) {
3 CF_Q = ExtractCategoryFeature(q)	6 return
4 DF_Q = ExtractDistributionFeature(q)	7 }
5 $Result$ = null, H = DBL_MAX	8 if (N is unleaf node) {
6 while ($Result.Size < k$) {	9 for each child node NC of N
7 SearchQuadTree($T.root$, m--)	10 SearchQuadTree(NC, cm)
8 }	11 } else if (N is leaf node) {
9 return $Result$	12 for each region R
	13 if ($R.size >= SL$ && $R.size <= SU$)
	14 Try to insert R to $Result$ and update H
	15 }
	16 }

For each region whose size is in the previously determined range, we try to insert it into result set and then update the result set. If the size of result set is bigger than k after insertion of new region, we must remove the most dissimilar region from the result set. Then the threshold is updated to the Euclidean distance between the query region and the most similar region in the result set.

5 EXPERIMENTAL EVALUATION

To the best of our knowledge, SVSM (Sheng et al., 2010) is the only existing approach to similar region search. So we only compared with SVSM in our experiments. All the algorithms were implemented in Java. All the experiments were performed on a computer with an AMD Athlon™ 64 X2 Dual Core 4800+ @ 2.50 GHz CPU and 2GB RAM.

The real Beijing data set obtained from the CloudMade project (http://cloudmade.com/) is used in our experiments. The map is 20 kilometers long and 20 kilometers wide with 52, 347 POIs, which is classified into 32 categories. In map partition process, square cell's edge length is 25 meters. The smallest candidate region is 250 meters long and 250 meters wide. The largest candidate region is 3000 meters long and 3000 meters wide. We use 24 MZMs to build distribution feature vector.

Effectiveness Evaluation. We select three typical types of query regions as the test queries. The first type is shopping mall, whose spatial points are usually clustered in small regions. The second type is commercial street, whose spatial points are distributed along the streets. The third type is university, which is a star-like distribution where the institutes are located at the center and other facilities such as hotels and restaurants are located around the university.

Each answer region is manually scored. Score of result set is average one of all regions in the result set. For each type, 20 queries with different query regions are performed. So, score of each type of query regions is also average one. In the effectiveness evaluation, number of answer regions for each query is set to 5. In order to study the significance of the number of common representative categories, m is set to one of four values: 3, 5, 7, and 9. Among the 20 queries, each value is used 5 times.

Figure 2 shows the results of effectiveness evaluation. We can see that both SVSM and our approach are effective in querying shopping mall and street, and our approach has no significant effectiveness improvement to SVSM in query the two types of regions. But in querying university, our approach outperforms SVSM. It is because in querying university, rotation transform has negative influence on similar region search, due to the star-like distribution. SVSM doesn't deal with rotation transform perfectly, and our approach is superior to SVSM in handling rotation transform. We can also see that both small m values and large m values don't contribute to improve effectiveness, so modest values are best choice. It is because small m values are not enough to differentiate region functionality, and large m values are likely to include some noise categories.

Efficiency Evaluation. This set of experiments evaluates the efficiency of our approach and SVSM. For each type of query regions, we conducts 40 queries. Number of answer regions for each query is set to 5, and on the basis of effectiveness evaluation, we set the number of common representative categories to 5. In order to study the

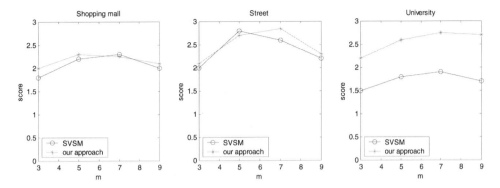

Figure 2.   Effectiveness evaluation results.

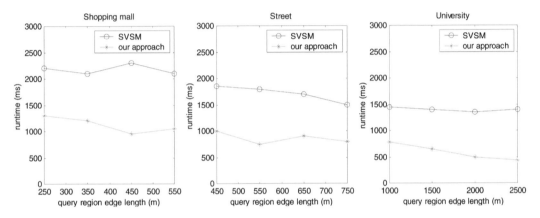

Figure 3.   Efficiency evaluation results.

influence of query region size on the runtime, for each type of query regions, we use multiple kinds of query region edge length.

Figure 3 shows the results of efficiency evaluation. We can see that for each type of query regions, our approach outperforms SVSM obviously. The reason is that region expansion in SVSM is very time-consuming operation, while our approach doesn't need region expansion, and also have two efficient pruning strategies. We can also find that with the increase of query region edge length, the runtime decreases. That is because a larger query region has less candidate regions to handle than a smaller query region.

6   CONCLUSION

To deal with region's rotation transform problem, we first introduce modified Zernike moments, and adopt modified Zernike moments to define region's distribution feature. On the basis of modified Zernike moments, we propose a distribution-aware approach to similar region search. Our approach is based on quadtree, and has two efficient pruning strategies: category based pruning and PCA based pruning. In online process, the two pruning strategies are employed to prune as many cluster as possible. Compared with existing method, our approach is more effective and more efficient to find top-k similar regions.

REFERENCES

Berchtold, S., Böhm, C., Kriegal, H.-P., 1998. The pyramid-technique: Towards breaking the curse of dimensionality. SIGMOD Rec. 27 (2), 142–153.

Cui, J.T., An, Z.Y., 2010. Efficient nearest neighbor query based on extended B+-tree in high-dimensional space. Pattern Recogn. Lett. 31, 12, 1740–1748.

Hwang, S.K., Kim, W.Y., 2006. A novel approach to the fast computation of Zernike moments, Pattern Recognition, Volume 39, Issue 11, Pages 2065–2076.

Kim, W.Y., Kim, Y.S., 1999. Robust rotation angle estimator, IEEE Trans. Pattern Anal. Mach. Intell. 21 (8), 768–773.

Kim, W.Y., Yuan, P., 1994. A practical pattern recognition system for translation, scale and rotation invariance, Proceedings of IEEE International Conference on Computer Vision and Pattern Recognition, pp. 391–396.

Kim, Y.S., Kim, W.Y., 1998. Content-based trademark retrieval system using visually salient feature, J. Image Vision Comput. 16, 931–939.

Salton, G., Wong, A., Yang, C.S., 1975. A vector space model for automatic indexing. Commun. ACM 18(11), 613–620.

Sheng, C., Zheng, Y., 2010. Answering top-k similar region queries. In Proceedings of the 15th international conference on Database Systems for Advanced Applications—Volume Part I (DASFAA'10), Vol. Part I. 186–201.

Yu, C., Ooi, B.C., Tan, K.-L., Jagadish, H.V., 2001. Indexing the distance: An efficient method to knn processing. In: VLDB '01: Proc. 27th Internet. Conf. on Very Large Data Bases. Morgan Kaufmann Publishers Inc., San Francisco, CA, USA, pp. 421–430.

Zernike, F., 1934. "Diffraction theory of the cut procedure and its improved form, the phase contrast method," Physics, vol. 1, no. 689–704, pp. 56.

Author index

Wei, J.-L. 1295
Wei, K.-F. 91
Wei, Y.G. 641
Wei, Z.Q. 13
Wen, Q. 941
Wen, S.T. 851
Wu, B. 209
Wu, F. 277, 765
Wu, F. 1103
Wu, F.-F. 187, 915
Wu, F.-T. 771
Wu, F.Y. 155
Wu, J. 183
Wu, J.-Y. 1335
Wu, L. 1441
Wu, M.-Q. 831
Wu, M.W. 329
Wu, Q.L. 569
Wu, R.C. 513
Wu, S.-L. 225
Wu, X.-W. 417
Wu, Y. 349
Wu, Y.H. 605
Wu, Y.-L. 1223
Wu, Y.L. 277
Wu, Z.-Y. 893

Xia, J.-S. 1281
Xia, X. 1147
Xia, Y.-J. 689
Xiang, L.Q. 393
Xiang, Y.-X. 429
Xiao, H. 115
Xiao, N. 367, 373
Xiao, Q. 317
Xiao, T. 573
Xiao, X.-C. 75
Xiao, X.F. 919
Xie, B. 151
Xie, H. 711
Xie, K. 645
Xie, Z.F. 799
Xiong, C.X. 55
Xiong, J.-Y. 1377
Xiong, Q. 1163
Xu, B.Q. 221
Xu, D. 1123
Xu, D.-Z. 665, 1397
Xu, L. 1045
Xu, M. 1015
Xu, R. 1127
Xu, S. 1265
Xu, S.-H. 131
Xu, T. 3
Xu, W. 29
Xu, W.P. 255

Xu, X.-H. 1281, 1287
Xu, X.-J. 1095
Xu, X.Q. 267
Xu, Y. 115
Xu, Y.-W. 273
Xu, Z.H. 865
Xu, Z.Q. 1151
Xue, C.-N. 893
Xue, J. 969

Yan, G.-G. 175
Yan, L. 497, 501
Yan, T.-Y. 421, 425
Yan, Z.-L. 819
Yang, C.W. 1147
Yang, D.L. 477
Yang, D.M. 887
Yang, D.-M. 983, 987
Yang, H.T. 699
Yang, J. 887
Yang, J.-H. 563
Yang, P. 317
Yang, Q.L. 685
Yang, S.R. 1123
Yang, Y. 485
Yang, Y. 513
Yang, Z.-L. 731
Yao, X.H. 531, 535, 539, 543
Ye, X.-M. 451
Yi, F. 103
Yin, J.-H. 125, 855
Yin, X.J. 809
Ying, F.T. 1209
Ying, W.Q. 1209
Yong, Z.-Q. 447
You, W.-Q. 447
You, X.-C. 9, 755
Yu, C.Y. 259
Yu, H.Z. 1175, 1205
Yu, H.-Z. 731
Yu, M.J. 1193
Yu, M.-N. 1387
Yu, Q.-S. 1335
Yu, S.-C. 1387
Yu, S.Y. 641
Yu, T. 49, 793
Yu, T.-F. 689
Yu, W.L. 443
Yu, Y. 477
Yuan, J.S. 477
Yuan, M. 477
Yuan, P.F. 573, 579
Yuan, S.F. 255
Yuan, S.S.X. 653
Yuan, Y. 299

Yuan, Z.-W. 403
Yue, G.L. 961
Yue, J. 289
Yun, H. 1057

Zang, P. 523, 905
Zang, Y.-F. 749
Zeng, L. 1127
Zeng, X. 595, 1361
Zhai, Y.Z. 1039
Zhan, Q.L. 1227
Zhan, T. 323
Zhan, Y. 1029
Zhang, A.H. 1189
Zhang, B. 91
Zhang, C.-Q. 717
Zhang, D.-D. 737
Zhang, F.L. 513
Zhang, F.-L. 617, 1373
Zhang, G. 29
Zhang, G.F. 55
Zhang, H.-G. 457
Zhang, H.-M. 429
Zhang, H.S. 201
Zhang, H.Y. 909
Zhang, H.Y. 1085
Zhang, J. 669
Zhang, J. 1259
Zhang, J.B. 267, 909
Zhang, J.B. 513
Zhang, J.F. 293
Zhang, K. 195, 703, 1445
Zhang, K.F. 481
Zhang, L. 707
Zhang, L.C. 685
Zhang, L.-L. 131
Zhang, L.M. 573, 579
Zhang, L.-X. 1429
Zhang, M. 69
Zhang, M. 675
Zhang, P.Y. 45, 473
Zhang, Q. 1231
Zhang, Q.J. 1011
Zhang, S.L. 377
Zhang, S.P. 1015
Zhang, T.Z. 313
Zhang, X.H. 951
Zhang, X.-M. 1307
Zhang, X.Y. 1155
Zhang, Y. 255
Zhang, Y. 1251
Zhang, Y. 1295
Zhang, Y.F. 657
Zhang, Y.F. 1133
Zhang, Y.-T. 1077
Zhang, Y.-Y. 1303